INSTRUCTOR'S SOLUTIONS MANUAL

VOLUME II

Mark McCombs

ALGEBRA & TRIGONOMETRY

SIXTH EDITION

Michael Sullivan

Prentice Hall

Upper Saddle River, NJ 07458

Editor in Chief: Sally Yagan
Associate Editor: Dawn Murrin
Assistant Managing Editor: John Matthews
Production Editor: Donna Crilly
Supplement Cover Manager: Paul Gourhan
Supplement Cover Designer: PM Workshop Inc.
Manufacturing Buyer: Lisa McDowell

Upper Saddle River, NJ 07458

Printed in the United States of America

10 9 8 7 6 5 4 3 2 1

ISBN 0-13-097062-X

Prentice-Hall International (UK) Limited, London
Prentice-Hall of Australia Pty. Limited, Sydney
Prentice-Hall Canada, Inc., Toronto
Prentice-Hall Hispanoamericana, S.A., Mexico City
Prentice-Hall of India Private Limited, New Delhi
Pearson Education Asia Pte. Ltd., Singapore
Prentice-Hall of Japan, Inc., Tokyo
Editora Prentice-Hall do Brazil, Ltda., Rio de Janeiro

Chapter 7

Trigonometric Functions

7.1 Angles and Their Measure

1.

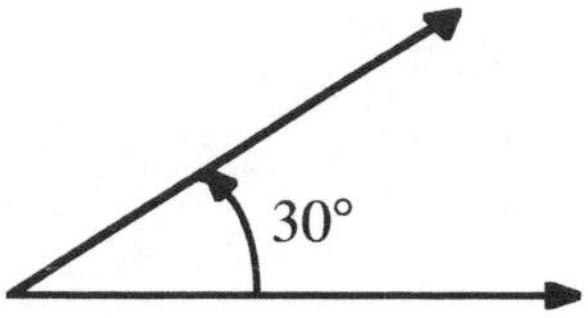

2.

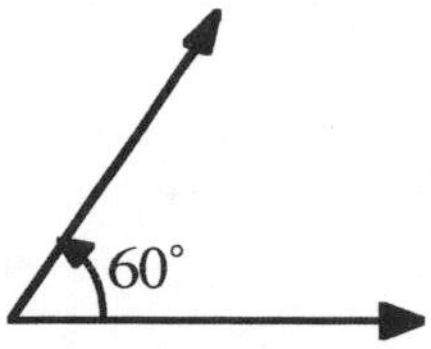

3.

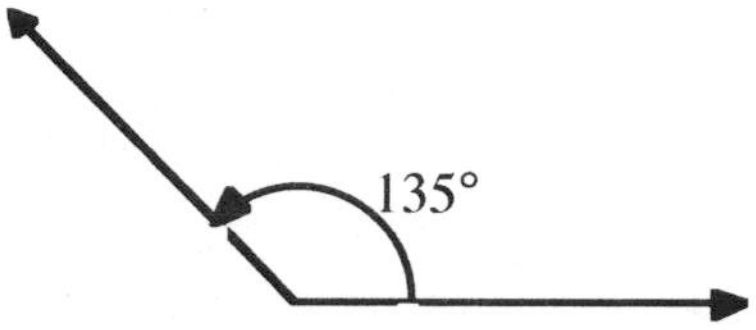

4.

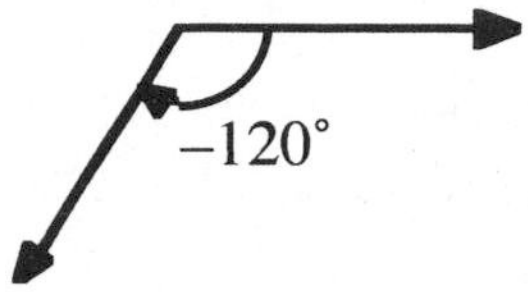

5.

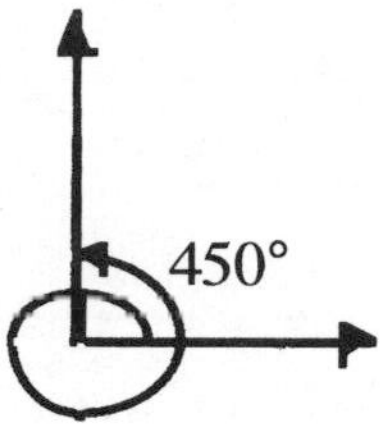

6.

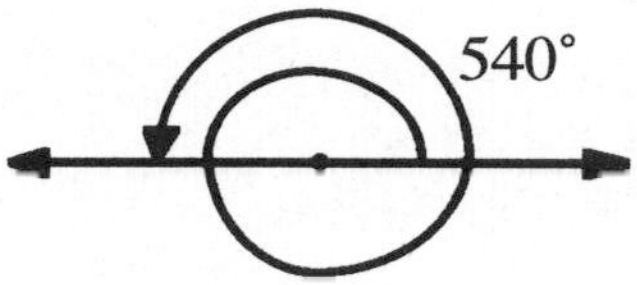

7.

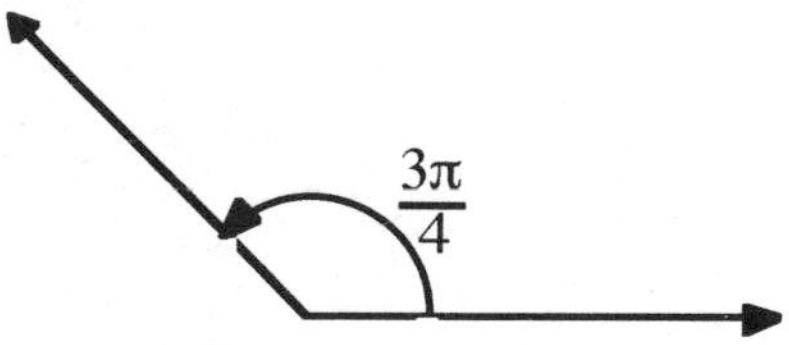

8.

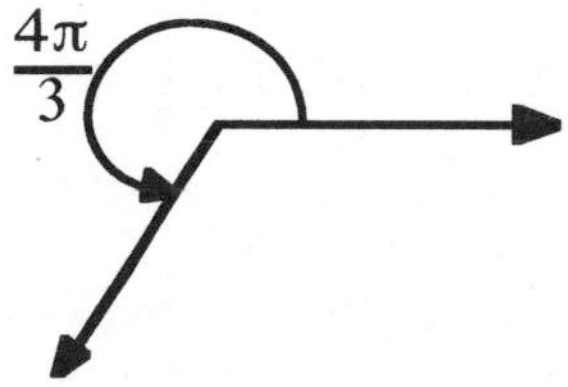

9.

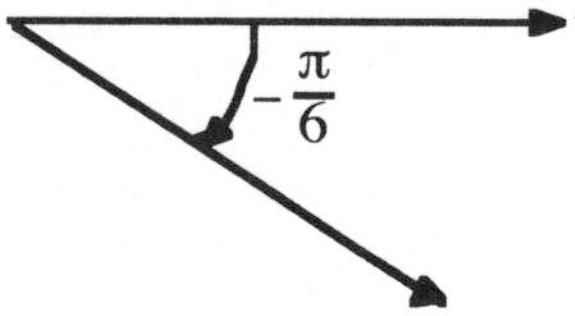

10.

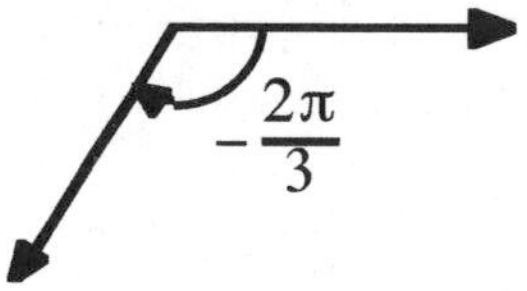

11.

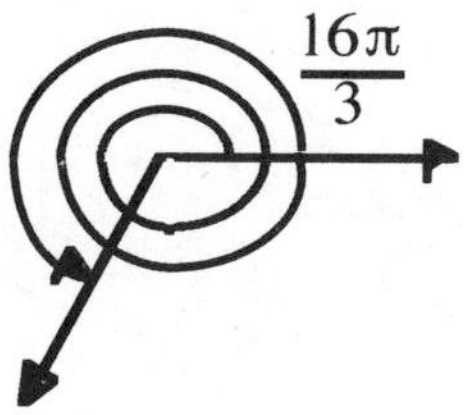

12.

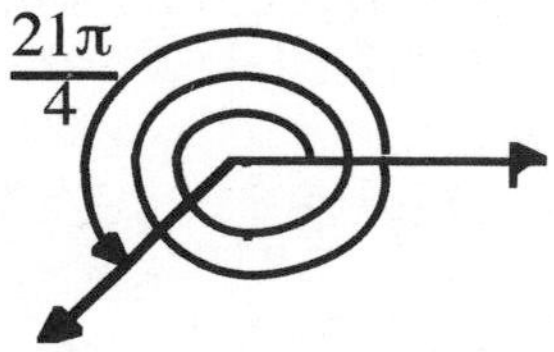

13. $30° = 30 \cdot \frac{\pi}{180}$ radian $= \frac{\pi}{6}$ radians

14. $120° = 120 \cdot \frac{\pi}{180}$ radian $= \frac{2\pi}{3}$ radians

15. $240° = 240 \cdot \frac{\pi}{180}$ radian $= \frac{4\pi}{3}$ radians

16. $330° = 330 \cdot \frac{\pi}{180}$ radian $= \frac{11\pi}{6}$ radians

17. $-60° = -60 \cdot \frac{\pi}{180}$ radian $= -\frac{\pi}{3}$ radians

18. $-30° = -30 \cdot \frac{\pi}{180}$ radian $= -\frac{\pi}{6}$ radians

19. $180° = 180 \cdot \frac{\pi}{180}$ radian $= \pi$ radians

20. $270° = 270 \cdot \frac{\pi}{180}$ radian $= \frac{3\pi}{2}$ radians

21. $-135° = -135 \cdot \frac{\pi}{180}$ radian $= -\frac{3\pi}{4}$ radians

22. $-225° = -225 \cdot \frac{\pi}{180}$ radian $= -\frac{5\pi}{4}$ radians

23. $-90° = -90 \cdot \frac{\pi}{180}$ radian $= -\frac{\pi}{2}$ radians

24. $-180° = -180 \cdot \frac{\pi}{180}$ radian $= -\pi$ radians

25. $\frac{\pi}{3} = \frac{\pi}{3} \cdot \frac{180}{\pi}$ degrees $= 60°$

26. $\frac{5\pi}{6} = \frac{5\pi}{6} \cdot \frac{180}{\pi}$ degrees $= 150°$

27. $-\frac{5\pi}{4} = -\frac{5\pi}{4} \cdot \frac{180}{\pi}$ degrees $= -225°$

28. $-\frac{2\pi}{3} = -\frac{2\pi}{3} \cdot \frac{180}{\pi}$ degrees $= -120°$

29. $\frac{\pi}{2} = \frac{\pi}{2} \cdot \frac{180}{\pi}$ degrees $= 90°$

30. $4\pi = 4\pi \cdot \frac{180}{\pi}$ degrees $= 720°$

31. $\frac{\pi}{12}=\frac{\pi}{12}\cdot\frac{180}{\pi}$ degrees $=15°$

32. $\frac{5\pi}{12}=\frac{5\pi}{12}\cdot\frac{180}{\pi}$ degrees $=75°$

33. $-\frac{\pi}{2}=-\frac{\pi}{2}\cdot\frac{180}{\pi}$ degrees $=-90°$

34. $-\pi=-\pi\cdot\frac{180}{\pi}$ degrees $=-180°$

35. $-\frac{\pi}{6}=-\frac{\pi}{6}\cdot\frac{180}{\pi}$ degrees $=-30°$

36. $-\frac{3\pi}{4}=-\frac{3\pi}{4}\cdot\frac{180}{\pi}$ degrees $=-135°$

37. $r=10$ meters; $\theta=\frac{1}{2}$ radian; $s=r\theta=10\cdot\frac{1}{2}=5$ meters

38. $r=6$ feet; $\theta=2$ radian; $s=r\theta=6\cdot 2=12$ feet

39. $\theta=\frac{1}{3}$ radian; $s=2$ feet; $s=r\theta$ or $r=\frac{s}{\theta}=\frac{2}{\left(\frac{1}{3}\right)}=6$ feet

40. $\theta=\frac{1}{4}$ radian; $s=6$ cm; $s=r\theta$ or $r=\frac{s}{\theta}=\frac{6}{\left(\frac{1}{4}\right)}=24$ cm

41. $r=5$ miles; $s=3$ miles; $s=r\theta$ or $\theta=\frac{s}{r}=\frac{3}{5}=0.6$ radians

42. $r=6$ meters; $s=8$ meters; $s=r\theta$ or $\theta=\frac{s}{r}=\frac{8}{6}=\frac{4}{3}$ radians

43. $r=2$ inches; $\theta=30°$; Convert to radians: $30°=30\cdot\frac{\pi}{180}=\frac{\pi}{6}$ radians

$s=r\theta=2\cdot\frac{\pi}{6}=\frac{\pi}{3}$ inches

44. $r=3$ meters; $\theta=120°$; Convert to radians: $120°=120\cdot\frac{\pi}{180}=\frac{2\pi}{3}$ radians

$s=r\theta=3\cdot\frac{2\pi}{3}=2\pi$ meters

45. $r = 10$ meters; $\theta = \dfrac{1}{2}$ radian

$$A = \frac{1}{2}r^2\theta = \frac{1}{2}(10)^2\left(\frac{1}{2}\right) = \frac{100}{4} = 25 \text{ square meters}$$

46. $r = 6$ feet; $\theta = 2$ radians

$$A = \frac{1}{2}r^2\theta = \frac{1}{2}(6)^2(2) = 36 \text{ square feet}$$

47. $\theta = \dfrac{1}{3}$ radian; $A = 2$ square feet

$$A = \frac{1}{2}r^2\theta \rightarrow 2 = \frac{1}{2}r^2\left(\frac{1}{3}\right) = \frac{1}{6}r^2$$

$$2 = \frac{1}{6}r^2 \rightarrow 12 = r^2 \rightarrow r = \sqrt{12} \approx 3.464 \text{ feet}$$

48. $\theta = \dfrac{1}{4}$ radian; $A = 6$ square centimeters

$$A = \frac{1}{2}r^2\theta \rightarrow 6 = \frac{1}{2}r^2\left(\frac{1}{4}\right) = \frac{1}{4}r^2$$

$$6 = \frac{1}{8}r^2 \rightarrow 48 = r^2 \rightarrow r = \sqrt{48} \approx 6.928 \text{ cm}$$

49. $r = 5$ miles; $A = 3$ square miles

$$A = \frac{1}{2}r^2\theta \rightarrow 3 = \frac{1}{2}(5)^2\theta = \frac{25}{2}\theta$$

$$3 = \frac{25}{2}\theta \rightarrow \frac{6}{25} = \theta \rightarrow \theta \approx 0.24 \text{ radians}$$

50. $r = 6$ meters; $A = 8$ square meters

$$A = \frac{1}{2}r^2\theta \rightarrow 8 = \frac{1}{2}(6)^2\theta = \frac{36}{2}\theta = 18\theta$$

$$8 = 18\theta \rightarrow \frac{8}{18} = \theta \rightarrow \theta = \frac{4}{9} \approx 0.167 \text{ radians}$$

51. $r = 2$ inches; $\theta = 30°$; Convert to radians: $30° = 30 \cdot \dfrac{\pi}{180} = \dfrac{\pi}{6}$ radians

$$A = \frac{1}{2}r^2\theta = \frac{1}{2}(2)^2\left(\frac{\pi}{6}\right) = \frac{1}{2}\cdot 4\left(\frac{\pi}{6}\right) = \frac{\pi}{3} \approx 1.047 \text{ square inches}$$

52. $r = 3$ meters; $\theta = 120°$; Convert to radians: $120° = 120 \cdot \dfrac{\pi}{180} = \dfrac{2\pi}{3}$ radians

$$A = \frac{1}{2}r^2\theta = \frac{1}{2}(3)^2\left(\frac{2\pi}{3}\right) = \frac{1}{2}\cdot 9\left(\frac{2\pi}{3}\right) = 3\pi \approx 9.425 \text{ square meters}$$

53. $r=2$ feet; $\theta=\dfrac{\pi}{3}$ radians

$$s=r\theta=2\cdot\frac{\pi}{3}=\frac{2\pi}{3}\approx 2.094 \text{ feet}$$

$$A=\frac{1}{2}r^2\theta=\frac{1}{2}(2)^2\left(\frac{\pi}{3}\right)=\frac{1}{2}\cdot 4\left(\frac{\pi}{3}\right)=\frac{2\pi}{3}\approx 2.094 \text{ square feet}$$

54. $r=4$ meters; $\theta=\dfrac{\pi}{6}$ radians

$$s=r\theta=4\cdot\frac{\pi}{6}=\frac{2\pi}{3}\approx 2.094 \text{ meters}$$

$$A=\frac{1}{2}r^2\theta=\frac{1}{2}(4)^2\left(\frac{\pi}{6}\right)=\frac{1}{2}\cdot 16\left(\frac{\pi}{6}\right)=\frac{4\pi}{3}\approx 4.189 \text{ square meters}$$

55. $r=12$ yards; $\theta=70°$; Convert to radians: $70°=70\cdot\dfrac{\pi}{180}=\dfrac{7\pi}{18}$ radians

$$s=r\theta=12\cdot\frac{7\pi}{18}\approx 14.661 \text{ yards}$$

$$A=\frac{1}{2}r^2\theta=\frac{1}{2}(12)^2\left(\frac{7\pi}{18}\right)=\frac{1}{2}\cdot 144\left(\frac{7\pi}{18}\right)=72\left(\frac{7\pi}{18}\right)\approx 87.965 \text{ square yards}$$

56. $r=9$ cm; $\theta=50°$; Convert to radians: $50°=50\cdot\dfrac{\pi}{180}=\dfrac{5\pi}{18}$ radians

$$s=r\theta=9\cdot\frac{5\pi}{18}\approx 7.854 \text{ cm}$$

$$A=\frac{1}{2}r^2\theta=\frac{1}{2}(9)^2\left(\frac{5\pi}{18}\right)=\frac{1}{2}\cdot 81\left(\frac{5\pi}{18}\right)\approx 35.343 \text{ square cm}$$

57. $17°=17\cdot\dfrac{\pi}{180}$ radian $=\dfrac{17\pi}{180}$ radians ≈ 0.30 radians

58. $73°=73\cdot\dfrac{\pi}{180}$ radian $=\dfrac{73\pi}{180}$ radians ≈ 1.27 radians

59. $-40°=-40\cdot\dfrac{\pi}{180}$ radian $=-\dfrac{2\pi}{9}$ radians ≈ -0.70 radians

60. $-51°=-51\cdot\dfrac{\pi}{180}$ radian $=-\dfrac{17\pi}{60}$ radians ≈ -0.89 radians

61. $125°=125\cdot\dfrac{\pi}{180}$ radian $=\dfrac{25\pi}{36}$ radians ≈ 2.18 radians

62. $350°=350\cdot\dfrac{\pi}{180}$ radian $=\dfrac{35\pi}{18}$ radians ≈ 6.11 radians

63. $3.14 \text{ radians} = 3.14 \cdot \frac{180}{\pi} \text{ degrees} \approx 179.91^\circ$

64. $0.75 \text{ radians} = 0.75 \cdot \frac{180}{\pi} \text{ degrees} \approx 42.97^\circ$

65. $2 \text{ radians} = 2 \cdot \frac{180}{\pi} \text{ degrees} \approx 114.59^\circ$

66. $3 \text{ radians} = 3 \cdot \frac{180}{\pi} \text{ degrees} \approx 171.89^\circ$

67. $6.32 \text{ radians} = 6.32 \cdot \frac{180}{\pi} \text{ degrees} \approx 362.11^\circ$

68. $\sqrt{2} \text{ radians} = \sqrt{2} \cdot \frac{180}{\pi} \text{ degrees} \approx 81.03^\circ$

69. $40^\circ 10' 25'' = \left(40 + 10 \cdot \frac{1}{60} + 25 \cdot \frac{1}{60} \cdot \frac{1}{60}\right)^\circ \approx (40 + 0.1667 + 0.00694)^\circ \approx 40.17^\circ$

70. $61^\circ 42' 21'' = \left(61 + 42 \cdot \frac{1}{60} + 21 \cdot \frac{1}{60} \cdot \frac{1}{60}\right)^\circ \approx (61 + 0.7000 + 0.00583)^\circ \approx 61.71^\circ$

71. $1^\circ 2' 3'' = \left(1 + 2 \cdot \frac{1}{60} + 3 \cdot \frac{1}{60} \cdot \frac{1}{60}\right)^\circ \approx (1 + 0.0333 + 0.00083)^\circ \approx 1.03^\circ$

72. $73^\circ 40' 40'' = \left(73 + 40 \cdot \frac{1}{60} + 40 \cdot \frac{1}{60} \cdot \frac{1}{60}\right)^\circ \approx (73 + 0.6667 + 0.0111)^\circ \approx 73.68^\circ$

73. $9^\circ 9' 9'' = \left(9 + 9 \cdot \frac{1}{60} + 9 \cdot \frac{1}{60} \cdot \frac{1}{60}\right)^\circ = (9 + 0.15 + 0.0025)^\circ \approx 9.15^\circ$

74. $98^\circ 22' 45'' = \left(98 + 22 \cdot \frac{1}{60} + 45 \cdot \frac{1}{60} \cdot \frac{1}{60}\right)^\circ \approx (98 + 0.3667 + 0.0125)^\circ \approx 98.38^\circ$

75. $40.32^\circ = ?$

$0.32^\circ = 0.32(1^\circ) = 0.32(60') = 19.2'$

$0.2' = 0.2(1') = 0.2(60'') = 12''$

$40.32^\circ = 40^\circ + 0.32^\circ = 40^\circ + 19.2' = 40^\circ + 19' + 0.2' = 40^\circ + 19' + 12'' = 40^\circ 19' 12''$

76. $61.24^\circ = ?$

$0.24^\circ = 0.24(1^\circ) = 0.24(60') = 14.4'$

$0.4' = 0.4(1') = 0.4(60'') = 24''$

$61.24^\circ = 61^\circ + 0.24^\circ = 61^\circ + 14.4' = 61^\circ + 14' + 0.4' = 61^\circ + 14' + 24'' = 61^\circ 14' 24''$

77. $18.255° = ?$

$0.255° = 0.255(1°) = 0.255(60') = 15.3'$

$0.3' = 0.3(1') = 0.3(60'') = 18''$

$18.255° = 18° + 0.255° = 18° + 15.3' = 18° + 15' + 0.3' = 18° + 15' + 18'' = 18°15'18''$

78. $29.411° = ?$

$0.411° = 0.411(1°) = 0.411(60') = 24.66'$

$0.66' = 0.66(1') = 0.66(60'') = 39.6''$

$29.411° = 29° + 0.411° = 29° + 24.66' = 29° + 24' + 0.66' = 29° + 24' + 39.6'' = 29°24'40''$

79. $19.99° = ?$

$0.99° = 0.99(1°) = 0.99(60') = 59.4'$

$0.4' = 0.4(1') = 0.4(60'') = 24''$

$19.99° = 19° + 0.99° = 19° + 59.4' = 19° + 59' + 0.4' = 19° + 59' + 24'' = 19°59'24''$

80. $44.01° = ?$

$0.01° = 0.01(1°) = 0.01(60') = 0.6'$

$0.6' = 0.6(1') = 0.6(60'') = 36''$

$44.01° = 44° + 0.01° = 44° + 0.6' = 44° + 0' + 0.6' = 44° + 0' + 36'' = 44°0'36''$

81. $r = 6$ inches; $\theta = 90° = \frac{\pi}{2}$ radians

$s = r\theta = 6 \cdot \frac{\pi}{2} = 3\pi \text{ inches} \approx 9.42 \text{ inches}$

$r = 6$ inches; $\theta = \frac{25}{60} \text{ rev} = \frac{5}{12} \cdot 360° = 150° = \frac{5\pi}{6}$ radians

$s = r\theta = 6 \cdot \frac{5\pi}{6} = 5\pi \text{ inches} \approx 15.71 \text{ inches}$

82. $r = 40$ inches; $\theta = 20° = \frac{\pi}{9}$ radians

$s = r\theta = 40 \cdot \frac{\pi}{9} = \frac{40\pi}{9} \text{ inches} \approx 13.96 \text{ inches}$

83. $r = 4$ m; $\theta = 45°$; Convert to radians: $45° = 45 \cdot \frac{\pi}{180} = \frac{\pi}{4}$ radians

$$A = \frac{1}{2}r^2\theta = \frac{1}{2}(4)^2\left(\frac{\pi}{4}\right) = \frac{1}{2} \cdot 16\left(\frac{\pi}{4}\right) = 2\pi \approx 6.283 \text{ square meters}$$

84. $r = 3$ cm; $\theta = 60°$; Convert to radians: $60° = 60 \cdot \frac{\pi}{180} = \frac{\pi}{3}$ radians

$$A = \frac{1}{2}r^2\theta = \frac{1}{2}(3)^2\left(\frac{\pi}{3}\right) = \frac{1}{2} \cdot 9\left(\frac{\pi}{3}\right) = \frac{3\pi}{2} \approx 4.712 \text{ square cm}$$

85. $r = 30$ feet; $\theta = 135°$; Convert to radians : $135° = 135 \cdot \frac{\pi}{180} = \frac{3\pi}{4}$ radians

$$A = \frac{1}{2} r^2 \theta = \frac{1}{2}(30)^2\left(\frac{3\pi}{4}\right) = \frac{1}{2}\cdot(900)\left(\frac{3\pi}{4}\right) = \frac{2700\pi}{8} \approx 1060.29 \text{ square feet}$$

86. $r = 50$ yards; $A = 100$ square yards

$$A = \frac{1}{2} r^2 \theta \rightarrow 100 = \frac{1}{2}(50)^2 \theta = \frac{2500}{2}\theta = 1250 \cdot \theta$$

$$100 = 1250 \cdot \theta \rightarrow \frac{100}{1250} = \theta \rightarrow \theta \approx 0.08 \text{ radians}$$

87. $r = 5$ cm.; $t = 20$ seconds; $\theta = \frac{1}{3}$ radian

$$\omega = \frac{\theta}{t} = \frac{\left(\frac{1}{3}\right)}{20} = \frac{1}{3}\cdot\frac{1}{20} = \frac{1}{60} \text{ radian/sec}$$

$$v = \frac{s}{t} = \frac{r\theta}{t} = \frac{5\cdot\left(\frac{1}{3}\right)}{20} = \frac{5}{3}\cdot\frac{1}{20} = \frac{1}{12} \text{ cm/sec}$$

88. $r = 2$ meters; $t = 20$ seconds; $s = 5$ meters

$$\omega = \frac{\theta}{t} = \frac{\left(\frac{s}{r}\right)}{t} = \frac{\left(\frac{5}{2}\right)}{20} = \frac{5}{2}\cdot\frac{1}{20} = \frac{1}{8} \text{ radian/sec}$$

$$v = \frac{s}{t} = \frac{5}{20} = \frac{1}{4} \text{ m/sec}$$

89. $d = 26$ inches; $r = 13$ inches; $v = 35$ mi / hr

$$v = \frac{35 \text{ mi}}{\text{hr}}\cdot\frac{5280 \text{ ft}}{\text{mi}}\cdot\frac{12 \text{ in}}{\text{ft}}\cdot\frac{1 \text{ hr}}{60 \text{ min}} = 36960 \text{ in/min}$$

$$\omega = \frac{v}{r} = \frac{36960 \text{ in/min}}{13 \text{ in}} = 2843.08 \text{ radians/min}$$

$$= \frac{2843.08 \text{ rad}}{\text{min}}\cdot\frac{1 \text{ rev}}{2\pi \text{ rad}} \approx 452.5 \text{ rev/min}$$

90. $r = 15$ inches; $\omega = 3$ rev / sec $= 6\pi$ rad / sec

$v = r\omega = 15 \cdot 6\pi$ in/sec $= 90\pi \approx 282.74$ in/sec

$$v = 90\pi \frac{\text{in}}{\text{sec}}\cdot\frac{1 \text{ ft}}{12 \text{ in}}\cdot\frac{1}{5280}\frac{\text{mi}}{\text{ft}}\cdot\frac{3600}{1}\frac{\text{sec}}{\text{hr}} \approx 16.06 \text{ mi/hr}$$

91. $r = 3960$ miles; $\theta = 35°9' - 29°57' = 5°12' = 5.2° = 5.2 \cdot \frac{\pi}{180} \approx 0.09076$ radian

$$s = r\theta = 3960 \cdot 0.09076 \approx 359.4 \text{ miles}$$

92. $r = 3960$ miles; $\theta = 38°21' - 30°20' = 8°1' = 8.017° = 8.017 \cdot \frac{\pi}{180} \approx 0.1399$ radian

$$s = r\theta = 3960 \cdot 0.1399 \approx 554 \text{ miles}$$

93. $r = 3429.5$ miles; $\omega = 1 \text{ rev / day} = 2\pi \text{ radians / day} = \frac{\pi}{12} \text{ radians / hr}$

$$v = r\omega = 3429.5 \cdot \frac{\pi}{12} \approx 897.8 \text{ miles/hr}$$

94. $r = 3033.5$ miles; $\omega = 1 \text{ rev / day} = 2\pi \text{ radians / day} = \frac{\pi}{12} \text{ radians / hr}$

$$v = r\omega = 3033.5 \cdot \frac{\pi}{12} \approx 794.2 \text{ miles/hr}$$

95. $r = 2.39 \times 10^5$ miles;

$$\omega = 1 \text{ rev/27.3 days} = 2\pi \text{ radians/27.3 day} = \frac{\pi}{12 \cdot 27.3} \text{ radians/hr}$$

$$v = r\omega = \left(2.39 \times 10^5\right) \cdot \frac{\pi}{327.6} \approx 2292 \text{ miles/hr}$$

96. $r = 9.29 \times 10^7$ miles;

$$\omega = 1 \text{ rev / 365 days} = 2\pi \text{ radians / 365 day} = \frac{\pi}{12 \cdot 365} \text{ radians / hr}$$

$$v = r\omega = \left(9.29 \times 10^7\right) \cdot \frac{\pi}{4380} \approx 66{,}633 \text{ miles / hr}$$

97. $r_1 = 2$ inches; $r_2 = 8$ inches; $\omega_1 = 3 \text{ rev / min} = 6\pi \text{ radians / min}$
Find ω_2:

$$v_1 = v_2$$

$$r_1\omega_1 = r_2\omega_2 \rightarrow 2(6\pi) = 8\omega_2$$

$$\omega_2 = \frac{12\pi}{8} = 1.5\pi \text{ radians/min} = \frac{1.5\pi}{2\pi} \text{ rev/min} = \frac{3}{4} \text{ rev/min}$$

98. $r = 30$ feet; $\omega = \frac{1 \text{ rev}}{70 \text{ sec}} = \frac{2\pi}{70 \text{ sec}} = \frac{\pi}{35} \text{ rad / sec}$

$$v = r\omega = 30 \text{ feet} \cdot \frac{\pi \text{ rad}}{35 \text{ sec}} = \frac{6\pi}{7} \frac{\text{ft}}{\text{sec}} \approx 2.69 \text{ feet / sec}$$

99. $r = 4$ feet; $\omega = 10 \text{ rev / min} = 20\pi \text{ radians / min}$

$$v = r\omega = 4 \cdot 20\pi = 80\pi \frac{\text{ft}}{\text{min}} = \frac{80\pi \text{ ft}}{\text{min}} \cdot \frac{1 \text{ mi}}{5280 \text{ ft}} \cdot \frac{60 \text{ min}}{\text{hr}} \approx 2.86 \text{ mi/hr}$$

100. $d = 26$ inches; $r = 13$ inches; $\omega = 480 \text{ rev / min} = 960\pi \text{ radians / min}$

$$v = r\omega = 13 \cdot 960\pi = 12480\pi \frac{\text{in}}{\text{min}} = \frac{12480\pi \text{ in}}{\text{min}} \cdot \frac{1 \text{ ft}}{12 \text{ in}} \cdot \frac{1 \text{ mi}}{5280 \text{ ft}} \cdot \frac{60 \text{ min}}{\text{hr}}$$

$$\approx 37.13 \text{ mi / hr}$$

$$\omega = \frac{v}{r} = \frac{80 \text{ mi / hr}}{13 \text{ in}} \cdot \frac{12 \text{ in}}{1 \text{ ft}} \cdot \frac{5280 \text{ ft}}{1 \text{ mi}} \cdot \frac{1 \text{ hr}}{60 \text{ min}} \cdot \frac{1 \text{ rev}}{2\pi \text{ rad}} \approx 1034 \text{ rev / min}$$

101. $d = 8.5$ feet; $r = 4.25$ feet; $v = 9.55$ mi/hr

$$\omega = \frac{v}{r} = \frac{9.55\text{ mi/hr}}{4.25\text{ ft}} = \frac{9.55\text{ mi}}{\text{hr}} \cdot \frac{1}{4.25\text{ ft}} \cdot \frac{5280\text{ ft}}{\text{mi}} \cdot \frac{1\text{ hr}}{60\text{ min}} \cdot \frac{1\text{ rev}}{2\pi} \approx 31.47\text{ rev/min}$$

102. Let t represent the time for the earth to rotate 90 miles.

$$\frac{t}{90} = \frac{24}{2\pi(3559)} \rightarrow t = \frac{90(24)}{2\pi(3559)} \approx 0.0966\text{ hours} \approx 5.8\text{ minutes}$$

103. The earth makes one full rotation in 24 hours. The distance traveled in 24 hours is the circumference of the earth. At the equator the circumference is $2\pi(3960)$ miles. Therefore, the linear velocity a person must travel to keep up with the sun is:

$$v = \frac{s}{t} = \frac{2\pi(3960)}{24} \approx 1037\text{ miles / hr}$$

104. Find s, when $r = 3960$ miles and $\theta = 1'$.

$$\theta = 1' \cdot \frac{1\text{ degree}}{60\text{ min}} \cdot \frac{\pi\text{ radians}}{180\text{ degrees}} \approx 0.00029\text{ radians}$$

$$s = r\theta = 3960(0.00029) \approx 1.1484\text{ miles}$$

1 nautical mile is approximately 1.15 statute miles.

105. r_1 rotates at ω_1 rev / min; r_2 rotates at ω_2 rev / min;

$v = r_1\omega_1 = r_2\omega_2$

So, $\dfrac{r_1}{r_2} = \dfrac{\omega_2}{\omega_1}$

Chapter 7

Trigonometric Functions

7.2 Right Triangle Trigonometry

1. opposite = 5; adjacent = 12
   Find the hypotenuse:
   $$5^2+12^2=(\text{hypotenuse})^2$$
   $$(\text{hypotenuse})^2=25+144=169\rightarrow\text{hypotenuse}=13$$
   $\sin\theta=\dfrac{\text{opp}}{\text{hyp}}=\dfrac{5}{13}$ $\quad\cos\theta=\dfrac{\text{adj}}{\text{hyp}}=\dfrac{12}{13}$ $\quad\tan\theta=\dfrac{\text{opp}}{\text{adj}}=\dfrac{5}{12}$

   $\csc\theta=\dfrac{\text{hyp}}{\text{opp}}=\dfrac{13}{5}$ $\quad\sec\theta=\dfrac{\text{hyp}}{\text{adj}}=\dfrac{13}{12}$ $\quad\cot\theta=\dfrac{\text{adj}}{\text{opp}}=\dfrac{12}{5}$

2. opposite = 3; adjacent = 4
   Find the hypotenuse:
   $$3^2+4^2=(\text{hypotenuse})^2$$
   $$(\text{hypotenuse})^2=9+16=25\rightarrow\text{hypotenuse}=5$$
   $\sin\theta=\dfrac{\text{opp}}{\text{hyp}}=\dfrac{3}{5}$ $\quad\cos\theta=\dfrac{\text{adj}}{\text{hyp}}=\dfrac{4}{5}$ $\quad\tan\theta=\dfrac{\text{opp}}{\text{adj}}=\dfrac{3}{4}$

   $\csc\theta=\dfrac{\text{hyp}}{\text{opp}}=\dfrac{5}{3}$ $\quad\sec\theta=\dfrac{\text{hyp}}{\text{adj}}=\dfrac{5}{4}$ $\quad\cot\theta=\dfrac{\text{adj}}{\text{opp}}=\dfrac{4}{3}$

3. opposite = 2; adjacent = 3
   Find the hypotenuse:
   $$2^2+3^2=(\text{hypotenuse})^2$$
   $$(\text{hypotenuse})^2=4+9=13\rightarrow\text{hypotenuse}=\sqrt{13}$$
   $\sin\theta=\dfrac{\text{opp}}{\text{hyp}}=\dfrac{2}{\sqrt{13}}=\dfrac{2\sqrt{13}}{13}$ $\quad\cos\theta=\dfrac{\text{adj}}{\text{hyp}}=\dfrac{3}{\sqrt{13}}=\dfrac{3\sqrt{13}}{13}$ $\quad\tan\theta=\dfrac{\text{opp}}{\text{adj}}=\dfrac{2}{3}$

   $\csc\theta=\dfrac{\text{hyp}}{\text{opp}}=\dfrac{\sqrt{13}}{2}$ $\quad\sec\theta=\dfrac{\text{hyp}}{\text{adj}}=\dfrac{\sqrt{13}}{3}$ $\quad\cot\theta=\dfrac{\text{adj}}{\text{opp}}=\dfrac{3}{2}$

4. opposite = 3; adjacent = 3
   Find the hypotenuse:
   $$3^2+3^2=(\text{hypotenuse})^2$$
   $$(\text{hypotenuse})^2=9+9=18\rightarrow\text{hypotenuse}=\sqrt{18}=3\sqrt{2}$$
   $\sin\theta=\dfrac{\text{opp}}{\text{hyp}}=\dfrac{3}{3\sqrt{2}}=\dfrac{\sqrt{2}}{2}$ $\quad\cos\theta=\dfrac{\text{adj}}{\text{hyp}}=\dfrac{3}{3\sqrt{2}}=\dfrac{\sqrt{2}}{2}$ $\quad\tan\theta=\dfrac{\text{opp}}{\text{adj}}=\dfrac{3}{3}=1$

   $\csc\theta=\dfrac{\text{hyp}}{\text{opp}}=\dfrac{3\sqrt{2}}{3}=\sqrt{2}$ $\quad\sec\theta=\dfrac{\text{hyp}}{\text{adj}}=\dfrac{3\sqrt{2}}{3}=\sqrt{2}$ $\quad\cot\theta=\dfrac{\text{adj}}{\text{opp}}=\dfrac{3}{3}=1$

5. adjacent = 2; hypotenuse = 4

Find the opposite side:

$$(\text{opposite})^2 + 2^2 = 4^2$$

$$(\text{opposite})^2 = 16 - 4 = 12 \rightarrow \text{opposite} = \sqrt{12} = 2\sqrt{3}$$

$$\sin\theta = \frac{\text{opp}}{\text{hyp}} = \frac{2\sqrt{3}}{4} = \frac{\sqrt{3}}{2} \quad \cos\theta = \frac{\text{adj}}{\text{hyp}} = \frac{2}{4} = \frac{1}{2} \quad \tan\theta = \frac{\text{opp}}{\text{adj}} = \frac{2\sqrt{3}}{2} = \sqrt{3}$$

$$\csc\theta = \frac{\text{hyp}}{\text{opp}} = \frac{4}{2\sqrt{3}} = \frac{2\sqrt{3}}{3} \quad \sec\theta = \frac{\text{hyp}}{\text{adj}} = \frac{4}{2} = 2 \quad \cot\theta = \frac{\text{adj}}{\text{opp}} = \frac{2}{2\sqrt{3}} = \frac{\sqrt{3}}{3}$$

6. opposite = 3; hypotenuse = 4

Find the adjacent side:

$$3^2 + (\text{adjacent})^2 = 4^2$$

$$(\text{adjacent})^2 = 16 - 9 = 7 \rightarrow \text{adjacent} = \sqrt{7}$$

$$\sin\theta = \frac{\text{opp}}{\text{hyp}} = \frac{3}{4} \quad \cos\theta = \frac{\text{adj}}{\text{hyp}} = \frac{\sqrt{7}}{4} \quad \tan\theta = \frac{\text{opp}}{\text{adj}} = \frac{3}{\sqrt{7}} = \frac{3\sqrt{7}}{7}$$

$$\csc\theta = \frac{\text{hyp}}{\text{opp}} = \frac{4}{3} \quad \sec\theta = \frac{\text{hyp}}{\text{adj}} = \frac{4}{\sqrt{7}} = \frac{4\sqrt{7}}{7} \quad \cot\theta = \frac{\text{adj}}{\text{opp}} = \frac{\sqrt{7}}{3}$$

7. opposite = $\sqrt{2}$; adjacent = 1

Find the hypotenuse:

$$\left(\sqrt{2}\right)^2 + 1^2 = (\text{hypotenuse})^2$$

$$(\text{hypotenuse})^2 = 2 + 1 = 3 \rightarrow \text{hypotenuse} = \sqrt{3}$$

$$\sin\theta = \frac{\text{opp}}{\text{hyp}} = \frac{\sqrt{2}}{\sqrt{3}} = \frac{\sqrt{6}}{3} \quad \cos\theta = \frac{\text{adj}}{\text{hyp}} = \frac{1}{\sqrt{3}} = \frac{\sqrt{3}}{3} \quad \tan\theta = \frac{\text{opp}}{\text{adj}} = \frac{\sqrt{2}}{1} = \sqrt{2}$$

$$\csc\theta = \frac{\text{hyp}}{\text{opp}} = \frac{\sqrt{3}}{\sqrt{2}} = \frac{\sqrt{6}}{2} \quad \sec\theta = \frac{\text{hyp}}{\text{adj}} = \frac{\sqrt{3}}{1} = \sqrt{3} \quad \cot\theta = \frac{\text{adj}}{\text{opp}} = \frac{1}{\sqrt{2}} = \frac{\sqrt{2}}{2}$$

8. opposite = 2; adjacent = $\sqrt{3}$

Find the hypotenuse:

$$2^2 + \left(\sqrt{3}\right)^2 = (\text{hypotenuse})^2$$

$$(\text{hypotenuse})^2 = 4 + 3 = 7 \rightarrow \text{hypotenuse} = \sqrt{7}$$

$$\sin\theta = \frac{\text{opp}}{\text{hyp}} = \frac{2}{\sqrt{7}} = \frac{2\sqrt{7}}{7} \quad \cos\theta = \frac{\text{adj}}{\text{hyp}} = \frac{\sqrt{3}}{\sqrt{7}} = \frac{\sqrt{21}}{7} \quad \tan\theta = \frac{\text{opp}}{\text{adj}} = \frac{2}{\sqrt{3}} = \frac{2\sqrt{3}}{3}$$

$$\csc\theta = \frac{\text{hyp}}{\text{opp}} = \frac{\sqrt{7}}{2} \quad \sec\theta = \frac{\text{hyp}}{\text{adj}} = \frac{\sqrt{7}}{\sqrt{3}} = \frac{\sqrt{21}}{3} \quad \cot\theta = \frac{\text{adj}}{\text{opp}} = \frac{\sqrt{3}}{2}$$

9. opposite = 1; hypotenuse = $\sqrt{5}$
Find the adjacent side:

$$1^2 + (\text{adjacent})^2 = \left(\sqrt{5}\right)^2$$

$$(\text{adjacent})^2 = 5 - 1 = 4 \rightarrow \text{adjacent} = 2$$

$\sin\theta = \dfrac{\text{opp}}{\text{hyp}} = \dfrac{1}{\sqrt{5}} = \dfrac{\sqrt{5}}{5}$ $\cos\theta = \dfrac{\text{adj}}{\text{hyp}} = \dfrac{2}{\sqrt{5}} = \dfrac{2\sqrt{5}}{5}$ $\tan\theta = \dfrac{\text{opp}}{\text{adj}} = \dfrac{1}{2}$

$\csc\theta = \dfrac{\text{hyp}}{\text{opp}} = \dfrac{\sqrt{5}}{1} = \sqrt{5}$ $\sec\theta = \dfrac{\text{hyp}}{\text{adj}} = \dfrac{\sqrt{5}}{2}$ $\cot\theta = \dfrac{\text{adj}}{\text{opp}} = \dfrac{2}{1} = 2$

10. adjacent = 2; hypotenuse = $\sqrt{5}$
Find the opposite side:

$$(\text{opposite})^2 + 2^2 = \left(\sqrt{5}\right)^2$$

$$(\text{opposite})^2 = 5 - 4 = 1 \rightarrow \text{opposite} = 1$$

$\sin\theta = \dfrac{\text{opp}}{\text{hyp}} = \dfrac{1}{\sqrt{5}} = \dfrac{\sqrt{5}}{5}$ $\cos\theta = \dfrac{\text{adj}}{\text{hyp}} = \dfrac{2}{\sqrt{5}} = \dfrac{2\sqrt{5}}{5}$ $\tan\theta = \dfrac{\text{opp}}{\text{adj}} = \dfrac{1}{2}$

$\csc\theta = \dfrac{\text{hyp}}{\text{opp}} = \dfrac{\sqrt{5}}{1} = \sqrt{5}$ $\sec\theta = \dfrac{\text{hyp}}{\text{adj}} = \dfrac{\sqrt{5}}{2}$ $\cot\theta = \dfrac{\text{adj}}{\text{opp}} = \dfrac{2}{1} = 2$

11. $\sin\theta = \dfrac{1}{2}$; $\cos\theta = \dfrac{\sqrt{3}}{2}$

$\tan\theta = \dfrac{\sin\theta}{\cos\theta} = \dfrac{\left(\frac{1}{2}\right)}{\left(\frac{\sqrt{3}}{2}\right)} = \dfrac{1}{2} \cdot \dfrac{2}{\sqrt{3}} = \dfrac{1}{\sqrt{3}} \dfrac{\sqrt{3}}{\sqrt{3}} = \dfrac{\sqrt{3}}{3}$ $\cot\theta = \dfrac{1}{\tan\theta} = \dfrac{1}{\left(\frac{\sqrt{3}}{3}\right)} = \dfrac{3}{\sqrt{3}} \dfrac{\sqrt{3}}{\sqrt{3}} = \dfrac{3\sqrt{3}}{3} = \sqrt{3}$

$\sec\theta = \dfrac{1}{\cos\theta} = \dfrac{1}{\left(\frac{\sqrt{3}}{2}\right)} = \dfrac{2}{\sqrt{3}} \dfrac{\sqrt{3}}{\sqrt{3}} = \dfrac{2\sqrt{3}}{3}$ $\csc\theta = \dfrac{1}{\sin\theta} = \dfrac{1}{\left(\frac{1}{2}\right)} = 2$

12. $\sin\theta = \dfrac{\sqrt{3}}{2}$; $\cos\theta = \dfrac{1}{2}$

$\tan\theta = \dfrac{\sin\theta}{\cos\theta} = \dfrac{\left(\frac{\sqrt{3}}{2}\right)}{\left(\frac{1}{2}\right)} = \dfrac{\sqrt{3}}{2} \cdot \dfrac{2}{1} = \sqrt{3}$ $\cot\theta = \dfrac{1}{\tan\theta} = \dfrac{1}{\sqrt{3}} \dfrac{\sqrt{3}}{\sqrt{3}} = \dfrac{\sqrt{3}}{3}$

$\sec\theta = \dfrac{1}{\cos\theta} = \dfrac{1}{\left(\frac{1}{2}\right)} = 2$ $\csc\theta = \dfrac{1}{\sin\theta} = \dfrac{1}{\left(\frac{\sqrt{3}}{2}\right)} = \dfrac{2}{\sqrt{3}} \dfrac{\sqrt{3}}{\sqrt{3}} = \dfrac{2\sqrt{3}}{3}$

13. $\sin\theta = \dfrac{2}{3}; \quad \cos\theta = \dfrac{\sqrt{5}}{3}$

$$\tan\theta = \frac{\sin\theta}{\cos\theta} = \frac{\left(\frac{2}{3}\right)}{\left(\frac{\sqrt{5}}{3}\right)} = \frac{2}{3}\cdot\frac{3}{\sqrt{5}} = \frac{2}{\sqrt{5}}\frac{\sqrt{5}}{\sqrt{5}} = \frac{2\sqrt{5}}{5} \qquad \cot\theta = \frac{1}{\tan\theta} = \frac{1}{\left(\frac{2\sqrt{5}}{5}\right)} = \frac{5}{2\sqrt{5}}\frac{\sqrt{5}}{\sqrt{5}} = \frac{5\sqrt{5}}{10} = \frac{\sqrt{5}}{2}$$

$$\sec\theta = \frac{1}{\cos\theta} = \frac{1}{\left(\frac{\sqrt{5}}{3}\right)} = \frac{3}{\sqrt{5}}\frac{\sqrt{5}}{\sqrt{5}} = \frac{3\sqrt{5}}{5} \qquad \csc\theta = \frac{1}{\sin\theta} = \frac{1}{\left(\frac{2}{3}\right)} = \frac{3}{2}$$

14. $\sin\theta = \dfrac{1}{3}; \quad \cos\theta = \dfrac{2\sqrt{2}}{3}$

$$\tan\theta = \frac{\sin\theta}{\cos\theta} = \frac{\left(\frac{1}{3}\right)}{\left(\frac{2\sqrt{2}}{3}\right)} = \frac{1}{3}\cdot\frac{3}{2\sqrt{2}} = \frac{1}{2\sqrt{2}}\frac{\sqrt{2}}{\sqrt{2}} = \frac{\sqrt{2}}{4}$$

$$\cot\theta = \frac{1}{\tan\theta} = \frac{1}{\left(\frac{\sqrt{2}}{4}\right)} = \frac{4}{\sqrt{2}}\frac{\sqrt{2}}{\sqrt{2}} = \frac{4\sqrt{2}}{2} = 2\sqrt{2}$$

$$\sec\theta = \frac{1}{\cos\theta} = \frac{1}{\left(\frac{2\sqrt{2}}{3}\right)} = \frac{3}{2\sqrt{2}}\frac{\sqrt{2}}{\sqrt{2}} = \frac{3\sqrt{2}}{4} \qquad \csc\theta = \frac{1}{\sin\theta} = \frac{1}{\left(\frac{1}{3}\right)} = 3$$

15. $\sin\theta = \dfrac{\sqrt{2}}{2}$ corresponds to the right triangle

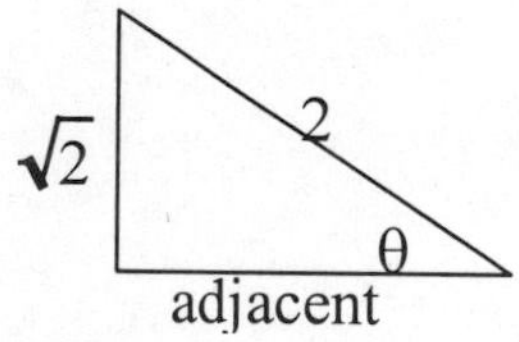

Using the Pythagorean Theorem:

$$(adjacent)^2 + \left(\sqrt{2}\right)^2 = 2^2$$

$$(adjacent)^2 + 2 = 4 \rightarrow (adjacent)^2 = 2 \rightarrow adjacent = \sqrt{2}$$

So the triangle becomes

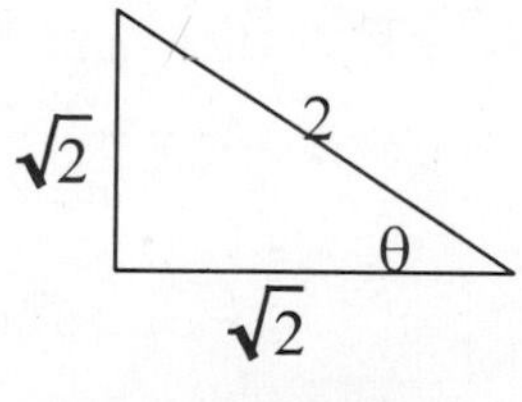

$$\cos\theta = \frac{\text{adj}}{\text{hyp}} = \frac{\sqrt{2}}{2} = \frac{2\sqrt{2}}{2} \qquad \tan\theta = \frac{\text{opp}}{\text{adj}} = \frac{\sqrt{2}}{\sqrt{2}} = 1 \qquad \cot\theta = \frac{\text{adj}}{\text{opp}} = \frac{\sqrt{2}}{\sqrt{2}} = 1$$

$$\csc\theta = \frac{\text{hyp}}{\text{opp}} = \frac{2}{\sqrt{2}} = \sqrt{2} \qquad \sec\theta = \frac{\text{hyp}}{\text{adj}} = \frac{2}{\sqrt{2}} = \sqrt{2}$$

16. $\cos\theta = \dfrac{\sqrt{2}}{2}$ corresponds to the right triangle

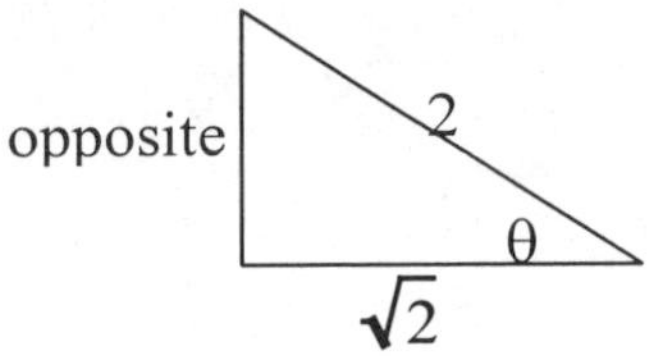

Using the Pythagorean Theorem:

$$(opposite)^2 + \left(\sqrt{2}\right)^2 = 2^2$$

$$(opposite)^2 + 2 = 4 \rightarrow (opposite)^2 = 2 \rightarrow opposite = \sqrt{2}$$

So the triangle becomes

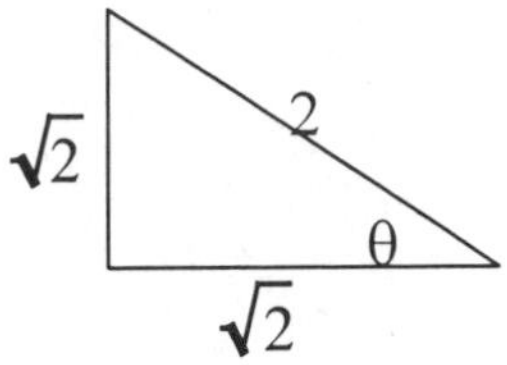

$$\sin\theta = \frac{\text{opp}}{\text{hyp}} = \frac{\sqrt{2}}{2} = \frac{2\sqrt{2}}{2} \qquad \tan\theta = \frac{\text{opp}}{\text{adj}} = \frac{\sqrt{2}}{\sqrt{2}} = 1 \qquad \cot\theta = \frac{\text{adj}}{\text{opp}} = \frac{\sqrt{2}}{\sqrt{2}} = 1$$

$$\csc\theta = \frac{\text{hyp}}{\text{opp}} = \frac{2}{\sqrt{2}} = \sqrt{2} \qquad \sec\theta = \frac{\text{hyp}}{\text{adj}} = \frac{2}{\sqrt{2}} = \sqrt{2}$$

17. $\cos\theta = \dfrac{1}{3}$ corresponds to the right triangle

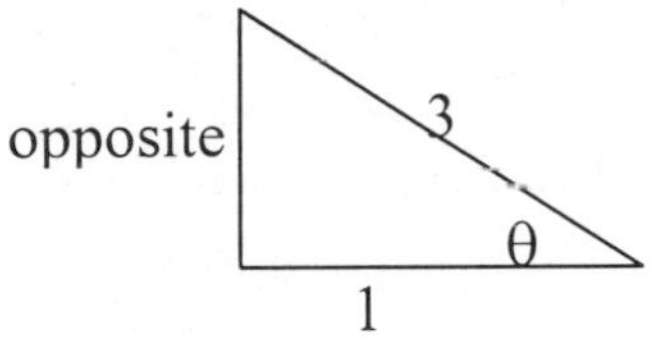

Using the Pythagorean Theorem:

$$(opposite)^2 + (1)^2 = 3^2$$

$$(opposite)^2 + 1 = 9 \rightarrow (opposite)^2 = 8 \rightarrow opposite = \sqrt{8}$$

So the triangle becomes

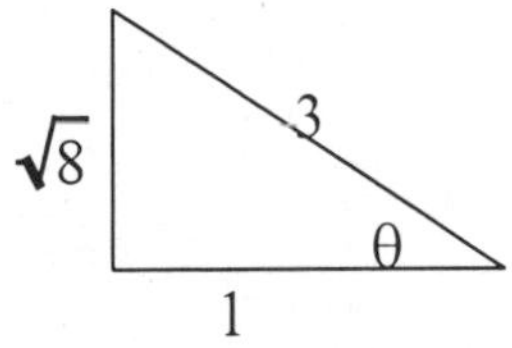

$$\sin\theta = \frac{\text{opp}}{\text{hyp}} = \frac{\sqrt{8}}{3} = \frac{2\sqrt{2}}{3} \qquad \tan\theta = \frac{\text{opp}}{\text{adj}} = \frac{\sqrt{8}}{1} = 2\sqrt{2} \qquad \cot\theta = \frac{\text{adj}}{\text{opp}} = \frac{1}{\sqrt{8}}\frac{\sqrt{8}}{\sqrt{8}}$$

$$\csc\theta = \frac{\text{hyp}}{\text{opp}} = \frac{3}{\sqrt{8}}\frac{\sqrt{8}}{\sqrt{8}} = \frac{3\sqrt{8}}{8} \qquad \sec\theta = \frac{\text{hyp}}{\text{adj}} = \frac{3}{1} = 3 \qquad = \frac{\sqrt{8}}{8} = \frac{2\sqrt{2}}{8} = \frac{\sqrt{2}}{4}$$

18. $\sin\theta = \dfrac{\sqrt{3}}{4}$ corresponds to the right triangle

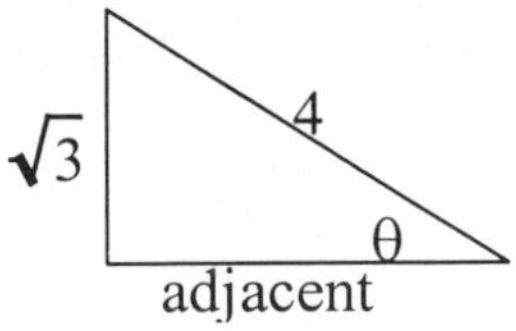

Using the Pythagorean Theorem:

$$(adjacent)^2 + \left(\sqrt{3}\right)^2 = 4^2$$

$$(adjacent)^2 + 3 = 16 \rightarrow (adjacent)^2 = 13 \rightarrow adjacent = \sqrt{13}$$

So the triangle becomes

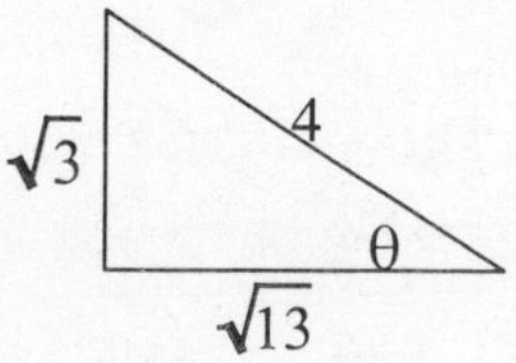

$\cos\theta = \frac{\text{adj}}{\text{hyp}} = \frac{\sqrt{13}}{4}$ $\tan\theta = \frac{\text{opp}}{\text{adj}} = \frac{\sqrt{3}}{\sqrt{13}}\frac{\sqrt{13}}{\sqrt{13}} = \frac{\sqrt{39}}{13}$

$\csc\theta = \frac{\text{hyp}}{\text{opp}} = \frac{4}{\sqrt{3}}\frac{\sqrt{3}}{\sqrt{3}} = \frac{4\sqrt{3}}{3}$ $\sec\theta = \frac{\text{hyp}}{\text{adj}} = \frac{4}{\sqrt{13}}\frac{\sqrt{13}}{\sqrt{13}} = \frac{4\sqrt{13}}{13}$

$\cot\theta = \frac{\text{adj}}{\text{opp}} = \frac{\sqrt{13}}{\sqrt{3}}\frac{\sqrt{3}}{\sqrt{3}} = \frac{\sqrt{39}}{3}$

19. $\tan\theta = \frac{1}{2}$ corresponds to the right triangle

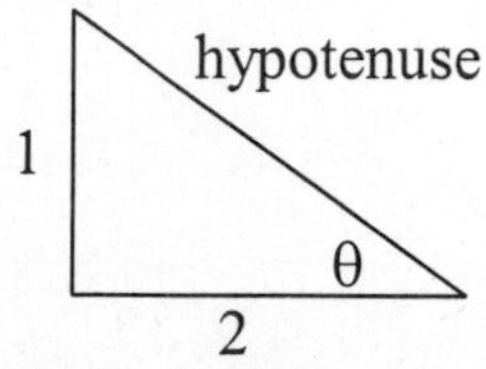

Using the Pythagorean Theorem:

$(1)^2 + (2)^2 = (hypotenuse)^2$

$1 + 4 = (hypotenuse)^2 \rightarrow 5 = (hypotenuse)^2 \rightarrow hypotenuse = \sqrt{5}$

So the triangle becomes

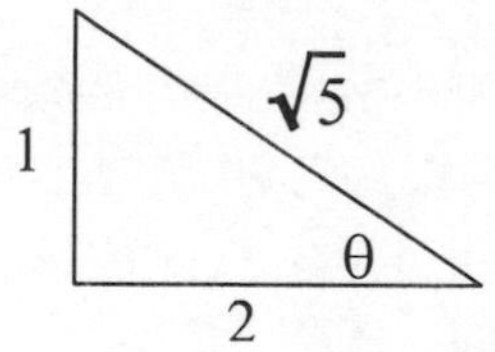

$\cos\theta = \frac{\text{adj}}{\text{hyp}} = \frac{2}{\sqrt{5}}\frac{\sqrt{5}}{\sqrt{5}} = \frac{2\sqrt{5}}{5}$ $\sin\theta = \frac{\text{opp}}{\text{hyp}} = \frac{1}{\sqrt{5}}\frac{\sqrt{5}}{\sqrt{5}} = \frac{\sqrt{5}}{5}$ $\cot\theta = \frac{\text{adj}}{\text{opp}} = \frac{2}{1} = 2$

$\csc\theta = \frac{\text{hyp}}{\text{opp}} = \frac{\sqrt{5}}{1} = \sqrt{5}$ $\sec\theta = \frac{\text{hyp}}{\text{adj}} = \frac{\sqrt{5}}{2}$

20. $\cot\theta = \frac{1}{2}$ corresponds to the right triangle

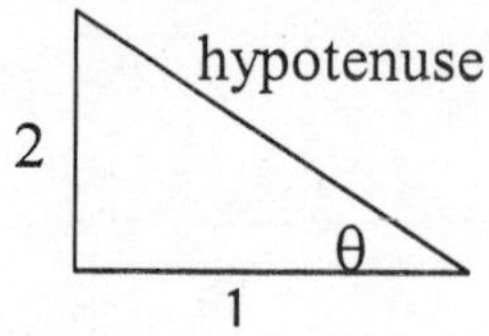

Using the Pythagorean Theorem:

$(1)^2 + (2)^2 = (hypotenuse)^2$

$1 + 4 = (hypotenuse)^2 \rightarrow 5 = (hypotenuse)^2 \rightarrow hypotenuse = \sqrt{5}$

So the triangle becomes

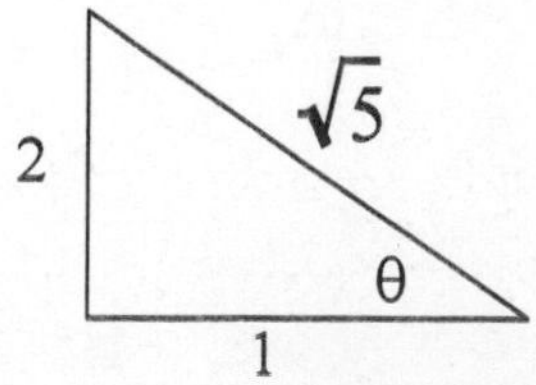

$\cos\theta = \frac{\text{adj}}{\text{hyp}} = \frac{1}{\sqrt{5}}\frac{\sqrt{5}}{\sqrt{5}} = \frac{\sqrt{5}}{5}$ $\sin\theta = \frac{\text{opp}}{\text{hyp}} = \frac{2}{\sqrt{5}}\frac{\sqrt{5}}{\sqrt{5}} = \frac{2\sqrt{5}}{5}$ $\tan\theta = \frac{\text{opp}}{\text{adj}} = \frac{2}{1} = 2$

$\csc\theta = \frac{\text{hyp}}{\text{opp}} = \frac{\sqrt{5}}{2}$ $\sec\theta = \frac{\text{hyp}}{\text{adj}} = \frac{\sqrt{5}}{1} = \sqrt{5}$

21. $\sec\theta = 3$ corresponds to the right triangle

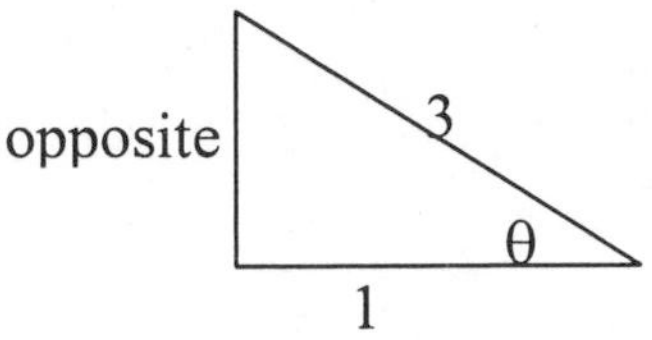

Using the Pythagorean Theorem:

$(opposite)^2 + (1)^2 = 3^2$

$(opposite)^2 + 1 = 9 \rightarrow (opposite)^2 = 8 \rightarrow opposite = \sqrt{8}$

So the triangle becomes

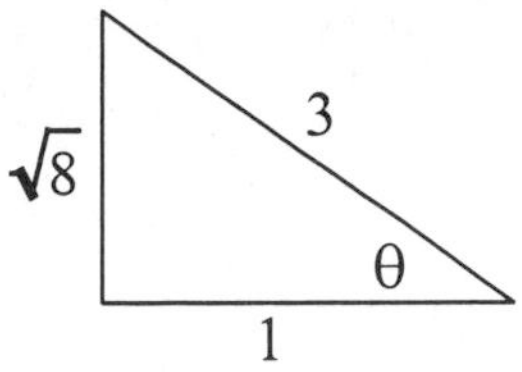

$\sin\theta = \dfrac{\text{opp}}{\text{hyp}} = \dfrac{\sqrt{8}}{3} = \dfrac{2\sqrt{2}}{3}$ $\tan\theta = \dfrac{\text{opp}}{\text{adj}} = \dfrac{\sqrt{8}}{1} = 2\sqrt{2}$ $\cot\theta = \dfrac{\text{adj}}{\text{opp}} = \dfrac{1}{\sqrt{8}} \cdot \dfrac{\sqrt{8}}{\sqrt{8}}$

$\csc\theta = \dfrac{\text{hyp}}{\text{opp}} = \dfrac{3}{\sqrt{8}} \cdot \dfrac{\sqrt{8}}{\sqrt{8}} = \dfrac{3\sqrt{8}}{8}$ $\cos\theta = \dfrac{\text{adj}}{\text{hyp}} = \dfrac{1}{3}$ $= \dfrac{\sqrt{8}}{8} = \dfrac{2\sqrt{2}}{8} = \dfrac{\sqrt{2}}{4}$

22. $\csc\theta = 5$ corresponds to the right triangle

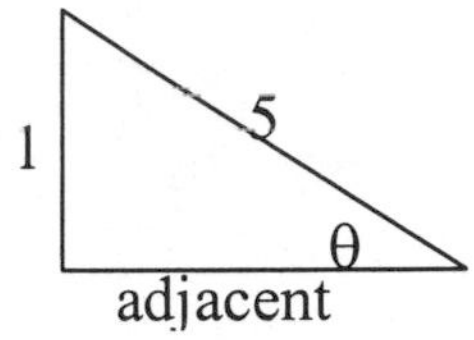

Using the Pythagorean Theorem:

$(adjacent)^2 + (1)^2 = 5^2$

$(adjacent)^2 + 1 = 25 \rightarrow (adjacent)^2 = 24 \rightarrow adjacent = \sqrt{24}$

So the triangle becomes

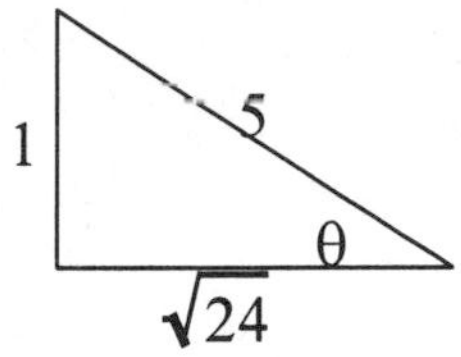

$\cos\theta = \dfrac{\text{adj}}{\text{hyp}} = \dfrac{\sqrt{24}}{5} = \dfrac{4\sqrt{6}}{5}$ $\tan\theta = \dfrac{\text{opp}}{\text{adj}} = \dfrac{1}{\sqrt{24}} \cdot \dfrac{\sqrt{24}}{\sqrt{24}} = \dfrac{4\sqrt{6}}{24} = \dfrac{\sqrt{6}}{6}$

$\sin\theta = \dfrac{\text{opp}}{\text{hyp}} = \dfrac{1}{5}$ $\sec\theta = \dfrac{\text{hyp}}{\text{adj}} = \dfrac{5}{\sqrt{24}} \cdot \dfrac{\sqrt{24}}{\sqrt{24}} = \dfrac{20\sqrt{6}}{24} = \dfrac{5\sqrt{6}}{6}$

$\cot\theta = \dfrac{\text{adj}}{\text{opp}} = \dfrac{\sqrt{24}}{1} = 4\sqrt{6}$

23. $\tan\theta = \sqrt{2}$ corresponds to the right triangle

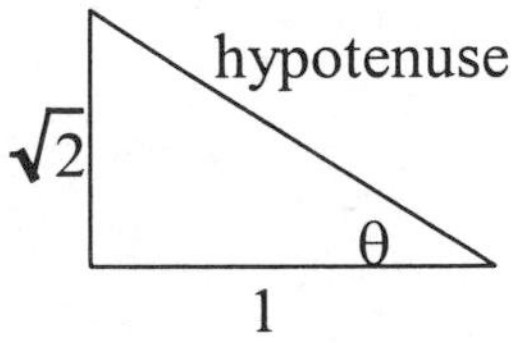

Using the Pythagorean Theorem:

$(1)^2 + \left(\sqrt{2}\right)^2 = (hypotenuse)^2$

$1 + 2 = (hypotenuse)^2 \rightarrow 3 = (hypotenuse)^2 \rightarrow hypotenuse = \sqrt{3}$

So the triangle becomes

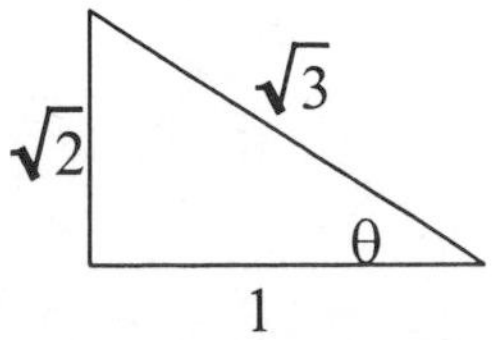

$$\cos\theta = \frac{\text{adj}}{\text{hyp}} = \frac{1}{\sqrt{3}}\frac{\sqrt{3}}{\sqrt{3}} = \frac{\sqrt{3}}{3} \qquad \sin\theta = \frac{\text{opp}}{\text{hyp}} = \frac{\sqrt{2}}{\sqrt{3}}\frac{\sqrt{3}}{\sqrt{3}} = \frac{\sqrt{6}}{3}$$

$$\csc\theta = \frac{\text{hyp}}{\text{opp}} = \frac{\sqrt{3}}{\sqrt{2}}\frac{\sqrt{2}}{\sqrt{2}} = \frac{\sqrt{6}}{2} \qquad \sec\theta = \frac{\text{hyp}}{\text{adj}} = \frac{\sqrt{3}}{1} = \sqrt{3}$$

$$\cot\theta = \frac{\text{adj}}{\text{opp}} = \frac{1}{\sqrt{2}}\frac{\sqrt{2}}{\sqrt{2}} = \frac{\sqrt{2}}{2}$$

24. $\sec\theta = \frac{5}{3}$ corresponds to the right triangle

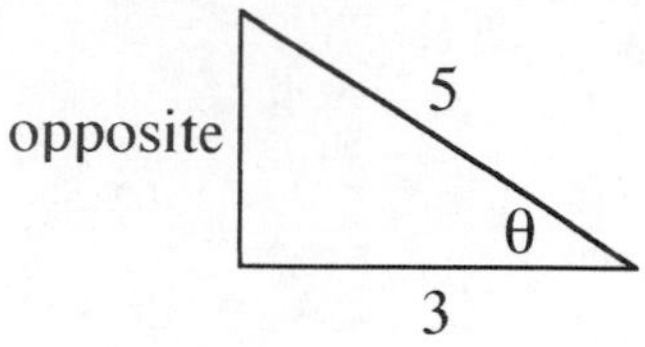

Using the Pythagorean Theorem:

$$(opposite)^2 + (3)^2 = 5^2$$

$$(opposite)^2 + 9 = 25 \to (opposite)^2 = 16 \to opposite = 4$$

So the triangle becomes

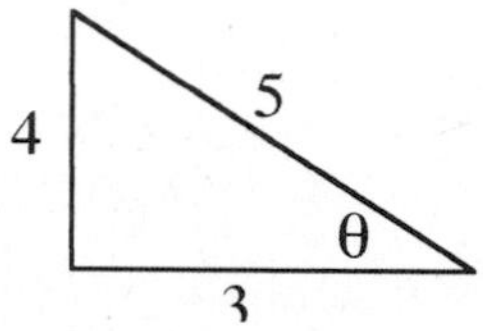

$$\sin\theta = \frac{\text{opp}}{\text{hyp}} = \frac{4}{5} \qquad \tan\theta = \frac{\text{opp}}{\text{adj}} = \frac{4}{3} \qquad \cot\theta = \frac{\text{adj}}{\text{opp}} = \frac{3}{4}$$

$$\csc\theta = \frac{\text{hyp}}{\text{opp}} = \frac{5}{4} \qquad \cos\theta = \frac{\text{adj}}{\text{hyp}} = \frac{3}{5}$$

25. $\csc\theta = 2$ corresponds to the right triangle

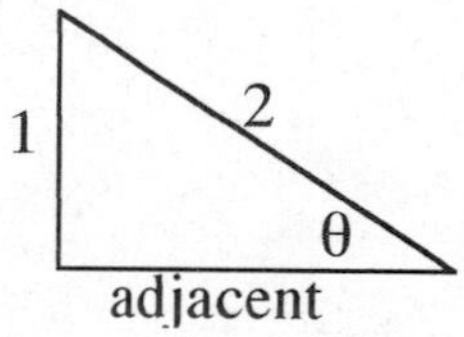

Using the Pythagorean Theorem:

$$(adjacent)^2 + (1)^2 = 2^2$$

$$(adjacent)^2 + 1 = 4 \to (adjacent)^2 = 3 \to adjacent = \sqrt{3}$$

So the triangle becomes

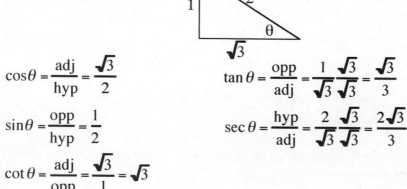

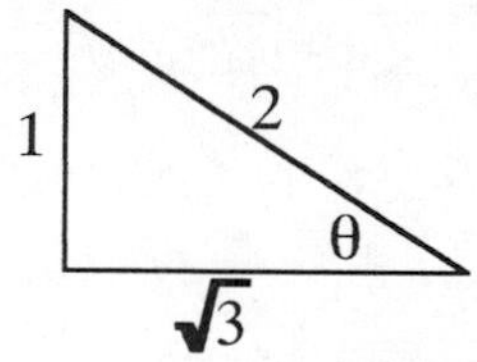

$$\cos\theta = \frac{\text{adj}}{\text{hyp}} = \frac{\sqrt{3}}{2} \qquad \tan\theta = \frac{\text{opp}}{\text{adj}} = \frac{1}{\sqrt{3}}\frac{\sqrt{3}}{\sqrt{3}} = \frac{\sqrt{3}}{3}$$

$$\sin\theta = \frac{\text{opp}}{\text{hyp}} = \frac{1}{2} \qquad \sec\theta = \frac{\text{hyp}}{\text{adj}} = \frac{2}{\sqrt{3}}\frac{\sqrt{3}}{\sqrt{3}} = \frac{2\sqrt{3}}{3}$$

$$\cot\theta = \frac{\text{adj}}{\text{opp}} = \frac{\sqrt{3}}{1} = \sqrt{3}$$

26. $\cot\theta = 2$ corresponds to the right triangle

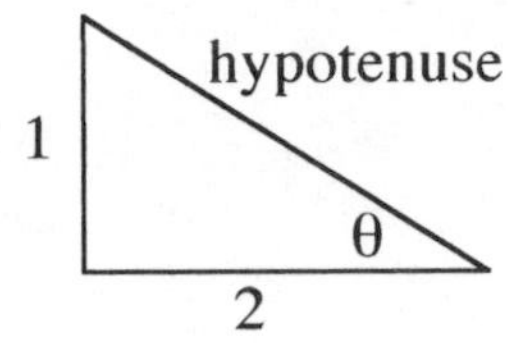

Using the Pythagorean Theorem:

$(1)^2 + (2)^2 = (hypotenuse)^2$

$1 + 4 = (hypotenuse)^2 \rightarrow 5 = (hypotenuse)^2 \rightarrow hypotenuse = \sqrt{5}$

So the triangle becomes

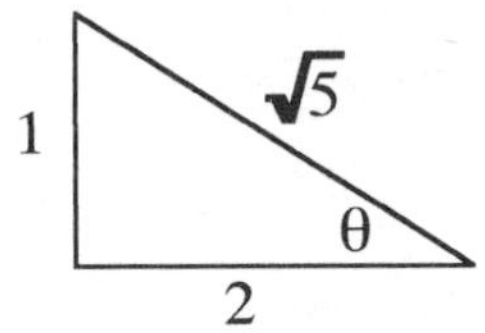

$\cos\theta = \frac{\text{adj}}{\text{hyp}} = \frac{2}{\sqrt{5}}\frac{\sqrt{5}}{\sqrt{5}} = \frac{2\sqrt{5}}{5}$ $\quad \sin\theta = \frac{\text{opp}}{\text{hyp}} = \frac{1}{\sqrt{5}}\frac{\sqrt{5}}{\sqrt{5}} = \frac{\sqrt{5}}{5}$ $\quad \tan\theta = \frac{\text{opp}}{\text{adj}} = \frac{1}{2}$

$\csc\theta = \frac{\text{hyp}}{\text{opp}} = \frac{\sqrt{5}}{1} = \sqrt{5}$ $\quad \sec\theta = \frac{\text{hyp}}{\text{adj}} = \frac{\sqrt{5}}{2}$

27. $\sin^2(20°) + \cos^2(20°) = 1$, using the identity $\sin^2\theta + \cos^2\theta = 1$

28. $\sec^2(28°) - \tan^2(28°) = 1$, using the identity $\tan^2\theta + 1 = \sec^2\theta$

29. $\sin(80°)\csc(80°) = \sin(80°)\cdot\frac{1}{\sin(80°)} = 1$, using the identity $\csc\theta = \frac{1}{\sin\theta}$

30. $\tan(10°)\cot(10°) = \tan(10°)\cdot\frac{1}{\tan(10°)} = 1$, using the identity $\cot\theta = \frac{1}{\tan\theta}$

31. $\tan(50°) - \frac{\sin(50°)}{\cos(50°)} = \frac{\sin(50°)}{\cos(50°)} - \frac{\sin(50°)}{\cos(50°)} = 0$, using the identity $\tan\theta = \frac{\sin\theta}{\cos\theta}$

32. $\cot(25°) - \frac{\cos(25°)}{\sin(25°)} = \frac{\cos(25°)}{\sin(25°)} - \frac{\cos(25°)}{\sin(25°)} = 0$, using the identity $\cot\theta = \frac{\cos\theta}{\sin\theta}$

33. $\sin(38°) - \cos(52°) = \sin(38°) - \sin(90° - 52°) = \sin(38°) - \sin(38°) = 0$

34. $\tan(12°) - \cot(78°) = \tan(12°) - \tan(90° - 78°) = \tan(12°) - \tan(12°) = 0$

35. $\frac{\cos(10°)}{\sin(80°)} = \frac{\sin(90° - 10°)}{\sin(80°)} = \frac{\sin(80°)}{\sin(80°)} = 1$

36. $\frac{\cos(40°)}{\sin(50°)} = \frac{\sin(90° - 40°)}{\sin(50°)} = \frac{\sin(50°)}{\sin(50°)} = 1$

37. $1 - \cos^2(20°) - \cos^2(70°) = \sin^2(20°) - \sin^2(90° - 70°) = \sin^2(20°) - \sin^2(20°) = 0$

38. $1+\tan^2(5°)-\csc^2(85°)=\sec^2(5°)-\sec^2(90°-85°)=\sec^2(5°)-\sec^2(5°)=0$

39. $\tan(20°)-\dfrac{\cos(70°)}{\cos(20°)}=\tan 20°-\dfrac{\sin(90°-70°)}{\cos(20°)}=\tan(20°)-\dfrac{\sin(20°)}{\cos(20°)}=\tan(20°)-\tan(20°)=0$

40. $\cot(40°)-\dfrac{\sin(50°)}{\sin(40°)}=\cot(40°)-\dfrac{\cos(90°-50°)}{\sin(40°)}=\cot(40°)-\dfrac{\cos(40°)}{\sin(40°)}=\cot(40°)-\cot(40°)=0$

41. $\tan(35°)\sec(55°)\cos(35°)=\left(\dfrac{\sin(35°)}{\cos(35°)}\right)\sec(55°)\cos(35°)=\sin(35°)\sec(55°)$

$=\sin(35°)\csc(90°-55°)=\sin(35°)\csc(35°)=\sin(35°)\cdot\dfrac{1}{\sin(35°)}=1$

42. $\cot(25°)\csc(65°)\sin(25°)$

$=\left(\dfrac{\cos(25°)}{\sin(25°)}\right)\csc(65°)\sin(25°)=\cos(25°)\csc(65°)=\cos(25°)\sec(90°-65°)$

$=\cos(25°)\sec(25°)=\cos(25°)\cdot\dfrac{1}{\cos(25°)}=1$

43. $\cos(35°)\sin(55°)+\cos(55°)\sin(35°)=\sin(55°+35°)=\sin(90°)=1$

44. $\sec(35°)\csc(55°)-\tan(35°)\cot(55°)=\sec(35°)\sec(35°)-\tan(35°)\tan(35°)$

$=\sec^2 35°-\tan^2 35°=1$

45. Given: $\sin(30°)=\dfrac{1}{2}$

(a) $\cos(60°)=\sin(90°-60°)=\sin(30°)=\dfrac{1}{2}$

(b) $\cos^2(30°)=1-\sin^2(30°)=1-\left(\dfrac{1}{2}\right)^2=1-\dfrac{1}{4}=\dfrac{3}{4}$

(c) $\csc\left(\dfrac{\pi}{6}\right)=\csc(30°)=\dfrac{1}{\sin(30°)}=\dfrac{1}{\left(\dfrac{1}{2}\right)}=2$

(d) $\sec\left(\dfrac{\pi}{3}\right)=\sec(60°)=\csc(90°-60°)=\csc(30°)=2$

46. Given: $\sin 60°=\dfrac{\sqrt{3}}{2}$

(a) $\cos(30°)=\sin(90°-30°)=\sin(60°)=\dfrac{\sqrt{3}}{2}$

(b) $\cos^2(60^\circ) = 1 - \sin^2(60^\circ) = 1 - \left(\frac{\sqrt{3}}{2}\right)^2 = 1 - \frac{3}{4} = \frac{1}{4}$

(c) $\sec\left(\frac{\pi}{6}\right) = \sec(30^\circ) = \frac{1}{\cos(30^\circ)} = \frac{1}{\left(\frac{\sqrt{3}}{2}\right)} = \frac{2}{\sqrt{3}}\frac{\sqrt{3}}{\sqrt{3}} = \frac{2\sqrt{3}}{3}$

(d) $\csc\left(\frac{\pi}{3}\right) = \csc(60^\circ) = \sec(90^\circ - 60^\circ) = \sec(30^\circ) = \frac{2\sqrt{3}}{3}$

47. Given: $\tan\theta = 4$

(a) $\sec^2\theta = 1 + \tan^2\theta = 1 + 4^2 = 1 + 16 = 17$

(b) $\cot\theta = \frac{1}{\tan\theta} = \frac{1}{4}$

(c) $\cot\left(\frac{\pi}{2} - \theta\right) = \tan\theta = 4$

(d) $\csc^2\theta = 1 + \cot^2\theta = 1 + \frac{1}{\tan^2\theta} = 1 + \frac{1}{4^2} = 1 + \frac{1}{16} = \frac{17}{16}$

48. Given: $\sec\theta = 3$

(a) $\cos\theta = \frac{1}{\sec\theta} = \frac{1}{3}$

(b) $\tan^2\theta = \sec^2\theta - 1 = 3^2 - 1 = 9 - 1 = 8$

(c) $\csc(90^\circ - \theta) = \sec\theta = 3$

(d) $\sin^2\theta = 1 - \cos^2\theta = 1 - \frac{1}{\sec^2\theta} = 1 - \frac{1}{3^2} = 1 - \frac{1}{9} = \frac{8}{9}$

49. Given: $\csc\theta = 4$

(a) $\sin\theta = \frac{1}{\csc\theta} = \frac{1}{4}$

(b) $\cot^2\theta = \csc^2\theta - 1 = 4^2 - 1 = 16 - 1 = 15$

(c) $\sec(90^\circ - \theta) = \csc\theta = 4$

(d) $\sec^2\theta = 1 + \tan^2\theta = 1 + \frac{1}{\cot^2\theta} = 1 + \frac{1}{\csc^2\theta - 1} = 1 + \frac{1}{4^2 - 1} = 1 + \frac{1}{15} = \frac{16}{15}$

50. Given: $\cot\theta = 2$

(a) $\tan\theta = \frac{1}{\cot\theta} = \frac{1}{2}$

(b) $\csc^2\theta = \cot^2\theta + 1 = 2^2 + 1 = 4 + 1 = 5$

(c) $\tan\left(\frac{\pi}{2} - \theta\right) = \cot\theta = 2$

(d) $\sec^2\theta = 1 + \tan^2\theta = 1 + \frac{1}{\cot^2\theta} = 1 + \frac{1}{2^2} = 1 + \frac{1}{4} = \frac{5}{4}$

51. Given: $\sin(38^\circ) \approx 0.62$

(a) $\cos(38^\circ) \approx ?$

$\sin^2(38^\circ) + \cos^2(38^\circ) = 1$

$\cos^2(38^\circ) = 1 - \sin^2(38^\circ) \rightarrow \cos(38^\circ) = \sqrt{1 - \sin^2(38^\circ)} \approx \sqrt{1 - (0.62)^2} \approx 0.785$

(b) $\tan(38^\circ) \approx ?$

$\tan(38^\circ) = \dfrac{\sin(38^\circ)}{\cos(38^\circ)} \approx \dfrac{0.62}{0.785} \approx 0.79$

(c) $\cot(38^\circ) \approx ?$

$\cot(38^\circ) = \dfrac{\cos(38^\circ)}{\sin(38^\circ)} \approx \dfrac{0.785}{0.62} \approx 1.266$

(d) $\sec(38^\circ) \approx ?$

$\sec(38^\circ) = \dfrac{1}{\cos(38^\circ)} \approx \dfrac{1}{0.785} \approx 1.274$

(e) $\csc(38^\circ) \approx ?$

$\csc(38^\circ) = \dfrac{1}{\sin(38^\circ)} \approx \dfrac{1}{0.62} \approx 1.613$

(f) $\sin(52)^\circ \approx ?$

$\sin(52^\circ) = \cos(90^\circ - 52^\circ)$

$= \cos(38^\circ) \approx 0.785$

(g) $\cos(52^\circ) \approx ?$

$\cos(52^\circ) = \sin(90^\circ - 52^\circ)$

$= \sin(38^\circ) \approx 0.62$

(h) $\tan(52^\circ) \approx ?$

$\tan(52^\circ) = \cot(90^\circ - 52^\circ) = \cot(38^\circ) \approx 1.266$

52. Given: $\cos(21^\circ) \approx 0.93$

(a) $\sin(21^\circ) \approx ?$

$\sin^2(21^\circ) + \cos^2(21^\circ) = 1$

$\sin^2(21^\circ) = 1 - \cos^2(21^\circ) \rightarrow \sin(21^\circ) = \sqrt{1 - \cos^2(21^\circ)} \approx \sqrt{1 - (0.93)^2} \approx 0.368$

(b) $\tan(21^\circ) \approx ?$

$\tan(21^\circ) = \dfrac{\sin(21^\circ)}{\cos(21^\circ)} \approx \dfrac{0.368}{0.93} = 0.396$

(c) $\cot(21^\circ) \approx ?$

$\cot(21^\circ) = \dfrac{\cos(21^\circ)}{\sin(21^\circ)} \approx \dfrac{0.93}{0.368} = 2.527$

(d) $\sec(21^\circ) \approx ?$

$\sec(21^\circ) = \dfrac{1}{\cos(21^\circ)} \approx \dfrac{1}{0.93} \approx 1.075$

(e) $\csc(21^\circ) \approx ?$

$\csc(21^\circ) = \dfrac{1}{\sin(21^\circ)} \approx \dfrac{1}{0.368} \approx 2.717$

(f) $\sin(69^\circ) \approx ?$

$\sin(69^\circ) = \cos(90^\circ - 69^\circ)$

$= \cos(21^\circ) \approx 0.93$

(g) $\cos(69^\circ) \approx ?$

$\cos(69^\circ) = \sin(90^\circ - 69^\circ)$

$= \sin(21^\circ) \approx 0.368$

(h) $\tan(69^\circ) \approx ?$

$\tan(69^\circ) = \cot(90^\circ - 69^\circ) = \cot(21^\circ) \approx 2.527$

53. Given: $\sin\theta = 0.3$

$\sin\theta + \cos\left(\dfrac{\pi}{2} - \theta\right) = \sin\theta + \sin\theta = 0.3 + 0.3 = 0.6$

54. Given: $\tan\theta = 4$

$$\tan\theta + \tan\left(\frac{\pi}{2} - \theta\right) = \tan\theta + \cot\theta = \tan\theta + \frac{1}{\tan\theta} = 4 + \frac{1}{4} = \frac{17}{4}$$

55. $\sin\theta = \cos(2\theta + 30^\circ) = \cos(90^\circ - (60^\circ - 2\theta)) = \sin(60^\circ - 2\theta)$

The equation $\sin\theta = \sin(60^\circ - 2\theta)$ will be true when

$$\theta = 60^\circ - 2\theta \to 3\theta = 60^\circ \to \theta = \frac{60^\circ}{3} = 20^\circ.$$

56. $\tan\theta = \cot(\theta + 45^\circ) = \cot(90^\circ - (45^\circ - \theta)) = \tan(45^\circ - \theta)$

The equation $\tan\theta = \tan(45^\circ - \theta)$ will be true when

$$\theta = 45^\circ - \theta \to 2\theta = 45^\circ \to \theta = \frac{45^\circ}{2} = 22.5^\circ.$$

57. (a) $T = \dfrac{1500}{300} + \dfrac{500}{100} = 5 + 5 = 10$ minutes

(b) $T = \dfrac{500}{100} + \dfrac{1500}{100} = 5 + 15 = 20$ minutes

(c) $\tan\theta = \dfrac{500}{x} \quad \rightarrow \quad x = \dfrac{500}{\tan\theta}$

$$\sin\theta = \frac{500}{\text{distance in sand}} \quad \rightarrow \quad \text{distance in sand} = \frac{500}{\sin\theta}$$

$$T = \frac{1500 - x}{300} + \frac{\text{distance in sand}}{100} = \frac{1\left(500 - \frac{500}{\tan\theta}\right)}{300} + \frac{\left(\frac{500}{\sin\theta}\right)}{100} = 5 - \frac{5}{3\tan\theta} + \frac{5}{\sin\theta}$$

(d) $\tan\theta = \dfrac{500}{1500} = \dfrac{1}{3}$, so we can consider the triangle

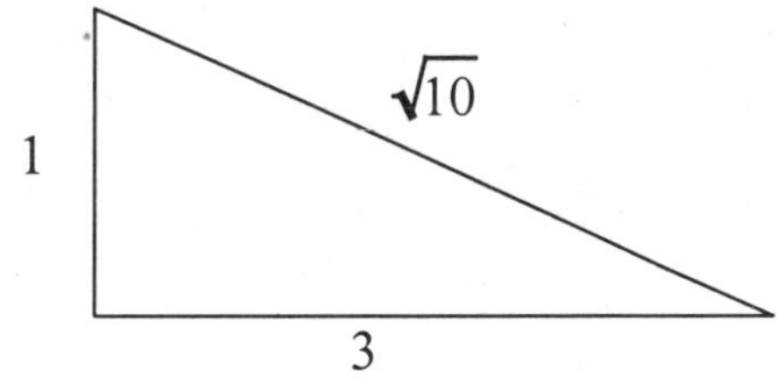

$$T = 5 - \frac{5}{3\tan\theta} + \frac{5}{\sin\theta} = 5 - \frac{5}{3\left(\frac{1}{3}\right)} + \frac{5}{\left(\frac{1}{\sqrt{10}}\right)} = 5 - 5 + 5\sqrt{10} \approx 15.81 \text{ minutes}$$

(e) 1000 feet along the paved path leaves an additional 500 feet in the direction of the path, so the angle of the path across the sand is 45°.

$$T = 5 - \frac{5}{3\tan(45^\circ)} + \frac{5}{\sin(45^\circ)} = 5 - \frac{5}{3 \cdot 1} + \frac{5}{\left(\frac{\sqrt{2}}{2}\right)} = 5 - \frac{5}{3} + \frac{10}{\sqrt{2}} \approx 10.4 \text{ minutes}$$

(f) Graph:

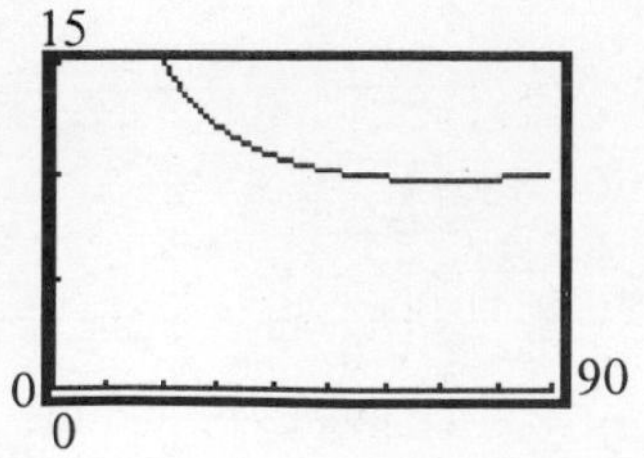

The time is least when the angle is approximately 70.53°. The least time is approximately 9.71 minutes. The value of x is:

$$x = \frac{500}{\tan(70.53^\circ)} \approx 176.8 \text{ feet}$$

58. Consider the length of the ladder in two sections, x, the portion across the hall that is 3 feet wide and y, the portion across that hall that is 4 feet wide. Then,

$$\cos\theta = \frac{3}{x} \rightarrow x = \frac{3}{\cos\theta} \text{ and } \sin\theta = \frac{4}{y} \rightarrow y = \frac{4}{\sin\theta}$$

$$L = x + y = \frac{3}{\cos\theta} + \frac{4}{\sin\theta}$$

59. (a) $|OA| = |OC| = 1; \quad \angle OAC = \angle OCA;$

$\angle OAC + \angle OAC + 180^\circ - \theta = 180^\circ$

$$2(\angle OAC) = \theta \rightarrow \angle OAC = \frac{\theta}{2}$$

(b) $\sin\theta = \dfrac{|CD|}{|OC|} = |CD| \qquad \cos\theta = \dfrac{|OD|}{|OC|} = |OD|$

(c) $\tan\dfrac{\theta}{2} = \dfrac{|CD|}{|AD|} = \dfrac{|CD|}{1+|OD|} = \dfrac{\sin\theta}{1+\cos\theta}$

60. Let h be the height of the triangle and b be the base of the triangle.

$$\sin\theta = \frac{h}{a} \rightarrow h = a\sin\theta \qquad \cos\theta = \frac{\left(\frac{1}{2}b\right)}{a} \rightarrow b = 2a\cos\theta$$

$$A = \frac{1}{2}bh = \frac{1}{2}(2a\cos\theta)(a\sin\theta) = a^2\sin\theta\cos\theta$$

61. $h = x\cdot\dfrac{h}{x} = x\tan\theta; \quad h = (1-x)\cdot\dfrac{h}{1-x} = (1-x)\tan(n\theta)$

$x\tan\theta = (1-x)\tan(n\theta)$

$x\tan\theta = \tan(n\theta) - x\tan(n\theta) \rightarrow x(\tan\theta + \tan n\theta) = \tan(n\theta)$

$$x = \frac{\tan n\theta}{\tan\theta + \tan(n\theta)}$$

62. $\sin\theta = \dfrac{a}{x+a} = \dfrac{b}{x+2a+b}$

$xb + ab = xa + 2a^2 + ab$

$x(b-a) = 2a^2$

$x = \dfrac{2a^2}{b-a}$

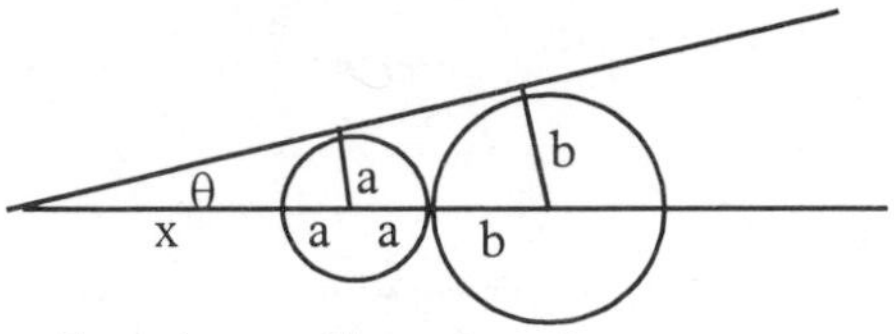

$$\sin\theta = \frac{a}{x+a} = \frac{a}{\left(\dfrac{2a^2}{b-a}+a\right)} = \frac{a}{\left(\dfrac{2a^2+ab-a^2}{b-a}\right)} = \frac{a(b-a)}{a^2+ab} = \frac{a(b-a)}{a(b+a)} = \frac{b-a}{b+a}$$

$$\cos\theta = \sqrt{1-\sin^2\theta} = \sqrt{1-\left(\frac{b-a}{b+a}\right)^2} = \sqrt{1-\frac{b^2-2ab+a^2}{b^2+2ab+a^2}}$$

$$= \sqrt{\frac{b^2+2ab+a^2-b^2+2ab-a^2}{b^2+2ab+a^2}} = \sqrt{\frac{4ab}{(a+b)^2}} = \frac{2\sqrt{ab}}{a+b} = \frac{\sqrt{ab}}{\left(\dfrac{a+b}{2}\right)}$$

63. (a) Area $\Delta OAC = \frac{1}{2}|OC|\cdot|AC| = \frac{1}{2}\cdot\frac{|OC|}{1}\cdot\frac{|AC|}{1} = \frac{1}{2}\cos\alpha\sin\alpha = \frac{1}{2}\sin\alpha\cos\alpha$

(b) Area $\Delta OCB = \frac{1}{2}|OC|\cdot|BC| = \frac{1}{2}\cdot|OB|^2\cdot\frac{|OC|}{|OB|}\cdot\frac{|BC|}{|OB|} = \frac{1}{2}|OB|^2\cos\beta\sin\beta$

$= \frac{1}{2}|OB|^2\sin\beta\cos\beta$

(c) Area $\Delta OAB = \frac{1}{2}|BD|\cdot|OA| = \frac{1}{2}|BD|\cdot 1 = \frac{1}{2}\cdot|OB|\cdot\frac{|BD|}{|OB|} = \frac{1}{2}|OB|\sin(\alpha+\beta)$

(d) $\dfrac{\cos\alpha}{\cos\beta} = \dfrac{\left(\dfrac{|OC|}{|OA|}\right)}{\left(\dfrac{|OC|}{|OB|}\right)} = \dfrac{|OC|}{1}\cdot\dfrac{|OB|}{|OC|} = |OB|$

(e) Area ΔOAB = Area ΔOAC + Area ΔOCB

$\frac{1}{2}|OB|\sin(\alpha+\beta) = \frac{1}{2}\sin\alpha\cos\alpha + \frac{1}{2}|OB|^2\sin\beta\cos\beta$

$\dfrac{\cos\alpha}{\cos\beta}\sin(\alpha+\beta) = \sin\alpha\cos\alpha + \dfrac{\cos^2\alpha}{\cos^2\beta}\sin\beta\cos\beta$

$\sin(\alpha+\beta) = \dfrac{\cos\beta}{\cos\alpha}\sin\alpha\cos\alpha + \dfrac{\cos\alpha}{\cos\beta}\sin\beta\cos\beta$

$\sin(\alpha+\beta) = \sin\alpha\cos\beta + \cos\alpha\sin\beta$

64. (a) Area of $\Delta OBC = \frac{1}{2}\cdot 1\cdot 1\cdot\sin\theta = \frac{1}{2}\sin\theta$

(b) Area of $\Delta OBD = \frac{1}{2}\cdot 1\cdot\tan\theta = \frac{1}{2}\tan\theta = \dfrac{\sin\theta}{2\cos\theta}$

(c) Area $\Delta OBC <$ Area arc $OBC <$ Area ΔOBD

$$\frac{1}{2}\sin\theta < \frac{1}{2}\theta < \frac{\sin\theta}{2\cos\theta} \rightarrow \frac{\sin\theta`}{\sin\theta} < \frac{\theta}{\sin\theta} < \frac{\sin\theta}{\sin\theta\cos\theta}$$

$$1 < \frac{\theta}{\sin\theta} < \frac{1}{\cos\theta}$$

65. $\sin\alpha = \frac{\sin\alpha}{\cos\alpha}\cdot\cos\alpha = \tan\alpha\cos\alpha = \cos\beta\cos\alpha = \cos\beta\tan\beta = \cos\beta\cdot\frac{\sin\beta}{\cos\beta} = \sin\beta$

$$\sin^2\alpha + \cos^2\alpha = 1$$

$$\sin^2\alpha + \tan^2\beta = 1 \rightarrow \sin^2\alpha + \frac{\sin^2\beta}{\cos^2\beta} = 1 \rightarrow \sin^2\alpha + \frac{\sin^2\alpha}{1-\sin^2\alpha} = 1$$

$$(1-\sin^2\alpha)\left(\sin^2\alpha + \frac{\sin^2\alpha}{1-\sin^2\alpha}\right) = (1)(1-\sin^2\alpha) \rightarrow \sin^2\alpha - \sin^4\alpha + \sin^2\alpha = 1 - \sin^2\alpha$$

$$\sin^4\alpha - 3\sin^2\alpha + 1 = 0 \rightarrow \sin^2\alpha = \frac{3\pm\sqrt{5}}{2} \rightarrow \sin\alpha = \sqrt{\frac{3\pm\sqrt{5}}{2}}$$

66. Consider the right triangle:

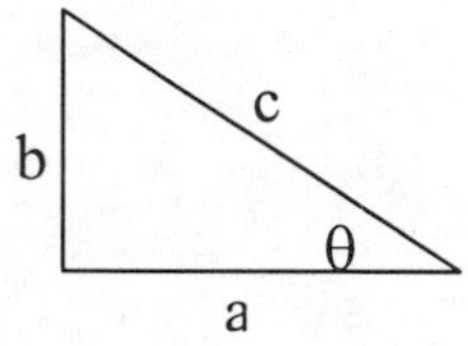

If θ is an acute angle in this triangle, then $a>0,\ b>0$ and $c>0$.

So $\cos\theta = \frac{a}{c} > 0$. Also, since $a^2 + b^2 = c^2$, we know that $0 < a^2 < c^2 \rightarrow 0 < a < c$.

Now $0 < a < c \rightarrow 0 < \frac{a}{c} < 1$. So we now know that $0 < \cos\theta < 1$, which implies that $\frac{1}{\cos\theta} > \frac{1}{1} \rightarrow \frac{1}{\cos\theta} > 1 \rightarrow \sec\theta > 1$.

67. Consider the right triangle:

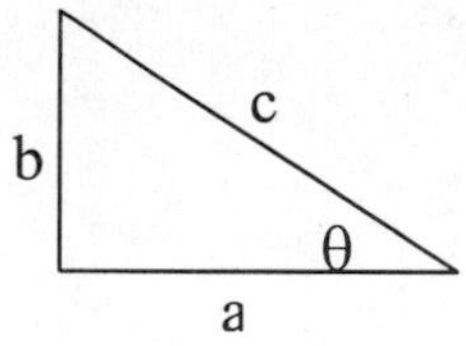

If θ is an acute angle in this triangle, then $a>0,\ b>0$ and $c>0$.

So $\sin\theta = \frac{b}{c} > 0$. Also, since $a^2 + b^2 = c^2$, we know that $0 < b^2 < c^2 \rightarrow 0 < b < c$.

Now $0 < b < c \rightarrow 0 < \frac{b}{c} < 1$. Therefore, $0 < \sin\theta < 1$.

Chapter 7

Trigonometric Functions

7.3 Computing the Values of Trigonometric Functions of Given Angles

1.

θ	$\sin\theta$	$\cos\theta$	$\tan\theta$	$\cot\theta$	$\sec\theta$	$\csc\theta$
$\frac{\pi}{4}$	$\frac{\sqrt{2}}{2}$	$\frac{\sqrt{2}}{2}$	1	1	$\sqrt{2}$	$\sqrt{2}$

2.

θ	$\sin\theta$	$\cos\theta$	$\tan\theta$	$\cot\theta$	$\sec\theta$	$\csc\theta$
30°	$\frac{1}{2}$	$\frac{\sqrt{3}}{2}$	$\frac{\sqrt{3}}{3}$	$\sqrt{3}$	$\frac{2\sqrt{3}}{3}$	2
60°	$\frac{\sqrt{3}}{2}$	$\frac{1}{2}$	$\sqrt{3}$	$\frac{\sqrt{3}}{3}$	2	$\frac{2\sqrt{3}}{3}$

3. $\sin(60^\circ)=\frac{\sqrt{3}}{2}$

4. $\cos(60^\circ)=\frac{1}{2}$

5. $\sin(30^\circ)=\frac{1}{2}$

6. $\cos(30^\circ)=\frac{\sqrt{3}}{2}$

7. $(\sin(60^\circ))^2=\left(\frac{\sqrt{3}}{2}\right)^2=\frac{3}{4}$

8. $(\cos(60^\circ))^2=\left(\frac{1}{2}\right)^2=\frac{1}{4}$

9. $2\sin(60^\circ)=2\cdot\frac{\sqrt{3}}{2}=\sqrt{3}$

10. $2\cos(60^\circ)=2\cdot\frac{1}{2}=1$

11. $\frac{\sin(60^\circ)}{2}=\frac{\left(\frac{\sqrt{3}}{2}\right)}{2}=\frac{\sqrt{3}}{4}$

12. $\frac{\cos(60^\circ)}{2}=\frac{\left(\frac{1}{2}\right)}{2}=\frac{1}{4}$

13. $4\cos(45^\circ)-2\sin(45^\circ)=4\cdot\frac{\sqrt{2}}{2}-2\cdot\frac{\sqrt{2}}{2}$
$=2\sqrt{2}-\sqrt{2}=\sqrt{2}$

14. $2\sin(45^\circ)+\cos(30^\circ)=2\cdot\frac{\sqrt{2}}{2}+\frac{\sqrt{3}}{2}$
$=\sqrt{2}+\frac{\sqrt{3}}{2}=\frac{2\sqrt{2}+\sqrt{3}}{2}$

15. $6\tan(45^\circ)-8\cos(60^\circ)=6\cdot1-8\cdot\frac{1}{2}$
$=6-4=2$

16. $\sin(30^\circ)\tan(60^\circ)=\frac{1}{2}\cdot\sqrt{3}=\frac{\sqrt{3}}{2}$

17. $\sec\left(\frac{\pi}{4}\right)+2\csc\left(\frac{\pi}{3}\right)=\sqrt{2}+2\cdot\frac{\sqrt{3}}{3}$
$=\frac{3\sqrt{2}+2\sqrt{3}}{3}$

18. $\tan\left(\frac{\pi}{4}\right)+\cot\left(\frac{\pi}{4}\right)=1+1=2$

19. $\sec^2\left(\frac{\pi}{6}\right)-4=\left(\frac{2\sqrt{3}}{3}\right)^2-4=\frac{12}{9}-4$
$=\frac{4}{3}-4=\frac{4-12}{3}=-\frac{8}{3}$

20. $4+\tan^2\left(\frac{\pi}{3}\right)=4+\left(\sqrt{3}\right)^2$
$=4+3=7$

21. $\sin^2(30^\circ)+\cos^2(60^\circ)=\left(\frac{1}{2}\right)^2+\left(\frac{1}{2}\right)^2$
$=\frac{1}{4}+\frac{1}{4}=\frac{2}{4}=\frac{1}{2}$

22. $\sec^2(60^\circ)-\tan^2(45^\circ)=(2)^2-(1)^2$
$=4-1=3$

23. $1-\cos^2(30^\circ)-\cos^2(60^\circ)=1-\left(\frac{\sqrt{3}}{2}\right)^2-\left(\frac{1}{2}\right)^2$
$=1-\frac{3}{4}-\frac{1}{4}=1-1=0$

24. $1+\tan^2(30^\circ)-\csc^2(45^\circ)=1+\left(\frac{\sqrt{3}}{3}\right)^2-\left(\sqrt{2}\right)^2=1+\frac{3}{9}-2=-\frac{2}{3}$

25. Set the calculator to degree mode: $\sin(28^\circ)\approx 0.47$.

26. Set the calculator to degree mode: $\cos(14^\circ)\approx 0.97$.

27. Set the calculator to degree mode: $\tan(21^\circ)\approx 0.38$.

28. Set the calculator to degree mode: $\cot(70^\circ)=\frac{1}{\tan(70^\circ)}\approx 0.36$.

29. Set the calculator to degree mode: $\sec(41^\circ)=\frac{1}{\cos(41^\circ)}\approx 1.33$.

30. Set the calculator to degree mode: $\csc(55^\circ)=\frac{1}{\sin(55^\circ)}\approx 1.22$.

31. Set the calculator to radian mode: $\sin\left(\frac{\pi}{10}\right)\approx 0.31$.

32. Set the calculator to radian mode: $\cos\left(\frac{\pi}{8}\right) \approx 0.92$.

33. Set the calculator to radian mode: $\tan\left(\frac{5\pi}{12}\right) \approx 3.73$.

34. Set the calculator to radian mode: $\cot\left(\frac{\pi}{18}\right) = \frac{1}{\tan\left(\frac{\pi}{18}\right)} \approx 5.67$

35. Set the calculator to radian mode: $\sec\left(\frac{\pi}{12}\right) = \frac{1}{\cos\left(\frac{\pi}{12}\right)} \approx 1.04$.

36. Set the calculator to radian mode: $\csc\left(\frac{5\pi}{13}\right) = \frac{1}{\sin\left(\frac{5\pi}{13}\right)} \approx 1.07$.

37. Set the calculator to radian mode: $\sin(1) \approx 0.84$.

38. Set the calculator to radian mode: $\tan(1) \approx 1.56$.

39. Set the calculator to degree mode: $\sin(1°) \approx 0.02$.

40. Set the calculator to degree mode: $\tan(1°) \approx 0.02$.

41. Set the calculator to radian mode: $\tan(0.3) \approx 0.31$.

42. Set the calculator to radian mode: $\tan(0.1) \approx 0.1$.

43. Use the formula $R = \frac{v_0^2 \sin(2\theta)}{g}$ with $g = 32.2 \text{ft}/\sec^2$; $\theta = 45°$; $v_0 = 100$ ft / sec:

$$R = \frac{100^2 \sin(2(45°))}{32.2} = \frac{10000 \sin(90°)}{32.2} = \frac{10000}{32.2} \approx 310.56 \text{ feet}$$

Use the formula $H = \frac{v_0^2 \sin^2\theta}{2g}$ with $g = 32.2 \text{ft}/\sec^2$; $\theta = 45°$; $v_0 = 100$ ft / sec:

$$H = \frac{100^2 \sin^2(45°)}{2(32.2)} \approx \frac{10000(0.7071)^2}{64.4} \approx 77.64 \text{ feet}$$

44. Use the formula $R = \frac{v_0^2 \sin(2\theta)}{g}$ with $g = 9.8 \text{ m}/\sec^2$; $\theta = 30°$; $v_0 = 150$ m / sec:

$$R = \frac{150^2 \sin(2(30°))}{9.8} = \frac{22500 \sin(60°)}{9.8} \approx 1988.32 \text{ meters}$$

Use the formula $H = \dfrac{v_0^2 \sin^2\theta}{2g}$ with $g = 9.8 \text{ m/sec}^2$; $\theta = 30°$; $v_0 = 150 \text{ m/sec}$:

$$H = \frac{150^2 \sin^2(30°)}{2(9.8)} = \frac{22500(0.5)^2}{19.6} \approx 286.99 \text{ meters}$$

45. Use the formula $R = \dfrac{v_0^2 \sin(2\theta)}{g}$ with $g = 9.8 \text{ m/sec}^2$; $\theta = 25°$; $v_0 = 500 \text{ m/sec}$:

$$R = \frac{500^2 \sin(2(25°))}{9.8} = \frac{250{,}000 \sin(50°)}{9.8} \approx 19{,}542 \text{ meters}$$

Use the formula $H = \dfrac{v_0^2 \sin^2\theta}{2g}$ with $g = 9.8 \text{ m/sec}^2$; $\theta = 25°$; $v_0 = 500 \text{ m/sec}$:

$$H = \frac{500^2 \sin^2(25°)}{2(9.8)} \approx \frac{250{,}000(0.4226)^2}{19.6} \approx 2278 \text{ meters}$$

46. Use the formula $R = \dfrac{v_0^2 \sin(2\theta)}{g}$ with $g = 32.2 \text{ ft/sec}^2$; $\theta = 50°$; $v_0 = 200 \text{ ft/sec}$:

$$R = \frac{200^2 \sin(2(50°))}{32.2} = \frac{40000 \sin(100°)}{32.2} \approx 1223.36 \text{ feet}$$

Use the formula $H = \dfrac{v_0^2 \sin^2\theta}{2g}$ with $g = 32.2 \text{ ft/sec}^2$; $\theta = 50°$; $v_0 = 200 \text{ ft/sec}$:

$$H = \frac{200^2 \sin^2(50°)}{2(32.2)} \approx \frac{40000(0.7660)^2}{64.4} \approx 364.49 \text{ feet}$$

47. Use the formula $t = \sqrt{\dfrac{2a}{g \sin\theta \cos\theta}}$ with $g = 32 \text{ ft/sec}^2$ and $a = 10$ feet:

(a) $$t = \sqrt{\frac{2(10)}{32\sin(30°)\cos(30°)}} = \sqrt{\frac{20}{\left(32 \cdot \frac{1}{2} \cdot \frac{\sqrt{3}}{2}\right)}} = \sqrt{\frac{20}{8\sqrt{3}}} = \sqrt{\frac{5}{2\sqrt{3}}} \approx 1.20 \text{ seconds}$$

(b) $$t = \sqrt{\frac{2(10)}{32\sin(45°)\cos(45°)}} = \sqrt{\frac{20}{\left(32 \cdot \frac{\sqrt{2}}{2} \cdot \frac{\sqrt{2}}{2}\right)}} = \sqrt{\frac{20}{16}} = \sqrt{\frac{5}{4}} \approx 1.12 \text{ seconds}$$

(c) $$t = \sqrt{\frac{2(10)}{32\sin(60°)\cos(60°)}} = \sqrt{\frac{20}{\left(32 \cdot \frac{\sqrt{3}}{2} \cdot \frac{1}{2}\right)}} = \sqrt{\frac{20}{8\sqrt{3}}} = \sqrt{\frac{5}{2\sqrt{3}}} \approx 1.20 \text{ seconds}$$

48. Use the formula $x = \cos\theta + \sqrt{16 + 0.5\cos(2\theta)}$.

When $\theta = 30°$:

$$x = \cos(30°) + \sqrt{16 + 0.5\cos(2 \cdot 30°)} = \cos(30°) + \sqrt{16 + 0.5\cos(60°)} \approx 4.897 \text{ m}$$

When $\theta = 45°$:

$$x = \cos(45°) + \sqrt{16 + 0.5\cos(2 \cdot 45°)} = \cos(45°) + \sqrt{16 + 0.5\cos(90°)} \approx 4.707 \text{ m}$$

49. (a) $T(30°)=1+\frac{2}{3\sin(30°)}-\frac{1}{4\tan(30°)}=1+\frac{2}{\left(3\cdot\frac{1}{2}\right)}-\frac{1}{\left(4\cdot\frac{1}{\sqrt{3}}\right)}=1+\frac{4}{3}-\frac{\sqrt{3}}{4}\approx 1.9\text{ hrs}$

$\frac{1}{x}=\tan\theta \rightarrow x=\frac{1}{\tan\theta}$

Distance traveled on road is : $8-2x=8-\frac{2}{\tan\theta}$

$$\text{Time on road} = \frac{\text{distance on road}}{\text{rate on road}}=\frac{\left(8-\frac{2}{\tan\theta}\right)}{8}\approx 0.57\text{ hours}$$

(b) $T(45°)=1+\frac{2}{3\sin(45°)}-\frac{1}{4\tan(45°)}=1+\frac{2}{\left(3\cdot\frac{1}{\sqrt{2}}\right)}-\frac{1}{4\cdot 1}=1+\frac{2\sqrt{2}}{3}-\frac{1}{4}\approx 1.69\text{ hrs}$

$$\text{Time on road} = \frac{\left(8-\frac{2}{\tan(45°)}\right)}{8}\approx 0.75\text{ hours}$$

(c) $T(60°)=1+\frac{2}{3\sin(60°)}-\frac{1}{4\tan(60°)}=1+\frac{2}{\left(3\cdot\frac{\sqrt{3}}{2}\right)}-\frac{1}{4\cdot\sqrt{3}}$

$=1+\frac{4}{3\sqrt{3}}-\frac{1}{4\sqrt{3}}\approx 1.63\text{ hrs}$ Time on road $=\frac{\left(8-\frac{2}{\tan(60°)}\right)}{8}\approx 0.86\text{ hours}$

(d) $T(90°)=1+\frac{2}{3\sin(90°)}-\frac{1}{4\tan(90°)}=(\tan 90°\text{ is undefined})$

The distance would be 2 miles in the sand and 8 miles on the road. The total time would be: $\frac{2}{3}+1=\frac{5}{3}\approx 1.67$ hours.

50. Use the formula: $V(\theta)=\frac{1}{3}\pi\cdot R^3\frac{(1+\sec\theta)^3}{\tan^2\theta}$

When $\theta=30°$:

$$V(30°)=\left(\frac{1}{3}\right)\left(\pi\cdot 2^3\right)\frac{(1+\sec(30°))^3}{\tan^2(30°)}\approx\left(\frac{8}{3}\right)(\pi)\frac{(1+1.1547)^3}{(0.5774)^2}\approx 251.4\text{ cm}^3$$

When $\theta=45°$:

$$V(45°)=\left(\frac{1}{3}\right)\left(\pi\cdot 2^3\right)\frac{(1+\sec(45°))^3}{\tan^2(45°)}\approx\left(\frac{8}{3}\right)(\pi)\frac{(1+1.4142)^3}{(1)^2}\approx 117.9\text{ cm}^3$$

When $\theta=60°$:

$$V(60°)=\left(\frac{1}{3}\right)\left(\pi\cdot 2^3\right)\frac{(1+\sec(60°))^3}{\tan^2(60°)}=\left(\frac{8}{3}\right)(\pi)\frac{(1+2)^3}{(1.7321)^2}\approx 75.4\text{ cm}^3$$

51. Complete the table:

θ	0.5	0.4	0.2	0.1	0.01	0.001	0.0001	0.00001
$\sin\theta$	0.4794	0.3894	0.1987	0.0998	0.0100	0.0010	0.0001	0.00001
$\dfrac{\sin\theta}{\theta}$	0.9589	0.9735	0.9933	0.9983	1.0000	1.0000	1.0000	1.0000

The ratio $\frac{\sin\theta}{\theta}$ as θ approaches 0 is 1.

52. Complete the table:

θ	0.5	0.4	0.2	0.1	0.01	0.001	0.0001	0.00001
$\cos\theta-1$	–0.1224	–0.0789	–0.0199	–0.0050	–0.0000	–0.0000	–0.0000	–0.0000
$\dfrac{\cos\theta-1}{\theta}$	–0.2448	–0.1973	–0.0997	–0.0500	–0.0050	–0.0005	–0.0000	–0.0000

The ratio $\frac{\cos\theta-1}{\theta}$ as θ approaches 0 is 0.

53. $\tan 1^\circ \cdot \tan 2^\circ \cdot \tan 3^\circ \cdot \ldots \cdot \tan 89^\circ = 1$

We can rearrange the order of the terms in this product as follows:

$$(\tan(1^\circ)\cdot\tan(89^\circ))\cdot(\tan(2^\circ)\cdot\tan(88^\circ))\cdot(\tan(3^\circ)\cdot\tan(87^\circ))\cdot\ldots\cdot(\tan(44^\circ)\cdot\tan(46^\circ))\cdot\tan(45^\circ)$$

Now each set of parentheses contains a pair of complementary angles.

For example, $(\tan(1^\circ)\cdot\tan(89^\circ))$. Using cofunction properties we have:

$$(\tan(1^\circ)\cdot\tan(89^\circ))=(\tan(1^\circ)\cdot\tan(90^\circ-1^\circ))=(\tan(1^\circ)\cdot\cot(1^\circ))=1$$

This result holds for each pair in our product. And since we know that $\tan(45^\circ)=1$, our product can be rewritten as $1\cdot1\cdot1\cdot\ldots\cdot1=1$. Therefore, $\tan 1^\circ\cdot\tan 2^\circ\cdot\tan 3^\circ\cdot\ldots\cdot\tan 89^\circ=1$.

54. $\cot(1^\circ)\cdot\cot(2^\circ)\cdot\cot(3^\circ)\cdot\ldots\cdot\cot(89^\circ)=1$

We can rearrange the order of the terms in this product as follows:

$$(\cot(1^\circ)\cdot\cot(89^\circ))\cdot(\cot(2^\circ)\cdot\cot(88^\circ))\cdot(\cot(3^\circ)\cdot\cot(87^\circ))\cdot\ldots\cdot(\cot(44^\circ)\cdot\cot(46^\circ))\cdot\cot(45^\circ)$$

Now follow the strategy used in Problem 53.

55. $\cos(1^\circ)\cdot\cos(2^\circ)\cdot\ldots\cdot\cos(45^\circ)\cdot\csc(46^\circ)\cdot\ldots\cdot\csc(89^\circ)$

We can rearrange the order of the terms in this product as follows:

$$(\cos(1^\circ)\cdot\csc(89^\circ))\cdot(\cos(2^\circ)\cdot\csc(88^\circ))\cdot(\cos(3^\circ)\cdot\csc(87^\circ))\cdot\ldots\cdot(\cos(44^\circ)\cdot\csc(46^\circ))\cdot\cos(45^\circ)$$

Now each set of parentheses contains a pair of complementary angles.

For example, $(\cos(1^\circ)\cdot\csc(89^\circ))$. Using cofunction properties we have:

$$(\cos(1^\circ)\cdot\csc(89^\circ))=(\cos(1^\circ)\cdot\csc(90^\circ-1^\circ))=(\cos(1^\circ)\cdot\sec(1^\circ))=1$$

This result holds for each pair in our product. And since we know that $\cos(45^\circ)=\frac{\sqrt{2}}{2}$,

Our product can be rewritten as $1\cdot1\cdot1\cdot\ldots\cdot1\cdot\frac{\sqrt{2}}{2}=\frac{\sqrt{2}}{2}$.

56. $\sin(1^\circ)\cdot\sin(2^\circ)\cdot\ldots\cdot\sin(45^\circ)\cdot\sec(46^\circ)\cdot\ldots\cdot\sec(89^\circ)=\dfrac{\sqrt{2}}{2}$

We can rearrange the order of the terms in this product as follows:

$$(\sin(1^\circ)\cdot\sec(89^\circ))\cdot(\sin(2^\circ)\cdot\sec(88^\circ))\cdot(\sin(3^\circ)\cdot\sec(87^\circ))\cdot\ldots\cdot(\sin(44^\circ)\cdot\sec(46^\circ))\cdot\sin(45^\circ)$$

Now each set of parentheses contains a pair of complementary angles.

For example, $(\sin(1^\circ)\cdot\sec(89^\circ))$. Using cofunction properties we have:

$$(\sin(1^\circ)\cdot\sec(89^\circ))=(\sin(1^\circ)\cdot\sec(90^\circ-1^\circ))=(\sin(1^\circ)\cdot\csc(1^\circ))=1$$

This result holds for each pair in our product. And since we know that $\sin(45^\circ)=\dfrac{\sqrt{2}}{2}$,

Our product can be rewritten as $1\cdot1\cdot1\cdot\ldots\cdot1\cdot\dfrac{\sqrt{2}}{2}=\dfrac{\sqrt{2}}{2}$.

Chapter 7

Trigonometric Functions

7.4 Trigonometric Functions of General Angles

1. $(-3,4) \rightarrow a=-3, b=4$ $\quad r=\sqrt{a^2+b^2}=\sqrt{(-3)^2+4^2}=\sqrt{9+16}=\sqrt{25}=5$

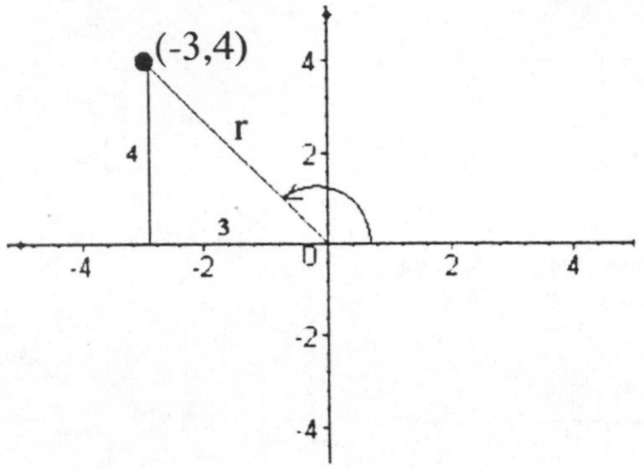

$\sin\theta=\frac{b}{r}=\frac{4}{5}$ $\quad \cos\theta=\frac{a}{r}=\frac{-3}{5}=-\frac{3}{5}$

$\tan\theta=\frac{b}{a}=\frac{4}{-3}=-\frac{4}{3}$ $\quad \cot\theta=\frac{a}{b}=\frac{-3}{4}=-\frac{3}{4}$

$\sec\theta=\frac{r}{a}=\frac{5}{-3}=-\frac{5}{3}$ $\quad \csc\theta=\frac{r}{b}=\frac{5}{4}$

2. $(5,-12)$ $\quad r=\sqrt{a^2+b^2}=\sqrt{5^2+12^2}=\sqrt{25+144}=\sqrt{169}=13$

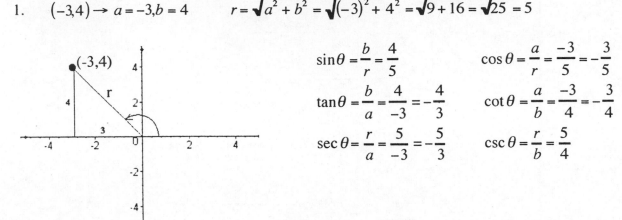

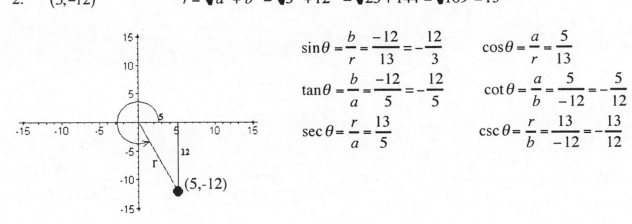

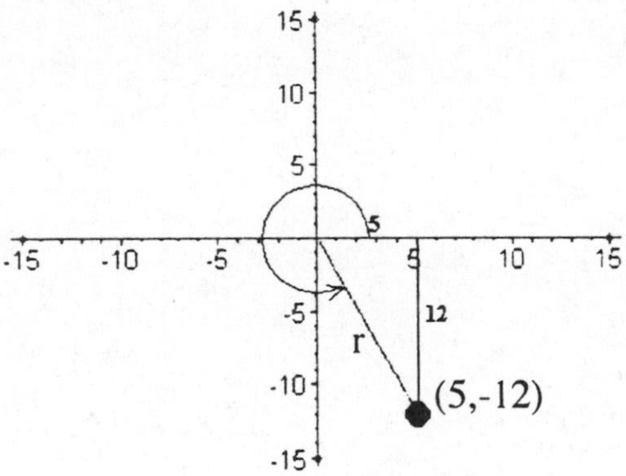

$\sin\theta=\frac{b}{r}=\frac{-12}{13}=-\frac{12}{3}$ $\quad \cos\theta=\frac{a}{r}=\frac{5}{13}$

$\tan\theta=\frac{b}{a}=\frac{-12}{5}=-\frac{12}{5}$ $\quad \cot\theta=\frac{a}{b}=\frac{5}{-12}=-\frac{5}{12}$

$\sec\theta=\frac{r}{a}=\frac{13}{5}$ $\quad \csc\theta=\frac{r}{b}=\frac{13}{-12}=-\frac{13}{12}$

3. $(2,-3)$ $\quad r=\sqrt{a^2+b^2}=\sqrt{2^2+(-3)^2}=\sqrt{4+9}=\sqrt{13}$

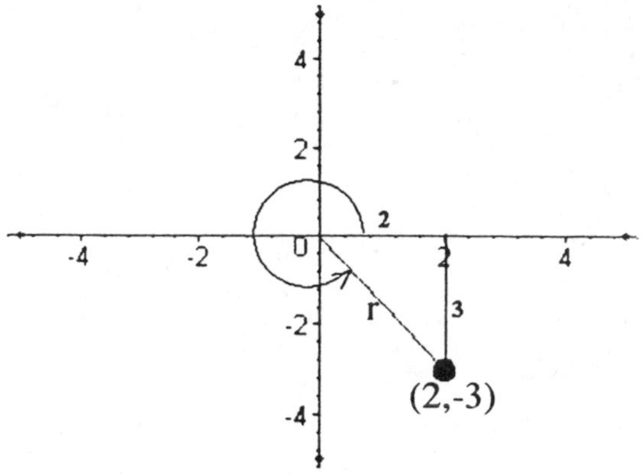

$$\sin\theta=\frac{b}{r}=\frac{-3}{\sqrt{13}}\cdot\frac{\sqrt{13}}{\sqrt{13}}=-\frac{3\sqrt{13}}{13}$$

$$\cos\theta=\frac{a}{r}=\frac{2}{\sqrt{13}}\cdot\frac{\sqrt{13}}{\sqrt{13}}=-\frac{2\sqrt{13}}{13}$$

$$\tan\theta=\frac{b}{a}=\frac{-3}{2}=-\frac{3}{2} \qquad \cot\theta=\frac{a}{b}=\frac{2}{-3}=-\frac{2}{3}$$

$$\sec\theta=\frac{r}{a}=\frac{\sqrt{13}}{2} \qquad \csc\theta=\frac{r}{b}=\frac{\sqrt{13}}{-3}=-\frac{\sqrt{13}}{3}$$

4. $(-1,-2)$ $\quad r=\sqrt{a^2+b^2}=\sqrt{(-1)^2+(-2)^2}=\sqrt{1+4}=\sqrt{5}$

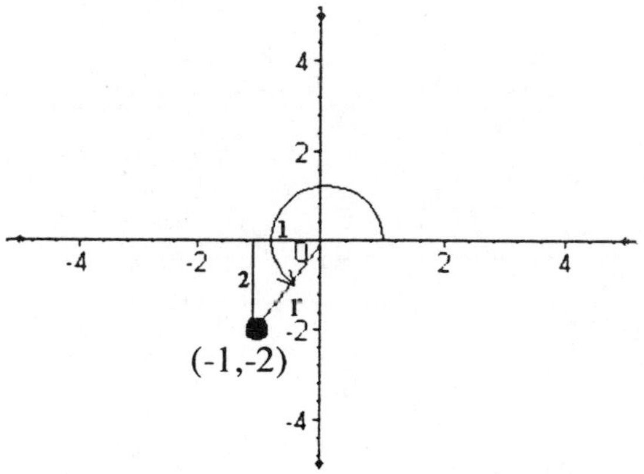

$$\sin\theta=\frac{b}{r}=\frac{-2}{\sqrt{5}}\cdot\frac{\sqrt{5}}{\sqrt{5}}=-\frac{2\sqrt{5}}{5}$$

$$\cos\theta=\frac{a}{r}=\frac{-1}{\sqrt{5}}\cdot\frac{\sqrt{5}}{\sqrt{5}}=-\frac{\sqrt{5}}{5}$$

$$\tan\theta=\frac{b}{a}=\frac{-2}{-1}=2 \qquad \cot\theta=\frac{a}{b}=\frac{-1}{-2}=\frac{1}{2}$$

$$\sec\theta=\frac{r}{a}=\frac{\sqrt{5}}{-1}=-\sqrt{5} \qquad \csc\theta=\frac{r}{b}=\frac{\sqrt{5}}{-2}=-\frac{\sqrt{5}}{2}$$

5. $(-3,-3)$ $\quad r=\sqrt{a^2+b^2}=\sqrt{(-3)^2+(-3)^2}=\sqrt{9+9}=\sqrt{18}=3\sqrt{2}$

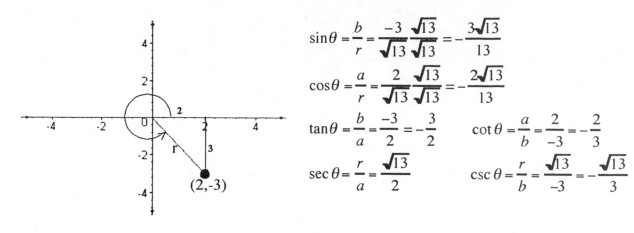

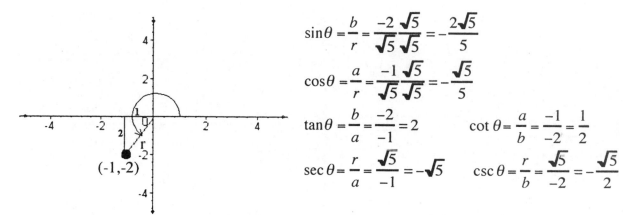

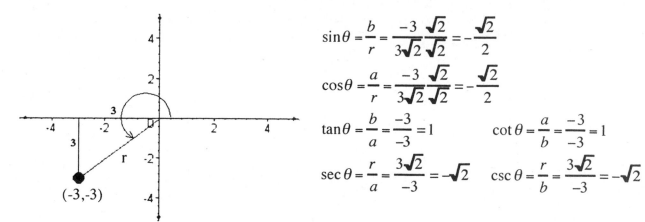

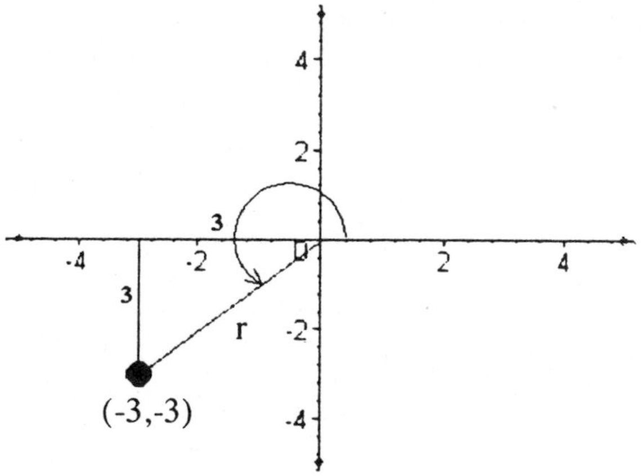

$$\sin\theta=\frac{b}{r}=\frac{-3}{3\sqrt{2}}\cdot\frac{\sqrt{2}}{\sqrt{2}}=-\frac{\sqrt{2}}{2}$$

$$\cos\theta=\frac{a}{r}=\frac{-3}{3\sqrt{2}}\cdot\frac{\sqrt{2}}{\sqrt{2}}=-\frac{\sqrt{2}}{2}$$

$$\tan\theta=\frac{b}{a}=\frac{-3}{-3}=1 \qquad \cot\theta=\frac{a}{b}=\frac{-3}{-3}=1$$

$$\sec\theta=\frac{r}{a}=\frac{3\sqrt{2}}{-3}=-\sqrt{2} \qquad \csc\theta=\frac{r}{b}=\frac{3\sqrt{2}}{-3}=-\sqrt{2}$$

6. $(2,-2)$

$$r=\sqrt{a^2+b^2}=\sqrt{2^2+(-2)^2}=\sqrt{4+4}=\sqrt{8}=2\sqrt{2}$$

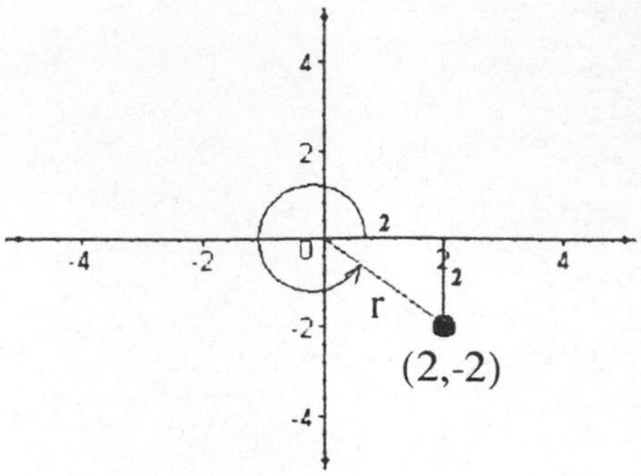

$$\sin\theta=\frac{b}{r}=\frac{-2}{2\sqrt{2}}\frac{\sqrt{2}}{\sqrt{2}}=-\frac{\sqrt{2}}{2}$$

$$\cos\theta=\frac{a}{r}=\frac{2}{2\sqrt{2}}\frac{\sqrt{2}}{\sqrt{2}}=\frac{\sqrt{2}}{2}$$

$$\tan\theta=\frac{b}{a}=\frac{-2}{2}=-1 \qquad \cot\theta=\frac{a}{b}=\frac{2}{-2}=-1$$

$$\sec\theta=\frac{r}{a}=\frac{2\sqrt{2}}{2}=\sqrt{2} \qquad \csc\theta=\frac{r}{b}=\frac{2\sqrt{2}}{-2}=-\sqrt{2}$$

7. $\left(\frac{\sqrt{3}}{2},\frac{1}{2}\right)$

$$r=\sqrt{a^2+b^2}=\sqrt{\left(\frac{\sqrt{3}}{2}\right)^2+\left(\frac{1}{2}\right)^2}=\sqrt{\frac{3}{4}+\frac{1}{4}}=\sqrt{1}=1$$

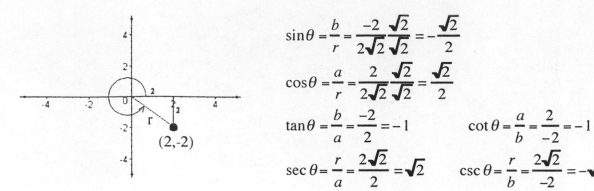

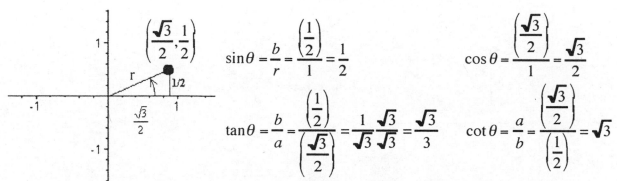

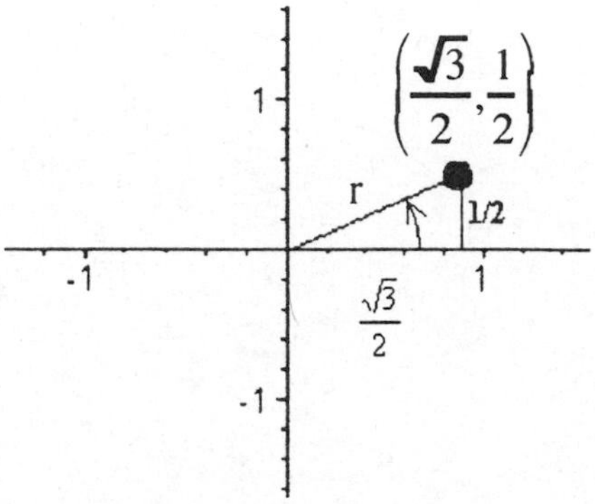

$$\sin\theta=\frac{b}{r}=\frac{\left(\frac{1}{2}\right)}{1}=\frac{1}{2} \qquad \cos\theta=\frac{\left(\frac{\sqrt{3}}{2}\right)}{1}=\frac{\sqrt{3}}{2}$$

$$\tan\theta=\frac{b}{a}=\frac{\left(\frac{1}{2}\right)}{\left(\frac{\sqrt{3}}{2}\right)}=\frac{1}{\sqrt{3}}\frac{\sqrt{3}}{\sqrt{3}}=\frac{\sqrt{3}}{3} \qquad \cot\theta=\frac{a}{b}=\frac{\left(\frac{\sqrt{3}}{2}\right)}{\left(\frac{1}{2}\right)}=\sqrt{3}$$

$$\sec\theta=\frac{r}{a}=\frac{1}{\left(\frac{\sqrt{3}}{2}\right)}=\frac{2}{\sqrt{3}}\frac{\sqrt{3}}{\sqrt{3}}=\frac{2\sqrt{3}}{3} \qquad \csc\theta=\frac{r}{b}=\frac{1}{\left(\frac{1}{2}\right)}=2$$

8. $\left(-\frac{1}{2}, \frac{\sqrt{3}}{2}\right)$

$$r = \sqrt{a^2 + b^2} = \sqrt{\left(-\frac{1}{2}\right)^2 + \left(\frac{\sqrt{3}}{2}\right)^2} = \sqrt{\frac{1}{4} + \frac{3}{4}} = \sqrt{1} = 1$$

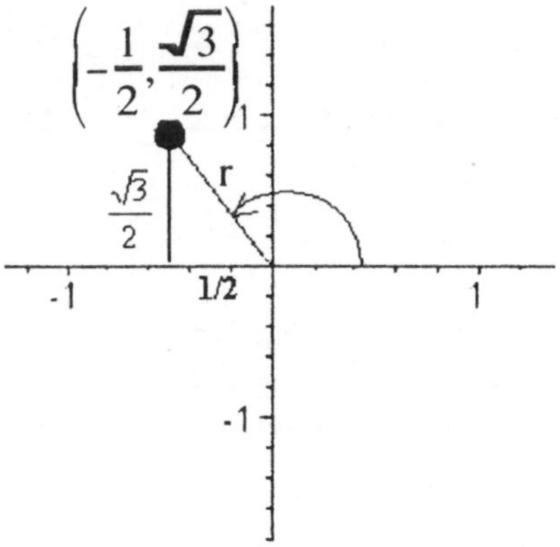

$$\sin\theta = \frac{b}{r} = \frac{\left(\frac{\sqrt{3}}{2}\right)}{1} = \frac{\sqrt{3}}{2} \qquad \cos\theta = \frac{a}{r} = \frac{\left(-\frac{1}{2}\right)}{1} = -\frac{1}{2}$$

$$\tan\theta = \frac{b}{a} = \frac{\left(\frac{\sqrt{3}}{2}\right)}{\left(-\frac{1}{2}\right)} = -\sqrt{3} \qquad \cot\theta = \frac{a}{b} = \frac{\left(-\frac{1}{2}\right)}{\left(\frac{\sqrt{3}}{2}\right)} = \frac{-1}{\sqrt{3}}\frac{\sqrt{3}}{\sqrt{3}} = -\frac{\sqrt{3}}{3}$$

$$\sec\theta = \frac{r}{a} = \frac{1}{\left(-\frac{1}{2}\right)} = -2 \qquad \csc\theta = \frac{r}{b} = \frac{1}{\left(\frac{\sqrt{3}}{2}\right)} = \frac{2}{\sqrt{3}}\frac{\sqrt{3}}{\sqrt{3}} = \frac{2\sqrt{3}}{3}$$

9. $\left(\frac{\sqrt{2}}{2}, -\frac{\sqrt{2}}{2}\right)$

$$r = \sqrt{a^2 + b^2} = \sqrt{\left(\frac{\sqrt{2}}{2}\right)^2 + \left(-\frac{\sqrt{2}}{2}\right)^2} = \sqrt{\frac{2}{4} + \frac{2}{4}} = \sqrt{1} = 1$$

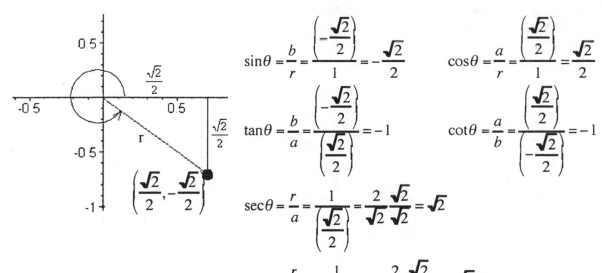

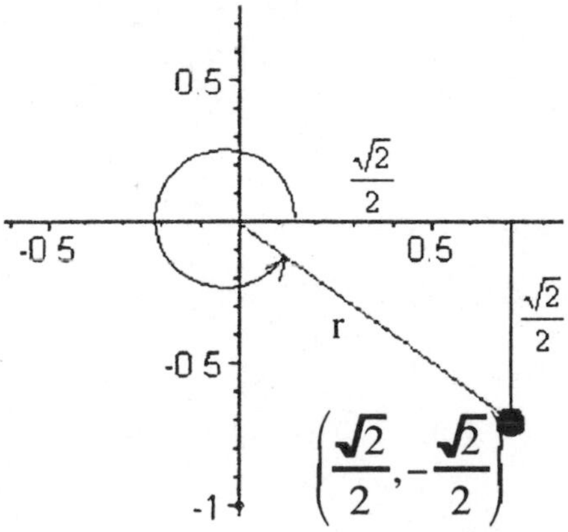

$$\sin\theta = \frac{b}{r} = \frac{\left(-\frac{\sqrt{2}}{2}\right)}{1} = -\frac{\sqrt{2}}{2} \qquad \cos\theta = \frac{a}{r} = \frac{\left(\frac{\sqrt{2}}{2}\right)}{1} = \frac{\sqrt{2}}{2}$$

$$\tan\theta = \frac{b}{a} = \frac{\left(-\frac{\sqrt{2}}{2}\right)}{\left(\frac{\sqrt{2}}{2}\right)} = -1 \qquad \cot\theta = \frac{a}{b} = \frac{\left(\frac{\sqrt{2}}{2}\right)}{\left(-\frac{\sqrt{2}}{2}\right)} = -1$$

$$\sec\theta = \frac{r}{a} = \frac{1}{\left(\frac{\sqrt{2}}{2}\right)} = \frac{2}{\sqrt{2}}\frac{\sqrt{2}}{\sqrt{2}} = \sqrt{2}$$

$$\csc\theta = \frac{r}{b} = \frac{1}{\left(-\frac{\sqrt{2}}{2}\right)} = -\frac{2}{\sqrt{2}}\frac{\sqrt{2}}{\sqrt{2}} = -\sqrt{2}$$

10. $\left(-\frac{\sqrt{2}}{2},-\frac{\sqrt{2}}{2}\right)$ $r=\sqrt{a^2+b^2}=\sqrt{\left(-\frac{\sqrt{2}}{2}\right)^2+\left(-\frac{\sqrt{2}}{2}\right)^2}=\sqrt{\frac{2}{4}+\frac{2}{4}}=\sqrt{1}=1$

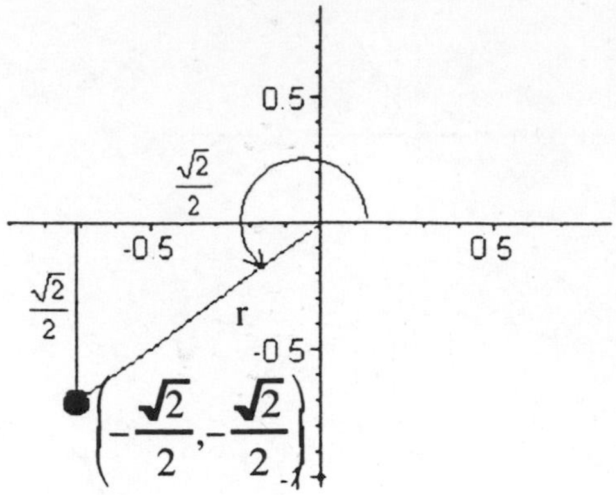

$$\sin\theta=\frac{b}{r}=\frac{\left(-\frac{\sqrt{2}}{2}\right)}{1}=-\frac{\sqrt{2}}{2} \qquad \cos\theta=\frac{a}{r}=\frac{\left(-\frac{\sqrt{2}}{2}\right)}{1}=-\frac{\sqrt{2}}{2}$$

$$\tan\theta=\frac{b}{a}=\frac{\left(-\frac{\sqrt{2}}{2}\right)}{\left(-\frac{\sqrt{2}}{2}\right)}=1 \qquad \cot\theta=\frac{a}{b}=\frac{\left(-\frac{\sqrt{2}}{2}\right)}{\left(-\frac{\sqrt{2}}{2}\right)}=1$$

$$\sec\theta=\frac{r}{a}=\frac{1}{\left(-\frac{\sqrt{2}}{2}\right)}=-\frac{2}{\sqrt{2}}\frac{\sqrt{2}}{\sqrt{2}}=-\sqrt{2}$$

$$\csc\theta=\frac{r}{b}=\frac{1}{\left(-\frac{\sqrt{2}}{2}\right)}=-\frac{2}{\sqrt{2}}\frac{\sqrt{2}}{\sqrt{2}}=-\sqrt{2}$$

11. Since $\sin\theta>0$ for points in quadrants I and II, and $\cos\theta<0$ for points in quadrants II and III, the angle θ lies in quadrant II.

12. Since $\sin\theta<0$ for points in quadrants III and IV, and $\cos\theta>0$ for points in quadrants I and IV, the angle θ lies in quadrant IV.

13. Since $\sin\theta<0$ for points in quadrants III and IV, and $\tan\theta<0$ for points in quadrants II and IV, the angle θ lies in quadrant IV.

14. Since $\cos\theta>0$ for points in quadrants I and IV, and $\tan\theta>0$ for points in quadrants I and III, the angle θ lies in quadrant I.

15. Since $\cos\theta>0$ for points in quadrants I and IV, and $\cot\theta<0$ for points in quadrants II and IV, the angle θ lies in quadrant IV.

16. Since $\sin\theta<0$ for points in quadrants II and III, and $\cot\theta>0$ for points in quadrants I and III, the angle θ lies in quadrant III.

17. Since $\sec\theta<0$ for points in quadrants II and III, and $\tan\theta>0$ for points in quadrants I and III, the angle θ lies in quadrant III.

18. Since $\csc\theta>0$ for points in quadrants I and II, and $\cot\theta<0$ for points in quadrants II and IV, the angle θ lies in quadrant II.

19. $\theta = -30^\circ + 360^\circ = 330^\circ$;
$\Rightarrow \theta$ in quadrant IV
reference angle $\alpha = 360^\circ - 330^\circ = 30^\circ$

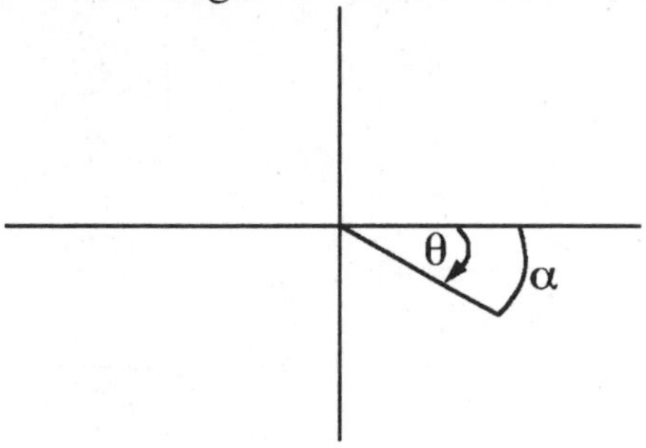

20. $\theta = 60^\circ \Rightarrow \theta$ in quadrant I
reference angle $\alpha = 60^\circ$

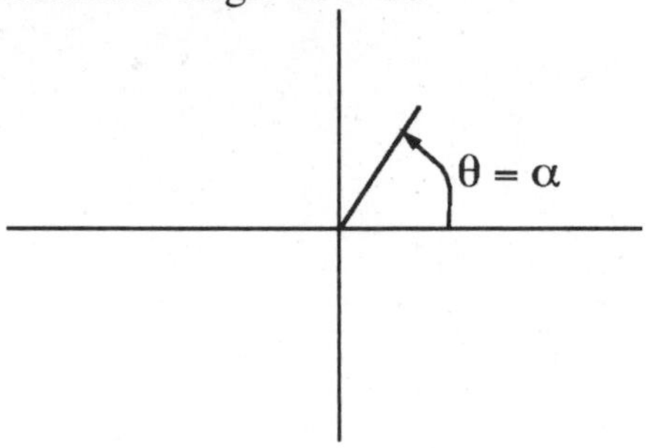

21. $\theta = 120^\circ \Rightarrow \theta$ in quadrant II
reference angle $\alpha = 180^\circ - 120^\circ = 60^\circ$

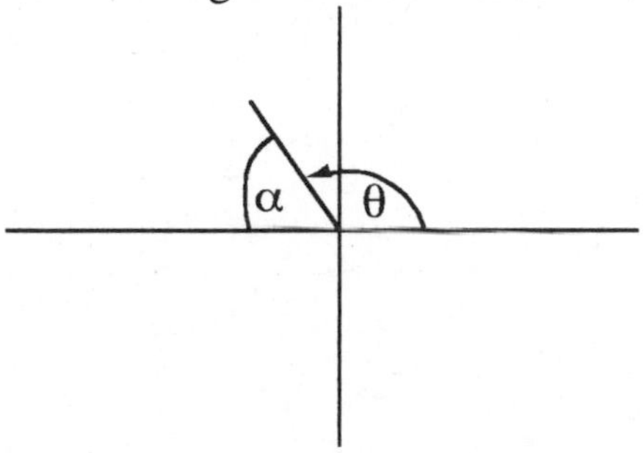

22. $\theta = 300^\circ \Rightarrow \theta$ in quadrant IV
reference angle $\alpha = 360^\circ - 300^\circ = 60^\circ$

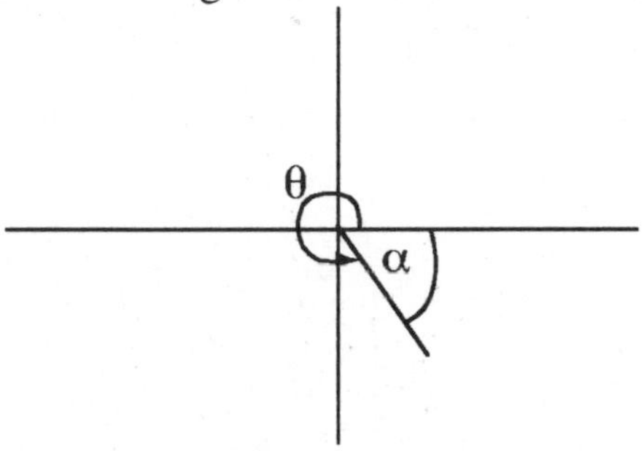

23. $\theta = 210^\circ \Rightarrow \theta$ in quadrant III
reference angle $\alpha = 210^\circ - 180^\circ = 30^\circ$

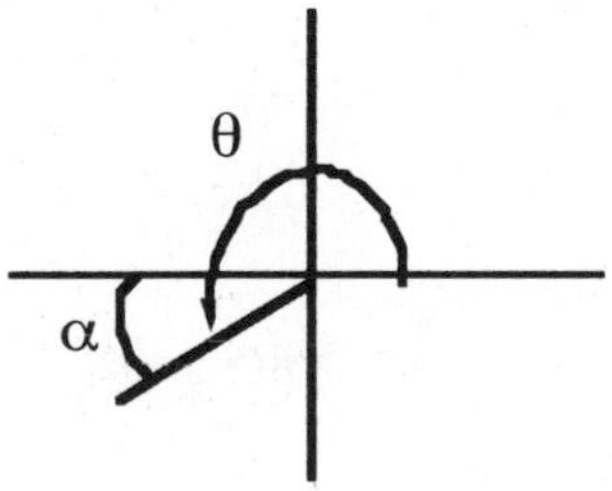

24. $\theta = 330^\circ \Rightarrow \theta$ in quadrant IV
reference angle $\alpha = 360^\circ - 330^\circ = 30^\circ$

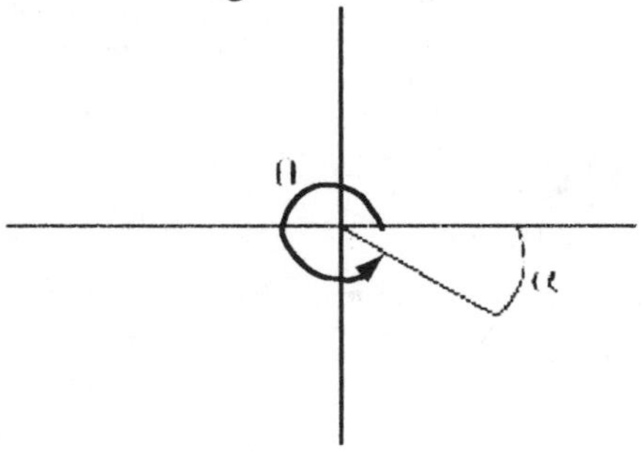

25. $\theta = \dfrac{5\pi}{4} \Rightarrow \theta$ in quadrant III

reference angle $\alpha = \dfrac{5\pi}{4} - \pi = \dfrac{\pi}{4}$

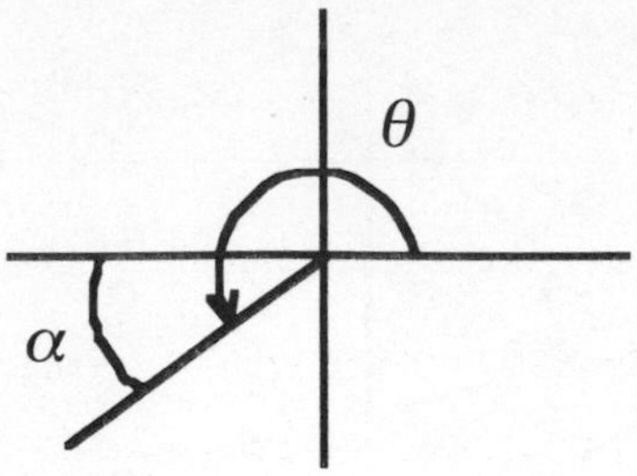

26. $\theta = \dfrac{5\pi}{6} \Rightarrow \theta$ in quadrant II

reference angle $\alpha = \pi - \dfrac{5\pi}{6} = \dfrac{\pi}{6}$

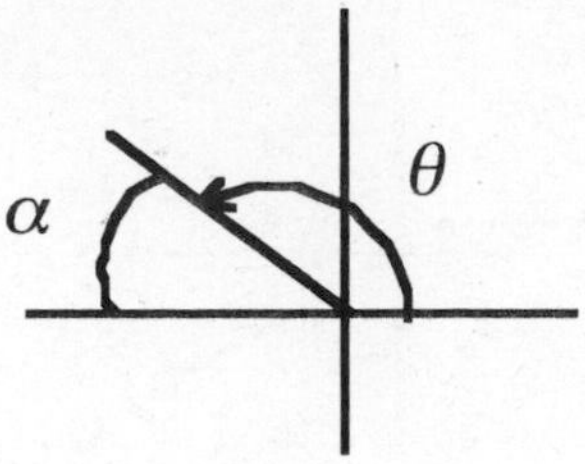

27. $\theta = \dfrac{8\pi}{3} - 2\pi = \dfrac{2\pi}{3} \Rightarrow \theta$ in quadrant II

reference angle $\alpha = \pi - \dfrac{2\pi}{3} = \dfrac{\pi}{3}$

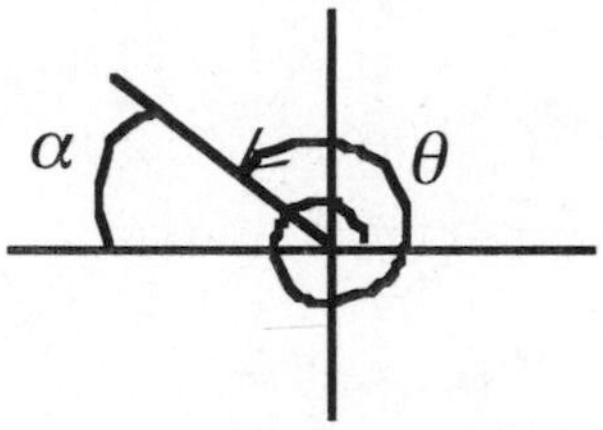

28. $\theta = \dfrac{7\pi}{4} \Rightarrow \theta$ in quadrant IV

reference angle $\alpha = 2\pi - \dfrac{7\pi}{4} = \dfrac{\pi}{4}$

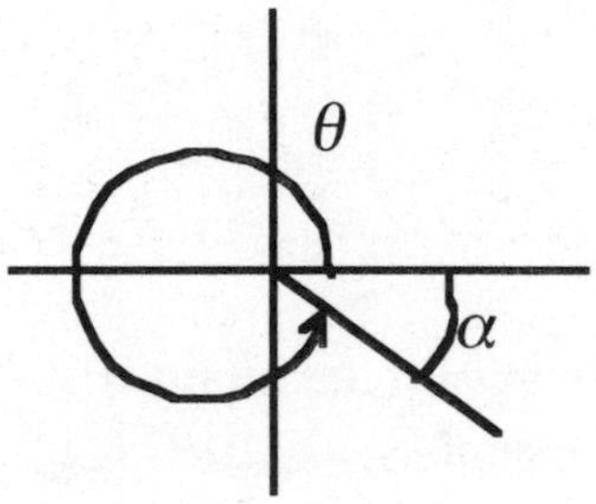

29. $\theta = -135^\circ + 360^\circ = 225^\circ$
$\Rightarrow \theta$ in quadrant III
reference angle $\alpha = 225^\circ - 180^\circ = 45^\circ$

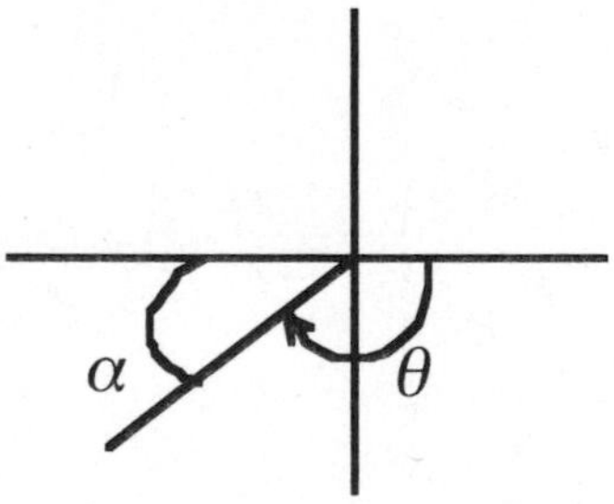

30. $\theta = -240^\circ + 360^\circ = 120^\circ$
$\Rightarrow \theta$ in quadrant II
reference angle $\alpha = 180^\circ - 120^\circ = 60^\circ$

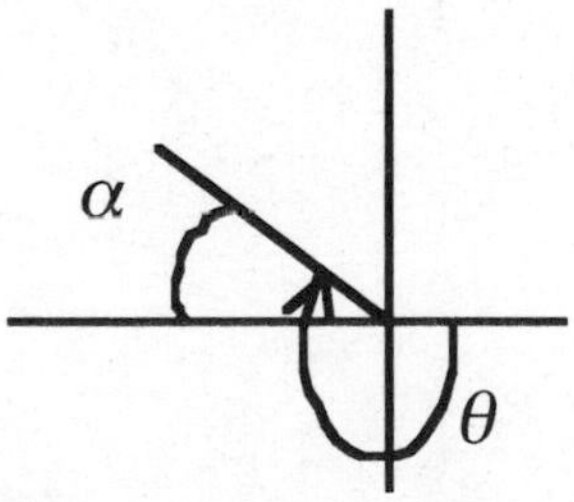

31. $\theta = -\frac{2\pi}{3} + 2\pi = \frac{4\pi}{3}$
$\Rightarrow \theta$ in quadrant III
reference angle $\alpha = \frac{4\pi}{3} - \pi = \frac{\pi}{3}$

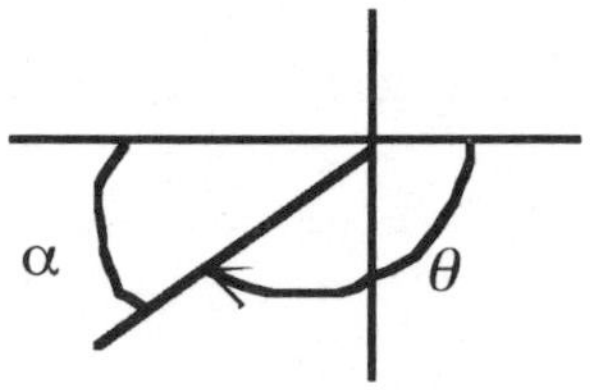

32. $\theta = -\frac{7\pi}{6} + 2\pi = \frac{5\pi}{6}$
$\Rightarrow \theta$ in quadrant II
reference angle $\alpha = \pi - \frac{5\pi}{6} = \frac{\pi}{6}$

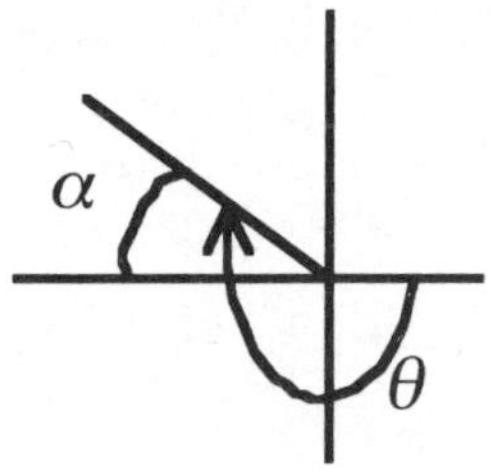

33. $\theta = 440^\circ - 360^\circ = 80^\circ \Rightarrow \theta$ in quadrant I
reference angle $\alpha = 80^\circ$

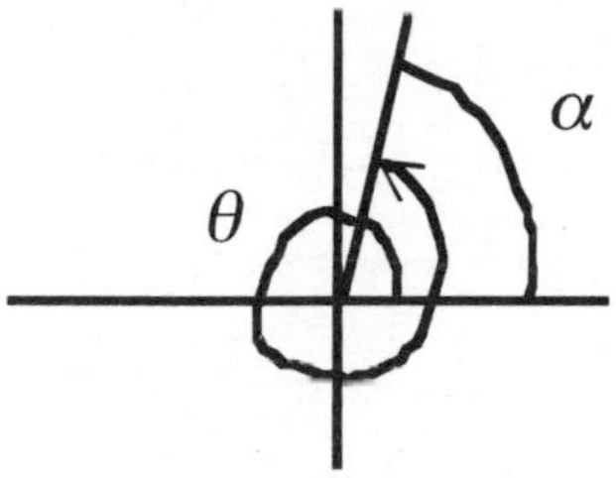

34. $\theta = 490^\circ - 360^\circ = 130^\circ \Rightarrow \theta$ in quadrant II
reference angle $\alpha = 50^\circ$

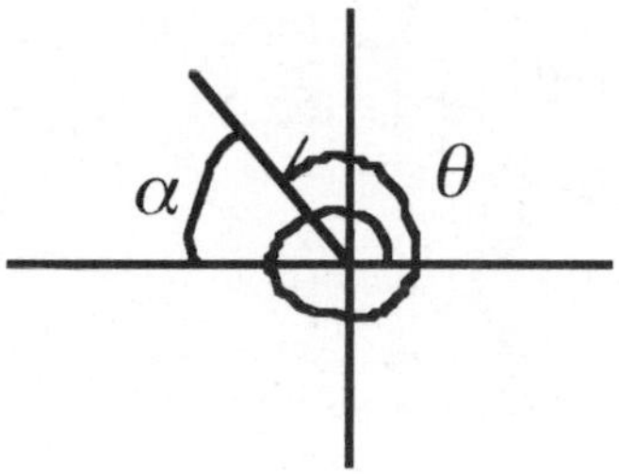

35. $\theta = -\frac{3\pi}{4} + 2\pi = \frac{5\pi}{4} \Rightarrow \theta$ in quadrant III
reference angle $\alpha = \frac{5\pi}{4} - \pi = \frac{\pi}{4}$

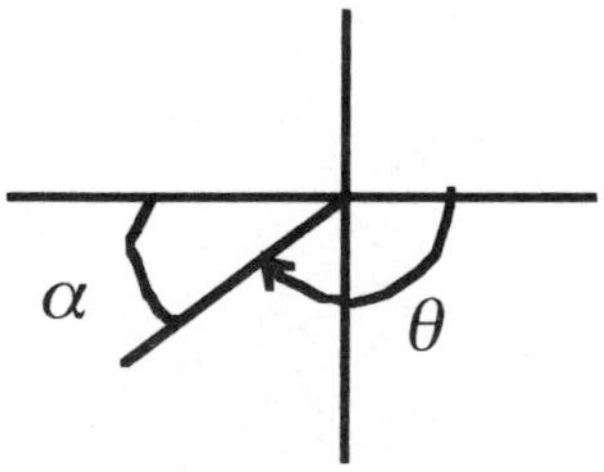

36. $\theta = -\frac{11\pi}{6} + 2\pi = \frac{\pi}{6} \Rightarrow \theta$ in quadrant I
reference angle $\alpha = \frac{\pi}{6}$

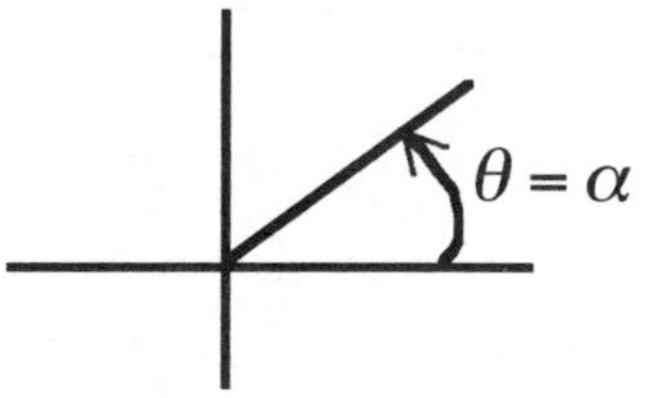

37. $\sin(405°) = \sin(360° + 45°) = \sin(45°) = \dfrac{\sqrt{2}}{2}$

38. $\cos(420°) = \cos(360° + 60°) = \cos(60°) = \dfrac{1}{2}$

39. $\tan(405°) = \tan(180° + 180° + 45°) = \tan(45°) = 1$

40. $\sin(390°) = \sin(360° + 30°) = \sin(30°) = \dfrac{1}{2}$

41. $\csc(450°) = \csc(360° + 90°) = \csc(90°) = 1$

42. $\sec(540°) = \sec(360° + 180°) = \sec(180°) = -1$

43. $\cot(390°) = \cot(180° + 180° + 30°) = \cot(30°) = \sqrt{3}$

44. $\sec(420°) = \sec(360° + 60°) = \sec(60°) = 2$

45. $\cos\left(\dfrac{33\pi}{4}\right) = \cos\left(\dfrac{\pi}{4} + \dfrac{32\pi}{4}\right) = \cos\left(\dfrac{\pi}{4} + 8\pi\right) = \cos\left(\dfrac{\pi}{4} + 4 \cdot 2\pi\right) = \cos\left(\dfrac{\pi}{4}\right) = \dfrac{\sqrt{2}}{2}$

46. $\sin\left(\dfrac{9\pi}{4}\right) = \sin\left(\dfrac{\pi}{4} + \dfrac{8\pi}{4}\right) = \sin\left(\dfrac{\pi}{4} + 2\pi\right) = \sin\left(\dfrac{\pi}{4}\right) = \dfrac{\sqrt{2}}{2}$

47. $\tan(21\pi) = \tan(0 + 21\pi) = \tan(0) = 0$

48. $\csc\left(\dfrac{9\pi}{2}\right) = \csc\left(\dfrac{\pi}{2} + \dfrac{8\pi}{2}\right) = \csc\left(\dfrac{\pi}{2} + 4\pi\right) = \csc\left(\dfrac{\pi}{2} + 2 \cdot 2\pi\right) = \csc\left(\dfrac{\pi}{2}\right) = 1$

49. $\sec\left(\dfrac{17\pi}{4}\right) = \sec\left(\dfrac{\pi}{4} + \dfrac{16\pi}{4}\right) = \sec\left(\dfrac{\pi}{4} + 4\pi\right) = \sec\left(\dfrac{\pi}{4} + 2 \cdot 2\pi\right) = \sec\left(\dfrac{\pi}{4}\right) = \sqrt{2}$

50. $\cot\left(\dfrac{17\pi}{4}\right) = \cot\left(\dfrac{\pi}{4} + \dfrac{16\pi}{4}\right) = \cot\left(\dfrac{\pi}{4} + 4\pi\right) = \cot\left(\dfrac{\pi}{4} + 2 \cdot 2\pi\right) = \cot\left(\dfrac{\pi}{4}\right) = 1$

51. $\tan\left(\dfrac{19\pi}{6}\right) = \tan\left(\dfrac{\pi}{6} + \dfrac{18\pi}{6}\right) = \tan\left(\dfrac{\pi}{6} + 3\pi\right) = \tan\left(\dfrac{\pi}{6}\right) = \dfrac{\sqrt{3}}{3}$

52. $\sec\left(\dfrac{25\pi}{6}\right) = \sec\left(\dfrac{\pi}{6} + \dfrac{24\pi}{6}\right) = \sec\left(\dfrac{\pi}{6} + 4\pi\right) = \sec\left(\dfrac{\pi}{6} + 2 \cdot 2\pi\right) = \sec\left(\dfrac{\pi}{6}\right) = \dfrac{2\sqrt{3}}{3}$

53. $\sin(150°) = \sin(30°) = \dfrac{1}{2}$, since $\theta = 150°$ has reference angle $\alpha = 30°$ in quadrant II.

54. $\cos(210^\circ) = -\cos(30^\circ) = -\dfrac{\sqrt{3}}{2}$, since $\theta = 210^\circ$ has reference angle $\alpha = 30^\circ$ in quadrant III.

55. $\cos(315^\circ) = \cos(45^\circ) = \dfrac{\sqrt{2}}{2}$, since $\theta = 315^\circ$ has reference angle $\alpha = 45^\circ$ in quadrant IV.

56. $\sin(120^\circ) = \sin(60^\circ) = \dfrac{\sqrt{3}}{2}$, since $\theta = 120^\circ$ has reference angle $\alpha = 60^\circ$ in quadrant II.

57. $\sec(240^\circ) = -\sec(60^\circ) = -2$, since $\theta = 240^\circ$ has reference angle $\alpha = 60^\circ$ in quadrant III.

58. $\csc(300^\circ) = -\csc(60^\circ) = -\dfrac{2\sqrt{3}}{3}$, since $\theta = 300^\circ$ has reference angle $\alpha = 60^\circ$ in quadrant IV.

59. $\cot(330^\circ) = -\cot(30^\circ) = -\sqrt{3}$, since $\theta = 330^\circ$ has reference angle $\alpha = 30^\circ$ in quadrant IV.

60. $\tan(225^\circ) = \tan(45^\circ) = 1$, since $\theta = 225^\circ$ has reference angle $\alpha = 45^\circ$ in quadrant III.

61. $\sin\left(\dfrac{3\pi}{4}\right) = \sin\left(\dfrac{\pi}{4}\right) = \dfrac{\sqrt{2}}{2}$, since $\theta = \dfrac{3\pi}{4}$ has reference angle $\alpha = \dfrac{\pi}{4}$ in quadrant III.

62. $\cos\left(\dfrac{2\pi}{3}\right) = -\cos\left(\dfrac{\pi}{3}\right) = -\dfrac{1}{2}$, since $\theta = \dfrac{2\pi}{3}$ has reference angle $\alpha = \dfrac{\pi}{3}$ in quadrant II.

63. $\cot\left(\dfrac{7\pi}{6}\right) = \cot\left(\dfrac{\pi}{6}\right) = \sqrt{3}$, since $\theta = \dfrac{7\pi}{6}$ has reference angle $\alpha = \dfrac{\pi}{6}$ in quadrant III.

64. $\csc\left(\dfrac{7\pi}{4}\right) = -\csc\left(\dfrac{\pi}{4}\right) = -\sqrt{2}$, since $\theta = \dfrac{7\pi}{4}$ has reference angle $\alpha = \dfrac{\pi}{4}$ in quadrant IV.

65. $\cos(-60^\circ) = \cos(60^\circ) = \dfrac{1}{2}$, since $\theta = -60^\circ$ has reference angle $\alpha = 60^\circ$ in quadrant IV.

66. $\tan(-120^\circ) = \tan(60^\circ) = \sqrt{3}$, since $\theta = -120^\circ$ has reference angle $\alpha = 60^\circ$ in quadrant III.

67. $\sin\left(-\dfrac{2\pi}{3}\right) = -\sin\left(\dfrac{\pi}{3}\right) = -\dfrac{\sqrt{3}}{2}$, since $\theta = -\dfrac{2\pi}{3}$ has reference angle $\alpha = \dfrac{\pi}{3}$ in quadrant III.

68. $\cot\left(-\dfrac{\pi}{6}\right) = -\cot\left(\dfrac{\pi}{6}\right) = -\sqrt{3}$, since $\theta = -\dfrac{\pi}{6}$ has reference angle $\alpha = \dfrac{\pi}{6}$ in quadrant IV.

69. $\tan\left(\frac{14\pi}{3}\right) = -\tan\left(\frac{\pi}{3}\right) = -\sqrt{3}$, since $\theta = \frac{14\pi}{3}$ has reference angle $\alpha = \frac{\pi}{3}$ in quadrant II.

70. $\sec\left(\frac{11\pi}{4}\right) = -\sec\left(\frac{\pi}{4}\right) = -\sqrt{2}$, since $\theta = \frac{11\pi}{4}$ has reference angle $\alpha = \frac{\pi}{4}$ in quadrant II.

71. $\csc(-315^\circ) = \csc(45^\circ) = \sqrt{2}$, since $\theta = -315^\circ$ has reference angle $\alpha = 45^\circ$ in quadrant I.

72. $\sec(-225^\circ) = -\sec(45^\circ) = -\sqrt{2}$, since $\theta = -225^\circ$ has reference angle $\alpha = 45^\circ$ in quadrant II.

73. $\sin(8\pi) = \sin(0 + 8\pi) = \sin(0) = 0$

74. $\cos(-2\pi) = \cos(0 - 2\pi) = \cos(0) = 1$

75. $\tan(7\pi) = \tan(\pi + 6\pi) = \tan(\pi) = 0$

76. $\cot(5\pi) = \cot(\pi + 4\pi) = \cot(\pi)$, which is undefined

77. $\sec(-3\pi) = \sec(\pi) = -1$, since $\theta = -3\pi$ is coterminal with $\alpha = \pi$.

78. $\csc\left(-\frac{5\pi}{2}\right) = \csc\left(\frac{3\pi}{2}\right) = -1$, since $\theta = -\frac{5\pi}{2}$ is coterminal with $\alpha = \frac{3\pi}{2}$.

79. $\sin\theta = \frac{12}{13}$, θ in quadrant II

Since θ is in quadrant II, we know that $\sin\theta > 0$ and $\csc\theta > 0$;
while $\cos\theta < 0$, $\sec\theta < 0$, $\tan\theta < 0$ and $\cot\theta < 0$.

If α is the reference angle for θ, then $\sin\alpha = \frac{12}{13}$.

Now draw the appropriate triangle and use the Pythagorean Theorem to find the values of the other trigonometric functions of α.

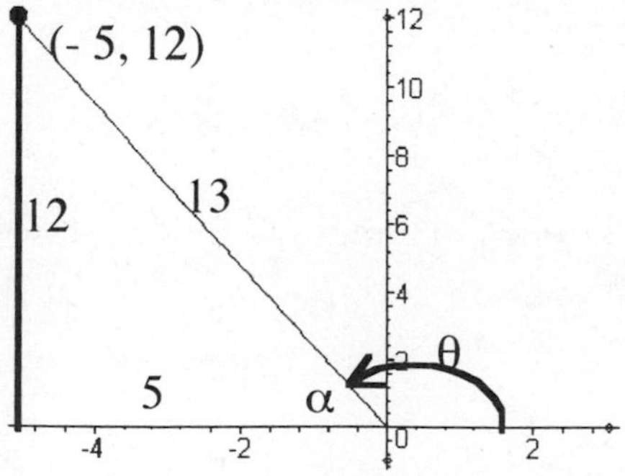

$\cos\alpha = \frac{5}{13}$ $\tan\alpha = \frac{12}{5}$ $\sec\alpha = \frac{13}{5}$

$\csc\alpha = \frac{13}{12}$ $\cot\alpha = \frac{5}{12}$

Finally, we assign the appropriate sign to find the values of the other trigonometric functions of θ.

$\cos\theta = -\frac{5}{13}$ $\tan\theta = -\frac{12}{5}$ $\sec\theta = -\frac{13}{5}$

$\csc\theta = \frac{13}{12}$ $\cot\theta = -\frac{5}{12}$

80. $\cos\theta = \frac{3}{5}$, θ in quadrant IV

Since θ is in quadrant IV, we know that $\cos\theta > 0$ and $\sec\theta > 0$;
while $\sin\theta < 0$, $\csc\theta < 0$, $\tan\theta < 0$ and $\cot\theta < 0$.
If α is the reference angle for θ, then $\cos\alpha = \frac{3}{5}$.
Now draw the appropriate triangle and use the Pythagorean Theorem to find the values of the other trigonometric functions of α.

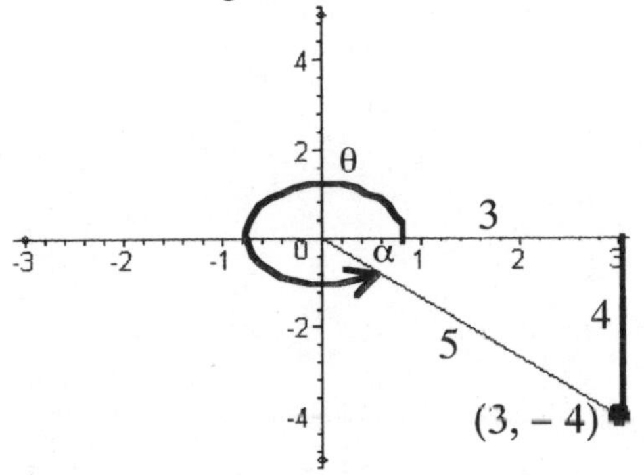

$\sin\alpha = \frac{4}{5}$ $\tan\alpha = \frac{4}{3}$ $\sec\alpha = \frac{5}{3}$

$\csc\alpha = \frac{5}{4}$ $\cot\alpha = \frac{3}{4}$

Finally, we assign the appropriate sign to find the values of the other trigonometric functions of θ.

$\sin\theta = -\frac{4}{5}$ $\tan\theta = -\frac{4}{3}$ $\sec\theta = \frac{5}{3}$

$\csc\theta = -\frac{5}{4}$ $\cot\theta = -\frac{3}{4}$

81. $\cos\theta = -\frac{4}{5}$, θ in quadrant III

Since θ is in quadrant III, we know that $\cos\theta < 0$, $\sec\theta < 0$, $\sin\theta < 0$ and $\csc\theta < 0$;
while $\tan\theta > 0$ and $\cot\theta > 0$.
If α is the reference angle for θ, then $\cos\alpha = \frac{4}{5}$.
Now draw the appropriate triangle and use the Pythagorean Theorem to find the values of the other trigonometric functions of α.

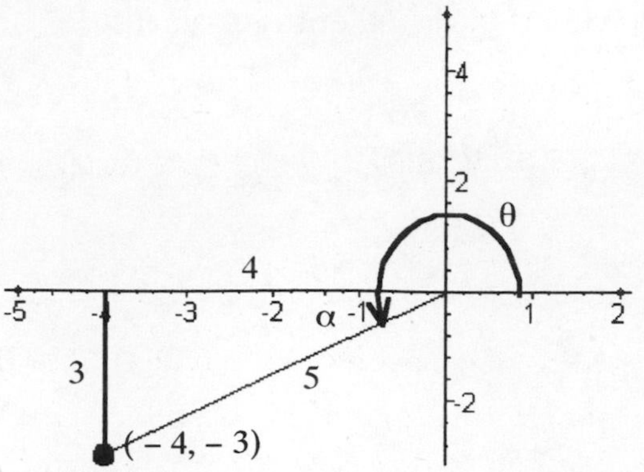

$\sin\alpha = \frac{3}{5}$ $\tan\alpha = \frac{3}{4}$ $\sec\alpha = \frac{5}{4}$

$\csc\alpha = \frac{5}{3}$ $\cot\alpha = \frac{4}{3}$

Finally, we assign the appropriate sign to find the values of the other trigonometric functions of θ.

$\sin\theta = -\frac{3}{5}$ $\tan\theta = \frac{3}{4}$ $\sec\theta = -\frac{5}{4}$

$\csc\theta = -\frac{5}{3}$ $\cot\theta = \frac{4}{3}$

82. $\sin\theta = -\frac{5}{13}$, θ in quadrant III

Since θ is in quadrant III, we know that $\cos\theta < 0$, $\sec\theta < 0$, $\sin\theta < 0$ and $\csc\theta < 0$; while $\tan\theta > 0$ and $\cot\theta > 0$.

If α is the reference angle for θ, then $\sin\alpha = \frac{5}{13}$.

Now draw the appropriate triangle and use the Pythagorean Theorem to find the values of the other trigonometric functions of α.

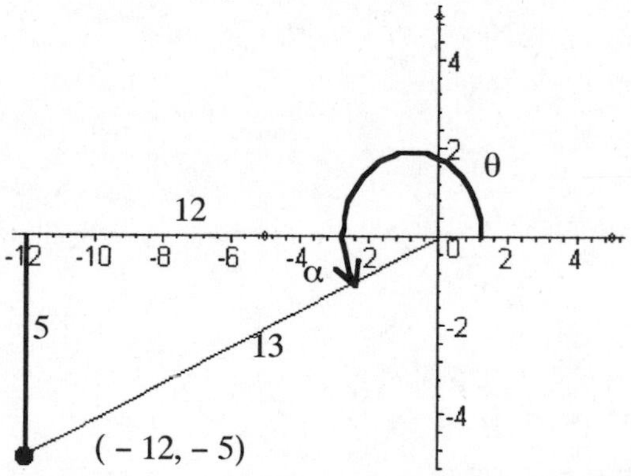

$\cos\alpha = \frac{12}{13}$ $\tan\alpha = \frac{5}{12}$ $\sec\alpha = \frac{13}{12}$

$\csc\alpha = \frac{13}{5}$ $\cot\alpha = \frac{12}{5}$

Finally, we assign the appropriate sign to find the values of the other trigonometric functions of θ.

$\cos\theta = -\frac{12}{13}$ $\tan\theta = \frac{5}{12}$ $\sec\theta = -\frac{13}{12}$

$\csc\theta = -\frac{13}{5}$ $\cot\theta = \frac{12}{5}$

83. $\sin\theta = \frac{5}{13}$, $90° < \theta < 180° \Rightarrow \theta$ in quadrant II

Since θ is in quadrant II, we know that $\cos\theta < 0$, $\sec\theta < 0$, $\tan\theta < 0$ and $\cot\theta < 0$; while $\sin\theta > 0$ and $\csc\theta > 0$.

If α is the reference angle for θ, then $\sin\alpha = \frac{5}{13}$.

Now draw the appropriate triangle and use the Pythagorean Theorem to find the values of the other trigonometric functions of α.

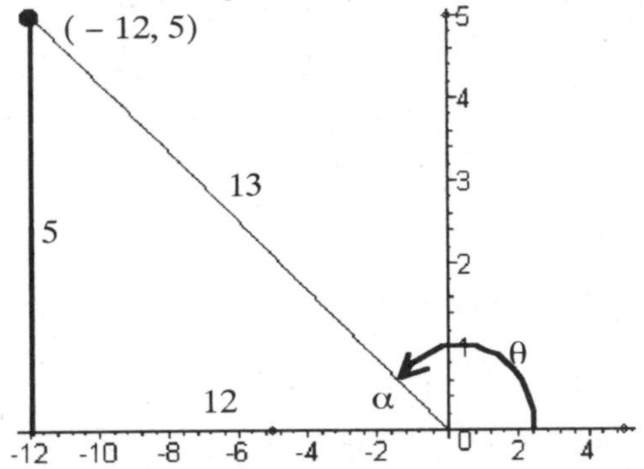

$\cos\alpha = \frac{12}{13}$ $\tan\alpha = \frac{5}{12}$ $\sec\alpha = \frac{13}{12}$

$\csc\alpha = \frac{13}{5}$ $\cot\alpha = \frac{12}{5}$

Finally, we assign the appropriate sign to find the values of the other trigonometric functions of θ.

$\cos\theta = -\frac{12}{13}$ $\tan\theta = -\frac{5}{12}$ $\sec\theta = -\frac{13}{12}$

$\csc\theta = \frac{13}{5}$ $\cot\theta = -\frac{12}{5}$

84. $\cos\theta = \frac{4}{5}$, $270° < \theta < 360° \Rightarrow \theta$ in quadrant IV

Since θ is in quadrant IV, we know that $\sin\theta < 0$, $\csc\theta < 0$, $\tan\theta < 0$ and $\cot\theta < 0$; while $\cos\theta > 0$ and $\sec\theta > 0$.

If α is the reference angle for θ, then $\cos\alpha = \frac{4}{5}$.

Now draw the appropriate triangle and use the Pythagorean Theorem to find the values of the other trigonometric functions of α.

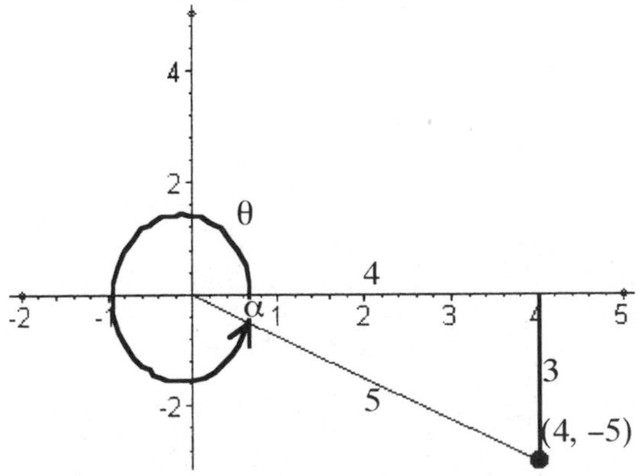

$\sin\alpha = \frac{3}{5}$ $\tan\alpha = \frac{3}{4}$ $\sec\alpha = \frac{5}{4}$

$\csc\alpha = \frac{5}{3}$ $\cot\alpha = \frac{4}{3}$

Finally, we assign the appropriate sign to find the values of the other trigonometric functions of θ.

$\sin\theta = -\frac{3}{5}$ $\tan\theta = -\frac{3}{4}$ $\sec\theta = \frac{5}{4}$

$\csc\theta = -\frac{5}{3}$ $\cot\theta = -\frac{4}{3}$

85. $\cos\theta = -\frac{1}{3}$, $180^\circ < \theta < 270^\circ \Rightarrow \theta$ in quadrant III

Since θ is in quadrant III, we know that $\cos\theta < 0$, $\sec\theta < 0$, $\sin\theta < 0$ and $\csc\theta < 0$; while $\tan\theta > 0$ and $\cot\theta > 0$.

If α is the reference angle for θ, then $\cos\alpha = \frac{1}{3}$.

Now draw the appropriate triangle and use the Pythagorean Theorem to find the values of the other trigonometric functions of α.

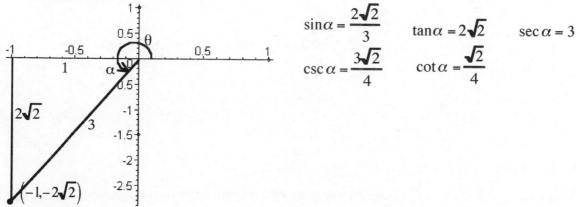

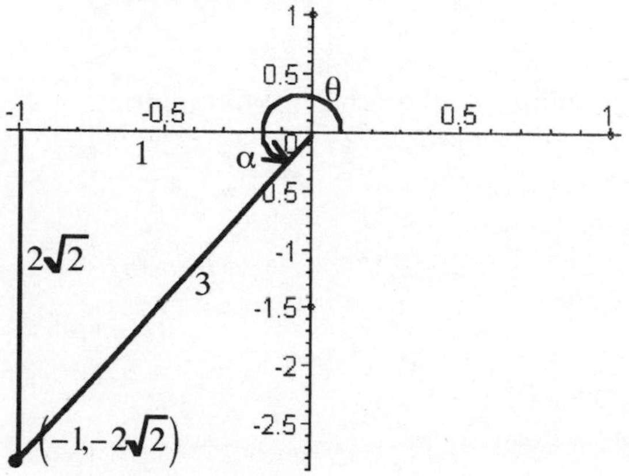

$\sin\alpha = \frac{2\sqrt{2}}{3}$ $\tan\alpha = 2\sqrt{2}$ $\sec\alpha = 3$

$\csc\alpha = \frac{3\sqrt{2}}{4}$ $\cot\alpha = \frac{\sqrt{2}}{4}$

Finally, we assign the appropriate sign to find the values of the other trigonometric functions of θ.

$\sin\theta = -\frac{2\sqrt{2}}{3}$ $\tan\theta = 2\sqrt{2}$ $\sec\theta = -3$

$\csc\theta = -\frac{3\sqrt{2}}{4}$ $\cot\theta = \frac{\sqrt{2}}{4}$

86. $\sin\theta = -\frac{2}{3}$, $180^\circ < \theta < 270^\circ \Rightarrow \theta$ in quadrant III

Since θ is in quadrant III, we know that $\cos\theta < 0$, $\sec\theta < 0$, $\sin\theta < 0$ and $\csc\theta < 0$; while $\tan\theta > 0$ and $\cot\theta > 0$.

If α is the reference angle for θ, then $\sin\alpha = \frac{2}{3}$.

Now draw the appropriate triangle and use the Pythagorean Theorem to find the values of the other trigonometric functions of α.

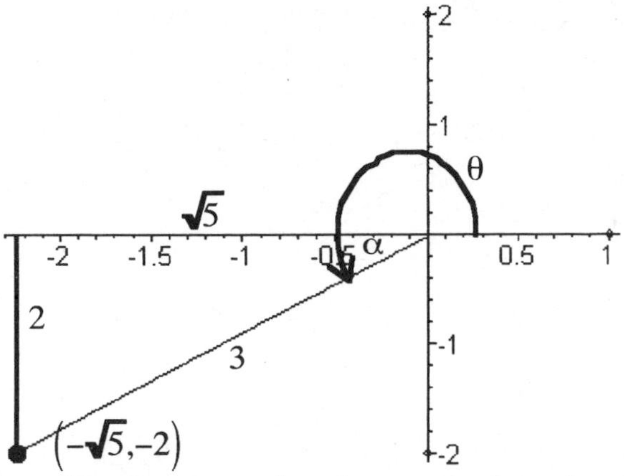

$\cos\alpha = \frac{\sqrt{5}}{3}$ $\tan\alpha = \frac{2\sqrt{5}}{5}$ $\sec\alpha = \frac{3\sqrt{5}}{5}$

$\csc\alpha = \frac{3}{2}$ $\cot\alpha = \frac{\sqrt{5}}{2}$

Finally, we assign the appropriate sign to find the values of the other trigonometric functions of θ.

$\cos\theta = -\frac{\sqrt{5}}{3}$ $\tan\theta = \frac{2\sqrt{5}}{5}$ $\sec\theta = -\frac{3\sqrt{5}}{5}$

$\csc\theta = -\frac{3}{2}$ $\cot\theta = \frac{\sqrt{5}}{2}$

87. $\sin\theta = \frac{2}{3}$, $\tan\theta < 0 \Rightarrow \theta$ in quadrant II

Since θ is in quadrant II, we know that $\cos\theta < 0$, $\sec\theta < 0$, $\tan\theta < 0$ and $\cot\theta < 0$; while $\sin\theta > 0$ and $\csc\theta > 0$.

If α is the reference angle for θ, then $\sin\alpha = \frac{2}{3}$.

Now draw the appropriate triangle and use the Pythagorean Theorem to find the values of the other trigonometric functions of α.

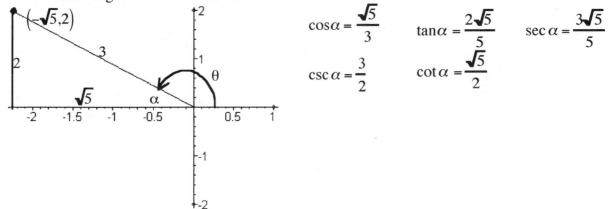

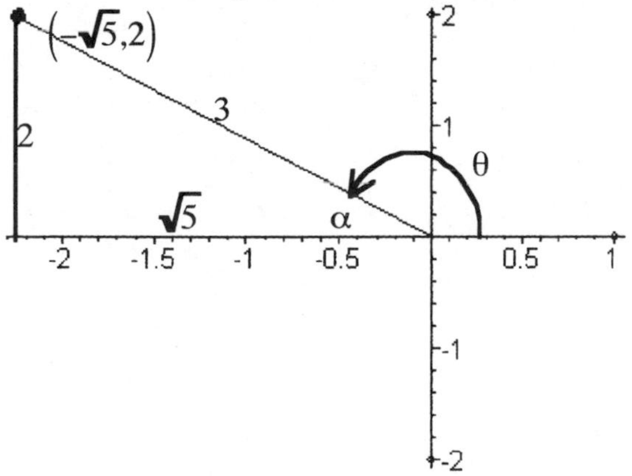

$\cos\alpha = \frac{\sqrt{5}}{3}$ $\tan\alpha = \frac{2\sqrt{5}}{5}$ $\sec\alpha = \frac{3\sqrt{5}}{5}$

$\csc\alpha = \frac{3}{2}$ $\cot\alpha = \frac{\sqrt{5}}{2}$

Finally, we assign the appropriate sign to find the values of the other trigonometric functions of θ.

$\cos\theta = -\frac{\sqrt{5}}{3}$ $\tan\theta = -\frac{2\sqrt{5}}{5}$ $\sec\theta = -\frac{3\sqrt{5}}{5}$

$\csc\theta = \frac{3}{2}$ $\cot\theta = -\frac{\sqrt{5}}{2}$

88. $\cos\theta = -\frac{1}{4}$, $\tan\theta > 0 \Rightarrow$ θ in quadrant III

Since θ is in quadrant III, we know that $\cos\theta < 0$, $\sec\theta < 0$, $\sin\theta < 0$ and $\csc\theta < 0$; while $\tan\theta > 0$ and $\cot\theta > 0$.

If α is the reference angle for θ, then $\cos\alpha = \frac{1}{4}$.

Now draw the appropriate triangle and use the Pythagorean Theorem to find the values of the other trigonometric functions of α.

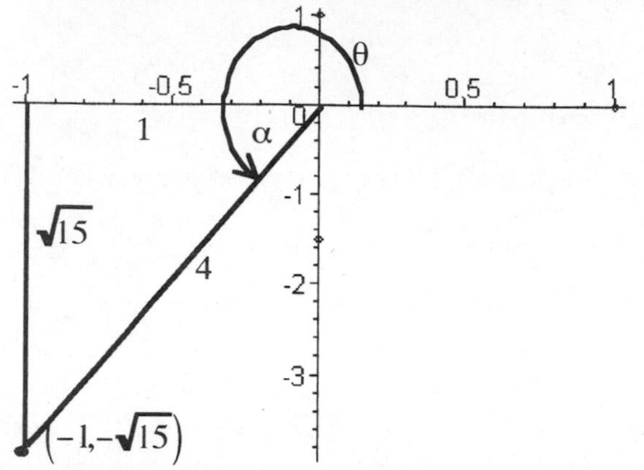

$\sin\alpha = \frac{\sqrt{15}}{4}$ $\tan\alpha = \sqrt{15}$ $\sec\alpha = 4$

$\csc\alpha = \frac{4\sqrt{15}}{15}$ $\cot\alpha = \frac{\sqrt{15}}{15}$

Finally, we assign the appropriate sign to find the values of the other trigonometric functions of θ.

$\sin\theta = -\frac{\sqrt{15}}{4}$ $\tan\theta = \sqrt{15}$ $\sec\theta = -4$

$\csc\theta = -\frac{4\sqrt{15}}{15}$ $\cot\theta = \frac{\sqrt{15}}{15}$

89. $\sec\theta = 2$, $\sin\theta < 0$, $\Rightarrow$ θ in quadrant IV

Since θ is in quadrant IV, we know that $\sin\theta < 0$, $\csc\theta < 0$, $\tan\theta < 0$ and $\cot\theta < 0$; while $\cos\theta > 0$ and $\sec\theta > 0$.

If α is the reference angle for θ, then $\sec\alpha = 2$.

Now draw the appropriate triangle and use the Pythagorean Theorem to find the values of the other trigonometric functions of α.

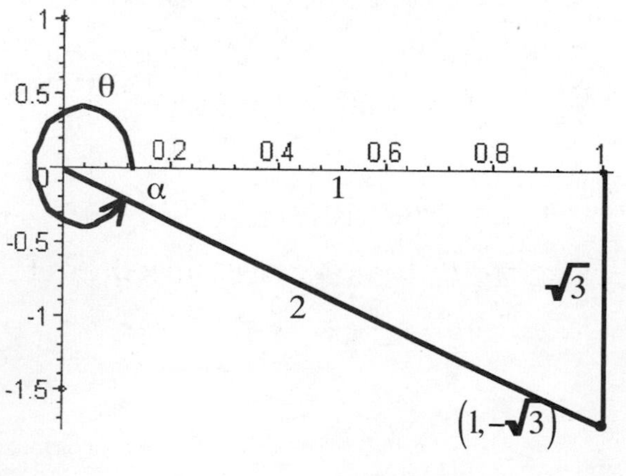

$\cos\alpha = \frac{1}{2}$ $\sin\alpha = \frac{\sqrt{3}}{2}$ $\tan\alpha = \sqrt{3}$

$\csc\alpha = \frac{2\sqrt{3}}{3}$ $\cot\alpha = \frac{\sqrt{3}}{3}$

Finally, we assign the appropriate sign to find the values of the other trigonometric functions of θ.

$$\cos\theta = \frac{1}{2} \qquad \sin\theta = -\frac{\sqrt{3}}{2} \qquad \tan\theta = -\sqrt{3}$$

$$\csc\theta = -\frac{2\sqrt{3}}{3} \qquad \cot\theta = -\frac{\sqrt{3}}{3}$$

90. $\csc\theta = 3$, $\cot\theta < 0$, $\Rightarrow$ θ in quadrant II

Since θ is in quadrant II, we know that $\cos\theta < 0$, $\sec\theta < 0$, $\tan\theta < 0$ and $\cot\theta < 0$; while $\sin\theta > 0$ and $\csc\theta > 0$.
If α is the reference angle for θ, then $\csc\alpha = 3$.
Now draw the appropriate triangle and use the Pythagorean Theorem to find the values of the other trigonometric functions of α.

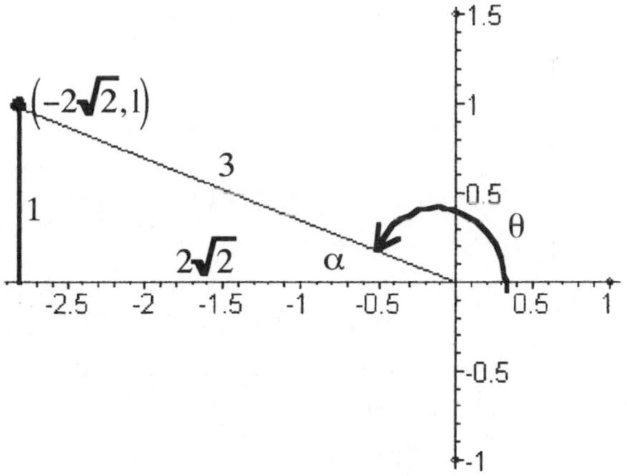

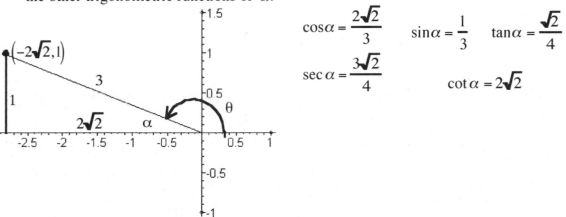

$$\cos\alpha = \frac{2\sqrt{2}}{3} \qquad \sin\alpha = \frac{1}{3} \qquad \tan\alpha = \frac{\sqrt{2}}{4}$$

$$\sec\alpha = \frac{3\sqrt{2}}{4} \qquad \cot\alpha = 2\sqrt{2}$$

Finally, we assign the appropriate sign to find the values of the other trigonometric functions of θ.

$$\cos\theta = -\frac{2\sqrt{2}}{3} \qquad \sin\theta = \frac{1}{3} \qquad \tan\theta = -\frac{\sqrt{2}}{4}$$

$$\csc\theta = \frac{3\sqrt{2}}{4} \qquad \cot\theta = -2\sqrt{2}$$

91. $\tan\theta = \frac{3}{4}$, $\sin\theta < 0$, $\Rightarrow$ θ in quadrant III

Since θ is in quadrant III, we know that $\cos\theta < 0$, $\sec\theta < 0$, $\sin\theta < 0$ and $\csc\theta < 0$; while $\tan\theta > 0$ and $\cot\theta > 0$.
If α is the reference angle for θ, then $\tan\alpha = \frac{3}{4}$.
Now draw the appropriate triangle and use the Pythagorean Theorem to find the values of the other trigonometric functions of α.

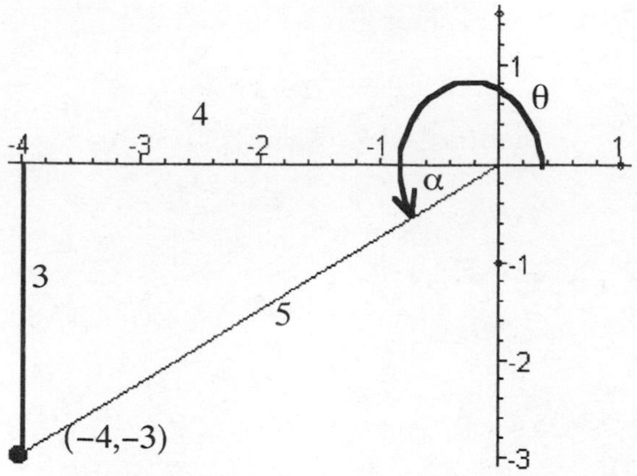

$\cos\alpha = \frac{4}{5}$ $\sin\alpha = \frac{3}{5}$ $\sec\alpha = \frac{5}{4}$

$\csc\alpha = \frac{5}{3}$ $\cot\alpha = \frac{4}{3}$

Finally, we assign the appropriate sign to find the values of the other trigonometric functions of θ.

$\cos\theta = -\frac{4}{5}$ $\sin\theta = -\frac{3}{5}$ $\sec\theta = -\frac{5}{4}$

$\csc\theta = -\frac{5}{3}$ $\cot\theta = \frac{4}{3}$

92. $\cot\theta = \frac{4}{3}$, $\cos\theta < 0$, $\Rightarrow$ θ in quadrant III

Since θ is in quadrant III, we know that $\cos\theta < 0$, $\sec\theta < 0$, $\sin\theta < 0$ and $\csc\theta < 0$; while $\tan\theta > 0$ and $\cot\theta > 0$.

If α is the reference angle for θ, then $\cot\alpha = \frac{4}{3}$.

Now draw the appropriate triangle and use the Pythagorean Theorem to find the values of the other trigonometric functions of α.

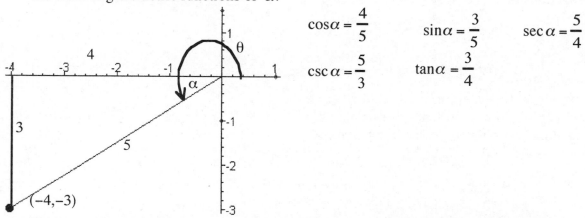

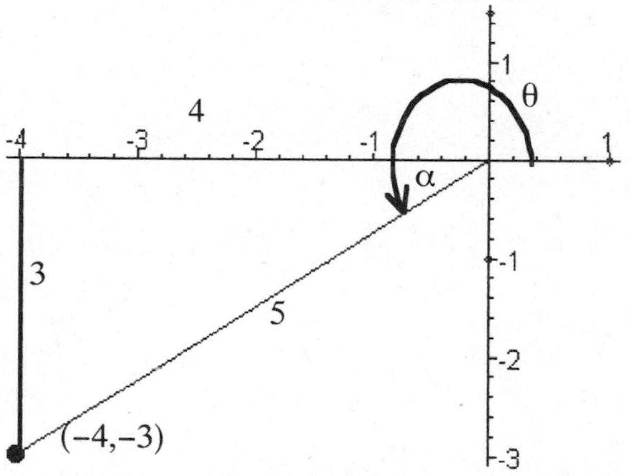

$\cos\alpha = \frac{4}{5}$ $\sin\alpha = \frac{3}{5}$ $\sec\alpha = \frac{5}{4}$

$\csc\alpha = \frac{5}{3}$ $\tan\alpha = \frac{3}{4}$

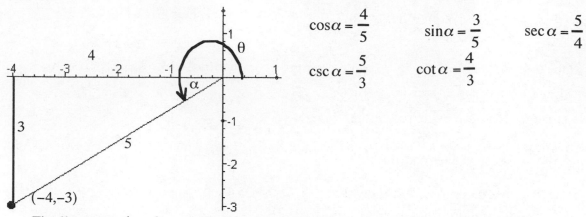

Finally, we assign the appropriate sign to find the values of the other trigonometric functions of θ.

$\cos\theta = -\frac{4}{5}$ $\sin\theta = -\frac{3}{5}$ $\sec\theta = -\frac{5}{4}$

$\csc\theta = -\frac{5}{3}$ $\tan\theta = \frac{3}{4}$

93. $\tan\theta = -\frac{1}{3}, \ \sin\theta > 0 \ \Rightarrow \ \theta$ in quadrant II

Since θ is in quadrant II, we know that $\cos\theta < 0$, $\sec\theta < 0$, $\tan\theta < 0$ and $\cot\theta < 0$; while $\sin\theta > 0$ and $\csc\theta > 0$.

If α is the reference angle for θ, then $\tan\alpha = \frac{1}{3}$.

Now draw the appropriate triangle and use the Pythagorean Theorem to find the values of the other trigonometric functions of α.

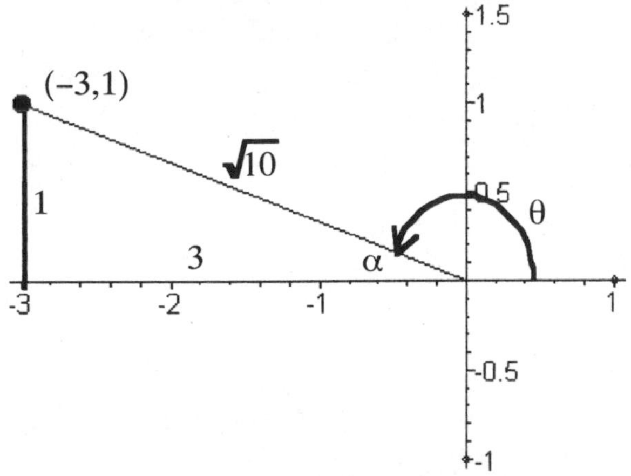

$\cos\alpha = \frac{3\sqrt{10}}{10}$ $\quad \sin\alpha = \frac{\sqrt{10}}{10}$ $\quad \sec\alpha = \frac{\sqrt{10}}{3}$

$\csc\alpha = \sqrt{10}$ $\quad \cot\alpha = 3$

Finally, we assign the appropriate sign to find the values of the other trigonometric functions of θ.

$\cos\theta = -\frac{3\sqrt{10}}{10}$ $\quad \sin\theta = \frac{\sqrt{10}}{10}$ $\quad \sec\theta = -\frac{\sqrt{10}}{3}$

$\csc\theta = \sqrt{10}$ $\quad \cot\theta = -3$

94. $\sec\theta = -2, \ \tan\theta > 0 \ \Rightarrow \ \theta$ in quadrant III

Since θ is in quadrant III, we know that $\cos\theta < 0$, $\sec\theta < 0$, $\sin\theta < 0$ and $\csc\theta < 0$; while $\tan\theta > 0$ and $\cot\theta > 0$.

If α is the reference angle for θ, then $\sec\alpha = 2$.

Now draw the appropriate triangle and use the Pythagorean Theorem to find the values of the other trigonometric functions of α.

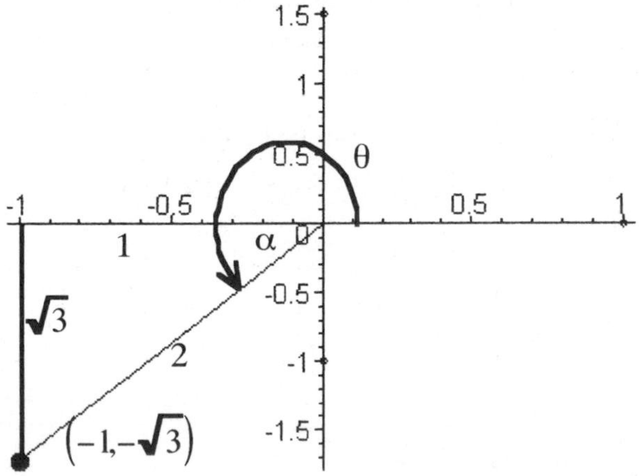

$\cos\alpha = \frac{1}{2}$ $\quad \sin\alpha = \frac{\sqrt{3}}{2}$ $\quad \cot\alpha = \frac{\sqrt{3}}{3}$

$\csc\alpha = \frac{2\sqrt{3}}{3}$ $\quad \tan\alpha = \sqrt{3}$

Finally, we assign the appropriate sign to find the values of the other trigonometric functions of θ.

$\cos\theta = -\dfrac{1}{2}$ $\sin\theta = -\dfrac{\sqrt{3}}{2}$ $\cot\theta = -\dfrac{\sqrt{3}}{3}$

$\csc\theta = -\dfrac{2\sqrt{3}}{3}$ $\tan\theta = \sqrt{3}$

95. $\csc\theta = -2,\ \tan\theta > 0 \Rightarrow \theta$ in quadrant III

Since θ is in quadrant III, we know that $\cos\theta < 0$, $\sec\theta < 0$, $\sin\theta < 0$ and $\csc\theta < 0$; while $\tan\theta > 0$ and $\cot\theta > 0$.
If α is the reference angle for θ, then $\csc\alpha = 2$.
Now draw the appropriate triangle and use the Pythagorean Theorem to find the values of the other trigonometric functions of α.

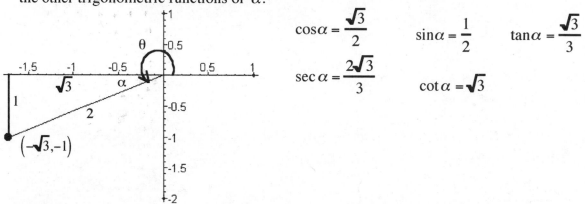

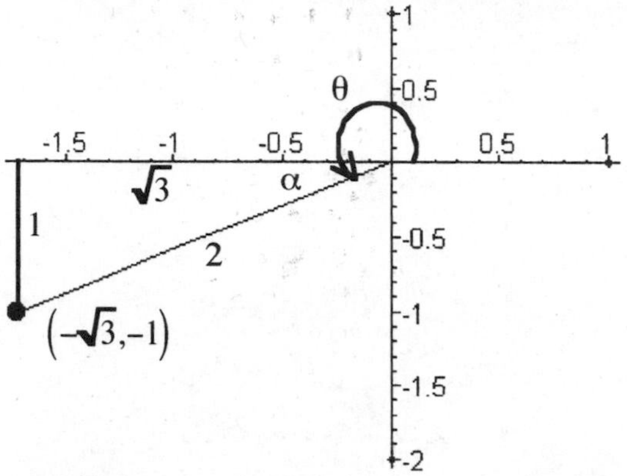

$\cos\alpha = \dfrac{\sqrt{3}}{2}$ $\sin\alpha = \dfrac{1}{2}$ $\tan\alpha = \dfrac{\sqrt{3}}{3}$

$\sec\alpha = \dfrac{2\sqrt{3}}{3}$ $\cot\alpha = \sqrt{3}$

Finally, we assign the appropriate sign to find the values of the other trigonometric functions of θ.

$\cos\theta = -\dfrac{\sqrt{3}}{2}$ $\sin\theta = -\dfrac{1}{2}$ $\cot\theta = \sqrt{3}$

$\sec\theta = -\dfrac{2\sqrt{3}}{3}$ $\tan\theta = \dfrac{\sqrt{3}}{3}$

96. $\cot\theta = -2,\ \sec\theta > 0 \Rightarrow \theta$ in quadrant IV

Since θ is in quadrant IV, we know that $\cos\theta > 0$ and $\sec\theta > 0$; while $\sin\theta < 0$, $\csc\theta < 0$, $\tan\theta < 0$ and $\cot\theta < 0$.
If α is the reference angle for θ, then $\cot\alpha = 2$.
Now draw the appropriate triangle and use the Pythagorean Theorem to find the values of the other trigonometric functions of α.

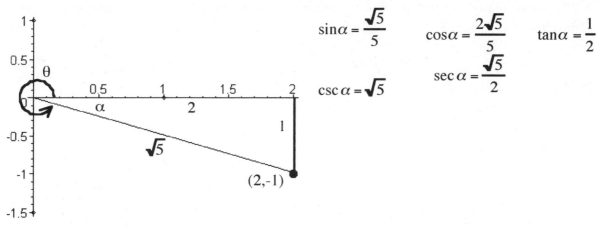

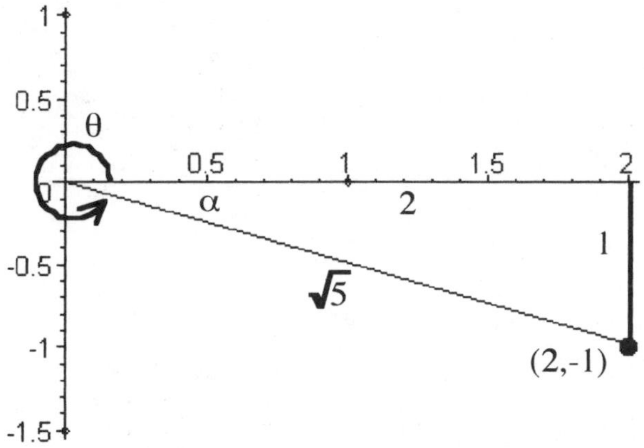

$\sin\alpha = \frac{\sqrt{5}}{5}$ $\cos\alpha = \frac{2\sqrt{5}}{5}$ $\tan\alpha = \frac{1}{2}$

$\csc\alpha = \sqrt{5}$ $\sec\alpha = \frac{\sqrt{5}}{2}$

Finally, we assign the appropriate sign to find the values of the other trigonometric functions of θ.

$\sin\theta = -\frac{\sqrt{5}}{5}$ $\cos\theta = \frac{2\sqrt{5}}{5}$ $\tan\theta = -\frac{1}{2}$

$\csc\theta = -\sqrt{5}$ $\sec\theta = \frac{\sqrt{5}}{2}$

97. $\sin(45°)+\sin(135°)+\sin(225°)+\sin(315°)$

$= \sin(45°)+\sin(45°+90°)+\sin(45°+180°)+\sin(45°+270°)$

$= \frac{\sqrt{2}}{2}+\frac{\sqrt{2}}{2}+\left(-\frac{\sqrt{2}}{2}\right)+\left(-\frac{\sqrt{2}}{2}\right)=0$

98. $\tan(60°)+\tan(150°)=\tan(60°)+\tan(180°-30°)$

So the reference angle for 150° is 30°, and since 150° lies in Quadrant II we have:

$\tan(60°)+\tan(150°)=\tan(60°)-\tan(30°)=\sqrt{3}-\frac{\sqrt{3}}{3}=\frac{2\sqrt{3}}{3}$

99. Given: $\sin\theta = 0.2 \Rightarrow$ θ in quadrant I
Therefore, $\theta+\pi$ is in quadrant III $\therefore$ $\sin(\theta+\pi) = -0.2$

100. Given: $\cos\theta = 0.4 \Rightarrow$ θ in quadrant I
Therefore, $\theta+\pi$ is in quadrant III $\therefore$ $\cos(\theta+\pi) = -0.4$

101. Given: $\tan\theta = 3 \Rightarrow \theta$ in quadrant I or III
Therefore, $\theta+\pi$ is in quadrant III or I $\therefore$ $\tan(\theta+\pi) = 3$

102. Given: $\cot\theta = -2 \Rightarrow \theta$ in quadrant II or IV
Therefore, $\theta+\pi$ is in quadrant IV or II $\therefore$ $\cot(\theta+\pi) = -2$

103. Given $\sin\theta = \frac{1}{5}$, then $\csc\theta = \frac{1}{\sin\theta} = \frac{1}{\left(\frac{1}{5}\right)} = 5$

104. Given $\cos\theta = \frac{2}{3}$, then $\sec\theta = \frac{1}{\cos\theta} = \frac{1}{\left(\frac{2}{3}\right)} = \frac{3}{2}$

105. Find the value:

$$\sin(1°) + \sin(2°) + \sin(3°) + \ldots + \sin(357°) + \sin(358°) + \sin(359°)$$
$$= \sin(1°) + \sin(2°) + \sin(3°) + \ldots + \sin(360° - 3°) + \sin(360° - 2°) + \sin(360° - 1°)$$
$$= \sin(1°) + \sin(2°) + \sin(3°) + \ldots + \sin(-3°) + \sin(-2°) + \sin(-1°)$$
$$= \sin(1°) + \sin(2°) + \sin(3°) + \ldots - \sin(3°) - \sin(2°) - \sin(1°)$$
$$= \sin(180°) = 0$$

106. Find the value:

$$\cos(1°) + \cos(2°) + \cos(3°) + \ldots + \cos(357°) + \cos(358°) + \cos(359°)$$
$$= \cos(1°) + \cos(2°) + \cos(3°) + \ldots + \cos(360° - 3°) + \cos(360° - 2°) + \cos(360° - 1°)$$
$$= \cos(1°) + \cos(2°) + \cos(3°) + \ldots + \cos(-3°) + \cos(-2°) + \cos(-1°)$$
$$= \cos(1°) + \cos(2°) + \cos(3°) + \ldots + \cos(3°) + \cos(2°) + \cos(1°)$$
$$= 2\cos(1°) + 2\cos(2°) + 2\cos(3°) + \ldots + 2\cos(178°) + 2\cos(179°) + \cos(180°)$$
$$= 2\cos(1°) + 2\cos(2°) + 2\cos(3°) + \ldots + 2\cos(180° - 2°) + 2\cos(180° - 1°) + \cos(180°)$$
$$= 2\cos(1°) + 2\cos(2°) + 2\cos(3°) + \ldots - 2\cos(2°) - 2\cos(1°) + \cos(180°)$$
$$= \cos(180°) = -1$$

107. (a) $R = \frac{32^2\sqrt{2}}{32}\left[\sin(2(60°)) - \cos(2(60°)) - 1\right] \approx 32\sqrt{2}(0.866 - (-0.5) - 1) \approx 16.6$ ft

(b) Graph:

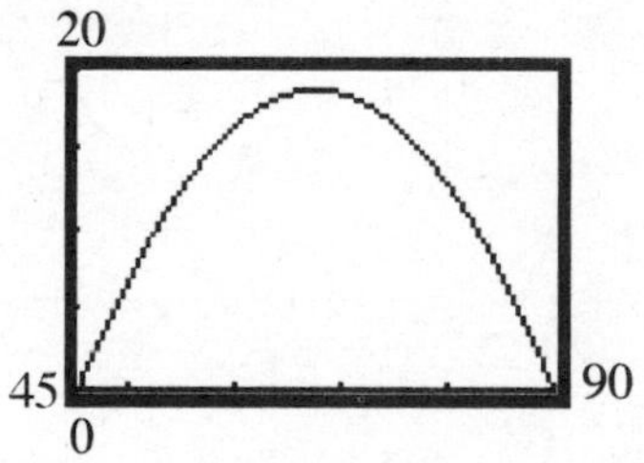

(c) Using MAXIMUM, R is largest when $\theta = 67.5°$.

Chapter 7

Trigonometric Functions

7.5 Trigonometric Functions: Unit Circle Approach

1. $P=\left(\frac{\sqrt{3}}{2},-\frac{1}{2}\right)\Rightarrow a=\frac{\sqrt{3}}{2}, b=-\frac{1}{2}$

$\sin t=-\frac{1}{2};$ $\qquad \csc t=\frac{1}{\left(-\frac{1}{2}\right)}=1\cdot\left(-\frac{2}{1}\right)=-2$

$\cos t=\frac{\sqrt{3}}{2};$ $\qquad \sec t=\frac{1}{\left(\frac{\sqrt{3}}{2}\right)}=1\cdot\left(\frac{2}{\sqrt{3}}\right)=\frac{2}{\sqrt{3}}\cdot\frac{\sqrt{3}}{\sqrt{3}}=\frac{2\sqrt{3}}{3}$

$\tan t=\frac{\left(-\frac{1}{2}\right)}{\left(\frac{\sqrt{3}}{2}\right)}=\left(-\frac{1}{2}\right)\cdot\left(\frac{2}{\sqrt{3}}\right)$ $\qquad \cot t=\frac{\left(\frac{\sqrt{3}}{2}\right)}{\left(-\frac{1}{2}\right)}=\left(\frac{\sqrt{3}}{2}\right)\cdot\left(-\frac{2}{1}\right)=-\sqrt{3}$

$=-\frac{1}{\sqrt{3}}\cdot\frac{\sqrt{3}}{\sqrt{3}}=-\frac{\sqrt{3}}{3}$

2. $P=\left(-\frac{\sqrt{3}}{2},-\frac{1}{2}\right)\Rightarrow a=-\frac{\sqrt{3}}{2}, b=-\frac{1}{2}$

$\sin t=-\frac{1}{2}$ $\qquad \csc t=\frac{1}{\left(-\frac{1}{2}\right)}=1\cdot\left(-\frac{2}{1}\right)\cdot=-2$

$\cos t=-\frac{\sqrt{3}}{2}$ $\qquad \sec t=\frac{1}{\left(-\frac{\sqrt{3}}{2}\right)}=1\cdot\left(-\frac{2}{\sqrt{3}}\right)=-\frac{2}{\sqrt{3}}\cdot\frac{\sqrt{3}}{\sqrt{2}}=-\frac{2\sqrt{3}}{3}$

$\tan t=\frac{\left(-\frac{1}{2}\right)}{\left(-\frac{\sqrt{3}}{2}\right)}=\left(-\frac{1}{2}\right)\cdot\left(-\frac{2}{\sqrt{3}}\right)$ $\qquad \cot t=\frac{\left(-\frac{\sqrt{3}}{2}\right)}{\left(-\frac{1}{2}\right)}=\left(-\frac{\sqrt{3}}{2}\right)\cdot\left(-\frac{2}{1}\right)=\sqrt{3}$

$=\frac{1}{\sqrt{3}}\cdot\frac{\sqrt{3}}{\sqrt{3}}=\frac{\sqrt{3}}{3}$

3. $P=\left(-\frac{\sqrt{2}}{2},-\frac{\sqrt{2}}{2}\right)\Rightarrow a=-\frac{\sqrt{2}}{2},b=-\frac{\sqrt{2}}{2}$

$\sin t=-\frac{\sqrt{2}}{2}$

$\csc t=\frac{1}{\left(-\frac{\sqrt{2}}{2}\right)}=1\cdot\left(-\frac{2}{\sqrt{2}}\right)=-\frac{2}{\sqrt{2}}\cdot\frac{\sqrt{2}}{\sqrt{2}}=-\sqrt{2}$

$\cos t=-\frac{\sqrt{2}}{2}$

$\sec t=\frac{1}{\left(-\frac{\sqrt{2}}{2}\right)}=1\cdot\left(-\frac{2}{\sqrt{2}}\right)=-\frac{2}{\sqrt{2}}\cdot\frac{\sqrt{2}}{\sqrt{2}}=-\sqrt{2}$

$\tan t=\frac{\left(-\frac{\sqrt{2}}{2}\right)}{\left(-\frac{\sqrt{2}}{2}\right)}=1$

$\cot t=\frac{\left(-\frac{\sqrt{2}}{2}\right)}{\left(-\frac{\sqrt{2}}{2}\right)}=1$

4. $P=\left(\frac{\sqrt{2}}{2},-\frac{\sqrt{2}}{2}\right)\Rightarrow a=\frac{\sqrt{2}}{2},b=-\frac{\sqrt{2}}{2}$

$\sin t=-\frac{\sqrt{2}}{2}$

$\csc t=\frac{1}{\left(-\frac{\sqrt{2}}{2}\right)}=1\cdot\left(-\frac{2}{\sqrt{2}}\right)=-\frac{2}{\sqrt{2}}\cdot\frac{\sqrt{2}}{\sqrt{2}}=-\sqrt{2}$

$\cos t=\frac{\sqrt{2}}{2}$

$\sec t=\frac{1}{\left(\frac{\sqrt{2}}{2}\right)}=1\cdot\left(\frac{2}{\sqrt{2}}\right)=\frac{2}{\sqrt{2}}\cdot\frac{\sqrt{2}}{\sqrt{2}}=\sqrt{2}$

$\tan t=\frac{\left(-\frac{\sqrt{2}}{2}\right)}{\left(\frac{\sqrt{2}}{2}\right)}=-1$

$\cot t=\frac{\left(\frac{\sqrt{2}}{2}\right)}{\left(-\frac{\sqrt{2}}{2}\right)}=-1$

5. $P=\left(\frac{\sqrt{5}}{3},\frac{2}{3}\right)\Rightarrow a=\frac{\sqrt{5}}{3},b=\frac{2}{3}$

$\sin t=\frac{2}{3}$

$\csc t=\frac{1}{\left(\frac{2}{3}\right)}=1\cdot\left(\frac{3}{2}\right)=\frac{3}{2}$

$\cos t=\frac{\sqrt{5}}{3}$

$\sec t=\frac{1}{\left(\frac{\sqrt{5}}{3}\right)}=1\cdot\left(\frac{3}{\sqrt{5}}\right)=\frac{3}{\sqrt{5}}\cdot\frac{\sqrt{5}}{\sqrt{5}}=\frac{3\sqrt{5}}{5}$

$$\tan t=\frac{\left(\frac{2}{3}\right)}{\left(\frac{\sqrt{5}}{3}\right)}=\left(\frac{2}{3}\right)\cdot\left(\frac{3}{\sqrt{5}}\right)=\frac{2}{\sqrt{5}}\cdot\frac{\sqrt{5}}{\sqrt{5}}=\frac{2\sqrt{5}}{5}\qquad \cot t=\frac{\left(\frac{\sqrt{5}}{3}\right)}{\left(\frac{2}{3}\right)}=\left(\frac{\sqrt{5}}{3}\right)\cdot\left(\frac{3}{2}\right)=\frac{\sqrt{5}}{2}$$

6. $P=\left(-\frac{\sqrt{5}}{5},\frac{2\sqrt{5}}{5}\right)\Rightarrow a=-\frac{\sqrt{5}}{5},b=\frac{2\sqrt{5}}{5}$

$$\sin t=\frac{2\sqrt{5}}{5}\qquad \csc t=\frac{1}{\left(\frac{2\sqrt{5}}{5}\right)}=1\cdot\left(\frac{5}{2\sqrt{5}}\right)\cdot\frac{\sqrt{5}}{\sqrt{5}}=\frac{\sqrt{5}}{2}$$

$$\cos t=-\frac{\sqrt{5}}{5}\qquad \sec t=\frac{1}{\left(-\frac{\sqrt{5}}{5}\right)}=1\cdot\left(-\frac{5}{\sqrt{5}}\right)\cdot\frac{\sqrt{5}}{\sqrt{5}}=-\sqrt{5}$$

$$\tan t=\frac{\left(\frac{2\sqrt{5}}{5}\right)}{\left(-\frac{\sqrt{5}}{5}\right)}=\left(\frac{2\sqrt{5}}{5}\right)\cdot\left(-\frac{5}{\sqrt{5}}\right)=-2\qquad \cot t=\frac{\left(-\frac{\sqrt{5}}{5}\right)}{\left(\frac{2\sqrt{5}}{5}\right)}=\left(-\frac{\sqrt{5}}{5}\right)\cdot\left(\frac{5}{2\sqrt{5}}\right)=-\frac{1}{2}$$

7. For the point (3, -4), $x=3,\ y=-4,\ r=\sqrt{x^2+y^2}=\sqrt{9+16}=\sqrt{25}=5$

$$\sin\theta=-\frac{4}{5}\qquad \cos\theta=\frac{3}{5}\qquad \tan\theta=-\frac{4}{3}$$

$$\csc\theta=-\frac{5}{4}\qquad \sec\theta=\frac{5}{3}\qquad \cot\theta=-\frac{3}{4}$$

8. For the point (4, –3), $x=4,\ y=-3,\ r=\sqrt{x^2+y^2}=\sqrt{16+9}=\sqrt{25}=5$

$$\sin\theta=-\frac{3}{5}\qquad \cos\theta=\frac{4}{5}\qquad \tan\theta=-\frac{3}{4}$$

$$\csc\theta=\frac{5}{3}\qquad \sec\theta=\frac{5}{4}\qquad \cot\theta=-\frac{4}{3}$$

9. For the point (-2, 3), $x=-2,\ y=3,\ r=\sqrt{x^2+y^2}=\sqrt{4+9}=\sqrt{13}$

$$\sin\theta=\frac{3}{\sqrt{13}}\cdot\frac{\sqrt{13}}{\sqrt{13}}=\frac{3\sqrt{13}}{13}\qquad \cos\theta=-\frac{2}{\sqrt{13}}\cdot\frac{\sqrt{13}}{\sqrt{13}}=-\frac{2\sqrt{13}}{13}\qquad \tan\theta=-\frac{3}{2}$$

$$\csc\theta=\frac{\sqrt{13}}{3}\qquad \sec\theta=-\frac{\sqrt{13}}{2}\qquad \cot\theta=-\frac{2}{3}$$

10. For the point (2, -4), $x=2,\ y=-4,\ r=\sqrt{x^2+y^2}=\sqrt{4+16}=\sqrt{20}=2\sqrt{5}$

$$\sin\theta=\frac{-4}{2\sqrt{5}}\cdot\frac{\sqrt{5}}{\sqrt{5}}=-\frac{2\sqrt{5}}{5}\qquad \cos\theta=\frac{2}{\sqrt{5}}\cdot\frac{\sqrt{5}}{\sqrt{5}}=\frac{2\sqrt{5}}{5}\qquad \tan\theta=\frac{-4}{2}=-2$$

$$\csc\theta=\frac{2\sqrt{5}}{-4}=-\frac{\sqrt{5}}{2}\qquad \sec\theta=\frac{\sqrt{5}}{2}\qquad \cot\theta=-\frac{1}{2}$$

11. For the point (–1, –1), $x=-1,\ y=-1,\ r=\sqrt{x^2+y^2}=\sqrt{1+1}=\sqrt{2}=\sqrt{2}$

$$\sin\theta=\frac{-1}{\sqrt{2}}\cdot\frac{\sqrt{2}}{\sqrt{2}}=-\frac{\sqrt{2}}{2}\qquad \cos\theta=\frac{-1}{\sqrt{2}}\cdot\frac{\sqrt{2}}{\sqrt{2}}=-\frac{\sqrt{2}}{2}\qquad \tan\theta=\frac{-1}{-1}=1$$

$$\csc\theta=\frac{\sqrt{2}}{-1}=-\sqrt{2}\qquad \sec\theta=\frac{\sqrt{2}}{-1}=-\sqrt{2}\qquad \cot\theta=\frac{-1}{-1}=1$$

12. For the point (–3, 1), $x=-3,\ y=1,\ r=\sqrt{x^2+y^2}=\sqrt{9+1}=\sqrt{10}$

$$\sin\theta=\frac{1}{\sqrt{10}}\cdot\frac{\sqrt{10}}{\sqrt{10}}=\frac{\sqrt{10}}{10}\qquad \cos\theta=\frac{-3}{\sqrt{10}}\cdot\frac{\sqrt{10}}{\sqrt{10}}=-\frac{3\sqrt{10}}{13}\qquad \tan\theta=\frac{1}{-3}=-\frac{1}{3}$$

$$\csc\theta=\frac{\sqrt{10}}{1}=\sqrt{10}\qquad \sec\theta=\frac{\sqrt{10}}{-3}=-\frac{\sqrt{10}}{3}\qquad \cot\theta=\frac{-3}{1}=-3$$

13. $\sin(405^\circ)=\sin(360^\circ+45^\circ)=\sin(45^\circ)=\frac{\sqrt{2}}{2}$

14. $\cos(420^\circ)=\cos(360^\circ+60^\circ)=\cos(60^\circ)=\frac{1}{2}$

15. $\tan(405^\circ)=\tan(180^\circ+180^\circ+45^\circ)=\tan(45^\circ)=1$

16. $\sin(390^\circ)=\sin(360^\circ+30^\circ)=\sin(30^\circ)=\frac{1}{2}$

17. $\csc(450^\circ)=\csc(360^\circ+90^\circ)=\csc(90^\circ)=1$

18. $\sec(540^\circ)=\sec(360^\circ+180^\circ)=\sec(180^\circ)=-1$

19. $\cot(390^\circ)=\cot(180^\circ+180^\circ+30^\circ)=\cot(30^\circ)=\sqrt{3}$

20. $\sec(420^\circ)=\sec(360^\circ+60^\circ)=\sec(60^\circ)=2$

21. $\cos\left(\frac{33\pi}{4}\right)=\cos\left(\frac{\pi}{4}+\frac{32\pi}{4}\right)=\cos\left(\frac{\pi}{4}+8\pi\right)=\cos\left(\frac{\pi}{4}+4\cdot 2\pi\right)=\cos\left(\frac{\pi}{4}\right)=\frac{\sqrt{2}}{2}$

22. $\sin\left(\frac{9\pi}{4}\right)=\sin\left(\frac{\pi}{4}+\frac{8\pi}{4}\right)=\sin\left(\frac{\pi}{4}+2\pi\right)=\sin\left(\frac{\pi}{4}\right)=\frac{\sqrt{2}}{2}$

23. $\tan(21\pi)=\tan(0+21\pi)=\tan(0)=0$

24. $\csc\left(\frac{9\pi}{2}\right)=\csc\left(\frac{\pi}{2}+\frac{8\pi}{2}\right)=\csc\left(\frac{\pi}{2}+4\pi\right)=\csc\left(\frac{\pi}{2}+2\cdot 2\pi\right)=\csc\left(\frac{\pi}{2}\right)=1$

25. $\sec\left(\frac{17\pi}{4}\right)=\sec\left(\frac{\pi}{4}+\frac{16\pi}{4}\right)=\sec\left(\frac{\pi}{4}+4\pi\right)=\sec\left(\frac{\pi}{4}+2\cdot 2\pi\right)=\sec\left(\frac{\pi}{4}\right)=\sqrt{2}$

26. $\cot\left(\frac{17\pi}{4}\right)=\cot\left(\frac{\pi}{4}+\frac{16\pi}{4}\right)=\cot\left(\frac{\pi}{4}+4\pi\right)=\cot\left(\frac{\pi}{4}+2\cdot 2\pi\right)=\cot\left(\frac{\pi}{4}\right)=1$

27. $\tan\left(\frac{19\pi}{6}\right)=\tan\left(\frac{\pi}{6}+\frac{18\pi}{6}\right)=\tan\left(\frac{\pi}{6}+3\pi\right)=\tan\left(\frac{\pi}{6}\right)=\frac{\sqrt{3}}{3}$

28. $\sec\left(\frac{25\pi}{6}\right)=\sec\left(\frac{\pi}{6}+\frac{24\pi}{6}\right)=\sec\left(\frac{\pi}{6}+4\pi\right)=\sec\left(\frac{\pi}{6}+2\cdot 2\pi\right)=\sec\left(\frac{\pi}{6}\right)=\frac{2\sqrt{3}}{3}$

29. $\sin(-60°)=-\sin(60°)=-\frac{\sqrt{3}}{2}$

30. $\cos(-30°)=\cos(30°)=\frac{\sqrt{3}}{2}$

31. $\tan(-30°)=-\tan(30°)=-\frac{\sqrt{3}}{3}$

32. $\sin(-135°)=-\sin(135°)=-\frac{\sqrt{2}}{2}$

33. $\sec(-60°)=\sec(60°)=2$

34. $\csc(-30°)=-\csc(30°)=-2$

35. $\sin(-90°)=-\sin(90°)=-1$

36. $\cos(-270°)=\cos(270°)=0$

37. $\tan\left(-\frac{\pi}{4}\right)=-\tan\left(\frac{\pi}{4}\right)=-1$

38. $\sin(-\pi)=-\sin(\pi)=0$

39. $\cos\left(-\frac{\pi}{4}\right)=\cos\left(\frac{\pi}{4}\right)=\frac{\sqrt{2}}{2}$

40. $\sin\left(-\frac{\pi}{3}\right)=-\sin\left(\frac{\pi}{3}\right)=-\frac{\sqrt{3}}{2}$

41. $\tan(-\pi)=-\tan(\pi)=0$

42. $\sin\left(-\frac{3\pi}{2}\right)=-\sin\left(\frac{3\pi}{2}\right)=-(-1)=1$

43. $\csc\left(-\frac{\pi}{4}\right)=-\csc\left(\frac{\pi}{4}\right)=-\sqrt{2}$

44. $\sec(-\pi)=\sec(\pi)=-1$

45. $\sec\left(-\frac{\pi}{6}\right)=\sec\left(\frac{\pi}{6}\right)=\frac{2\sqrt{3}}{3}$

46. $\csc\left(-\frac{\pi}{3}\right)=-\csc\left(\frac{\pi}{3}\right)=-\frac{2\sqrt{3}}{3}$

47. $\sin(-\pi)+\cos(5\pi)=-\sin(\pi)+\cos(\pi+4\pi)=0+\cos(\pi)=-1$

48. $\tan\left(-\frac{5\pi}{6}\right)-\cot\left(\frac{7\pi}{2}\right)=-\tan\left(\frac{5\pi}{6}\right)-\cot\left(\frac{3\pi}{2}+2\pi\right)=-\tan\left(\frac{5\pi}{6}\right)-\cot\left(\frac{3\pi}{2}\right)$

$$=-\frac{\sqrt{3}}{3}-0=\frac{\sqrt{3}}{3}$$

49. $\sec(-\pi)+\csc\left(-\frac{\pi}{2}\right)=\sec(\pi)-\csc\left(\frac{\pi}{2}\right)=-1-1=-2$

50. $\tan(-6\pi)+\cos\left(\frac{9\pi}{4}\right)=-\tan(0+6\pi)+\cos\left(\frac{\pi}{4}+2\pi\right)=-\tan(0)+\cos\left(\frac{\pi}{4}\right)=0+\frac{\sqrt{2}}{2}=\frac{\sqrt{2}}{2}$

51. $\sin\left(-\frac{9\pi}{4}\right)-\tan\left(-\frac{9\pi}{4}\right)=-\sin\left(\frac{9\pi}{4}\right)+\tan\left(\frac{9\pi}{4}\right)=-\sin\left(\frac{\pi}{4}+\frac{8\pi}{4}\right)+\tan\left(\frac{\pi}{4}+\frac{8\pi}{4}\right)$

$$=-\sin\left(\frac{\pi}{4}\right)+\tan\left(\frac{\pi}{4}\right)=-\frac{\sqrt{2}}{2}+1$$

52. $\cos\left(-\frac{17\pi}{4}\right)-\sin\left(-\frac{3\pi}{2}\right)=\cos\left(\frac{17\pi}{4}\right)+\sin\left(\frac{3\pi}{2}\right)=\cos\left(\frac{\pi}{4}+2\cdot 2\pi\right)+\sin\left(\frac{3\pi}{2}\right)$

$$=\cos\left(\frac{\pi}{4}\right)+\sin\left(\frac{3\pi}{2}\right)=\frac{\sqrt{2}}{2}+(-1)=\frac{\sqrt{2}}{2}-1$$

53. The domain of the sine function is the set of all real numbers.

54. The domain of the cosine function is the set of all real numbers.

55. $f(\theta)=\tan\theta$ is not defined for numbers that are odd multiples of $\frac{\pi}{2}$.

56. $f(\theta)=\cot\theta$ is not defined for numbers that are multiples of π.

57. $f(\theta)=\sec\theta$ is not defined for numbers that are odd multiples of $\frac{\pi}{2}$.

58. $f(\theta)=\csc\theta$ is not defined for numbers that are multiples of π.

59. The range of the sine function is the set of all real numbers between –1 and 1, inclusive.

60. The range of the cosine function is the set of all real numbers between –1 and 1, inclusive.

61. The range of the tangent function is the set of all real numbers.

62. The range of the cotangent function is the set of all real numbers.

63. The range of the secant function is the set of all real number greater than or equal to 1 and all real numbers less than or equal to –1.

64. The range of the cosecant function is the set of all real number greater than or equal to 1 and all real numbers less than or equal to –1.

65. The sine function is odd because $\sin(-\theta) = -\sin\theta$. Its graph is symmetric to the origin.

66. The cosine function is even because $\cos(-\theta) = \cos\theta$. Its graph is symmetric to the y-axis.

67. The tangent function is odd because $\tan(-\theta) = -\tan\theta$. Its graph is symmetric to the origin.

68. The cotangent function is odd because $\cot(-\theta) = -\cot\theta$. Its graph is symmetric to the origin.

69. The secant function is even because $\sec(-\theta) = \sec\theta$. Its graph is symmetric to the y-axis.

70. The cosecant function is odd because $\csc(-\theta) = -\csc\theta$. Its graph is symmetric to the origin.

71. If $\sin\theta = 0.3$, then $\sin(\theta + \pi) = -0.3$

72. If $\cos\theta = 0.2$, then $\cos(\theta + \pi) = -0.2$

73. If $\tan\theta = 3$, then $\tan(\theta + \pi) = 3$

74. If $\cot\theta = -2$, then $\cot(\theta + \pi) = -2$

75. (a) $f(-a) = -f(a) = -\frac{1}{3}$

(b) $f(a) + f(a + 2\pi) + f(a + 4\pi) = f(a) + f(a) + f(a) = \frac{1}{3} + \frac{1}{3} + \frac{1}{3} = 1$

76. (a) $f(-a) = f(a) = \frac{1}{4}$

(b) $f(a) + f(a + 2\pi) + f(a - 2\pi) = f(a) + f(a) + f(a) = \frac{1}{4} + \frac{1}{4} + \frac{1}{4} = \frac{3}{4}$

77. (a) $f(-a) = -f(a) = -2$

(b) $f(a) + f(a + \pi) + f(a + 2\pi) = f(a) + f(a) + f(a) = 2 + 2 + 2 = 6$

78. (a) $f(-a) = -f(a) = -(-3) = 3$

(b) $f(a) + f(a + \pi) + f(a + 4\pi) = f(a) + f(a) + f(a) = -3 + (-3) + (-3) = -9$

79. (a) $f(-a) = f(a) = -4$
(b) $f(a) + f(a+2\pi) + f(a+4\pi) = f(a) + f(a) + f(a) = (-4) + (-4) + (-4) = -12$

80. (a) $f(-a) = -f(a) = -2$
(b) $f(a) + f(a+2\pi) + f(a+4\pi) = f(a) + f(a) + f(a) = 2 + 2 + 2 = 6$

81. Let $P = (x, y)$ be the point on the unit circle that corresponds to an angle θ. Consider the equation $\tan\theta = \frac{y}{x} = a$. Then $y = ax$. Now $x^2 + y^2 = 1$, so $x^2 + a^2x^2 = 1$. Thus, $x = \pm\frac{1}{\sqrt{1+a^2}}$ and $y = \pm\frac{a}{\sqrt{1+a^2}}$; that is, for any real number a, there is a point $P = (x, y)$ on the unit circle for which $\tan\theta = a$. In other words, $-\infty < \tan\theta < +\infty$, and the range of the tangent function is the set of all real numbers.

82. Let $P = (x, y)$ be the point on the unit circle that corresponds to an angle θ. Consider the equation $\cot\theta = \frac{x}{y} = a$. Then $x = ay$. Now $x^2 + y^2 = 1$, so $a^2y^2 + y^2 = 1$. Thus, $y = \pm\frac{1}{\sqrt{1+a^2}}$ and $x = \pm\frac{a}{\sqrt{1+a^2}}$; that is, for any real number a, there is a point $P = (x, y)$ on the unit circle for which $\cot\theta = a$. In other words, $-\infty < \cot\theta < +\infty$, and the range of the tangent function is the set of all real numbers.

83. Suppose there is a number p, $0 < p < 2\pi$, for which $\sin(\theta + p) = \sin\theta$ for all θ. If $\theta = 0$, then $\sin(0 + p) = \sin p = \sin 0 = 0$; so that $p = \pi$. If $\theta = \frac{\pi}{2}$, then $\sin\left(\frac{\pi}{2} + p\right) = \sin\left(\frac{\pi}{2}\right)$. But $p = \pi$. Thus, $\sin\left(\frac{3\pi}{2}\right) = -1 = \sin\left(\frac{\pi}{2}\right) = 1$, or $-1 = 1$. This is impossible. The smallest positive number p for which $\sin(\theta + p) = \sin\theta$ for all θ is therefore $p = 2\pi$.

84. Suppose there is a number p, $0 < p < 2\pi$, for which $\cos(\theta + p) = \cos\theta$ for all θ. If $\theta = \frac{\pi}{2}$, then $\cos\left(\frac{\pi}{2} + p\right) = \cos\left(\frac{\pi}{2}\right) = 0$; so that $p = \pi$. If $\theta = 0$, then $\cos(0 + p) = \cos 0$. But $p = \pi$. Thus, $\cos(\pi) = -1 = \cos(0) = 1$, or $-1 = 1$. This is impossible. The smallest positive number p for which $\cos(\theta + p) = \cos\theta$ for all θ is therefore $p = 2\pi$.

85. $\sec\theta = \frac{1}{\cos\theta}$: since $\cos\theta$ has period 2π, so does $\sec\theta$.

86. $\csc\theta = \frac{1}{\sin\theta}$: since $\sin\theta$ has period 2π, so does $\csc\theta$.

87. If $P = (a,b)$ is the point on the unit circle corresponding to θ, then $Q = (-a,-b)$ is the point on the unit circle corresponding to $\theta + \pi$.

Thus, $\tan(\theta + \pi) = \frac{-b}{-a} = \frac{b}{a} = \tan\theta$. If there exists a number p, $0 < p < \pi$, for which $\tan(\theta + p) = \tan\theta$ for all θ, then if $\theta = 0$, then $\tan(p) = \tan(0) = 0$.
But this means that p is a multiple of π. Since no multiple of π exists in the interval $(0, \pi)$, this is impossible. Therefore, the fundamental period of $f(\theta) = \tan\theta$ is π.

88. We know that $\cot\theta = \dfrac{1}{\tan\theta}$.

Since the period of $f(\theta) = \tan\theta$ is π (see problem 87), the period of $g(\theta) = \cot\theta$ is also π

89. Slope of $L^* = \dfrac{\sin\theta - 0}{\cos\theta - 0} = \dfrac{\sin\theta}{\cos\theta} = \tan\theta$
Since L is parallel to L^*, then the slope of $L = \tan\theta$.

Chapter 7

Trigonometric Functions

7.6 Graphs of the Sine and Cosine Functions

1. 0

2. 1

3. The graph of $y = \sin x$ is increasing for $-\frac{\pi}{2} < x < \frac{\pi}{2}$.

4. The graph of $y = \cos x$ is decreasing for $0 < x < \pi$.

5. The greatest value of $y = \sin x$ is 1.

6. The least value of $y = \cos x$ is –1.

7. $\sin x = 0$ when $x = 0, \pi, 2\pi$

8. $\cos x = 0$ when $x = \frac{\pi}{2}, \frac{3\pi}{2}$

9. $\sin x = 1$ when $x = -\frac{3\pi}{2}, \frac{\pi}{2}$; $\sin x = -1$ when $x = -\frac{\pi}{2}, \frac{3\pi}{2}$

10. $\cos x = 1$ when $x = -2\pi, 0, 2\pi$; $\cos x = -1$ when $x = -\pi, \pi$

11. B, C, F

12. A, D, E

13. $y = 3\sin x$

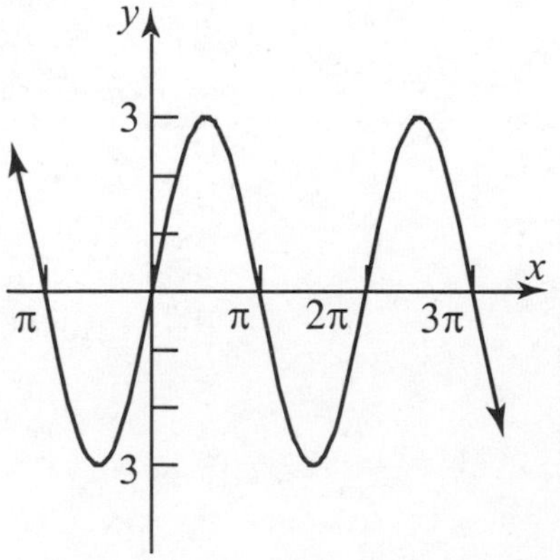

14. $y = 4\cos x$

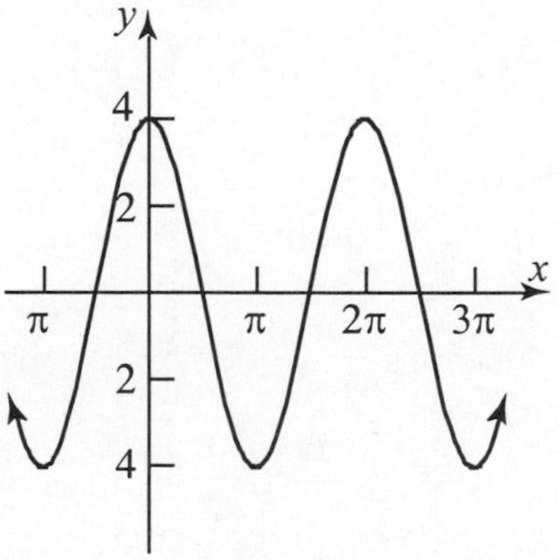

15. $y = \cos\left(x + \frac{\pi}{4}\right)$

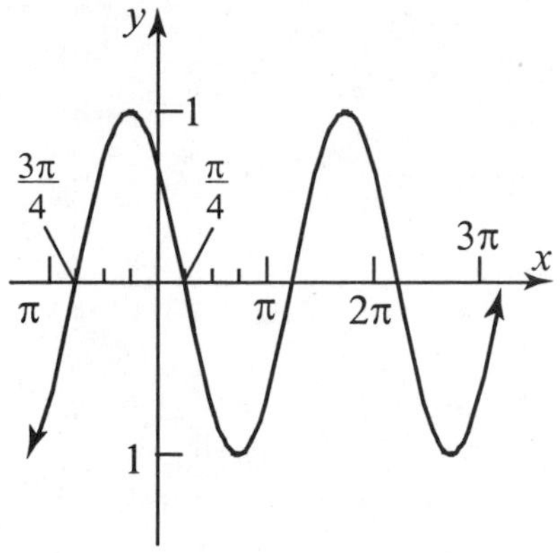

16. $y = \sin(x - \pi)$

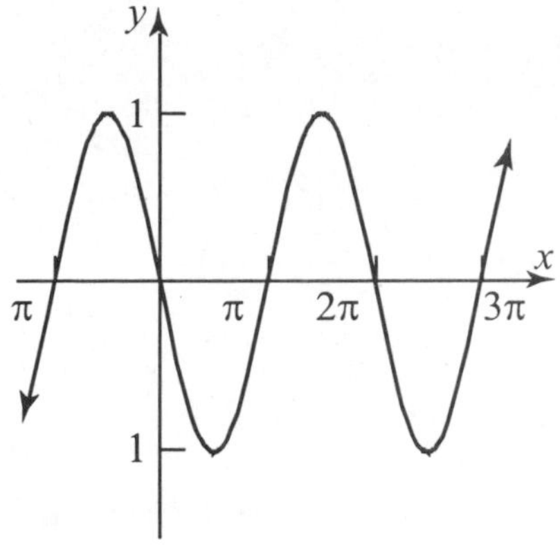

17. $y = \sin x - 1$

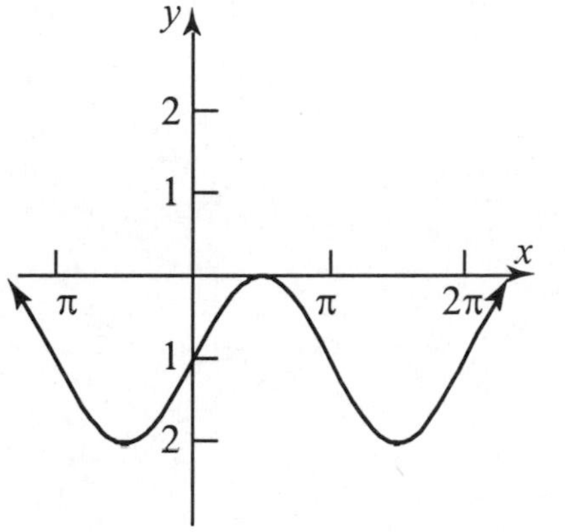

18. $y = \cos x + 1$

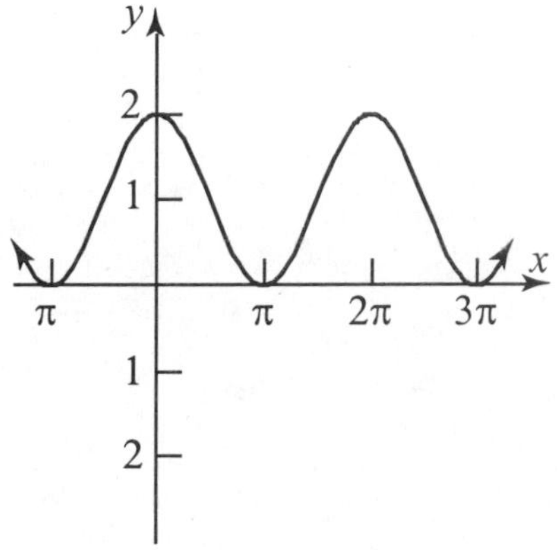

19. $y = -2\sin x$

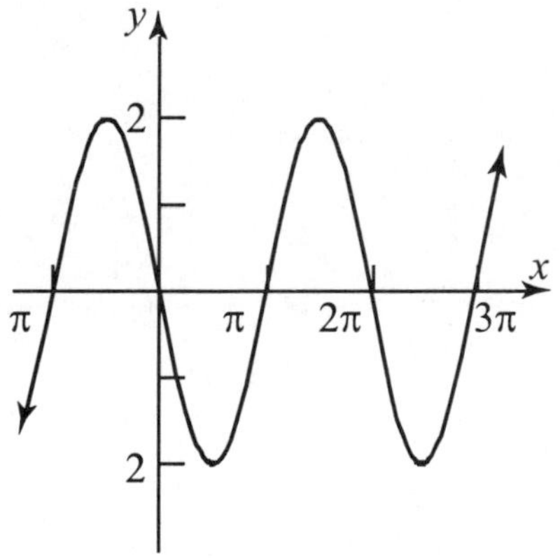

20. $y = -3\cos x$

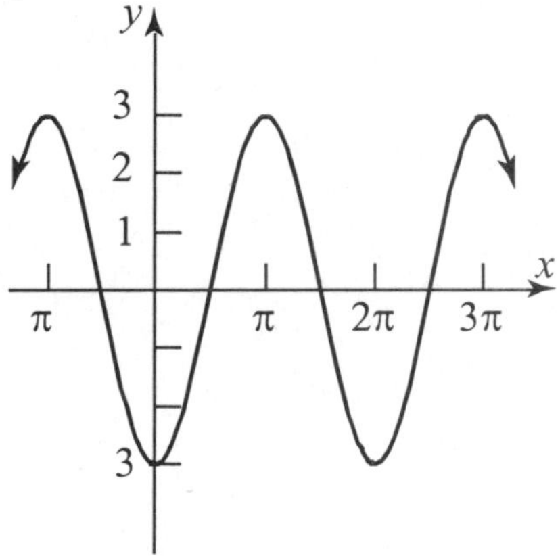

21. $y = \sin(\pi x)$

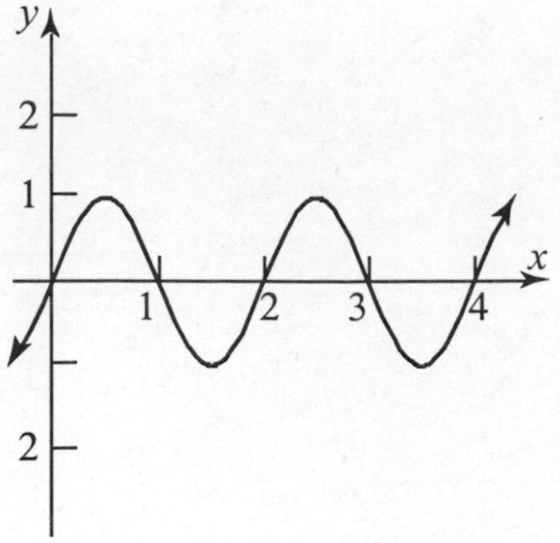

22. $y = \cos\left(\frac{\pi}{2} x\right)$

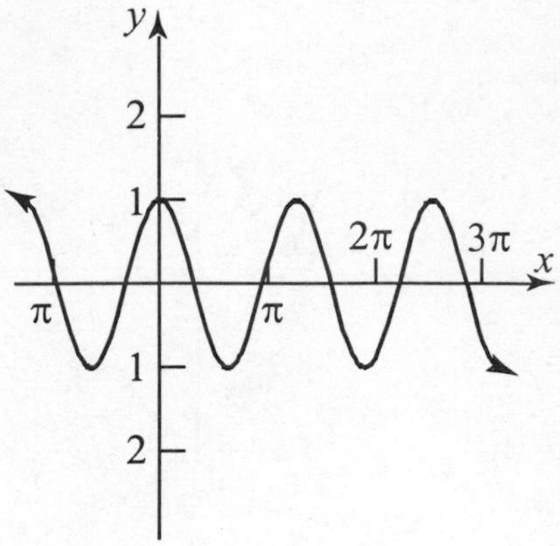

23. $y = 2\sin x + 2$

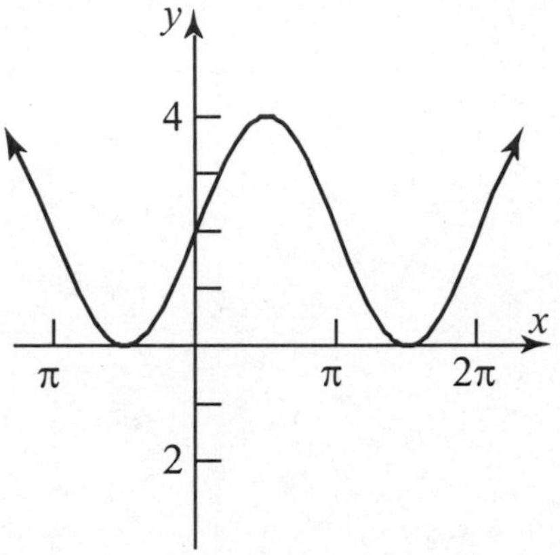

24. $y = 3\cos x + 3$

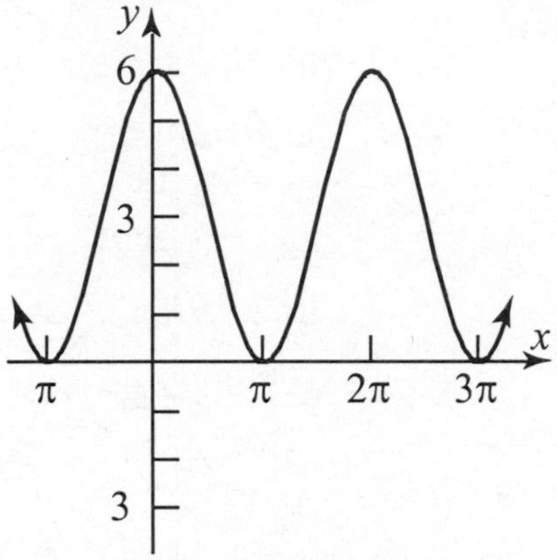

25. $y = -2\cos\left(x - \frac{\pi}{2}\right)$

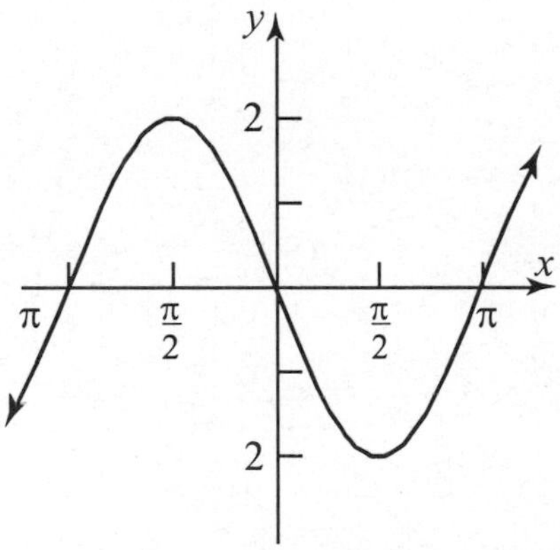

26. $y = -3\sin\left(x + \frac{\pi}{2}\right)$

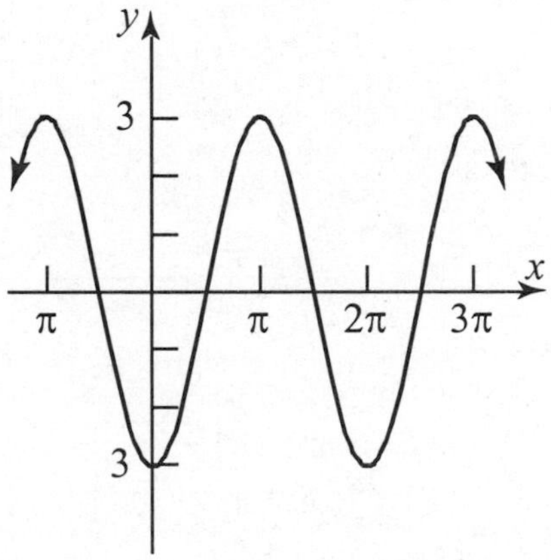

27. $y = 3\sin(\pi - x)$

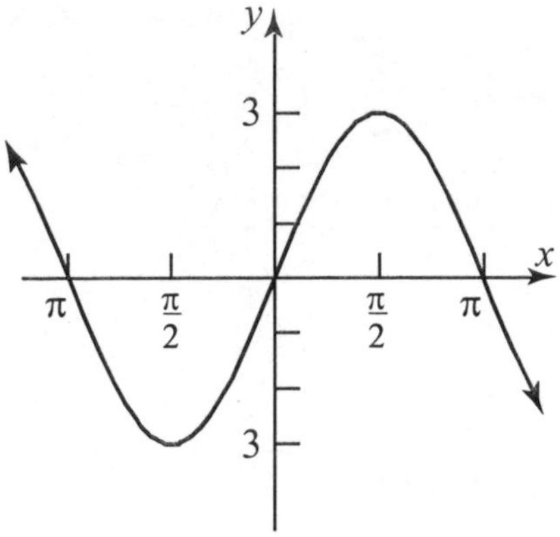

28. $y = 2\cos(\pi - x)$

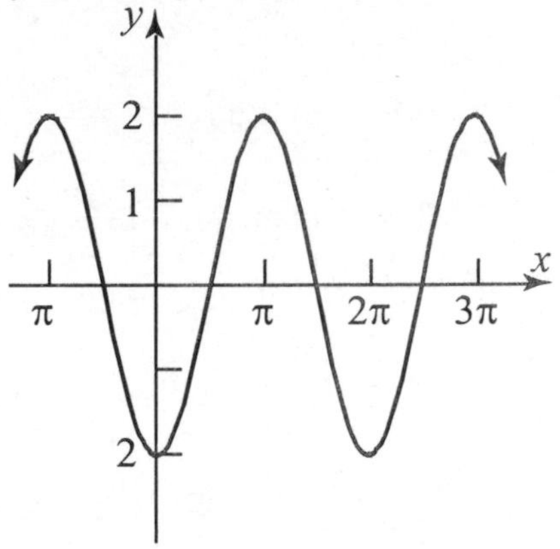

29. $y = 2\sin x$

This is in the form $y = A\sin(\omega x)$ where $A = 2$ and $\omega = 1$.

Thus, the amplitude is $|A| = |2| = 2$ and the period is $T = \frac{2\pi}{\omega} = \frac{2\pi}{1} = 2\pi$.

30. $y = 3\cos x$

This is in the form $y = A\cos(\omega x)$ where $A = 3$ and $\omega = 1$.

Thus, the amplitude is $|A| = |3| = 3$ and the period is $T = \frac{2\pi}{\omega} = \frac{2\pi}{1} = 2\pi$.

31. $y = -4\cos(2x)$

This is in the form $y = A\cos(\omega x)$ where $A = -4$ and $\omega = 2$.

Thus, the amplitude is $|A| = |-4| = 4$ and the period is $T = \frac{2\pi}{\omega} = \frac{2\pi}{2} = \pi$.

32. $y = -\sin\left(\frac{1}{2}x\right)$

This is in the form $y = A\sin(\omega x)$ where $A = -1$ and $\omega = \frac{1}{2}$.

Thus, the amplitude is $|A| = |-1| = 1$ and the period is $T = \frac{2\pi}{\omega} = \frac{2\pi}{\left(\frac{1}{2}\right)} = 4\pi$.

33. $y = 6\sin(\pi x)$

This is in the form $y = A\sin(\omega x)$ where $A = 6$ and $\omega = \pi$.

Thus, the amplitude is $|A| = |6| = 6$ and the period is $T = \frac{2\pi}{\omega} = \frac{2\pi}{\pi} = 2$.

34. $y = -3\cos(3x)$

This is in the form $y = A\cos(\omega x)$ where $A = -3$ and $\omega = 3$.

Thus, the amplitude is $|A| = |-3| = 3$ and the period is $T = \frac{2\pi}{\omega} = \frac{2\pi}{3}$.

35. $y=-\frac{1}{2}\cos\left(\frac{3}{2}x\right)$

This is in the form $y=A\cos(\omega x)$ where $A=-\frac{1}{2}$ and $\omega=\frac{3}{2}$.

Thus, the amplitude is $|A|=\left|-\frac{1}{2}\right|=\frac{1}{2}$ and the period is $T=\frac{2\pi}{\omega}=\frac{2\pi}{\left(\frac{3}{2}\right)}=\frac{4\pi}{3}$.

36. $y=\frac{4}{3}\sin\left(\frac{2}{3}x\right)$

This is in the form $y=A\sin(\omega x)$ where $A=\frac{4}{3}$ and $\omega=\frac{2}{3}$.

Thus, the amplitude is $|A|=\left|\frac{4}{3}\right|=\frac{4}{3}$ and the period is $T=\frac{2\pi}{\omega}=\frac{2\pi}{\left(\frac{2}{3}\right)}=3\pi$.

37. $y=\frac{5}{3}\sin\left(-\frac{2\pi}{3}x\right)=-\frac{5}{3}\sin\left(\frac{2\pi}{3}x\right)$

This is in the form $y=A\sin(\omega x)$ where $A=-\frac{5}{3}$ and $\omega=\frac{2\pi}{3}$.

Thus, the amplitude is $|A|=\left|-\frac{5}{3}\right|=\frac{5}{3}$ and the period is $T=\frac{2\pi}{\omega}=\frac{2\pi}{\left(\frac{2\pi}{3}\right)}=3$.

38. $y=\frac{9}{5}\cos\left(-\frac{3\pi}{2}x\right)=\frac{9}{5}\cos\left(\frac{3\pi}{2}x\right)$

This is in the form $y=A\cos(\omega x)$ where $A=\frac{9}{5}$ and $\omega=\frac{3\pi}{2}$.

Thus, the amplitude is $|A|=\left|\frac{9}{5}\right|=\frac{9}{5}$ and the period is $T=\frac{2\pi}{\omega}=\frac{2\pi}{\left(\frac{3\pi}{2}\right)}=\frac{4\pi}{3\pi}=\frac{4}{3}$.

39. F
40. E
41. A
42. I
43. H
44. B
45. C
46. G
47. J
48. D
49. A
50. C
51. B
52. D

53. $y = 5\sin(4x)$ $A = 5;\ T = \frac{\pi}{2}$

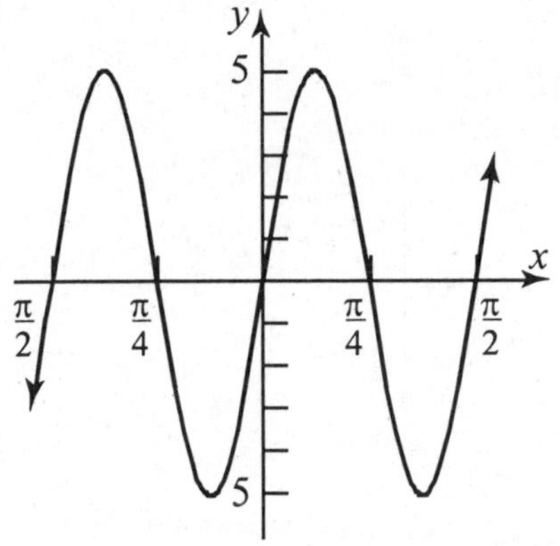

54. $y = 4\cos(6x)$ $A = 4;\ T = \frac{\pi}{3}$

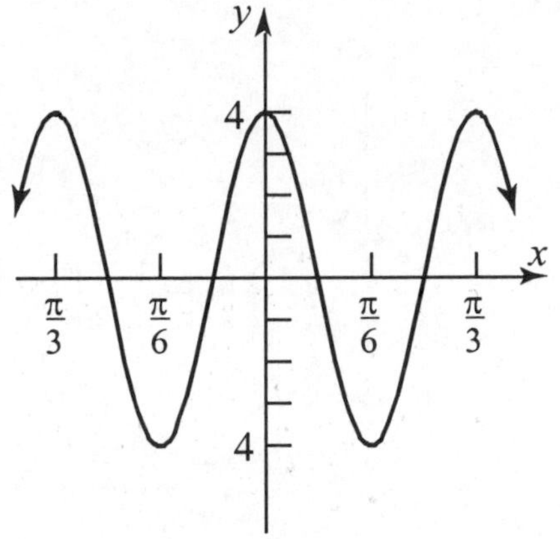

55. $y = 5\cos(\pi x)$ $A = 5;\ T = 2$

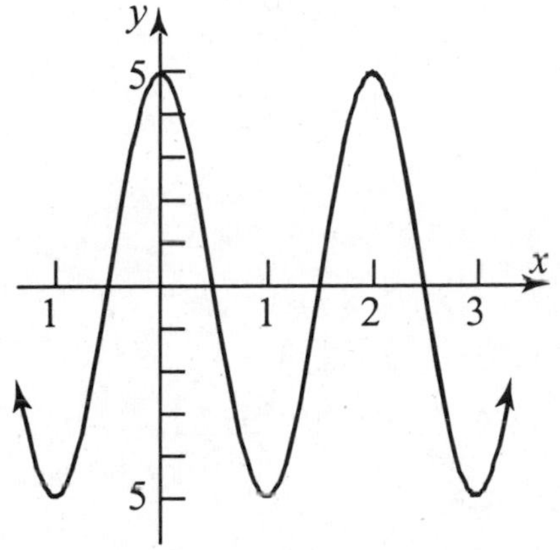

56. $y = 2\sin(\pi x)$ $A = 2;\ T = 2$

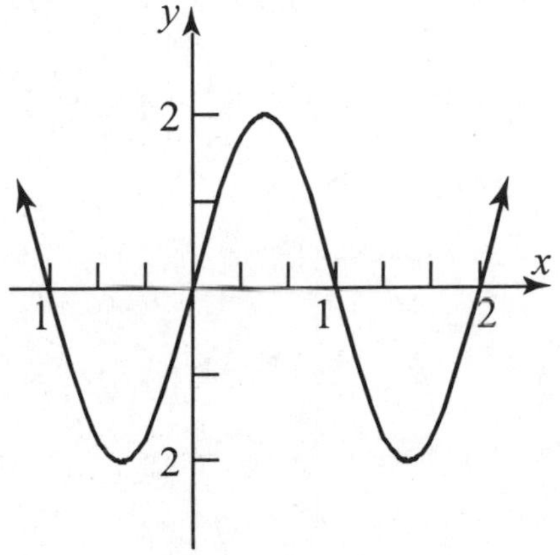

57. $y = -2\cos(2\pi x)$ $A = -2;\ T = 1$

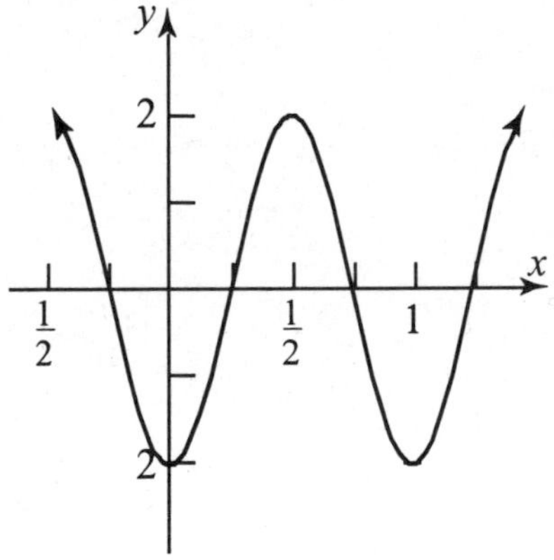

58. $y = -5\cos(2\pi x)$ $A = -5;\ T = 1$

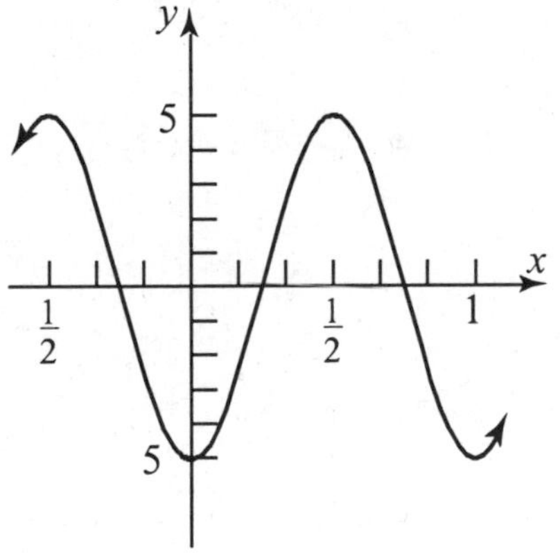

59. $y = -4\sin\left(\frac{1}{2}x\right)$ $A = -4;\ T = 4\pi$

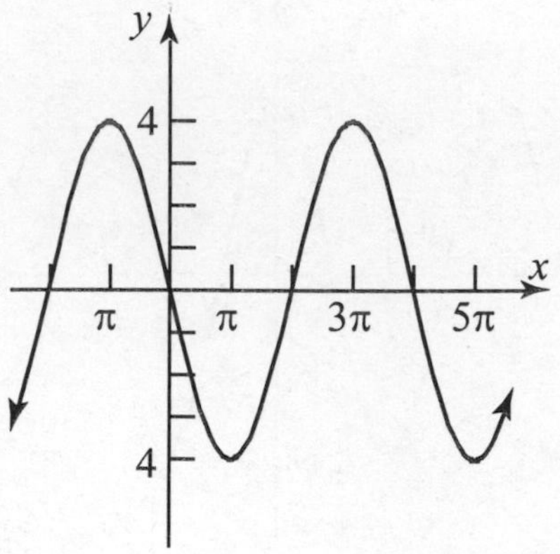

60. $y = -2\cos\left(\frac{1}{2}x\right)$ $A = -2;\ T = 4\pi$

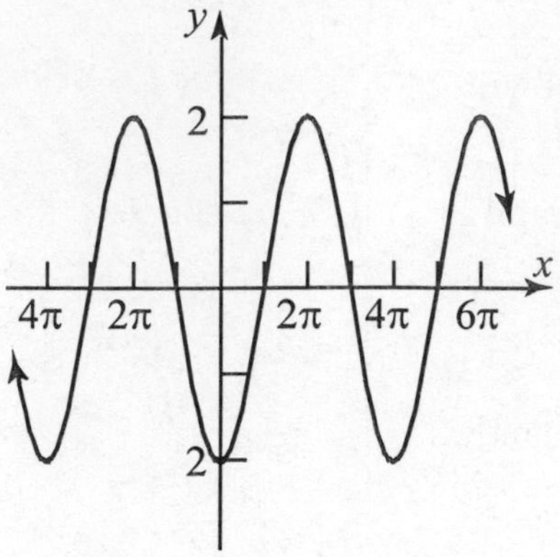

61. $y = \frac{3}{2}\sin\left(-\frac{2}{3}x\right) = -\frac{3}{2}\sin\left(\frac{2}{3}x\right)$

$A = -\frac{3}{2};\ T = 3\pi$

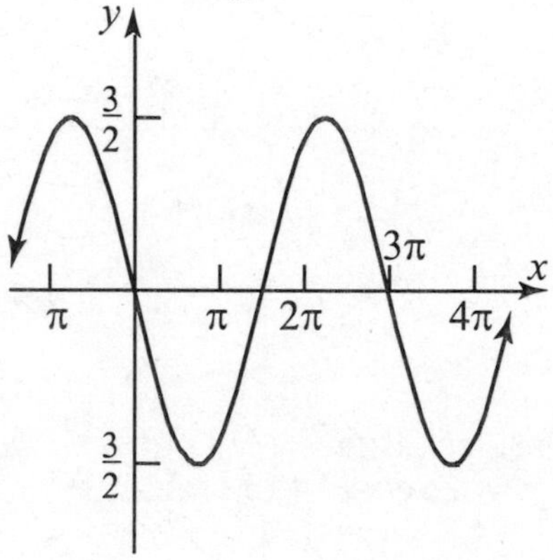

62. $y = \frac{4}{3}\cos\left(-\frac{1}{3}x\right) = \frac{4}{3}\cos\left(\frac{1}{3}x\right)$

$A = \frac{4}{3};\ T = 6\pi$

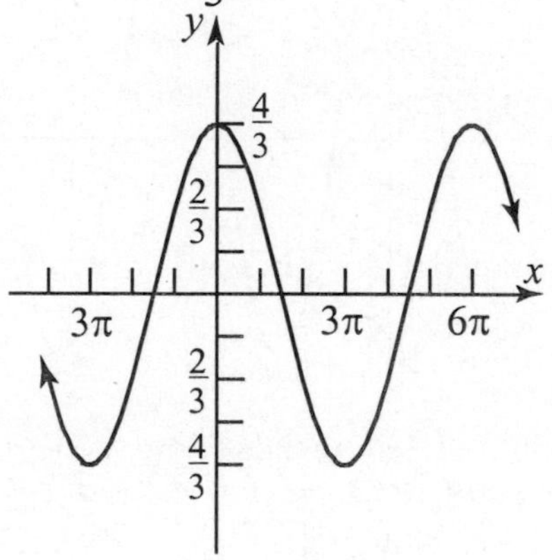

63. $|A| = 3;\ T = \pi;\ \omega = \frac{2\pi}{T} = \frac{2\pi}{\pi} = 2;\qquad y = 3\sin(2x)$

64. $|A| = 2;\ T = 4\pi;\ \omega = \frac{2\pi}{T} = \frac{2\pi}{4\pi} = \frac{1}{2};\qquad y = 2\sin\left(\frac{1}{2}x\right)$

65. $|A| = 3;\ T = 2;\ \omega = \frac{2\pi}{T} = \frac{2\pi}{2} = \pi;\qquad y = 3\sin(\pi x)$

66. $|A| = 4;\ T = 1;\ \omega = \frac{2\pi}{T} = \frac{2\pi}{1} = 2\pi;\qquad y = 4\sin(2\pi x)$

67. The graph is a cosine graph with an amplitude of 5 and a period of 8. Find ω:

$$8 = \frac{2\pi}{\omega} \rightarrow 8\omega = 2\pi \rightarrow \omega = \frac{2\pi}{8} = \frac{\pi}{4}$$

The equation is: $y = 5\cos\left(\frac{\pi}{4}x\right)$.

68. The graph is a sine graph with an amplitude of 4 and a period of 8π. Find ω:

$$8\pi = \frac{2\pi}{\omega} \rightarrow 8\pi\omega = 2\pi \rightarrow \omega = \frac{2\pi}{8\pi} = \frac{1}{4}$$

The equation is: $y = 4\sin\left(\frac{1}{4}x\right)$.

69. The graph is a reflected cosine graph with an amplitude of 3 and a period of 4π. Find ω:

$$4\pi = \frac{2\pi}{\omega} \rightarrow 4\pi\omega = 2\pi \rightarrow \omega = \frac{2\pi}{4\pi} = \frac{1}{2}$$

The equation is: $y = -3\cos\left(\frac{1}{2}x\right)$.

70. The graph is a reflected sine graph with an amplitude of 2 and a period of 4. Find ω:

$$4 = \frac{2\pi}{\omega} \rightarrow 4\omega = 2\pi \rightarrow \omega = \frac{2\pi}{4} = \frac{\pi}{2}$$

The equation is: $y = -2\sin\left(\frac{\pi}{2}x\right)$.

71. The graph is a sine graph with an amplitude of $\frac{3}{4}$ and a period of 1. Find ω:

$$1 = \frac{2\pi}{\omega} \rightarrow \omega = 2\pi$$

The equation is: $y = \frac{3}{4}\sin(2\pi x)$.

72. The graph is a reflected cosine graph with an amplitude of $\frac{5}{2}$ and a period of 2. Find ω:

$$2 = \frac{2\pi}{\omega} \rightarrow 2\omega = 2\pi \rightarrow \omega = \frac{2\pi}{2} = \pi$$

The equation is: $y = -\frac{5}{2}\cos(\pi x)$.

73. The graph is a reflected sine graph with an amplitude of 1 and a period of $\frac{4\pi}{3}$. Find ω:

$$\frac{4\pi}{3} = \frac{2\pi}{\omega} \rightarrow 4\pi\omega = 6\pi \rightarrow \omega = \frac{6\pi}{4\pi} = \frac{3}{2}$$

The equation is: $y = -\sin\left(\frac{3}{2}x\right)$.

74. The graph is a reflected cosine graph with an amplitude of π and a period of 2π. Find ω:

$$2\pi = \frac{2\pi}{\omega} \rightarrow 2\pi\omega = 2\pi \rightarrow \omega = \frac{2\pi}{2\pi} = 1$$

The equation is: $y = -\pi\cos x$.

75. The graph is a reflected cosine graph with an amplitude of 2 and a period of $\frac{4}{3}$.
Find ω:
$$\frac{4}{3}=\frac{2\pi}{\omega} \rightarrow 4\omega=6\pi \rightarrow \omega=\frac{6\pi}{4}=\frac{3\pi}{2}$$
The equation is: $y=-2\cos\left(\frac{3\pi}{2}x\right)$.

76. The graph is a reflected sine graph with an amplitude of $\frac{1}{2}$ and a period of $\frac{4\pi}{3}$.
Find ω:
$$\frac{4\pi}{3}=\frac{2\pi}{\omega} \rightarrow 4\pi\omega=6\pi \rightarrow \omega=\frac{6\pi}{4\pi}=\frac{3}{2}$$
The equation is: $y=-\frac{1}{2}\sin\left(\frac{3}{2}x\right)$.

77. The graph is a sine graph with an amplitude of 3 and a period of 4. Find ω:
$$4=\frac{2\pi}{\omega} \rightarrow 4\omega=2\pi \rightarrow \omega=\frac{2\pi}{4}=\frac{\pi}{2}$$
The equation is: $y=3\sin\left(\frac{\pi}{2}x\right)$.

78. The graph is a reflected cosine graph with an amplitude of 2 and a period of 2.
Find ω:
$$2=\frac{2\pi}{\omega} \rightarrow 2\omega=2\pi \rightarrow \omega=\frac{2\pi}{2}=\pi$$
The equation is: $y=-2\cos(\pi x)$.

79. The graph is a reflected cosine graph with an amplitude of 4 and a period of $\frac{2\pi}{3}$.
Find ω:
$$\frac{2\pi}{3}=\frac{2\pi}{\omega} \rightarrow 2\pi\omega=6\pi \rightarrow \omega=\frac{6\pi}{2\pi}=3$$
The equation is: $y=-4\cos(3x)$.

80. The graph is a sine graph with an amplitude of 4 and a period of π. Find ω:
$$\pi=\frac{2\pi}{\omega} \rightarrow \pi\omega=2\pi \rightarrow \omega=\frac{2\pi}{\pi}=2$$
The equation is: $y=4\sin(2x)$.

81. $I=220\sin(60\pi t),\ t\geq 0$

Period: $T=\frac{2\pi}{\omega}=\frac{2\pi}{60\pi}=\frac{1}{30}$

Amplitude: $|A|=|220|=220$

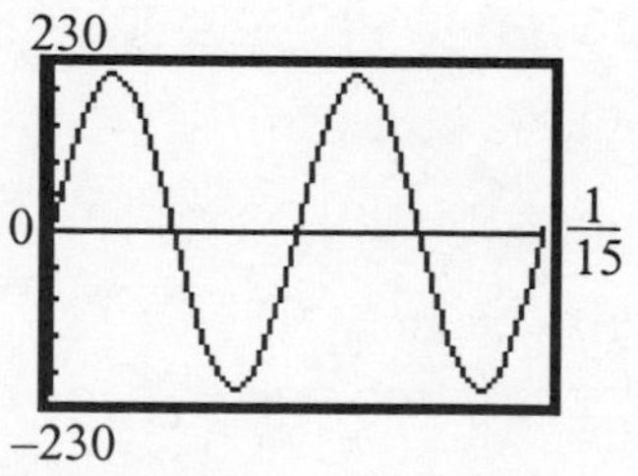

82. $I = 120\sin(30\pi t),\ t \geq 0$

Period: $T = \frac{2\pi}{\omega} = \frac{2\pi}{30\pi} = \frac{1}{15}$

Amplitude: $|A| = |120| = 120$

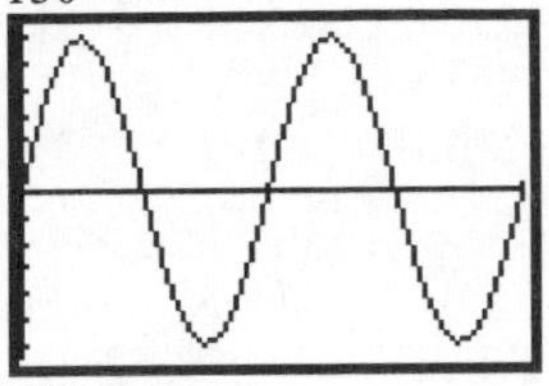

83. $V = 220\sin(120\pi t)$

(a) Amplitude: $|A| = |220| = 220$

Period: $T = \frac{2\pi}{\omega} = \frac{2\pi}{120\pi} = \frac{1}{60}$

(b)

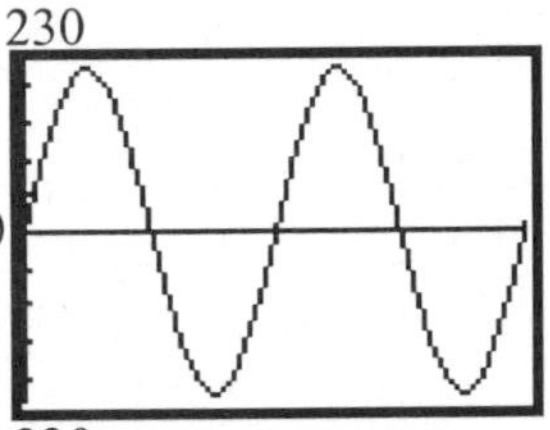

(c) $V = IR$

$220\sin(120\pi t) = 10I$

$22\sin(120\pi t) = I$

(d) Amplitude: $|A| = |22| = 22$

Period: $T = \frac{2\pi}{\omega} = \frac{2\pi}{120\pi} = \frac{1}{60}$

(e)

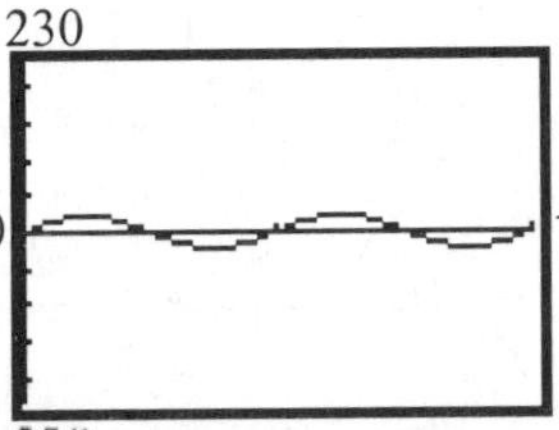

84. $V = 120\sin(120\pi t)$

(a) Amplitude: $|A| = |120| = 120$

Period: $T = \frac{2\pi}{\omega} = \frac{2\pi}{120\pi} = \frac{1}{60}$

(b)

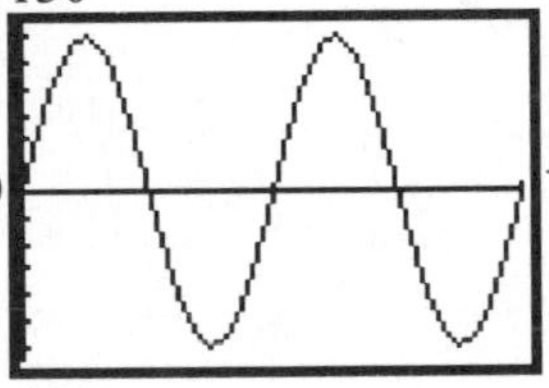

(c) $V = IR$

$120\sin(120\pi t) = 20I$

$6\sin(120\pi t) = I$

(d) Amplitude: $|A| = |6| = 6$

Period: $T = \frac{2\pi}{\omega} = \frac{2\pi}{120\pi} = \frac{1}{60}$

(e)

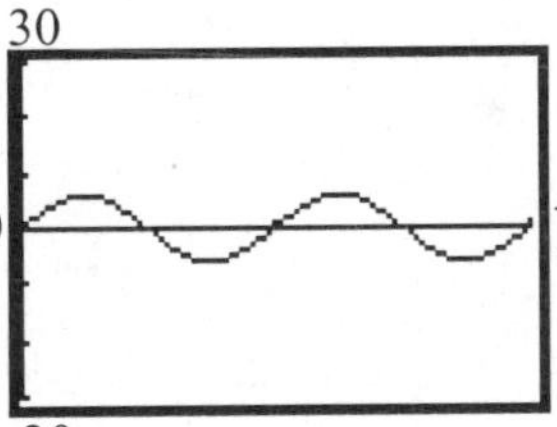

85. (a) $P = \frac{V^2}{R} = \frac{(V_0\sin(2\pi f t))^2}{R} = \frac{V_0^2\sin^2(2\pi f t)}{R}$

(b) The graph is the reflected cosine graph translated up a distance equivalent to the amplitude. The period is $\frac{1}{2f}$, so $\omega = 4\pi f$. The amplitude is $\frac{1}{2}\cdot\frac{V_0^2}{R} = \frac{V_0^2}{2R}$.

The equation is: $P = -\frac{V_0^2}{2R}\cos(4\pi f t) + \frac{V_0^2}{2R} = \frac{V_0^2}{R}\cdot\frac{1}{2}(1-\cos(4\pi f t))$

(c) Comparing the formulas:

$\sin^2(2\pi f t) = \frac{1}{2}(1-\cos(4\pi f t))$

86. (a) Physical potential: $\omega = \frac{2\pi}{23}$; Emotional potential: $\omega = \frac{2\pi}{28} = \frac{\pi}{14}$;

Intellectual potential: $\omega = \frac{2\pi}{33}$

(b) Graphing:

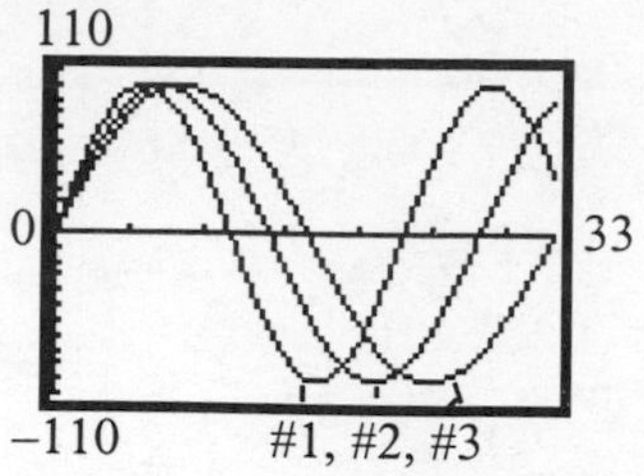

#1: $P = 100\sin\left(\frac{2\pi}{23}t\right)$

#2: $P = 100\sin\left(\frac{\pi}{14}t\right)$

#3: $P = 100\sin\left(\frac{2\pi}{33}t\right)$

(c) No

(d) Graphing:

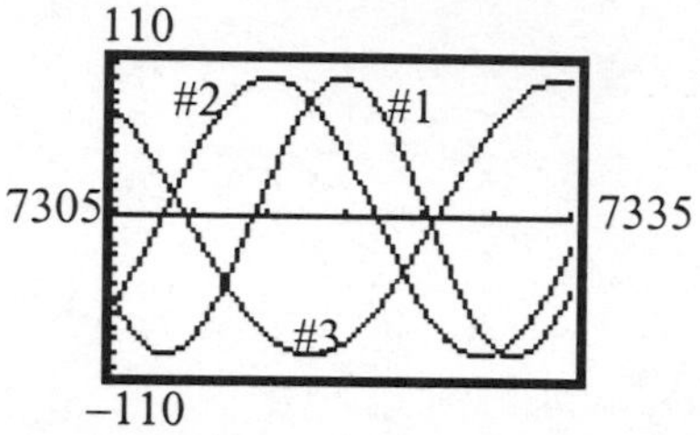

Physical potential peaks 15 days after the 20th birthday. Emotional potential has a maximum at 10 days and a minimum at the 24th day. Intellectual potential peaks on the 29th day and is at a minimum on the 13th day.

87. $y = |\cos x|, \ -2\pi \le x \le 2\pi$

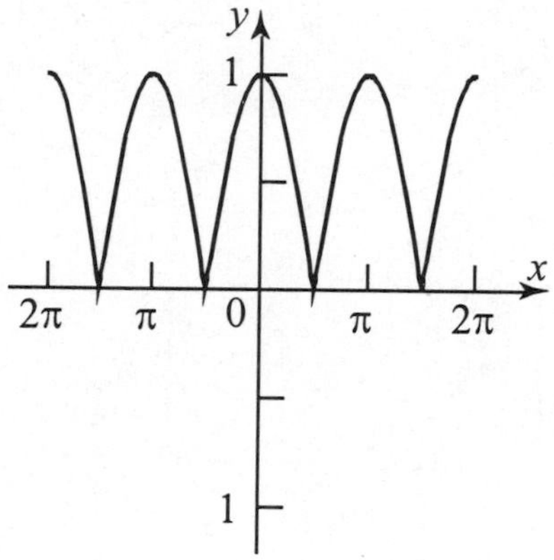

88. $y = |\sin x|, \ -2\pi \le x \le 2\pi$

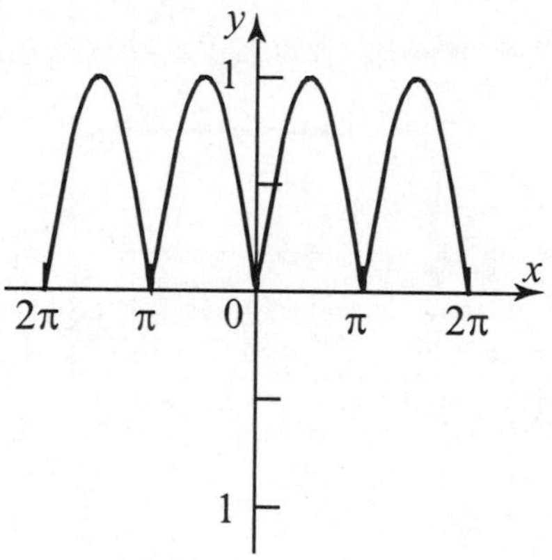

Trigonometric Functions

7.7 Graphs of the Tangent, Cotangent, Cosecant and Secant Functions

1. y-intercept: 0

2. No y-intercept.

3. y-intercept: 1

4. No y-intercept.

5. $\sec x = 1$ for $x = -2\pi, 0, 2\pi$; $\sec x = -1$ for $x = -\pi, \pi$

6. $\csc x = 1$ when $x = -\frac{3\pi}{2}, \frac{\pi}{2}$; $\csc x = -1$ when $x = -\frac{\pi}{2}, \frac{3\pi}{2}$

7. $y = \sec x$ has vertical asymptotes for $x = -\frac{3\pi}{2}, -\frac{\pi}{2}, \frac{\pi}{2}, \frac{3\pi}{2}$

8. $y = \csc x$ has vertical asymptotes for $x = -2\pi, -\pi, 0, \pi, 2\pi$

9. $y = \tan x$ has vertical asymptotes for $x = -\frac{3\pi}{2}, -\frac{\pi}{2}, \frac{\pi}{2}, \frac{3\pi}{2}$

10. $y = \cot x$ has vertical asymptotes for $x = -2\pi, -\pi, 0, \pi, 2\pi$

11. B   12. D   13. A   14. C

15. $y = -\sec x$

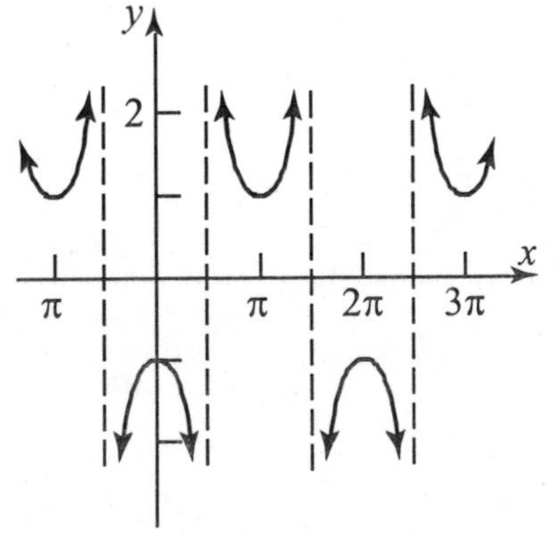

16. $y = -\cot x$

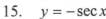

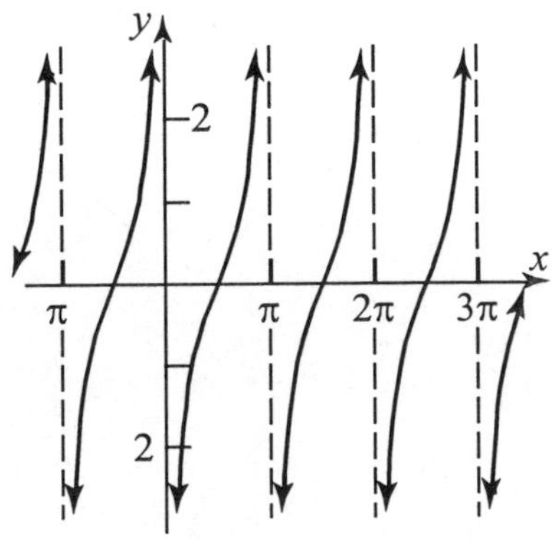

17. $y = \sec\left(x - \frac{\pi}{2}\right)$

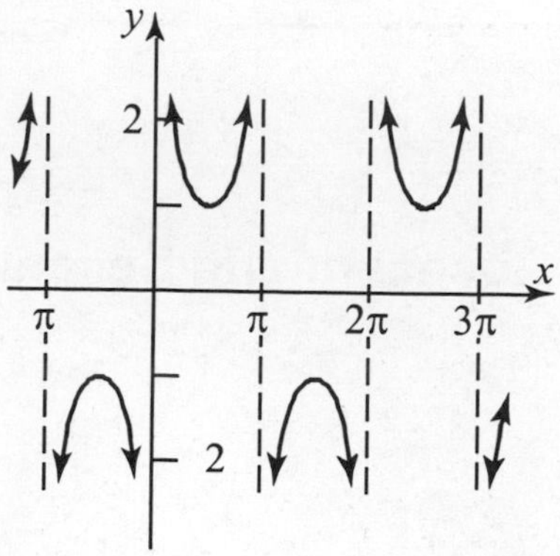

18. $y = \csc(x - \pi)$

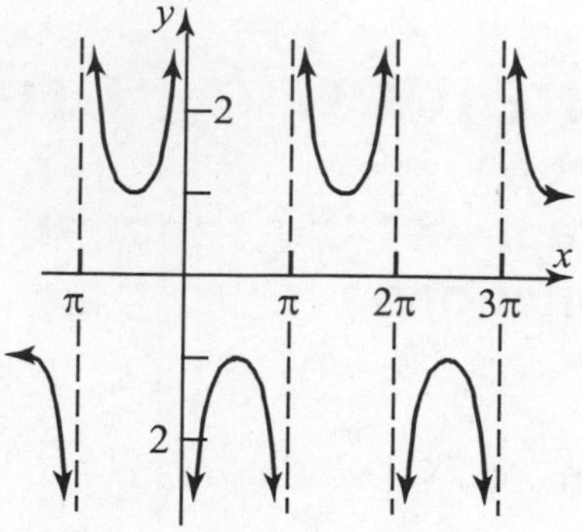

19. $y = \tan(x - \pi)$

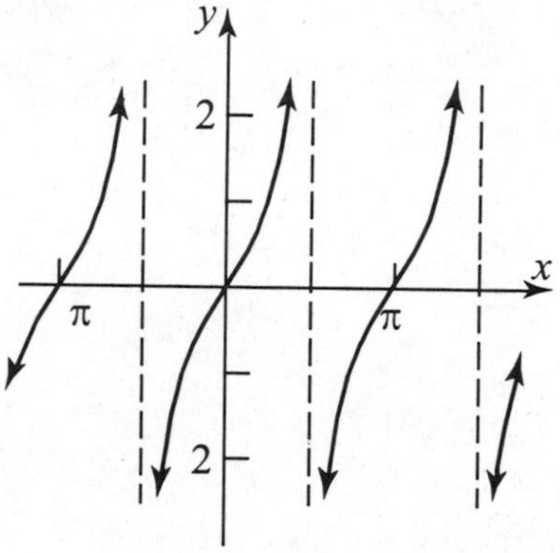

20. $y = \cot(x - \pi)$

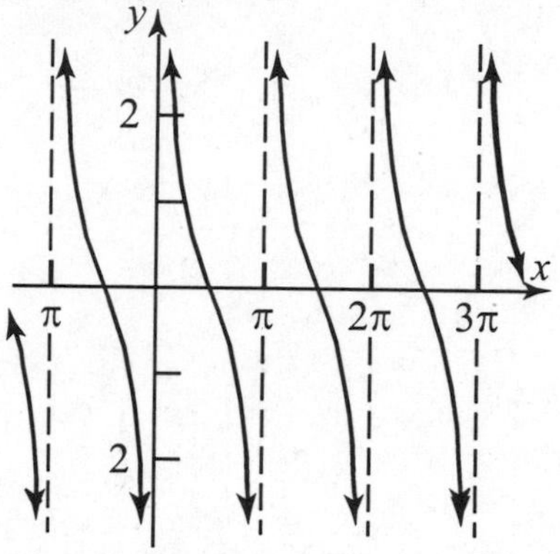

21. $y = 3\tan(2x)$

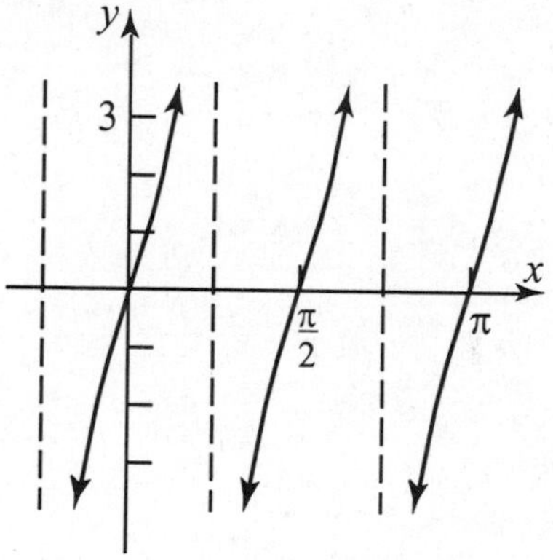

22. $y = 4\tan\left(\frac{1}{2}x\right)$

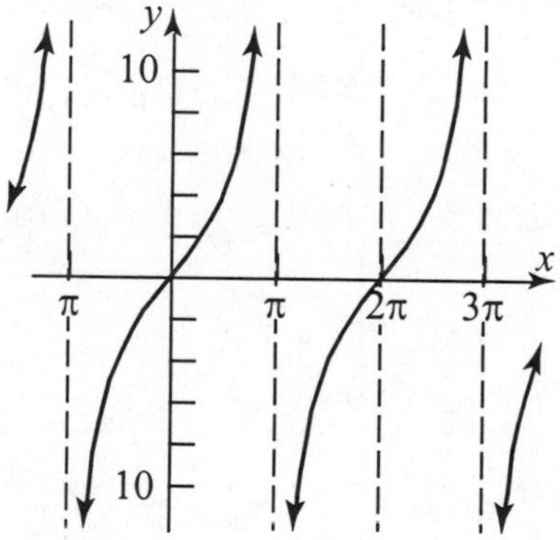

23. $y = \sec(2x)$

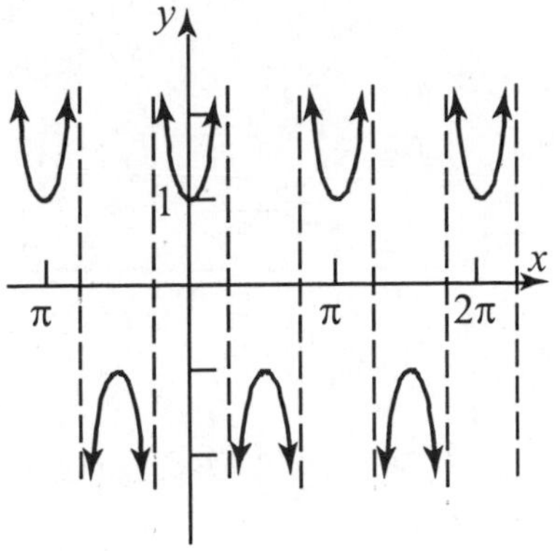

24. $y = \csc\left(\frac{1}{2}x\right)$

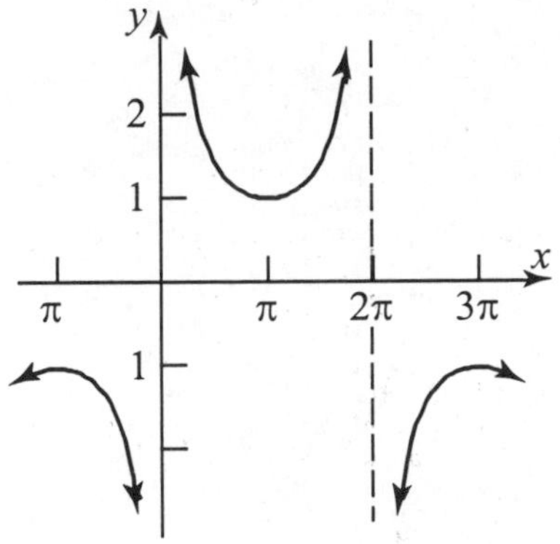

25. $y = \cot(\pi x)$

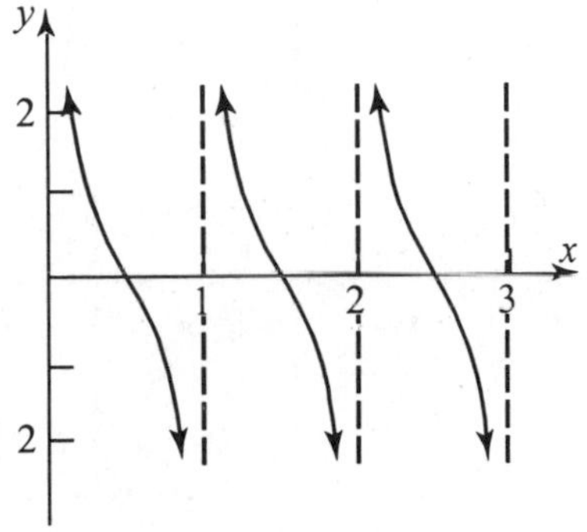

26. $y = \cot(2x)$

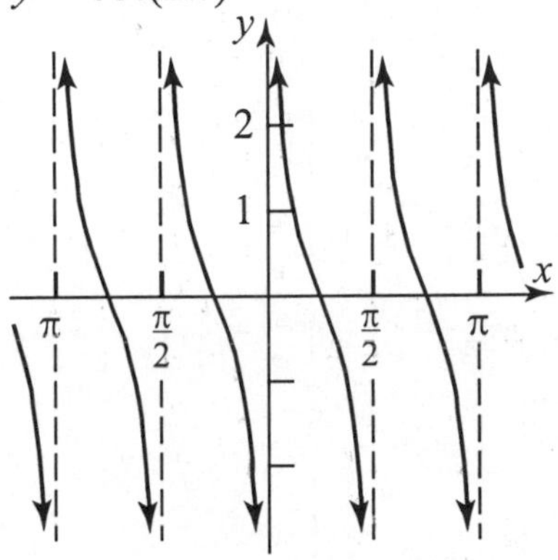

27. $y = -3\tan(4x)$

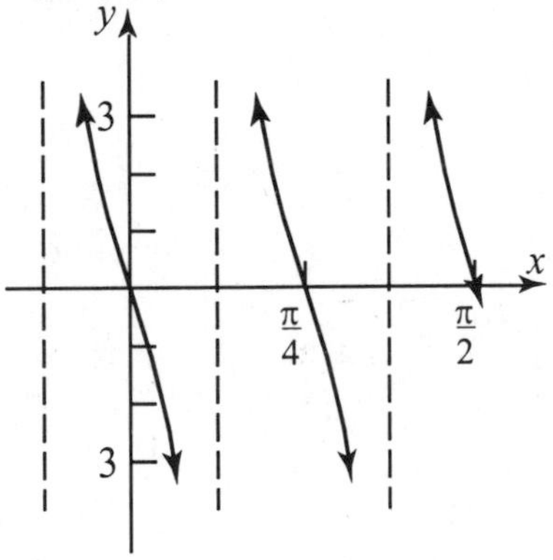

28. $y = -3\tan(2x)$

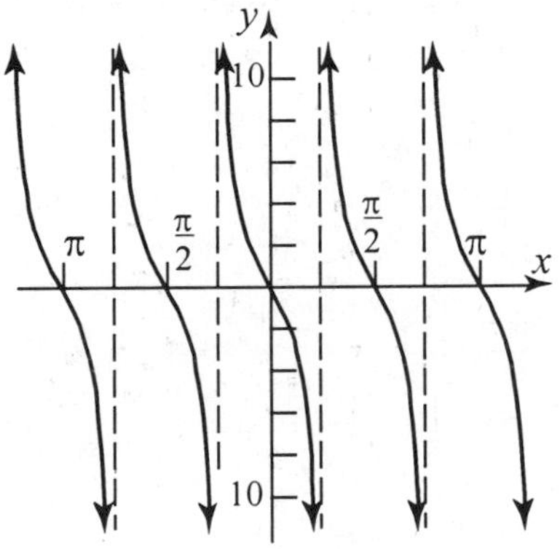

29. $y = 2\sec\left(\frac{1}{2}x\right)$

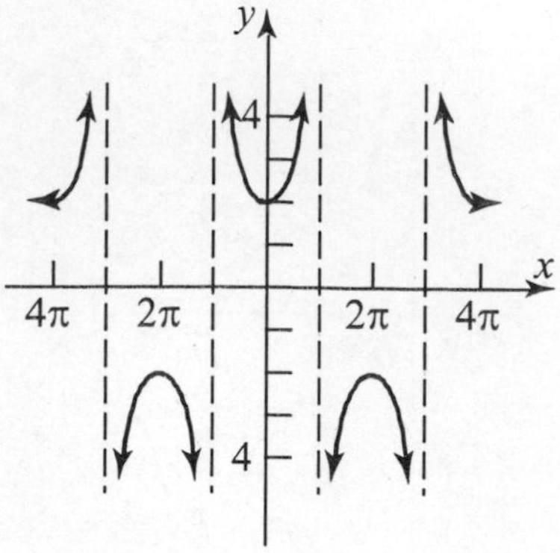

30. $y = 2\sec(3x)$

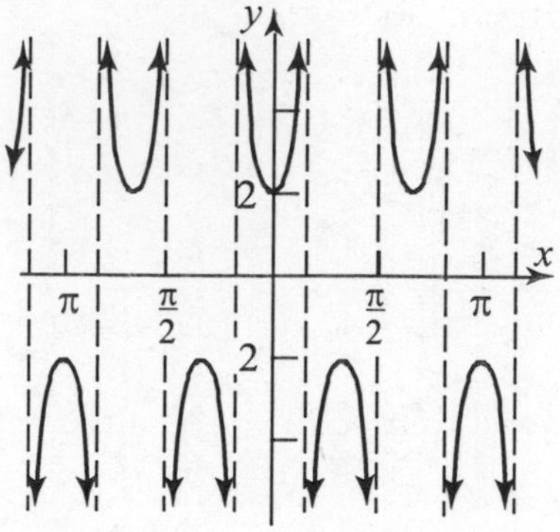

31. $y = -3\csc\left(x + \frac{\pi}{4}\right)$

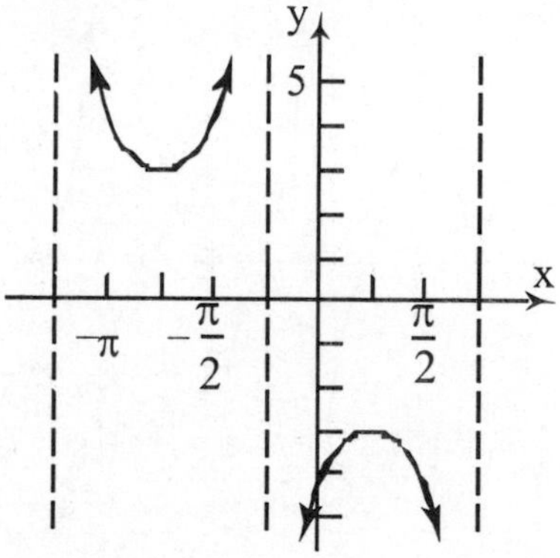

32. $y = -2\tan\left(x + \frac{\pi}{4}\right)$

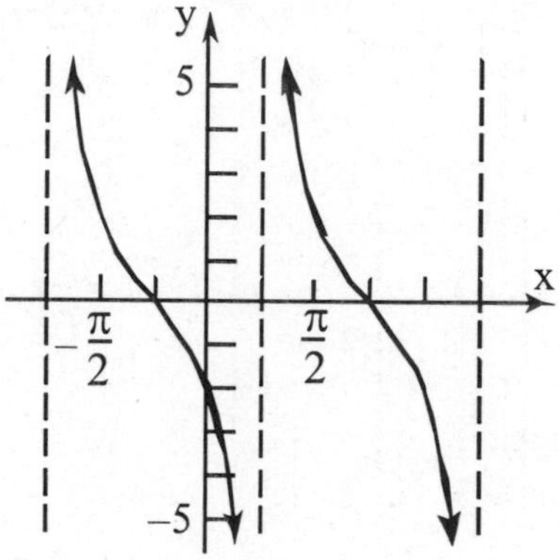

33. $y = \frac{1}{2}\cot\left(x + \frac{\pi}{4}\right)$

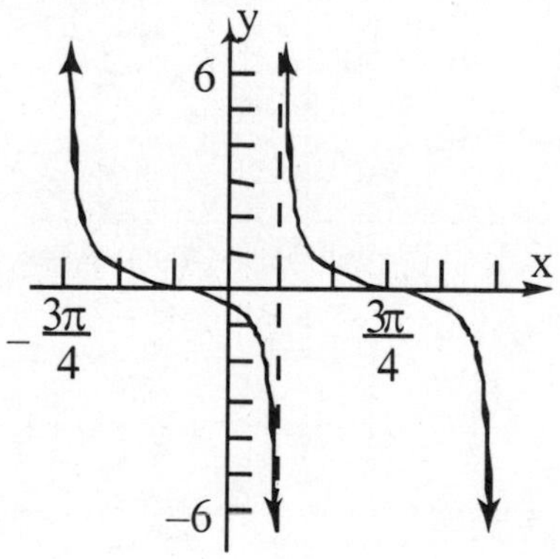

34. $y = 3\sec\left(x + \frac{\pi}{2}\right)$

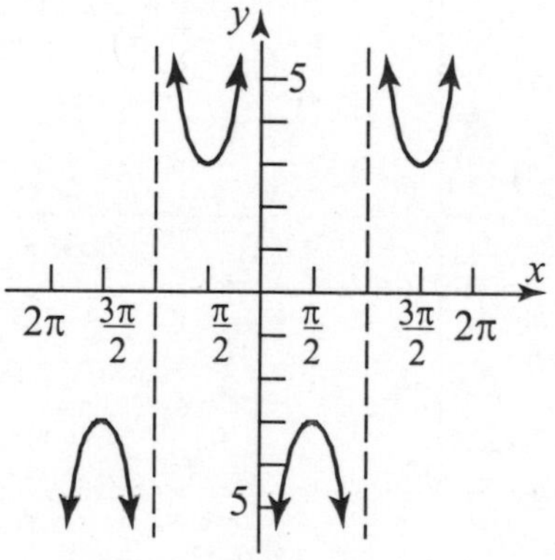

35. (a) $L = \dfrac{3}{\cos\theta} + \dfrac{4}{\sin\theta} = 3\sec\theta + 4\csc\theta$

(b) Graph:

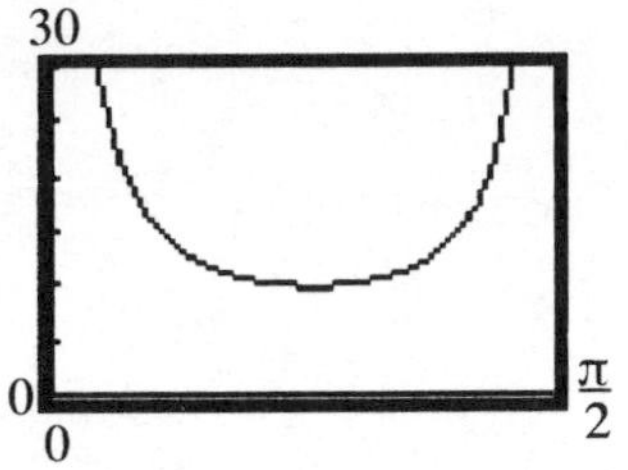

(c) Use MINIMUM to find the least value: L is least when $\theta = 0.83$.

(d) $L = \dfrac{3}{\cos(0.83)} + \dfrac{4}{\sin(0.83)} \approx 9.86$ feet

36. Graph:

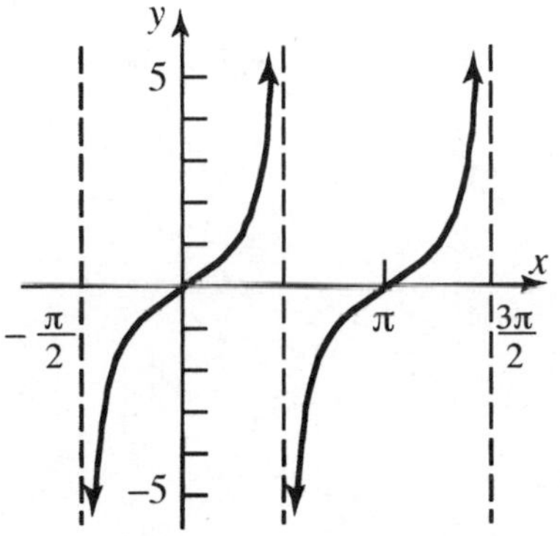

$y = \tan x$

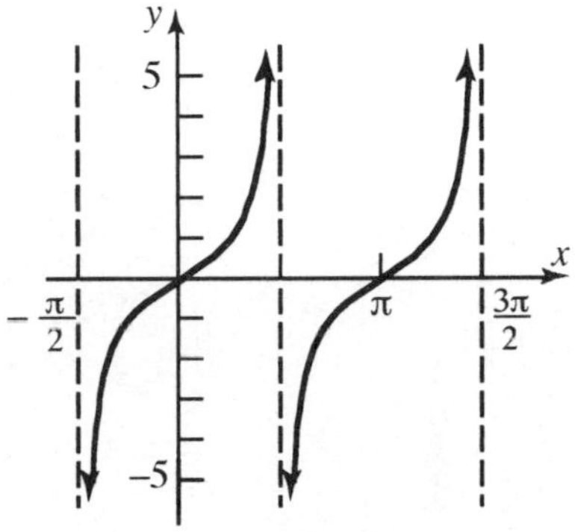

$y = -\cot\left(x + \frac{\pi}{2}\right)$

The two functions are equal to each other.

Trigonometric Functions

7.8 Phase Shift; Sinusoidal Curve Fitting

1. $y = 4\sin(2x - \pi)$

   Amplitude: $|A| = |4| = 4$

   Period: $T = \dfrac{2\pi}{\omega} = \dfrac{2\pi}{2} = \pi$

   Phase Shift: $\dfrac{\phi}{\omega} = \dfrac{\pi}{2}$

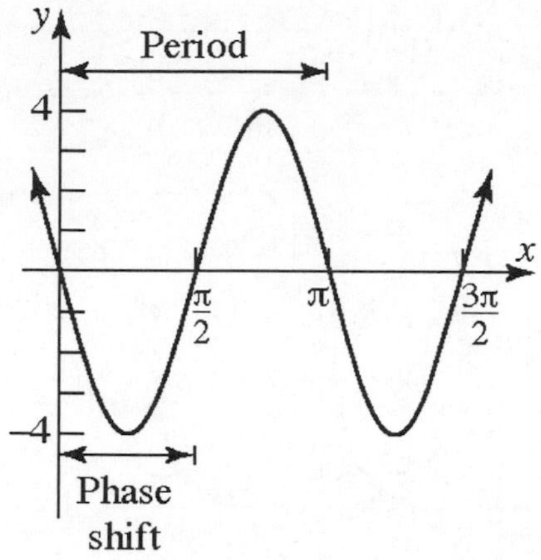

2. $y = 3\sin(3x - \pi)$

   Amplitude: $|A| = |3| = 3$

   Period: $T = \dfrac{2\pi}{\omega} = \dfrac{2\pi}{3}$

   Phase Shift: $\dfrac{\phi}{\omega} = \dfrac{\pi}{3}$

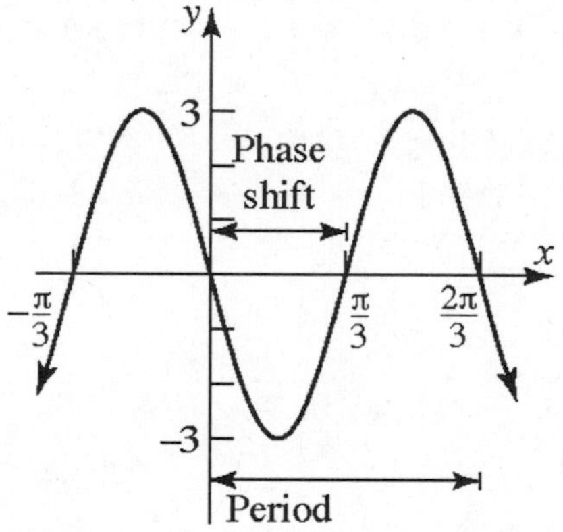

3. $y = 2\cos\left(3x + \dfrac{\pi}{2}\right)$

   Amplitude: $|A| = |2| = 2$

   Period: $T = \dfrac{2\pi}{\omega} = \dfrac{2\pi}{3}$

   Phase Shift: $\dfrac{\phi}{\omega} = \dfrac{\left(-\dfrac{\pi}{2}\right)}{3} = -\dfrac{\pi}{6}$

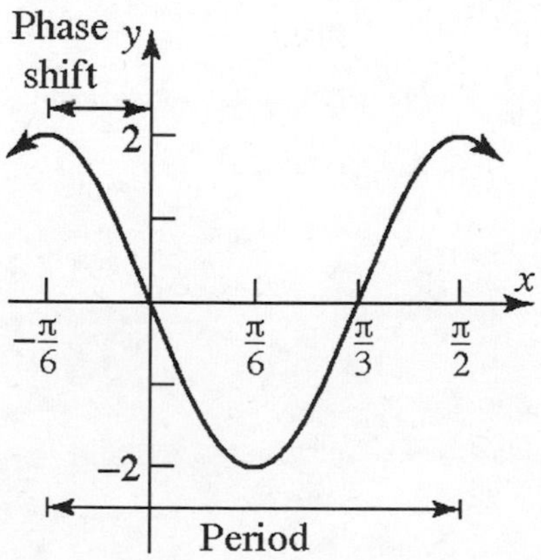

4. $y = 3\cos(2x + \pi)$

Amplitude: $|A| = |3| = 3$

Period: $T = \frac{2\pi}{\omega} = \frac{2\pi}{2} = \pi$

Phase Shift: $\frac{\phi}{\omega} = \frac{-\pi}{2} = -\frac{\pi}{2}$

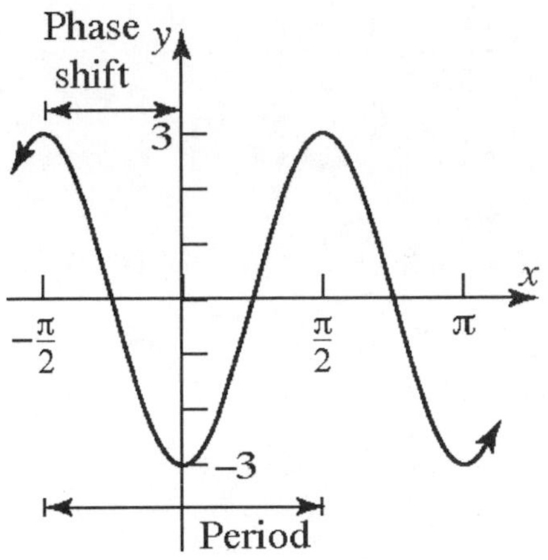

5. $y = -3\sin\left(2x + \frac{\pi}{2}\right)$

Amplitude: $|A| = |-3| = 3$

Period: $T = \frac{2\pi}{\omega} = \frac{2\pi}{2} = \pi$

Phase Shift: $\frac{\phi}{\omega} = \frac{\left(-\frac{\pi}{2}\right)}{2} = -\frac{\pi}{4}$

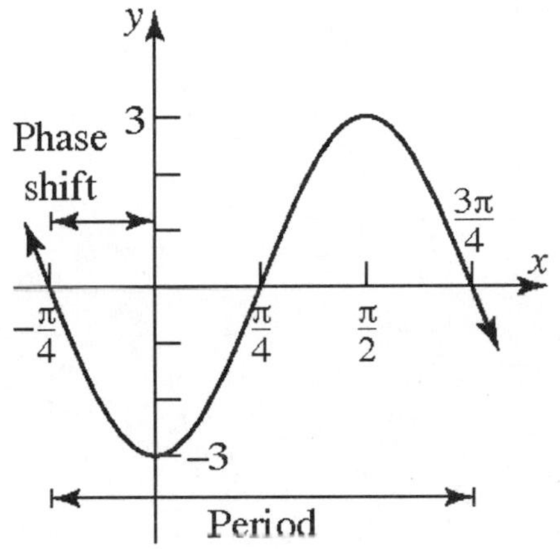

6. $y = -2\cos\left(2x - \frac{\pi}{2}\right)$

Amplitude: $|A| = |-2| = 2$

Period: $T = \frac{2\pi}{\omega} = \frac{2\pi}{2} = \pi$

Phase Shift: $\frac{\phi}{\omega} = \frac{\left(\frac{\pi}{2}\right)}{2} = \frac{\pi}{4}$

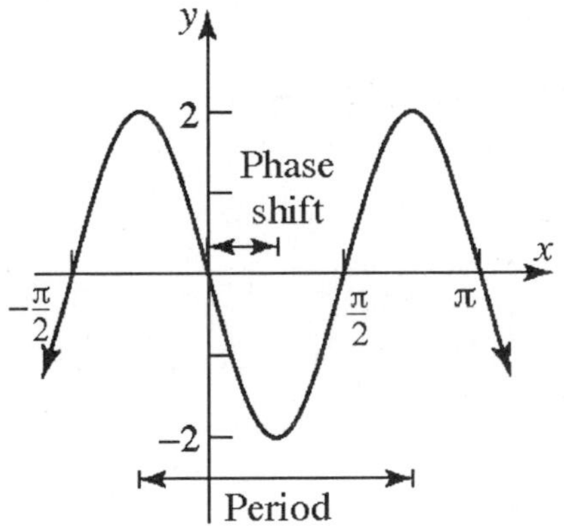

7. $y = 4\sin(\pi x + 2)$

Amplitude: $|A| = |4| = 4$

Period: $T = \dfrac{2\pi}{\omega} = \dfrac{2\pi}{\pi} = 2$

Phase Shift: $\dfrac{\phi}{\omega} = -\dfrac{2}{\pi}$

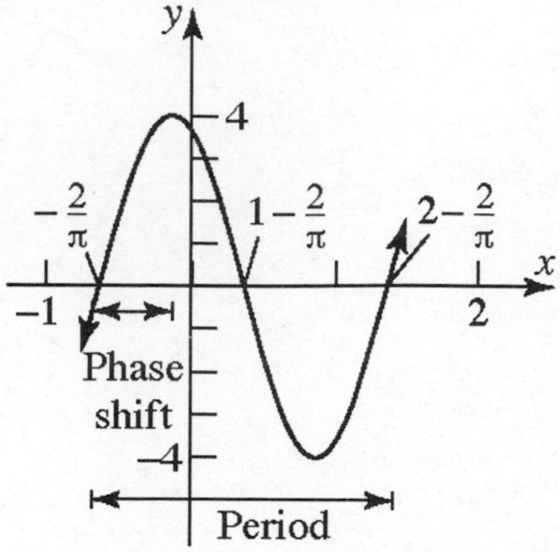

8. $y = 2\cos(2\pi x + 4)$

Amplitude: $|A| = |2| = 2$

Period: $T = \dfrac{2\pi}{\omega} = \dfrac{2\pi}{2\pi} = 1$

Phase Shift: $\dfrac{\phi}{\omega} = \dfrac{-4}{2\pi} = -\dfrac{2}{\pi}$

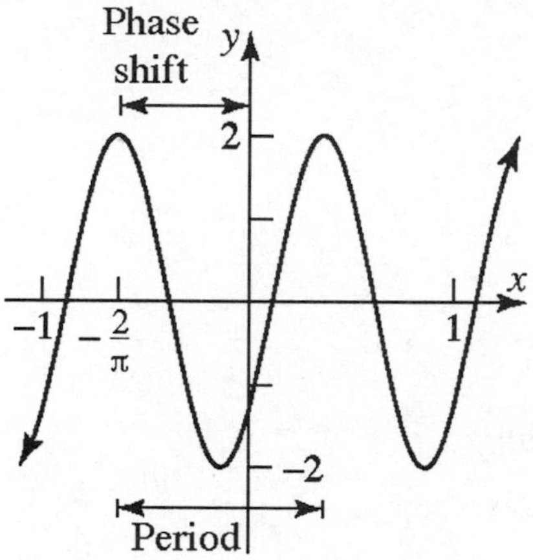

9. $y = 3\cos(\pi x - 2)$

Amplitude: $|A| = |3| = 3$

Period: $T = \dfrac{2\pi}{\omega} = \dfrac{2\pi}{\pi} = 2$

Phase Shift: $\dfrac{\phi}{\omega} = \dfrac{2}{\pi}$

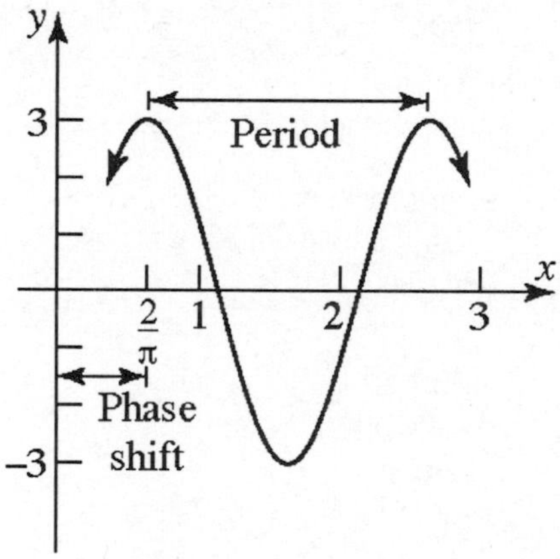

10. $y = 2\cos(2\pi x - 4)$

Amplitude: $|A| = |2| = 2$

Period: $T = \dfrac{2\pi}{\omega} = \dfrac{2\pi}{2\pi} = 1$

Phase Shift: $\dfrac{\phi}{\omega} = \dfrac{4}{2\pi} = \dfrac{2}{\pi}$

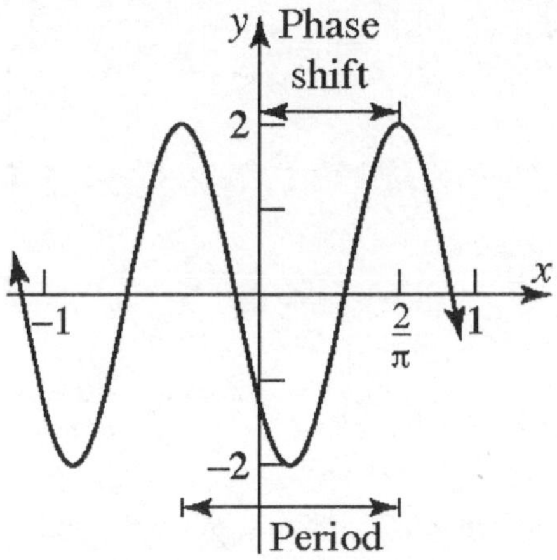

11. $y = 3\sin\left(-2x + \dfrac{\pi}{2}\right) = -3\sin\left(2x - \dfrac{\pi}{2}\right)$

Amplitude: $|A| = |-3| = 3$

Period: $T = \dfrac{2\pi}{\omega} = \dfrac{2\pi}{2} = \pi$

Phase Shift: $\dfrac{\phi}{\omega} = \dfrac{\left(\dfrac{\pi}{2}\right)}{2} = \dfrac{\pi}{4}$

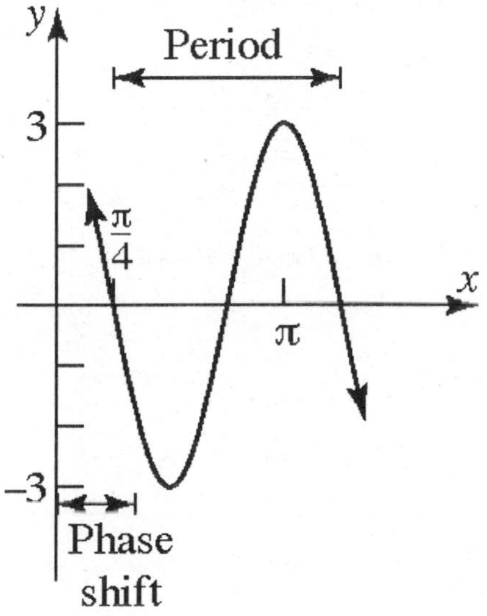

12. $y = 3\cos\left(-2x + \dfrac{\pi}{2}\right)$

Amplitude: $|A| = |3| = 3$

Period: $T = \dfrac{2\pi}{\omega} = \dfrac{2\pi}{2} = \pi$

Phase Shift: $\dfrac{\phi}{\omega} = \dfrac{\left(-\dfrac{\pi}{2}\right)}{-2} = \dfrac{\pi}{4}$

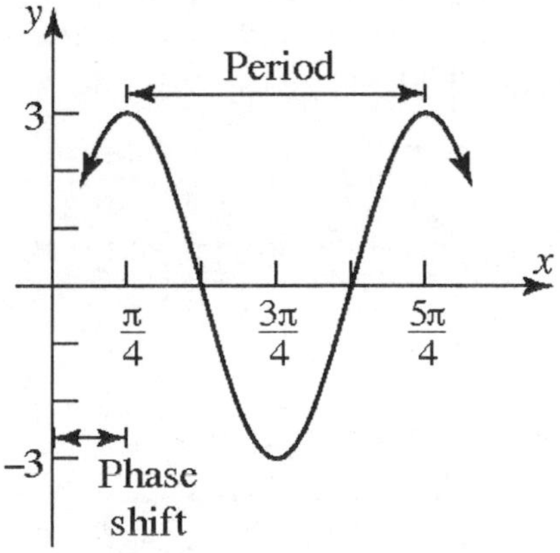

13. $|A| = 2;\quad T = \pi;\quad \dfrac{\phi}{\omega} = \dfrac{1}{2};\quad \omega = \dfrac{2\pi}{T} = \dfrac{2\pi}{\pi} = 2;\quad \dfrac{\phi}{\omega} = \dfrac{\phi}{2} = \dfrac{1}{2} \rightarrow \phi = 1$

$$y = 2\sin(2x - 1) = 2\sin\left[2\left(x - \frac{1}{2}\right)\right]$$

14. $|A| = 3;\ T = \frac{\pi}{2};\ \frac{\phi}{\omega} = 2;\ \omega = \frac{2\pi}{T} = \frac{2\pi}{\left(\frac{\pi}{2}\right)} = 4;\ \frac{\phi}{\omega} = \frac{\phi}{4} = 2 \rightarrow \phi = 8$

$y = 3\sin(4x - 8) = 3\sin[4(x-2)]$

15. $|A| = 3;\ T = 3\pi;\ \frac{\phi}{\omega} = -\frac{1}{3};\ \omega = \frac{2\pi}{T} = \frac{2\pi}{3\pi} = \frac{2}{3};$

$\frac{\phi}{\omega} = \frac{\phi}{\frac{2}{3}} = -\frac{1}{3} \rightarrow \phi = -\frac{1}{3}\cdot\frac{2}{3} = -\frac{2}{9} \qquad y = 3\sin\left(\frac{2}{3}x + \frac{2}{9}\right) = 3\sin\left[\frac{2}{3}\left(x + \frac{1}{3}\right)\right]$

16. $|A| = 2;\ T = \pi;\ \frac{\phi}{\omega} = -2;\ \omega = \frac{2\pi}{T} = \frac{2\pi}{\pi} = 2;\ \frac{\phi}{\omega} = \frac{\phi}{2} = -2 \rightarrow \phi = -4$

$y = 2\sin(2x + 4) = 2\sin[2(x+2)]$

17. $I = 120\sin\left(30\pi t - \frac{\pi}{3}\right),\quad t \geq 0$

Period: $T = \frac{2\pi}{\omega} = \frac{2\pi}{30\pi} = \frac{1}{15}$

Amplitude: $|A| = |120| = 120$

Phase Shift: $\frac{\phi}{\omega} = \frac{\left(\frac{\pi}{3}\right)}{30\pi} = \frac{1}{90}$

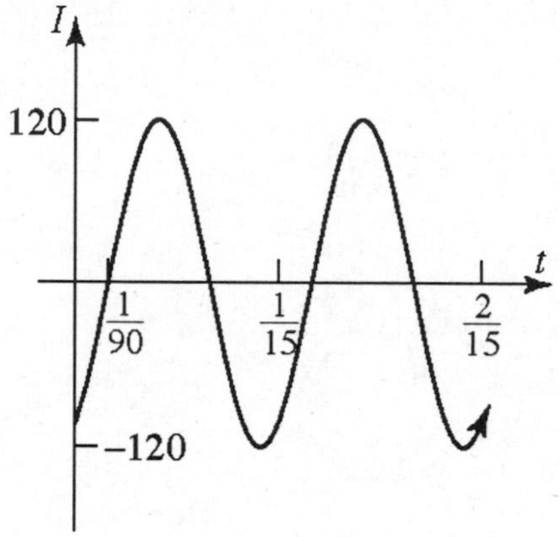

18. $I = 220\sin\left(60\pi t - \frac{\pi}{6}\right),\quad t \geq 0$

Period: $T = \frac{2\pi}{\omega} = \frac{2\pi}{60\pi} = \frac{1}{30}$

Amplitude: $|A| = |220| = 220$

Phase Shift: $\frac{\phi}{\omega} = \frac{\left(\frac{\pi}{6}\right)}{60\pi} = \frac{1}{360}$

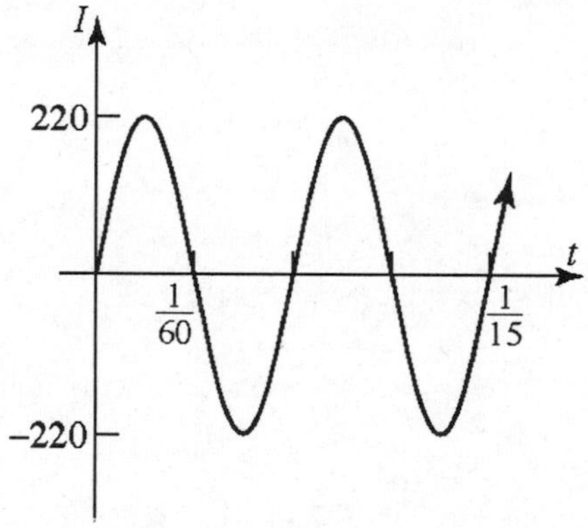

19. (a) Draw a scatter diagram:

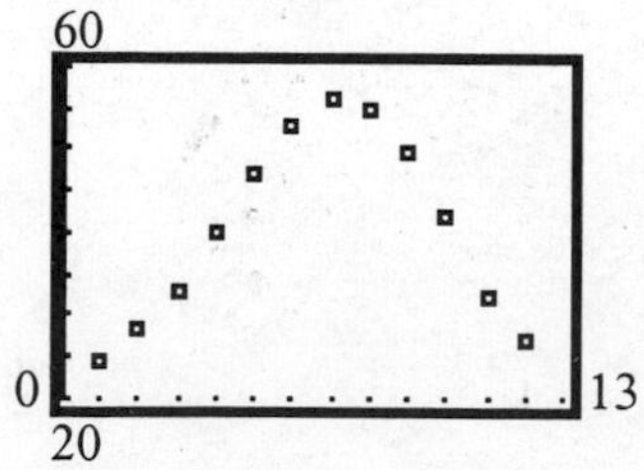

(b) Amplitude: $A = \dfrac{56.0 - 24.2}{2} = \dfrac{31.8}{2} = 15.9$

Vertical Shift: $\dfrac{56.0 + 24.2}{2} = \dfrac{80.2}{2} = 40.1$

$\omega = \dfrac{2\pi}{12} = \dfrac{\pi}{6}$

Phase shift (use $y = 24.2$, $x = 1$):

$$24.2 = 15.9\sin\left(\frac{\pi}{6}\cdot 1 - \phi\right) + 40.1$$

$$-15.9 = 15.9\sin\left(\frac{\pi}{6} - \phi\right) \to -1 = \sin\left(\frac{\pi}{6} - \phi\right) \to -\frac{\pi}{2} = \frac{\pi}{6} - \phi$$

$$\phi = \frac{2\pi}{3}$$

Thus, $y = 15.9\sin\left(\dfrac{\pi}{6}x - \dfrac{2\pi}{3}\right) + 40.1$

(c)

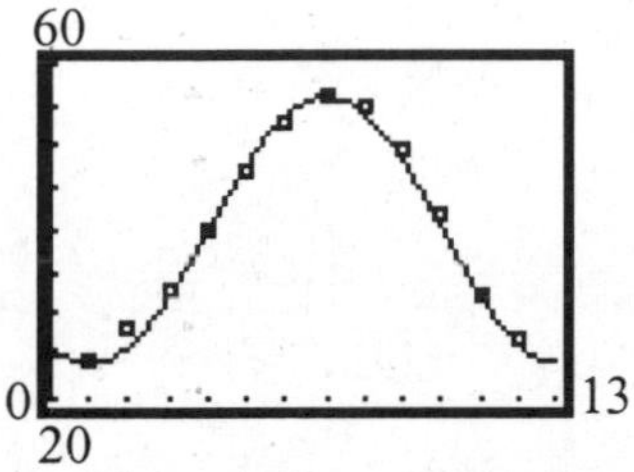

(e)

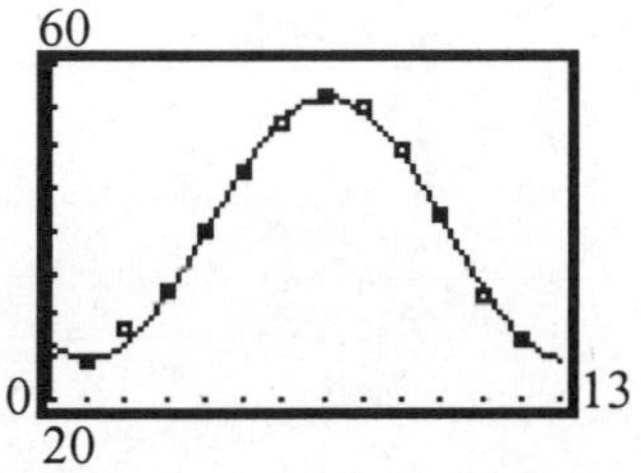

(d) $y = 15.62\sin(0.517x - 2.096) + 40.377$

20. (a) Draw a scatter diagram:

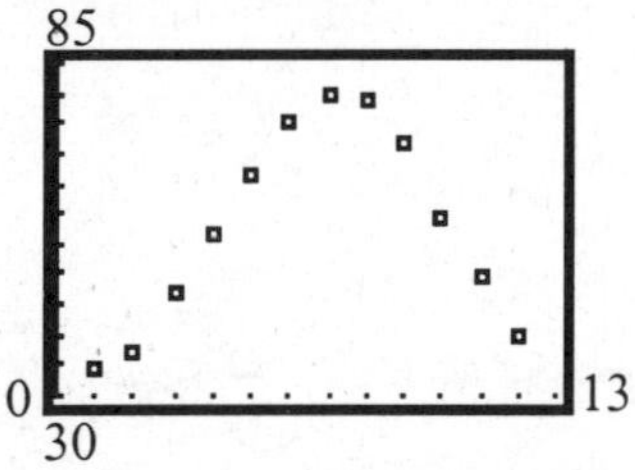

(b) Amplitude: $A = \dfrac{80.0 - 34.6}{2} = \dfrac{45.4}{2} = 22.7$

Vertical Shift: $\dfrac{80.0 + 34.6}{2} = \dfrac{114.6}{2} = 57.3$

$\omega = \dfrac{2\pi}{12} = \dfrac{\pi}{6}$

Phase shift (use $y = 34.6$, $x = 1$):

$$34.6 = 22.7\sin\left(\frac{\pi}{6}\cdot 1 - \phi\right) + 57.3$$

$$-22.7 = 22.7\sin\left(\frac{\pi}{6} - \phi\right) \to -1 = \sin\left(\frac{\pi}{6} - \phi\right) \to -\frac{\pi}{2} = \frac{\pi}{6} - \phi$$

$$\phi = \frac{2\pi}{3}$$

Thus, $y = 22.7\sin\left(\frac{\pi}{6}x - \frac{2\pi}{3}\right) + 57.3$

(c)

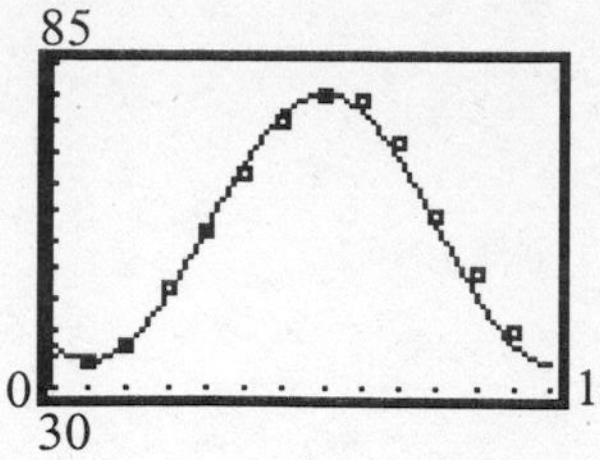

(e)

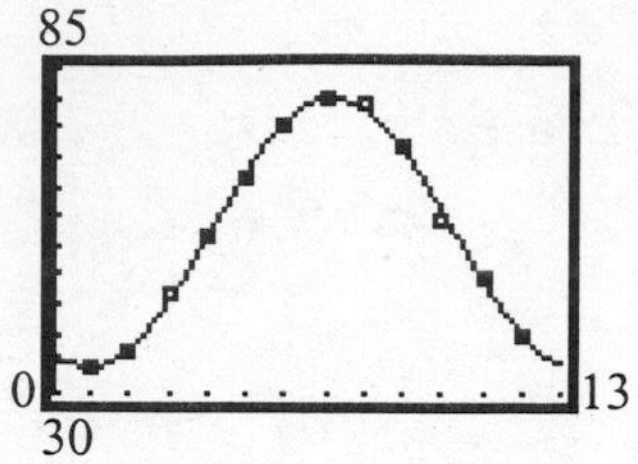

(d) $y = 22.6128\sin(0.5032x - 2.0384) + 57.1686$

21. (a) Draw a scatter diagram:

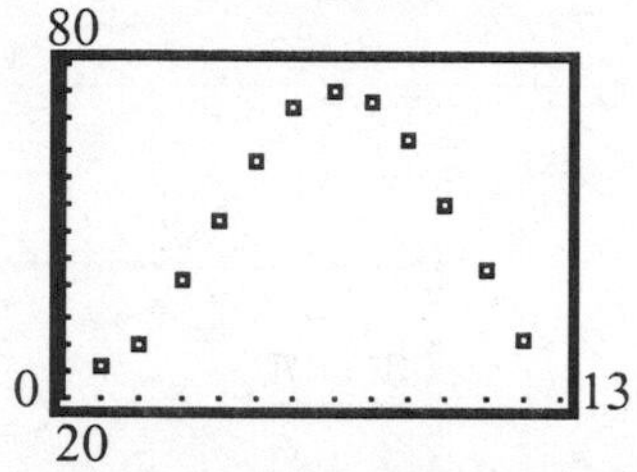

(b) Amplitude: $A = \frac{75.4 - 25.5}{2} = \frac{49.9}{2} = 24.95$

Vertical Shift: $\frac{75.4 + 25.5}{2} = \frac{100.9}{2} = 50.45$

$\omega = \frac{2\pi}{12} = \frac{\pi}{6}$

Phase shift (use $y = 25.5$, $x = 1$):

$$25.5 = 24.95\sin\left(\frac{\pi}{6}\cdot 1 - \phi\right) + 50.45$$

$$-24.95 = 24.95\sin\left(\frac{\pi}{6} - \phi\right) \rightarrow -1 = \sin\left(\frac{\pi}{6} - \phi\right) \rightarrow -\frac{\pi}{2} = \frac{\pi}{6} - \phi$$

$$\phi = \frac{2\pi}{3}$$

Thus, $y = 24.95\sin\left(\frac{\pi}{6}x - \frac{2\pi}{3}\right) + 50.45$

(c)

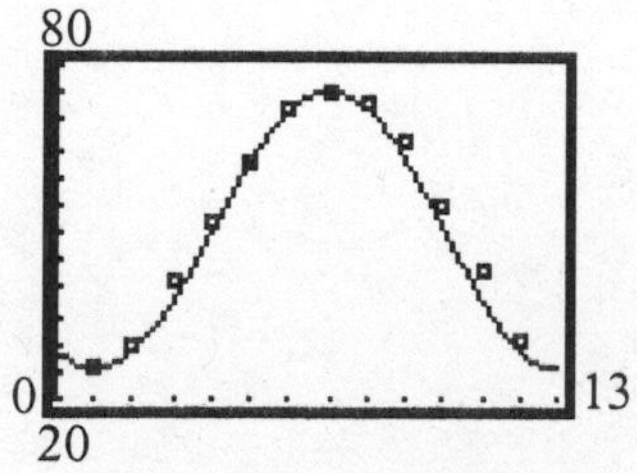

(e)

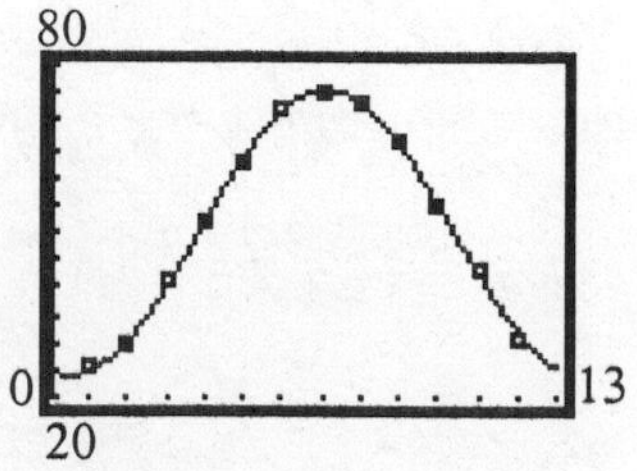

(d) $y = 25.693\sin(0.476x - 1.814) + 49.854$

22. (a) Draw a scatter diagram:

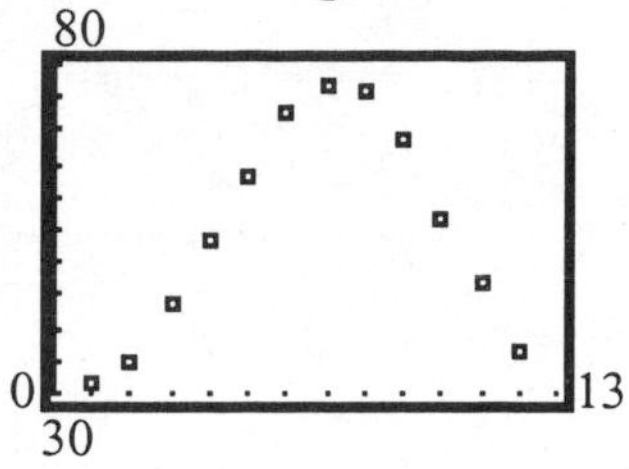

(b) Amplitude: $A = \dfrac{77.0 - 31.8}{2} = \dfrac{45.2}{2} = 22.6$

Vertical Shift: $\dfrac{77.0 + 31.8}{2} = \dfrac{108.8}{2} = 54.4$

$\omega = \dfrac{2\pi}{12} = \dfrac{\pi}{6}$

Phase shift (use $y = 31.8$, $x = 1$):

$$31.8 = 22.6\sin\left(\frac{\pi}{6}\cdot 1 - \phi\right) + 54.4$$

$$-22.6 = 22.6\sin\left(\frac{\pi}{6} - \phi\right) \rightarrow -1 = \sin\left(\frac{\pi}{6} - \phi\right) \rightarrow -\frac{\pi}{2} = \frac{\pi}{6} - \phi$$

$$\phi = \frac{2\pi}{3}$$

Thus, $y = 22.6\sin\left(\dfrac{\pi}{6}x - \dfrac{2\pi}{3}\right) + 54.4$

(c)

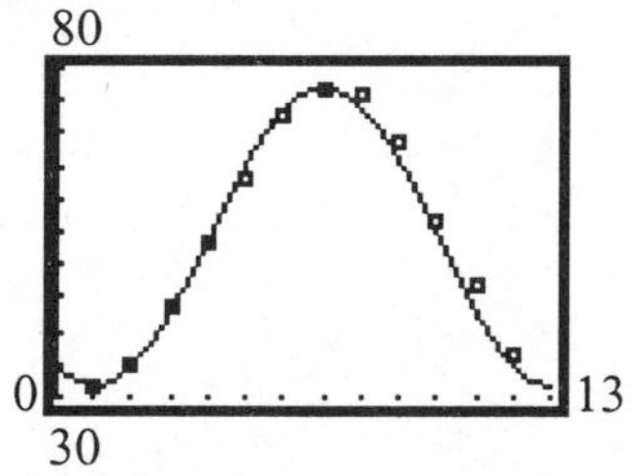

(e)

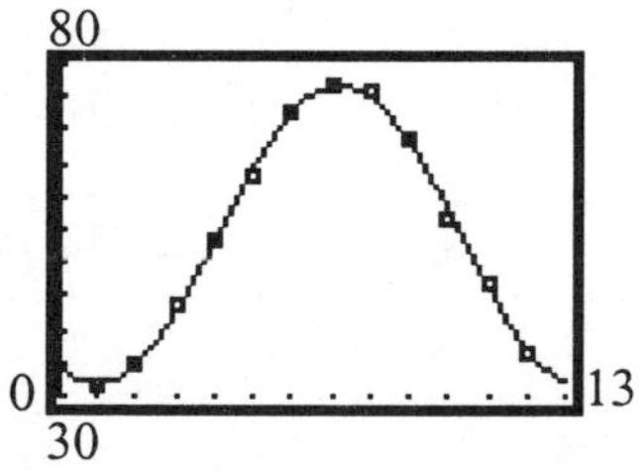

(d) $y = 22.4587\sin(0.5058x - 2.0602) + 54.3482$

23. (a) $3.6333 + 12.5 = 16.1333$ hours which is at 4:08 p.m.

(b) Amplitude: $A = \dfrac{8.2 - (-0.6)}{2} = \dfrac{8.8}{2} = 4.4$

Vertical Shift: $\dfrac{8.2 + (-0.6)}{2} = \dfrac{7.6}{2} = 3.8$

$\omega = \dfrac{2\pi}{12.5} = \dfrac{\pi}{6.25}$

Phase shift (use $y = -0.6$, $x = 10.1333$):

$$-0.6 = 4.4\sin\left(\frac{\pi}{6.25}\cdot 10.1333 - \phi\right) + 3.8$$

$$-4.4 = 4.4\sin\left(\frac{\pi}{6.25}\cdot 10.1333 - \phi\right) \rightarrow -1 = \sin\left(\frac{10.1333\pi}{6.25} - \phi\right)$$

$$-\frac{\pi}{2}=\frac{10.1333\pi}{6.25}-\phi \rightarrow \phi = 6.6643$$

Thus, $y = 4.4\sin\left(\frac{\pi}{6.25}x - 6.6643\right) + 3.8$

(c)

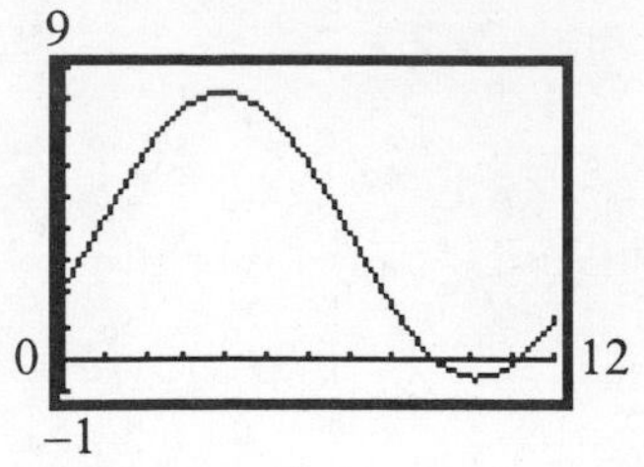

(d) $y = 4.4\sin\left(\frac{\pi}{6.25}(16.1333) - 6.6643\right) + 3.8 = 8.2$ feet

24. (a) $8.1833 + 12.5 = 20.6833$ hours which is at 8:41 p.m.

(b) Amplitude: $A = \frac{13.2-2.2}{2} = \frac{11}{2} = 5.5$

Vertical Shift: $\frac{13.2+2.2}{2} = \frac{15.4}{2} = 7.7$

$\omega = \frac{2\pi}{12.5} = \frac{\pi}{6.25}$

Phase shift (use $y = 2.2$, $x = 14.2333$):

$$2.2 = 5.5\sin\left(\frac{\pi}{6.25}\cdot 14.2333 - \phi\right) + 7.7$$

$$-5.5 = 5.5\sin\left(\frac{\pi}{6.25}\cdot 14.2333 - \phi\right) \rightarrow -1 = \sin\left(\frac{14.2333\pi}{6.25} - \phi\right)$$

$$-\frac{\pi}{2}=\frac{14.2333\pi}{6.25}-\phi \rightarrow \phi = 8.7252$$

Thus, $y = 5.5\sin\left(\frac{\pi}{6.25}x - 8.7252\right) + 7.7$

(c)

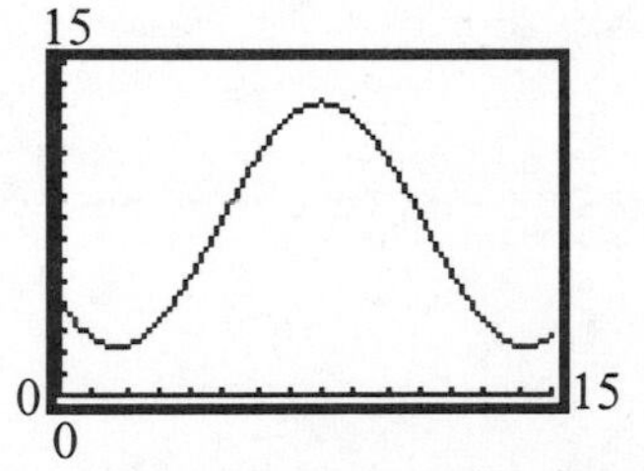

(d) $y = 5.5\sin\left(\frac{\pi}{6.25}(20.6833) - 8.7252\right) + 7.7 = 13.2$ feet

25. (a) Amplitude: $A=\dfrac{12.75-10.583}{2}=\dfrac{2.167}{2}=1.0835$

Vertical Shift: $\dfrac{12.75+10.583}{2}=\dfrac{23.333}{2}=11.6665$

$\omega=\dfrac{2\pi}{365}$

Phase shift (use $y=10.583$, $x=356$):

$$10.583=1.0835\sin\left(\frac{2\pi}{365}\cdot 356-\phi\right)+11.6665$$

$$-1.0835=1.0835\sin\left(\frac{2\pi}{365}\cdot 356-\phi\right)\to -1=\sin\left(\frac{712\pi}{365}-\phi\right)$$

$$-\frac{\pi}{2}=\frac{712\pi}{365}-\phi\to\phi=7.6991$$

Thus, $y=1.0835\sin\left(\frac{2\pi}{365}x-7.6991\right)+11.6665$

(b)

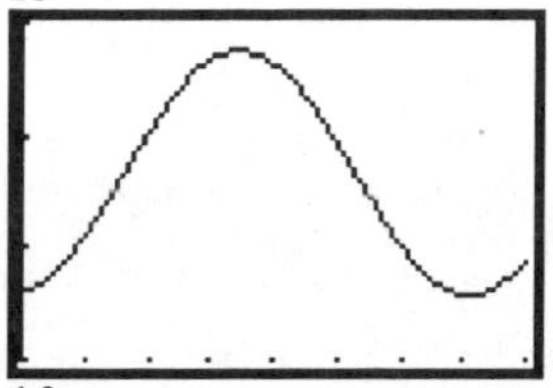

(c) $y=1.0835\sin\left(\frac{2\pi}{365}(92)-7.6991\right)+11.6665=11.85$ hours

26. (a) Amplitude: $A=\dfrac{13.65-9.067}{2}=\dfrac{4.583}{2}=2.2915$

Vertical Shift: $\dfrac{13.65+9.067}{2}=\dfrac{22.717}{2}=11.3585$

$\omega=\dfrac{2\pi}{365}$

Phase shift (use $y=9.067$, $x=356$):

$$9.067=2.2915\sin\left(\frac{2\pi}{365}\cdot 356-\phi\right)+11.3585$$

$$-2.2915=2.2915\sin\left(\frac{2\pi}{365}\cdot 356-\phi\right)\to -1=\sin\left(\frac{712\pi}{365}-\phi\right)$$

$$-\frac{\pi}{2}=\frac{712\pi}{365}-\phi\to\phi=7.6991$$

Thus, $y=2.2915\sin\left(\frac{2\pi}{365}x-7.6991\right)+11.3585$

(b)

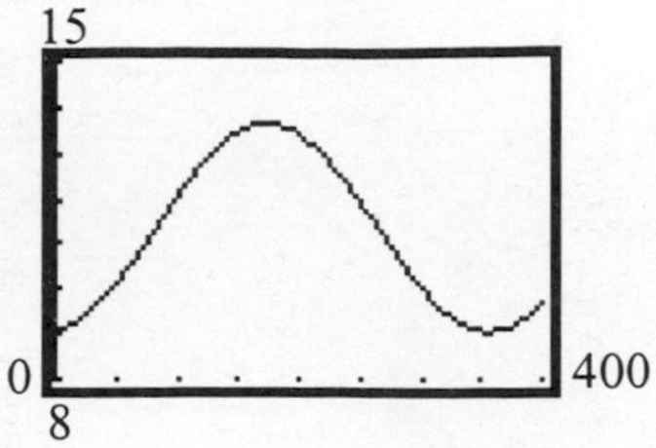

(c) $y = 2.2915\sin\left(\frac{2\pi}{365}(92) - 7.6991\right) + 11.3585 = 11.7$ hours

27. (a) Amplitude: $A = \frac{16.233 - 5.45}{2} = \frac{10.783}{2} = 5.3915$

Vertical Shift: $\frac{16.233 + 5.45}{2} = \frac{21.683}{2} = 10.8415$

$\omega = \frac{2\pi}{365}$

Phase shift (use $y = 5.45$, $x = 356$):

$$5.45 = 5.3915\sin\left(\frac{2\pi}{365}\cdot 356 - \phi\right) + 10.8415$$

$$-5.3915 = 5.3915\sin\left(\frac{2\pi}{365}\cdot 356 - \phi\right) \rightarrow -1 = \sin\left(\frac{712\pi}{365} - \phi\right)$$

$$-\frac{\pi}{2} = \frac{712\pi}{365} - \phi \rightarrow \phi = 7.6991$$

Thus, $y = 5.3915\sin\left(\frac{2\pi}{365}x - 7.6991\right) + 10.8415$

(b)

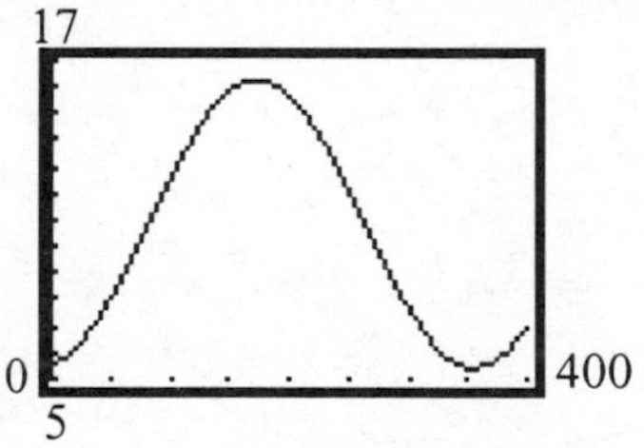

(c) $y = 5.3915\sin\left(\frac{2\pi}{365}(92) - 7.6991\right) + 10.8415 = 11.74$ hours

28. (a) Amplitude: $A = \frac{12.767 - 10.783}{2} = \frac{1.984}{2} = 0.992$

Vertical Shift: $\frac{12.767 + 10.783}{2} = \frac{23.55}{2} = 11.775$

$\omega = \frac{2\pi}{365}$

Phase shift (use $y = 10.783$, $x = 356$):

$$10.783 = 0.992\sin\left(\frac{2\pi}{365}\cdot 356 - \phi\right) + 11.775$$

$$-0.992 = 0.992\sin\left(\frac{2\pi}{365}\cdot 356 - \phi\right)$$

$$-1=\sin\left(\frac{712\pi}{365}-\phi\right)\rightarrow-\frac{\pi}{2}=\frac{712\pi}{365}-\phi\rightarrow\phi=7.6991$$

Thus, $y=0.992\sin\left(\frac{2\pi}{365}x-7.6991\right)+11.775$

(b)

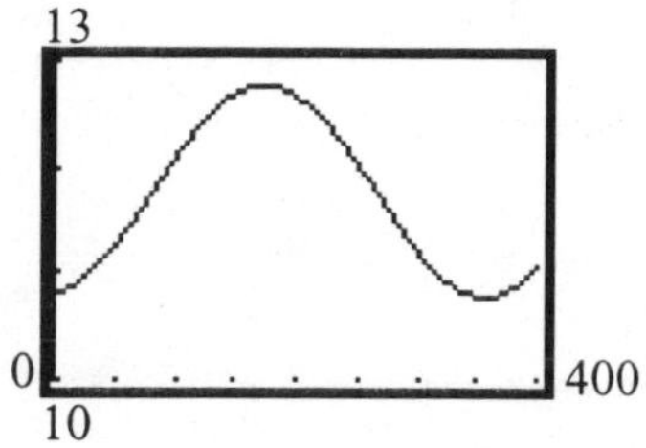

(c) $y=0.992\sin\left(\frac{2\pi}{365}(92)-7.6991\right)+11.775=11.9$ hours

Chapter 7

Trigonometric Functions

7.R Chapter Review

1. $135° = 135 \cdot \frac{\pi}{180}$ radian $= \frac{3\pi}{4}$ radians

2. $210° = 210 \cdot \frac{\pi}{180}$ radian $= \frac{7\pi}{6}$ radians

3. $18° = 18 \cdot \frac{\pi}{180}$ radian $= \frac{\pi}{10}$ radians

4. $15° = 15 \cdot \frac{\pi}{180}$ radian $= \frac{\pi}{12}$ radians

5. $\frac{3\pi}{4} = \frac{3\pi}{4} \cdot \frac{180}{\pi}$ degrees $= 135°$

6. $\frac{2\pi}{3} = \frac{2\pi}{3} \cdot \frac{180}{\pi}$ degrees $= 120°$

7. $-\frac{5\pi}{2} = -\frac{5\pi}{2} \cdot \frac{180}{\pi}$ degrees $= -450°$

8. $-\frac{3\pi}{2} = -\frac{3\pi}{2} \cdot \frac{180}{\pi}$ degrees $= -270°$

9. $\tan\left(\frac{\pi}{4}\right) - \sin\left(\frac{\pi}{6}\right) = 1 - \frac{1}{2} = \frac{1}{2}$

10. $\cos\left(\frac{\pi}{3}\right) + \sin\left(\frac{\pi}{2}\right) = \frac{1}{2} + 1 = \frac{3}{2}$

11. $3\sin(45°) - 4\tan\left(\frac{\pi}{6}\right) = 3 \cdot \frac{\sqrt{2}}{2} - 4 \cdot \frac{\sqrt{3}}{3} = \frac{3\sqrt{2}}{2} - \frac{4\sqrt{3}}{3}$

12. $4\cos(60°) + 3\tan\left(\frac{\pi}{3}\right) = 4 \cdot \frac{1}{2} + 3 \cdot \sqrt{3} = 2 + 3\sqrt{3}$

13. $6\cos\left(\frac{3\pi}{4}\right) + 2\tan\left(-\frac{\pi}{3}\right) = 6\left(-\frac{\sqrt{2}}{2}\right) + 2\left(-\sqrt{3}\right) = -3\sqrt{2} - 2\sqrt{3}$

14. $3\sin\left(\frac{2\pi}{3}\right)-4\cos\left(\frac{5\pi}{2}\right)=3\left(\frac{\sqrt{3}}{2}\right)-4(0)=\frac{3\sqrt{3}}{2}$

15. $\sec\left(-\frac{\pi}{3}\right)-\cot\left(-\frac{5\pi}{4}\right)=\sec\left(\frac{\pi}{3}\right)+\cot\left(\frac{5\pi}{4}\right)=2+1=3$

16. $4\csc\left(\frac{3\pi}{4}\right)-\cot\left(-\frac{\pi}{4}\right)=4\csc\left(\frac{3\pi}{4}\right)+\cot\left(\frac{\pi}{4}\right)=4\sqrt{2}+1$

17. $\tan(\pi)+\sin(\pi)=0+0=0$

18. $\cos\left(\frac{\pi}{2}\right)-\csc\left(-\frac{\pi}{2}\right)=\cos\left(\frac{\pi}{2}\right)+\csc\left(\frac{\pi}{2}\right)=0+1=1$

19. $\cos(180°)-\tan(-45°)=-1-(-1)=-1+1=0$

20. $\sin(270°)+\cos(-180°)=-1+(-1)=-2$

21. $\sin^2(20°)+\frac{1}{\sec^2(20°)}=\sin^2(20°)+\cos^2(20°)=1$

22. $\frac{1}{\cos^2(40°)}-\frac{1}{\cot^2(20°)}=\sec^2(40°)-\tan^2(40°)=1$

23. $\sec(50°)\cos(50°)=\frac{1}{\cos(50°)}\cdot\cos(50°)=1$

24. $\tan(10°)\cot(10°)=\tan(10°)\cdot\frac{1}{\tan(10°)}=1$

25. $\frac{\sin(50°)}{\cos(40°)}=\frac{\cos(40°)}{\cos(40°)}=1$

26. $\frac{\tan(20°)}{\cot(70°)}=\frac{\tan(20°)}{\tan(20°)}=1$

27. $\frac{\sin(-40°)}{\cos(50°)}=\frac{-\sin(40°)}{\cos(50°)}=\frac{-\cos(50°)}{\cos(50°)}=-1$

28. $\tan(-20°)\cot(20°)=-\tan(20°)\cot(20°)=-\tan(20°)\cdot\frac{1}{\cot(20°)}=-1$

29. $\sin(400°)\sec(-50°) = \sin(40°+360°)\sec(50°) = \sin(40°)\csc(40°) = \sin(40°)\cdot\dfrac{1}{\sin(40°)} = 1$

30. $\cot(200°)\cot(-70°) = \cot(20°+180°)(-\cot 70°) = \cot(20°)(-\tan 20°) = \cot(20°)\cdot\dfrac{-1}{\cot(20°)} = -1$

31. $\sin\theta = -\dfrac{4}{5},\ \cos\theta > 0,\ \Rightarrow\ \theta$ in quadrant IV

Solve for $\cos\theta$:

$$\sin^2\theta + \cos^2\theta = 1 \to \cos^2\theta = 1-\sin^2\theta \to \cos\theta = \pm\sqrt{1-\sin^2\theta}$$

Since θ is in quadrant IV, $\cos\theta > 0$.

$$\cos\theta = \sqrt{1-\sin^2\theta} = \sqrt{1-\left(-\frac{4}{5}\right)^2} = \sqrt{1-\frac{16}{25}} = \sqrt{\frac{9}{25}} = \frac{3}{5}$$

$$\tan\theta = \frac{\sin\theta}{\cos\theta} = \frac{\left(-\frac{4}{5}\right)}{\left(\frac{3}{5}\right)} = -\frac{4}{5}\cdot\frac{5}{3} = -\frac{4}{3} \qquad \sec\theta = \frac{1}{\cos\theta} = \frac{1}{\left(\frac{3}{5}\right)} = \frac{5}{3}$$

$$\csc\theta = \frac{1}{\sin\theta} = \frac{1}{\left(-\frac{4}{5}\right)} = -\frac{5}{4} \qquad \cot\theta = \frac{1}{\tan\theta} = \frac{1}{\left(-\frac{4}{3}\right)} = -\frac{3}{4}$$

32. $\cos\theta = -\dfrac{3}{5},\ \sin\theta < 0,\ \Rightarrow\ \theta$ in quadrant III

Solve for $\sin\theta$:

$$\sin^2\theta + \cos^2\theta = 1 \to \sin^2\theta = 1-\cos^2\theta \to \sin\theta = \pm\sqrt{1-\cos^2\theta}$$

$$\sin\theta = -\sqrt{1-\cos^2\theta} = -\sqrt{1-\left(-\frac{3}{5}\right)^2} = -\sqrt{1-\frac{9}{25}} = -\sqrt{\frac{16}{25}} = -\frac{4}{5}$$

$$\tan\theta = \frac{\sin\theta}{\cos\theta} = \frac{\left(-\frac{4}{5}\right)}{\left(-\frac{3}{5}\right)} = -\frac{4}{5}\cdot -\frac{5}{3} = \frac{4}{3} \qquad \sec\theta = \frac{1}{\cos\theta} = \frac{1}{\left(-\frac{3}{5}\right)} = -\frac{5}{3}$$

$$\csc\theta = \frac{1}{\sin\theta} = \frac{1}{\left(-\frac{4}{5}\right)} = -\frac{5}{4} \qquad \cot\theta = \frac{1}{\tan\theta} = \frac{1}{\left(\frac{4}{3}\right)} = \frac{3}{4}$$

33. $\tan\theta = \dfrac{12}{5},\ \sin\theta < 0,\ \Rightarrow\ \theta$ in quadrant III

Solve for $\sec\theta$:

$$\sec^2\theta = 1+\tan^2\theta \to \sec\theta = \pm\sqrt{1+\tan^2\theta}$$

Since θ is in quadrant III, $\sec\theta < 0$.

$$\sec\theta = -\sqrt{1+\tan^2\theta} = -\sqrt{1+\left(\frac{12}{5}\right)^2} = -\sqrt{1+\frac{144}{25}} = -\sqrt{\frac{169}{25}} = -\frac{13}{5}$$

$$\cos\theta = -\frac{5}{13}$$

$$\sin\theta = -\sqrt{1-\cos^2\theta} = -\sqrt{1-\left(-\frac{5}{13}\right)^2} = -\sqrt{1-\frac{25}{169}} = -\sqrt{\frac{144}{169}} = -\frac{12}{13}$$

$$\csc\theta = \frac{1}{\sin\theta} = \frac{1}{\left(-\frac{12}{13}\right)} = -\frac{13}{12} \qquad \cot\theta = \frac{1}{\tan\theta} = \frac{1}{\left(\frac{12}{5}\right)} = \frac{5}{12}$$

34. $\cot\theta = \frac{12}{5}$, $\cos\theta < 0$, $\Rightarrow$ θ in quadrant III

Solve for $\csc\theta$:

$$\csc^2\theta = 1+\cot^2\theta \rightarrow \csc\theta = \pm\sqrt{1+\cot^2\theta}$$

Since θ is in quadrant III, $\csc\theta < 0$.

$$\csc\theta = -\sqrt{1+\cot^2\theta} = -\sqrt{1+\left(\frac{12}{5}\right)^2} = -\sqrt{1+\frac{144}{25}} = -\sqrt{\frac{169}{25}} = -\frac{13}{5}$$

$$\sin\theta = -\frac{5}{13}$$

$$\cos\theta = -\sqrt{1-\sin^2\theta} = -\sqrt{1-\left(-\frac{5}{13}\right)^2} = -\sqrt{1-\frac{25}{169}} = -\sqrt{\frac{144}{169}} = -\frac{12}{13}$$

$$\sec\theta = \frac{1}{\cos\theta} = \frac{1}{\left(-\frac{12}{13}\right)} = -\frac{13}{12} \qquad \tan\theta = \frac{1}{\cot\theta} = \frac{1}{\left(\frac{12}{5}\right)} = \frac{5}{12}$$

35. $\sec\theta = -\frac{5}{4}$, $\tan\theta < 0$, $\Rightarrow$ θ in quadrant II

Solve for $\cos\theta$:

$$\cos\theta = \frac{1}{\sec\theta} = \frac{1}{\left(-\frac{5}{4}\right)} = -\frac{4}{5}$$

Solve for $\sin\theta$:

$$\sin^2\theta + \cos^2\theta = 1 \rightarrow \sin^2\theta = 1-\cos^2\theta \rightarrow \sin\theta = \pm\sqrt{1-\cos^2\theta}$$

Since θ is in quadrant II, $\sin\theta > 0$.

$$\sin\theta = \sqrt{1-\cos^2\theta} = \sqrt{1-\left(-\frac{4}{5}\right)^2} = \sqrt{1-\frac{16}{25}} = \sqrt{\frac{9}{25}} = \frac{3}{5}$$

$$\tan\theta = \frac{\sin\theta}{\cos\theta} = \frac{\left(\frac{3}{5}\right)}{\left(-\frac{4}{5}\right)} = \frac{3}{5}\cdot -\frac{5}{4} = -\frac{3}{4}$$

$\csc\theta = \dfrac{1}{\sin\theta} = \dfrac{1}{\left(\frac{3}{5}\right)} = \dfrac{5}{3}$ $\cot\theta = \dfrac{1}{\tan\theta} = \dfrac{1}{\left(-\frac{3}{4}\right)} = -\dfrac{4}{3}$

36. $\csc\theta = -\dfrac{5}{3}, \quad \cot\theta < 0, \quad \Rightarrow \quad \theta$ in quadrant IV

$\sin\theta = \dfrac{1}{\csc\theta} = \dfrac{1}{\left(-\frac{5}{3}\right)} = -\dfrac{3}{5}$

Solve for $\cos\theta$:

$$\sin^2\theta + \cos^2\theta = 1 \rightarrow \cos^2\theta = 1 - \sin^2\theta \rightarrow \cos\theta = \pm\sqrt{1-\sin^2\theta}$$

Since θ is in quadrant IV, $\cos\theta > 0$.

$\cos\theta = \sqrt{1-\sin^2\theta} = \sqrt{1-\left(-\frac{3}{5}\right)^2} = \sqrt{1-\frac{9}{25}} = \sqrt{\frac{16}{25}} = \frac{4}{5}$

$\sec\theta = \dfrac{1}{\cos\theta} = \dfrac{1}{\left(\frac{4}{5}\right)} = \dfrac{5}{4}$

$\tan\theta = \dfrac{\sin\theta}{\cos\theta} = \dfrac{\left(-\frac{3}{5}\right)}{\left(\frac{4}{5}\right)} = -\dfrac{3}{5}\cdot\dfrac{5}{4} = -\dfrac{3}{4}$ $\cot\theta = \dfrac{1}{\tan\theta} = \dfrac{1}{\left(-\frac{3}{4}\right)} = -\dfrac{4}{3}$

37. $\sin\theta = \dfrac{12}{13}, \quad \theta$ in quadrant II

Solve for $\cos\theta$:

$$\sin^2\theta + \cos^2\theta = 1 \rightarrow \cos^2\theta = 1 - \sin^2\theta \rightarrow \cos\theta = \pm\sqrt{1-\sin^2\theta}$$

Since θ is in quadrant II, $\cos\theta < 0$.

$\cos\theta = -\sqrt{1-\sin^2\theta} = -\sqrt{1-\left(\frac{12}{13}\right)^2} = -\sqrt{1-\frac{144}{169}} = -\sqrt{\frac{25}{169}} = -\frac{5}{13}$

$\tan\theta = \dfrac{\sin\theta}{\cos\theta} = \dfrac{\left(\frac{12}{13}\right)}{\left(-\frac{5}{13}\right)} = \dfrac{12}{13}\cdot -\dfrac{13}{5} = -\dfrac{12}{5}$ $\sec\theta = \dfrac{1}{\cos\theta} = \dfrac{1}{\left(-\frac{5}{13}\right)} = -\dfrac{13}{5}$

$\csc\theta = \dfrac{1}{\sin\theta} = \dfrac{1}{\left(\frac{12}{13}\right)} = \dfrac{13}{12}$ $\cot\theta = \dfrac{1}{\tan\theta} = \dfrac{1}{\left(-\frac{12}{5}\right)} = -\dfrac{5}{12}$

38. $\cos\theta = -\frac{3}{5}$, θ in quadrant III

Solve for $\sin\theta$:

$$\sin^2\theta + \cos^2\theta = 1 \rightarrow \sin^2\theta = 1 - \cos^2\theta \rightarrow \sin\theta = \pm\sqrt{1-\cos^2\theta}$$

Since θ is in quadrant III, $\sin\theta < 0$.

$$\sin\theta = -\sqrt{1-\cos^2\theta} = -\sqrt{1-\left(-\frac{3}{5}\right)^2} = -\sqrt{1-\frac{9}{25}} = -\sqrt{\frac{16}{25}} = -\frac{4}{5}$$

$$\tan\theta = \frac{\sin\theta}{\cos\theta} = \frac{\left(-\frac{4}{5}\right)}{\left(-\frac{3}{5}\right)} = -\frac{4}{5}\cdot -\frac{5}{3} = \frac{4}{3}$$

$$\sec\theta = \frac{1}{\cos\theta} = \frac{1}{\left(-\frac{3}{5}\right)} = -\frac{5}{3}$$

$$\csc\theta = \frac{1}{\sin\theta} = \frac{1}{\left(-\frac{4}{5}\right)} = -\frac{5}{4}$$

$$\cot\theta = \frac{1}{\tan\theta} = \frac{1}{\left(\frac{4}{3}\right)} = \frac{3}{4}$$

39. $\sin\theta = -\frac{5}{13}$, $\frac{3\pi}{2} < \theta < 2\pi$, $\Rightarrow \theta$ in quadrant IV

Solve for $\cos\theta$:

$$\sin^2\theta + \cos^2\theta = 1 \rightarrow \cos^2\theta = 1 - \sin^2\theta \rightarrow \cos\theta = \pm\sqrt{1-\sin^2\theta}$$

Since θ is in quadrant IV, $\cos\theta > 0$.

$$\cos\theta = \sqrt{1-\sin^2\theta} = \sqrt{1-\left(-\frac{5}{13}\right)^2} = \sqrt{1-\frac{25}{169}} = \sqrt{\frac{144}{169}} = \frac{12}{13}$$

$$\tan\theta = \frac{\sin\theta}{\cos\theta} = \frac{\left(-\frac{5}{13}\right)}{\left(\frac{12}{13}\right)} = -\frac{5}{13}\cdot\frac{13}{12} = -\frac{5}{12}$$

$$\sec\theta = \frac{1}{\cos\theta} = \frac{1}{\left(\frac{12}{13}\right)} = \frac{13}{12}$$

$$\csc\theta = \frac{1}{\sin\theta} = \frac{1}{\left(-\frac{5}{13}\right)} = -\frac{13}{5}$$

$$\cot\theta = \frac{1}{\tan\theta} = \frac{1}{\left(-\frac{5}{12}\right)} = -\frac{12}{5}$$

40. $\cos\theta = \frac{12}{13}$, $\frac{3\pi}{2} < \theta < 2\pi$, $\Rightarrow \theta$ in quadrant IV

Solve for $\sin\theta$:

$$\sin^2\theta + \cos^2\theta = 1 \rightarrow \sin^2\theta = 1 - \cos^2\theta \rightarrow \sin\theta = \pm\sqrt{1-\cos^2\theta}$$

Since θ is in quadrant IV, $\sin\theta < 0$.

$$\sin\theta = -\sqrt{1-\cos^2\theta} = -\sqrt{1-\left(\frac{12}{13}\right)^2} = -\sqrt{1-\frac{144}{169}} = -\sqrt{\frac{25}{169}} = -\frac{5}{13}$$

$$\tan\theta=\frac{\sin\theta}{\cos\theta}=\frac{\left(-\frac{5}{13}\right)}{\left(\frac{12}{13}\right)}=-\frac{5}{13}\cdot\frac{13}{12}=-\frac{5}{12}\qquad \sec\theta=\frac{1}{\cos\theta}=\frac{1}{\left(\frac{12}{13}\right)}=\frac{13}{12}$$

$$\csc\theta=\frac{1}{\sin\theta}=\frac{1}{\left(-\frac{5}{13}\right)}=-\frac{13}{5}\qquad \cot\theta=\frac{1}{\tan\theta}=\frac{1}{\left(-\frac{5}{12}\right)}=-\frac{12}{5}$$

41. $\tan\theta=\frac{1}{3},\ 180^\circ<\theta<270^\circ,\ \Rightarrow\ \theta$ in quadrant III

Solve for $\sec\theta$:

$$\sec^2\theta=1+\tan^2\theta\rightarrow\sec\theta=\pm\sqrt{1+\tan^2\theta}$$

Since θ is in quadrant III, $\sec\theta<0$.

$$\sec\theta=-\sqrt{1+\tan^2\theta}=-\sqrt{1+\left(\frac{1}{3}\right)^2}=-\sqrt{1+\frac{1}{9}}=-\sqrt{\frac{10}{9}}=-\frac{\sqrt{10}}{3}$$

$$\cos\theta=\frac{1}{\sec\theta}=\frac{1}{\left(-\frac{\sqrt{10}}{3}\right)}=-\frac{3}{\sqrt{10}}\cdot\frac{\sqrt{10}}{\sqrt{10}}=-\frac{3\sqrt{10}}{10}$$

$$\sin\theta=-\sqrt{1-\cos^2\theta}=-\sqrt{1-\left(-\frac{3\sqrt{10}}{3}\right)^2}=-\sqrt{1-\frac{90}{100}}=-\sqrt{\frac{10}{100}}=-\frac{\sqrt{10}}{10}$$

$$\csc\theta=\frac{1}{\sin\theta}=\frac{1}{\left(-\frac{\sqrt{10}}{10}\right)}=-\frac{10}{\sqrt{10}}=-\sqrt{10}\qquad \cot\theta=\frac{1}{\tan\theta}=\frac{1}{\left(\frac{1}{3}\right)}=3$$

42. $\tan\theta=-\frac{2}{3},\ 90^\circ<\theta<180^\circ,\ \Rightarrow\ \theta$ in quadrant II

Solve for $\sec\theta$:

$$\sec^2\theta=1+\tan^2\theta\ \rightarrow\ \sec\theta=\pm\sqrt{1+\tan^2\theta}$$

Since θ is in quadrant II, $\sec\theta<0$.

$$\sec\theta=-\sqrt{1+\tan^2\theta}=-\sqrt{1+\left(-\frac{2}{3}\right)^2}=-\sqrt{1+\frac{4}{9}}=-\sqrt{\frac{13}{9}}=-\frac{\sqrt{13}}{3}$$

$$\cos\theta=\frac{1}{\sec\theta}=\frac{1}{\left(-\frac{\sqrt{13}}{3}\right)}=-\frac{3}{\sqrt{13}}\cdot\frac{\sqrt{13}}{\sqrt{13}}=-\frac{3\sqrt{13}}{13}$$

$$\sin\theta=\sqrt{1-\cos^2\theta}=\sqrt{1-\left(-\frac{3\sqrt{13}}{13}\right)^2}=\sqrt{1-\frac{117}{169}}=\sqrt{\frac{52}{169}}=\frac{2\sqrt{13}}{13}$$

$$\csc\theta=\frac{1}{\sin\theta}=\frac{1}{\left(\frac{2\sqrt{13}}{13}\right)}=\frac{13}{2\sqrt{13}}=\frac{\sqrt{13}}{2}\qquad \cot\theta=\frac{1}{\tan\theta}=\frac{1}{\left(-\frac{2}{3}\right)}=-\frac{3}{2}$$

43. $\sec\theta = 3,\ \dfrac{3\pi}{2} < \theta < 2\pi,\ \Rightarrow\ \theta$ in quadrant IV

$\cos\theta = \dfrac{1}{\sec\theta} = \dfrac{1}{3}$

Solve for $\sin\theta$:

$$\sin^2\theta + \cos^2\theta = 1 \ \rightarrow\ \sin^2\theta = 1 - \cos^2\theta \ \rightarrow\ \sin\theta = \pm\sqrt{1-\cos^2\theta}$$

Since θ is in quadrant IV, $\sin\theta < 0$.

$$\sin\theta = -\sqrt{1-\cos^2\theta} = -\sqrt{1-\left(\frac{1}{3}\right)^2} = -\sqrt{1-\frac{1}{9}} = -\sqrt{\frac{8}{9}} = -\frac{2\sqrt{2}}{3}$$

$$\tan\theta = \frac{\sin\theta}{\cos\theta} = \frac{\left(-\frac{2\sqrt{2}}{3}\right)}{\left(\frac{1}{3}\right)} = -\frac{2\sqrt{2}}{3}\cdot\frac{3}{1} = -2\sqrt{2}$$

$$\csc\theta = \frac{1}{\sin\theta} = \frac{1}{\left(-\frac{2\sqrt{2}}{3}\right)} = -\frac{3}{2\sqrt{2}} = -\frac{3\sqrt{2}}{4} \qquad \cot\theta = \frac{1}{\tan\theta} = \frac{1}{-2\sqrt{2}} = -\frac{\sqrt{2}}{4}$$

44. $\csc\theta = -4,\ \pi < \theta < \dfrac{3\pi}{2},\ \Rightarrow\ \theta$ in quadrant III

$\sin\theta = \dfrac{1}{\csc\theta} = \dfrac{1}{-4} = -\dfrac{1}{4}$

Solve for $\cos\theta$:

$$\sin^2\theta + \cos^2\theta = 1 \ \rightarrow\ \cos^2\theta = 1 - \sin^2\theta \ \rightarrow\ \cos\theta = \pm\sqrt{1-\sin^2\theta}$$

Since θ is in quadrant III, $\cos\theta < 0$.

$$\cos\theta = -\sqrt{1-\sin^2\theta} = -\sqrt{1-\left(-\frac{1}{4}\right)^2} = -\sqrt{1-\frac{1}{16}} = -\sqrt{\frac{15}{16}} = -\frac{\sqrt{15}}{4}$$

$$\sec\theta = \frac{1}{\cos\theta} = \frac{1}{\left(-\frac{\sqrt{15}}{4}\right)} = -\frac{4}{\sqrt{15}}\cdot\frac{\sqrt{15}}{\sqrt{15}} = -\frac{4\sqrt{15}}{15}$$

$$\tan\theta = \frac{\sin\theta}{\cos\theta} = \frac{\left(-\frac{1}{4}\right)}{\left(-\frac{\sqrt{15}}{4}\right)} = -\frac{1}{4}\cdot-\frac{4}{\sqrt{15}}\cdot\frac{\sqrt{15}}{\sqrt{15}} = \frac{\sqrt{15}}{15}$$

$$\cot\theta = \frac{1}{\tan\theta} = \frac{1}{\left(\frac{\sqrt{15}}{5}\right)} = \frac{15}{\sqrt{15}} = \sqrt{15}$$

45. $\cot\theta = -2,\ \frac{\pi}{2} < \theta < \pi,\ \Rightarrow\ \theta$ in quadrant II

$\tan\theta = \frac{1}{\cot\theta} = \frac{1}{-2} = -\frac{1}{2}$

Solve for $\sec\theta$:

$$\sec^2\theta = 1 + \tan^2\theta \rightarrow \sec\theta = \pm\sqrt{1+\tan^2\theta}$$

Since θ is in quadrant II, $\sec\theta < 0$.

$$\sec\theta = -\sqrt{1+\tan^2\theta} = -\sqrt{1+\left(-\frac{1}{2}\right)^2} = -\sqrt{1+\frac{1}{4}} = -\sqrt{\frac{5}{4}} = -\frac{\sqrt{5}}{2}$$

$$\cos\theta = \frac{1}{\sec\theta} = \frac{1}{\left(-\frac{\sqrt{5}}{2}\right)} = -\frac{2}{\sqrt{5}}\cdot\frac{\sqrt{5}}{\sqrt{5}} = -\frac{2\sqrt{5}}{5}$$

$$\sin\theta = \sqrt{1-\cos^2\theta} = \sqrt{1-\left(-\frac{2\sqrt{5}}{2}\right)^2} = \sqrt{1-\frac{20}{25}} = \sqrt{\frac{5}{25}} = \frac{\sqrt{5}}{5}$$

$$\csc\theta = \frac{1}{\sin\theta} = \frac{1}{\left(\frac{\sqrt{5}}{5}\right)} = \frac{5}{\sqrt{5}} = \sqrt{5}$$

46. $\tan\theta = -2,\ \frac{3\pi}{2} < \theta < 2\pi,\ \Rightarrow\ \theta$ in quadrant IV

$\cot\theta = \frac{1}{\tan\theta} = \frac{1}{-2} = -\frac{1}{2}$

Solve for $\sec\theta$:

$$\sec^2\theta = 1 + \tan^2\theta \rightarrow \sec\theta = \pm\sqrt{1+\tan^2\theta}$$

Since θ is in quadrant IV, $\sec\theta > 0$.

$$\sec\theta = \sqrt{1+\tan^2\theta} = \sqrt{1+(-2)^2} = \sqrt{1+4} = \sqrt{5}$$

$$\cos\theta = \frac{1}{\sec\theta} = \frac{1}{\sqrt{5}} = \frac{\sqrt{5}}{5}$$

$$\sin\theta = -\sqrt{1-\cos^2\theta} = -\sqrt{1-\left(\frac{\sqrt{5}}{5}\right)^2} = -\sqrt{1-\frac{5}{25}} = -\sqrt{\frac{20}{25}} = -\frac{2\sqrt{5}}{5}$$

$$\csc\theta = \frac{1}{\sin\theta} = \frac{1}{\left(-\frac{2\sqrt{5}}{5}\right)} = -\frac{5}{2\sqrt{5}} = -\frac{\sqrt{5}}{2}$$

47. $y = 2\sin(4x)$

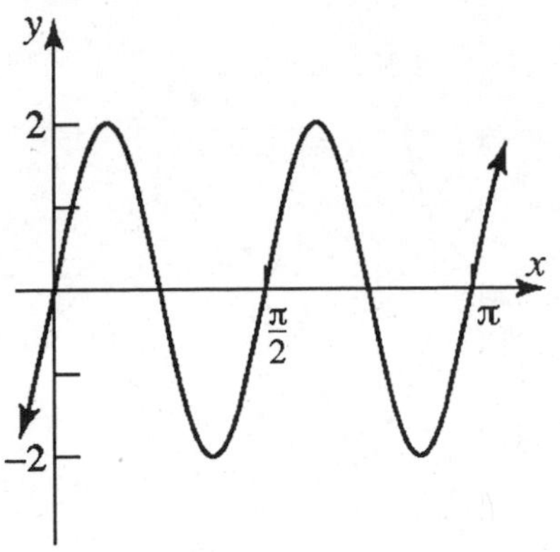

48. $y = -3\cos(2x)$

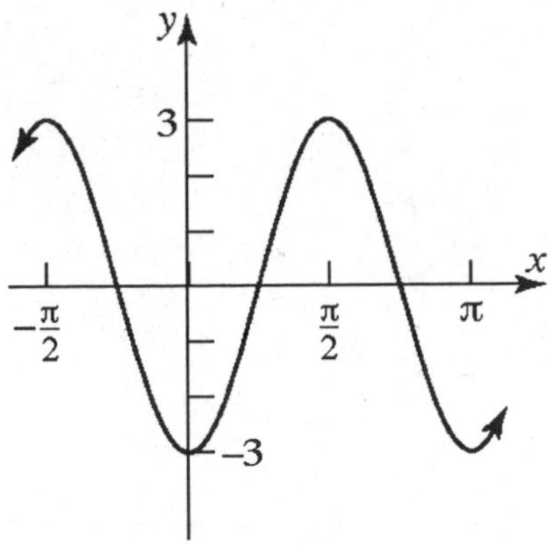

49. $y = -2\cos\left(x + \frac{\pi}{2}\right)$

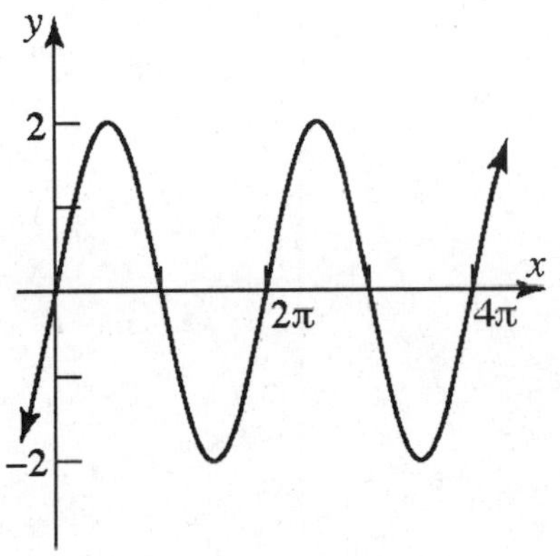

50. $y = 3\sin(x - \pi)$

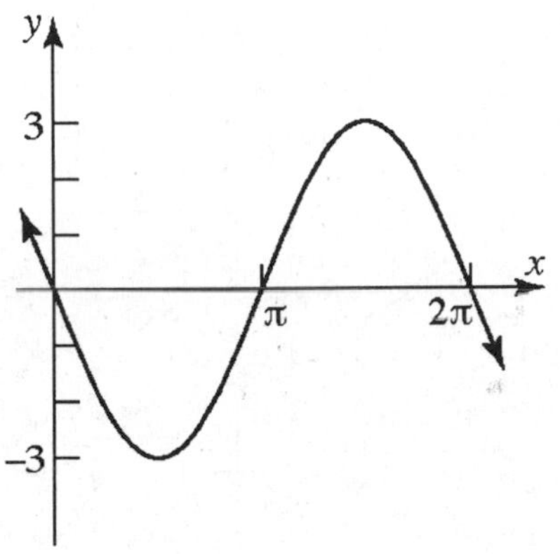

51. $y = \tan(x + \pi)$

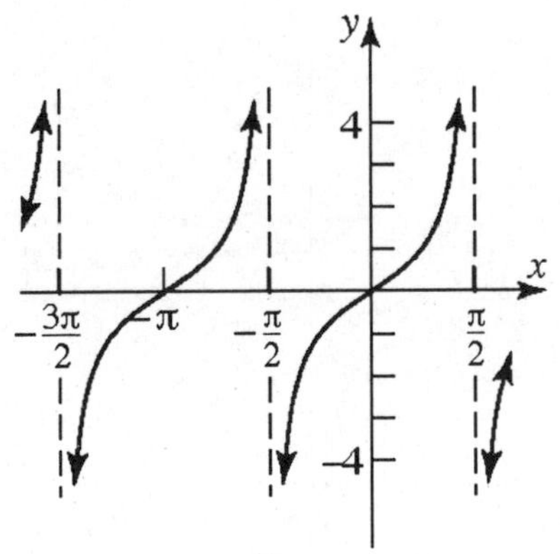

52. $y = -\tan\left(x - \frac{\pi}{2}\right)$

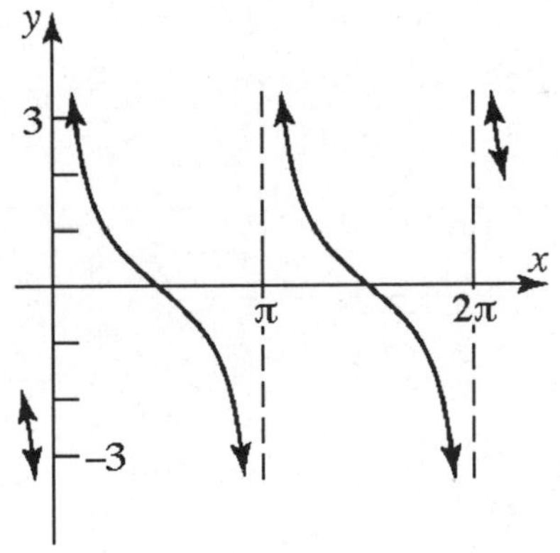

53. $y=-2\tan(3x)$

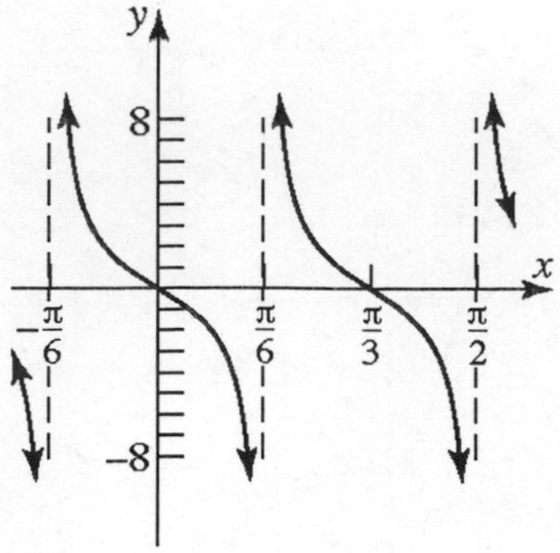

54. $y=4\tan(2x)$

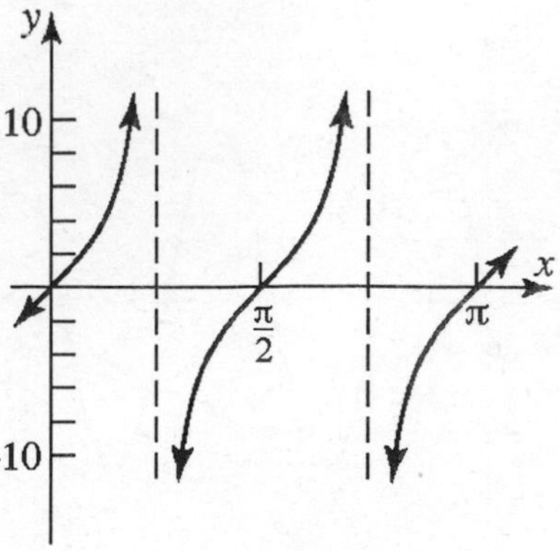

55. $y=\cot\left(x+\dfrac{\pi}{4}\right)$

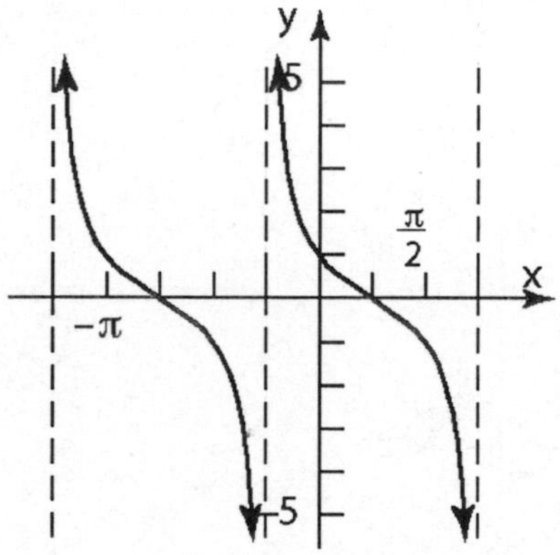

56. $y=-4\cot(2x)$

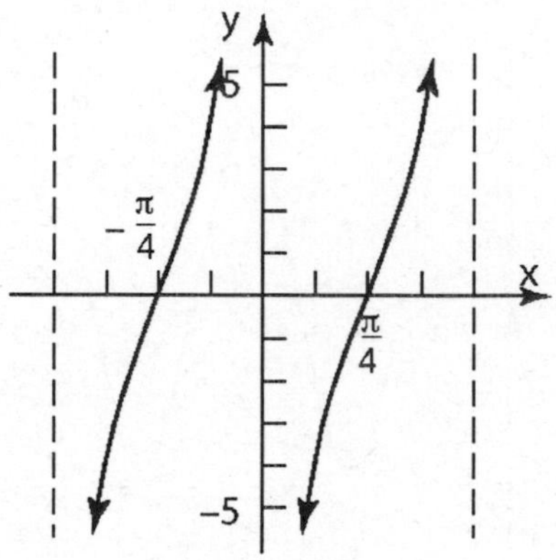

57. $y=\sec\left(x-\dfrac{\pi}{4}\right)$

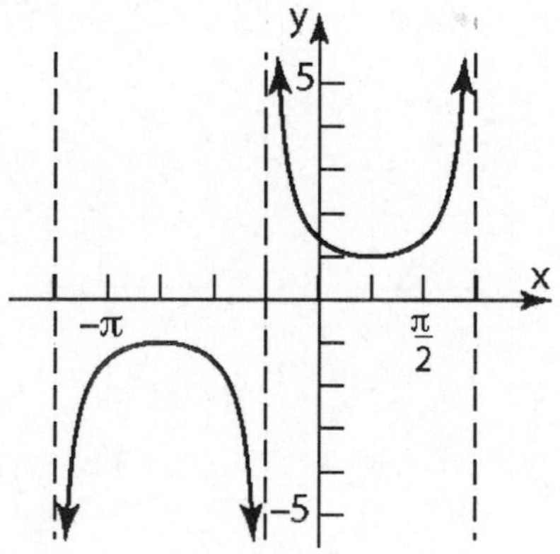

58. $y=\csc\left(x+\dfrac{\pi}{4}\right)$

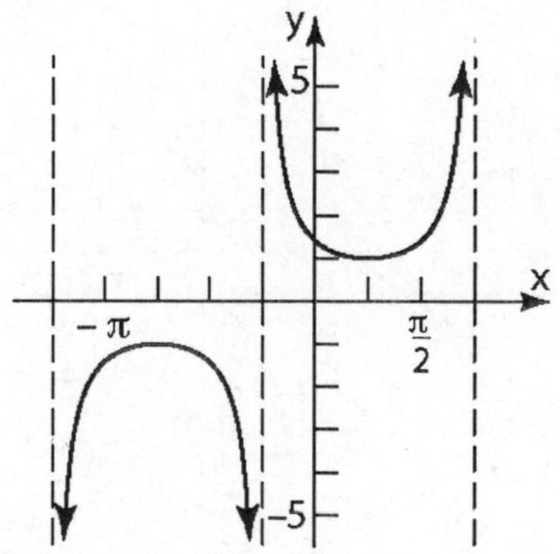

59. $y=4\cos x$
Amplitude = 4
Period = 2π

60. $y=\sin(2x)$
Amplitude = 1
Period = π

61. $y = -8\sin\left(\frac{\pi}{2}x\right)$

Amplitude = 8

Period = 4

62. $y = -2\cos(3\pi x)$

Amplitude = 2

Period = $\frac{2}{3}$

63. $y = 4\sin(3x)$

Amplitude: $|A| = |4| = 4$

Period: $T = \frac{2\pi}{\omega} = \frac{2\pi}{3}$

Phase Shift: $\frac{\phi}{\omega} = \frac{0}{3} = 0$

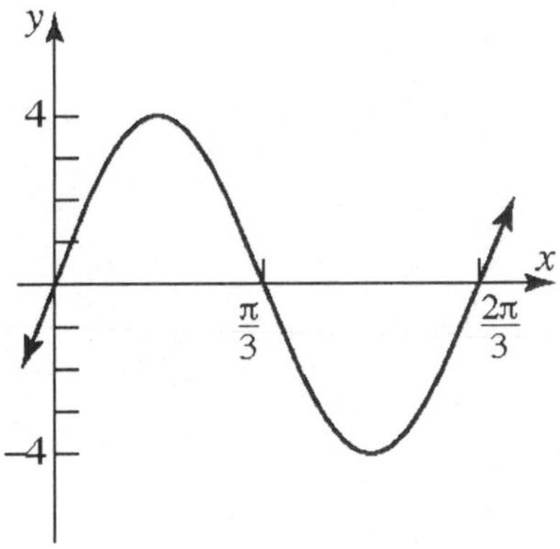

64. $y = 2\cos\left(\frac{1}{3}x\right)$

Amplitude: $|A| = |2| = 2$

Period: $T = \frac{2\pi}{\omega} = \frac{2\pi}{\left(\frac{1}{3}\right)} = 6\pi$

Phase Shift: $\frac{\phi}{\omega} = \frac{0}{\left(\frac{1}{3}\right)} = 0$

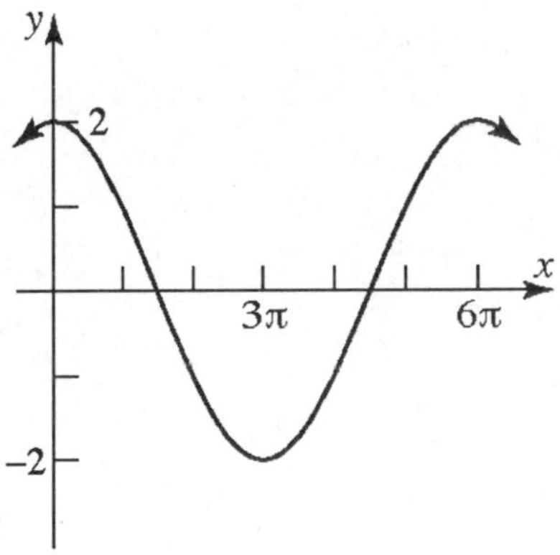

65. $y = 2\sin(2x - \pi)$

Amplitude: $|A| = |2| = 2$

Period: $T = \frac{2\pi}{\omega} = \frac{2\pi}{2} = \pi$

Phase Shift: $\frac{\phi}{\omega} = \frac{-\pi}{2} = -\frac{\pi}{2}$

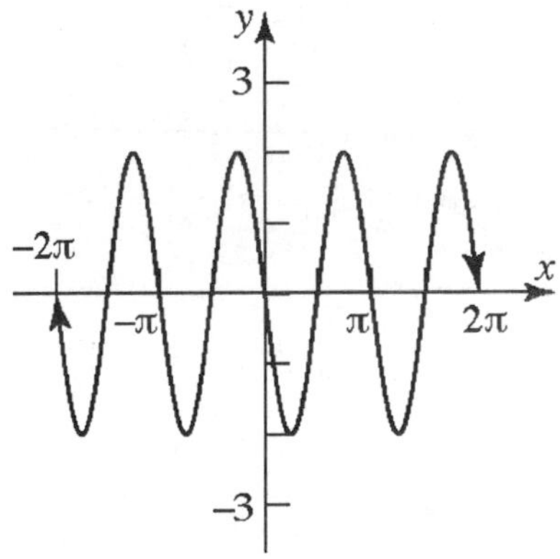

66. $y = -\cos\left(\frac{1}{2}x + \frac{\pi}{2}\right)$

Amplitude: $|A| = |-1| = 1$

Period: $T = \frac{2\pi}{\omega} = \frac{2\pi}{\left(\frac{1}{2}\right)} = 4\pi$

Phase Shift: $\frac{\phi}{\omega} = \frac{\left(-\frac{\pi}{2}\right)}{\left(\frac{1}{2}\right)} = -\pi$

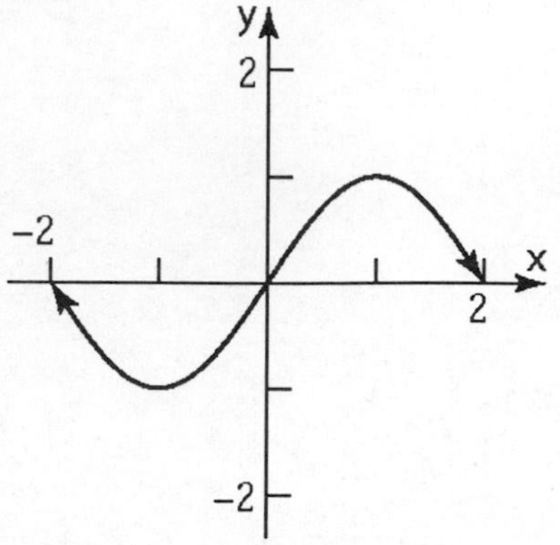

67. $y = \frac{1}{2}\sin\left(\frac{3}{2}x - \pi\right)$

Amplitude: $|A| = \left|\frac{1}{2}\right| = \frac{1}{2}$

Period: $T = \frac{2\pi}{\omega} = \frac{2\pi}{\left(\frac{3}{2}\right)} = \frac{4\pi}{3}$

Phase Shift: $\frac{\phi}{\omega} = \frac{\pi}{\left(\frac{3}{2}\right)} = \frac{2\pi}{3}$

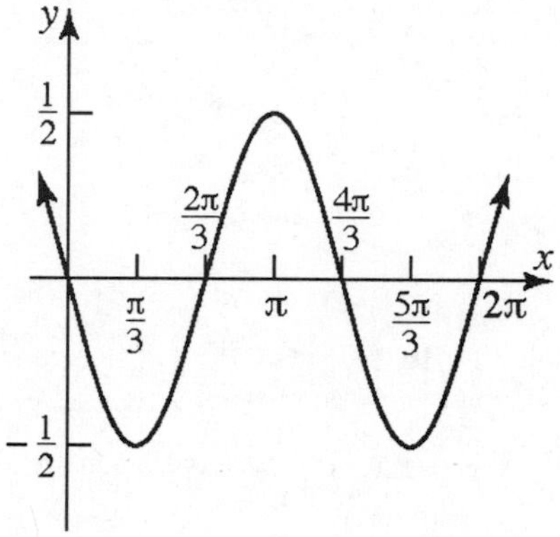

68. $y = \frac{3}{2}\cos(6x + 3\pi)$

Amplitude: $|A| = \left|\frac{3}{2}\right| = \frac{3}{2}$

Period: $T = \frac{2\pi}{\omega} = \frac{2\pi}{6} = \frac{\pi}{3}$

Phase Shift: $\frac{\phi}{\omega} = \frac{-3\pi}{6} = -\frac{\pi}{2}$

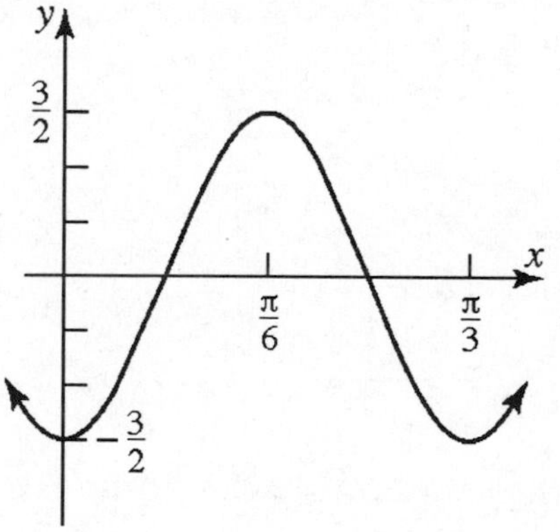

69. $y = -\frac{2}{3}\cos(\pi x - 6)$

Amplitude: $|A| = \left|-\frac{2}{3}\right| = \frac{2}{3}$

Period: $T = \frac{2\pi}{\omega} = \frac{2\pi}{\pi} = 2$

Phase Shift: $\frac{\phi}{\omega} = \frac{6}{\pi}$

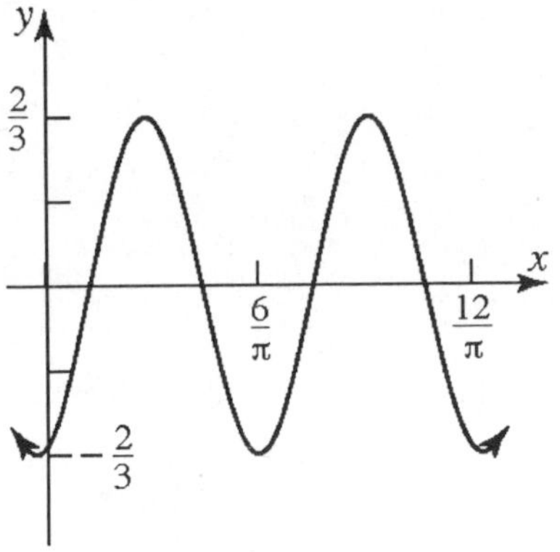

70. $y = -7\sin\left(\frac{\pi}{3}x + \frac{4}{3}\right)$

Amplitude: $|A| = |-7| = 7$

Period: $T = \frac{2\pi}{\omega} = \frac{2\pi}{\left(\frac{\pi}{3}\right)} = 6$

Phase Shift: $\frac{\phi}{\omega} = \frac{\left(-\frac{4}{3}\right)}{\left(\frac{\pi}{3}\right)} = -\frac{4}{\pi}$

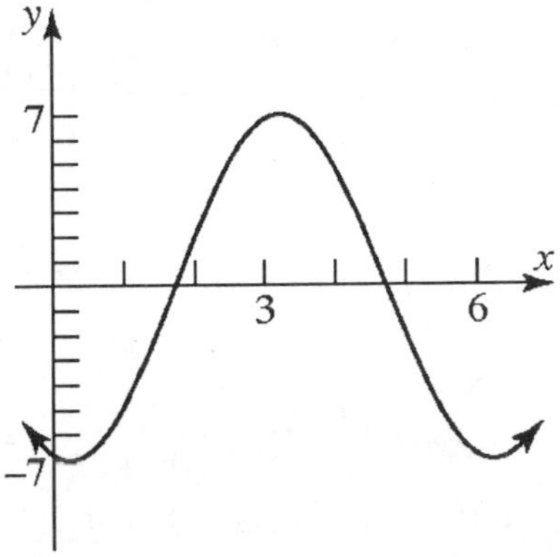

71. The graph is a cosine graph with an amplitude of 5 and a period of 8π. Find ω:

$$8\pi = \frac{2\pi}{\omega} \rightarrow 8\pi\omega = 2\pi \rightarrow \omega = \frac{2\pi}{8\pi} = \frac{1}{4}$$

The equation is: $y = 5\cos\left(\frac{1}{4}x\right)$.

72. The graph is a sine graph with an amplitude of 4 and a period of 8π. Find ω:

$$8\pi = \frac{2\pi}{\omega} \rightarrow 8\pi\omega = 2\pi \rightarrow \omega = \frac{2\pi}{8\pi} = \frac{1}{4}$$

The equation is: $y = 4\sin\left(\frac{1}{4}x\right)$.

73. The graph is a reflected cosine graph with an amplitude of 6 and a period of 8. Find ω:

$$8 = \frac{2\pi}{\omega} \rightarrow 8\omega = 2\pi \rightarrow \omega = \frac{2\pi}{8} = \frac{\pi}{4}$$

The equation is: $y = -6\cos\left(\frac{\pi}{4}x\right)$.

74. The graph is a reflected sine graph with an amplitude of 7 and a period of 8. Find ω:

$$8 = \frac{2\pi}{\omega} \rightarrow 8\omega = 2\pi \rightarrow \omega = \frac{2\pi}{8} = \frac{\pi}{4}$$

The equation is: $y = -7\sin\left(\frac{\pi}{4}x\right)$.

75. $r = 2$ feet, $\theta = 30°$ or $\theta = \frac{\pi}{6}$

$$s = r\theta = 2 \cdot \frac{\pi}{6} = \frac{\pi}{3} \text{ feet}$$

$$A = \frac{1}{2} \cdot r^2\theta = \frac{1}{2} \cdot (2)^2 \cdot \frac{\pi}{6} = \frac{\pi}{3} \text{ square feet}$$

76. $r = 8$ inches, $\theta = 180°$ or $\theta = \pi$

$$s = r\theta = 8 \cdot \pi = 8\pi \text{ inches in 30 minutes}$$

$r = 8$ inches, $\theta = 120°$ or $\theta = \frac{2\pi}{3}$

$$s = r\theta = 8 \cdot \frac{2\pi}{3} = \frac{16\pi}{3} \text{ inches in 20 minutes}$$

77. $v = 180$ mi/hr, $d = \frac{1}{2}$ mile $\rightarrow r = \frac{1}{4} = 0.25$ mile

$$\omega = \frac{v}{r} = \frac{180 \text{ mi/hr}}{0.25 \text{ mi}} = 720 \text{ rad/hr} = \frac{720 \text{ rad}}{\text{hr}} \cdot \frac{1 \text{ rev}}{2\pi \text{ rad}} = \frac{360 \text{ rev}}{\pi \text{ hr}} \approx 114.6 \text{ rev/hr}$$

78. $r = 25$ feet; $\omega = \frac{1 \text{ rev}}{30 \text{ sec}} = \frac{1 \text{ rev}}{30 \text{ sec}} \cdot \frac{2\pi \text{ radians}}{1 \text{ rev}} = \frac{\pi}{15} \text{ rad / sec}$

$$v = r\omega = 25 \cdot \frac{\pi}{15} = \frac{5\pi}{3} \text{ ft / sec} \approx 5.2 \text{ ft / sec.}$$

79. Since there are two lights on opposite sides and the light is seen every 5 seconds, the beacon makes 1 revolution every 10 seconds.

$$\omega = \frac{1 \text{ rev}}{10 \text{ sec}} \cdot \frac{2\pi}{1 \text{ rev}} = \frac{\pi}{5} \text{ radians / second}$$

80. $r = 16$ inches; $v = 90$ mi / hr

$$\omega = \frac{v}{r} = \frac{90 \text{ mi / hr}}{16 \text{ in}} \cdot \frac{12 \text{ in}}{1 \text{ ft}} \cdot \frac{5280 \text{ ft}}{1 \text{ mi}} \cdot \frac{1 \text{ hr}}{60 \text{ min}} \cdot \frac{1 \text{ rev}}{2\pi \text{ rad}} \approx 945.38 \text{ rev / min}$$

$r = 14$ inches; $v = 90$ mi / hr

$$\omega = \frac{v}{r} = \frac{90 \text{ mi / hr}}{14 \text{ in}} \cdot \frac{12 \text{ in}}{1 \text{ ft}} \cdot \frac{5280 \text{ ft}}{1 \text{ mi}} \cdot \frac{1 \text{ hr}}{60 \text{ min}} \cdot \frac{1 \text{ rev}}{2\pi \text{ rad}} \approx 1080.43 \text{ rev / min}$$

81. $E(t) = 120\sin(120\pi t)$, $t \geq 0$

(a) The maximum value of E is the amplitude which is 120.

(b) Period $= \frac{2\pi}{120\pi} = \frac{1}{60}$ seconds

(c) Graphing:

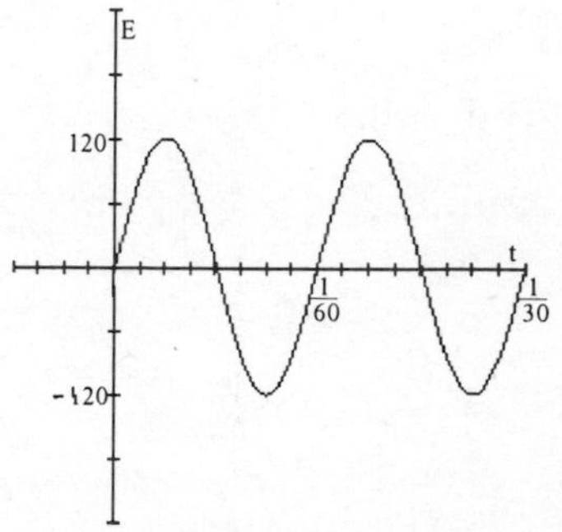

82. $I(t) = 220\sin\left(30\pi t + \frac{\pi}{6}\right), \quad t \ge 0$

(a) Period $= \frac{2\pi}{30\pi} = \frac{1}{15}$

(b) The amplitude is 220.

(c) The phase shift is: $\frac{\phi}{\omega} = \frac{\left(-\frac{\pi}{6}\right)}{30\pi} = -\frac{\pi}{6}\cdot\frac{1}{30\pi} = -\frac{1}{180}$

(d) Graphing:

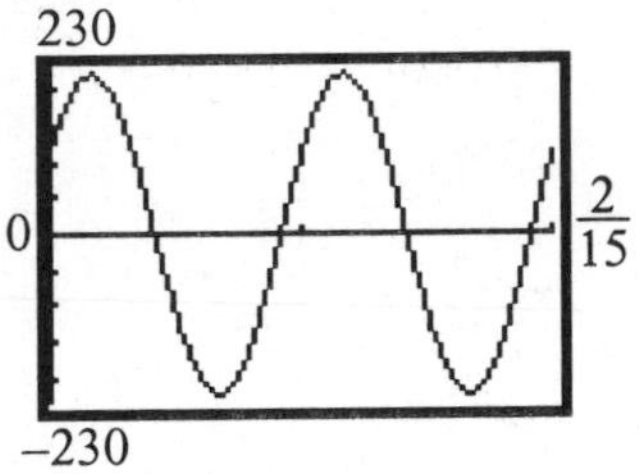

83. (a) Draw a scatter diagram:

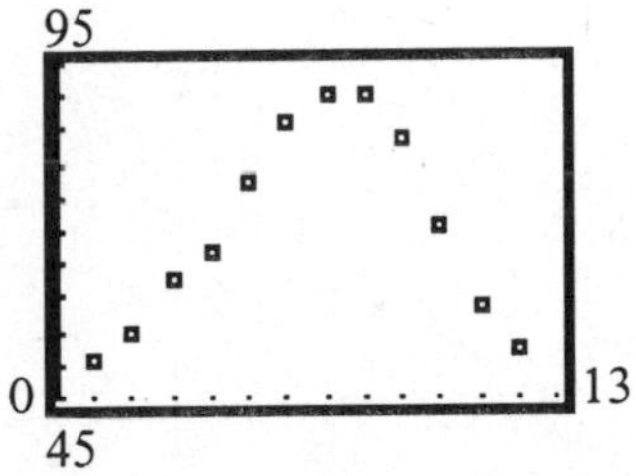

(b) Amplitude: $A = \frac{90-51}{2} = \frac{39}{2} = 19.5$

Vertical Shift: $\frac{90+51}{2} = \frac{141}{2} = 70.5$

$\omega = \frac{2\pi}{12} = \frac{\pi}{6}$

Phase shift (use $y = 51$, $x = 1$):

$$51 = 19.5\sin\left(\frac{\pi}{6}\cdot 1 - \phi\right) + 70.5$$

$$-19.5 = 19.5\sin\left(\frac{\pi}{6} - \phi\right) \rightarrow -1 = \sin\left(\frac{\pi}{6} - \phi\right)$$

$$-\frac{\pi}{2} = \frac{\pi}{6} - \phi \rightarrow \phi = \frac{2\pi}{3}$$

Thus, $y = 19.5\sin\left(\frac{\pi}{6}x - \frac{2\pi}{3}\right) + 70.5$

(c)

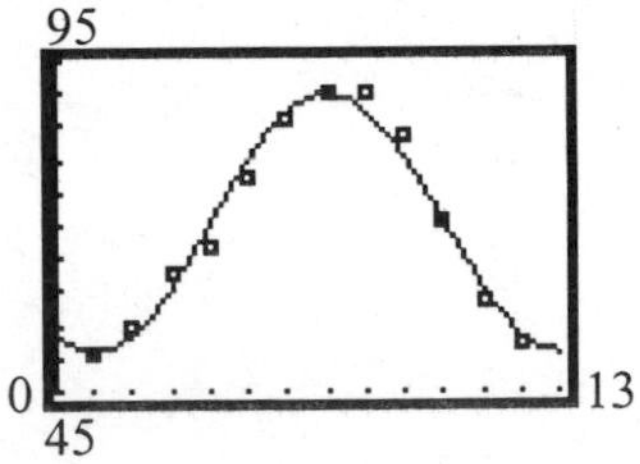

(e)

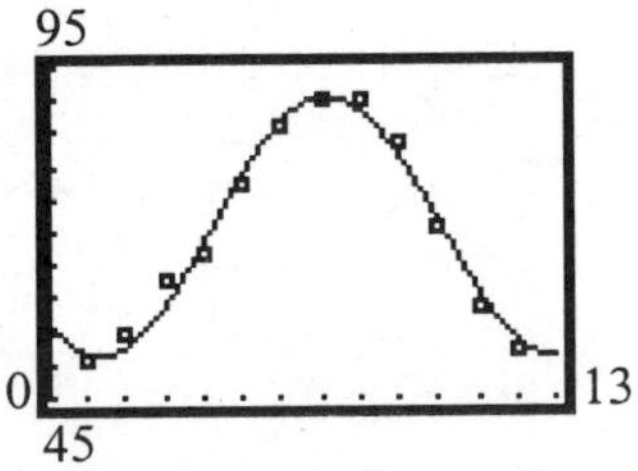

(d) $y = 19.518\sin(0.541x - 2.283) + 71.01$

84. (a) Draw a scatter diagram:

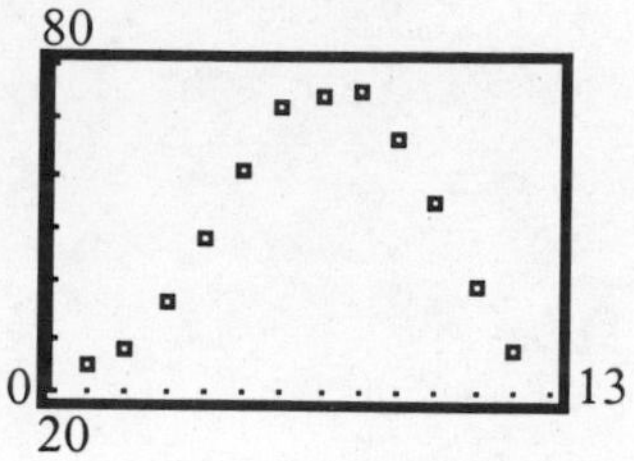

(b) Amplitude: $A = \dfrac{75 - 25}{2} = \dfrac{50}{2} = 25$

Vertical Shift: $\dfrac{75 + 25}{2} = \dfrac{100}{2} = 50$

$\omega = \dfrac{2\pi}{12} = \dfrac{\pi}{6}$

Phase shift (use $y = 25$, $x = 1$):

$$25 = 25\sin\left(\frac{\pi}{6} \cdot 1 - \phi\right) + 50$$

$$-25 = 25\sin\left(\frac{\pi}{6} - \phi\right) \rightarrow -1 = \sin\left(\frac{\pi}{6} - \phi\right)$$

$$-\frac{\pi}{2} = \frac{\pi}{6} - \phi \rightarrow \phi = \frac{2\pi}{3}$$

Thus, $y = 25\sin\left(\dfrac{\pi}{6}x - \dfrac{2\pi}{3}\right) + 50$

(c)

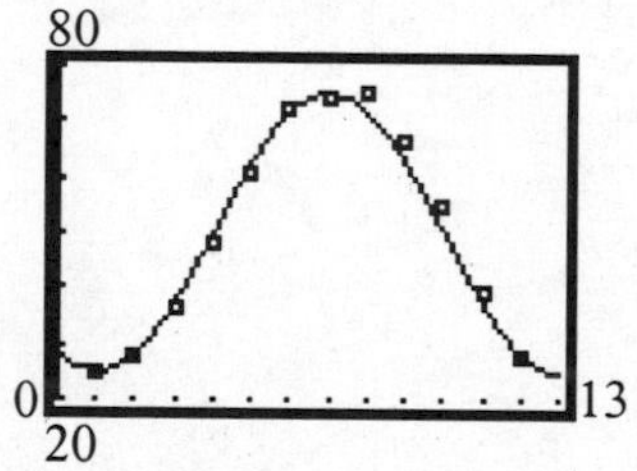

(e)

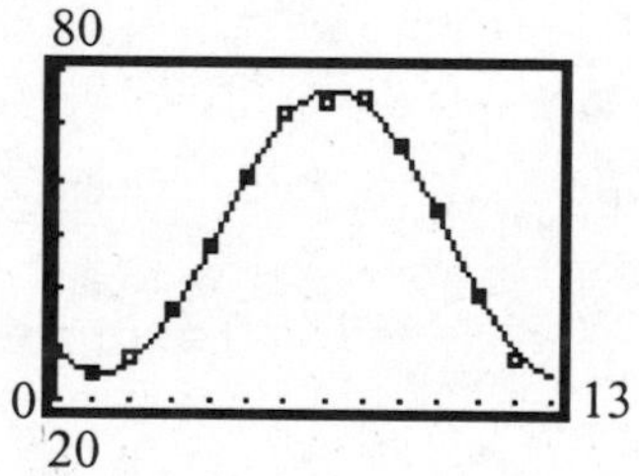

(d) $y = 25.815\sin(0.521x - 2.175) + 50.46$

85. (a) Amplitude: $A = \dfrac{13.367 - 9.667}{2} = \dfrac{3.7}{2} = 1.85$

Vertical Shift: $\dfrac{13.367 + 9.667}{2} = \dfrac{23.034}{2} = 11.517$

$\omega = \dfrac{2\pi}{365}$

Phase shift (use $y = 9.667$, $x = 355$):

$$9.667 = 1.85\sin\left(\frac{2\pi}{365} \cdot 355 - \phi\right) + 11.517$$

$$-1.85 = 1.85\sin\left(\frac{2\pi}{365}\cdot 355 - \phi\right) \to -1 = \sin\left(\frac{710\pi}{365} - \phi\right)$$

$$-\frac{\pi}{2} = \frac{710\pi}{365} - \phi \to \phi = 7.6818$$

Thus, $y = 1.85\sin\left(\frac{2\pi}{365}x - 7.6818\right) + 11.517$

(b)

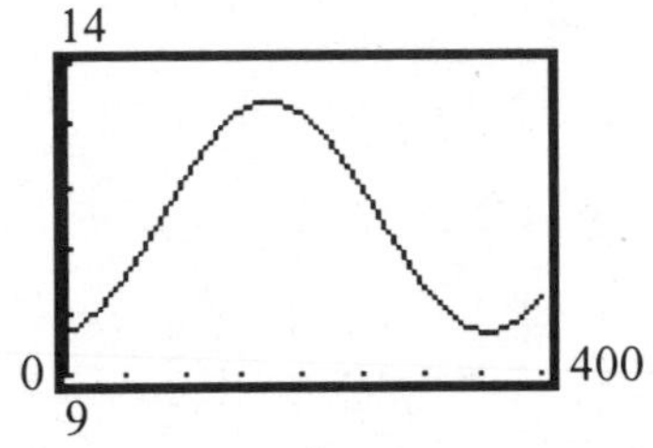

(c) $y = 1.85\sin\left(\frac{2\pi}{365}(91) - 7.6818\right) + 11.517 = 11.83$ hours

86. (a) Amplitude: $A = \frac{13.967 - 8.417}{2} = \frac{5.55}{2} = 2.775$

Vertical Shift: $\frac{13.967 + 8.417}{2} = \frac{22.384}{2} = 11.192$

$\omega = \frac{2\pi}{365}$

Phase shift (use $y = 8.417$, $x = 355$):

$$8.417 = 2.775\sin\left(\frac{2\pi}{365}\cdot 355 - \phi\right) + 11.192$$

$$-2.775 = 2.775\sin\left(\frac{2\pi}{365}\cdot 355 - \phi\right) \to -1 = \sin\left(\frac{710\pi}{365} - \phi\right)$$

$$-\frac{\pi}{2} = \frac{710\pi}{365} - \phi \to \phi = 7.6818$$

Thus, $y = 2.775\sin\left(\frac{2\pi}{365}x - 7.6818\right) + 11.192$

(b)

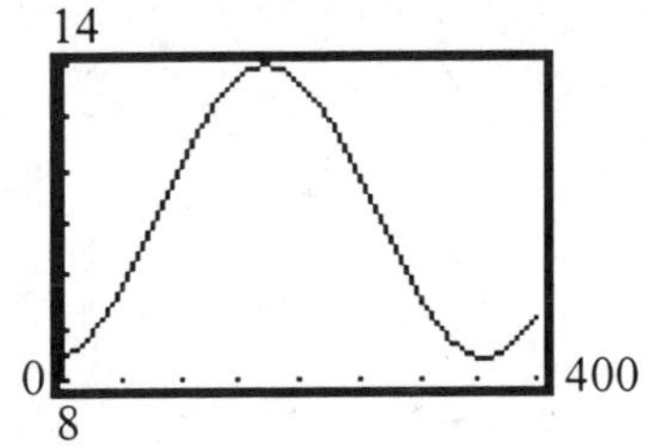

(c) $y = 2.775\sin\left(\frac{2\pi}{365}(91) - 7.6818\right) + 11.192 \approx 11.66$ hours

Chapter 8

Analytic Trigonometry

8.1 The Inverse Sine, Cosine and Tangent Functions

1. $\sin^{-1}(0)$

   We are finding the angle θ, $-\frac{\pi}{2} \le \theta \le \frac{\pi}{2}$, whose sine equals 0.

   $$\sin\theta = 0 \qquad -\frac{\pi}{2} \le \theta \le \frac{\pi}{2}$$
   $$\theta = 0 \rightarrow \sin^{-1}(0) = 0$$

2. $\cos^{-1}(1)$

   We are finding the angle θ, $0 \le \theta \le \pi$, whose cosine equals 1.

   $$\cos\theta = 1 \qquad 0 \le \theta \le \pi$$
   $$\theta = 0 \rightarrow \cos^{-1}(1) = 0$$

3. $\sin^{-1}(-1)$

   We are finding the angle θ, $-\frac{\pi}{2} \le \theta \le \frac{\pi}{2}$, whose sine equals -1.

   $$\sin\theta = -1 \qquad -\frac{\pi}{2} \le \theta \le \frac{\pi}{2}$$
   $$\theta = -\frac{\pi}{2} \rightarrow \sin^{-1}(-1) = -\frac{\pi}{2}$$

4. $\cos^{-1}(-1)$

   We are finding the angle θ, $0 \le \theta \le \pi$, whose cosine equals -1.

   $$\cos\theta = -1 \qquad 0 \le \theta \le \pi$$
   $$\theta = \pi \rightarrow \cos^{-1}(-1) = \pi$$

5. $\tan^{-1}(0)$

   We are finding the angle θ, $-\frac{\pi}{2} < \theta < \frac{\pi}{2}$, whose tangent equals 0.

   $$\tan\theta = 0 \qquad -\frac{\pi}{2} < \theta < \frac{\pi}{2}$$
   $$\theta = 0 \rightarrow \tan^{-1}(0) = 0$$

6. $\tan^{-1}(-1)$

We are finding the angle $\theta, -\frac{\pi}{2} < \theta < \frac{\pi}{2}$, whose tangent equals -1.

$$\tan\theta = -1 \qquad -\frac{\pi}{2} < \theta < \frac{\pi}{2}$$

$$\theta = -\frac{\pi}{4} \rightarrow \tan^{-1}(-1) = -\frac{\pi}{4}$$

7. $\sin^{-1}\left(\frac{\sqrt{2}}{2}\right)$

We are finding the angle $\theta, -\frac{\pi}{2} \le \theta \le \frac{\pi}{2}$, whose sine equals $\frac{\sqrt{2}}{2}$.

$$\sin\theta = \frac{\sqrt{2}}{2} \qquad -\frac{\pi}{2} \le \theta \le \frac{\pi}{2}$$

$$\theta = \frac{\pi}{4} \rightarrow \sin^{-1}\left(\frac{\sqrt{2}}{2}\right) = \frac{\pi}{4}$$

8. $\tan^{-1}\left(\frac{\sqrt{3}}{3}\right)$

We are finding the angle $\theta, -\frac{\pi}{2} < \theta < \frac{\pi}{2}$, whose tangent equals $\frac{\sqrt{3}}{3}$.

$$\tan\theta = \frac{\sqrt{3}}{3} \qquad -\frac{\pi}{2} < \theta < \frac{\pi}{2}$$

$$\theta = \frac{\pi}{6} \rightarrow \tan^{-1}\left(\frac{\sqrt{3}}{3}\right) = \frac{\pi}{6}$$

9. $\tan^{-1}\left(\sqrt{3}\right)$

We are finding the angle $\theta, -\frac{\pi}{2} < \theta < \frac{\pi}{2}$, whose tangent equals $\sqrt{3}$.

$$\tan\theta = \sqrt{3} \qquad -\frac{\pi}{2} < \theta < \frac{\pi}{2}$$

$$\theta = \frac{\pi}{3} \rightarrow \tan^{-1}\left(\sqrt{3}\right) = \frac{\pi}{3}$$

10. $\sin^{-1}\left(-\frac{\sqrt{3}}{2}\right)$

We are finding the angle $\theta, -\frac{\pi}{2} \le \theta \le \frac{\pi}{2}$, whose sine equals $-\frac{\sqrt{3}}{2}$.

$$\sin\theta = -\frac{\sqrt{3}}{2} \qquad -\frac{\pi}{2} \le \theta \le \frac{\pi}{2}$$

$$\theta = -\frac{\pi}{3} \rightarrow \sin^{-1}\left(-\frac{\sqrt{3}}{2}\right) = -\frac{\pi}{3}$$

11. $\cos^{-1}\left(-\frac{\sqrt{3}}{2}\right)$

We are finding the angle θ, $0 \le \theta \le \pi$, whose cosine equals $-\frac{\sqrt{3}}{2}$.

$$\cos\theta = -\frac{\sqrt{3}}{2} \qquad 0 \le \theta \le \pi$$

$$\theta = \frac{5\pi}{6} \rightarrow \cos^{-1}\left(-\frac{\sqrt{3}}{2}\right) = \frac{5\pi}{6}$$

12. $\sin^{-1}\left(-\frac{\sqrt{2}}{2}\right)$

We are finding the angle θ, $-\frac{\pi}{2} \le \theta \le \frac{\pi}{2}$, whose sine equals $-\frac{\sqrt{2}}{2}$.

$$\sin\theta = -\frac{\sqrt{2}}{2} \qquad -\frac{\pi}{2} \le \theta \le \frac{\pi}{2}$$

$$\theta = -\frac{\pi}{4} \rightarrow \sin^{-1}\left(-\frac{\sqrt{2}}{2}\right) = -\frac{\pi}{4}$$

13. $\sin^{-1}(0.1) \approx 0.10$

14. $\cos^{-1}(0.6) \approx 0.93$

15. $\tan^{-1}(5) \approx 1.37$

16. $\tan^{-1}(0.2) \approx 0.20$

17. $\cos^{-1}\left(\frac{7}{8}\right) \approx 0.51$

18. $\sin^{-1}\left(\frac{1}{8}\right) \approx 0.13$

19. $\tan^{-1}(-0.4) \approx -0.38$

20. $\tan^{-1}(-3) \approx -1.25$

21. $\sin^{-1}(-0.12) \approx -0.12$

22. $\cos^{-1}(-0.44) \approx 2.03$

23. $\cos^{-1}\left(\frac{\sqrt{2}}{3}\right) \approx 1.08$

24. $\sin^{-1}\left(\frac{\sqrt{3}}{5}\right) \approx 0.35$

25. $\sin\left[\sin^{-1}(0.54)\right] = 0.54$

26. $\tan\left[\tan^{-1}(7.4)\right] = 7.4$

27. $\cos^{-1}\left[\cos\left(\frac{4\pi}{5}\right)\right] = \frac{4\pi}{5}$

28. $\sin^{-1}\left[\sin\left(-\frac{\pi}{10}\right)\right] = -\frac{\pi}{10}$

29. $\tan\left[\tan^{-1}(-3.5)\right]=-3.5$

30. $\cos\left[\cos^{-1}(-0.05)\right]=-0.05$

31. $\sin^{-1}\left[\sin\left(-\frac{3\pi}{7}\right)\right]=-\frac{3\pi}{7}$

32. $\tan^{-1}\left[\tan\left(\frac{2\pi}{5}\right)\right]=\frac{2\pi}{5}$

33. yes, $\sin^{-1}\left[\sin\left(-\frac{\pi}{6}\right)\right]=-\frac{\pi}{6}$ since $\sin^{-1}[\sin(x)]=x$ where $-\frac{\pi}{2}\le x\le\frac{\pi}{2}$
and $-\frac{\pi}{6}$ is in the restricted domain of $f(x)=\sin(x)$.

34. no, $\sin^{-1}\left[\sin\left(\frac{2\pi}{3}\right)\right]\neq\frac{2\pi}{3}$ since $\sin^{-1}[\sin(x)]=x$ where $-\frac{\pi}{2}\le x\le\frac{\pi}{2}$
and $\frac{2\pi}{3}$ is not in the restricted domain of $f(x)=\sin(x)$.

35. no, $\sin\left[\sin^{-1}(2)\right]\neq 2$ since $\sin\left[\sin^{-1}(x)\right]=x$ where $-1\le x\le 1$
and 2 is not in the domain of $f(x)=\sin^{-1}(x)$.

36. yes, $\sin\left[\sin^{-1}\left(-\frac{1}{2}\right)\right]=-\frac{1}{2}$ since $\sin\left[\sin^{-1}(x)\right]=x$ where $-1\le x\le 1$
and $-\frac{1}{2}$ is in the domain of $f(x)=\sin^{-1}(x)$.

37. no, $\cos^{-1}\left[\cos\left(-\frac{\pi}{6}\right)\right]\neq-\frac{\pi}{6}$ since $\cos^{-1}[\cos(x)]=x$ where $0\le x\le\pi$
and $-\frac{\pi}{6}$ is not in the restricted domain of $f(x)=\cos(x)$.

38. yes, $\cos^{-1}\left[\cos\left(\frac{2\pi}{3}\right)\right]=\frac{2\pi}{3}$ since $\cos^{-1}[\cos(x)]=x$ where $0\le x\le\pi$
and $\frac{2\pi}{3}$ is in the restricted domain of $f(x)=\cos(x)$.

39. yes, $\cos\left[\cos^{-1}\left(-\frac{1}{2}\right)\right]=-\frac{1}{2}$ since $\cos\left[\cos^{-1}(x)\right]=x$ where $-1\le x\le 1$

and $-\frac{1}{2}$ is in the domain of $f(x)=\cos^{-1}(x)$.

40. no, $\cos\left[\cos^{-1}(2)\right]\neq 2$ since $\cos\left[\cos^{-1}(x)\right]=x$ where $-1\le x\le 1$
and 2 is not in the domain of $f(x)=\cos^{-1}(x)$.

41. yes, $\tan^{-1}\left[\tan\left(-\frac{\pi}{3}\right)\right]=-\frac{\pi}{3}$ since $\tan^{-1}[\tan(x)]=x$ where $-\frac{\pi}{2}<x<\frac{\pi}{2}$ and $-\frac{\pi}{3}$ is in the restricted domain of $f(x)=\tan(x)$.

42. no, $\tan^{-1}\left[\tan\left(\frac{2\pi}{3}\right)\right]\neq\frac{2\pi}{3}$ since $\tan^{-1}[\tan(x)]=x$ where $-\frac{\pi}{2}<x<\frac{\pi}{2}$ and $\frac{2\pi}{3}$ is not in the restricted domain of $f(x)=\tan(x)$.

43. yes, $\tan\left[\tan^{-1}(2)\right]=2$ since $\tan\left[\tan^{-1}(x)\right]=x$ where $-\infty<x<\infty$

44. yes, $\tan\left[\tan^{-1}\left(-\frac{1}{2}\right)\right]=-\frac{1}{2}$ since $\tan\left[\tan^{-1}(x)\right]=x$ where $-\infty<x<\infty$

45. (a) $D=24\cdot\left[1-\frac{\cos^{-1}\left(\tan\left(23.5\cdot\frac{\pi}{180}\right)\tan\left(29.75\cdot\frac{\pi}{180}\right)\right)}{\pi}\right]\approx 13.92$ hours

(b) $D=24\cdot\left[1-\frac{\cos^{-1}\left(\tan\left(0\cdot\frac{\pi}{180}\right)\tan\left(29.75\cdot\frac{\pi}{180}\right)\right)}{\pi}\right]\approx 12$ hours

(c) $D=24\cdot\left[1-\frac{\cos^{-1}\left(\tan\left(22.8\cdot\frac{\pi}{180}\right)\tan\left(29.75\cdot\frac{\pi}{180}\right)\right)}{\pi}\right]\approx 13.85$ hours

46. (a) $D=24\cdot\left(1-\frac{\cos^{-1}\left(\tan\left(23.5\cdot\frac{\pi}{180}\right)\tan\left(40.75\cdot\frac{\pi}{180}\right)\right)}{\pi}\right)\approx 14.93$ hours

(b) $D=24\cdot\left(1-\frac{\cos^{-1}\left(\tan\left(0\cdot\frac{\pi}{180}\right)\tan\left(40.75\cdot\frac{\pi}{180}\right)\right)}{\pi}\right)\approx 12$ hours

(c) $D = 24 \cdot \left(1 - \dfrac{\cos^{-1}\left(\tan\left(22.8 \cdot \dfrac{\pi}{180} \right) \tan\left(40.75 \cdot \dfrac{\pi}{180} \right) \right)}{\pi} \right) \approx 14.83$ hours

47. (a) $D = 24 \cdot \left(1 - \dfrac{\cos^{-1}\left(\tan\left(23.5 \cdot \dfrac{\pi}{180} \right) \tan\left(21.3 \cdot \dfrac{\pi}{180} \right) \right)}{\pi} \right) \approx 13.30$ hours

(b) $D = 24 \cdot \left(1 - \dfrac{\cos^{-1}\left(\tan\left(0 \cdot \dfrac{\pi}{180} \right) \tan\left(21.3 \cdot \dfrac{\pi}{180} \right) \right)}{\pi} \right) \approx 12$ hours

(c) $D = 24 \cdot \left(1 - \dfrac{\cos^{-1}\left(\tan\left(22.8 \cdot \dfrac{\pi}{180} \right) \tan\left(21.3 \cdot \dfrac{\pi}{180} \right) \right)}{\pi} \right) \approx 13.26$ hours

48. (a) $D = 24 \cdot \left(1 - \dfrac{\cos^{-1}\left(\tan\left(23.5 \cdot \dfrac{\pi}{180} \right) \tan\left(61.167 \cdot \dfrac{\pi}{180} \right) \right)}{\pi} \right) \approx 18.96$ hours

(b) $D = 24 \cdot \left(1 - \dfrac{\cos^{-1}\left(\tan\left(0 \cdot \dfrac{\pi}{180} \right) \tan\left(61.167 \cdot \dfrac{\pi}{180} \right) \right)}{\pi} \right) \approx 12$ hours

(c) $D = 24 \cdot \left(1 - \dfrac{\cos^{-1}\left(\tan\left(22.8 \cdot \dfrac{\pi}{180} \right) \tan\left(61.167 \cdot \dfrac{\pi}{180} \right) \right)}{\pi} \right) \approx 18.64$ hours

49. (a) $D = 24 \cdot \left(1 - \dfrac{\cos^{-1}\left(\tan\left(23.5 \cdot \dfrac{\pi}{180} \right) \tan\left(0 \cdot \dfrac{\pi}{180} \right) \right)}{\pi} \right) \approx 12$ hours

(b) $D = 24 \cdot \left(1 - \dfrac{\cos^{-1}\left(\tan\left(0 \cdot \dfrac{\pi}{180} \right) \tan\left(0 \cdot \dfrac{\pi}{180} \right) \right)}{\pi} \right) \approx 12$ hours

(c) $D = 24 \cdot \left(1 - \dfrac{\cos^{-1}\left(\tan\left(22.8 \cdot \frac{\pi}{180} \right) \tan\left(0 \cdot \frac{\pi}{180} \right) \right)}{\pi} \right) \approx 12$ hours

(d) The number of hours of daylight per day is approximately 12 hours throughout the year.

50. (a) $D = 24 \cdot \left(1 - \dfrac{\cos^{-1}\left(\tan\left(23.5 \cdot \frac{\pi}{180} \right) \tan\left(66.5 \cdot \frac{\pi}{180} \right) \right)}{\pi} \right) \approx 24$ hours

(b) $D = 24 \cdot \left(1 - \dfrac{\cos^{-1}\left(\tan\left(0 \cdot \frac{\pi}{180} \right) \tan\left(66.5 \cdot \frac{\pi}{180} \right) \right)}{\pi} \right) \approx 12$ hours

(c) $D = 24 \cdot \left(1 - \dfrac{\cos^{-1}\left(\tan\left(22.8 \cdot \frac{\pi}{180} \right) \tan\left(66.5 \cdot \frac{\pi}{180} \right) \right)}{\pi} \right) \approx 22.02$ hours

(d) The number of hours of daylight at this location on the winter solstice is: $24 - 24 = 0$. On the winter solstice, there is no daylight.

51. $1530 \text{ ft} \cdot \dfrac{1 \text{ mile}}{5280 \text{ feet}} = 0.29$ mile

$\cos\theta = \dfrac{3960}{3960.29}$

$\theta \approx 0.0121$ radians

$s = r\theta = 3960(0.0121) = 47.92$ miles

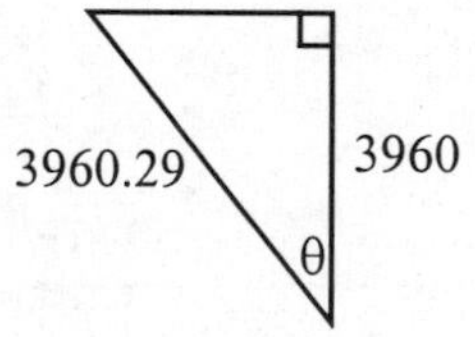

$\dfrac{2\pi(2710)}{24} = \dfrac{47.92}{t}$

$t \approx 0.0675$ hour $= 4.05$ minutes

Chapter 8

Analytic Trigonometry

8.2 The Inverse Trigonometric Functions (Continued)

1. $\cos\left(\sin^{-1}\left(\frac{\sqrt{2}}{2}\right)\right)$

   Find the angle θ, $-\frac{\pi}{2} \le \theta \le \frac{\pi}{2}$, whose sine equals $\frac{\sqrt{2}}{2}$.

   $$\sin\theta = \frac{\sqrt{2}}{2} \qquad -\frac{\pi}{2} \le \theta \le \frac{\pi}{2}$$

   $$\theta = \frac{\pi}{4} \rightarrow \cos\left(\sin^{-1}\left(\frac{\sqrt{2}}{2}\right)\right) = \cos\left(\frac{\pi}{4}\right) = \frac{\sqrt{2}}{2}$$

2. $\sin\left(\cos^{-1}\left(\frac{1}{2}\right)\right)$

   Find the angle θ, $0 \le \theta \le \pi$, whose cosine equals $\frac{1}{2}$.

   $$\cos\theta = \frac{1}{2} \qquad 0 \le \theta \le \pi$$

   $$\theta = \frac{\pi}{3} \rightarrow \sin\left(\cos^{-1}\left(\frac{1}{2}\right)\right) = \sin\left(\frac{\pi}{3}\right) = \frac{\sqrt{3}}{2}$$

3. $\tan\left(\cos^{-1}\left(-\frac{\sqrt{3}}{2}\right)\right)$

   Find the angle θ, $0 \le \theta \le \pi$, whose cosine equals $-\frac{\sqrt{3}}{2}$.

   $$\cos\theta = -\frac{\sqrt{3}}{2} \qquad 0 \le \theta \le \pi$$

   $$\theta = \frac{5\pi}{6} \rightarrow \tan\left(\cos^{-1}\left(-\frac{\sqrt{3}}{2}\right)\right) = \tan\left(\frac{5\pi}{6}\right) = -\frac{\sqrt{3}}{3}$$

4. $\tan\left(\sin^{-1}\left(-\frac{1}{2}\right)\right)$

Find the angle θ, $-\frac{\pi}{2} \le \theta \le \frac{\pi}{2}$, whose sine equals $-\frac{1}{2}$.

$$\sin\theta = -\frac{1}{2} \qquad -\frac{\pi}{2} \le \theta \le \frac{\pi}{2}$$

$$\theta = -\frac{\pi}{6} \rightarrow \tan\left(\sin^{-1}\left(-\frac{1}{2}\right)\right) = \tan\left(-\frac{\pi}{6}\right) = -\frac{\sqrt{3}}{3}$$

5. $\sec\left(\cos^{-1}\left(\frac{1}{2}\right)\right)$

Find the angle θ, $0 \le \theta \le \pi$, whose cosine equals $\frac{1}{2}$.

$$\cos\theta = \frac{1}{2} \qquad 0 \le \theta \le \pi$$

$$\theta = \frac{\pi}{3} \rightarrow \sec\left(\cos^{-1}\left(\frac{1}{2}\right)\right) = \sec\left(\frac{\pi}{3}\right) = 2$$

6. $\cot\left(\sin^{-1}\left(-\frac{1}{2}\right)\right)$

Find the angle θ, $-\frac{\pi}{2} \le \theta \le \frac{\pi}{2}$, whose sine equals $-\frac{1}{2}$.

$$\sin\theta = -\frac{1}{2} \qquad -\frac{\pi}{2} \le \theta \le \frac{\pi}{2}$$

$$\theta = -\frac{\pi}{6} \rightarrow \cot\left(\sin^{-1}\left(-\frac{1}{2}\right)\right) = \cot\left(-\frac{\pi}{6}\right) = -\sqrt{3}$$

7. $\csc\left(\tan^{-1}(1)\right)$

Find the angle θ, $-\frac{\pi}{2} < \theta < \frac{\pi}{2}$, whose tangent equals 1.

$$\tan\theta = 1 \qquad -\frac{\pi}{2} < \theta < \frac{\pi}{2}$$

$$\theta = \frac{\pi}{4} \rightarrow \csc\left(\tan^{-1}(1)\right) = \csc\left(\frac{\pi}{4}\right) = \sqrt{2}$$

8. $\sec\left(\tan^{-1}\left(\sqrt{3}\right)\right)$

Find the angle θ, $-\frac{\pi}{2} < \theta < \frac{\pi}{2}$, whose tangent equals $\sqrt{3}$.

$$\tan\theta = \sqrt{3} \qquad -\frac{\pi}{2} < \theta < \frac{\pi}{2}$$

$$\theta = \frac{\pi}{3} \rightarrow \sec\left(\tan^{-1}\left(\sqrt{3}\right)\right) = \sec\left(\frac{\pi}{3}\right) = 2$$

9. $\sin\left(\tan^{-1}(-1)\right)$

Find the angle θ, $-\frac{\pi}{2} < \theta < \frac{\pi}{2}$, whose tangent equals -1.

$$\tan\theta = -1 \qquad -\frac{\pi}{2} < \theta < \frac{\pi}{2}$$

$$\theta = -\frac{\pi}{4} \rightarrow \sin\left(\tan^{-1}(-1)\right) = \sin\left(-\frac{\pi}{4}\right) = -\frac{\sqrt{2}}{2}$$

10. $\cos\left(\sin^{-1}\left(-\frac{\sqrt{3}}{2}\right)\right)$

Find the angle θ, $-\frac{\pi}{2} \le \theta \le \frac{\pi}{2}$, whose sine equals $-\frac{\sqrt{3}}{2}$.

$$\sin\theta = -\frac{\sqrt{3}}{2} \qquad -\frac{\pi}{2} \le \theta \le \frac{\pi}{2}$$

$$\theta = -\frac{\pi}{3} \rightarrow \cos\left(\sin^{-1}\left(-\frac{\sqrt{3}}{2}\right)\right) = \cos\left(-\frac{\pi}{3}\right) = \frac{1}{2}$$

11. $\sec\left(\sin^{-1}\left(-\frac{1}{2}\right)\right)$

Find the angle θ, $-\frac{\pi}{2} \le \theta \le \frac{\pi}{2}$, whose sine equals $-\frac{1}{2}$.

$$\sin\theta = -\frac{1}{2} \qquad -\frac{\pi}{2} \le \theta \le \frac{\pi}{2}$$

$$\theta = -\frac{\pi}{6} \rightarrow \sec\left(\sin^{-1}\left(-\frac{1}{2}\right)\right) = \sec\left(-\frac{\pi}{6}\right) = \frac{2\sqrt{3}}{3}$$

12. $\csc\left(\cos^{-1}\left(-\frac{\sqrt{3}}{2}\right)\right)$

Find the angle θ, $0 \le \theta \le \pi$, whose cosine equals $-\frac{\sqrt{3}}{2}$.

$$\cos\theta = -\frac{\sqrt{3}}{2} \qquad 0 \le \theta \le \pi$$

$$\theta = \frac{5\pi}{6} \rightarrow \csc\left(\cos^{-1}\left(-\frac{\sqrt{3}}{2}\right)\right) = \csc\left(\frac{5\pi}{6}\right) = 2$$

13. $\cos^{-1}\left(\cos\frac{5\pi}{4}\right) = \cos^{-1}\left(-\frac{\sqrt{2}}{2}\right)$

Find the angle θ, $0 \le \theta \le \pi$, whose cosine equals $-\frac{\sqrt{2}}{2}$.

$$\cos\theta = -\frac{\sqrt{2}}{2} \qquad 0 \le \theta \le \pi$$
$$\theta = \frac{3\pi}{4}$$

14. $\tan^{-1}\left(\tan\left(\frac{2\pi}{3}\right)\right) = \tan^{-1}\left(-\sqrt{3}\right)$

Find the angle θ, $-\frac{\pi}{2} < \theta < \frac{\pi}{2}$, whose tangent equals $-\sqrt{3}$.

$$\tan\theta = -\sqrt{3} \qquad -\frac{\pi}{2} < \theta < \frac{\pi}{2}$$
$$\theta = -\frac{\pi}{3}$$

15. $\sin^{-1}\left(\sin\left(-\frac{7\pi}{6}\right)\right) = \sin^{-1}\left(\frac{1}{2}\right)$

Find the angle θ, $-\frac{\pi}{2} \le \theta \le \frac{\pi}{2}$, whose sine equals $\frac{1}{2}$.

$$\sin\theta = \frac{1}{2} \qquad -\frac{\pi}{2} \le \theta \le \frac{\pi}{2}$$
$$\theta = \frac{\pi}{6}$$

16. $\cos^{-1}\left(\cos\left(-\frac{\pi}{3}\right)\right) = \cos^{-1}\left(\frac{1}{2}\right)$

Find the angle θ, $0 \le \theta \le \pi$, whose cosine equals $\frac{1}{2}$.

$$\cos\theta = \frac{1}{2} \qquad 0 \le \theta \le \pi$$
$$\theta = \frac{\pi}{3}$$

17. $\tan\left(\sin^{-1}\left(\frac{1}{3}\right)\right)$

Since $\sin\theta = \frac{1}{3}$, $-\frac{\pi}{2} \le \theta \le \frac{\pi}{2}$, let $y = 1$ and $r = 3$. Solve for x:

$$x^2 + 1 = 9 \to x^2 = 8 \to x = \pm\sqrt{8} = \pm 2\sqrt{2}$$

Since θ is in quadrant I, $x = 2\sqrt{2}$.

$$\tan\left(\sin^{-1}\left(\frac{1}{3}\right)\right) = \tan\theta = \frac{y}{x} = \frac{1}{2\sqrt{2}} \cdot \frac{\sqrt{2}}{\sqrt{2}} = \frac{\sqrt{2}}{4}$$

18. $\tan\left(\cos^{-1}\left(\frac{1}{3}\right)\right)$

Since $\cos\theta = \frac{1}{3}$, $0 \le \theta \le \pi$, let $x = 1$ and $r = 3$. Solve for y:

$$1 + y^2 = 9 \to y^2 = 8 \to y = \pm\sqrt{8} = \pm 2\sqrt{2}$$

Since θ is in quadrant I, $y = 2\sqrt{2}$.

$$\tan\left(\cos^{-1}\left(\frac{1}{3}\right)\right) = \tan\theta = \frac{y}{x} = \frac{2\sqrt{2}}{1} = 2\sqrt{2}$$

19. $\sec\left(\tan^{-1}\left(\frac{1}{2}\right)\right)$

Since $\tan\theta = \frac{1}{2}$, $-\frac{\pi}{2} < \theta < \frac{\pi}{2}$, let $x = 2$ and $y = 1$. Solve for r:

$$2^2 + 1 = r^2 \to r^2 = 5 \to r = \sqrt{5}$$

θ is in quadrant I.

$$\sec\left(\tan^{-1}\left(\frac{1}{2}\right)\right) = \sec\theta = \frac{r}{x} = \frac{\sqrt{5}}{2}$$

20. $\cos\left(\sin^{-1}\left(\frac{\sqrt{2}}{3}\right)\right)$

Since $\sin\theta = \frac{\sqrt{2}}{3}$, $-\frac{\pi}{2} \le \theta \le \frac{\pi}{2}$, let $y = \sqrt{2}$ and $r = 3$. Solve for x:

$$x^2 + 2 = 9 \to x^2 = 7 \to x = \pm\sqrt{7}$$

Since θ is in quadrant I, $x = \sqrt{7}$.

$$\cos\left(\sin^{-1}\left(\frac{\sqrt{2}}{3}\right)\right) = \cos\theta = \frac{x}{r} = \frac{\sqrt{7}}{3}$$

21. $\cot\left(\sin^{-1}\left(-\frac{\sqrt{2}}{3}\right)\right)$

Since $\sin\theta = -\frac{\sqrt{2}}{3}$, $-\frac{\pi}{2} \le \theta \le \frac{\pi}{2}$, let $y = -\sqrt{2}$ and $r = 3$. Solve for x:

$$x^2 + 2 = 9 \to x^2 = 7 \to x = \pm\sqrt{7}$$

Since θ is in quadrant IV, $x = \sqrt{7}$.

$$\cot\left(\sin^{-1}\left(-\frac{\sqrt{2}}{3}\right)\right) = \cot\theta = \frac{x}{y} = \frac{\sqrt{7}}{-\sqrt{2}} \cdot \frac{\sqrt{2}}{\sqrt{2}} = -\frac{\sqrt{14}}{2}$$

22. $\csc\left(\tan^{-1}(-2)\right)$

Since $\tan\theta = -2$, $-\frac{\pi}{2} < \theta < \frac{\pi}{2}$, let $x = 1$ and $y = -2$. Solve for r:

$$1 + 4 = r^2 \quad \to \quad r^2 = 5 \quad \to \quad r = \sqrt{5}; \ \theta \text{ is in quadrant IV.}$$

$$\csc\left(\tan^{-1}(-2)\right) = \csc\theta = \frac{r}{y} = \frac{\sqrt{5}}{-2} = -\frac{\sqrt{5}}{2}$$

23. $\sin\left(\tan^{-1}(-3)\right)$

Since $\tan\theta = -3$, $-\frac{\pi}{2} < \theta < \frac{\pi}{2}$, let $x = 1$ and $y = -3$. Solve for r:

$$1+9=r^2 \quad \rightarrow \quad r^2=10 \quad \rightarrow \quad r=\sqrt{10}\text{; } \theta \text{ is in quadrant IV.}$$

$$\sin\left(\tan^{-1}(-3)\right)=\sin\theta=\frac{y}{r}=\frac{-3}{\sqrt{10}}\cdot\frac{\sqrt{10}}{\sqrt{10}}=-\frac{3\sqrt{10}}{10}$$

24. $\cot\left(\cos^{-1}\left(-\frac{\sqrt{3}}{3}\right)\right)$

Since $\cos\theta = -\frac{\sqrt{3}}{3}$, $0 \le \theta \le \pi$, let $x = -\sqrt{3}$ and $r = 3$. Solve for y:

$$3+y^2=9 \rightarrow y^2=6 \rightarrow y=\pm\sqrt{6}$$

Since θ is in quadrant II, $y=\sqrt{6}$.

$$\cot\left(\cos^{-1}\left(-\frac{\sqrt{3}}{3}\right)\right)=\cot\theta=\frac{x}{y}=\frac{-\sqrt{3}}{\sqrt{6}}=\frac{-1}{\sqrt{2}}\cdot\frac{\sqrt{2}}{\sqrt{2}}=-\frac{\sqrt{2}}{2}$$

25. $\sec\left(\sin^{-1}\left(\frac{2\sqrt{5}}{5}\right)\right)$

Since $\sin\theta = \frac{2\sqrt{5}}{5}$, $-\frac{\pi}{2} \le \theta \le \frac{\pi}{2}$, let $y = 2\sqrt{5}$ and $r = 5$. Solve for x:

$$x^2+20=25 \rightarrow x^2=5 \rightarrow x=\pm\sqrt{5}$$

Since θ is in quadrant I, $x=\sqrt{5}$.

$$\sec\left(\sin^{-1}\left(\frac{2\sqrt{5}}{5}\right)\right)=\sec\theta=\frac{r}{x}=\frac{5}{\sqrt{5}}\cdot\frac{\sqrt{5}}{\sqrt{5}}=\sqrt{5}$$

26. $\csc\left(\tan^{-1}\left(\frac{1}{2}\right)\right)$

Since $\tan\theta = \frac{1}{2}$, $-\frac{\pi}{2} < \theta < \frac{\pi}{2}$, let $x = 2$ and $y = 1$. Solve for r:

$$2^2+1=r^2 \quad \rightarrow \quad r^2=5 \quad \rightarrow \quad r=\sqrt{5}\text{; } \theta \text{ is in quadrant I.}$$

$$\csc\left(\tan^{-1}\left(\frac{1}{2}\right)\right)=\csc\theta=\frac{r}{y}=\frac{\sqrt{5}}{1}=\sqrt{5}$$

27. $\sin^{-1}\left(\cos\frac{3\pi}{4}\right)=\sin^{-1}\left(-\frac{\sqrt{2}}{2}\right)=-\frac{\pi}{4}$

28. $\cos^{-1}\left(\sin\frac{7\pi}{6}\right)=\cos^{-1}\left(-\frac{1}{2}\right)=\frac{2\pi}{3}$

29. $\cot^{-1}\left(\sqrt{3}\right)$

We are finding the angle θ, $0 < \theta < \pi$, whose cotangent equals $\sqrt{3}$.

$\cot\theta = \sqrt{3} \qquad 0 < \theta < \pi$

$$\theta = \frac{\pi}{6} \rightarrow \cot^{-1}\left(\sqrt{3}\right) = \frac{\pi}{6}$$

30. $\cot^{-1}(1)$

We are finding the angle θ, $0 < \theta < \pi$, whose cotangent equals 1.

$\cot\theta = 1 \qquad 0 < \theta < \pi$

$$\theta = \frac{\pi}{4} \rightarrow \cot^{-1}(1) = \frac{\pi}{4}$$

31. $\csc^{-1}(-1)$

We are finding the angle θ, $-\frac{\pi}{2} \le \theta \le \frac{\pi}{2}$, $\theta \ne 0$, whose cosecant equals -1.

$\csc\theta = -1 \qquad -\frac{\pi}{2} \le \theta \le \frac{\pi}{2}, \ \theta \ne 0$

$$\theta = -\frac{\pi}{2} \rightarrow \csc^{-1}(-1) = -\frac{\pi}{2}$$

32. $\csc^{-1}\left(\sqrt{2}\right)$

We are finding the angle θ, $-\frac{\pi}{2} \le \theta \le \frac{\pi}{2}$, $\theta \ne 0$, whose cosecant equals $\sqrt{2}$.

$\csc\theta = \sqrt{2} \qquad -\frac{\pi}{2} \le \theta \le \frac{\pi}{2}, \ \theta \ne 0$

$$\theta = \frac{\pi}{4} \rightarrow \csc^{-1}\left(\sqrt{2}\right) = \frac{\pi}{4}$$

33. $\sec^{-1}\left(\frac{2\sqrt{3}}{3}\right)$

We are finding the angle θ, $0 \le \theta \le \pi$, $\theta \ne \frac{\pi}{2}$, whose secant equals $\frac{2\sqrt{3}}{3}$.

$\sec\theta = \frac{2\sqrt{3}}{3} \qquad 0 \le \theta \le \pi, \ \theta \ne \frac{\pi}{2}$

$$\theta = \frac{\pi}{6} \rightarrow \sec^{-1}\left(\frac{2\sqrt{3}}{3}\right) = \frac{\pi}{6}$$

34. $\sec^{-1}(-2)$

We are finding the angle θ, $0 \le \theta \le \pi$, $\theta \ne \frac{\pi}{2}$, whose secant equals –2.

$$\sec\theta = -2 \qquad 0 \le \theta \le \pi,\ \theta \ne \frac{\pi}{2}$$

$$\theta = \frac{2\pi}{3} \rightarrow \sec^{-1}(-2) = \frac{2\pi}{3}$$

35. $\cot^{-1}\left(-\frac{\sqrt{3}}{3}\right)$

We are finding the angle θ, $0 < \theta < \pi$, whose cotangent equals $-\frac{\sqrt{3}}{3}$.

$$\cot\theta = -\frac{\sqrt{3}}{3} \qquad 0 < \theta < \pi$$

$$\theta = \frac{2\pi}{3} \rightarrow \cot^{-1}\left(-\frac{\sqrt{3}}{3}\right) = \frac{2\pi}{3}$$

36. $\csc^{-1}\left(-\frac{2\sqrt{3}}{3}\right)$

We are finding the angle θ, $-\frac{\pi}{2} \le \theta \le \frac{\pi}{2}$, $\theta \ne 0$, whose cosecant equals $-\frac{2\sqrt{3}}{3}$.

$$\csc\theta = -\frac{2\sqrt{3}}{3} \qquad -\frac{\pi}{2} \le \theta \le \frac{\pi}{2},\ \theta \ne 0$$

$$\theta = -\frac{\pi}{3} \rightarrow \csc^{-1}\left(-\frac{2\sqrt{3}}{3}\right) = -\frac{\pi}{3}$$

37. $\sec^{-1}(4) = \cos^{-1}\left(\frac{1}{4}\right)$

We are finding the angle θ, $0 \le \theta \le \pi$, whose cosine equals $\frac{1}{4}$.

$$\cos\theta = \frac{1}{4} \Rightarrow \theta \text{ in quadrant I}$$

The calculator yields $\theta = \cos^{-1}\left(\frac{1}{4}\right) \approx 1.32$, which is an angle in quadrant I.

$\therefore\ \sec^{-1}(4) \approx 1.32$

38. $\csc^{-1}(5)=\sin^{-1}\left(\frac{1}{5}\right)$

We are finding the angle $\theta,\ -\frac{\pi}{2}\le\theta\le\frac{\pi}{2}$, whose sine equals $\frac{1}{5}$.

$\sin\theta=\frac{1}{5}\ \Rightarrow\theta$ in quadrant I

The calculator yields $\theta=\sin^{-1}\left(\frac{1}{5}\right)\approx 0.20$, which is an angle in quadrant I.

$\therefore\ \csc^{-1}(5)\approx 0.20$

39. $\cot^{-1}(2)=\tan^{-1}\left(\frac{1}{2}\right)$

We are finding the angle $\theta,\ 0\le\theta\le\pi,$ whose tangent equals $\frac{1}{2}$.

$\tan\theta=\frac{1}{2}\ \Rightarrow\theta$ in quadrant I

The calculator yields $\theta=\tan^{-1}\left(\frac{1}{2}\right)\approx 0.46$, which is an angle in quadrant I.

$\therefore\ \cot^{-1}(2)\approx 0.46$

40. $\sec^{-1}(-3)=\cos^{-1}\left(-\frac{1}{3}\right)$

We are finding the angle $\theta,\ 0\le\theta\le\pi,$ whose cosine equals $-\frac{1}{3}$.

$\cos\theta=-\frac{1}{3}\ \Rightarrow\theta$ in quadrant II

The calculator yields $\theta=\cos^{-1}\left(-\frac{1}{3}\right)\approx 1.91$, which is an angle in quadrant II.

$\therefore\ \sec^{-1}(-3)\approx 1.91$

41. $\csc^{-1}(-3)=\sin^{-1}\left(-\frac{1}{3}\right)\approx -0.34$

We are finding the angle $\theta,\ -\frac{\pi}{2}\le\theta\le\frac{\pi}{2}$, whose sine equals $-\frac{1}{3}$.

$\sin\theta=-\frac{1}{3}\ \Rightarrow\theta$ in quadrant IV

The calculator yields $\theta=\sin^{-1}\left(-\frac{1}{3}\right)\approx -0.34$, which is an angle in quadrant IV.

$\therefore\ \csc^{-1}(-3)\approx -0.34$

42. $\cot^{-1}\left(-\frac{1}{2}\right) = \tan^{-1}(-2)$

We are finding the angle $\theta,\ 0 \le \theta \le \pi,$ whose tangent equals -2.

$\tan\theta = -2 \Rightarrow \theta$ in quadrant II

The calculator yields $\tan^{-1}(-2) \approx -1.11$, which is an angle in quadrant IV.

Since θ is in quadrant II, $\theta \approx -1.11 + \pi \approx 2.03$.

$\therefore\ \cot^{-1}\left(-\frac{1}{2}\right) \approx 2.03$

43. $\cot^{-1}\left(-\sqrt{5}\right) = \tan^{-1}\left(-\frac{1}{\sqrt{5}}\right)$

We are finding the angle $\theta,\ 0 \le \theta \le \pi,$ whose tangent equals $-\frac{1}{\sqrt{5}}$.

$\tan\theta = -\frac{1}{\sqrt{5}} \Rightarrow \theta$ in quadrant II

The calculator yields $\tan^{-1}\left(-\frac{1}{\sqrt{5}}\right) \approx -0.42$, which is an angle in quadrant IV.

Since θ is in quadrant II, $\theta \approx -0.42 + \pi \approx 2.72$.

$\therefore\ \cot^{-1}\left(-\sqrt{5}\right) \approx 2.72$

44. $\cot^{-1}(-8.1) = \tan^{-1}\left(-\frac{1}{8.1}\right)$

We are finding the angle $\theta,\ 0 \le \theta \le \pi,$ whose tangent equals $-\frac{1}{8.1}$.

$\tan\theta = -\frac{1}{8.1} \Rightarrow \theta$ in quadrant II

The calculator yields $\tan^{-1}\left(-\frac{1}{8.1}\right) \approx -0.12$, which is an angle in quadrant IV.

Since θ is in quadrant II, $\theta \approx -0.12 + \pi \approx 3.02$.

$\therefore\ \cot^{-1}(-8.1) \approx 3.02$

45. $\csc^{-1}\left(-\frac{3}{2}\right) = \sin^{-1}\left(-\frac{2}{3}\right)$

We are finding the angle $\theta,\ -\frac{\pi}{2} \le \theta \le \frac{\pi}{2},$ whose sine equals $-\frac{2}{3}$.

$\sin\theta = -\frac{2}{3} \Rightarrow \theta$ in quadrant IV

The calculator yields $\sin^{-1}\left(-\frac{2}{3}\right) \approx -0.73$, which is an angle in quadrant IV.

$\therefore\ \csc^{-1}\left(-\frac{3}{2}\right) \approx -0.73$

46. $\sec^{-1}\left(-\frac{4}{3}\right) = \cos^{-1}\left(-\frac{3}{4}\right)$

We are finding the angle $\theta,\ 0 \le \theta \le \pi,$ whose cosine equals $-\frac{3}{4}$.

$\cos\theta = -\frac{3}{4} \Rightarrow \theta$ in quadrant II

The calculator yields $\cos^{-1}\left(-\frac{3}{4}\right) \approx 2.42$, which is an angle in quadrant II.

$\therefore\ \sec^{-1}\left(-\frac{4}{3}\right) \approx 2.42$

47. $\cot^{-1}\left(-\frac{3}{2}\right) = \tan^{-1}\left(-\frac{2}{3}\right)$

We are finding the angle $\theta,\ 0 \le \theta \le \pi,$ whose tangent equals $-\frac{2}{3}$.

$\tan\theta = -\frac{2}{3} \Rightarrow \theta$ in quadrant II

The calculator yields $\tan^{-1}\left(-\frac{2}{3}\right) \approx -0.59$, which is an angle in quadrant IV.

Since θ is in quadrant II, $\theta \approx -0.59 + \pi \approx 2.55$.

$\therefore\ \cot^{-1}\left(-\frac{3}{2}\right) \approx 2.55$

48. $\cot^{-1}\left(-\sqrt{10}\right) = \tan^{-1}\left(-\frac{1}{\sqrt{10}}\right)$

We are finding the angle $\theta,\ 0 \le \theta \le \pi,$ whose tangent equals $-\frac{1}{\sqrt{10}}$.

$\tan\theta = -\frac{1}{\sqrt{10}} \Rightarrow \theta$ in quadrant II

The calculator yields $\tan^{-1}\left(-\frac{1}{\sqrt{10}}\right) \approx -0.31$, which is an angle in quadrant IV.

Since θ is in quadrant II, $\theta \approx -0.31 + \pi \approx 2.84$.

$\therefore\ \cot^{-1}\left(-\sqrt{10}\right) \approx 2.84$

49. $y = \cot^{-1} x$

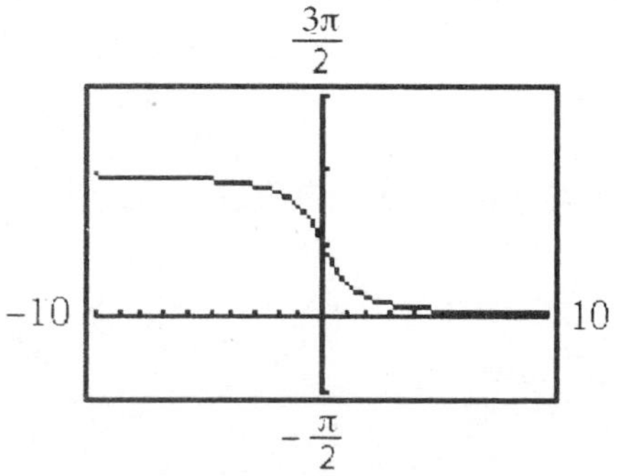

50. $y = \sec^{-1} x$

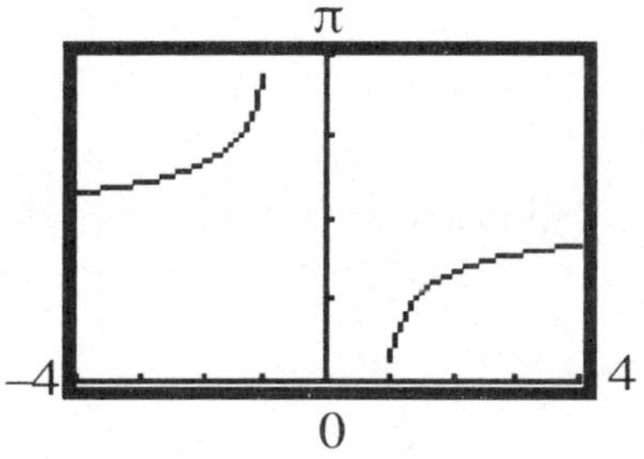

51. $y = \csc^{-1} x$

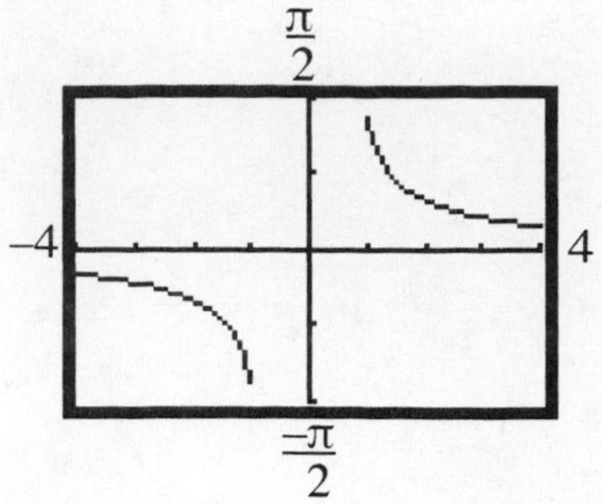

Chapter 8

Analytic Trigonometry

8.3 Trigonometric Identities

1. $\csc\theta \cdot \cos\theta = \dfrac{1}{\sin\theta} \cdot \cos\theta = \dfrac{\cos\theta}{\sin\theta} = \cot\theta$

2. $\sec\theta \cdot \sin\theta = \dfrac{1}{\cos\theta} \cdot \sin\theta = \dfrac{\sin\theta}{\cos\theta} = \tan\theta$

3. $1 + \tan^2(-\theta) = 1 + (-\tan\theta)^2 = 1 + \tan^2\theta = \sec^2\theta$

4. $1 + \cot^2(-\theta) = 1 + (-\cot\theta)^2 = 1 + \cot^2\theta = \csc^2\theta$

5. $\cos\theta(\tan\theta + \cot\theta) = \cos\theta\left(\dfrac{\sin\theta}{\cos\theta} + \dfrac{\cos\theta}{\sin\theta}\right) = \cos\theta\left(\dfrac{\sin^2\theta + \cos^2\theta}{\cos\theta\sin\theta}\right) = \dfrac{1}{\sin\theta} = \csc\theta$

6. $\sin\theta(\cot\theta + \tan\theta) = \sin\theta\left(\dfrac{\cos\theta}{\sin\theta} + \dfrac{\sin\theta}{\cos\theta}\right) = \sin\theta\left(\dfrac{\cos^2\theta + \sin^2\theta}{\sin\theta\cos\theta}\right) = \dfrac{1}{\cos\theta} = \sec\theta$

7. $\tan\theta\cot\theta - \cos^2\theta = \tan\theta \cdot \dfrac{1}{\tan\theta} - \cos^2\theta = 1 - \cos^2\theta = \sin^2\theta$

8. $\sin\theta\csc\theta - \cos^2\theta = \sin\theta \cdot \dfrac{1}{\sin\theta} - \cos^2\theta = 1 - \cos^2\theta = \sin^2\theta$

9. $(\sec\theta - 1)(\sec\theta + 1) = \sec^2\theta - 1 = \tan^2\theta$

10. $(\csc\theta - 1)(\csc\theta + 1) = \csc^2\theta - 1 = \cot^2\theta$

11. $(\sec\theta + \tan\theta)(\sec\theta - \tan\theta) = \sec^2\theta - \tan^2\theta = 1$

12. $(\csc\theta + \cot\theta)(\csc\theta - \cot\theta) = \csc^2\theta - \cot^2\theta = 1$

13. $\cos^2\theta(1 + \tan^2\theta) = \cos^2\theta \cdot \sec^2\theta = \cos^2\theta \cdot \dfrac{1}{\cos^2\theta} = 1$

14. $(1 - \cos^2\theta)(1 + \cot^2\theta) = \sin^2\theta \cdot \csc^2\theta = \sin^2\theta \cdot \dfrac{1}{\sin^2\theta} = 1$

15. $(\sin\theta+\cos\theta)^2+(\sin\theta-\cos\theta)^2$
$= \sin^2\theta+2\sin\theta\cos\theta+\cos^2\theta+\sin^2\theta-2\sin\theta\cos\theta+\cos^2\theta$
$= 2\sin^2\theta+2\cos^2\theta = 2(\sin^2\theta+\cos^2\theta) = 2\cdot 1 = 2$

16. $\tan^2\theta\cos^2\theta+\cot^2\theta\sin^2\theta = \dfrac{\sin^2\theta}{\cos^2\theta}\cdot\cos^2\theta+\dfrac{\cos^2\theta}{\sin^2\theta}\cdot\sin^2\theta = \sin^2\theta+\cos^2\theta = 1$

17. $\sec^4\theta-\sec^2\theta = \sec^2\theta(\sec^2\theta-1) = (\tan^2\theta+1)\tan^2\theta = \tan^4\theta+\tan^2\theta$

18. $\csc^4\theta-\csc^2\theta = \csc^2\theta(\csc^2\theta-1) = (\cot^2\theta+1)\cot^2\theta = \cot^4\theta+\cot^2\theta$

19. $\sec\theta-\tan\theta = \dfrac{1}{\cos\theta}-\dfrac{\sin\theta}{\cos\theta} = \left(\dfrac{1-\sin\theta}{\cos\theta}\right)\cdot\left(\dfrac{1+\sin\theta}{1+\sin\theta}\right) = \dfrac{1-\sin^2\theta}{\cos\theta(1+\sin\theta)}$
$= \dfrac{\cos^2\theta}{\cos\theta(1+\sin\theta)} = \dfrac{\cos\theta}{1+\sin\theta}$

20. $\csc\theta-\cot\theta = \dfrac{1}{\sin\theta}-\dfrac{\cos\theta}{\sin\theta} = \left(\dfrac{1-\cos\theta}{\sin\theta}\right)\cdot\left(\dfrac{1+\cos\theta}{1+\cos\theta}\right) = \dfrac{1-\cos^2\theta}{\sin\theta(1+\cos\theta)}$
$= \dfrac{\sin^2\theta}{\sin\theta(1+\cos\theta)} = \dfrac{\sin\theta}{1+\cos\theta}$

21. $3\sin^2\theta+4\cos^2\theta = 3\sin^2\theta+3\cos^2\theta+\cos^2\theta = 3(\sin^2\theta+\cos^2\theta)+\cos^2\theta$
$= 3\cdot 1+\cos^2\theta = 3+\cos^2\theta$

22. $9\sec^2\theta-5\tan^2\theta = 4\sec^2\theta+5\sec^2\theta-5\tan^2\theta = 4\sec^2\theta+5(\sec^2\theta-\tan^2\theta)$
$= 4\sec^2\theta+5\cdot 1 = 5+4\sec^2\theta$

23. $1-\dfrac{\cos^2\theta}{1+\sin\theta} = 1-\dfrac{1-\sin^2\theta}{1+\sin\theta} = 1-\dfrac{(1-\sin\theta)(1+\sin\theta)}{1+\sin\theta} = 1-1+\sin\theta = \sin\theta$

24. $1-\dfrac{\sin^2\theta}{1-\cos\theta} = 1-\dfrac{1-\cos^2\theta}{1-\cos\theta} = 1-\dfrac{(1-\cos\theta)(1+\cos\theta)}{1-\cos\theta} = 1-1-\cos\theta = -\cos\theta$

25. $\dfrac{1+\tan\theta}{1-\tan\theta} = \dfrac{\left(1+\dfrac{1}{\cot\theta}\right)}{\left(1-\dfrac{1}{\cot\theta}\right)} = \dfrac{\left(\dfrac{\cot\theta+1}{\cot\theta}\right)}{\left(\dfrac{\cot\theta-1}{\cot\theta}\right)} = \dfrac{\cot\theta+1}{\cot\theta}\cdot\dfrac{\cot\theta}{\cot\theta-1} = \dfrac{\cot\theta+1}{\cot\theta-1}$

26. $\dfrac{\csc\theta-1}{\csc\theta+1} = \dfrac{\left(\dfrac{1}{\sin\theta}-1\right)}{\left(\dfrac{1}{\sin\theta}+1\right)} = \dfrac{\left(\dfrac{1-\sin\theta}{\sin\theta}\right)}{\left(\dfrac{1+\sin\theta}{\sin\theta}\right)} = \dfrac{1-\sin\theta}{\sin\theta}\cdot\dfrac{\sin\theta}{1+\sin\theta} = \dfrac{1-\sin\theta}{1+\sin\theta}$

27. $$\frac{\sec\theta}{\csc\theta}+\frac{\sin\theta}{\cos\theta}=\frac{\left(\frac{1}{\cos\theta}\right)}{\left(\frac{1}{\sin\theta}\right)}+\frac{\sin\theta}{\cos\theta}=\frac{\sin\theta}{\cos\theta}+\frac{\sin\theta}{\cos\theta}=\tan\theta+\tan\theta=2\tan\theta$$

28. $$\frac{\csc\theta-1}{\cot\theta}=\frac{\csc\theta-1}{\cot\theta}\cdot\frac{\csc\theta+1}{\csc\theta+1}=\frac{\csc^2\theta-1}{\cot\theta(\csc\theta+1)}=\frac{\cot^2\theta}{\cot\theta(\csc\theta+1)}=\frac{\cot\theta}{\csc\theta+1}$$

29. $$\frac{1+\sin\theta}{1-\sin\theta}=\frac{\left(1+\frac{1}{\csc\theta}\right)}{\left(1-\frac{1}{\csc\theta}\right)}=\frac{\left(\frac{\csc\theta+1}{\csc\theta}\right)}{\left(\frac{\csc\theta-1}{\csc\theta}\right)}=\frac{\csc\theta+1}{\csc\theta}\cdot\frac{\csc\theta}{\csc\theta-1}=\frac{\csc\theta+1}{\csc\theta-1}$$

30. $$\frac{\cos\theta+1}{\cos\theta-1}=\frac{(\cos\theta+1)\cdot\left(\frac{1}{\cos\theta}\right)}{(\cos\theta-1)\cdot\left(\frac{1}{\cos\theta}\right)}=\frac{\left(1+\frac{1}{\cos\theta}\right)}{\left(1-\frac{1}{\cos\theta}\right)}=\frac{1+\sec\theta}{1-\sec\theta}$$

31. $$\frac{1-\sin\theta}{\cos\theta}+\frac{\cos\theta}{1-\sin\theta}=\frac{(1-\sin\theta)^2+\cos^2\theta}{\cos\theta(1-\sin\theta)}=\frac{1-2\sin\theta+\sin^2\theta+\cos^2\theta}{\cos\theta(1-\sin\theta)}$$
$$=\frac{1-2\sin\theta+1}{\cos\theta(1-\sin\theta)}=\frac{2-2\sin\theta}{\cos\theta(1-\sin\theta)}=\frac{2(1-\sin\theta)}{\cos\theta(1-\sin\theta)}=\frac{2}{\cos\theta}=2\sec\theta$$

32. $$\frac{\cos\theta}{1+\sin\theta}+\frac{1+\sin\theta}{\cos\theta}=\frac{\cos^2\theta+(1+\sin\theta)^2}{\cos\theta(1+\sin\theta)}=\frac{\cos^2\theta+1+2\sin\theta+\sin^2\theta}{\cos\theta(1+\sin\theta)}$$
$$=\frac{1+2\sin\theta+1}{\cos\theta(1+\sin\theta)}=\frac{2+2\sin\theta}{\cos\theta(1+\sin\theta)}=\frac{2(1+\sin\theta)}{\cos\theta(1+\sin\theta)}=\frac{2}{\cos\theta}=2\sec\theta$$

33. $$\frac{\sin\theta}{\sin\theta-\cos\theta}=\frac{\sin\theta}{\sin\theta-\cos\theta}\cdot\frac{\left(\frac{1}{\sin\theta}\right)}{\left(\frac{1}{\sin\theta}\right)}=\frac{1}{\left(1-\frac{\cos\theta}{\sin\theta}\right)}=\frac{1}{1-\cot\theta}$$

34. $$1-\frac{\sin^2\theta}{1+\cos\theta}=\frac{1+\cos\theta-\sin^2\theta}{1+\cos\theta}=\frac{1+\cos\theta-(1-\cos^2\theta)}{1+\cos\theta}=\frac{\cos\theta+\cos^2\theta}{1+\cos\theta}$$
$$=\frac{\cos\theta(1+\cos\theta)}{1+\cos\theta}=\cos\theta$$

35. $$(\sec\theta-\tan\theta)^2=\sec^2\theta-2\sec\theta\tan\theta+\tan^2\theta=\frac{1}{\cos^2\theta}-2\cdot\frac{1}{\cos\theta}\cdot\frac{\sin\theta}{\cos\theta}+\frac{\sin^2\theta}{\cos^2\theta}$$
$$=\frac{1-2\sin\theta+\sin^2\theta}{\cos^2\theta}=\frac{(1-\sin\theta)(1-\sin\theta)}{1-\sin^2\theta}=\frac{(1-\sin\theta)(1-\sin\theta)}{(1-\sin\theta)(1+\sin\theta)}=\frac{1-\sin\theta}{1+\sin\theta}$$

36. $(\csc\theta-\cot\theta)^2=\csc^2\theta-2\csc\theta\cot\theta+\cot^2\theta=\dfrac{1}{\sin^2\theta}-2\cdot\dfrac{1}{\sin\theta}\cdot\dfrac{\cos\theta}{\sin\theta}+\dfrac{\cos^2\theta}{\sin^2\theta}$

$$=\frac{1-2\cos\theta+\cos^2\theta}{\sin^2\theta}=\frac{(1-\cos\theta)(1-\cos\theta)}{1-\cos^2\theta}=\frac{(1-\cos\theta)(1-\cos\theta)}{(1-\cos\theta)(1+\cos\theta)}=\frac{1-\cos\theta}{1+\cos\theta}$$

37. $\dfrac{\cos\theta}{1-\tan\theta}+\dfrac{\sin\theta}{1-\cot\theta}=\dfrac{\cos\theta}{\left(1-\dfrac{\sin\theta}{\cos\theta}\right)}+\dfrac{\sin\theta}{\left(1-\dfrac{\cos\theta}{\sin\theta}\right)}=\dfrac{\cos\theta}{\left(\dfrac{\cos\theta-\sin\theta}{\cos\theta}\right)}+\dfrac{\sin\theta}{\left(\dfrac{\sin\theta-\cos\theta}{\sin\theta}\right)}$

$$=\frac{\cos^2\theta}{\cos\theta-\sin\theta}+\frac{\sin^2\theta}{\sin\theta-\cos\theta}=\frac{\cos^2\theta-\sin^2\theta}{\cos\theta-\sin\theta}$$

$$=\frac{(\cos\theta-\sin\theta)(\cos\theta+\sin\theta)}{\cos\theta-\sin\theta}=\cos\theta+\sin\theta=\sin\theta+\cos\theta$$

38. $\dfrac{\cot\theta}{1-\tan\theta}+\dfrac{\tan\theta}{1-\cot\theta}=\dfrac{\left(\dfrac{\cos\theta}{\sin\theta}\right)}{\left(1-\dfrac{\sin\theta}{\cos\theta}\right)}+\dfrac{\left(\dfrac{\sin\theta}{\cos\theta}\right)}{\left(1-\dfrac{\cos\theta}{\sin\theta}\right)}=\dfrac{\left(\dfrac{\cos\theta}{\sin\theta}\right)}{\left(\dfrac{\cos\theta-\sin\theta}{\cos\theta}\right)}+\dfrac{\left(\dfrac{\sin\theta}{\cos\theta}\right)}{\left(\dfrac{\sin\theta-\cos\theta}{\sin\theta}\right)}$

$$=\frac{\cos^2\theta}{\sin\theta(\cos\theta-\sin\theta)}+\frac{\sin^2\theta}{\cos\theta(\sin\theta-\cos\theta)}$$

$$=\frac{-\cos^2\theta\cdot\cos\theta+\sin^2\theta\cdot\sin\theta}{\sin\theta\cos\theta(\sin\theta-\cos\theta)}=\frac{\sin^3\theta-\cos^3\theta}{\sin\theta\cos\theta(\sin\theta-\cos\theta)}$$

$$=\frac{(\sin\theta-\cos\theta)(\sin^2\theta+\sin\theta\cos\theta+\cos^2\theta)}{\sin\theta\cos\theta(\sin\theta-\cos\theta)}$$

$$=\frac{\sin^2\theta+\sin\theta\cos\theta+\cos^2\theta}{\sin\theta\cos\theta}=\frac{\sin^2\theta}{\sin\theta\cos\theta}+\frac{\sin\theta\cos\theta}{\sin\theta\cos\theta}+\frac{\cos^2\theta}{\sin\theta\cos\theta}$$

$$=\frac{\sin\theta}{\cos\theta}+1+\frac{\cos\theta}{\sin\theta}=1+\tan\theta+\cot\theta$$

39. $\tan\theta+\dfrac{\cos\theta}{1+\sin\theta}=\dfrac{\sin\theta}{\cos\theta}+\dfrac{\cos\theta}{1+\sin\theta}=\dfrac{\sin\theta(1+\sin\theta)+\cos^2\theta}{\cos\theta(1+\sin\theta)}$

$$=\frac{\sin\theta+\sin^2\theta+\cos^2\theta}{\cos\theta(1+\sin\theta)}=\frac{\sin\theta+1}{\cos\theta(1+\sin\theta)}=\frac{1}{\cos\theta}=\sec\theta$$

40. $\dfrac{\sin\theta\cos\theta}{\cos^2\theta-\sin^2\theta}=\dfrac{(\sin\theta\cos\theta)\cdot\left(\dfrac{1}{\cos^2\theta}\right)}{(\cos^2\theta-\sin^2\theta)\cdot\left(\dfrac{1}{\cos^2\theta}\right)}=\dfrac{\left(\dfrac{\sin\theta}{\cos\theta}\right)}{\left(1-\dfrac{\sin^2\theta}{\cos^2\theta}\right)}=\dfrac{\tan\theta}{1-\tan^2\theta}$

41. $\dfrac{\tan\theta+\sec\theta-1}{\tan\theta-\sec\theta+1}=\dfrac{\tan\theta+(\sec\theta-1)}{\tan\theta-(\sec\theta-1)}\cdot\dfrac{\tan\theta+(\sec\theta-1)}{\tan\theta+(\sec\theta-1)}$

$$= \frac{\tan^2\theta + 2\tan\theta(\sec\theta - 1) + \sec^2\theta - 2\sec\theta + 1}{\tan^2\theta - (\sec^2\theta - 2\sec\theta + 1)}$$
$$= \frac{\sec^2\theta - 1 + 2\tan\theta(\sec\theta - 1) + \sec^2\theta - 2\sec\theta + 1}{\sec^2\theta - 1 - \sec^2\theta + 2\sec\theta - 1}$$
$$= \frac{2\sec^2\theta - 2\sec\theta + 2\tan\theta(\sec\theta - 1)}{2\sec\theta - 2}$$
$$= \frac{2\sec\theta(\sec\theta - 1) + 2\tan\theta(\sec\theta - 1)}{2\sec\theta - 2}$$
$$= \frac{2(\sec\theta - 1)(\sec\theta + \tan\theta)}{2(\sec\theta - 1)} = \sec\theta + \tan\theta = \tan\theta + \sec\theta$$

42. $$\frac{\sin\theta - \cos\theta + 1}{\sin\theta + \cos\theta - 1} = \frac{(\sin\theta - \cos\theta) + 1}{(\sin\theta + \cos\theta) - 1} \cdot \frac{(\sin\theta + \cos\theta) + 1}{(\sin\theta + \cos\theta) + 1}$$
$$= \frac{\sin^2\theta - \cos^2\theta + \sin\theta + \cos\theta + \sin\theta - \cos\theta + 1}{(\sin\theta + \cos\theta)^2 - 1}$$
$$= \frac{\sin^2\theta - \cos^2\theta + 2\sin\theta + 1}{\sin^2\theta + 2\sin\theta\cos\theta + \cos^2\theta - 1} = \frac{\sin^2\theta - (1 - \sin^2\theta) + 2\sin\theta + 1}{2\sin\theta\cos\theta + 1 - 1}$$
$$= \frac{2\sin^2\theta + 2\sin\theta}{2\sin\theta\cos\theta} = \frac{2\sin\theta(\sin\theta + 1)}{2\sin\theta\cos\theta} = \frac{\sin\theta + 1}{\cos\theta}$$

43. $$\frac{\tan\theta - \cot\theta}{\tan\theta + \cot\theta} = \frac{\left(\frac{\sin\theta}{\cos\theta} - \frac{\cos\theta}{\sin\theta}\right)}{\left(\frac{\sin\theta}{\cos\theta} + \frac{\cos\theta}{\sin\theta}\right)} = \frac{\left(\frac{\sin^2\theta - \cos^2\theta}{\cos\theta\sin\theta}\right)}{\left(\frac{\sin^2\theta + \cos^2\theta}{\cos\theta\sin\theta}\right)} = \frac{\sin^2\theta - \cos^2\theta}{1} = \sin^2\theta - \cos^2\theta$$

44. $$\frac{\sec\theta - \cos\theta}{\sec\theta + \cos\theta} = \frac{\left(\frac{1}{\cos\theta} - \frac{\cos^2\theta}{\cos\theta}\right)}{\left(\frac{1}{\cos\theta} + \frac{\cos^2\theta}{\cos\theta}\right)} = \frac{\left(\frac{1 - \cos^2\theta}{\cos\theta}\right)}{\left(\frac{1 + \cos^2\theta}{\cos\theta}\right)} = \frac{\sin^2\theta}{1 + \cos^2\theta}$$

45. $$\frac{\tan\theta - \cot\theta}{\tan\theta + \cot\theta} + 1 = \frac{\left(\frac{\sin\theta}{\cos\theta} - \frac{\cos\theta}{\sin\theta}\right)}{\left(\frac{\sin\theta}{\cos\theta} + \frac{\cos\theta}{\sin\theta}\right)} + 1 = \frac{\left(\frac{\sin^2\theta - \cos^2\theta}{\cos\theta\sin\theta}\right)}{\left(\frac{\sin^2\theta + \cos^2\theta}{\cos\theta\sin\theta}\right)} + 1 = \frac{\sin^2\theta - \cos^2\theta}{1} + 1$$
$$= \sin^2\theta - \cos^2\theta + 1 = \sin^2\theta + (1 - \cos^2\theta) = \sin^2\theta + \sin^2\theta = 2\sin^2\theta$$

46. $$\frac{\tan\theta - \cot\theta}{\tan\theta + \cot\theta} + 2\cos^2\theta = \frac{\left(\frac{\sin\theta}{\cos\theta} - \frac{\cos\theta}{\sin\theta}\right)}{\left(\frac{\sin\theta}{\cos\theta} + \frac{\cos\theta}{\sin\theta}\right)} + 2\cos^2\theta = \frac{\left(\frac{\sin^2\theta - \cos^2\theta}{\cos\theta\sin\theta}\right)}{\left(\frac{\sin^2\theta + \cos^2\theta}{\cos\theta\sin\theta}\right)} + 2\cos^2\theta$$
$$= \frac{\sin^2\theta - \cos^2\theta}{1} + 2\cos^2\theta = \sin^2\theta + \cos^2\theta = 1$$

47. $$\frac{\sec\theta+\tan\theta}{\cot\theta+\cos\theta}=\frac{\left(\frac{1}{\cos\theta}+\frac{\sin\theta}{\cos\theta}\right)}{\left(\frac{\cos\theta}{\sin\theta}+\cos\theta\right)}=\frac{\left(\frac{1+\sin\theta}{\cos\theta}\right)}{\left(\frac{\cos\theta+\cos\theta\sin\theta}{\sin\theta}\right)}=\frac{1+\sin\theta}{\cos\theta}\cdot\frac{\sin\theta}{\cos\theta(1+\sin\theta)}$$
$$=\frac{\sin\theta}{\cos\theta}\cdot\frac{1}{\cos\theta}=\tan\theta\sec\theta$$

48. $$\frac{\sec\theta}{1+\sec\theta}=\frac{\left(\frac{1}{\cos\theta}\right)}{\left(1+\frac{1}{\cos\theta}\right)}=\frac{\left(\frac{1}{\cos\theta}\right)}{\left(\frac{\cos\theta+1}{\cos\theta}\right)}=\left(\frac{1}{1+\cos\theta}\right)\cdot\left(\frac{1-\cos\theta}{1-\cos\theta}\right)=\frac{1-\cos\theta}{1-\cos^2\theta}=\frac{1-\cos\theta}{\sin^2\theta}$$

49. $$\frac{1-\tan^2\theta}{1+\tan^2\theta}+1=\frac{1-\tan^2\theta+1+\tan^2\theta}{1+\tan^2\theta}=\frac{2}{\sec^2\theta}=2\cdot\frac{1}{\sec^2\theta}=2\cos^2\theta$$

50. $$\frac{1-\cot^2\theta}{1+\cot^2\theta}+2\cos^2\theta=\frac{1-\cot^2\theta}{\csc^2\theta}+2\cos^2\theta=\frac{1}{\csc^2\theta}-\frac{\cot^2\theta}{\csc^2\theta}+2\cos^2\theta$$
$$=\sin^2\theta-\frac{\left(\frac{\cos^2\theta}{\sin^2\theta}\right)}{\left(\frac{1}{\sin^2\theta}\right)}+2\cos^2\theta=\sin^2\theta-\cos^2\theta+2\cos^2\theta=\sin^2\theta+\cos^2\theta=1$$

51. $$\frac{\sec\theta-\csc\theta}{\sec\theta\csc\theta}=\frac{\left(\frac{1}{\cos\theta}-\frac{1}{\sin\theta}\right)}{\left(\frac{1}{\cos\theta}\cdot\frac{1}{\sin\theta}\right)}=\frac{\left(\frac{\sin\theta-\cos\theta}{\cos\theta\sin\theta}\right)}{\left(\frac{1}{\cos\theta\sin\theta}\right)}=\sin\theta-\cos\theta$$

52. $$\frac{\sin^2\theta-\tan\theta}{\cos^2\theta-\cot\theta}=\frac{\left(\sin^2\theta-\frac{\sin\theta}{\cos\theta}\right)}{\left(\cos^2\theta-\frac{\cos\theta}{\sin\theta}\right)}=\frac{\left(\frac{\sin^2\theta\cos\theta-\sin\theta}{\cos\theta}\right)}{\left(\frac{\cos^2\theta\sin\theta-\cos\theta}{\sin\theta}\right)}=\frac{\left(\frac{\sin\theta(\sin\theta\cos\theta-1)}{\cos\theta}\right)}{\left(\frac{\cos\theta(\cos\theta\sin\theta-1)}{\sin\theta}\right)}$$
$$=\frac{\sin^2\theta}{\cos^2\theta}=\tan^2\theta$$

53. $$\sec\theta-\cos\theta-\sin\theta\tan\theta=\frac{1}{\cos\theta}-\cos\theta-\sin\theta\cdot\frac{\sin\theta}{\cos\theta}=\frac{1-\cos^2\theta-\sin^2\theta}{\cos\theta}$$
$$=\frac{\sin^2\theta-\sin^2\theta}{\cos\theta}=0$$

54. $$\tan\theta+\cot\theta-\sec\theta\csc\theta=\frac{\sin\theta}{\cos\theta}+\frac{\cos\theta}{\sin\theta}-\frac{1}{\cos\theta}\cdot\frac{1}{\sin\theta}=\frac{\sin^2\theta+\cos^2\theta-1}{\cos\theta\sin\theta}$$
$$=\frac{1-1}{\cos\theta\sin\theta}=0$$

55. $$\frac{1}{1-\sin\theta}+\frac{1}{1+\sin\theta}=\frac{1+\sin\theta+1-\sin\theta}{(1-\sin\theta)(1+\sin\theta)}=\frac{2}{1-\sin^2\theta}=\frac{2}{\cos^2\theta}=2\sec^2\theta$$

56. $$\frac{1+\sin\theta}{1-\sin\theta}-\frac{1-\sin\theta}{1+\sin\theta}=\frac{(1+\sin\theta)^2-(1-\sin\theta)^2}{(1-\sin\theta)(1+\sin\theta)}$$
$$=\frac{1+2\sin\theta+\sin^2\theta-(1-2\sin\theta+\sin^2\theta)}{1-\sin^2\theta}$$
$$=\frac{4\sin\theta}{\cos^2\theta}=4\cdot\frac{\sin\theta}{\cos\theta}\cdot\frac{1}{\cos\theta}=4\tan\theta\sec\theta$$

57. $$\frac{\sec\theta}{1-\sin\theta}=\left(\frac{\sec\theta}{1-\sin\theta}\right)\cdot\left(\frac{1+\sin\theta}{1+\sin\theta}\right)=\frac{\sec\theta(1+\sin\theta)}{1-\sin^2\theta}=\frac{\sec\theta(1+\sin\theta)}{\cos^2\theta}$$
$$=\frac{1}{\cos\theta}\cdot\frac{1+\sin\theta}{\cos^2\theta}=\frac{1+\sin\theta}{\cos^3\theta}$$

58. $$(\sec\theta-\tan\theta)^2=\sec^2\theta-2\sec\theta\tan\theta+\tan^2\theta=\frac{1}{\cos^2\theta}-2\cdot\frac{1}{\cos\theta}\cdot\frac{\sin\theta}{\cos\theta}+\frac{\sin^2\theta}{\cos^2\theta}$$
$$=\frac{1-2\sin\theta+\sin^2\theta}{\cos^2\theta}=\frac{(1-\sin\theta)(1-\sin\theta)}{1-\sin^2\theta}=\frac{(1-\sin\theta)(1-\sin\theta)}{(1-\sin\theta)(1+\sin\theta)}=\frac{1-\sin\theta}{1+\sin\theta}$$

59. $$\frac{(\sec\theta-\tan\theta)^2+1}{\csc\theta(\sec\theta-\tan\theta)}=\frac{\sec^2\theta-2\sec\theta\tan\theta+\tan^2\theta+1}{\csc\theta(\sec\theta-\tan\theta)}=\frac{2\sec^2\theta-2\sec\theta\tan\theta}{\csc\theta(\sec\theta-\tan\theta)}$$
$$=\frac{2\sec\theta(\sec\theta-\tan\theta)}{\csc\theta(\sec\theta-\tan\theta)}=\frac{2\sec\theta}{\csc\theta}=\frac{\left(2\cdot\frac{1}{\cos\theta}\right)}{\left(\frac{1}{\sin\theta}\right)}=2\cdot\frac{1}{\cos\theta}\cdot\frac{\sin\theta}{1}=2\tan\theta$$

60. $$\frac{\sec^2\theta-\tan^2\theta+\tan\theta}{\sec\theta}=\frac{1+\tan\theta}{\sec\theta}=\frac{\left(1+\frac{\sin\theta}{\cos\theta}\right)}{\left(\frac{1}{\cos\theta}\right)}=\left(1+\frac{\sin\theta}{\cos\theta}\right)\cos\theta=\cos\theta+\sin\theta$$

61. $$\frac{\sin\theta+\cos\theta}{\cos\theta}-\frac{\sin\theta-\cos\theta}{\sin\theta}=\frac{\sin\theta}{\cos\theta}+\frac{\cos\theta}{\cos\theta}-\frac{\sin\theta}{\sin\theta}+\frac{\cos\theta}{\sin\theta}=\frac{\sin\theta}{\cos\theta}+1-1+\frac{\cos\theta}{\sin\theta}$$
$$=\frac{\sin^2\theta+\cos^2\theta}{\cos\theta\sin\theta}=\frac{1}{\cos\theta\sin\theta}=\sec\theta\csc\theta$$

62. $$\frac{\sin\theta+\cos\theta}{\sin\theta}-\frac{\cos\theta-\sin\theta}{\cos\theta}=\frac{\sin\theta}{\sin\theta}+\frac{\cos\theta}{\sin\theta}-\frac{\cos\theta}{\cos\theta}+\frac{\sin\theta}{\cos\theta}=1+\frac{\cos\theta}{\sin\theta}-1+\frac{\sin\theta}{\cos\theta}$$
$$=\frac{\cos^2\theta+\sin^2\theta}{\cos\theta\sin\theta}=\frac{1}{\cos\theta\sin\theta}=\sec\theta\csc\theta$$

63. $$\frac{\sin^3\theta+\cos^3\theta}{\sin\theta+\cos\theta}=\frac{(\sin\theta+\cos\theta)(\sin^2\theta-\sin\theta\cos\theta+\cos^2\theta)}{\sin\theta+\cos\theta}=1-\sin\theta\cos\theta$$

64. $$\frac{\sin^3\theta+\cos^3\theta}{1-2\cos^2\theta}=\frac{(\sin\theta+\cos\theta)(\sin^2\theta-\sin\theta\cos\theta+\cos^2\theta)}{1-\cos^2\theta-\cos^2\theta}$$

$$=\frac{(\sin\theta+\cos\theta)(1-\sin\theta\cos\theta)}{\sin^2\theta-\cos^2\theta}=\frac{(\sin\theta+\cos\theta)(1-\sin\theta\cos\theta)}{(\sin\theta+\cos\theta)(\sin\theta-\cos\theta)}$$

$$=\frac{1-\sin\theta\cos\theta}{(\sin\theta-\cos\theta)}\cdot\frac{\left(\frac{1}{\cos\theta}\right)}{\left(\frac{1}{\cos\theta}\right)}=\frac{\left(\frac{1}{\cos\theta}-\sin\theta\right)}{\left(\frac{\sin\theta}{\cos\theta}-1\right)}=\frac{\sec\theta-\sin\theta}{\tan\theta-1}$$

65. $$\frac{\cos^2\theta-\sin^2\theta}{1-\tan^2\theta}=\frac{\cos^2\theta-\sin^2\theta}{\left(1-\frac{\sin^2\theta}{\cos^2\theta}\right)}=\frac{\cos^2\theta-\sin^2\theta}{\left(\frac{\cos^2\theta-\sin^2\theta}{\cos^2\theta}\right)}=\cos^2\theta$$

66. $$\frac{\cos\theta+\sin\theta-\sin^3\theta}{\sin\theta}=\frac{\cos\theta}{\sin\theta}+\frac{\sin\theta}{\sin\theta}-\frac{\sin^3\theta}{\sin\theta}=\cot\theta+1-\sin^2\theta=\cot\theta+\cos^2\theta$$

67. $$\frac{(2\cos^2\theta-1)^2}{\cos^4\theta-\sin^4\theta}=\frac{\left[2\cos^2\theta-(\sin^2\theta+\cos^2\theta)\right]^2}{(\cos^2\theta-\sin^2\theta)(\cos^2\theta+\sin^2\theta)}$$

$$=\frac{(\cos^2\theta-\sin^2\theta)^2}{(\cos^2\theta-\sin^2\theta)(\cos^2\theta+\sin^2\theta)}=\frac{\cos^2\theta-\sin^2\theta}{\cos^2\theta+\sin^2\theta}$$

$$=\cos^2\theta-\sin^2\theta=1-\sin^2\theta-\sin^2\theta=1-2\sin^2\theta$$

68. $$\frac{1-2\cos^2\theta}{\sin\theta\cos\theta}=\frac{1-\cos^2\theta-\cos^2\theta}{\sin\theta\cos\theta}=\frac{\sin^2\theta-\cos^2\theta}{\sin\theta\cos\theta}=\frac{\sin^2\theta}{\sin\theta\cos\theta}-\frac{\cos^2\theta}{\sin\theta\cos\theta}$$

$$=\frac{\sin\theta}{\cos\theta}-\frac{\cos\theta}{\sin\theta}=\tan\theta-\cot\theta$$

69. $$\frac{1+\sin\theta+\cos\theta}{1+\sin\theta-\cos\theta}=\frac{(1+\sin\theta)+\cos\theta}{(1+\sin\theta)-\cos\theta}\cdot\frac{(1+\sin\theta)+\cos\theta}{(1+\sin\theta)+\cos\theta}$$

$$=\frac{1+2\sin\theta+\sin^2\theta+2\cos\theta(1+\sin\theta)+\cos^2\theta}{1+2\sin\theta+\sin^2\theta-\cos^2\theta}$$

$$=\frac{1+2\sin\theta+\sin^2\theta+2\cos\theta(1+\sin\theta)+(1-\sin^2\theta)}{1+2\sin\theta+\sin^2\theta-(1-\sin^2\theta)}$$

$$=\frac{2+2\sin\theta+2\cos\theta(1+\sin\theta)}{2\sin\theta+2\sin^2\theta}=\frac{2(1+\sin\theta)+2\cos\theta(1+\sin\theta)}{2\sin\theta(1+\sin\theta)}$$

$$=\frac{2(1+\sin\theta)(1+\cos\theta)}{2\sin\theta(1+\sin\theta)}=\frac{1+\cos\theta}{\sin\theta}$$

70. $$\frac{1+\cos\theta+\sin\theta}{1+\cos\theta-\sin\theta}=\frac{(1+\cos\theta)+\sin\theta}{(1+\cos\theta)-\sin\theta}\cdot\frac{(1+\cos\theta)+\sin\theta}{(1+\cos\theta)+\sin\theta}$$

$$=\frac{1+2\cos\theta+\cos^2\theta+2\sin\theta(1+\cos\theta)+\sin^2\theta}{1+2\cos\theta+\cos^2\theta-\sin^2\theta}$$

$$=\frac{1+2\cos\theta+\cos^2\theta+2\sin\theta(1+\cos\theta)+1-\cos^2\theta}{1+2\cos\theta+\cos^2\theta-(1-\cos^2\theta)}$$

$$= \frac{2+2\cos\theta+2\sin\theta(1+\cos\theta)}{2\cos\theta+2\cos^2\theta} = \frac{2(1+\cos\theta)+2\sin\theta(1+\cos\theta)}{2\cos\theta(1+\cos\theta)}$$
$$= \frac{2(1+\cos\theta)(1+\sin\theta)}{2\cos\theta(1+\cos\theta)} = \frac{1+\sin\theta}{\cos\theta} = \frac{1}{\cos\theta} + \frac{\sin\theta}{\cos\theta} = \sec\theta + \tan\theta$$

71. $(a\sin\theta + b\cos\theta)^2 + (a\cos\theta - b\sin\theta)^2$
$$= a^2\sin^2\theta + 2ab\sin\theta\cos\theta + b^2\cos^2\theta + a^2\cos^2\theta - 2ab\sin\theta\cos\theta + b^2\sin^2\theta$$
$$= a^2(\sin^2\theta + \cos^2\theta) + b^2(\sin^2\theta + \cos^2\theta) = a^2 + b^2$$

72. $(2a\sin\theta\cos\theta)^2 + a^2(\cos^2\theta - \sin^2\theta)^2$
$$= 4a^2\sin^2\theta\cos^2\theta + a^2\left(\cos^4\theta - 2\cos^2\theta\sin^2\theta + \sin^4\theta\right)$$
$$= a^2\left(4\sin^2\theta\cos^2\theta + \cos^4\theta - 2\cos^2\theta\sin^2\theta + \sin^4\theta\right)$$
$$= a^2\left(\cos^4\theta + 2\cos^2\theta\sin^2\theta + \sin^4\theta\right)$$
$$= a^2\left(\cos^2\theta + \sin^2\theta\right)^2 = a^2(1)^2 = a^2$$

73. $\dfrac{\tan\alpha + \tan\beta}{\cot\alpha + \cot\beta} = \dfrac{\tan\alpha + \tan\beta}{\left(\dfrac{1}{\tan\alpha} + \dfrac{1}{\tan\beta}\right)} = \dfrac{\tan\alpha + \tan\beta}{\left(\dfrac{\tan\beta + \tan\alpha}{\tan\alpha\tan\beta}\right)}$
$$= (\tan\alpha + \tan\beta)\cdot\left(\frac{\tan\alpha\tan\beta}{\tan\alpha + \tan\beta}\right) = \tan\alpha\tan\beta$$

74. $(\tan\alpha + \tan\beta)(1 - \cot\alpha\cot\beta) + (\cot\alpha + \cot\beta)(1 - \tan\alpha\tan\beta)$
$$= \tan\alpha + \tan\beta - \tan\alpha\cot\alpha\cot\beta - \tan\beta\cot\alpha\cot\beta$$
$$+ \cot\alpha + \cot\beta - \cot\alpha\tan\alpha\tan\beta - \cot\beta\tan\alpha\tan\beta$$
$$= \tan\alpha + \tan\beta - \cot\beta - \cot\alpha + \cot\alpha + \cot\beta - \tan\beta - \tan\alpha = 0$$

75. $(\sin\alpha + \cos\beta)^2 + (\cos\beta + \sin\alpha)(\cos\beta - \sin\alpha)$
$$= \sin^2\alpha + 2\sin\alpha\cos\beta + \cos^2\beta + \cos^2\beta - \sin^2\alpha$$
$$= 2\sin\alpha\cos\beta + 2\cos^2\beta = 2\cos\beta(\sin\alpha + \cos\beta)$$

76. $(\sin\alpha - \cos\beta)^2 + (\cos\beta + \sin\alpha)(\cos\beta - \sin\alpha)$
$$= \sin^2\alpha - 2\sin\alpha\cos\beta + \cos^2\beta + \cos^2\beta - \sin^2\alpha$$
$$= -2\sin\alpha\cos\beta + 2\cos^2\beta = -2\cos\beta(\sin\alpha - \cos\beta)$$

77. $\ln|\sec\theta| = \ln\left|\dfrac{1}{\cos\theta}\right| = \ln|\cos\theta|^{-1} = -\ln|\cos\theta|$

78. $\ln|\tan\theta| = \ln\left|\dfrac{\sin\theta}{\cos\theta}\right| = \ln|\sin\theta| - \ln|\cos\theta|$

79. $\ln|1 + \cos\theta| + \ln|1 - \cos\theta| = \ln\left(|1 + \cos\theta|\cdot|1 - \cos\theta|\right) = \ln|1 - \cos^2\theta|$
$$= \ln|\sin^2\theta| = 2\ln|\sin\theta|$$

80. $\ln|\sec\theta+\tan\theta|+\ln|\sec\theta-\tan\theta| = \ln\left(|\sec\theta+\tan\theta|\cdot|\sec\theta-\tan\theta|\right)$
$= \ln|\sec^2\theta-\tan^2\theta| = \ln|1| = 0$

81. Show that $\sec\left(\tan^{-1}v\right)=\sqrt{1+v^2}$.
Let $\alpha=\tan^{-1}v$. Then $\tan\alpha = v$, $-\frac{\pi}{2}<\alpha<\frac{\pi}{2}$.
$\sec\left(\tan^{-1}v\right)=\sec\alpha=\sqrt{1+\tan^2\alpha}=\sqrt{1+v^2}$

82. Show that $\tan\left(\sin^{-1}v\right)=\frac{v}{\sqrt{1-v^2}}$.
Let $\alpha=\sin^{-1}v$. Then $\sin\alpha = v$, $-\frac{\pi}{2}\le\alpha\le\frac{\pi}{2}$.
$\tan\left(\sin^{-1}v\right)=\tan\alpha=\frac{\sin\alpha}{\cos\alpha}=\frac{\sin\alpha}{\sqrt{1-\sin^2\alpha}}=\frac{v}{\sqrt{1-v^2}}$

83. Show that $\tan\left(\cos^{-1}v\right)=\frac{\sqrt{1-v^2}}{v}$.
Let $\alpha=\cos^{-1}v$. Then $\cos\alpha = v$, $0\le\alpha\le\pi$.
$\tan\left(\cos^{-1}v\right)=\tan\alpha=\frac{\sin\alpha}{\cos\alpha}=\frac{\sqrt{1-\cos^2\alpha}}{\cos\alpha}=\frac{\sqrt{1-v^2}}{v}$

84. Show that $\sin\left(\cos^{-1}v\right)=\sqrt{1-v^2}$.
Let $\alpha=\cos^{-1}v$. Then $\cos\alpha = v$, $0\le\alpha\le\pi$.
$\sin\left(\cos^{-1}v\right)=\sin\alpha=\sqrt{1-\cos^2\alpha}=\sqrt{1-v^2}$

85. Show that $\cos\left(\sin^{-1}v\right)=\sqrt{1-v^2}$.
Let $\alpha=\sin^{-1}v$. Then $\sin\alpha = v$, $-\frac{\pi}{2}\le\alpha\le\frac{\pi}{2}$.
$\cos\left(\sin^{-1}v\right)=\cos\alpha=\sqrt{1-\sin^2\alpha}=\sqrt{1-v^2}$

86. From Problem 81 we know that $\sec\left(\tan^{-1}v\right)=\sqrt{1+v^2}$.
Since $\sec\alpha=\frac{1}{\cos\alpha}$, then $\cos\left(\tan^{-1}v\right)=\frac{1}{\sqrt{1+v^2}}$.

Analytic Trigonometry

8.4 Sum and Difference Formulas

1. $\sin\left(\frac{5\pi}{12}\right)=\sin\left(\frac{3\pi}{12}+\frac{2\pi}{12}\right)=\sin\left(\frac{\pi}{4}\right)\cos\left(\frac{\pi}{6}\right)+\cos\left(\frac{\pi}{4}\right)\sin\left(\frac{\pi}{6}\right)=\frac{\sqrt{2}}{2}\cdot\frac{\sqrt{3}}{2}+\frac{\sqrt{2}}{2}\cdot\frac{1}{2}$
$=\frac{1}{4}\left(\sqrt{6}+\sqrt{2}\right)$

2. $\sin\left(\frac{\pi}{12}\right)=\sin\left(\frac{3\pi}{12}-\frac{2\pi}{12}\right)=\sin\left(\frac{\pi}{4}\right)\cos\left(\frac{\pi}{6}\right)-\cos\left(\frac{\pi}{4}\right)\sin\left(\frac{\pi}{6}\right)=\frac{\sqrt{2}}{2}\cdot\frac{\sqrt{3}}{2}-\frac{\sqrt{2}}{2}\cdot\frac{1}{2}$
$=\frac{1}{4}\left(\sqrt{6}-\sqrt{2}\right)$

3. $\cos\left(\frac{7\pi}{12}\right)=\cos\left(\frac{4\pi}{12}+\frac{3\pi}{12}\right)=\cos\left(\frac{\pi}{3}\right)\cos\left(\frac{\pi}{4}\right)-\sin\left(\frac{\pi}{3}\right)\sin\left(\frac{\pi}{4}\right)=\frac{1}{2}\cdot\frac{\sqrt{2}}{2}-\frac{\sqrt{3}}{2}\cdot\frac{\sqrt{2}}{2}$
$=\frac{1}{4}\left(\sqrt{2}-\sqrt{6}\right)$

4. $\tan\left(\frac{7\pi}{12}\right)=\tan\left(\frac{3\pi}{12}+\frac{4\pi}{12}\right)=\frac{\tan\left(\frac{\pi}{4}\right)+\tan\left(\frac{\pi}{3}\right)}{1-\tan\left(\frac{\pi}{4}\right)\tan\left(\frac{\pi}{3}\right)}=\frac{1+\sqrt{3}}{1-1\cdot\sqrt{3}}=\left(\frac{1+\sqrt{3}}{1-\sqrt{3}}\right)\cdot\left(\frac{1+\sqrt{3}}{1+\sqrt{3}}\right)$
$=\frac{1+2\sqrt{3}+3}{1-3}=\frac{4+2\sqrt{3}}{-2}=-2-\sqrt{3}$

5. $\cos(165^\circ)=\cos(120^\circ+45^\circ)=\cos(120^\circ)\cos(45^\circ)-\sin(120^\circ)\sin(45^\circ)$
$=-\frac{1}{2}\cdot\frac{\sqrt{2}}{2}-\frac{\sqrt{3}}{2}\cdot\frac{\sqrt{2}}{2}=-\frac{1}{4}\left(\sqrt{2}+\sqrt{6}\right)$

6. $\sin(105^\circ)=\sin(60^\circ+45^\circ)=\sin(60^\circ)\cos(45^\circ)+\cos(60^\circ)\sin(45^\circ)$
$=\frac{\sqrt{3}}{2}\cdot\frac{\sqrt{2}}{2}+\frac{1}{2}\cdot\frac{\sqrt{2}}{2}=\frac{1}{4}\left(\sqrt{6}+\sqrt{2}\right)$

7. $\tan(15^\circ)=\tan(45^\circ-30^\circ)=\dfrac{\tan(45^\circ)-\tan(30^\circ)}{1+\tan(45^\circ)\tan(30^\circ)}=\dfrac{\left(1-\dfrac{\sqrt{3}}{3}\right)}{\left(1+1\cdot\dfrac{\sqrt{3}}{3}\right)}=\dfrac{\left(\dfrac{3-\sqrt{3}}{3}\right)}{\left(\dfrac{3+\sqrt{3}}{3}\right)}$

$=\left(\dfrac{3-\sqrt{3}}{3+\sqrt{3}}\right)\cdot\left(\dfrac{3-\sqrt{3}}{3-\sqrt{3}}\right)=\dfrac{9-6\sqrt{3}+3}{9-3}=\dfrac{12-6\sqrt{3}}{6}=\dfrac{6(2-\sqrt{3})}{6}=2-\sqrt{3}$

8. $\tan(195^\circ)=\tan(135^\circ+60^\circ)=\dfrac{\tan(135^\circ)+\tan(60^\circ)}{1-\tan(135^\circ)\tan(60^\circ)}=\dfrac{-1+\sqrt{3}}{1-(-1)\cdot\sqrt{3}}=\left(\dfrac{-1+\sqrt{3}}{1+\sqrt{3}}\right)\cdot\left(\dfrac{1-\sqrt{3}}{1-\sqrt{3}}\right)$

$=\dfrac{-1+2\sqrt{3}-3}{1-3}=\dfrac{-4+2\sqrt{3}}{-2}=2-\sqrt{3}$

9. $\sin\left(\dfrac{17\pi}{12}\right)=\sin\left(\dfrac{15\pi}{12}+\dfrac{2\pi}{12}\right)=\sin\left(\dfrac{5\pi}{4}\right)\cos\left(\dfrac{\pi}{6}\right)+\cos\left(\dfrac{5\pi}{4}\right)\sin\left(\dfrac{\pi}{6}\right)=-\dfrac{\sqrt{2}}{2}\cdot\dfrac{\sqrt{3}}{2}+-\dfrac{\sqrt{2}}{2}\cdot\dfrac{1}{2}$

$=-\dfrac{1}{4}\left(\sqrt{6}+\sqrt{2}\right)$

10. $\tan\left(\dfrac{19\pi}{12}\right)=\tan\left(\dfrac{15\pi}{12}+\dfrac{4\pi}{12}\right)=\dfrac{\tan\left(\dfrac{5\pi}{4}\right)+\tan\left(\dfrac{\pi}{3}\right)}{1-\tan\left(\dfrac{5\pi}{4}\right)\tan\left(\dfrac{\pi}{3}\right)}=\dfrac{1+\sqrt{3}}{1-1\cdot\sqrt{3}}=\left(\dfrac{1+\sqrt{3}}{1-\sqrt{3}}\right)\cdot\left(\dfrac{1+\sqrt{3}}{1+\sqrt{3}}\right)$

$=\dfrac{1+2\sqrt{3}+3}{1-3}=\dfrac{4+2\sqrt{3}}{-2}=-2-\sqrt{3}$

11. $\sec\left(-\dfrac{\pi}{12}\right)=\dfrac{1}{\cos\left(-\dfrac{\pi}{12}\right)}=\dfrac{1}{\cos\left(\dfrac{3\pi}{12}-\dfrac{4\pi}{12}\right)}=\dfrac{1}{\cos\left(\dfrac{\pi}{4}\right)\cos\left(\dfrac{\pi}{3}\right)+\sin\left(\dfrac{\pi}{4}\right)\sin\left(\dfrac{\pi}{3}\right)}$

$=\dfrac{1}{\left(\dfrac{\sqrt{2}}{2}\cdot\dfrac{1}{2}+\dfrac{\sqrt{2}}{2}\cdot\dfrac{\sqrt{3}}{2}\right)}=\dfrac{1}{\left(\dfrac{\sqrt{2}+\sqrt{6}}{4}\right)}=\left(\dfrac{4}{\sqrt{2}+\sqrt{6}}\right)\cdot\left(\dfrac{\sqrt{2}-\sqrt{6}}{\sqrt{2}-\sqrt{6}}\right)$

$=\dfrac{4\left(\sqrt{2}-\sqrt{6}\right)}{2-6}=\dfrac{4\left(\sqrt{2}-\sqrt{6}\right)}{-4}=-\left(\sqrt{2}-\sqrt{6}\right)=\sqrt{6}-\sqrt{2}$

12. $\cot\left(-\dfrac{5\pi}{12}\right)=-\cot\dfrac{5\pi}{12}=\dfrac{-1}{\tan\left(\dfrac{5\pi}{12}\right)}=\dfrac{-1}{\tan\left(\dfrac{3\pi}{12}+\dfrac{2\pi}{12}\right)}=\dfrac{-1}{\left(\dfrac{\tan\left(\dfrac{\pi}{4}\right)+\tan\left(\dfrac{\pi}{6}\right)}{1-\tan\left(\dfrac{\pi}{4}\right)\tan\left(\dfrac{\pi}{6}\right)}\right)}$

$$= -\left(\frac{1-\tan\left(\frac{\pi}{4}\right)\tan\left(\frac{\pi}{6}\right)}{\tan\left(\frac{\pi}{4}\right)+\tan\left(\frac{\pi}{6}\right)}\right) = -\left(\frac{\left(1-1\cdot\frac{1}{\sqrt{3}}\right)}{\left(1+\frac{1}{\sqrt{3}}\right)}\right) = -\left(\frac{\left(\frac{\sqrt{3}-1}{\sqrt{3}}\right)}{\left(\frac{\sqrt{3}+1}{\sqrt{3}}\right)}\right)$$

$$= -\left(\frac{\sqrt{3}-1}{\sqrt{3}+1}\right)\cdot\left(\frac{1-\sqrt{3}}{1-\sqrt{3}}\right) = -\left(\frac{\sqrt{3}-3-1+\sqrt{3}}{1-3}\right) = -\left(\frac{-4+2\sqrt{3}}{-2}\right) = -2+\sqrt{3}$$

13. $\sin(20^\circ)\cos(10^\circ)+\cos(20^\circ)\sin(10^\circ)=\sin(20^\circ+10^\circ)=\sin(30^\circ)=\frac{1}{2}$

14. $\sin(20^\circ)\cos(80^\circ)-\cos(20^\circ)\sin(80^\circ)=\sin(20^\circ-80^\circ)=\sin(-60^\circ)=-\sin(60^\circ)=-\frac{\sqrt{3}}{2}$

15. $\cos(70^\circ)\cos(20^\circ)-\sin(70^\circ)\sin(20^\circ)=\cos(70^\circ+20^\circ)=\cos(90^\circ)=0$

16. $\cos(40^\circ)\cos(10^\circ)+\sin(40^\circ)\sin(10^\circ)=\cos(40^\circ-10^\circ)=\cos(30^\circ)=\frac{\sqrt{3}}{2}$

17. $\frac{\tan(20^\circ)+\tan(25^\circ)}{1-\tan(20^\circ)\tan(25^\circ)}=\tan(20^\circ+25^\circ)=\tan(45^\circ)=1$

18. $\frac{\tan(40^\circ)-\tan(10^\circ)}{1+\tan(40^\circ)\tan(10^\circ)}=\tan(40^\circ-10^\circ)=\tan(30^\circ)=\frac{\sqrt{3}}{3}$

19. $\sin\left(\frac{\pi}{12}\right)\cos\left(\frac{7\pi}{12}\right)-\cos\left(\frac{\pi}{12}\right)\sin\left(\frac{7\pi}{12}\right)=\sin\left(\frac{\pi}{12}-\frac{7\pi}{12}\right)=\sin\left(-\frac{\pi}{2}\right)=-1$

20. $\cos\left(\frac{5\pi}{12}\right)\cos\left(\frac{7\pi}{12}\right)-\sin\left(\frac{5\pi}{12}\right)\sin\left(\frac{7\pi}{12}\right)=\cos\left(\frac{5\pi}{12}+\frac{7\pi}{12}\right)=\cos\left(\frac{12\pi}{12}\right)=\cos(\pi)=-1$

21. $\cos\left(\frac{\pi}{12}\right)\cos\left(\frac{5\pi}{12}\right)+\sin\left(\frac{5\pi}{12}\right)\sin\left(\frac{\pi}{12}\right)=\cos\left(\frac{\pi}{12}-\frac{5\pi}{12}\right)=\cos\left(-\frac{\pi}{3}\right)=\cos\left(\frac{\pi}{3}\right)=\frac{1}{2}$

22. $\sin\left(\frac{\pi}{18}\right)\cos\left(\frac{5\pi}{18}\right)+\cos\left(\frac{\pi}{18}\right)\sin\left(\frac{5\pi}{18}\right)=\sin\left(\frac{\pi}{18}+\frac{5\pi}{18}\right)=\sin\left(\frac{6\pi}{18}\right)=\sin\left(\frac{\pi}{3}\right)=\frac{\sqrt{3}}{2}$

23. $\sin\alpha = \frac{3}{5},\ 0 < \alpha < \frac{\pi}{2};$ $\cos\beta = \frac{2\sqrt{5}}{5},\ -\frac{\pi}{2} < \beta < 0$

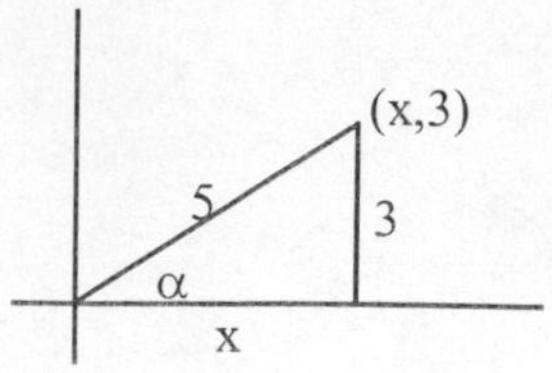

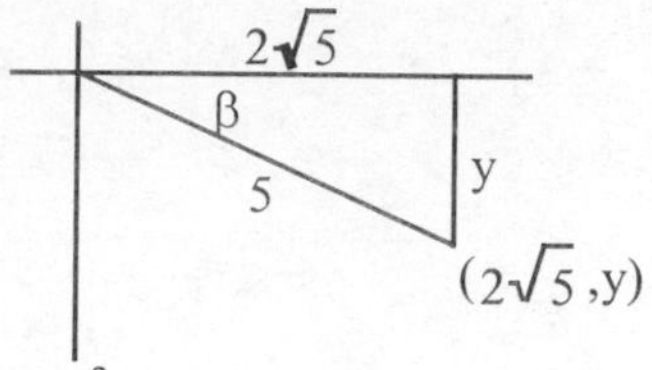

$$x^2 + 3^2 = 5^2,\ x > 0$$
$$x^2 = 25 - 9 = 16,\ x > 0$$
$$x = 4$$
$$\cos\alpha = \frac{4}{5},\ \tan\alpha = \frac{3}{4}$$

$$\left(2\sqrt{5}\right)^2 + y^2 = 5^2,\ y < 0$$
$$y^2 = 25 - 20 = 5.\ y < 0$$
$$y = -\sqrt{5}$$
$$\sin\beta = -\frac{\sqrt{5}}{5},\quad \tan\beta = \frac{-\sqrt{5}}{2\sqrt{5}} = -\frac{1}{2}$$

(a) $\sin(\alpha + \beta) = \sin\alpha\cos\beta + \cos\alpha\sin\beta = \frac{3}{5}\cdot\frac{2\sqrt{5}}{5} + \frac{4}{5}\cdot -\frac{\sqrt{5}}{5} = \frac{6\sqrt{5} - 4\sqrt{5}}{25} = \frac{2\sqrt{5}}{25}$

(b) $\cos(\alpha + \beta) = \cos\alpha\cos\beta - \sin\alpha\sin\beta = \frac{4}{5}\cdot\frac{2\sqrt{5}}{5} - \frac{3}{5}\cdot -\frac{\sqrt{5}}{5} = \frac{8\sqrt{5} + 3\sqrt{5}}{25} = \frac{11\sqrt{5}}{25}$

(c) $\sin(\alpha - \beta) = \sin\alpha\cos\beta - \cos\alpha\sin\beta = \frac{3}{5}\cdot\frac{2\sqrt{5}}{5} - \frac{4}{5}\cdot -\frac{\sqrt{5}}{5} = \frac{6\sqrt{5} + 4\sqrt{5}}{25}$

$$= \frac{10\sqrt{5}}{25} = \frac{2\sqrt{5}}{5}$$

(d) $\tan(\alpha - \beta) = \frac{\tan\alpha - \tan\beta}{1 + \tan\alpha\tan\beta} = \frac{\left(\frac{3}{4} - \left(-\frac{1}{2}\right)\right)}{\left(1 + \left(\frac{3}{4}\right)\cdot\left(-\frac{1}{2}\right)\right)} = \frac{\left(\frac{5}{4}\right)}{\left(\frac{5}{8}\right)} = 2$

24. $\cos\alpha = \frac{\sqrt{5}}{5},\ 0 < \alpha < \frac{\pi}{2};$ $\sin\beta = -\frac{4}{5},\ -\frac{\pi}{2} < \beta < 0$

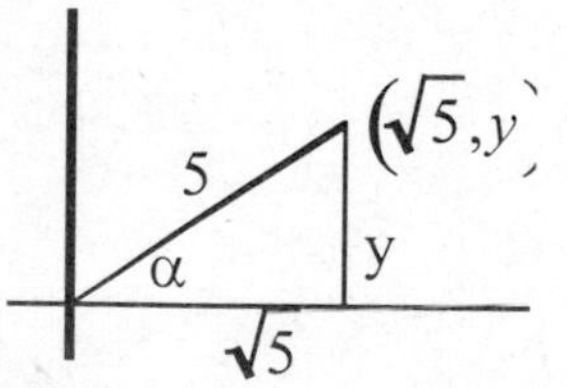

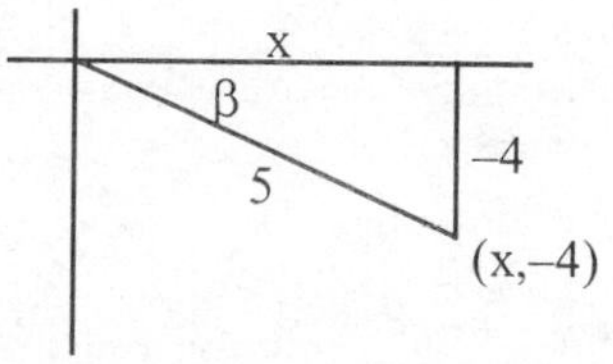

$$\left(\sqrt{5}\right)^2 + y^2 = 5^2,\ y > 0$$
$$y^2 = 25 - 5 = 20,\ y > 0$$
$$y = \sqrt{20} = 2\sqrt{5}$$
$$\sin\alpha = \frac{2\sqrt{5}}{5},\ \tan\alpha = \frac{2\sqrt{5}}{\sqrt{5}} = 2$$

$$x^2 + (-4)^2 = 5^2,\ x > 0$$
$$x^2 = 25 - 16 = 9.\ x > 0$$
$$x = 3$$
$$\cos\beta = \frac{3}{5},\ \tan\beta = \frac{-4}{3} = -\frac{4}{3}$$

(a) $\sin(\alpha+\beta)=\sin\alpha\cos\beta+\cos\alpha\sin\beta=\left(\frac{2\sqrt{5}}{5}\right)\cdot\left(\frac{3}{5}\right)+\left(\frac{\sqrt{5}}{5}\right)\cdot\left(-\frac{4}{5}\right)=\frac{6\sqrt{5}-4\sqrt{5}}{25}=\frac{2\sqrt{5}}{25}$

(b) $\cos(\alpha+\beta)=\cos\alpha\cos\beta-\sin\alpha\sin\beta=\left(\frac{\sqrt{5}}{5}\right)\cdot\left(\frac{3}{5}\right)-\left(\frac{2\sqrt{5}}{5}\right)\cdot\left(-\frac{4}{5}\right)=\frac{3\sqrt{5}+8\sqrt{5}}{25}=\frac{11\sqrt{5}}{25}$

(c) $\sin(\alpha-\beta)=\sin\alpha\cos\beta-\cos\alpha\sin\beta=\left(\frac{2\sqrt{5}}{5}\right)\cdot\left(\frac{3}{5}\right)-\left(\frac{\sqrt{5}}{5}\right)\cdot\left(-\frac{4}{5}\right)=\frac{6\sqrt{5}+4\sqrt{5}}{25}$

$=\frac{10\sqrt{5}}{25}=\frac{2\sqrt{5}}{5}$

(d) $\tan(\alpha-\beta)=\frac{\tan\alpha-\tan\beta}{1+\tan\alpha\tan\beta}=\frac{\left(2-\left(-\frac{4}{3}\right)\right)}{\left(1+2\cdot\left(-\frac{4}{3}\right)\right)}=\frac{\left(\frac{10}{3}\right)}{\left(-\frac{5}{3}\right)}=-2$

25. $\tan\alpha=-\frac{4}{3},\ \frac{\pi}{2}<\alpha<\pi;$ $\qquad\cos\beta=\frac{1}{2},\ 0<\beta<\frac{\pi}{2}$

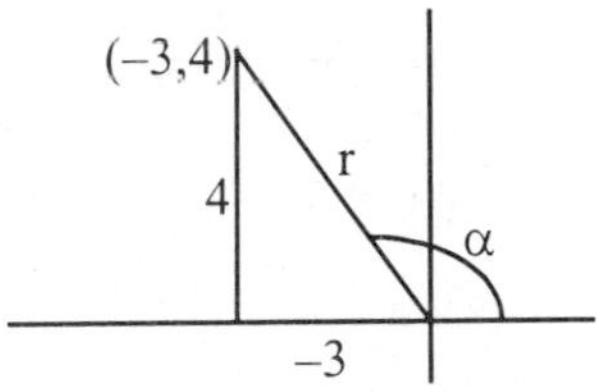

$r^2=(-3)^2+4^2=25$

$r=5$

$\sin\alpha=\frac{4}{5},\ \cos\alpha=\frac{-3}{5}=-\frac{3}{5}$

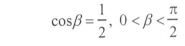

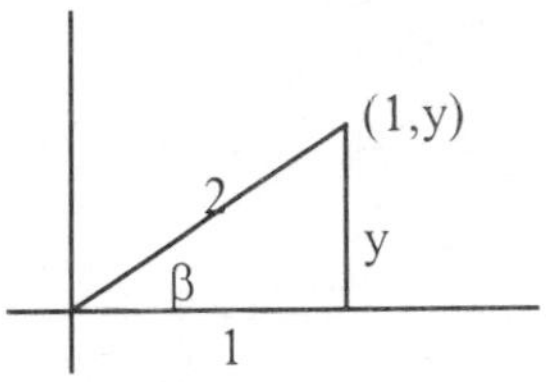

$1^2+y^2=2^2,\ y>0$

$y^2=4-1=3.\ y>0$

$y=\sqrt{3}$

$\sin\beta=\frac{\sqrt{3}}{2},\quad \tan\beta=\frac{\sqrt{3}}{1}=\sqrt{3}$

(a) $\sin(\alpha+\beta)=\sin\alpha\cos\beta+\cos\alpha\sin\beta=\left(\frac{4}{5}\right)\cdot\left(\frac{1}{2}\right)+\left(-\frac{3}{5}\right)\cdot\left(\frac{\sqrt{3}}{2}\right)=\frac{4-3\sqrt{3}}{10}$

(b) $\cos(\alpha+\beta)=\cos\alpha\cos\beta-\sin\alpha\sin\beta=\left(-\frac{3}{5}\right)\cdot\left(\frac{1}{2}\right)-\left(\frac{4}{5}\right)\cdot\left(\frac{\sqrt{3}}{2}\right)=\frac{-3-4\sqrt{3}}{10}$

(c) $\sin(\alpha-\beta)=\sin\alpha\cos\beta-\cos\alpha\sin\beta=\left(\frac{4}{5}\right)\cdot\left(\frac{1}{2}\right)-\left(-\frac{3}{5}\right)\cdot\left(\frac{\sqrt{3}}{2}\right)=\frac{4+3\sqrt{3}}{10}$

(d) $\tan(\alpha-\beta)=\frac{\tan\alpha-\tan\beta}{1+\tan\alpha\tan\beta}=\frac{\left(-\frac{4}{3}-\sqrt{3}\right)}{\left(1+\left(-\frac{4}{3}\right)\cdot\sqrt{3}\right)}=\frac{\left(\frac{-4-3\sqrt{3}}{3}\right)}{\left(\frac{3-4\sqrt{3}}{3}\right)}=\left(\frac{-4-3\sqrt{3}}{3-4\sqrt{3}}\right)\cdot\left(\frac{3+4\sqrt{3}}{3+4\sqrt{3}}\right)$

$=\frac{-48-25\sqrt{3}}{-39}=\frac{48+25\sqrt{3}}{39}$

26. $\tan\alpha = \frac{5}{12},\ \pi < \alpha < \frac{3\pi}{2};$ $\sin\beta = -\frac{1}{2},\ \pi < \beta < \frac{3\pi}{2}$

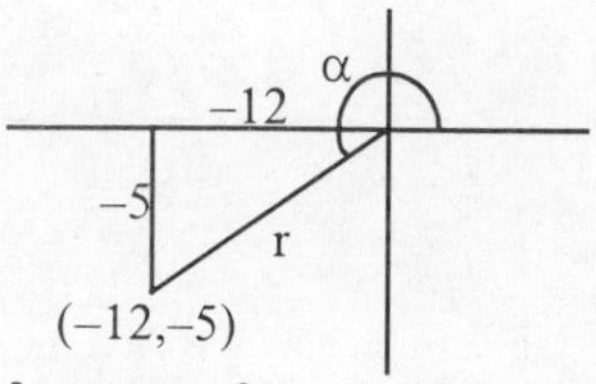

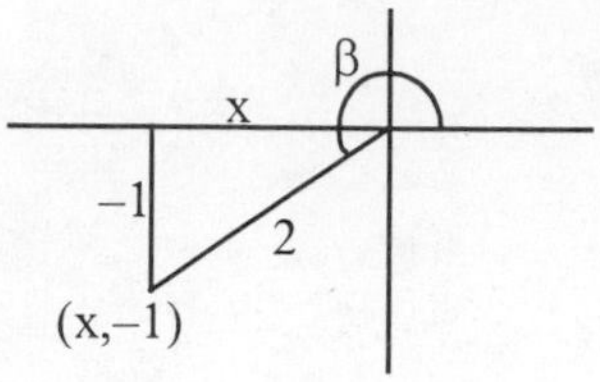

$r^2 = (-12)^2 + (-5)^2 = 169$

$r = 13$

$\sin\alpha = \frac{-5}{13} = -\frac{5}{13},\ \cos\alpha = \frac{-12}{13} = -\frac{12}{13}$

$x^2 + (-1)^2 = 2^2,\ x < 0$

$x^2 = 4 - 1 = 3.\ x < 0$

$x = -\sqrt{3}$

$\cos\beta = -\frac{\sqrt{3}}{2},\quad \tan\beta = \frac{-1}{-\sqrt{3}} = \frac{\sqrt{3}}{3}$

(a) $\sin(\alpha+\beta) = \sin\alpha\cos\beta + \cos\alpha\sin\beta = \left(-\frac{5}{13}\right)\cdot\left(-\frac{\sqrt{3}}{2}\right) + \left(-\frac{12}{13}\right)\cdot\left(-\frac{1}{2}\right) = \frac{5\sqrt{3}+12}{26}$

(b) $\cos(\alpha+\beta) = \cos\alpha\cos\beta - \sin\alpha\sin\beta = \left(-\frac{12}{13}\right)\cdot\left(-\frac{\sqrt{3}}{2}\right) - \left(-\frac{5}{13}\right)\cdot\left(-\frac{1}{2}\right) = \frac{12\sqrt{3}-5}{26}$

(c) $\sin(\alpha-\beta) = \sin\alpha\cos\beta - \cos\alpha\sin\beta = \left(-\frac{5}{13}\right)\cdot\left(-\frac{\sqrt{3}}{2}\right) - \left(-\frac{12}{13}\right)\cdot\left(-\frac{1}{2}\right) = \frac{5\sqrt{3}-12}{26}$

(d) $\tan(\alpha-\beta) = \frac{\tan\alpha - \tan\beta}{1+\tan\alpha\tan\beta} = \frac{\left(\frac{5}{12} - \frac{\sqrt{3}}{3}\right)}{\left(1 + \frac{5}{12}\cdot\frac{\sqrt{3}}{3}\right)} = \frac{\left(\frac{5-4\sqrt{3}}{12}\right)}{\left(\frac{36+5\sqrt{3}}{36}\right)} = \left(\frac{15-12\sqrt{3}}{36+5\sqrt{3}}\right)\cdot\left(\frac{36-5\sqrt{3}}{36-5\sqrt{3}}\right)$

$= \frac{540 - 507\sqrt{3} + 180}{1296 - 75} = \frac{720 - 507\sqrt{3}}{1221} = \frac{240 - 169\sqrt{3}}{407}$

27. $\sin\alpha = \frac{5}{13},\ -\frac{3\pi}{2} < \alpha < -\pi;$ $\tan\beta = -\sqrt{3},\ \frac{\pi}{2} < \beta < \pi$

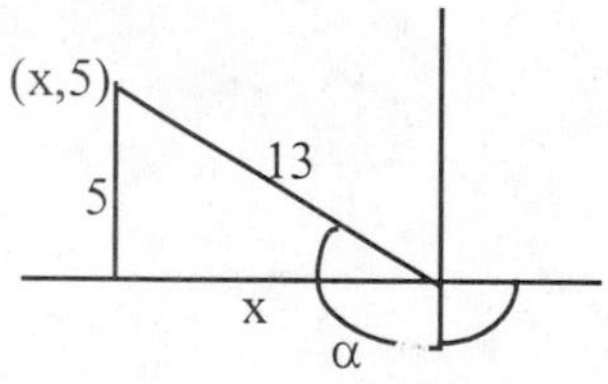

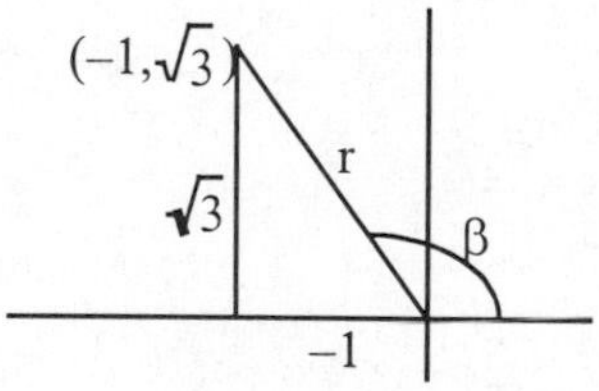

$x^2 + 5^2 = 13^2,\ x < 0$

$x^2 = 169 - 25 = 144,\ x < 0$

$x = -12$

$\cos\alpha = \frac{-12}{13} = -\frac{12}{13},\ \tan\alpha = -\frac{5}{12}$

$r^2 = (-1)^2 + \sqrt{3}^2 = 4$

$r = 2$

$\sin\beta = \frac{\sqrt{3}}{2},\ \cos\beta = \frac{-1}{2} = -\frac{1}{2}$

(a) $\sin(\alpha+\beta)=\sin\alpha\cos\beta+\cos\alpha\sin\beta=\left(\frac{5}{13}\right)\cdot\left(-\frac{1}{2}\right)+\left(-\frac{12}{13}\right)\cdot\left(\frac{\sqrt{3}}{2}\right)=\frac{-5-12\sqrt{3}}{26}$

(b) $\cos(\alpha+\beta)=\cos\alpha\cos\beta-\sin\alpha\sin\beta=\left(-\frac{12}{13}\right)\cdot\left(-\frac{1}{2}\right)-\left(\frac{5}{13}\right)\cdot\left(\frac{\sqrt{3}}{2}\right)=\frac{12-5\sqrt{3}}{26}$

(c) $\sin(\alpha-\beta)=\sin\alpha\cos\beta-\cos\alpha\sin\beta=\left(\frac{5}{13}\right)\cdot\left(-\frac{1}{2}\right)-\left(-\frac{12}{13}\right)\cdot\left(\frac{\sqrt{3}}{2}\right)=\frac{-5+12\sqrt{3}}{26}$

(d) $\tan(\alpha-\beta)=\frac{\tan\alpha-\tan\beta}{1+\tan\alpha\tan\beta}=\frac{\left(-\frac{5}{12}-(-\sqrt{3})\right)}{\left(1+\left(-\frac{5}{12}\right)\cdot(-\sqrt{3})\right)}=\frac{\left(\frac{-5+12\sqrt{3}}{12}\right)}{\left(\frac{12+5\sqrt{3}}{12}\right)}$

$=\left(\frac{-5+12\sqrt{3}}{12+5\sqrt{3}}\right)\cdot\left(\frac{12-5\sqrt{3}}{12-5\sqrt{3}}\right)=\frac{-240+169\sqrt{3}}{69}$

28. $\cos\alpha=\frac{1}{2},\ -\frac{\pi}{2}<\alpha<0;$ $\qquad\sin\beta=\frac{1}{3},\ 0<\beta<\frac{\pi}{2}$

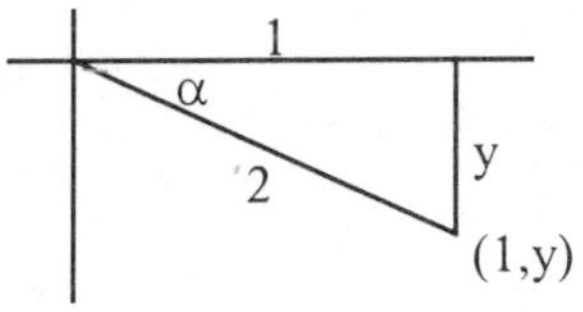

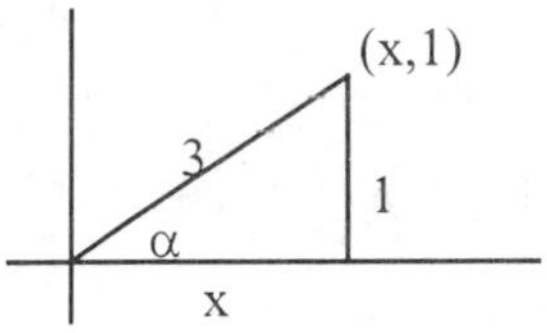

$1^2+y^2=2^2,\ y<0$

$y^2=4-1=3,\ y<0$

$y=-\sqrt{3}$

$\sin\alpha=\frac{-\sqrt{3}}{2}=-\frac{\sqrt{3}}{2},\ \tan\alpha=\frac{-\sqrt{3}}{1}=-\sqrt{3}$

$x^2+1^2=3^2,\ x>0$

$x^2=9-1=8.\ x>0$

$x=\sqrt{8}=2\sqrt{2}$

$\cos\beta=\frac{2\sqrt{2}}{3},\ \tan\beta=\frac{1}{2\sqrt{2}}=\frac{\sqrt{2}}{4}$

(a) $\sin(\alpha+\beta)=\sin\alpha\cos\beta+\cos\alpha\sin\beta=\left(-\frac{\sqrt{3}}{2}\right)\cdot\left(\frac{2\sqrt{2}}{3}\right)+\left(\frac{1}{2}\right)\cdot\left(\frac{1}{3}\right)=\frac{-2\sqrt{6}+1}{6}$

(b) $\cos(\alpha+\beta)=\cos\alpha\cos\beta-\sin\alpha\sin\beta=\left(\frac{1}{2}\right)\cdot\left(\frac{2\sqrt{2}}{3}\right)-\left(-\frac{\sqrt{3}}{2}\right)\cdot\left(\frac{1}{3}\right)=\frac{2\sqrt{2}+\sqrt{3}}{6}$

(c) $\sin(\alpha-\beta)=\sin\alpha\cos\beta-\cos\alpha\sin\beta=\left(-\frac{\sqrt{3}}{2}\right)\cdot\left(\frac{2\sqrt{2}}{3}\right)-\left(\frac{1}{2}\right)\cdot\left(\frac{1}{3}\right)=\frac{-2\sqrt{6}-1}{6}$

(d) $\tan(\alpha-\beta)=\frac{\tan\alpha-\tan\beta}{1+\tan\alpha\tan\beta}=\frac{\left(-\sqrt{3}-\frac{\sqrt{2}}{4}\right)}{\left(1+(-\sqrt{3})\cdot\frac{\sqrt{2}}{4}\right)}=\frac{\left(\frac{-4\sqrt{3}-\sqrt{2}}{4}\right)}{\left(\frac{4-\sqrt{6}}{4}\right)}$

$$=\left(\frac{-4\sqrt{3}-\sqrt{2}}{4-\sqrt{6}}\right)\cdot\left(\frac{4+\sqrt{6}}{4+\sqrt{6}}\right)=\frac{-16\sqrt{3}-4\sqrt{2}-4\sqrt{18}-\sqrt{12}}{16-6}$$

$$=\frac{-18\sqrt{3}-16\sqrt{2}}{10}=\frac{-9\sqrt{3}-8\sqrt{2}}{5}$$

29. $\sin\theta=\frac{1}{3}$, θ in quadrant II

(a) $\cos\theta=-\sqrt{1-\sin^2\theta}=-\sqrt{1-\left(\frac{1}{3}\right)^2}=-\sqrt{1-\frac{1}{9}}=-\sqrt{\frac{8}{9}}=-\frac{2\sqrt{2}}{3}$

(b) $\sin\left(\theta+\frac{\pi}{6}\right)=\sin\theta\cos\left(\frac{\pi}{6}\right)+\cos\theta\sin\left(\frac{\pi}{6}\right)=\left(\frac{1}{3}\right)\cdot\left(\frac{\sqrt{3}}{2}\right)+\left(-\frac{2\sqrt{2}}{3}\right)\cdot\left(\frac{1}{2}\right)=\frac{\sqrt{3}-2\sqrt{2}}{6}$

(c) $\cos\left(\theta-\frac{\pi}{3}\right)=\cos\theta\cos\left(\frac{\pi}{3}\right)+\sin\theta\sin\left(\frac{\pi}{3}\right)=\left(-\frac{2\sqrt{2}}{3}\right)\cdot\left(\frac{1}{2}\right)+\left(\frac{1}{3}\right)\cdot\left(\frac{\sqrt{3}}{2}\right)=\frac{-2\sqrt{2}+\sqrt{3}}{6}$

(d) $\tan\left(\theta+\frac{\pi}{4}\right)=\dfrac{\tan\theta+\tan\left(\frac{\pi}{4}\right)}{1-\tan\theta\tan\left(\frac{\pi}{4}\right)}=\dfrac{\left(-\frac{1}{2\sqrt{2}}+1\right)}{\left(1-\left(-\frac{1}{2\sqrt{2}}\right)\cdot 1\right)}=\dfrac{\left(\frac{-1+2\sqrt{2}}{2\sqrt{2}}\right)}{\left(\frac{2\sqrt{2}+1}{2\sqrt{2}}\right)}$

$$=\left(\frac{2\sqrt{2}-1}{2\sqrt{2}+1}\right)\cdot\left(\frac{2\sqrt{2}-1}{2\sqrt{2}-1}\right)=\frac{9-4\sqrt{2}}{7}$$

30. $\cos\theta=\frac{1}{4}$, θ in quadrant IV

(a) $\sin\theta=-\sqrt{1-\cos^2\theta}=-\sqrt{1-\left(\frac{1}{4}\right)^2}=-\sqrt{1-\frac{1}{16}}=-\sqrt{\frac{15}{16}}=-\frac{\sqrt{15}}{4}$

(b) $\sin\left(\theta-\frac{\pi}{6}\right)=\sin\theta\cos\left(\frac{\pi}{6}\right)-\cos\theta\sin\left(\frac{\pi}{6}\right)=\left(-\frac{\sqrt{15}}{4}\right)\cdot\left(\frac{\sqrt{3}}{2}\right)-\left(\frac{1}{4}\right)\left(\frac{1}{2}\right)=\frac{-3\sqrt{5}-1}{8}$

(c) $\cos\left(\theta+\frac{\pi}{3}\right)=\cos\theta\cos\left(\frac{\pi}{3}\right)-\sin\theta\sin\left(\frac{\pi}{3}\right)=\left(\frac{1}{4}\right)\cdot\left(\frac{1}{2}\right)-\left(-\frac{\sqrt{15}}{4}\right)\cdot\left(\frac{\sqrt{3}}{2}\right)=\frac{1+3\sqrt{5}}{8}$

(d) $\tan\left(\theta-\frac{\pi}{4}\right)=\dfrac{\tan\theta-\tan\left(\frac{\pi}{4}\right)}{1+\tan\theta\tan\left(\frac{\pi}{4}\right)}=\dfrac{-\sqrt{15}-1}{1+\left(-\sqrt{15}\right)\cdot 1}=\left(\frac{-1-\sqrt{15}}{1-\sqrt{15}}\right)\cdot\left(\frac{1+\sqrt{15}}{1+\sqrt{15}}\right)$

$$=\frac{-1-2\sqrt{15}-15}{1-15}=\frac{-16-2\sqrt{15}}{-14}=\frac{-8-\sqrt{15}}{-7}$$

31. $\sin\left(\frac{\pi}{2}+\theta\right)=\sin\left(\frac{\pi}{2}\right)\cos\theta+\cos\left(\frac{\pi}{2}\right)\sin\theta=1\cdot\cos\theta+0\cdot\sin\theta=\cos\theta$

32. $\cos\left(\frac{\pi}{2}+\theta\right)=\cos\left(\frac{\pi}{2}\right)\cos\theta-\sin\left(\frac{\pi}{2}\right)\sin\theta=0\cdot\cos\theta-1\cdot\sin\theta=-\sin\theta$

33. $\sin(\pi-\theta)=\sin(\pi)\cos\theta-\cos(\pi)\sin\theta=0\cdot\cos\theta-(-1)\sin\theta=\sin\theta$

34. $\cos(\pi-\theta)=\cos(\pi)\cos\theta+\sin(\pi)\sin\theta=-1\cdot\cos\theta+(0)\sin\theta=-\cos\theta$

35. $\sin(\pi+\theta)=\sin(\pi)\cos\theta+\cos(\pi)\sin\theta=0\cdot\cos\theta+(-1)\sin\theta=-\sin\theta$

36. $\cos(\pi+\theta)=\cos(\pi)\cos\theta-\sin(\pi)\sin\theta=-1\cdot\cos\theta-(0)\sin\theta=-\cos\theta$

37. $\tan(\pi-\theta)=\dfrac{\tan(\pi)-\tan\theta}{1+\tan(\pi)\tan\theta}=\dfrac{0-\tan\theta}{1+0\cdot\tan\theta}=\dfrac{-\tan\theta}{1}=-\tan\theta$

38. $\tan(2\pi-\theta)=\dfrac{\tan(2\pi)-\tan\theta}{1+\tan(2\pi)\tan\theta}=\dfrac{0-\tan\theta}{1+0\cdot\tan\theta}=\dfrac{-\tan\theta}{1}=-\tan\theta$

39. $\sin\left(\frac{3\pi}{2}+\theta\right)=\sin\left(\frac{3\pi}{2}\right)\cos\theta+\cos\left(\frac{3\pi}{2}\right)\sin\theta=-1\cdot\cos\theta+0\cdot\sin\theta=-\cos\theta$

40. $\cos\left(\frac{3\pi}{2}+\theta\right)=\cos\left(\frac{3\pi}{2}\right)\cos\theta-\sin\left(\frac{3\pi}{2}\right)\sin\theta=0\cdot\cos\theta-(-1)\cdot\sin\theta=\sin\theta$

41. $\sin(\alpha+\beta)+\sin(\alpha-\beta)=\sin\alpha\cos\beta+\cos\alpha\sin\beta+\sin\alpha\cos\beta-\cos\alpha\sin\beta$
$=2\sin\alpha\cos\beta$

42. $\cos(\alpha+\beta)+\cos(\alpha-\beta)=\cos\alpha\cos\beta-\sin\alpha\sin\beta+\cos\alpha\cos\beta+\sin\alpha\sin\beta$
$=2\cos\alpha\cos\beta$

43. $\dfrac{\sin(\alpha+\beta)}{\sin\alpha\cos\beta}=\dfrac{\sin\alpha\cos\beta+\cos\alpha\sin\beta}{\sin\alpha\cos\beta}=\dfrac{\sin\alpha\cos\beta}{\sin\alpha\cos\beta}+\dfrac{\cos\alpha\sin\beta}{\sin\alpha\cos\beta}=1+\cot\alpha\tan\beta$

44. $\dfrac{\sin(\alpha+\beta)}{\cos\alpha\cos\beta}=\dfrac{\sin\alpha\cos\beta+\cos\alpha\sin\beta}{\cos\alpha\cos\beta}=\dfrac{\sin\alpha\cos\beta}{\cos\alpha\cos\beta}+\dfrac{\cos\alpha\sin\beta}{\cos\alpha\cos\beta}=\tan\alpha+\tan\beta$

45. $\dfrac{\cos(\alpha+\beta)}{\cos\alpha\cos\beta}=\dfrac{\cos\alpha\cos\beta-\sin\alpha\sin\beta}{\cos\alpha\cos\beta}=\dfrac{\cos\alpha\cos\beta}{\cos\alpha\cos\beta}-\dfrac{\sin\alpha\sin\beta}{\cos\alpha\cos\beta}=1-\tan\alpha\tan\beta$

46. $\dfrac{\cos(\alpha-\beta)}{\sin\alpha\cos\beta}=\dfrac{\cos\alpha\cos\beta+\sin\alpha\sin\beta}{\sin\alpha\cos\beta}=\dfrac{\cos\alpha\cos\beta}{\sin\alpha\cos\beta}+\dfrac{\sin\alpha\sin\beta}{\sin\alpha\cos\beta}=\cot\alpha+\tan\beta$

47. $$\frac{\sin(\alpha+\beta)}{\sin(\alpha-\beta)}=\frac{\sin\alpha\cos\beta+\cos\alpha\sin\beta}{\sin\alpha\cos\beta-\cos\alpha\sin\beta}=\frac{\left(\frac{\sin\alpha\cos\beta}{\cos\alpha\cos\beta}+\frac{\cos\alpha\sin\beta}{\cos\alpha\cos\beta}\right)}{\left(\frac{\sin\alpha\cos\beta}{\cos\alpha\cos\beta}-\frac{\cos\alpha\sin\beta}{\cos\alpha\cos\beta}\right)}=\frac{\tan\alpha+\tan\beta}{\tan\alpha-\tan\beta}$$

48. $$\frac{\cos(\alpha+\beta)}{\cos(\alpha-\beta)}=\frac{\cos\alpha\cos\beta-\sin\alpha\sin\beta}{\cos\alpha\cos\beta+\sin\alpha\sin\beta}=\frac{\left(\frac{\cos\alpha\cos\beta}{\cos\alpha\cos\beta}-\frac{\sin\alpha\sin\beta}{\cos\alpha\cos\beta}\right)}{\left(\frac{\cos\alpha\cos\beta}{\cos\alpha\cos\beta}+\frac{\sin\alpha\sin\beta}{\cos\alpha\cos\beta}\right)}=\frac{1-\tan\alpha\tan\beta}{1+\tan\alpha\tan\beta}$$

49. $$\cot(\alpha+\beta)=\frac{\cos(\alpha+\beta)}{\sin(\alpha+\beta)}=\frac{\cos\alpha\cos\beta-\sin\alpha\sin\beta}{\sin\alpha\cos\beta+\cos\alpha\sin\beta}$$

$$=\frac{\left(\frac{\cos\alpha\cos\beta}{\sin\alpha\sin\beta}-\frac{\sin\alpha\sin\beta}{\sin\alpha\sin\beta}\right)}{\left(\frac{\sin\alpha\cos\beta}{\sin\alpha\sin\beta}+\frac{\cos\alpha\sin\beta}{\sin\alpha\sin\beta}\right)}=\frac{\cot\alpha\cot\beta-1}{\cot\beta+\cot\alpha}$$

50. $$\cot(\alpha-\beta)=\frac{\cos(\alpha-\beta)}{\sin(\alpha-\beta)}=\frac{\cos\alpha\cos\beta+\sin\alpha\sin\beta}{\sin\alpha\cos\beta-\cos\alpha\sin\beta}$$

$$=\frac{\left(\frac{\cos\alpha\cos\beta}{\sin\alpha\sin\beta}+\frac{\sin\alpha\sin\beta}{\sin\alpha\sin\beta}\right)}{\left(\frac{\sin\alpha\cos\beta}{\sin\alpha\sin\beta}-\frac{\cos\alpha\sin\beta}{\sin\alpha\sin\beta}\right)}=\frac{\cot\alpha\cot\beta+1}{\cot\beta-\cot\alpha}$$

51. $$\sec(\alpha+\beta)=\frac{1}{\cos(\alpha+\beta)}=\frac{1}{\cos\alpha\cos\beta-\sin\alpha\sin\beta}$$

$$=\frac{\left(\frac{1}{\sin\alpha\sin\beta}\right)}{\left(\frac{\cos\alpha\cos\beta}{\sin\alpha\sin\beta}-\frac{\sin\alpha\sin\beta}{\sin\alpha\sin\beta}\right)}=\frac{\csc\alpha\csc\beta}{\cot\alpha\cot\beta-1}$$

52. $$\sec(\alpha-\beta)=\frac{1}{\cos(\alpha-\beta)}=\frac{1}{\cos\alpha\cos\beta+\sin\alpha\sin\beta}$$

$$=\frac{\left(\frac{1}{\cos\alpha\cos\beta}\right)}{\left(\frac{\cos\alpha\cos\beta}{\cos\alpha\cos\beta}+\frac{\sin\alpha\sin\beta}{\cos\alpha\cos\beta}\right)}=\frac{\sec\alpha\sec\beta}{1+\tan\alpha\tan\beta}$$

53. $\sin(\alpha-\beta)\sin(\alpha+\beta) = (\sin\alpha\cos\beta - \cos\alpha\sin\beta)(\sin\alpha\cos\beta + \cos\alpha\sin\beta)$
$= \sin^2\alpha\cos^2\beta - \cos^2\alpha\sin^2\beta = \sin^2\alpha(1-\sin^2\beta) - (1-\sin^2\alpha)\sin^2\beta$
$\sin^2\alpha - \sin^2\alpha\sin^2\beta - \sin^2\beta + \sin^2\alpha\sin^2\beta = \sin^2\alpha - \sin^2\beta$

54. $\cos(\alpha-\beta)\cos(\alpha+\beta) = (\cos\alpha\cos\beta + \sin\alpha\sin\beta)(\cos\alpha\cos\beta - \sin\alpha\sin\beta)$
$= \cos^2\alpha\cos^2\beta - \sin^2\alpha\sin^2\beta = \cos^2\alpha(1-\sin^2\beta) - (1-\cos^2\alpha)\sin^2\beta$
$= \cos^2\alpha - \cos^2\alpha\sin^2\beta - \sin^2\beta + \cos^2\alpha\sin^2\beta = \cos^2\alpha - \sin^2\beta$

55. $\sin(\theta + k\pi) = \sin\theta\cos(k\pi) + \cos\theta\sin(k\pi) = \sin\theta(-1)^k + \cos\theta\cdot 0$
$= (-1)^k\sin\theta$, k any integer

56. $\cos(\theta + k\pi) = \cos\theta\cos(k\pi) - \sin\theta\sin(k\pi) = \cos\theta(-1)^k - \sin\theta\cdot 0$
$= (-1)^k\cos\theta$, k any integer

57. $\sin\left(\sin^{-1}\left(\frac{1}{2}\right) + \cos^{-1}(0)\right) = \sin\left(\frac{\pi}{6} + \frac{\pi}{2}\right) = \sin\left(\frac{\pi}{6}\right)\cos\left(\frac{\pi}{2}\right) + \cos\left(\frac{\pi}{6}\right)\sin\left(\frac{\pi}{2}\right) = \frac{1}{2}\cdot 0 + \frac{\sqrt{3}}{2}\cdot 1 = \frac{\sqrt{3}}{2}$

58. $\sin\left(\sin^{-1}\left(\frac{\sqrt{3}}{2}\right) + \cos^{-1}(1)\right) = \sin\left(\frac{\pi}{3} + 0\right) = \sin\left(\frac{\pi}{3}\right) = \frac{\sqrt{3}}{2}$

59. $\sin\left[\sin^{-1}\left(\frac{3}{5}\right) - \cos^{-1}\left(-\frac{4}{5}\right)\right]$

Let $\alpha = \sin^{-1}\left(\frac{3}{5}\right)$ and $\beta = \cos^{-1}\left(-\frac{4}{5}\right)$. α is in quadrant I; β is in quadrant II.

Then $\sin\alpha = \frac{3}{5}$, $-\frac{\pi}{2} \le \alpha \le \frac{\pi}{2}$, and $\cos\beta = -\frac{4}{5}, 0 \le \beta \le \pi$.

$$\cos\alpha = \sqrt{1-\sin^2\alpha} = \sqrt{1-\left(\frac{3}{5}\right)^2} = \sqrt{1-\frac{9}{25}} = \sqrt{\frac{16}{25}} = \frac{4}{5}$$

$$\sin\beta = \sqrt{1-\cos^2\beta} = \sqrt{1-\left(-\frac{4}{5}\right)^2} = \sqrt{1-\frac{16}{25}} = \sqrt{\frac{9}{25}} = \frac{3}{5}$$

$$\sin\left[\sin^{-1}\left(\frac{3}{5}\right) - \cos^{-1}\left(-\frac{4}{5}\right)\right] = \sin(\alpha-\beta) = \sin\alpha\cos\beta - \cos\alpha\sin\beta$$

$$= \left(\frac{3}{5}\right)\cdot\left(-\frac{4}{5}\right) - \left(\frac{4}{5}\right)\cdot\left(\frac{3}{5}\right) = -\frac{12}{25} - \frac{12}{25} = -\frac{24}{25}$$

60. $\sin\left(\sin^{-1}\left(-\frac{4}{5}\right) - \tan^{-1}\left(\frac{3}{4}\right)\right)$

Let $\alpha = \sin^{-1}\left(-\frac{4}{5}\right)$ and $\beta = \tan^{-1}\left(\frac{3}{4}\right)$. α is in quadrant IV; β is in quadrant I.

Then $\sin\alpha = -\frac{4}{5}$, $-\frac{\pi}{2} \le \alpha \le \frac{\pi}{2}$, and $\tan\beta = \frac{3}{4}, -\frac{\pi}{2} < \beta < \frac{\pi}{2}$.

$$\cos\alpha = \sqrt{1-\sin^2\alpha} = \sqrt{1-\left(-\frac{4}{5}\right)^2} = \sqrt{1-\frac{16}{25}} = \sqrt{\frac{9}{25}} = \frac{3}{5}$$

$$\sec\beta = \sqrt{1+\tan^2\beta} = \sqrt{1+\left(\frac{3}{4}\right)^2} = \sqrt{1+\frac{9}{16}} = \sqrt{\frac{25}{16}} = \frac{5}{4}; \quad \cos\beta = \frac{4}{5}$$

$$\sin\beta = \sqrt{1-\cos^2\beta} = \sqrt{1-\left(\frac{4}{5}\right)^2} = \sqrt{1-\frac{16}{25}} = \sqrt{\frac{9}{25}} = \frac{3}{5}$$

$$\sin\left(\sin^{-1}\left(-\frac{4}{5}\right) - \tan^{-1}\left(\frac{3}{4}\right)\right) = \sin(\alpha-\beta) = \sin\alpha\cos\beta - \cos\alpha\sin\beta$$

$$= \left(-\frac{4}{5}\right)\cdot\left(\frac{4}{5}\right) - \left(\frac{3}{5}\right)\cdot\left(\frac{3}{5}\right) = -\frac{16}{25} - \frac{9}{25} = -\frac{25}{25} = -1$$

61. $\cos\left(\tan^{-1}\left(\frac{4}{3}\right) + \cos^{-1}\left(\frac{5}{13}\right)\right)$

Let $\alpha = \tan^{-1}\left(\frac{4}{3}\right)$ and $\beta = \cos^{-1}\left(\frac{5}{13}\right)$. α is in quadrant I; β is in quadrant I.

Then $\tan\alpha = \frac{4}{3}$, $-\frac{\pi}{2} < \alpha < \frac{\pi}{2}$, and $\cos\beta = \frac{5}{13}, 0 \le \beta \le \pi$.

$$\sec\alpha = \sqrt{1+\tan^2\alpha} = \sqrt{1+\left(\frac{4}{3}\right)^2} = \sqrt{1+\frac{16}{9}} = \sqrt{\frac{25}{9}} = \frac{5}{3}; \quad \cos\alpha = \frac{3}{5}$$

$$\sin\alpha = \sqrt{1-\cos^2\alpha} = \sqrt{1-\left(\frac{3}{5}\right)^2} = \sqrt{1-\frac{9}{25}} = \sqrt{\frac{16}{25}} = \frac{4}{5}$$

$$\sin\beta = \sqrt{1-\cos^2\beta} = \sqrt{1-\left(\frac{5}{13}\right)^2} = \sqrt{1-\frac{25}{169}} = \sqrt{\frac{144}{169}} = \frac{12}{13}$$

$$\cos\left(\tan^{-1}\left(\frac{4}{3}\right) + \cos^{-1}\left(\frac{5}{13}\right)\right) = \cos(\alpha+\beta) = \cos\alpha\cos\beta - \sin\alpha\sin\beta$$

$$= \left(\frac{3}{5}\right)\cdot\left(\frac{5}{13}\right) - \left(\frac{4}{5}\right)\cdot\left(\frac{12}{13}\right) = \frac{15}{65} - \frac{48}{65} = -\frac{33}{65}$$

62. $\cos\left(\tan^{-1}\left(\frac{5}{12}\right) - \sin^{-1}\left(-\frac{3}{5}\right)\right)$

Let $\alpha = \tan^{-1}\left(\frac{5}{12}\right)$ and $\beta = \sin^{-1}\left(-\frac{3}{5}\right)$. α is in quadrant I; β is in quadrant IV.

Then $\tan\alpha = \frac{5}{12}$, $-\frac{\pi}{2} < \alpha < \frac{\pi}{2}$, and $\sin\beta = -\frac{3}{5}, -\frac{\pi}{2} < \alpha < \frac{\pi}{2}$.

$$\sec\alpha = \sqrt{1+\tan^2\alpha} = \sqrt{1+\left(\frac{5}{12}\right)^2} = \sqrt{1+\frac{25}{144}} = \sqrt{\frac{169}{144}} = \frac{13}{12};\quad \cos\alpha = \frac{12}{13}$$

$$\sin\alpha = \sqrt{1-\cos^2\alpha} = \sqrt{1-\left(\frac{12}{13}\right)^2} = \sqrt{1-\frac{144}{169}} = \sqrt{\frac{25}{169}} = \frac{5}{13}$$

$$\cos\beta = \sqrt{1-\sin^2\beta} = \sqrt{1-\left(-\frac{3}{5}\right)^2} = \sqrt{1-\frac{9}{25}} = \sqrt{\frac{16}{15}} = \frac{4}{5}$$

$$\cos\left(\tan^{-1}\left(\frac{5}{12}\right) - \sin^{-1}\left(-\frac{3}{5}\right)\right) = \cos(\alpha-\beta) = \cos\alpha\cos\beta + \sin\alpha\sin\beta$$

$$= \left(\frac{12}{13}\right)\cdot\left(\frac{4}{5}\right) + \left(\frac{5}{13}\right)\cdot\left(-\frac{3}{5}\right) = \frac{48}{65} - \frac{15}{65} = \frac{33}{65}$$

63. $\cos\left(\sin^{-1}\left(\frac{5}{13}\right) - \tan^{-1}\left(\frac{3}{4}\right)\right)$

Let $\alpha = \sin^{-1}\left(\frac{5}{13}\right)$ and $\beta = \tan^{-1}\left(\frac{3}{4}\right)$. α is in quadrant I; β is in quadrant I.

Then $\sin\alpha = \frac{5}{13},\ -\frac{\pi}{2} \le \alpha \le \frac{\pi}{2}$, and $\tan\beta = \frac{3}{4}, -\frac{\pi}{2} < \beta < \frac{\pi}{2}$.

$$\cos\alpha = \sqrt{1-\sin^2\alpha} = \sqrt{1-\left(\frac{5}{13}\right)^2} = \sqrt{1-\frac{25}{169}} = \sqrt{\frac{144}{169}} = \frac{12}{13}$$

$$\sec\beta = \sqrt{1+\tan^2\beta} = \sqrt{1+\left(\frac{3}{4}\right)^2} = \sqrt{1+\frac{9}{16}} = \sqrt{\frac{25}{16}} = \frac{5}{4};\quad \cos\beta = \frac{4}{5}$$

$$\sin\beta = \sqrt{1-\cos^2\beta} = \sqrt{1-\left(\frac{4}{5}\right)^2} = \sqrt{1-\frac{16}{25}} = \sqrt{\frac{9}{25}} = \frac{3}{5}$$

$$\cos\left[\sin^{-1}\left(\frac{5}{13}\right) - \tan^{-1}\left(\frac{3}{4}\right)\right] = \cos(\alpha-\beta)$$

$$= \cos\alpha\cos\beta + \sin\alpha\sin\beta = \frac{12}{13}\cdot\frac{4}{5} + \frac{5}{13}\cdot\frac{3}{5} = \frac{48}{65} + \frac{15}{65} = \frac{63}{65}$$

64. $\cos\left(\tan^{-1}\left(\frac{4}{3}\right) + \cos^{-1}\left(\frac{12}{13}\right)\right)$

Let $\alpha = \tan^{-1}\left(\frac{4}{3}\right)$ and $\beta = \cos^{-1}\left(\frac{12}{13}\right)$. α is in quadrant I; β is in quadrant I.

Then $\tan\alpha = \frac{4}{3},\ -\frac{\pi}{2} < \alpha < \frac{\pi}{2}$, and $\cos\beta = \frac{12}{13}, 0 \le \beta \le \pi$.

$$\sec\alpha = \sqrt{1+\tan^2\alpha} = \sqrt{1+\left(\frac{4}{3}\right)^2} = \sqrt{1+\frac{16}{9}} = \sqrt{\frac{25}{9}} = \frac{5}{3}; \quad \cos\alpha = \frac{3}{5}$$

$$\sin\alpha = \sqrt{1-\cos^2\alpha} = \sqrt{1-\left(\frac{3}{5}\right)^2} = \sqrt{1-\frac{9}{25}} = \sqrt{\frac{16}{25}} = \frac{4}{5}$$

$$\sin\beta = \sqrt{1-\cos^2\beta} = \sqrt{1-\left(\frac{12}{13}\right)^2} = \sqrt{1-\frac{144}{169}} = \sqrt{\frac{25}{169}} = \frac{5}{13}$$

$$\cos\left(\tan^{-1}\left(\frac{4}{3}\right)+\cos^{-1}\left(\frac{12}{13}\right)\right) = \cos(\alpha+\beta) = \cos\alpha\cos\beta - \sin\alpha\sin\beta$$

$$= \left(\frac{3}{5}\right)\cdot\left(\frac{12}{13}\right) - \left(\frac{4}{5}\right)\cdot\left(\frac{5}{13}\right) = \frac{36}{65} - \frac{20}{65} = \frac{16}{65}$$

65. $\tan\left(\sin^{-1}\left(\frac{5}{3}\right)+\frac{\pi}{6}\right)$

$\sin^{-1}\left(\frac{5}{3}\right)$ is undefined since $\frac{5}{3}$ is not in the domain of $f(x) = \sin^{-1}(x)$

therefore $\tan\left(\sin^{-1}\left(\frac{5}{3}\right)+\frac{\pi}{6}\right)$ is undefined.

66. $\tan\left(\frac{\pi}{4} - \cos^{-1}\left(\frac{3}{5}\right)\right)$

Let $\alpha = \cos^{-1}\left(\frac{3}{5}\right)$. α is in quadrant I.

Then $\cos\alpha = \frac{3}{5},\ 0 \le \alpha \le \pi$.

$$\sin\alpha = \sqrt{1-\cos^2\alpha} = \sqrt{1-\left(\frac{3}{5}\right)^2} = \sqrt{1-\frac{9}{25}} = \sqrt{\frac{16}{25}} = \frac{4}{5}$$

$$\tan\alpha = \frac{\sin\alpha}{\cos\alpha} = \frac{\left(\frac{4}{5}\right)}{\left(\frac{3}{5}\right)} = \frac{4}{5}\cdot\frac{5}{3} = \frac{4}{3}$$

$$\tan\left(\frac{\pi}{4} - \cos^{-1}\left(\frac{3}{5}\right)\right) = \frac{\tan\left(\frac{\pi}{4}\right) - \tan\left(\cos^{-1}\left(\frac{3}{5}\right)\right)}{1+\tan\left(\frac{\pi}{4}\right)\tan\left(\cos^{-1}\left(\frac{3}{5}\right)\right)} = \frac{\left(1-\frac{4}{3}\right)}{\left(1+1\cdot\frac{4}{3}\right)} = \frac{\left(-\frac{1}{3}\right)}{\left(\frac{7}{3}\right)} = -\frac{1}{3}\cdot\frac{3}{7} = -\frac{1}{7}$$

67. $\tan\left(\sin^{-1}\left(\frac{4}{5}\right)+\cos^{-1}(1)\right)$

Let $\alpha=\sin^{-1}\left(\frac{4}{5}\right)$ and $\beta=\cos^{-1}(1)$; α is in quadrant I.

Then $\sin\alpha=\frac{4}{5},\ -\frac{\pi}{2}\le\alpha\le\frac{\pi}{2}$ and $\cos\beta=1,\ 0\le\beta\le\pi$.

$$\cos\beta=1,\ 0\le\beta\le\pi\Rightarrow\beta=0\ \therefore\cos^{-1}1=0$$

$$\cos\alpha=\sqrt{1-\sin^2\alpha}=\sqrt{1-\left(\frac{4}{5}\right)^2}=\sqrt{1-\frac{16}{25}}=\sqrt{\frac{9}{25}}=\frac{3}{5}$$

$$\tan\alpha=\frac{\sin\alpha}{\cos\alpha}=\frac{\left(\frac{4}{5}\right)}{\left(\frac{3}{5}\right)}=\frac{4}{5}\cdot\frac{5}{3}=\frac{4}{3}$$

$$\tan\left(\sin^{-1}\left(\frac{4}{5}\right)+\cos^{-1}(1)\right)=\frac{\tan\left(\sin^{-1}\left(\frac{4}{5}\right)\right)+\tan\left(\cos^{-1}(1)\right)}{1-\tan\left(\sin^{-1}\left(\frac{4}{5}\right)\right)\tan\left(\cos^{-1}(1)\right)}=\frac{\left(\frac{4}{3}+0\right)}{\left(1-\frac{4}{3}\cdot 0\right)}=\frac{\left(\frac{4}{3}\right)}{(1)}=\frac{4}{3}$$

68. $\tan\left(\cos^{-1}\left(\frac{4}{5}\right)+\sin^{-1}(1)\right)$

Let $\alpha=\cos^{-1}\left(\frac{4}{5}\right)$ and $\beta=\sin^{-1}(1)$; α is in quadrant I.

Then $\cos\alpha=\frac{4}{5},\ 0\le\alpha\le\pi$ and $\sin\beta=1,\ -\frac{\pi}{2}\le\beta\le\frac{\pi}{2}$.

$$\sin\beta=1,\ -\frac{\pi}{2}\le\beta\le\frac{\pi}{2}\Rightarrow\beta=\frac{\pi}{2}\ \ \therefore\sin^{-1}(1)=\frac{\pi}{2}$$

$$\sin\alpha=\sqrt{1-\cos^2\alpha}=\sqrt{1-\left(\frac{4}{5}\right)^2}=\sqrt{1-\frac{16}{25}}=\sqrt{\frac{9}{25}}=\frac{3}{5}$$

$$\tan\alpha=\frac{\sin\alpha}{\cos\alpha}=\frac{\left(\frac{3}{5}\right)}{\left(\frac{4}{5}\right)}=\frac{3}{5}\cdot\frac{5}{4}=\frac{3}{4};\ \text{ but }\tan\left(\frac{\pi}{2}\right)\text{ is undefined.}$$

Therefore, we cannot use the sum formula for tangent.
Rewriting using sine and cosine,

$$\tan\left(\cos^{-1}\left(\frac{4}{5}\right)+\sin^{-1}(1)\right)=\frac{\sin\left(\cos^{-1}\left(\frac{4}{5}\right)+\sin^{-1}(1)\right)}{\tan\left(\cos^{-1}\left(\frac{4}{5}\right)+\sin^{-1}(1)\right)}=\frac{\sin(\alpha)\cos(\beta)+\cos(\alpha)\sin(\beta)}{\cos(\alpha)\cos(\beta)-\sin(\alpha)\sin(\beta)}$$

$$=\frac{\left(\frac{3}{5}\right)(0)+\left(\frac{4}{5}\right)(1)}{\left(\frac{4}{5}\right)(0)-\left(\frac{3}{5}\right)(1)}=\frac{\left(\frac{4}{5}\right)}{\left(-\frac{3}{5}\right)}=-\frac{4}{3} \quad \therefore \quad \tan\left(\cos^{-1}\left(\frac{4}{5}\right)+\sin^{-1}(1)\right)=-\frac{4}{3}$$

69. $\cos\left(\cos^{-1}u+\sin^{-1}v\right)$

Let $\alpha=\cos^{-1}u$ and $\beta=\sin^{-1}v$.

Then $\cos\alpha = u,\ 0 \le \alpha \le \pi,$ and $\sin\beta = v,\ -\frac{\pi}{2} \le \beta \le \frac{\pi}{2}$

$$\sin\alpha = \sqrt{1-\cos^2\alpha} = \sqrt{1-u^2}$$

$$\cos\beta = \sqrt{1-\sin^2\beta} = \sqrt{1-v^2}$$

$$\cos\left(\cos^{-1}u+\sin^{-1}v\right)=\cos(\alpha+\beta)=\cos\alpha\cos\beta-\sin\alpha\sin\beta=u\sqrt{1-v^2}-v\sqrt{1-u^2}$$

70. $\sin\left(\sin^{-1}u-\cos^{-1}v\right)$

Let $\alpha=\sin^{-1}u$ and $\beta=\cos^{-1}v$.

Then $\sin\alpha = u,\ -\frac{\pi}{2} \le \alpha \le \frac{\pi}{2},$ and $\cos\beta = v,\ 0 \le \beta \le \pi$

$$\cos\alpha = \sqrt{1-\sin^2\alpha} = \sqrt{1-u^2}$$

$$\sin\beta = \sqrt{1-\cos^2\beta} = \sqrt{1-v^2}$$

$$\sin\left(\sin^{-1}u-\cos^{-1}v\right)=\sin(\alpha-\beta)=\sin\alpha\cos\beta-\cos\alpha\sin\beta$$

$$=u\cdot v-\sqrt{1-u^2}\cdot\sqrt{1-v^2}$$

71. $\sin\left(\tan^{-1}u-\sin^{-1}v\right)$

Let $\alpha=\tan^{-1}u$ and $\beta=\sin^{-1}v$.

Then $\tan\alpha = u,\ -\frac{\pi}{2} < \alpha < \frac{\pi}{2},$ and $\sin\beta = v,\ -\frac{\pi}{2} \le \beta \le \frac{\pi}{2}$

$$\sec\alpha = \sqrt{\tan^2\alpha+1} = \sqrt{u^2+1}; \qquad \cos\alpha = \frac{1}{\sqrt{u^2+1}}$$

$$\sin\alpha = \sqrt{1-\cos^2\alpha} = \sqrt{1-\frac{1}{u^2+1}} = \sqrt{\frac{u^2+1-1}{u^2+1}} = \sqrt{\frac{u^2}{u^2+1}} = \frac{u}{\sqrt{u^2+1}}$$

$$\cos\beta = \sqrt{1-\sin^2\beta} = \sqrt{1-v^2}$$

$$\sin\left(\tan^{-1}u-\sin^{-1}v\right)=\sin(\alpha-\beta)=\sin\alpha\cos\beta-\cos\alpha\sin\beta$$

$$=\frac{u}{\sqrt{u^2+1}}\cdot\sqrt{1-v^2}-\frac{1}{\sqrt{u^2+1}}\cdot v=\frac{u\sqrt{1-v^2}-v}{\sqrt{u^2+1}}$$

72. $\cos\left(\tan^{-1}u+\tan^{-1}v\right)$

Let $\alpha=\tan^{-1}u$ and $\beta=\tan^{-1}v$.

Then $\tan\alpha = u,\ -\frac{\pi}{2} < \alpha < \frac{\pi}{2},$ and $\tan\beta = v,\ -\frac{\pi}{2} < \beta < \frac{\pi}{2}$

$$\sec\alpha = \sqrt{\tan^2\alpha + 1} = \sqrt{u^2+1}; \qquad \cos\alpha = \frac{1}{\sqrt{u^2+1}}$$

$$\sin\alpha = \sqrt{1-\cos^2\alpha} = \sqrt{1-\frac{1}{u^2+1}} = \sqrt{\frac{u^2+1-1}{u^2+1}} = \sqrt{\frac{u^2}{u^2+1}} = \frac{u}{\sqrt{u^2+1}}$$

$$\sec\beta = \sqrt{\tan^2\beta + 1} = \sqrt{v^2+1}; \qquad \cos\beta = \frac{1}{\sqrt{v^2+1}}$$

$$\sin\beta = \sqrt{1-\cos^2\beta} = \sqrt{1-\frac{1}{v^2+1}} = \sqrt{\frac{v^2+1-1}{v^2+1}} = \sqrt{\frac{v^2}{v^2+1}} = \frac{v}{\sqrt{v^2+1}}$$

$$\cos\left(\tan^{-1}u + \tan^{-1}v\right) = \cos(\alpha+\beta) = \cos\alpha\cos\beta - \sin\alpha\sin\beta$$

$$= \frac{1}{\sqrt{u^2+1}}\cdot\frac{1}{\sqrt{v^2+1}} - \frac{u}{\sqrt{u^2+1}}\cdot\frac{v}{\sqrt{v^2+1}} = \frac{1-uv}{\sqrt{u^2+1}\cdot\sqrt{v^2+1}}$$

73. $\tan\left(\sin^{-1}u - \cos^{-1}v\right)$

Let $\alpha = \sin^{-1}u$ and $\beta = \cos^{-1}v$.

Then $\sin\alpha = u,\ -\frac{\pi}{2} \le \alpha \le \frac{\pi}{2}$, and $\cos\beta = v,\ 0 \le \beta \le \pi$

$$\cos\alpha = \sqrt{1-\sin^2\alpha} = \sqrt{1-u^2}; \qquad \tan\alpha = \frac{\sin\alpha}{\cos\alpha} = \frac{u}{\sqrt{1-u^2}}$$

$$\sin\beta = \sqrt{1-\cos^2\beta} = \sqrt{1-v^2}; \qquad \tan\beta = \frac{\sin\beta}{\cos\beta} = \frac{\sqrt{1-v^2}}{v}$$

$$\tan\left(\sin^{-1}u - \cos^{-1}v\right) = \tan(\alpha-\beta) = \frac{\tan\alpha - \tan\beta}{1+\tan\alpha\tan\beta} = \frac{\left(\frac{u}{\sqrt{1-u^2}} - \frac{\sqrt{1-v^2}}{v}\right)}{\left(1+\frac{u}{\sqrt{1-u^2}}\cdot\frac{\sqrt{1-v^2}}{v}\right)}$$

$$= \frac{\left(\frac{uv-\sqrt{1-u^2}\sqrt{1-v^2}}{v\sqrt{1-u^2}}\right)}{\left(\frac{v\sqrt{1-u^2}+u\sqrt{1-v^2}}{v\sqrt{1-u^2}}\right)} = \frac{uv-\sqrt{1-u^2}\sqrt{1-v^2}}{v\sqrt{1-u^2}+u\sqrt{1-v^2}}$$

74. $\sec\left(\tan^{-1}u + \cos^{-1}v\right)$

Let $\alpha = \tan^{-1}u$ and $\beta = \cos^{-1}v$.

Then $\tan\alpha = u,\ -\frac{\pi}{2} < \alpha < \frac{\pi}{2}$, and $\cos\beta = v,\ 0 \le \beta \le \pi$

$$\sec\alpha = \sqrt{\tan^2\alpha + 1} = \sqrt{u^2+1}; \qquad \cos\alpha = \frac{1}{\sqrt{u^2+1}}$$

$$\sin\alpha = \sqrt{1-\cos^2\alpha} = \sqrt{1-\frac{1}{u^2+1}} = \sqrt{\frac{u^2+1-1}{u^2+1}} = \sqrt{\frac{u^2}{u^2+1}} = \frac{u}{\sqrt{u^2+1}}$$

$$\sin\beta = \sqrt{1-\cos^2\beta} = \sqrt{1-v^2}$$

$$\sec\left(\tan^{-1}u+\cos^{-1}v\right)=\sec(\alpha+\beta)=\frac{1}{\cos(\alpha+\beta)}=\frac{1}{\cos\alpha\cos\beta-\sin\alpha\sin\beta}$$

$$=\frac{1}{\left(\frac{1}{\sqrt{u^2+1}}\cdot v-\frac{u}{\sqrt{u^2+1}}\cdot\sqrt{1-v^2}\right)}=\frac{1}{\left(\frac{v}{\sqrt{u^2+1}}-\frac{u\sqrt{1-v^2}}{\sqrt{u^2+1}}\right)}$$

$$=\frac{1}{\left(\frac{v-u\sqrt{1-v^2}}{\sqrt{u^2+1}}\right)}=\frac{\sqrt{u^2+1}}{v-u\sqrt{1-v^2}}$$

75. Show that $\sin^{-1}v+\cos^{-1}v=\frac{\pi}{2}$.

Let $\alpha=\sin^{-1}v$ and $\beta=\cos^{-1}v$.

Then $\sin\alpha = v = \cos\beta$, and since $\sin\alpha = \cos\left(\frac{\pi}{2}-\alpha\right)$, $\cos\left(\frac{\pi}{2}-\alpha\right) = \cos\beta$.

If $v\ge 0$, then $0\le\alpha\le\frac{\pi}{2}$, so that $\left(\frac{\pi}{2}-\alpha\right)$ and β both lie in the interval $\left[0,\frac{\pi}{2}\right]$.

If $v<0$, then $-\frac{\pi}{2}\le\alpha<0$, so that $\left(\frac{\pi}{2}-\alpha\right)$ and β both lie in the interval $\left[\frac{\pi}{2},\pi\right]$. Either way, $\cos\left(\frac{\pi}{2}-\alpha\right) = \cos\beta$ implies $\frac{\pi}{2}-\alpha=\beta$, or $\alpha+\beta=\frac{\pi}{2}$. Thus, $\sin^{-1}v+\cos^{-1}v=\frac{\pi}{2}$.

76. Show that $\tan^{-1}v+\cot^{-1}v=\frac{\pi}{2}$.

Let $\alpha=\tan^{-1}v$ and $\beta=\cot^{-1}v$.

Then $\tan\alpha = v = \cot\beta$, and since $\tan\alpha = \cot\left(\frac{\pi}{2}-\alpha\right)$, $\cot\left(\frac{\pi}{2}-\alpha\right) = \cot\beta$.

If $v\ge 0$, then $0\le\alpha\le\frac{\pi}{2}$, so that $\left(\frac{\pi}{2}-\alpha\right)$ and β both lie in the interval $\left[0,\frac{\pi}{2}\right]$.

If $v<0$, then $-\frac{\pi}{2}\le\alpha<0$, so that $\left(\frac{\pi}{2}-\alpha\right)$ and β both lie in the interval $\left[\frac{\pi}{2},\pi\right]$. Either way, $\cot\left(\frac{\pi}{2}-\alpha\right) = \cot\beta$ implies $\frac{\pi}{2}-\alpha=\beta$, or $\alpha+\beta=\frac{\pi}{2}$. Thus, $\tan^{-1}v+\cot^{-1}v=\frac{\pi}{2}$.

77. Show that $\tan^{-1}\left(\frac{1}{v}\right)=\frac{\pi}{2}-\tan^{-1}v$, if $v>0$.

Let $\alpha=\tan^{-1}\left(\frac{1}{v}\right)$ and $\beta=\tan^{-1}v$. Because $\frac{1}{v}$ must be defined, $v\ne 0$ and so $\alpha,\beta\ne 0$.

Then $\tan\alpha=\frac{1}{v}=\frac{1}{\tan\beta}=\cot\beta$, and since $\tan\alpha=\cot\left(\frac{\pi}{2}-\alpha\right)$, $\cot\left(\frac{\pi}{2}-\alpha\right)=\cot\beta$.

Because $v>0$, $0<\alpha<\frac{\pi}{2}$ and so $\frac{\pi}{2}-\alpha$ and β both lie in the interval $\left(0,\frac{\pi}{2}\right)$. Then, $\cot\left(\frac{\pi}{2}-\alpha\right)=\cot\beta$ implies $\frac{\pi}{2}-\alpha=\beta$ or $\alpha=\frac{\pi}{2}-\beta$.

Thus, $\tan^{-1}\left(\frac{1}{v}\right)=\frac{\pi}{2}-\tan^{-1}v$, if $v>0$.

78. Show that $\cot^{-1}\left(e^{v}\right)=\tan^{-1}\left(e^{-v}\right)$.

Let $\theta=\tan^{-1}\left(e^{-v}\right)$. Then $\tan\theta = e^{-v}$, so $\cot\theta = \dfrac{1}{e^{-v}} = e^{v}$. Since $0 \le \theta \le \frac{\pi}{2}$ (because $e^{-v} > 0$), $\cot^{-1}\left(e^{v}\right)=\cot^{-1}(\cot\theta)=\theta=\tan^{-1}\left(e^{-v}\right)$.

79. $$\begin{aligned}\sin\left(\sin^{-1}v+\cos^{-1}v\right) &= \sin\left(\sin^{-1}v\right)\cos\left(\cos^{-1}v\right)+\cos\left(\sin^{-1}v\right)\sin\left(\cos^{-1}v\right)\\ &= v\cdot v+\sqrt{1-v^2}\sqrt{1-v^2} = v^2+1-v^2 = 1\end{aligned}$$

80. $$\begin{aligned}\cos\left(\sin^{-1}v+\cos^{-1}v\right) &= \cos\left(\sin^{-1}v\right)\cos\left(\cos^{-1}v\right)-\sin\left(\sin^{-1}v\right)\sin\left(\cos^{-1}v\right)\\ &= \sqrt{1-v^2}\cdot v-v\cdot\sqrt{1-v^2} = 0\end{aligned}$$

81. $$\begin{aligned}\frac{\sin(x+h)-\sin x}{h} &= \frac{\sin x\cos h+\cos x\sin h-\sin x}{h} = \frac{\cos x\sin h-\sin x+\sin x\cos h}{h}\\ &= \cos x\cdot\left(\frac{\sin h}{h}\right)-\sin x\cdot\left(\frac{1-\cos h}{h}\right)\end{aligned}$$

82. $$\begin{aligned}\frac{\cos(x+h)-\cos x}{h} &= \frac{\cos x\cos h-\sin x\sin h-\cos x}{h} = \frac{-\sin x\sin h+\cos x\cos h-\cos x}{h}\\ &= -\sin x\cdot\left(\frac{\sin h}{h}\right)-\cos x\cdot\left(\frac{1-\cos h}{h}\right)\end{aligned}$$

83. $\tan\left(\dfrac{\pi}{2}-\theta\right)=\dfrac{\tan\left(\frac{\pi}{2}\right)-\tan\theta}{1+\tan\left(\frac{\pi}{2}\right)\tan\theta}$ This is impossible because $\tan\left(\frac{\pi}{2}\right)$ is undefined.

$$\tan\left(\frac{\pi}{2}-\theta\right) = \frac{\sin\left(\frac{\pi}{2}-\theta\right)}{\cos\left(\frac{\pi}{2}-\theta\right)} = \frac{\cos\theta}{\sin\theta} = \cot\theta$$

84. If $\tan\alpha = x+1$ and $\tan\beta = x-1$, then

$$\begin{aligned}2\cot(\alpha-\beta) &= 2\cdot\frac{1}{\tan(\alpha-\beta)} = \frac{2}{\left(\dfrac{\tan\alpha-\tan\beta}{1+\tan\alpha\tan\beta}\right)} = \frac{2(1+\tan\alpha\tan\beta)}{\tan\alpha-\tan\beta}\\ &= \frac{2(1+(x+1)(x-1))}{x+1-(x-1)} = \frac{2\left(1+(x^2-1)\right)}{x+1-x+1} = \frac{2\left(1+x^2-1\right)}{2} = x^2\end{aligned}$$

85. $\tan\theta = \tan\left(\theta_2-\theta_1\right) = \dfrac{\tan\theta_2-\tan\theta_1}{1+\tan\theta_2\tan\theta_1} = \dfrac{m_2-m_1}{1+m_2m_1}$

86. $\sin(\alpha - \theta)\sin(\beta - \theta)\sin(\gamma - \theta)$

$$= (\sin\alpha\cos\theta - \cos\alpha\sin\theta)(\sin\beta\cos\theta - \cos\beta\sin\theta)(\sin\gamma\cos\theta - \cos\gamma\sin\theta)$$

$$= \sin\theta\left(\sin\alpha\left(\frac{\cos\theta}{\sin\theta}\right) - \cos\alpha\right)\sin\theta\left(\sin\beta\left(\frac{\cos\theta}{\sin\theta}\right) - \cos\beta\right)\sin\theta\left(\sin\gamma\left(\frac{\cos\theta}{\sin\theta}\right) - \cos\gamma\right)$$

$$= \sin^3\theta\left(\sin\alpha\left(\frac{\cos\theta}{\sin\theta} - \frac{\cos\alpha}{\sin\alpha}\right)\right)\left(\sin\beta\left(\frac{\cos\theta}{\sin\theta} - \frac{\cos\beta}{\sin\beta}\right)\right)\left(\sin\gamma\left(\frac{\cos\theta}{\sin\theta} - \frac{\cos\gamma}{\sin\gamma}\right)\right)$$

$$= \sin^3\theta(\sin\alpha(\cot\theta - \cot\alpha))(\sin\beta(\cot\theta - \cot\beta))(\sin\gamma(\cot\theta - \cot\gamma))$$

$$= \sin^3\theta\sin\alpha\sin\beta\sin\gamma(\cot\beta + \cot\gamma)(\cot\alpha + \cot\gamma)(\cot\alpha + \cot\beta)$$

$$= \sin^3\theta\sin\alpha\sin\beta\sin\gamma\left(\frac{\cos\beta}{\sin\beta} + \frac{\cos\gamma}{\sin\gamma}\right)\left(\frac{\cos\alpha}{\sin\alpha} + \frac{\cos\gamma}{\sin\gamma}\right)\left(\frac{\cos\alpha}{\sin\alpha} + \frac{\cos\beta}{\sin\beta}\right)$$

$$= \sin^3\theta\sin\alpha\sin\beta\sin\gamma\left(\frac{\sin(\gamma + \beta)}{\sin\beta\sin\gamma}\right)\left(\frac{\sin(\gamma + \alpha)}{\sin\alpha\sin\gamma}\right)\left(\frac{\sin(\beta + \alpha)}{\sin\alpha\sin\beta}\right)$$

$$= \sin^3\theta\sin\alpha\sin\beta\sin\gamma\left(\frac{\sin(180^\circ - \alpha)}{\sin\beta\sin\gamma}\right)\left(\frac{\sin(180^\circ - \beta)}{\sin\alpha\sin\gamma}\right)\left(\frac{\sin(180^\circ - \gamma)}{\sin\alpha\sin\beta}\right)$$

$$= \sin^3\theta\sin\alpha\sin\beta\sin\gamma\left(\frac{\sin\alpha}{\sin\beta\sin\gamma}\right)\left(\frac{\sin\beta}{\sin\alpha\sin\gamma}\right)\left(\frac{\sin\gamma}{\sin\alpha\sin\beta}\right)$$

$$= \sin^3\theta$$

87. The first step in the derivation

$$\tan\left(\theta + \frac{\pi}{2}\right) = \frac{\tan\theta + \tan\left(\frac{\pi}{2}\right)}{1 - \tan\theta\tan\left(\frac{\pi}{2}\right)}$$

is impossible because $\tan\left(\frac{\pi}{2}\right)$ is undefined.

Chapter 8

Analytic Trigonometry

8.5 Double-Angle and Half-Angle Formulas

1. $\sin\theta = \frac{3}{5},\ 0 < \theta < \frac{\pi}{2};$ thus, $0 < \frac{\theta}{2} < \frac{\pi}{4} \Rightarrow \frac{\theta}{2}$ is in quadrant I.

   $y = 3,\ r = 5$

   $x^2 + 3^2 = 5^2,\ x > 0 \ \rightarrow\ x^2 = 25 - 9 = 16,\ x > 0 \ \rightarrow\ x = 4$

   $\cos\theta = \frac{4}{5}$

   (a) $\sin(2\theta) = 2\sin\theta\cos\theta = 2\cdot\frac{3}{5}\cdot\frac{4}{5} = \frac{24}{25}$

   (b) $\cos(2\theta) = \cos^2\theta - \sin^2\theta = \left(\frac{4}{5}\right)^2 - \left(\frac{3}{5}\right)^2 = \frac{16}{25} - \frac{9}{25} = \frac{7}{25}$

   (c) $\sin\left(\frac{\theta}{2}\right) = \sqrt{\frac{1-\cos\theta}{2}} = \sqrt{\frac{\left(1-\frac{4}{5}\right)}{2}} = \sqrt{\frac{\left(\frac{1}{5}\right)}{2}} = \sqrt{\frac{1}{10}} = \frac{1}{\sqrt{10}} = \frac{\sqrt{10}}{10}$

   (d) $\cos\left(\frac{\theta}{2}\right) = \sqrt{\frac{1+\cos\theta}{2}} = \sqrt{\frac{\left(1+\frac{4}{5}\right)}{2}} = \sqrt{\frac{\left(\frac{9}{5}\right)}{2}} = \sqrt{\frac{9}{10}} = \frac{3}{\sqrt{10}} = \frac{3\sqrt{10}}{10}$

2. $\cos\theta = \frac{3}{5},\ 0 < \theta < \frac{\pi}{2};$ thus, $0 < \frac{\theta}{2} < \frac{\pi}{4} \Rightarrow \frac{\theta}{2}$ is in quadrant I.

   $x = 3,\ r = 5$

   $3^2 + y^2 = 5^2,\ y > 0 \ \rightarrow\ y^2 = 25 - 9 = 16,\ y > 0 \ \rightarrow\ y = 4$

   $\sin\theta = \frac{4}{5}$

   (a) $\sin(2\theta) = 2\sin\theta\cos\theta = 2\cdot\frac{4}{5}\cdot\frac{3}{5} = \frac{24}{25}$

   (b) $\cos(2\theta) = \cos^2\theta - \sin^2\theta = \left(\frac{3}{5}\right)^2 - \left(\frac{4}{5}\right)^2 = \frac{9}{25} - \frac{16}{25} = -\frac{7}{25}$

   (c) $\sin\left(\frac{\theta}{2}\right) = \sqrt{\frac{1-\cos\theta}{2}} = \sqrt{\frac{\left(1-\frac{3}{5}\right)}{2}} = \sqrt{\frac{\left(\frac{2}{5}\right)}{2}} = \sqrt{\frac{1}{5}} = \frac{1}{\sqrt{5}} = \frac{\sqrt{5}}{5}$

   (d) $\cos\left(\frac{\theta}{2}\right) = \sqrt{\frac{1+\cos\theta}{2}} = \sqrt{\frac{\left(1+\frac{3}{5}\right)}{2}} = \sqrt{\frac{\left(\frac{8}{5}\right)}{2}} = \sqrt{\frac{4}{5}} = \frac{2}{\sqrt{5}} = \frac{2\sqrt{5}}{5}$

3. $\tan\theta = \frac{4}{3}, \ \pi < \theta < \frac{3\pi}{2};$ thus, $\frac{\pi}{2} < \frac{\theta}{2} < \frac{3\pi}{4} \Rightarrow \frac{\theta}{2}$ is in quadrant II.

$x = -3, \ y = -4$

$r^2 = (-3)^2 + (-4)^2 = 9 + 16 = 25 \rightarrow r = 5$

$\sin\theta = -\frac{4}{5}, \ \cos\theta = -\frac{3}{5}$

(a) $\sin(2\theta) = 2\sin\theta\cos\theta = 2\cdot\left(-\frac{4}{5}\right)\cdot\left(-\frac{3}{5}\right) = \frac{24}{25}$

(b) $\cos(2\theta) = \cos^2\theta - \sin^2\theta = \left(-\frac{3}{5}\right)^2 - \left(-\frac{4}{5}\right)^2 = \frac{9}{25} - \frac{16}{25} = -\frac{7}{25}$

(c) $\sin\left(\frac{\theta}{2}\right) = \sqrt{\frac{1-\cos\theta}{2}} = \sqrt{\frac{1-\left(-\frac{3}{5}\right)}{2}} = \sqrt{\frac{\left(\frac{8}{5}\right)}{2}} = \sqrt{\frac{4}{5}} = \frac{2}{\sqrt{5}} = \frac{2\sqrt{5}}{5}$

(d) $\cos\left(\frac{\theta}{2}\right) = -\sqrt{\frac{1+\cos\theta}{2}} = -\sqrt{\frac{1+\left(-\frac{3}{5}\right)}{2}} = -\sqrt{\frac{\left(\frac{2}{5}\right)}{2}} = -\sqrt{\frac{1}{5}} = -\frac{1}{\sqrt{5}} = -\frac{\sqrt{5}}{5}$

4. $\tan\theta = \frac{1}{2}, \ \pi < \theta < \frac{3\pi}{2};$ thus, $\frac{\pi}{2} < \frac{\theta}{2} < \frac{3\pi}{4} \Rightarrow \frac{\theta}{2}$ is in quadrant II.

$x = -2, \ y = -1$

$r^2 = (-2)^2 + (-1)^2 = 4 + 1 = 5 \rightarrow r = \sqrt{5}$

$\sin\theta = -\frac{1}{\sqrt{5}} = -\frac{\sqrt{5}}{5}, \ \cos\theta = -\frac{2}{\sqrt{5}} = -\frac{2\sqrt{5}}{5}$

(a) $\sin(2\theta) = 2\sin\theta\cos\theta = 2\cdot\left(-\frac{\sqrt{5}}{5}\right)\cdot\left(-\frac{2\sqrt{5}}{5}\right) = \frac{4}{5}$

(b) $\cos(2\theta) = \cos^2\theta - \sin^2\theta = \left(-\frac{2\sqrt{5}}{5}\right)^2 - \left(-\frac{\sqrt{5}}{5}\right)^2 = \frac{20}{25} - \frac{5}{25} = \frac{15}{25} = \frac{3}{5}$

(c) $\sin\left(\frac{\theta}{2}\right) = \sqrt{\frac{1-\cos\theta}{2}} = \sqrt{\frac{1-\left(-\frac{2\sqrt{5}}{5}\right)}{2}} = \sqrt{\frac{\left(\frac{5+2\sqrt{5}}{5}\right)}{2}} = \sqrt{\frac{5+2\sqrt{5}}{10}}$

(d) $\cos\left(\frac{\theta}{2}\right) = -\sqrt{\frac{1+\cos\theta}{2}} = -\sqrt{\frac{1+\left(-\frac{2\sqrt{5}}{5}\right)}{2}} = -\sqrt{\frac{\left(\frac{5-2\sqrt{5}}{5}\right)}{2}} = -\sqrt{\frac{5-2\sqrt{5}}{10}}$

5. $\cos\theta = -\dfrac{\sqrt{6}}{3},\ \dfrac{\pi}{2} < \theta < \pi;$ thus, $\dfrac{\pi}{4} < \dfrac{\theta}{2} < \dfrac{\pi}{2} \Rightarrow \dfrac{\theta}{2}$ is in quadrant I.

$x = -\sqrt{6},\ r = 3$

$(-\sqrt{6})^2 + y^2 = 3^2 \ \rightarrow\ y^2 = 9 - 6 = 3 \ \rightarrow\ y = \sqrt{3}$

$\sin\theta = \dfrac{\sqrt{3}}{3}$

(a) $\sin(2\theta) = 2\sin\theta\cos\theta = 2\cdot\left(\dfrac{\sqrt{3}}{3}\right)\cdot\left(-\dfrac{\sqrt{6}}{3}\right) = -\dfrac{2\sqrt{18}}{9} = -\dfrac{6\sqrt{2}}{9} = -\dfrac{2\sqrt{2}}{3}$

(b) $\cos(2\theta) = \cos^2\theta - \sin^2\theta = \left(-\dfrac{\sqrt{6}}{3}\right)^2 - \left(\dfrac{\sqrt{3}}{3}\right)^2 = \dfrac{6}{9} - \dfrac{3}{9} = \dfrac{3}{9} = \dfrac{1}{3}$

(c) $\sin\left(\dfrac{\theta}{2}\right) = \sqrt{\dfrac{1-\cos\theta}{2}} = \sqrt{\dfrac{\left(1-\left(-\dfrac{\sqrt{6}}{3}\right)\right)}{2}} = \sqrt{\dfrac{\left(\dfrac{3+\sqrt{6}}{3}\right)}{2}} = \sqrt{\dfrac{3+\sqrt{6}}{6}}$

(d) $\cos\left(\dfrac{\theta}{2}\right) = \sqrt{\dfrac{1+\cos\theta}{2}} = \sqrt{\dfrac{\left(1+\left(-\dfrac{\sqrt{6}}{3}\right)\right)}{2}} = \sqrt{\dfrac{\left(\dfrac{3-\sqrt{6}}{3}\right)}{2}} = \sqrt{\dfrac{3-\sqrt{6}}{6}}$

6. $\sin\theta = -\dfrac{\sqrt{3}}{3},\ \dfrac{3\pi}{2} < \theta < 2\pi;$ thus, $\dfrac{3\pi}{4} < \dfrac{\theta}{2} < \pi \Rightarrow \dfrac{\theta}{2}$ is in quadrant II.

$y = -\sqrt{3},\ r = 3$

$x^2 + \left(-\sqrt{3}\right)^2 = 3^2 \ \rightarrow\ x^2 = 9 - 3 = 6 \ \rightarrow\ x = \sqrt{6}$

$\cos\theta = \dfrac{\sqrt{6}}{3}$

(a) $\sin(2\theta) = 2\sin\theta\cos\theta = 2\cdot\left(-\dfrac{\sqrt{3}}{3}\right)\cdot\left(\dfrac{\sqrt{6}}{3}\right) = -\dfrac{2\sqrt{18}}{9} = -\dfrac{6\sqrt{2}}{9} = -\dfrac{2\sqrt{2}}{3}$

(b) $\cos(2\theta) = \cos^2\theta - \sin^2\theta = \left(\dfrac{\sqrt{6}}{3}\right)^2 - \left(-\dfrac{\sqrt{3}}{3}\right)^2 = \dfrac{6}{9} - \dfrac{3}{9} = \dfrac{3}{9} = \dfrac{1}{3}$

(c) $\sin\left(\dfrac{\theta}{2}\right) = \sqrt{\dfrac{1-\cos\theta}{2}} = \sqrt{\dfrac{\left(1-\dfrac{\sqrt{6}}{3}\right)}{2}} = \sqrt{\dfrac{\left(\dfrac{3-\sqrt{6}}{3}\right)}{2}} = \sqrt{\dfrac{3-\sqrt{6}}{6}}$

(d) $\cos\left(\dfrac{\theta}{2}\right) = -\sqrt{\dfrac{1+\cos\theta}{2}} = -\sqrt{\dfrac{\left(1+\dfrac{\sqrt{6}}{3}\right)}{2}} = -\sqrt{\dfrac{\left(\dfrac{3+\sqrt{6}}{3}\right)}{2}} = -\sqrt{\dfrac{3+\sqrt{6}}{6}}$

7. $\sec\theta = 3,\ \sin\theta > 0;\quad 0 < \theta < \frac{\pi}{2};$ thus, $0 < \frac{\theta}{2} < \frac{\pi}{4} \Rightarrow \frac{\theta}{2}$ is in quadrant I.

$x = 1,\ r = 3$

$1^2 + y^2 = 3^2 \rightarrow y^2 = 9 - 1 = 8 \rightarrow y = 2\sqrt{2}$

$\sin\theta = \frac{2\sqrt{2}}{3},\quad \cos\theta = \frac{1}{3}$

(a) $\sin(2\theta) = 2\sin\theta\cos\theta = 2\cdot\frac{2\sqrt{2}}{3}\cdot\frac{1}{3} = \frac{4\sqrt{2}}{9}$

(b) $\cos(2\theta) = \cos^2\theta - \sin^2\theta = \left(\frac{1}{3}\right)^2 - \left(\frac{2\sqrt{2}}{3}\right)^2 = \frac{1}{9} - \frac{8}{9} = -\frac{7}{9}$

(c) $\sin\left(\frac{\theta}{2}\right) = \sqrt{\frac{1-\cos\theta}{2}} = \sqrt{\frac{\left(1-\frac{1}{3}\right)}{2}} = \sqrt{\frac{\left(\frac{2}{3}\right)}{2}} = \sqrt{\frac{1}{3}} = \frac{1}{\sqrt{3}} = \frac{\sqrt{3}}{3}$

(d) $\cos\left(\frac{\theta}{2}\right) = \sqrt{\frac{1+\cos\theta}{2}} = \sqrt{\frac{\left(1+\frac{1}{3}\right)}{2}} = \sqrt{\frac{\left(\frac{4}{3}\right)}{2}} = \sqrt{\frac{2}{3}} = \frac{\sqrt{6}}{3}$

8. $\csc\theta = -\sqrt{5},\ \cos\theta < 0 \rightarrow \pi < \theta < \frac{3\pi}{2};$

thus, $\frac{\pi}{2} < \frac{\theta}{2} < \frac{3\pi}{4} \Rightarrow \frac{\theta}{2}$ is in quadrant II.

$\sin\theta = \frac{-1}{\sqrt{5}} = -\frac{\sqrt{5}}{5}$

$r = \sqrt{5},\ y = -1$

$x^2 + (-1)^2 = \left(\sqrt{5}\right)^2 \rightarrow x^2 = 5 - 1 = 4 \rightarrow x = -2$

$\cos\theta = \frac{-2}{\sqrt{5}} = -\frac{2\sqrt{5}}{5}$

(a) $\sin(2\theta) = 2\sin\theta\cos\theta = 2\cdot\left(-\frac{\sqrt{5}}{5}\right)\cdot\left(-\frac{2\sqrt{5}}{5}\right) = \frac{4}{5}$

(b) $\cos(2\theta) = \cos^2\theta - \sin^2\theta = \left(-\frac{2\sqrt{5}}{5}\right)^2 - \left(-\frac{\sqrt{5}}{5}\right)^2 = \frac{20}{25} - \frac{5}{25} = \frac{15}{25} = \frac{3}{5}$

(c) $\sin\left(\frac{\theta}{2}\right) = \sqrt{\frac{1-\cos\theta}{2}} = \sqrt{\frac{\left(1-\left(-\frac{2\sqrt{5}}{5}\right)\right)}{2}} = \sqrt{\frac{\left(\frac{5+2\sqrt{5}}{5}\right)}{2}} = \sqrt{\frac{5+2\sqrt{5}}{10}}$

(d) $\cos\left(\frac{\theta}{2}\right)=-\sqrt{\frac{1+\cos\theta}{2}}=-\sqrt{\frac{1+\left(-\frac{2\sqrt{5}}{5}\right)}{2}}=-\sqrt{\frac{\left(\frac{5-2\sqrt{5}}{5}\right)}{2}}=-\sqrt{\frac{5-2\sqrt{5}}{10}}$

9. $\cot\theta=-2,\ \sec\theta<0;\ \frac{\pi}{2}<\theta<\pi;$ thus, $\frac{\pi}{4}<\frac{\theta}{2}<\frac{\pi}{2}\Rightarrow\frac{\theta}{2}$ is in quadrant I.

$x=-2,\ y=1$

$r^2=(-2)^2+1^2=4+1=5\ \rightarrow\ r=\sqrt{5}$

$\sin\theta=\frac{1}{\sqrt{5}}=\frac{\sqrt{5}}{5},\quad \cos\theta=-\frac{2}{\sqrt{5}}=-\frac{2\sqrt{5}}{5}$

(a) $\sin(2\theta)=2\sin\theta\cos\theta=2\cdot\left(\frac{\sqrt{5}}{5}\right)\cdot\left(-\frac{2\sqrt{5}}{5}\right)=-\frac{20}{25}=-\frac{4}{5}$

(b) $\cos(2\theta)=\cos^2\theta-\sin^2\theta=\left(-\frac{2\sqrt{5}}{5}\right)^2-\left(\frac{\sqrt{5}}{5}\right)^2=\frac{20}{25}-\frac{5}{25}=\frac{15}{25}=\frac{3}{5}$

(c) $\sin\left(\frac{\theta}{2}\right)=\sqrt{\frac{1-\cos\theta}{2}}=\sqrt{\frac{1-\left(-\frac{2\sqrt{5}}{5}\right)}{2}}=\sqrt{\frac{\left(\frac{5+2\sqrt{5}}{5}\right)}{2}}=\sqrt{\frac{5+2\sqrt{5}}{10}}$

(d) $\cos\left(\frac{\theta}{2}\right)=\sqrt{\frac{1+\cos\theta}{2}}=\sqrt{\frac{1+\left(-\frac{2\sqrt{5}}{5}\right)}{2}}=\sqrt{\frac{\left(\frac{5-2\sqrt{5}}{5}\right)}{2}}=\sqrt{\frac{5-2\sqrt{5}}{10}}$

10. $\sec\theta=2,\ \csc\theta<0;\ \frac{3\pi}{2}<\theta<2\pi;$ thus, $\frac{3\pi}{4}<\frac{\theta}{2}<\pi\Rightarrow\frac{\theta}{2}$ is in quadrant II.

$x=1,\ r=2$

$1^2+y^2=2^2\ \rightarrow\ y^2=4-1=3\ \rightarrow\ y=-\sqrt{3}$

$\sin\theta=-\frac{\sqrt{3}}{2},\quad \cos\theta=\frac{1}{2}$

(a) $\sin(2\theta)=2\sin\theta\cos\theta=2\cdot\left(-\frac{\sqrt{3}}{2}\right)\cdot\left(\frac{1}{2}\right)=-\frac{\sqrt{3}}{2}$

(b) $\cos(2\theta)=\cos^2\theta-\sin^2\theta=\left(\frac{1}{2}\right)^2-\left(-\frac{\sqrt{3}}{2}\right)^2=\frac{1}{4}-\frac{3}{4}=-\frac{1}{2}$

(c) $\sin\left(\frac{\theta}{2}\right)=\sqrt{\frac{1-\cos\theta}{2}}=\sqrt{\frac{\left(1-\frac{1}{2}\right)}{2}}=\sqrt{\frac{\left(\frac{1}{2}\right)}{2}}=\sqrt{\frac{1}{4}}=\frac{1}{2}$

(d) $\cos\left(\frac{\theta}{2}\right)=-\sqrt{\frac{1+\cos\theta}{2}}=-\sqrt{\frac{\left(1+\frac{1}{2}\right)}{2}}=-\sqrt{\frac{\left(\frac{3}{2}\right)}{2}}=-\sqrt{\frac{3}{4}}=-\frac{\sqrt{3}}{2}$

11. $\tan\theta=-3$, $\sin\theta<0$; $\frac{3\pi}{2}<\theta<2\pi$; thus, $\frac{3\pi}{4}<\frac{\theta}{2}<\pi$ or $\frac{\theta}{2}$ is in quadrant II.

$x=1,\ y=-3$

$r^2=1^2+(-3)^2=1+9=10 \rightarrow r=\sqrt{10}$

$\sin\theta=\frac{-3}{\sqrt{10}}=-\frac{3\sqrt{10}}{10}$, $\cos\theta=\frac{1}{\sqrt{10}}=\frac{\sqrt{10}}{10}$

(a) $\sin(2\theta)=2\sin\theta\cos\theta=2\cdot\left(-\frac{3\sqrt{10}}{10}\right)\cdot\left(\frac{\sqrt{10}}{10}\right)=-\frac{60}{100}=-\frac{3}{5}$

(b) $\cos(2\theta)=\cos^2\theta-\sin^2\theta=\left(\frac{\sqrt{10}}{10}\right)^2-\left(-\frac{3\sqrt{10}}{10}\right)^2=\frac{10}{100}-\frac{90}{100}=-\frac{80}{100}=-\frac{4}{5}$

(c) $\sin\left(\frac{\theta}{2}\right)=\sqrt{\frac{1-\cos\theta}{2}}=\sqrt{\frac{\left(1-\frac{\sqrt{10}}{10}\right)}{2}}=\sqrt{\frac{\left(\frac{10-\sqrt{10}}{10}\right)}{2}}=\sqrt{\frac{10-\sqrt{10}}{20}}=\frac{1}{2}\sqrt{\frac{10-\sqrt{10}}{5}}$

(d) $\cos\left(\frac{\theta}{2}\right)=-\sqrt{\frac{1+\cos\theta}{2}}=-\sqrt{\frac{\left(1+\frac{\sqrt{10}}{10}\right)}{2}}=-\sqrt{\frac{\left(\frac{10+\sqrt{10}}{10}\right)}{2}}=-\sqrt{\frac{10+\sqrt{10}}{20}}$

$=-\frac{1}{2}\sqrt{\frac{10+\sqrt{10}}{5}}$

12. $\cot\theta=3$, $\cos\theta<0$; $\pi<\theta<\frac{3\pi}{2}$; thus, $\frac{\pi}{2}<\frac{\theta}{2}<\frac{3\pi}{4} \Rightarrow \frac{\theta}{2}$ is in quadrant II.

$x=-3,\ y=-1$

$r^2=(-3)^2+(-1)^2=9+1=10 \rightarrow r=\sqrt{10}$

$\sin\theta=-\frac{1}{\sqrt{10}}=-\frac{\sqrt{10}}{10}$, $\cos\theta=-\frac{3}{\sqrt{10}}=-\frac{3\sqrt{10}}{10}$

(a) $\sin(2\theta)=2\sin\theta\cos\theta=2\cdot\left(-\frac{\sqrt{10}}{10}\right)\cdot\left(-\frac{3\sqrt{10}}{10}\right)=\frac{60}{100}=\frac{3}{5}$

(b) $\cos(2\theta) = \cos^2\theta - \sin^2\theta = \left(-\frac{3\sqrt{10}}{10}\right)^2 - \left(-\frac{\sqrt{10}}{10}\right)^2 = \frac{90}{100} - \frac{10}{100} = \frac{80}{100} = \frac{4}{5}$

(c) $\sin\left(\frac{\theta}{2}\right) = \sqrt{\frac{1-\cos\theta}{2}} = \sqrt{\frac{\left(1-\left(-\frac{3\sqrt{10}}{10}\right)\right)}{2}} = \sqrt{\frac{\left(\frac{10+3\sqrt{10}}{10}\right)}{2}} = \sqrt{\frac{10+3\sqrt{10}}{20}} = \frac{\sqrt{10+3\sqrt{10}}}{2\sqrt{5}}$

(d) $\cos\left(\frac{\theta}{2}\right) = -\sqrt{\frac{1+\cos\theta}{2}} = -\sqrt{\frac{\left(1+\left(-\frac{3\sqrt{10}}{10}\right)\right)}{2}} = -\sqrt{\frac{\left(\frac{10-3\sqrt{10}}{10}\right)}{2}} = -\sqrt{\frac{10-3\sqrt{10}}{20}}$

$= -\frac{\sqrt{10-3\sqrt{10}}}{2\sqrt{5}}$

13. $\sin(22.5^\circ) = \sin\left(\frac{45^\circ}{2}\right) = \sqrt{\frac{1-\cos(45^\circ)}{2}} = \sqrt{\frac{\left(1-\frac{\sqrt{2}}{2}\right)}{2}} = \sqrt{\frac{2-\sqrt{2}}{4}} = \frac{\sqrt{2-\sqrt{2}}}{2}$

14. $\cos(22.5^\circ) = \cos\left(\frac{45^\circ}{2}\right) = \sqrt{\frac{1+\cos(45^\circ)}{2}} = \sqrt{\frac{\left(1+\frac{\sqrt{2}}{2}\right)}{2}} = \sqrt{\frac{2+\sqrt{2}}{4}} = \frac{\sqrt{2+\sqrt{2}}}{2}$

15. $\tan\left(\frac{7\pi}{8}\right) = \tan\left(\frac{\left(\frac{7\pi}{4}\right)}{2}\right) = -\sqrt{\frac{\left(1-\cos\left(\frac{7\pi}{4}\right)\right)}{\left(1+\cos\left(\frac{7\pi}{4}\right)\right)}} = -\sqrt{\frac{\left(1-\frac{\sqrt{2}}{2}\right)}{\left(1+\frac{\sqrt{2}}{2}\right)}} = -\sqrt{\left(\frac{2-\sqrt{2}}{2+\sqrt{2}}\right)\cdot\left(\frac{2-\sqrt{2}}{2-\sqrt{2}}\right)}$

$= -\sqrt{\frac{6-4\sqrt{2}}{2}} = -\sqrt{3-2\sqrt{2}}$

16. $\tan\left(\frac{9\pi}{8}\right) = \tan\left(\frac{\left(\frac{9\pi}{4}\right)}{2}\right) = \sqrt{\frac{\left(1-\cos\left(\frac{9\pi}{4}\right)\right)}{\left(1+\cos\left(\frac{9\pi}{4}\right)\right)}} = \sqrt{\frac{\left(1-\frac{\sqrt{2}}{2}\right)}{\left(1+\frac{\sqrt{2}}{2}\right)}} = \sqrt{\left(\frac{2-\sqrt{2}}{2+\sqrt{2}}\right)\cdot\left(\frac{2-\sqrt{2}}{2-\sqrt{2}}\right)}$

$= \sqrt{\frac{6-4\sqrt{2}}{2}} = \sqrt{3-2\sqrt{2}}$

17. $\cos(165°)=\cos\left(\frac{330°}{2}\right)=-\sqrt{\frac{1+\cos(330°)}{2}}=-\sqrt{\frac{\left(1+\frac{\sqrt{3}}{2}\right)}{2}}=-\sqrt{\frac{2+\sqrt{3}}{4}}=-\frac{\sqrt{2+\sqrt{3}}}{2}$

18. $\sin(195°)=\sin\left(\frac{390°}{2}\right)=-\sqrt{\frac{1-\cos(390°)}{2}}=-\sqrt{\frac{\left(1-\frac{\sqrt{3}}{2}\right)}{2}}=-\sqrt{\frac{2-\sqrt{3}}{4}}=-\frac{\sqrt{2-\sqrt{3}}}{2}$

19.

$$\sec\left(\frac{15\pi}{8}\right)=\frac{1}{\cos\left(\frac{15\pi}{8}\right)}=\frac{1}{\cos\left(\frac{\left(\frac{15\pi}{4}\right)}{2}\right)}=\frac{1}{\sqrt{\frac{\left(1+\cos\left(\frac{15\pi}{4}\right)\right)}{2}}}=\frac{1}{\sqrt{\frac{\left(1+\frac{\sqrt{2}}{2}\right)}{2}}}=\frac{1}{\sqrt{\frac{2+\sqrt{2}}{4}}}$$

$$=\left(\frac{2}{\sqrt{2+\sqrt{2}}}\right)\cdot\left(\frac{\sqrt{2+\sqrt{2}}}{\sqrt{2+\sqrt{2}}}\right)=\left(\frac{2\sqrt{2+\sqrt{2}}}{2+\sqrt{2}}\right)\cdot\left(\frac{2-\sqrt{2}}{2-\sqrt{2}}\right)$$

$$=\frac{2\left(2-\sqrt{2}\right)\sqrt{2+\sqrt{2}}}{2}=\left(2-\sqrt{2}\right)\sqrt{2+\sqrt{2}}$$

20.

$$\csc\left(\frac{7\pi}{8}\right)=\frac{1}{\sin\left(\frac{7\pi}{8}\right)}=\frac{1}{\left(\sin\left(\frac{\left(\frac{7\pi}{4}\right)}{2}\right)\right)}=\frac{1}{\sqrt{\frac{\left(1-\cos\left(\frac{7\pi}{4}\right)\right)}{2}}}=\frac{1}{\sqrt{\frac{\left(1-\frac{\sqrt{2}}{2}\right)}{2}}}=\frac{1}{\sqrt{\frac{2-\sqrt{2}}{4}}}$$

$$=\left(\frac{2}{\sqrt{2-\sqrt{2}}}\right)\cdot\left(\frac{\sqrt{2-\sqrt{2}}}{\sqrt{2-\sqrt{2}}}\right)=\left(\frac{2\sqrt{2-\sqrt{2}}}{2-\sqrt{2}}\right)\cdot\left(\frac{2+\sqrt{2}}{2+\sqrt{2}}\right)$$

$$=\frac{2\left(2+\sqrt{2}\right)\sqrt{2-\sqrt{2}}}{2}=\left(2+\sqrt{2}\right)\sqrt{2-\sqrt{2}}$$

21. $\sin\left(-\frac{\pi}{8}\right)=\sin\left(\frac{\left(-\frac{\pi}{4}\right)}{2}\right)=-\sqrt{\frac{1-\cos\left(-\frac{\pi}{4}\right)}{2}}=-\sqrt{\frac{\left(1-\frac{\sqrt{2}}{2}\right)}{2}}=-\sqrt{\frac{2-\sqrt{2}}{4}}=-\frac{\sqrt{2-\sqrt{2}}}{2}$

22. $\cos\left(-\frac{3\pi}{8}\right)=\cos\left(\frac{\left(-\frac{3\pi}{4}\right)}{2}\right)=\sqrt{\frac{1+\cos\left(-\frac{3\pi}{4}\right)}{2}}=\sqrt{\frac{\left(1+\left(-\frac{\sqrt{2}}{2}\right)\right)}{2}}=\sqrt{\frac{2-\sqrt{2}}{4}}=\frac{\sqrt{2-\sqrt{2}}}{2}$

23. $\sin^4\theta = (\sin^2\theta)^2 = \left(\dfrac{1-\cos(2\theta)}{2}\right)^2 = \dfrac{1}{4}\left(1-2\cos(2\theta)+\cos^2(2\theta)\right)$

$$= \frac{1}{4}-\frac{1}{2}\cos(2\theta)+\frac{1}{4}\cos^2(2\theta) = \frac{1}{4}-\frac{1}{2}\cos(2\theta)+\frac{1}{4}\left(\frac{1+\cos(4\theta)}{2}\right)$$

$$= \frac{1}{4}-\frac{1}{2}\cos(2\theta)+\frac{1}{8}+\frac{1}{8}\cos(4\theta) = \frac{3}{8}-\frac{1}{2}\cos(2\theta)+\frac{1}{8}\cos(4\theta)$$

24. $\cos(3\theta) = \cos(2\theta+\theta) = \cos(2\theta)\cos\theta - \sin(2\theta)\sin\theta$

$$= \left(2\cos^2\theta-1\right)\cos\theta - 2\sin\theta\cos\theta\sin\theta = 2\cos^3\theta - \cos\theta - 2\sin^2\theta\cos\theta$$

$$= 2\cos^3\theta - \cos\theta - 2\left(1-\cos^2\theta\right)\cos\theta = 2\cos^3\theta - \cos\theta - 2\cos\theta + 2\cos^3\theta$$

$$= 4\cos^3\theta - 3\cos\theta$$

25. $\sin(4\theta) = \sin(2(2\theta)) = 2\sin(2\theta)\cos(2\theta) = 2(2\sin\theta\cos\theta)\left(1-2\sin^2\theta\right)$

$$= \cos\theta\left(4\sin\theta - 8\sin^3\theta\right)$$

26. $\cos(4\theta) = \cos(2(2\theta)) = 2\cos^2(2\theta) - 1 = 2\left(2\cos^2\theta - 1\right)^2 - 1$

$$= 2\left(4\cos^4\theta - 4\cos^2\theta + 1\right) - 1 = 8\cos^4\theta - 8\cos^2\theta + 2 - 1$$

$$= 8\cos^4\theta - 8\cos^2\theta + 1$$

27. Use the result of problem 25 to help solve the problem:

$$\sin(5\theta) = \sin(4\theta+\theta) = \sin(4\theta)\cos\theta + \cos(4\theta)\sin\theta$$

$$= \cos\theta\left(4\sin\theta - 8\sin^3\theta\right)\cos\theta + \cos(2(2\theta))\sin\theta$$

$$= \cos^2\theta\left(4\sin\theta - 8\sin^3\theta\right) + \left(1-2\sin^2(2\theta)\right)\sin\theta$$

$$= \left(1-\sin^2\theta\right)\left(4\sin\theta - 8\sin^3\theta\right) + \sin\theta\left(1-2(2\sin\theta\cos\theta)^2\right)$$

$$= 4\sin\theta - 12\sin^3\theta + 8\sin^5\theta + \sin\theta\left(1-8\sin^2\theta\cos^2\theta\right)$$

$$= 4\sin\theta - 12\sin^3\theta + 8\sin^5\theta + \sin\theta - 8\sin^3\theta\left(1-\sin^2\theta\right)$$

$$= 5\sin\theta - 12\sin^3\theta + 8\sin^5\theta - 8\sin^3\theta + 8\sin^5\theta$$

$$= 5\sin\theta - 20\sin^3\theta + 16\sin^5\theta$$

28. Use the result from problems 25 and 26 to help solve the problem:

$$\cos(5\theta) = \cos(4\theta+\theta) = \cos(4\theta)\cos\theta - \sin(4\theta)\sin\theta$$

$$= \left(8\cos^4\theta - 8\cos^2\theta + 1\right)\cos\theta - \left(\cos\theta\left(4\sin\theta - 8\sin^3\theta\right)\sin\theta\right)$$

$$= 8\cos^5\theta - 8\cos^3\theta + \cos\theta - 4\cos\theta\sin^2\theta + 8\cos\theta\sin^4\theta$$

$$= 8\cos^5\theta - 8\cos^3\theta + \cos\theta - 4\cos\theta(1-\cos^2\theta) + 8\cos\theta(1-\cos^2\theta)^2$$

$$= 8\cos^5\theta - 8\cos^3\theta + \cos\theta - 4\cos\theta + 4\cos^3\theta + 8\cos\theta(1 - 2\cos^2\theta + \cos^4\theta)$$
$$= 8\cos^5\theta - 4\cos^3\theta - 3\cos\theta + 8\cos\theta - 16\cos^3\theta + 8\cos^5\theta$$
$$= 16\cos^5\theta - 20\cos^3\theta + 5\cos\theta$$

29. $\cos^4\theta - \sin^4\theta = (\cos^2\theta + \sin^2\theta)(\cos^2\theta - \sin^2\theta) = 1 \cdot \cos(2\theta) = \cos(2\theta)$

30. $\dfrac{\cot\theta - \tan\theta}{\cot\theta + \tan\theta} = \dfrac{\left(\dfrac{\cos\theta}{\sin\theta} - \dfrac{\sin\theta}{\cos\theta}\right)}{\left(\dfrac{\cos\theta}{\sin\theta} + \dfrac{\sin\theta}{\cos\theta}\right)} = \dfrac{\left(\dfrac{\cos^2\theta - \sin^2\theta}{\sin\theta\cos\theta}\right)}{\left(\dfrac{\cos^2\theta + \sin^2\theta}{\sin\theta\cos\theta}\right)} = \dfrac{\cos(2\theta)}{\sin\theta\cos\theta} \cdot \dfrac{\sin\theta\cos\theta}{1} = \cos(2\theta)$

31. $\cot(2\theta) = \dfrac{1}{\tan(2\theta)} = \dfrac{1}{\left(\dfrac{2\tan\theta}{1 - \tan^2\theta}\right)} = \dfrac{1 - \tan^2\theta}{2\tan\theta} = \dfrac{\left(1 - \dfrac{1}{\cot^2\theta}\right)}{\left(\dfrac{2}{\cot\theta}\right)} = \dfrac{\left(\dfrac{\cot^2\theta - 1}{\cot^2\theta}\right)}{\left(\dfrac{2}{\cot\theta}\right)} = \dfrac{\cot^2\theta - 1}{2\cot\theta}$

32. $\cot(2\theta) = \dfrac{1}{\tan(2\theta)} = \dfrac{1}{\left(\dfrac{2\tan\theta}{1 - \tan^2\theta}\right)} = \dfrac{1 - \tan^2\theta}{2\tan\theta} = \dfrac{1}{2} \cdot \cot\theta(1 - \tan^2\theta) = \dfrac{1}{2} \cdot (\cot\theta - \tan\theta)$

33. $\sec(2\theta) = \dfrac{1}{\cos(2\theta)} = \dfrac{1}{2\cos^2\theta - 1} = \dfrac{1}{\left(\dfrac{2}{\sec^2\theta} - 1\right)} = \dfrac{1}{\left(\dfrac{2 - \sec^2\theta}{\sec^2\theta}\right)} = \dfrac{\sec^2\theta}{2 - \sec^2\theta}$

34. $\csc(2\theta) = \dfrac{1}{\sin(2\theta)} = \dfrac{1}{2\sin\theta\cos\theta} = \dfrac{1}{2} \cdot \csc\theta\sec\theta = \dfrac{1}{2} \cdot \sec\theta\csc\theta$

35. $\cos^2(2\theta) - \sin^2(2\theta) = \cos(2(2\theta)) = \cos(4\theta)$

36. $(4\sin\theta\cos\theta)(1 - 2\sin^2\theta) = (2\sin(2\theta))(\cos 2\theta) = \sin(4\theta)$

37. $\dfrac{\cos(2\theta)}{1 + \sin(2\theta)} = \dfrac{\cos^2\theta - \sin^2\theta}{1 + 2\sin\theta\cos\theta} = \dfrac{(\cos\theta - \sin\theta)(\cos\theta + \sin\theta)}{\cos^2\theta + \sin^2\theta + 2\sin\theta\cos\theta}$

$$= \frac{(\cos\theta - \sin\theta)(\cos\theta + \sin\theta)}{(\cos\theta + \sin\theta)(\cos\theta + \sin\theta)} = \frac{\cos\theta - \sin\theta}{\cos\theta + \sin\theta} = \frac{\left(\dfrac{\cos\theta}{\sin\theta} - \dfrac{\sin\theta}{\sin\theta}\right)}{\left(\dfrac{\cos\theta}{\sin\theta} + \dfrac{\sin\theta}{\sin\theta}\right)} = \frac{\cot\theta - 1}{\cot\theta + 1}$$

38. $\sin^2\theta\cos^2\theta = \dfrac{1}{4}(2\sin\theta\cos\theta)^2 = \dfrac{1}{4} \cdot (\sin(2\theta))^2 = \dfrac{1}{4} \cdot \left(\dfrac{1 - \cos(4\theta)}{2}\right) = \dfrac{1}{8} \cdot (1 - \cos(4\theta))$

39. $\sec^2\left(\frac{\theta}{2}\right)=\frac{1}{\cos^2\left(\frac{\theta}{2}\right)}=\frac{1}{\left(\frac{1+\cos\theta}{2}\right)}=\frac{2}{1+\cos\theta}$

40. $\csc^2\left(\frac{\theta}{2}\right)=\frac{1}{\sin^2\left(\frac{\theta}{2}\right)}=\frac{1}{\left(\frac{1-\cos\theta}{2}\right)}=\frac{2}{1-\cos\theta}$

41. $\cot^2\left(\frac{\theta}{2}\right)=\frac{1}{\tan^2\left(\frac{\theta}{2}\right)}=\frac{1}{\left(\frac{1-\cos\theta}{1+\cos\theta}\right)}=\frac{1+\cos\theta}{1-\cos\theta}=\frac{\left(1+\frac{1}{\sec\theta}\right)}{\left(1-\frac{1}{\sec\theta}\right)}=\frac{\left(\frac{\sec\theta+1}{\sec\theta}\right)}{\left(\frac{\sec\theta-1}{\sec\theta}\right)}=\frac{\sec\theta+1}{\sec\theta-1}$

42. $\tan\left(\frac{\theta}{2}\right)=\frac{1-\cos\theta}{\sin\theta}=\frac{1}{\sin\theta}-\frac{\cos\theta}{\sin\theta}=\csc\theta-\cot\theta$

43. $\frac{\left(1-\tan^2\left(\frac{\theta}{2}\right)\right)}{\left(1+\tan^2\left(\frac{\theta}{2}\right)\right)}=\frac{\left(1-\frac{1-\cos\theta}{1+\cos\theta}\right)}{\left(1+\frac{1-\cos\theta}{1+\cos\theta}\right)}=\frac{\left(\frac{1+\cos\theta-(1-\cos\theta)}{1+\cos\theta}\right)}{\left(\frac{1+\cos\theta+1-\cos\theta}{1+\cos\theta}\right)}=\frac{2\cos\theta}{2}=\cos\theta$

44. $\frac{\sin^3\theta+\cos^3\theta}{\sin\theta+\cos\theta}=\frac{(\sin\theta+\cos\theta)(\sin^2\theta-\sin\theta\cos\theta+\cos^2\theta)}{\sin\theta+\cos\theta}$

$=1-\sin\theta\cos\theta=1-\frac{1}{2}\cdot\sin(2\theta)$

45. $\frac{\sin(3\theta)}{\sin\theta}-\frac{\cos(3\theta)}{\cos\theta}=\frac{\sin(3\theta)\cos\theta-\cos(3\theta)\sin\theta}{\sin\theta\cos\theta}=\frac{\sin(3\theta-\theta)}{\sin\theta\cos\theta}$

$=\frac{\sin 2\theta}{\sin\theta\cos\theta}=\frac{2\sin\theta\cos\theta}{\sin\theta\cos\theta}=2$

46. $\frac{\cos\theta+\sin\theta}{\cos\theta-\sin\theta}-\frac{\cos\theta-\sin\theta}{\cos\theta+\sin\theta}=\frac{(\cos\theta+\sin\theta)^2-(\cos\theta-\sin\theta)^2}{(\cos\theta-\sin\theta)(\cos\theta+\sin\theta)}$

$=\frac{\cos^2\theta+2\cos\theta\sin\theta+\sin^2\theta-(\cos^2\theta-2\cos\theta\sin\theta+\sin^2\theta)}{\cos^2\theta-\sin^2\theta}$

$=\frac{1+2\cos\theta\sin\theta-1+2\cos\theta\sin\theta}{\cos 2\theta}=\frac{2(2\sin\theta\cos\theta)}{\cos 2\theta}=\frac{2\sin(2\theta)}{\cos(2\theta)}=2\tan(2\theta)$

47. $\tan(3\theta)=\tan(2\theta+\theta)=\dfrac{\tan(2\theta)+\tan\theta}{1-\tan(2\theta)\tan\theta}=\dfrac{\left(\dfrac{2\tan\theta}{1-\tan^2\theta}+\tan\theta\right)}{\left(1-\dfrac{2\tan\theta}{1-\tan^2\theta}\cdot\tan\theta\right)}$

$=\dfrac{\left(\dfrac{2\tan\theta+\tan\theta-\tan^3\theta}{1-\tan^2\theta}\right)}{\left(\dfrac{1-\tan^2\theta-2\tan^2\theta}{1-\tan^2\theta}\right)}=\dfrac{3\tan\theta-\tan^3\theta}{1-3\tan^2\theta}$

48. $\tan\theta+\tan(\theta+120^\circ)+\tan(\theta+240^\circ)=\tan\theta+\dfrac{\tan\theta+\tan(120^\circ)}{1-\tan\theta\tan(120^\circ)}+\dfrac{\tan\theta+\tan(240^\circ)}{1-\tan\theta\tan(240^\circ)}$

$=\tan\theta+\dfrac{\tan\theta-\sqrt{3}}{1-\tan\theta(-\sqrt{3})}+\dfrac{\tan\theta+\sqrt{3}}{1-\tan\theta(\sqrt{3})}=\tan\theta+\dfrac{\tan\theta-\sqrt{3}}{1+\sqrt{3}\tan\theta}+\dfrac{\tan\theta+\sqrt{3}}{1-\sqrt{3}\tan\theta}$

$=\dfrac{\tan\theta(1-3\tan^2\theta)+(\tan\theta-\sqrt{3})(1-\sqrt{3}\tan\theta)+(\tan\theta+\sqrt{3})(1+\sqrt{3}\tan\theta)}{1-3\tan^2\theta}$

$=\dfrac{\tan\theta-3\tan^3\theta+\tan\theta-\sqrt{3}\tan^2\theta-\sqrt{3}+3\tan\theta+\tan\theta+\sqrt{3}\tan^2\theta+\sqrt{3}+3\tan\theta}{1-3\tan^2\theta}$

$=\dfrac{-3\tan^3\theta+9\tan\theta}{1-3\tan^2\theta}=\dfrac{3(3\tan\theta-\tan^3\theta)}{1-3\tan^2\theta}=3\tan(3\theta)$ (by Problem 47)

49. $\dfrac{1}{2}\cdot(\ln|1-\cos(2\theta)|-\ln 2)=\dfrac{1}{2}\cdot\ln\left|\dfrac{1-\cos 2\theta}{2}\right|=\ln\left(\left|\dfrac{1-\cos(2\theta)}{2}\right|^{1/2}\right)=\ln\left(\left|\sin^2\theta\right|^{1/2}\right)=\ln|\sin\theta|$

50. $\dfrac{1}{2}\cdot(\ln|1+\cos(2\theta)|-\ln 2)=\dfrac{1}{2}\cdot\ln\left|\dfrac{1+\cos 2\theta}{2}\right|=\ln\left(\left|\dfrac{1+\cos(2\theta)}{2}\right|^{1/2}\right)=\ln\left(\left|\cos^2\theta\right|^{1/2}\right)=\ln|\cos\theta|$

51. $\sin\left(2\sin^{-1}\left(\dfrac{1}{2}\right)\right)=\sin\left(2\left(\dfrac{\pi}{6}\right)\right)=\sin\left(\dfrac{\pi}{3}\right)=\dfrac{\sqrt{3}}{2}$

52. $\sin\left(2\sin^{-1}\left(\dfrac{\sqrt{3}}{2}\right)\right)=\sin\left(2\left(\dfrac{\pi}{3}\right)\right)=\sin\left(\dfrac{2\pi}{3}\right)=\dfrac{\sqrt{3}}{2}$

53. $\cos\left(2\sin^{-1}\left(\dfrac{3}{5}\right)\right)=1-2\sin^2\left(\sin^{-1}\left(\dfrac{3}{5}\right)\right)=1-2\left(\dfrac{3}{5}\right)^2=1-2\left(\dfrac{9}{25}\right)=1-\dfrac{18}{25}=\dfrac{7}{25}$

54. $\cos\left(2\cos^{-1}\left(\dfrac{4}{5}\right)\right)=2\cos^2\left(\cos^{-1}\left(\dfrac{4}{5}\right)\right)-1=2\left(\dfrac{4}{5}\right)^2-1=2\left(\dfrac{16}{25}\right)-1=\dfrac{32}{25}-1=\dfrac{7}{25}$

55. $\tan\left[2\cos^{-1}\left(-\frac{3}{5}\right)\right]$

Let $\alpha=\cos^{-1}\left(-\frac{3}{5}\right)$. α is in quadrant II.

Then $\cos\alpha=-\frac{3}{5},\ 0\le\alpha\le\pi$.

$$\sec\alpha=-\frac{5}{3};\quad \tan\alpha=-\sqrt{\sec^2\alpha-1}=-\sqrt{\left(-\frac{5}{3}\right)^2-1}=-\sqrt{\frac{25}{9}-1}=-\sqrt{\frac{16}{9}}=-\frac{4}{3}$$

$$\tan\left[2\cos^{-1}\left(-\frac{3}{5}\right)\right]=\tan 2\alpha=\frac{2\tan\alpha}{1-\tan^2\alpha}=\frac{2\left(-\frac{4}{3}\right)}{\left(1-\left(-\frac{4}{3}\right)^2\right)}=\frac{\left(-\frac{8}{3}\right)}{\left(1-\frac{16}{9}\right)}=\frac{\left(-\frac{8}{3}\right)}{\left(-\frac{7}{9}\right)}=\left(-\frac{8}{3}\right)\cdot\left(-\frac{9}{7}\right)=\frac{24}{7}$$

56.

$$\tan\left(2\tan^{-1}\left(\frac{3}{4}\right)\right)=\frac{2\tan\left(\tan^{-1}\left(\frac{3}{4}\right)\right)}{1-\tan^2\left(\tan^{-1}\left(\frac{3}{4}\right)\right)}=\frac{2\cdot\left(\frac{3}{4}\right)}{\left(1-\left(\frac{3}{4}\right)^2\right)}=\frac{\left(\frac{3}{2}\right)}{\left(1-\frac{9}{16}\right)}=\frac{\left(\frac{3}{2}\right)}{\left(\frac{7}{16}\right)}=\frac{3}{2}\cdot\frac{16}{7}=\frac{24}{7}$$

57. $\sin\left(2\cos^{-1}\left(\frac{4}{5}\right)\right)$

Let $\alpha=\cos^{-1}\left(\frac{4}{5}\right)$. α is in quadrant I.

Then $\cos\alpha=\frac{4}{5},\ 0\le\alpha\le\pi$.

$$\sin\alpha=\sqrt{1-\cos^2\alpha}=\sqrt{1-\left(\frac{4}{5}\right)^2}=\sqrt{1-\frac{16}{25}}=\sqrt{\frac{9}{25}}=\frac{3}{5}$$

$$\sin\left[2\cos^{-1}\left(\frac{4}{5}\right)\right]=\sin 2\alpha=2\sin\alpha\cos\alpha=2\cdot\frac{3}{5}\cdot\frac{4}{5}=\frac{24}{25}$$

58. $\cos\left(2\tan^{-1}\left(-\frac{4}{3}\right)\right)$

Let $\alpha=\tan^{-1}\left(-\frac{4}{3}\right)$. α is in quadrant IV.

Then $\tan\alpha=-\frac{4}{3},\ -\frac{\pi}{2}<\alpha<\frac{\pi}{2}$.

$$\sec\alpha=\sqrt{\tan^2\alpha+1}=\sqrt{\left(-\frac{4}{3}\right)^2+1}=\sqrt{\frac{16}{9}+1}=\sqrt{\frac{25}{9}}=\frac{5}{3};\quad \cos\alpha=\frac{3}{5}$$

$$\cos\left[2\tan^{-1}\left(-\frac{4}{3}\right)\right]=\cos 2\alpha=2\cos^2\alpha-1=2\left(\frac{3}{5}\right)^2-1=2\cdot\frac{9}{25}-1=-\frac{7}{25}$$

59. $\sin^2\left[\frac{1}{2}\cdot\cos^{-1}\left(\frac{3}{5}\right)\right]=\frac{1-\cos\left(\cos^{-1}\left(\frac{3}{5}\right)\right)}{2}=\frac{\left(1-\frac{3}{5}\right)}{2}=\frac{\left(\frac{2}{5}\right)}{2}=\frac{1}{5}$

60. $\cos^2\left(\frac{1}{2}\cdot\sin^{-1}\left(\frac{3}{5}\right)\right)$

Let $\alpha=\sin^{-1}\left(\frac{3}{5}\right)$. α is in quadrant I.

Then $\sin\alpha=\frac{3}{5},\ -\frac{\pi}{2}<\alpha<\frac{\pi}{2}$.

$$\cos\alpha=\sqrt{1-\sin^2\alpha}=\sqrt{1-\left(\frac{3}{5}\right)^2}=\sqrt{1-\frac{9}{25}}=\sqrt{\frac{16}{25}}=\frac{4}{5}$$

$$\cos^2\left(\frac{1}{2}\cdot\sin^{-1}\left(\frac{3}{5}\right)\right)=\cos^2\left(\frac{1}{2}\cdot\alpha\right)=\frac{1+\cos\alpha}{2}=\frac{\left(1+\frac{4}{5}\right)}{2}=\frac{\left(\frac{9}{5}\right)}{2}=\frac{9}{10}$$

61. $\sec\left(2\tan^{-1}\left(\frac{3}{4}\right)\right)$

Let $\alpha=\tan^{-1}\left(\frac{3}{4}\right)$. α is in quadrant I.

Then $\tan\alpha=\frac{3}{4},\ -\frac{\pi}{2}<\alpha<\frac{\pi}{2}$.

$$\sec\alpha=\sqrt{\tan^2\alpha+1}=\sqrt{\left(\frac{3}{4}\right)^2+1}=\sqrt{\frac{9}{16}+1}=\sqrt{\frac{25}{16}}=\frac{5}{4};\quad \cos\alpha=\frac{4}{5}$$

$$\sec\left[2\tan^{-1}\left(\frac{3}{4}\right)\right]=\sec(2\alpha)=\frac{1}{\cos(2\alpha)}=\frac{1}{2\cos^2\alpha-1}=\frac{1}{\left(2\left(\frac{4}{5}\right)^2-1\right)}=\frac{1}{\left(2\cdot\left(\frac{16}{25}\right)-1\right)}=\frac{1}{\left(\frac{7}{25}\right)}=\frac{25}{7}$$

62. $\csc\left(2\sin^{-1}\left(-\frac{3}{5}\right)\right)$

Let $\alpha=\sin^{-1}\left(-\frac{3}{5}\right)$. α is in quadrant IV.

Then $\sin\alpha=-\frac{3}{5},\ -\frac{\pi}{2}\le\alpha\le\frac{\pi}{2}$.

$$\cos\alpha=\sqrt{1-\sin^2\alpha}=\sqrt{1-\left(-\frac{3}{5}\right)^2}=\sqrt{1-\frac{9}{25}}=\sqrt{\frac{16}{25}}=\frac{4}{5}$$

$$\csc\left(2\sin^{-1}\left(-\frac{3}{5}\right)\right)=\csc(2\alpha)=\frac{1}{\sin(2\alpha)}=\frac{1}{2\sin\alpha\cos\alpha}=\frac{1}{\left(2\cdot\left(-\frac{3}{5}\right)\cdot\left(\frac{4}{5}\right)\right)}=\frac{1}{\left(-\frac{24}{25}\right)}=-\frac{25}{24}$$

63. If $x = 2\tan\theta$, then:

$$\sin(2\theta) = 2\sin\theta\cos\theta = \frac{2\sin\theta}{\cos\theta}\cdot\frac{\cos^2\theta}{1} = \frac{\left(2\cdot\frac{\sin\theta}{\cos\theta}\right)}{\left(\frac{1}{\cos^2\theta}\right)} = \frac{2\tan\theta}{\sec^2\theta} = \frac{2\tan\theta}{1+\tan^2\theta}\cdot\frac{4}{4}$$

$$= \frac{4(2\tan\theta)}{4+(2\tan\theta)^2} = \frac{4x}{4+x^2}$$

64. $$\cos(2\theta) = \cos^2\theta - \sin^2\theta = \frac{\cos^2\theta-\sin^2\theta}{\cos^2\theta+\sin^2\theta} = \frac{\left(\frac{\cos^2\theta-\sin^2\theta}{\cos^2\theta}\right)}{\left(\frac{\cos^2\theta+\sin^2\theta}{\cos^2\theta}\right)} = \frac{1-\tan^2\theta}{1+\tan^2\theta}\cdot\frac{4}{4}$$

$$= \frac{4-4\tan^2\theta}{4+4\tan^2\theta} = \frac{4-x^2}{4+x^2}$$

65. Solve for C:

$$\frac{1}{2}\cdot\sin^2 x + C = -\frac{1}{4}\cdot\cos(2x)$$

$$C = -\frac{1}{4}\cdot\cos(2x) - \frac{1}{2}\cdot\sin^2 x = -\frac{1}{4}\cdot\left(\cos(2x)+2\sin^2 x\right)$$

$$= -\frac{1}{4}\cdot\left(1-2\sin^2 x+2\sin^2 x\right) = -\frac{1}{4}\cdot(1) = -\frac{1}{4}$$

66. $$\frac{1}{2}\cdot\cos^2 x + C = \frac{1}{4}\cdot\cos(2x)$$

$$C = \frac{1}{4}\cdot\cos(2x) - \frac{1}{2}\cdot\cos^2 x = \frac{1}{4}\cdot\left(2\cos^2 x - 1\right) - \frac{1}{2\cdot}\cos^2 x = \frac{1}{2}\cdot\cos^2 x - \frac{1}{4} - \frac{1}{2}\cos^2 x = -\frac{1}{4}$$

67. $$z = \tan\left(\frac{\alpha}{2}\right) = \frac{1-\cos\alpha}{\sin\alpha}$$

$$z\sin\alpha = 1-\cos\alpha$$

$$z\sin\alpha = 1-\sqrt{1-\sin^2\alpha}$$

$$z\sin\alpha - 1 = -\sqrt{1-\sin^2\alpha}$$

$$z^2\sin^2\alpha - 2z\sin\alpha + 1 = 1-\sin^2\alpha \rightarrow z^2\sin^2\alpha + \sin^2\alpha = 2z\sin\alpha$$

$$\sin^2\alpha(z^2+1) = 2z\sin\alpha \rightarrow \sin\alpha(z^2+1) = 2z \rightarrow \sin\alpha = \frac{2z}{z^2+1}$$

68.
$$z = \tan\left(\frac{\alpha}{2}\right) = \sqrt{\frac{1-\cos\alpha}{1+\cos\alpha}}$$
$$z^2 = \frac{1-\cos\alpha}{1+\cos\alpha} \rightarrow z^2 + z^2\cos\alpha = 1-\cos\alpha$$
$$z^2\cos\alpha + \cos\alpha = 1 - z^2 \rightarrow \cos\alpha(z^2+1) = 1-z^2 \rightarrow \cos\alpha = \frac{1-z^2}{1+z^2}$$

69. Let b represent the base of the triangle.

$$\cos\left(\frac{\theta}{2}\right) = \frac{h}{s} \rightarrow h = s\cos\left(\frac{\theta}{2}\right) \qquad \sin\left(\frac{\theta}{2}\right) = \frac{\left(\frac{1}{2}b\right)}{s} \rightarrow b = 2s\sin\left(\frac{\theta}{2}\right)$$
$$A = \frac{1}{2}b\cdot h = \frac{1}{2}\cdot\left(2s\sin\left(\frac{\theta}{2}\right)\right)\left(s\cos\left(\frac{\theta}{2}\right)\right) = s^2\sin\left(\frac{\theta}{2}\right)\cos\left(\frac{\theta}{2}\right) = \frac{1}{2}\cdot s^2\sin\theta$$

70. $\sin\theta = \frac{y}{1} = y; \qquad \cos\theta = \frac{x}{1} = x$

(a) $A = 2xy = 2\cos\theta\sin\theta$

(b) $2\cos\theta\sin\theta = 2\sin\theta\cos\theta = \sin(2\theta)$

(c) The largest value of the sine function is 1. Solve:

$$\sin(2\theta) = 1$$
$$2\theta = \frac{\pi}{2} \rightarrow \theta = \frac{\pi}{4}$$

(d) $x = \cos\left(\frac{\pi}{4}\right) = \frac{\sqrt{2}}{2} \qquad y = \sin\left(\frac{\pi}{4}\right) = \frac{\sqrt{2}}{2}$

The dimensions are $\sqrt{2}$ by $\frac{\sqrt{2}}{2}$.

71. $f(x) = \sin^2 x = \frac{1-\cos(2x)}{2}$

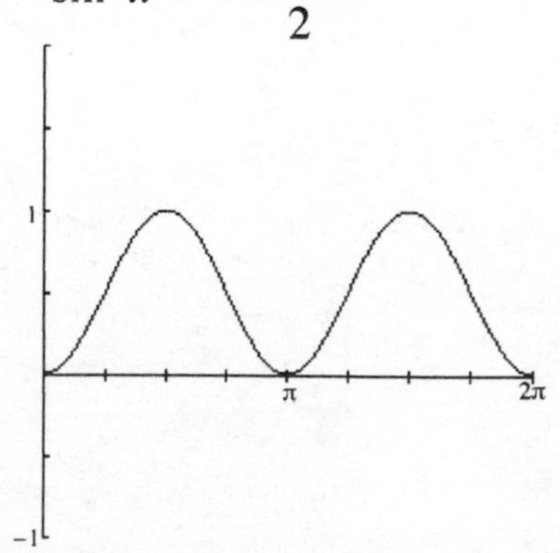

72. $g(x) = \cos^2 x = \frac{1+\cos(2x)}{2}$

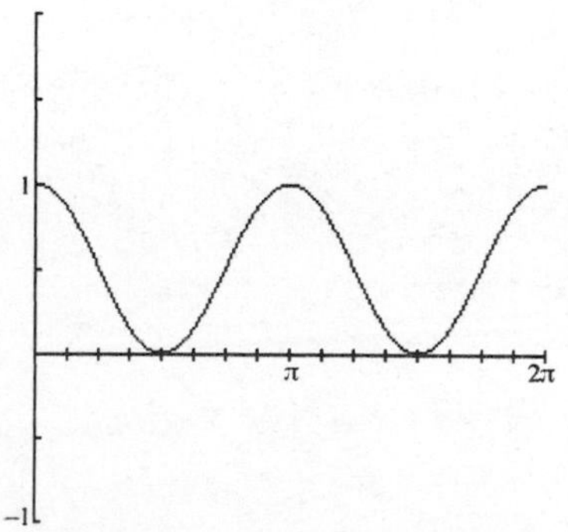

73.

$$\sin\left(\frac{\pi}{24}\right)=\sin\left(\frac{\left(\frac{\pi}{12}\right)}{2}\right)=\sqrt{\frac{\left(1-\cos\left(\frac{\pi}{12}\right)\right)}{2}}=\sqrt{\frac{1-\left(\frac{1}{4}\left(\sqrt{6}+\sqrt{2}\right)\right)}{2}}=\sqrt{\frac{1}{2}-\frac{1}{8}\left(\sqrt{6}+\sqrt{2}\right)}$$

$$=\sqrt{\frac{8-2\left(\sqrt{6}+\sqrt{2}\right)}{16}}=\frac{\sqrt{8-2\left(\sqrt{6}+\sqrt{2}\right)}}{4}$$

$$\cos\left(\frac{\pi}{24}\right)=\cos\left(\frac{\left(\frac{\pi}{12}\right)}{2}\right)=\sqrt{\frac{\left(1+\cos\left(\frac{\pi}{12}\right)\right)}{2}}=\sqrt{\frac{1+\left(\frac{1}{4}\left(\sqrt{6}+\sqrt{2}\right)\right)}{2}}=\sqrt{\frac{1}{2}+\frac{1}{8}\left(\sqrt{6}+\sqrt{2}\right)}$$

$$=\sqrt{\frac{8+2\left(\sqrt{6}+\sqrt{2}\right)}{16}}=\frac{\sqrt{8+2\left(\sqrt{6}+\sqrt{2}\right)}}{4}$$

74.

$$\cos\left(\frac{\pi}{8}\right)=\cos\left(\frac{\left(\frac{\pi}{4}\right)}{2}\right)=\sqrt{\frac{\left(1+\cos\left(\frac{\pi}{4}\right)\right)}{2}}=\sqrt{\frac{\left(1+\frac{\sqrt{2}}{2}\right)}{2}}=\sqrt{\frac{2+\sqrt{2}}{4}}=\frac{\sqrt{2+\sqrt{2}}}{2}$$

$$\sin\left(\frac{\pi}{16}\right)=\sin\left(\frac{\left(\frac{\pi}{8}\right)}{2}\right)=\sqrt{\frac{\left(1-\cos\left(\frac{\pi}{8}\right)\right)}{2}}=\sqrt{\frac{\left(1-\frac{\sqrt{2+\sqrt{2}}}{2}\right)}{2}}=\sqrt{\frac{2-\sqrt{2+\sqrt{2}}}{4}}=\frac{\sqrt{2-\sqrt{2+\sqrt{2}}}}{2}$$

$$\cos\left(\frac{\pi}{16}\right)=\cos\left(\frac{\left(\frac{\pi}{8}\right)}{2}\right)=\sqrt{\frac{\left(1+\cos\left(\frac{\pi}{8}\right)\right)}{2}}=\sqrt{\frac{\left(1+\frac{\sqrt{2+\sqrt{2}}}{2}\right)}{2}}=\sqrt{\frac{2+\sqrt{2+\sqrt{2}}}{4}}=\frac{\sqrt{2+\sqrt{2+\sqrt{2}}}}{2}$$

75. $\sin^3\theta+\sin^3(\theta+120^\circ)+\sin^3(\theta+240^\circ)$

$$=\sin^3\theta+\left(\sin\theta\cos(120^\circ)+\cos\theta\sin(120^\circ)\right)^3+\left(\sin\theta\cos(240^\circ)+\cos\theta\sin(240^\circ)\right)^3$$

$$=\sin^3\theta+\left(-\frac{1}{2}\cdot\sin\theta+\frac{\sqrt{3}}{2}\cdot\cos\theta\right)^3+\left(-\frac{1}{2}\cdot\sin\theta-\frac{\sqrt{3}}{2}\cdot\cos\theta\right)^3$$

$$= \sin^3\theta + \frac{1}{8}\cdot\left(-\sin^3\theta + 3\sqrt{3}\sin^2\theta\cos\theta - 9\sin\theta\cos^2\theta + 3\sqrt{3}\cos^3\theta\right)$$

$$-\frac{1}{8}\left(\sin^3\theta + 3\sqrt{3}\sin^2\theta\cos\theta + 9\sin\theta\cos^2\theta + 3\sqrt{3}\cos^3\theta\right)$$

$$= \sin^3\theta - \frac{1}{8}\cdot\sin^3\theta + \frac{3\sqrt{3}}{8}\cdot\sin^2\theta\cos\theta - \frac{9}{8}\cdot\sin\theta\cos^2\theta + \frac{3\sqrt{3}}{8}\cdot\cos^3\theta$$

$$-\frac{1}{8}\cdot\sin^3\theta - \frac{3\sqrt{3}}{8}\cdot\sin^2\theta\cos\theta - \frac{9}{8}\cdot\sin\theta\cos^2\theta - \frac{3\sqrt{3}}{8}\cdot\cos^3\theta$$

$$= \frac{3}{4}\cdot\sin^3\theta - \frac{9}{4}\cdot\sin\theta\cos^2\theta = \frac{3}{4}\cdot\left(\sin^3\theta - 3\sin\theta\left(1-\sin^2\theta\right)\right)$$

$$= \frac{3}{4}\cdot\left(\sin^3\theta - 3\sin\theta + 3\sin^3\theta\right) = \frac{3}{4}\cdot\left(4\sin^3\theta - 3\sin\theta\right) = -\frac{3}{4}\cdot\sin(3\theta)$$

(See the formula for $\sin(3\theta)$ on page 600 of the text.)

76. $$\tan\theta = \tan\left(3\left(\frac{\theta}{3}\right)\right) = \frac{3\tan\left(\frac{\theta}{3}\right) - \tan^3\left(\frac{\theta}{3}\right)}{1 - 3\tan^2\left(\frac{\theta}{3}\right)} = a\tan\left(\frac{\theta}{3}\right) \quad \text{(from Problem 47)}$$

$$3\tan\left(\frac{\theta}{3}\right) - \tan^3\left(\frac{\theta}{3}\right) = a\tan\left(\frac{\theta}{3}\right)\left(1 - 3\tan^2\left(\frac{\theta}{3}\right)\right)$$

$$3 - \tan^2\left(\frac{\theta}{3}\right) = a\left(1 - 3\tan^2\left(\frac{\theta}{3}\right)\right) \to 3 - \tan^2\left(\frac{\theta}{3}\right) = a - 3a\tan^2\left(\frac{\theta}{3}\right)$$

$$(3a-1)\tan^2\left(\frac{\theta}{3}\right) = a - 3 \to \tan^2\left(\frac{\theta}{3}\right) = \frac{a-3}{3a-1} \to \tan\left(\frac{\theta}{3}\right) = \pm\sqrt{\frac{a-3}{3a-1}}$$

77. (a) $$R(\theta) = \frac{v_0^2\sqrt{2}}{16}\cos\theta(\sin\theta - \cos\theta) = \frac{v_0^2\sqrt{2}}{16}(\cos\theta\sin\theta - \cos^2\theta)$$

$$= \frac{v_0^2\sqrt{2}}{16}\cdot\frac{1}{2}(2\cos\theta\sin\theta - 2\cos^2\theta) = \frac{v_0^2\sqrt{2}}{32}\left(\sin 2\theta - 2\left(\frac{1+\cos 2\theta}{2}\right)\right)$$

$$= \frac{v_0^2\sqrt{2}}{32}\left(\sin(2\theta) - 1 - \cos(2\theta)\right) = \frac{v_0^2\sqrt{2}}{32}\left(\sin(2\theta) - \cos(2\theta) - 1\right)$$

(b)

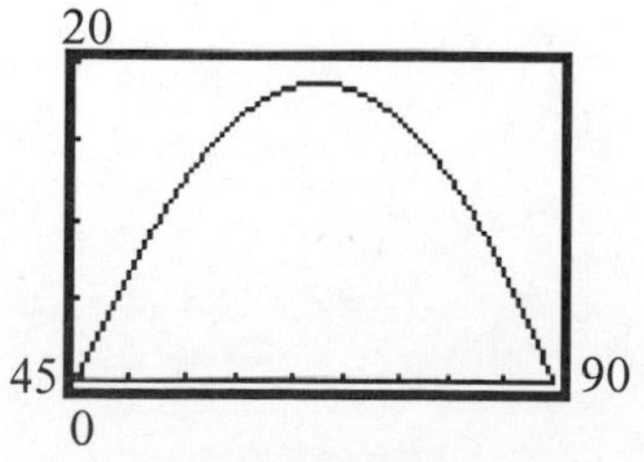

(c) Using the MAXIMUM feature on the calculator:
R has the largest value when $\theta \approx 67.5°$.

78. $$f(x)=\frac{1}{2}\cdot\sin(2\pi x)+\frac{1}{4}\cdot\sin(4\pi x)=\frac{1}{2}\cdot\sin(2\pi x)+\frac{1}{4}\cdot\big(2\sin(2\pi x)\cos(2\pi x)\big)$$
$$=\frac{1}{2}\cdot\sin(2\pi x)\big(1+\cos(2\pi x)\big)=\frac{1}{2}\cdot\sin(2\pi x)\big(1+(2\cos^2(\pi x)-1)\big)$$
$$=\frac{1}{2}\cdot\sin(2\pi x)\big(2\cos^2(\pi x)\big)=\sin(2\pi x)\cos^2(\pi x)$$

Chapter 8

Analytic Trigonometry

8.6 Product-to-Sum and Sum-to-Product Formulas

For Problems 1-10, use the formulas:

$$\sin\alpha\sin\beta = \frac{1}{2}\cdot[\cos(\alpha-\beta)-\cos(\alpha+\beta)] \qquad \cos\alpha\cos\beta = \frac{1}{2}\cdot[\cos(\alpha-\beta)+\cos(\alpha+\beta)]$$

$$\sin\alpha\cos\beta = \frac{1}{2}\cdot[\sin(\alpha+\beta)+\sin(\alpha-\beta)]$$

1. $\sin(4\theta)\sin(2\theta) = \frac{1}{2}\cdot[\cos(4\theta-2\theta)-\cos(4\theta+2\theta)] = \frac{1}{2}\cdot[\cos(2\theta)-\cos(6\theta)]$

2. $\cos(4\theta)\cos(2\theta) = \frac{1}{2}\cdot[\cos(4\theta-2\theta)+\cos(4\theta+2\theta)] = \frac{1}{2}\cdot[\cos(2\theta)+\cos(6\theta)]$

3. $\sin(4\theta)\cos(2\theta) = \frac{1}{2}\cdot[\sin(4\theta+2\theta)+\sin(4\theta-2\theta)] = \frac{1}{2}\cdot[\sin(6\theta)+\sin(2\theta)]$

4. $\sin(3\theta)\sin(5\theta) = \frac{1}{2}\cdot[\cos(3\theta-5\theta)-\cos(3\theta+5\theta)] = \frac{1}{2}\cdot[\cos(-2\theta)-\cos(8\theta)]$
$= \frac{1}{2}\cdot[\cos(2\theta)-\cos(8\theta)]$

5. $\cos(3\theta)\cos(5\theta) = \frac{1}{2}\cdot[\cos(3\theta-5\theta)+\cos(3\theta+5\theta)] = \frac{1}{2}\cdot[\cos(-2\theta)+\cos(8\theta)]$
$= \frac{1}{2}\cdot[\cos(2\theta)+\cos(8\theta)]$

6. $\sin(4\theta)\cos(6\theta) = \frac{1}{2}\cdot[\sin(4\theta+6\theta)+\sin(4\theta-6\theta)] = \frac{1}{2}\cdot[\sin(10\theta)+\sin(-2\theta)]$
$= \frac{1}{2}\cdot[\sin(10\theta)-\sin(2\theta)]$

7. $\sin\theta\sin(2\theta) = \frac{1}{2}\cdot[\cos(\theta-2\theta)-\cos(\theta+2\theta)] = \frac{1}{2}\cdot[\cos(-\theta)-\cos(3\theta)]$
$= \frac{1}{2}\cdot[\cos\theta-\cos(3\theta)]$

8. $\cos(3\theta)\cos(4\theta)=\frac{1}{2}\cdot[\cos(3\theta-4\theta)+\cos(3\theta+4\theta)]=\frac{1}{2}\cdot[\cos(-\theta)+\cos(7\theta)]$
$=\frac{1}{2}\cdot[\cos\theta+\cos(7\theta)]$

9. $\sin\left(\frac{3\theta}{2}\right)\cos\left(\frac{\theta}{2}\right)=\frac{1}{2}\cdot\left[\sin\left(\frac{3\theta}{2}+\frac{\theta}{2}\right)+\sin\left(\frac{3\theta}{2}-\frac{\theta}{2}\right)\right]=\frac{1}{2}\cdot[\sin(2\theta)+\sin\theta]$

10. $\sin\left(\frac{\theta}{2}\right)\cos\left(\frac{5\theta}{2}\right)=\frac{1}{2}\cdot\left[\sin\left(\frac{\theta}{2}+\frac{5\theta}{2}\right)+\sin\left(\frac{\theta}{2}-\frac{5\theta}{2}\right)\right]=\frac{1}{2}\cdot[\sin(3\theta)+\sin(-2\theta)]$
$=\frac{1}{2}[\sin(3\theta)-\sin(2\theta)]$

For Problems 11-18, use the formulas:

$\sin\alpha+\sin\beta=2\sin\left(\frac{\alpha+\beta}{2}\right)\cos\left(\frac{\alpha-\beta}{2}\right)$ $\quad$ $\sin\alpha-\sin\beta=2\sin\left(\frac{\alpha-\beta}{2}\right)\cos\left(\frac{\alpha+\beta}{2}\right)$

$\cos\alpha+\cos\beta=2\cos\left(\frac{\alpha+\beta}{2}\right)\cos\left(\frac{\alpha-\beta}{2}\right)$ $\quad$ $\cos\alpha-\cos\beta=-2\sin\left(\frac{\alpha+\beta}{2}\right)\sin\left(\frac{\alpha-\beta}{2}\right)$

11. $\sin(4\theta)-\sin(2\theta)=2\sin\left(\frac{4\theta-2\theta}{2}\right)\cos\left(\frac{4\theta+2\theta}{2}\right)=2\sin\theta\cos(3\theta)$

12. $\sin(4\theta)+\sin(2\theta)=2\sin\left(\frac{4\theta+2\theta}{2}\right)\cos\left(\frac{4\theta-2\theta}{2}\right)=2\sin(3\theta)\cos\theta$

13. $\cos(2\theta)+\cos(4\theta)=2\cos\left(\frac{2\theta+4\theta}{2}\right)\cos\left(\frac{2\theta-4\theta}{2}\right)=2\cos(3\theta)\cos(-\theta)=2\cos(3\theta)\cos\theta$

14. $\cos(5\theta)-\cos(3\theta)=-2\sin\left(\frac{5\theta+3\theta}{2}\right)\sin\left(\frac{5\theta-3\theta}{2}\right)=-2\sin(4\theta)\sin\theta$

15. $\sin\theta+\sin(3\theta)=2\sin\left(\frac{\theta+3\theta}{2}\right)\cos\left(\frac{\theta-3\theta}{2}\right)=2\sin(2\theta)\cos(-\theta)=2\sin(2\theta)\cos\theta$

16. $\cos\theta+\cos(3\theta)=2\cos\left(\frac{\theta+3\theta}{2}\right)\cos\left(\frac{\theta-3\theta}{2}\right)=2\cos(2\theta)\cos(-\theta)=2\cos(2\theta)\cos\theta$

17. $\cos\left(\frac{\theta}{2}\right)-\cos\left(\frac{3\theta}{2}\right)$
$=-2\sin\left(\frac{\left(\frac{\theta}{2}+\frac{3\theta}{2}\right)}{2}\right)\sin\left(\frac{\left(\frac{\theta}{2}-\frac{3\theta}{2}\right)}{2}\right)=-2\sin\theta\sin\left(-\frac{\theta}{2}\right)=-2\sin\theta\left(-\sin\left(\frac{\theta}{2}\right)\right)=2\sin\theta\sin\left(\frac{\theta}{2}\right)$

18. $\sin\left(\frac{\theta}{2}\right)-\sin\left(\frac{3\theta}{2}\right)$

$$=2\sin\left(\frac{\left(\frac{\theta}{2}-\frac{3\theta}{2}\right)}{2}\right)\cos\left(\frac{\left(\frac{\theta}{2}+\frac{3\theta}{2}\right)}{2}\right)=2\sin\left(-\frac{\theta}{2}\right)\cos\theta=-2\sin\left(\frac{\theta}{2}\right)\cos\theta$$

19. $\frac{\sin\theta+\sin(3\theta)}{2\sin(2\theta)}=\frac{2\sin(2\theta)\cos(-\theta)}{2\sin(2\theta)}=\cos(-\theta)=\cos\theta$

20. $\frac{\cos\theta+\cos(3\theta)}{2\cos(2\theta)}=\frac{2\cos(2\theta)\cos(-\theta)}{2\cos(2\theta)}=\cos(-\theta)=\cos\theta$

21. $\frac{\sin(4\theta)+\sin(2\theta)}{\cos(4\theta)+\cos(2\theta)}=\frac{2\sin(3\theta)\cos\theta}{2\cos(3\theta)\cos\theta}=\frac{\sin(3\theta)}{\cos(3\theta)}=\tan(3\theta)$

22. $\frac{\cos\theta-\cos(3\theta)}{\sin(3\theta)-\sin\theta}=\frac{-2\sin(2\theta)\sin(-\theta)}{2\sin\theta\cos(2\theta)}=\frac{-(-\sin\theta)\sin(2\theta)}{\sin\theta\cos(2\theta)}=\tan(2\theta)$

23. $\frac{\cos\theta-\cos(3\theta)}{\sin\theta+\sin(3\theta)}=\frac{-2\sin(2\theta)\sin(-\theta)}{2\sin(2\theta)\cos(-\theta)}=\frac{-(-\sin\theta)}{\cos\theta}=\tan\theta$

24. $\frac{\cos\theta-\cos(5\theta)}{\sin\theta+\sin(5\theta)}=\frac{-2\sin(3\theta)\sin(-2\theta)}{2\sin(3\theta)\cos(-2\theta)}=\frac{-(-\sin 2\theta)}{\cos(2\theta)}=\tan(2\theta)$

25. $\sin\theta[\sin\theta+\sin(3\theta)]=\sin\theta[2\sin(2\theta)\cos(-\theta)]=\cos\theta[2\sin(2\theta)\sin\theta]$

$$=\cos\theta\left[2\cdot\frac{1}{2}(\cos\theta-\cos(3\theta))\right]=\cos\theta(\cos\theta-\cos(3\theta))$$

26. $\sin\theta[\sin(3\theta)+\sin(5\theta)]=\sin\theta[2\sin(4\theta)\cos(-\theta)]=\cos\theta[2\sin(4\theta)\sin\theta]$

$$=\cos\theta\left[2\cdot\frac{1}{2}(\cos(3\theta)-\cos(5\theta))\right]=\cos\theta(\cos(3\theta)-\cos(5\theta))$$

27. $\frac{\sin(4\theta)+\sin(8\theta)}{\cos(4\theta)+\cos(8\theta)}=\frac{2\sin(6\theta)\cos(-2\theta)}{2\cos(6\theta)\cos(-2\theta)}=\frac{\sin(6\theta)}{\cos(6\theta)}=\tan(6\theta)$

28. $\frac{\sin(4\theta)-\sin(8\theta)}{\cos(4\theta)-\cos(8\theta)}=\frac{2\sin(-2\theta)\cos(6\theta)}{-2\sin(6\theta)\sin(-2\theta)}=\frac{\cos(6\theta)}{-\sin(6\theta)}=-\cot(6\theta)$

29. $\frac{\sin(4\theta)+\sin(8\theta)}{\sin(4\theta)-\sin(8\theta)}=\frac{2\sin(6\theta)\cos(-2\theta)}{2\sin(-2\theta)\cos(6\theta)}=\frac{\sin(6\theta)\cos(2\theta)}{-\sin(2\theta)\cos(6\theta)}$

$$=-\tan(6\theta)\cot(2\theta)=-\frac{\tan(6\theta)}{\tan(2\theta)}$$

30. $\frac{\cos(4\theta)-\cos(8\theta)}{\cos(4\theta)+\cos(8\theta)}=\frac{-2\sin(6\theta)\sin(-2\theta)}{2\cos(6\theta)\cos(-2\theta)}=-\tan(6\theta)\tan(-2\theta)=\tan(2\theta)\tan(6\theta)$

31. $$\frac{\sin\alpha+\sin\beta}{\sin\alpha-\sin\beta}=\frac{2\sin\left(\frac{\alpha+\beta}{2}\right)\cos\left(\frac{\alpha-\beta}{2}\right)}{2\sin\left(\frac{\alpha-\beta}{2}\right)\cos\left(\frac{\alpha+\beta}{2}\right)}=\tan\left(\frac{\alpha+\beta}{2}\right)\cot\left(\frac{\alpha-\beta}{2}\right)$$

32. $$\frac{\cos\alpha+\cos\beta}{\cos\alpha-\cos\beta}=\frac{2\cos\left(\frac{\alpha+\beta}{2}\right)\cos\left(\frac{\alpha-\beta}{2}\right)}{-2\sin\left(\frac{\alpha+\beta}{2}\right)\sin\left(\frac{\alpha-\beta}{2}\right)}=-\cot\left(\frac{\alpha+\beta}{2}\right)\cot\left(\frac{\alpha-\beta}{2}\right)$$

33. $$\frac{\sin\alpha+\sin\beta}{\cos\alpha+\cos\beta}=\frac{2\sin\left(\frac{\alpha+\beta}{2}\right)\cos\left(\frac{\alpha-\beta}{2}\right)}{2\cos\left(\frac{\alpha+\beta}{2}\right)\cos\left(\frac{\alpha-\beta}{2}\right)}=\tan\left(\frac{\alpha+\beta}{2}\right)$$

34. $$\frac{\sin\alpha-\sin\beta}{\cos\alpha-\cos\beta}=\frac{2\sin\left(\frac{\alpha-\beta}{2}\right)\cos\left(\frac{\alpha+\beta}{2}\right)}{-2\sin\left(\frac{\alpha+\beta}{2}\right)\sin\left(\frac{\alpha-\beta}{2}\right)}=-\cot\left(\frac{\alpha+\beta}{2}\right)$$

35. $$\begin{aligned}1+\cos(2\theta)+\cos(4\theta)+\cos(6\theta)&=\cos 0+\cos(6\theta)+\cos(2\theta)+\cos(4\theta)\\&=2\cos(3\theta)\cos(-3\theta)+2\cos(3\theta)\cos(-\theta)=2\cos^2(3\theta)+2\cos(3\theta)\cos\theta\\&=2\cos(3\theta)(\cos(3\theta)+\cos\theta)=2\cos(3\theta)2\cos(2\theta)\cos\theta\\&=4\cos\theta\cos(2\theta)\cos(3\theta)\end{aligned}$$

36. $$\begin{aligned}1-\cos(2\theta)+\cos(4\theta)-\cos(6\theta)&=\cos 0-\cos(6\theta)+\cos(4\theta)-\cos(2\theta)\\&=-2\sin(3\theta)\sin(-3\theta)-2\sin(3\theta)\sin(\theta)=2\sin^2(3\theta)-2\sin(3\theta)\sin\theta\\&=2\sin(3\theta)(\sin(3\theta)-\sin\theta)=2\sin(3\theta)2\sin\theta\cos(2\theta)\\&=4\sin\theta\cos(2\theta)\sin(3\theta)\end{aligned}$$

37. (a) $$\begin{aligned}y&=\sin[2\pi(852)t]+\sin[2\pi(1209)t]\\&=2\sin\left(\frac{2\pi(852)t+2\pi(1209)t}{2}\right)\cos\left(\frac{2\pi(852)t-2\pi(1209)t}{2}\right)\\&=2\sin(2061\pi t)\cos(357\pi t)\end{aligned}$$

(b) The maximum value of y is 2.

(c)

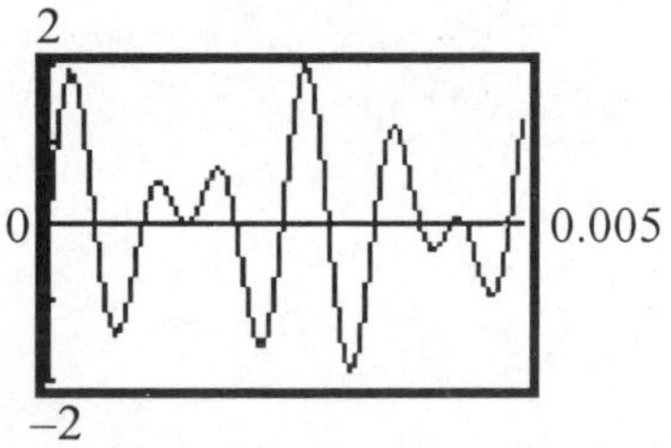

38. (a) $y = \sin[2\pi(941)t] + \sin[2\pi(1477)t]$

$$= 2\sin\left(\frac{2\pi(941)t + 2\pi(1477)t}{2}\right)\cos\left(\frac{2\pi(941)t - 2\pi(14779)t}{2}\right)$$

$$= 2\sin(2418\pi t)\cos(-536\pi t) = 2\sin(2418\pi t)\cos(536\pi t)$$

(b) The maximum value of y is 2.

(c)

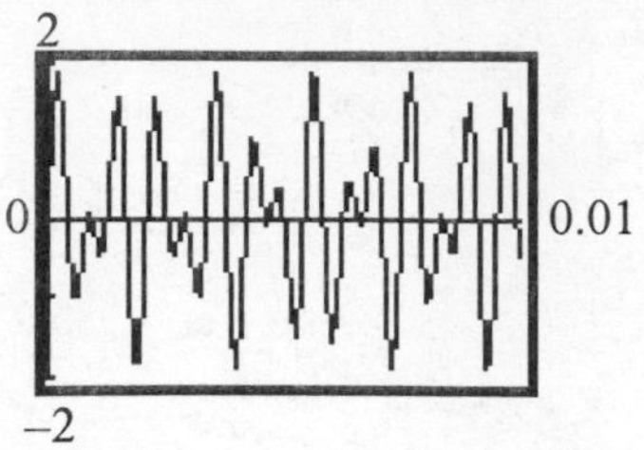

39. $\sin(2\alpha) + \sin(2\beta) + \sin(2\gamma)$

$$= 2\sin\left(\frac{2\alpha + 2\beta}{2}\right)\cos\left(\frac{2\alpha - 2\beta}{2}\right) + \sin(2\gamma)$$

$$= 2\sin(\alpha + \beta)\cos(\alpha - \beta) + 2\sin\gamma\cos\gamma$$

$$= 2\sin(\pi - \gamma)\cos(\alpha - \beta) + 2\sin\gamma\cos\gamma$$

$$= 2\sin\gamma\cos(\alpha - \beta) + 2\sin\gamma\cos\gamma = 2\sin\gamma[\cos(\alpha - \beta) + \cos\gamma]$$

$$= 2\sin\gamma\left(2\cos\left(\frac{\alpha - \beta + \gamma}{2}\right)\cos\left(\frac{\alpha - \beta - \gamma}{2}\right)\right)$$

$$= 4\sin\gamma\cos\left(\frac{\pi}{2} - \beta\right)\cos\left(\alpha - \frac{\pi}{2}\right) = 4\sin\gamma\sin\beta\sin\alpha$$

$$= 4\sin\alpha\sin\beta\sin\gamma$$

40. $\tan\alpha + \tan\beta + \tan\gamma = \dfrac{\sin\alpha}{\cos\alpha} + \dfrac{\sin\beta}{\cos\beta} + \dfrac{\sin\gamma}{\cos\gamma}$

$$= \frac{\sin\alpha\cos\beta\cos\gamma + \sin\beta\cos\alpha\cos\gamma + \sin\gamma\cos\alpha\cos\beta}{\cos\alpha\cos\beta\cos\gamma}$$

$$= \frac{\cos\gamma(\sin\alpha\cos\beta + \cos\alpha\sin\beta) + \sin\gamma\cos\alpha\cos\beta}{\cos\alpha\cos\beta\cos\gamma}$$

$$= \frac{\cos\gamma\sin(\alpha + \beta) + \sin\gamma\cos\alpha\cos\beta}{\cos\alpha\cos\beta\cos\gamma} = \frac{\cos\gamma\sin(\pi - \gamma) + \sin\gamma\cos\alpha\cos\beta}{\cos\alpha\cos\beta\cos\gamma}$$

$$= \frac{\cos\gamma\sin\gamma + \sin\gamma\cos\alpha\cos\beta}{\cos\alpha\cos\beta\cos\gamma} = \frac{\sin\gamma(\cos\gamma + \cos\alpha\cos\beta)}{\cos\alpha\cos\beta\cos\gamma}$$

$$= \frac{\sin\gamma(\cos(\pi - (\alpha + \beta)) + \cos\alpha\cos\beta)}{\cos\alpha\cos\beta\cos\gamma} = \frac{\sin\gamma(-\cos(\alpha + \beta) + \cos\alpha\cos\beta)}{\cos\alpha\cos\beta\cos\gamma}$$

$$= \frac{\sin\gamma(-\cos\alpha\cos\beta + \sin\alpha\sin\beta + \cos\alpha\cos\beta)}{\cos\alpha\cos\beta\cos\gamma} = \frac{\sin\gamma(\sin\alpha\sin\beta)}{\cos\alpha\cos\beta\cos\gamma}$$

$$= \tan\alpha\tan\beta\tan\gamma$$

41. Add the two sum formulas for $\sin(\alpha+\beta)$ and $\sin(\alpha-\beta)$ and solve:

$$\sin(\alpha+\beta)=\sin\alpha\cos\beta+\cos\alpha\sin\beta$$
$$\sin(\alpha-\beta)=\sin\alpha\cos\beta-\cos\alpha\sin\beta$$
$$\sin(\alpha+\beta)+\sin(\alpha-\beta)=2\sin\alpha\cos\beta$$
$$\sin\alpha\cos\beta=\frac{1}{2}\cdot[\sin(\alpha+\beta)+\sin(\alpha-\beta)]$$

42. $$2\sin\left(\frac{\alpha-\beta}{2}\right)\cos\left(\frac{\alpha+\beta}{2}\right)=2\cdot\frac{1}{2}\left[\sin\left(\frac{\alpha-\beta}{2}+\frac{\alpha+\beta}{2}\right)+\sin\left(\frac{\alpha-\beta}{2}-\frac{\alpha+\beta}{2}\right)\right]$$
$$=\sin\alpha+\sin(-\beta)=\sin\alpha-\sin\beta$$

Therefore, $\sin\alpha-\sin\beta=2\sin\left(\frac{\alpha-\beta}{2}\right)\cos\left(\frac{\alpha+\beta}{2}\right)$

43. $$2\cos\left(\frac{\alpha+\beta}{2}\right)\cos\left(\frac{\alpha-\beta}{2}\right)=2\cdot\frac{1}{2}\left[\cos\left(\frac{\alpha+\beta}{2}-\frac{\alpha-\beta}{2}\right)+\cos\left(\frac{\alpha+\beta}{2}+\frac{\alpha-\beta}{2}\right)\right]$$
$$=\cos\left(\frac{2\beta}{2}\right)+\cos\left(\frac{2\alpha}{2}\right)=\cos\beta+\cos\alpha$$

Therefore, $\cos\alpha+\cos\beta=2\cos\left(\frac{\alpha+\beta}{2}\right)\cos\left(\frac{\alpha-\beta}{2}\right)$

44. $$-2\sin\left(\frac{\alpha+\beta}{2}\right)\sin\left(\frac{\alpha-\beta}{2}\right)=-2\cdot\frac{1}{2}\left[\cos\left(\frac{\alpha+\beta}{2}-\frac{\alpha-\beta}{2}\right)-\cos\left(\frac{\alpha+\beta}{2}+\frac{\alpha-\beta}{2}\right)\right]$$
$$=-\left(\cos\left(\frac{2\beta}{2}\right)-\cos\left(\frac{2\alpha}{2}\right)\right)=\cos\alpha-\cos\beta$$

Therefore, $\cos\alpha-\cos\beta=-2\sin\left(\frac{\alpha+\beta}{2}\right)\sin\left(\frac{\alpha-\beta}{2}\right)$

Chapter 8

Analytic Trigonometry

8.7 Trigonometric Equations (I)

1. $\sin\theta = \frac{1}{2}$

$$\theta = \frac{\pi}{6} + 2k\pi \text{ or } \theta = \frac{5\pi}{6} + 2k\pi\text{, where } k \text{ is any integer}$$

Six solutions are $\theta = \frac{\pi}{6}, \frac{5\pi}{6}, \frac{13\pi}{6}, \frac{17\pi}{6}, \frac{25\pi}{6}, \frac{29\pi}{6}$

2. $\tan\theta = 1$

$$\theta = \frac{\pi}{4} + k\pi\text{, where } k \text{ is any integer}$$

Six solutions are $\theta = \frac{\pi}{4}, \frac{5\pi}{4}, \frac{9\pi}{4}, \frac{13\pi}{4}, \frac{17\pi}{4}, \frac{21\pi}{4}$

3. $\tan\theta = -\frac{\sqrt{3}}{3}$

$$\theta = \frac{5\pi}{6} + k\pi\text{, where } k \text{ is any integer}$$

Six solutions are $\theta = \frac{5\pi}{6}, \frac{11\pi}{6}, \frac{17\pi}{6}, \frac{23\pi}{6}, \frac{29\pi}{6}, \frac{35\pi}{6}$

4. $\cos\theta = -\frac{\sqrt{3}}{2}$

$$\theta = \frac{5\pi}{6} + 2k\pi \text{ or } \theta = \frac{7\pi}{6} + 2k\pi\text{, where } k \text{ is any integer}$$

Six solutions are $\theta = \frac{5\pi}{6}, \frac{7\pi}{6}, \frac{17\pi}{6}, \frac{19\pi}{6}, \frac{29\pi}{6}, \frac{31\pi}{6}$

5. $\cos\theta = 0$

$$\theta = \frac{\pi}{2} + 2k\pi \text{ or } \theta = \frac{3\pi}{2} + 2k\pi\text{, where } k \text{ is any integer}$$

Six solutions are $\theta = \frac{\pi}{2}, \frac{3\pi}{2}, \frac{5\pi}{2}, \frac{7\pi}{2}, \frac{9\pi}{2}, \frac{11\pi}{2}$

6. $\sin\theta = \frac{\sqrt{2}}{2}$

$$\theta = \frac{\pi}{4} + 2k\pi \text{ or } \theta = \frac{3\pi}{4} + 2k\pi\text{, where } k \text{ is any integer}$$

Six solutions are $\theta = \frac{\pi}{4}, \frac{3\pi}{4}, \frac{9\pi}{4}, \frac{11\pi}{4}, \frac{17\pi}{4}, \frac{19\pi}{4}$

7. $\cos(2\theta)=-\frac{1}{2}$

$2\theta=\frac{2\pi}{3}+2k\pi \rightarrow \theta=\frac{\pi}{3}+k\pi$, where k is any integer

$2\theta=\frac{4\pi}{3}+2k\pi \rightarrow \theta=\frac{2\pi}{3}+k\pi$, where k is any integer

Six solutions are $\theta=\frac{\pi}{3},\frac{2\pi}{3},\frac{4\pi}{3},\frac{5\pi}{3},\frac{7\pi}{3},\frac{8\pi}{3}$

8. $\sin(2\theta)=-1$

$2\theta=\frac{3\pi}{2}+2k\pi \rightarrow \theta=\frac{3\pi}{4}+k\pi$, where k is any integer

Six solutions are $\theta=\frac{3\pi}{4},\frac{7\pi}{4},\frac{11\pi}{4},\frac{15\pi}{4},\frac{19\pi}{4},\frac{23\pi}{4}$

9. $\sin\left(\frac{\theta}{2}\right)=-\frac{\sqrt{3}}{2}$

$\frac{\theta}{2}=\frac{4\pi}{3}+2k\pi \rightarrow \theta=\frac{8\pi}{3}+4k\pi$, where k is any integer

$\frac{\theta}{2}=\frac{5\pi}{3}+2k\pi \rightarrow \theta=\frac{10\pi}{3}+4k\pi$, where k is any integer

Six solutions are $\theta=\frac{8\pi}{3},\frac{10\pi}{3},\frac{20\pi}{3},\frac{22\pi}{3},\frac{32\pi}{3},\frac{34\pi}{3}$

10. $\tan\left(\frac{\theta}{2}\right)=-1$

$\frac{\theta}{2}=\frac{3\pi}{4}+2k\pi \rightarrow \theta=\frac{3\pi}{2}+4k\pi$, where k is any integer

$\frac{\theta}{2}=\frac{7\pi}{4}+2k\pi \rightarrow \theta=\frac{7\pi}{2}+4k\pi$, where k is any integer

Six solutions are $\theta=\frac{3\pi}{2},\frac{7\pi}{2},\frac{11\pi}{2},\frac{15\pi}{2},\frac{19\pi}{2},\frac{23\pi}{2}$

11. $2\sin\theta+3=2$

$2\sin\theta=-1 \rightarrow \sin\theta=-\frac{1}{2}$

$\theta=\frac{7\pi}{6}+2k\pi$ or $\theta=\frac{11\pi}{6}+2k\pi$, k is any integer

The solutions on the interval $[0, 2\pi)$ are $\theta=\frac{7\pi}{6},\frac{11\pi}{6}$.

12. $1-\cos\theta=\frac{1}{2}$

$$1-\cos\theta=\frac{1}{2}\rightarrow\frac{1}{2}=\cos\theta$$

$$\theta=\frac{\pi}{3}+2k\pi \quad\text{or}\quad \theta=\frac{5\pi}{3}+2k\pi,\ k \text{ is any integer}$$

The solutions on the interval $[0, 2\pi)$ are $\theta=\frac{\pi}{3},\frac{5\pi}{3}$.

13. $4\cos^2\theta=1$

$$\cos^2\theta=\frac{1}{4}\rightarrow\cos\theta=\pm\frac{1}{2}$$

$$\theta=\frac{\pi}{3}+k\pi \quad\text{or}\quad \theta=\frac{2\pi}{3}+k\pi,\ k \text{ is any integer}$$

The solutions on the interval $[0, 2\pi)$ are $\theta=\frac{\pi}{3},\frac{2\pi}{3},\frac{4\pi}{3},\frac{5\pi}{3}$.

14. $\tan^2\theta=\frac{1}{3}$

$$\tan\theta=\pm\sqrt{\frac{1}{3}}=\pm\frac{\sqrt{3}}{3}$$

$$\theta=\frac{\pi}{6}+k\pi \text{ or } \theta=\frac{5\pi}{6}+k\pi,\ k \text{ is any integer}$$

The solutions on the interval $[0, 2\pi)$ are $\theta=\frac{\pi}{6},\frac{5\pi}{6},\frac{7\pi}{6},\frac{11\pi}{6}$.

15. $2\sin^2\theta-1=0$

$$2\sin^2\theta=1\rightarrow\sin^2\theta=\frac{1}{2}\rightarrow\sin\theta=\pm\sqrt{\frac{1}{2}}=\pm\frac{\sqrt{2}}{2}$$

$$\theta=\frac{\pi}{4}+k\pi \quad\text{or}\quad \theta=\frac{3\pi}{4}+k\pi,\ k \text{ is any integer}$$

The solutions on the interval $[0, 2\pi)$ are $\theta=\frac{\pi}{4},\frac{3\pi}{4},\frac{5\pi}{4},\frac{7\pi}{4}$.

16. $4\cos^2\theta-3=0$

$$4\cos^2\theta=3\rightarrow\cos^2\theta=\frac{3}{4}\rightarrow\cos\theta=\pm\frac{\sqrt{3}}{2}$$

$$\theta=\frac{\pi}{6}+k\pi \quad\text{or}\quad \theta=\frac{5\pi}{6}+k\pi,\ k \text{ is any integer}$$

The solutions on the interval $[0, 2\pi)$ are $\theta=\frac{\pi}{6},\frac{5\pi}{6},\frac{7\pi}{6},\frac{11\pi}{6}$.

17. $\sin(3\theta) = -1$

$$3\theta = \frac{3\pi}{2} + 2k\pi \quad \rightarrow \quad \theta = \frac{\pi}{2} + \frac{2k\pi}{3}, \text{ where } k \text{ is any integer}$$

The solutions on the interval $[0, 2\pi)$ are $\theta = \frac{\pi}{2}, \frac{7\pi}{6}, \frac{11\pi}{6}$

18. $\tan\left(\frac{\theta}{2}\right) = \sqrt{3}$

$$\frac{\theta}{2} = \frac{\pi}{3} + k\pi \quad \rightarrow \quad \theta = \frac{2\pi}{3} + 2k\pi, \text{ where } k \text{ is any integer}$$

The solution on the interval $[0, 2\pi)$ is $\theta = \frac{2\pi}{3}$

19. $\cos(2\theta) = -\frac{1}{2}$

$$2\theta = \frac{2\pi}{3} + 2k\pi \quad \rightarrow \quad \theta = \frac{\pi}{3} + k\pi, \text{ where } k \text{ is any integer}$$

$$2\theta = \frac{4\pi}{3} + 2k\pi \quad \rightarrow \quad \theta = \frac{2\pi}{3} + k\pi, \text{ where } k \text{ is any integer}$$

The solutions on the interval $[0, 2\pi)$ are $\theta = \frac{\pi}{3}, \frac{2\pi}{3}, \frac{4\pi}{3}, \frac{5\pi}{3}$

20. $\tan(2\theta) = -1$

$$2\theta = \frac{3\pi}{4} + k\pi \quad \rightarrow \quad \theta = \frac{3\pi}{8} + \frac{k\pi}{2}, \text{ where } k \text{ is any integer}$$

The solutions on the interval $[0, 2\pi)$ are $\theta = \frac{3\pi}{8}, \frac{7\pi}{8}, \frac{11\pi}{8}, \frac{15\pi}{8}$

21. $\sec\left(\frac{3\theta}{2}\right) = -2$

$$\frac{3\theta}{2} = \frac{2\pi}{3} + 2k\pi \quad \rightarrow \quad \theta = \frac{4\pi}{9} + \frac{4k\pi}{3}, \text{ where } k \text{ is any integer}$$

$$\frac{3\theta}{2} = \frac{4\pi}{3} + 2k\pi \quad \rightarrow \quad \theta = \frac{8\pi}{9} + \frac{4k\pi}{3}, \text{ where } k \text{ is any integer}$$

The solutions on the interval $[0, 2\pi)$ are $\theta = \frac{4\pi}{9}, \frac{8\pi}{9}, \frac{16\pi}{9}$

22. $\cot\left(\frac{2\theta}{3}\right) = -\sqrt{3}$

$$\frac{2\theta}{3} = \frac{5\pi}{6} + k\pi \quad \rightarrow \quad \theta = \frac{5\pi}{4} + \frac{3k\pi}{2}, \text{ where } k \text{ is any integer}$$

The solution on the interval $[0, 2\pi)$ is $\theta = \frac{5\pi}{4}$

23. $\cos\left(2\theta - \frac{\pi}{2}\right) = -1$

$$2\theta - \frac{\pi}{2} = \pi + 2k\pi \quad \rightarrow \quad 2\theta = \frac{3\pi}{2} + 2k\pi \quad \rightarrow \quad \theta = \frac{3\pi}{4} + k\pi, \quad k \text{ is any integer}$$

The solutions on the interval $[0, 2\pi)$ are $\theta = \frac{3\pi}{4}, \frac{7\pi}{4}$.

24. $\sin\left(3\theta+\frac{\pi}{18}\right)=1$

$$3\theta+\frac{\pi}{18}=\frac{\pi}{2}+2k\pi \rightarrow 3\theta=\frac{4\pi}{9}+2k\pi \rightarrow \theta=\frac{4\pi}{27}+\frac{2k\pi}{3},\ k \text{ is any integer}$$

The solutions on the interval $[0, 2\pi)$ are $\theta=\frac{4\pi}{27}, \frac{22\pi}{27}, \frac{40\pi}{27}$.

25. $\tan\left(\frac{\theta}{2}+\frac{\pi}{3}\right)=1$

$$\frac{\theta}{2}+\frac{\pi}{3}=\frac{\pi}{4}+k\pi \rightarrow \frac{\theta}{2}=-\frac{\pi}{12}+k\pi \rightarrow \theta=-\frac{\pi}{6}+2k\pi,\ k \text{ is any integer}$$

The solution on the interval $[0, 2\pi)$ is $\theta=\frac{11\pi}{6}$.

26. $\cos\left(\frac{\theta}{3}-\frac{\pi}{4}\right)=\frac{1}{2}$

$$\frac{\theta}{3}-\frac{\pi}{4}=\frac{\pi}{3}+2k\pi \rightarrow \frac{\theta}{3}=\frac{7\pi}{12}+2k\pi \rightarrow \theta=\frac{7\pi}{4}+6k\pi,\ k \text{ is any integer}$$

$$\frac{\theta}{3}-\frac{\pi}{4}=\frac{5\pi}{3}+2k\pi \rightarrow \frac{\theta}{3}=\frac{23\pi}{12}+2k\pi \rightarrow \theta=\frac{23\pi}{4}+6k\pi,\ k \text{ is any integer}$$

The solution on the interval $[0, 2\pi)$ is $\theta=\frac{7\pi}{4}$.

27. $2\sin\theta+1=0 \rightarrow 2\sin\theta=-1 \rightarrow \sin\theta=-\frac{1}{2}$

$$\theta=\frac{7\pi}{6}+2k\pi \text{ or } \theta=\frac{11\pi}{6}+2k\pi,\ k \text{ is any integer}$$

The solutions on the interval $[0, 2\pi)$ are $\theta=\frac{7\pi}{6}, \frac{11\pi}{6}$.

28. $\cos\theta+1=0 \rightarrow \cos\theta=-1$

$$\theta=\pi+2k\pi,\ k \text{ is any integer}$$

The solution on the interval $[0, 2\pi)$ is $\theta=\pi$.

29. $\tan\theta+1=0 \rightarrow \tan\theta=-1$

$$\theta=\frac{3\pi}{4}+k\pi,\ k \text{ is any integer}$$

The solutions on the interval $[0, 2\pi)$ are $\theta=\frac{3\pi}{4}, \frac{7\pi}{4}$.

30. $\sqrt{3}\cot\theta+1=0 \rightarrow \sqrt{3}\cot\theta=-1 \rightarrow \cot\theta=-\frac{1}{\sqrt{3}}=-\frac{\sqrt{3}}{3}$

$$\theta=\frac{2\pi}{3}+k\pi,\ k \text{ is any integer}$$

The solutions on the interval $[0, 2\pi)$ are $\theta=\frac{2\pi}{3}, \frac{5\pi}{3}$.

31. $4\sec\theta + 6 = -2 \quad \rightarrow \quad 4\sec\theta = -8 \quad \rightarrow \quad \sec\theta = -2$

$$\theta = \frac{2\pi}{3} + 2k\pi \quad \text{or} \quad \theta = \frac{4\pi}{3} + 2k\pi, \ k \text{ is any integer}$$

The solutions on the interval $[0, 2\pi)$ are $\theta = \frac{2\pi}{3}, \frac{4\pi}{3}$.

32. $5\csc\theta - 3 = 2 \quad \rightarrow \quad 5\csc\theta = 5 \quad \rightarrow \quad \csc\theta = 1$

$$\theta = \frac{\pi}{2} + 2k\pi, \ k \text{ is any integer}$$

The solution on the interval $[0, 2\pi)$ is $\theta = \frac{\pi}{2}$.

33. $3\sqrt{2}\cos\theta + 2 = -1 \quad \rightarrow \quad 3\sqrt{2}\cos\theta = -3 \quad \rightarrow \quad \cos\theta = -\frac{1}{\sqrt{2}} = -\frac{\sqrt{2}}{2}$

$$\theta = \frac{3\pi}{4} + 2k\pi \quad \text{or} \quad \theta = \frac{5\pi}{4} + 2k\pi, \ k \text{ is any integer}$$

The solutions on the interval $[0, 2\pi)$ are $\theta = \frac{3\pi}{4}, \frac{5\pi}{4}$.

34. $4\sin\theta + 3\sqrt{3} = \sqrt{3} \quad \rightarrow \quad 4\sin\theta = -2\sqrt{3} \quad \rightarrow \quad \sin\theta = -\frac{2\sqrt{3}}{4} = -\frac{\sqrt{3}}{2}$

$$\theta = \frac{4\pi}{3} + 2k\pi \quad \text{or} \quad \theta = \frac{5\pi}{3} + 2k\pi, \ k \text{ is any integer}$$

The solutions on the interval $[0, 2\pi)$ are $\theta = \frac{4\pi}{3}, \frac{5\pi}{3}$.

35. $\sin\theta = 0.4$

$$\theta \approx 0.4115168 \quad \text{or} \quad \theta \approx \pi - 0.4115168 \approx 2.7300758$$

$\theta \approx 0.41, 2.73$

36. $\cos\theta = 0.6$

$$\theta \approx 0.92729522 \quad \text{or} \quad \theta \approx 2\pi - 0.92729522 \approx 5.35589009$$

$\theta \approx 0.93, 5.36$

37. $\tan\theta = 5$

$$\theta \approx 1.3734008 \quad \text{or} \quad \theta \approx \pi + 1.3734008 \approx 4.5149934$$

$\theta \approx 1.37, 4.51$

38. $\cot\theta = 2 \quad \rightarrow \quad \tan\theta = \frac{1}{2}$

$$\theta \approx 0.46364761 \quad \text{or} \quad \theta \approx \pi + 0.46364761 \approx 3.60524026$$

$\theta \approx 0.46, 3.61$

39. $\cos\theta = -0.9$

$$\theta \approx 2.6905658 \quad \text{or} \quad \theta \approx 2\pi - 2.6905658 \approx 3.5926195$$

$\theta \approx 2.69, 3.59$

40. $\sin\theta = -0.2$

$$\theta \approx -0.20135792 = 6.08182739 \quad \text{or} \quad \theta \approx \pi + 0.20135792 \approx 3.34295057$$

$\theta \approx 3.34, 6.08$

41. $\sec\theta = -4 \;\rightarrow\; \cos\theta = -\frac{1}{4}$

$\theta \approx 1.8234766$ or $\theta \approx 2\pi - 1.8234766 \approx 4.4597087$

$\theta \approx 1.82, 4.46$

42. $\csc\theta = -3 \;\rightarrow\; \sin\theta = -\frac{1}{3}$

$\theta \approx -0.33983691 = 5.94334840$ or $\theta \approx \pi + 0.33983691 \approx 3.48142956$

$\theta \approx 3.48, 5.94$

43. Use Snell's Law to solve:

$$\frac{\sin(40^\circ)}{\sin\theta_2} = 1.33 \rightarrow \sin(40^\circ) = 1.33\sin\theta_2 \rightarrow \sin\theta_2 = \frac{\sin(40^\circ)}{1.33} \approx 0.4833$$

$$\theta_2 = \sin^{-1}(0.4833) \approx 28.9^\circ$$

44. Use Snell's Law to solve:

$$\frac{\sin(50^\circ)}{\sin\theta_2} = 1.66 \rightarrow \sin(50^\circ) = 1.66\sin\theta_2 \rightarrow \sin\theta_2 = \frac{\sin(50^\circ)}{1.66} \approx 0.4615$$

$$\theta_2 = \sin^{-1}(0.4615) \approx 27.5^\circ$$

45. Calculate the index of refraction for each:

$\theta_1 = 10^\circ,\ \theta_2 = 7^\circ 45' = 7.75^\circ \qquad \frac{\sin\theta_1}{\sin\theta_2} = \frac{\sin(10^\circ)}{\sin(7.75^\circ)} \approx 1.2877$

$\theta_1 = 20^\circ,\ \theta_2 = 15^\circ 30' = 15.5^\circ \qquad \frac{\sin\theta_1}{\sin\theta_2} = \frac{\sin(20^\circ)}{\sin(15.5^\circ)} \approx 1.2798$

$\theta_1 = 30^\circ,\ \theta_2 = 22^\circ 30' = 22.5^\circ \qquad \frac{\sin\theta_1}{\sin\theta_2} = \frac{\sin(30^\circ)}{\sin(22.5^\circ)} \approx 1.3066$

$\theta_1 = 40^\circ,\ \theta_2 = 29^\circ 0' = 29^\circ \qquad \frac{\sin\theta_1}{\sin\theta_2} = \frac{\sin(40^\circ)}{\sin(29^\circ)} \approx 1.3259$

$\theta_1 = 50^\circ,\ \theta_2 = 35^\circ 0' = 35^\circ \qquad \frac{\sin\theta_1}{\sin\theta_2} = \frac{\sin(50^\circ)}{\sin(35^\circ)} \approx 1.3356$

$\theta_1 = 60^\circ,\ \theta_2 = 40^\circ 30' = 40.5^\circ \qquad \frac{\sin\theta_1}{\sin\theta_2} = \frac{\sin(60^\circ)}{\sin(40.5^\circ)} \approx 1.3335$

$\theta_1 = 70^\circ,\ \theta_2 = 45^\circ 30' = 45.5^\circ \qquad \frac{\sin\theta_1}{\sin\theta_2} = \frac{\sin(70^\circ)}{\sin(45.5^\circ)} \approx 1.3175$

$\theta_1 = 80^\circ,\ \theta_2 = 50^\circ 0' = 50^\circ \qquad \frac{\sin\theta_1}{\sin\theta_2} = \frac{\sin(80)^\circ}{\sin(50^\circ)} \approx 1.2856$

The results range from 1.28 to 1.34 and are surprisingly close to Snell's Law.

46. $\frac{v_1}{v_2} = \frac{2.99 \times 10^8}{1.92 \times 10^8} \approx 1.56$

The index of refraction for this liquid is 1.56.

47. Calculate the index of refraction:

$\theta_1 = 40°, \ \theta_2 = 26° \qquad \dfrac{\sin\theta_1}{\sin\theta_2} = \dfrac{\sin(40°)}{\sin(26°)} \approx 1.47$

48. The index of refraction of crown glass is 1.52.

$$\frac{\sin(30°)}{\sin\theta_2} = 1.52 \rightarrow \sin\theta_2 = \frac{\sin(30°)}{1.52} = 0.3289$$

$$\theta_2 = 19.2°$$

The angle of refraction is 19.2°.

49. If θ is the original angle of incidence and ϕ is the angle of refraction, then $\dfrac{\sin\theta}{\sin\phi} = n_2$. The angle of incidence of the emerging beam is also ϕ, and the index of refraction is $\dfrac{1}{n_2}$. Thus, θ is the angle of refraction of the emerging beam. The two beams are parallel since the original angle of incidence and the angle of refraction of the emerging beam are equal.

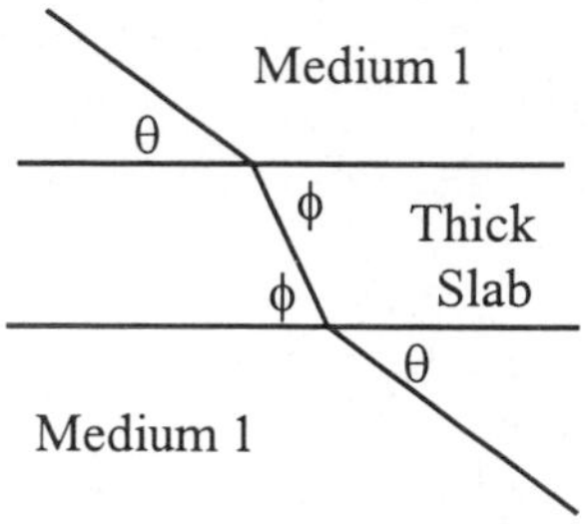

Chapter 8

Analytic Trigonometry

8.8 Trigonometric Equations (II)

1. $2\cos^2\theta + \cos\theta = 0 \rightarrow \cos\theta(2\cos\theta + 1) = 0$

$$\cos\theta = 0 \rightarrow \theta = \frac{\pi}{2}, \frac{3\pi}{2}$$

or $2\cos\theta + 1 = 0$

$$2\cos\theta = -1 \rightarrow \cos\theta = -\frac{1}{2} \rightarrow \theta = \frac{2\pi}{3}, \frac{4\pi}{3}$$

2. $\sin^2\theta - 1 = 0 \rightarrow (\sin\theta + 1)(\sin\theta - 1) = 0$

$$\sin\theta + 1 = 0 \rightarrow \sin\theta = -1 \rightarrow \theta = \frac{3\pi}{2}$$

or $\sin\theta - 1 = 0 \rightarrow \sin\theta = 1 \rightarrow \theta = \frac{\pi}{2}$

3. $2\sin^2\theta - \sin\theta - 1 = 0 \rightarrow (2\sin\theta + 1)(\sin\theta - 1) = 0$

$$2\sin\theta + 1 = 0 \rightarrow 2\sin\theta = -1 \rightarrow \sin\theta = -\frac{1}{2} \rightarrow \theta = \frac{7\pi}{6}, \frac{11\pi}{6}$$

or $\sin\theta - 1 = 0 \rightarrow \sin\theta = 1 \rightarrow \theta = \frac{\pi}{2}$

4. $2\cos^2\theta + \cos\theta - 1 = 0 \rightarrow (\cos\theta + 1)(2\cos\theta - 1) = 0$

$$\cos\theta + 1 = 0 \rightarrow \cos\theta = -1 \rightarrow \theta = \pi$$

or $2\cos\theta - 1 = 0 \rightarrow 2\cos\theta = 1 \rightarrow \cos\theta = \frac{1}{2} \rightarrow \theta = \frac{\pi}{3}, \frac{5\pi}{3}$

5. $(\tan\theta - 1)(\sec\theta - 1) = 0$

$$\tan\theta - 1 = 0 \rightarrow \tan\theta = 1 \rightarrow \theta = \frac{\pi}{4}, \frac{5\pi}{4}$$

or $\sec\theta - 1 = 0 \rightarrow \sec\theta = 1 \rightarrow \theta = 0$

6. $(\cot\theta + 1)\left(\csc\theta - \tfrac{1}{2}\right) = 0$

$$\cot\theta + 1 = 0 \rightarrow \cot\theta = -1 \rightarrow \theta = \frac{3\pi}{4}, \frac{7\pi}{4}$$

or $\csc\theta - \frac{1}{2} = 0 \rightarrow \csc\theta = \frac{1}{2}$, which is impossible

the solutions are $\theta = \frac{3\pi}{4}, \frac{7\pi}{4}$

7. $\sin^2\theta - \cos^2\theta = 1 + \cos\theta$

$$\left(1-\cos^2\theta\right) - \cos^2\theta = 1+\cos\theta \rightarrow 1-2\cos^2\theta = 1+\cos\theta$$

$$2\cos^2\theta + \cos\theta = 0 \rightarrow (\cos\theta)(2\cos\theta+1) = 0$$

$$\cos\theta = 0 \rightarrow\rightarrow \theta = \frac{\pi}{2}, \frac{3\pi}{2}$$

$$\text{or } 2\cos\theta + 1 = 0 \rightarrow \cos\theta = -\frac{1}{2} \rightarrow \theta = \frac{2\pi}{3}, \frac{4\pi}{3}$$

8. $\cos^2\theta - \sin^2\theta + \sin\theta = 0$

$$\left(1-\sin^2\theta\right) - \sin^2\theta + \sin\theta = 0 \rightarrow 1 - 2\sin^2\theta + \sin\theta = 0$$

$$2\sin^2\theta - \sin\theta - 1 = 0 \rightarrow (2\sin\theta + 1)(\sin\theta - 1) = 0$$

$$2\sin\theta + 1 = 0 \rightarrow \sin\theta = -\frac{1}{2} \rightarrow \theta = \frac{\pi}{6}, \frac{7\pi}{6}$$

$$\text{or } \sin\theta - 1 = 0 \rightarrow \sin\theta = 1 \rightarrow \theta = \frac{\pi}{2}$$

9. $\sin^2\theta = 6(\cos\theta + 1)$

$$1-\cos^2\theta = 6(\cos\theta+1) \rightarrow 1-\cos^2\theta = 6\cos\theta + 6$$

$$\cos^2\theta + 6\cos\theta + 5 = 0 \rightarrow (\cos\theta+5)(\cos\theta+1) = 0$$

$\cos\theta + 5 = 0 \rightarrow \cos\theta = -5$, which is impossible

$\text{or } \cos\theta + 1 \rightarrow \cos\theta = -1 \rightarrow \theta = \pi$

the solution is $\theta = \pi$.

10. $2\sin^2\theta = 3(1-\cos\theta)$

$$2\left(1-\cos^2\theta\right) = 3(1-\cos\theta) \rightarrow 2 - 2\cos^2\theta = 3 - 3\cos\theta$$

$$2\cos^2\theta - 3\cos\theta + 1 = 0 \rightarrow (2\cos\theta - 1)(\cos\theta - 1) = 0$$

$$2\cos\theta - 1 = 0 \rightarrow \cos\theta = \frac{1}{2} \rightarrow \theta = \frac{\pi}{3}, \frac{5\pi}{3}$$

$$\text{or } \cos\theta - 1 = 0 \rightarrow \cos\theta = 1 \rightarrow \theta = 0$$

11. $\cos(2\theta) + 6\sin^2\theta = 4$

$$1 - 2\sin^2\theta + 6\sin^2\theta = 4 \rightarrow 4\sin^2\theta = 3 \rightarrow \sin^2\theta = \frac{3}{4} \rightarrow \sin\theta = \pm\frac{\sqrt{3}}{2}$$

$$\theta = \frac{\pi}{3}, \frac{2\pi}{3}, \frac{4\pi}{3}, \frac{5\pi}{3}$$

12. $\cos(2\theta) = 2 - 2\sin^2\theta$

$1 - 2\sin^2\theta = 2 - 2\sin^2\theta \to 0 = 1$, which is impossible
therefore the equation has no real solution.

13. $\cos\theta = \sin\theta$

$\frac{\sin\theta}{\cos\theta} = 1 \to \tan\theta = 1$

$\theta = \frac{\pi}{4}, \frac{5\pi}{4}$

14. $\cos\theta + \sin\theta = 0$

$\sin\theta = -\cos\theta$

$\frac{\sin\theta}{\cos\theta} = -1 \to \tan\theta = -1$

$\theta = \frac{3\pi}{4}, \frac{7\pi}{4}$

15. $\tan\theta = 2\sin\theta$

$\frac{\sin\theta}{\cos\theta} = 2\sin\theta$

$\sin\theta = 2\sin\theta\cos\theta$

$0 = 2\sin\theta\cos\theta - \sin\theta$

$0 = \sin\theta(2\cos\theta - 1)$

$2\cos\theta - 1 = 0 \to \cos\theta = \frac{1}{2} \to \theta = \frac{\pi}{3}, \frac{5\pi}{3}$

or $\sin\theta = 0 \to \theta = 0, \pi$

16. $\sin(2\theta) = \cos\theta$

$2\sin\theta\cos\theta = \cos\theta$

$2\sin\theta\cos\theta - \cos\theta = 0$

$(\cos\theta)(2\sin\theta - 1) = 0$

$\cos\theta = 0 \to \cos\theta = 0 \to \theta = \frac{\pi}{2}, \frac{3\pi}{2}$

or $2\sin\theta = 1 \to \sin\theta = \frac{1}{2} \to \theta = \frac{\pi}{6}. \frac{5\pi}{6}$

17. $\sin\theta = \csc\theta$

$\sin\theta = \frac{1}{\sin\theta}$

$\sin^2\theta = 1 \to \sin\theta = \pm 1$

$\theta = \frac{\pi}{2}, \frac{3\pi}{2}$

18. $\tan\theta = \cot\theta$

$\tan\theta = \frac{1}{\tan\theta}$

$\tan^2\theta = 1 \to \tan\theta = \pm 1$

$\theta = \frac{\pi}{4}, \frac{3\pi}{4}, \frac{5\pi}{4}, \frac{7\pi}{4}$

19. $\cos(2\theta) = \cos\theta$

$2\cos^2\theta - 1 = \cos\theta \to 2\cos^2\theta - \cos\theta - 1 = 0 \to (2\cos\theta + 1)(\cos\theta - 1) = 0$

$2\cos\theta + 1 = 0 \to \cos\theta = -\frac{1}{2} \to \theta = \frac{2\pi}{3}, \frac{4\pi}{3}$

or $\cos\theta - 1 = 0 \to \cos\theta = 1 \to \theta = 0$

20. $\sin(2\theta)\sin\theta = \cos\theta$

$2\sin\theta\cos\theta\sin\theta = \cos\theta \to 2\sin^2\theta\cos\theta - \cos\theta = 0 \to (2\sin^2\theta - 1)\cos\theta = 0$

$2\sin^2\theta - 1 = 0 \to 2\sin^2\theta = 1 \to \sin^2\theta = \frac{1}{2} \to \sin\theta = \pm\frac{\sqrt{2}}{2}$

$\theta = \frac{\pi}{4}, \frac{3\pi}{4}, \frac{5\pi}{4}, \frac{7\pi}{4}$

or $\cos\theta = 0 \to \theta = \frac{\pi}{2}, \frac{3\pi}{2}$

21. $\sin(2\theta)+\sin(4\theta)=0$

$\sin(2\theta)+2\sin(2\theta)\cos(2\theta)=0 \rightarrow \sin(2\theta)(1+2\cos(2\theta))=0$

$$1+2\cos(2\theta)=0 \rightarrow \cos(2\theta)=-\frac{1}{2} \rightarrow 2\theta=\frac{2\pi}{3}+2k\pi \rightarrow \theta=\frac{\pi}{3}+k\pi$$

$$2\theta=\frac{4\pi}{3}+2k\pi \rightarrow \theta=\frac{2\pi}{3}+k\pi$$

$$\text{or } \sin(2\theta)=0 \rightarrow 2\theta=0+2k\pi \rightarrow \theta=k\pi$$

$$2\theta=\pi+2k\pi \rightarrow \theta=\frac{\pi}{2}+k\pi$$

$\theta=0, \frac{\pi}{3}, \frac{\pi}{2}, \frac{2\pi}{3}, \pi, \frac{4\pi}{3}, \frac{3\pi}{2}, \frac{5\pi}{3}$

22. $\cos(2\theta)+\cos(4\theta)=0$

$2\cos(3\theta)\cos(-\theta)=0 \rightarrow 2\cos(3\theta)\cos\theta=0$

$$\cos(3\theta)=0 \rightarrow 3\theta=\frac{\pi}{2}+2k\pi \rightarrow \theta=\frac{\pi}{6}+\frac{2k\pi}{3}$$

$$3\theta=\frac{3\pi}{2}+2k\pi \rightarrow \theta=\frac{\pi}{2}+\frac{2k\pi}{3}$$

$$\text{or } \cos\theta=0 \rightarrow \theta=\frac{\pi}{2}+2k\pi$$

$$\theta=\frac{3\pi}{2}+2k\pi$$

$\theta=\frac{\pi}{6}, \frac{\pi}{2}, \frac{5\pi}{6}, \frac{3\pi}{2}, \frac{7\pi}{6}, \frac{11\pi}{6}$

23. $\cos(4\theta)-\cos(6\theta)=0$

$\cos(5\theta-\theta)-\cos(5\theta+\theta)=0 \rightarrow -2\sin(5\theta)\sin(-\theta)=0$

$2\sin(5\theta)\sin\theta=0$

$$\sin(5\theta)=0 \rightarrow 5\theta=0+2k\pi \rightarrow \theta=\frac{2k\pi}{5}$$

$$5\theta=\pi+2k\pi \rightarrow \theta=\frac{\pi}{5}+\frac{2k\pi}{5}$$

$$\text{or } \sin\theta=0 \rightarrow \theta=0+2k\pi$$

$$\theta=\pi+2k\pi$$

$\theta=0, \frac{\pi}{5}, \frac{2\pi}{5}, \frac{3\pi}{5}, \frac{4\pi}{5}, \pi, \frac{6\pi}{5}, \frac{7\pi}{5}, \frac{8\pi}{5}, \frac{9\pi}{5}$

24. $\sin(4\theta) - \sin(6\theta) = 0$
$2\sin(-\theta)\cos(5\theta) = 0 \rightarrow -2\sin\theta\cos(5\theta) = 0$

$$\cos(5\theta) = 0 \rightarrow 5\theta = \frac{\pi}{2} + 2k\pi \rightarrow \theta = \frac{\pi}{10} + \frac{2k\pi}{5}$$

$$5\theta = \frac{3\pi}{2} + 2k\pi \rightarrow \theta = \frac{3\pi}{10} + \frac{2k\pi}{5}$$

or $\sin\theta = 0 \rightarrow \theta = 0 + 2k\pi$

$$\theta = \pi + 2k\pi$$

$$\theta = 0, \frac{\pi}{10}, \frac{3\pi}{10}, \frac{\pi}{2}, \frac{7\pi}{10}, \frac{9\pi}{10}, \pi, \frac{11\pi}{10}, \frac{13\pi}{10}, \frac{3\pi}{2}, \frac{17\pi}{10}, \frac{19\pi}{10}$$

25. $1 + \sin\theta = 2\cos^2\theta$

$1 + \sin\theta = 2(1 - \sin^2\theta) \rightarrow 1 + \sin\theta = 2 - 2\sin^2\theta$

$2\sin^2\theta + \sin\theta - 1 = 0 \rightarrow (2\sin\theta - 1)(\sin\theta + 1) = 0$

$$2\sin\theta - 1 = 0 \rightarrow \sin\theta = \frac{1}{2} \rightarrow \theta = \frac{\pi}{6}, \frac{5\pi}{6}$$

or $\sin\theta + 1 = 0 \rightarrow \sin\theta = -1 \rightarrow \theta = \frac{3\pi}{2}$

26. $\sin^2\theta = 2\cos\theta + 2$

$1 - \cos^2\theta = 2\cos\theta + 2 \rightarrow \cos^2\theta + 2\cos\theta + 1 = 0 \rightarrow (\cos\theta + 1)^2 = 0 \rightarrow \cos\theta + 1 = 0$

$\cos\theta = -1 \rightarrow \theta = \pi$

27. $\tan^2\theta = \frac{3}{2}\sec\theta$

$$\sec^2\theta - 1 = \frac{3}{2}\sec\theta \rightarrow 2\sec^2\theta - 2 = 3\sec\theta$$

$2\sec^2\theta - 3\sec\theta - 2 = 0 \rightarrow (2\sec\theta + 1)(\sec\theta - 2) = 0$

$2\sec\theta + 1 = 0 \rightarrow \sec\theta = -\frac{1}{2}$, which is impossible

or $\sec\theta - 2 = 0 \rightarrow \sec\theta = 2 \rightarrow \theta = \frac{\pi}{3}, \frac{5\pi}{3}$

the solutions are $\theta = \frac{\pi}{3}, \frac{5\pi}{3}$

28. $\csc^2\theta = \cot\theta + 1$

$1 + \cot^2\theta = \cot\theta + 1 \rightarrow \cot^2\theta - \cot\theta = 0 \rightarrow \cot\theta(\cot\theta - 1) = 0$

$\cot\theta = 0 \rightarrow \theta = \frac{\pi}{2}, \frac{3\pi}{2}$

or $\cot\theta = 1 \rightarrow \theta = \frac{\pi}{4}, \frac{5\pi}{4}$

29. $$3-\sin\theta=\cos(2\theta)$$
$$3-\sin\theta=1-2\sin^2\theta$$
$2\sin^2\theta-\sin\theta+2=0$
This is a quadratic equation in $\sin\theta$. The discriminant is $b^2-4ac=1-16=-15<0$.
The equation has no real solutions.

30. $$\cos(2\theta)+5\cos\theta+3=0$$
$$2\cos^2\theta-1+5\cos\theta+3=0\rightarrow 2\cos^2\theta+5\cos\theta+2=0$$
$$(2\cos\theta+1)(\cos\theta+2)=0$$
$$2\cos\theta=-1\ \rightarrow\cos\theta=-\frac{1}{2}\rightarrow\theta=\frac{2\pi}{3},\frac{4\pi}{3}$$
or $\cos\theta=-2$, which is impossible

the solutions are $\theta=\frac{2\pi}{3},\frac{4\pi}{3}$

31. $$\sec^2\theta+\tan\theta=0$$
$\tan^2\theta+1+\tan\theta=0$
This is a quadratic equation in $\tan\theta$. The discriminant is $b^2-4ac=1-4=-3<0$.
The equation has no real solutions.

32. $$\sec\theta=\tan\theta+\cot\theta$$
$$\frac{1}{\cos\theta}=\frac{\sin\theta}{\cos\theta}+\frac{\cos\theta}{\sin\theta}\rightarrow\frac{1}{\cos\theta}=\frac{\sin^2\theta+\cos^2\theta}{\sin\theta\cos\theta}$$
$$\frac{1}{\cos\theta}=\frac{1}{\sin\theta\cos\theta}\rightarrow\frac{\sin\theta\cos\theta}{\cos\theta}=1\rightarrow\sin\theta=1\rightarrow\theta=\frac{\pi}{2}$$
Since $\sec\left(\frac{\pi}{2}\right)$ and $\tan\left(\frac{\pi}{2}\right)$ do not exist, there is no real solution.

33. $\sin\theta-\sqrt{3}\cos\theta=1$
Divide each side by 2:
$$\frac{1}{2}\sin\theta-\frac{\sqrt{3}}{2}\cos\theta=\frac{1}{2}$$
Rewrite in the difference of two angles form where
$$\cos\phi=\frac{1}{2}\text{ and }\sin\phi=\frac{\sqrt{3}}{2}\text{ and }\phi=\frac{\pi}{3}:$$
$$\sin\theta\cos\phi-\cos\theta\sin\phi=\frac{1}{2}\rightarrow\sin(\theta-\phi)=\frac{1}{2}$$
$$\theta-\phi=\frac{\pi}{6}\quad\text{or}\quad\theta-\phi=\frac{5\pi}{6}$$
$$\theta-\frac{\pi}{3}=\frac{\pi}{6}\quad\text{or}\quad\theta-\frac{\pi}{3}=\frac{5\pi}{6}$$
$$\theta=\frac{\pi}{2}\quad\text{or}\quad\theta=\frac{7\pi}{6}$$

34. $\sqrt{3}\sin\theta+\cos\theta=1$

Divide each side by 2:

$$\frac{\sqrt{3}}{2}\sin\theta+\frac{1}{2}\cos\theta=\frac{1}{2}$$

Rewrite in the sum of two angles form where

$$\cos\phi=\frac{\sqrt{3}}{2}\text{ and }\sin\phi=\frac{1}{2}\text{ and }\phi=\frac{\pi}{6}:$$

$$\sin\theta\cos\phi+\cos\theta\sin\phi=\frac{1}{2}\rightarrow\sin(\theta+\phi)=\frac{1}{2}$$

$$\theta+\phi=\frac{\pi}{6}\quad\text{or}\quad\theta+\phi=\frac{5\pi}{6}$$

$$\theta+\frac{\pi}{6}=\frac{\pi}{6}\quad\text{or}\quad\theta+\frac{\pi}{6}=\frac{5\pi}{6}$$

$$\theta=0\quad\text{or}\quad\theta=\frac{2\pi}{3}$$

35. $\tan(2\theta)+2\sin\theta=0$

$$\frac{\sin(2\theta)}{\cos(2\theta)}+2\sin\theta=0$$

$$\frac{\sin2\theta+2\sin\theta\cos2\theta}{\cos2\theta}=0\rightarrow2\sin\theta\cos\theta+2\sin\theta(2\cos^2\theta-1)=0$$

$$2\sin\theta\left(\cos\theta+2\cos^2\theta-1\right)=0\rightarrow2\sin\theta\left(2\cos^2\theta+\cos\theta-1\right)=0$$

$$2\sin\theta(2\cos\theta-1)(\cos\theta+1)=0$$

$$2\cos\theta-1=0\rightarrow\cos\theta=\frac{1}{2}\rightarrow\theta=\frac{\pi}{3},\frac{5\pi}{3}$$

$$\text{or }2\sin\theta=0\rightarrow\sin\theta=0\rightarrow\theta=0,\pi$$

$$\text{or }\cos\theta+1=0\rightarrow\cos\theta=-1\rightarrow\theta=\pi$$

the solutions are $\theta=0,\frac{\pi}{3},\pi,\frac{5\pi}{3}$

36.

$$\tan(2\theta)+2\cos\theta=0$$

$$\frac{\sin(2\theta)}{\cos(2\theta)}+2\cos\theta=0$$

$$\frac{\sin(2\theta)+2\cos\theta\cos2\theta}{\cos(2\theta)}=0\rightarrow2\sin\theta\cos\theta+2\cos\theta(1-2\sin^2\theta)=0$$

$$2\cos\theta\left(\sin\theta+1-2\sin^2\theta\right)=0\rightarrow-2\cos\theta\left(2\sin^2\theta-\sin\theta-1\right)=0$$

$$-2\cos\theta(2\sin\theta+1)(\sin\theta-1)=0$$

$$2\sin\theta + 1 = 0 \rightarrow \sin\theta = -\frac{1}{2} \rightarrow \theta = \frac{7\pi}{6}, \frac{11\pi}{6}$$

$$\text{or } -2\cos\theta = 0 \rightarrow \cos\theta = 0 \rightarrow \theta = \frac{\pi}{2}, \frac{3\pi}{2}$$

$$\text{or } \sin\theta - 1 = 0 \rightarrow \sin\theta = 1 \rightarrow \theta = \frac{\pi}{2}$$

the solutions are $\theta = \frac{\pi}{2}, \frac{7\pi}{6}, \frac{3\pi}{2}, \frac{11\pi}{6}$

37. $\sin\theta + \cos\theta = \sqrt{2}$

Divide each side by $\sqrt{2}$: $\frac{1}{\sqrt{2}}\sin\theta + \frac{1}{\sqrt{2}}\cos\theta = 1$

Rewrite in the sum of two angles form where $\cos\phi = \frac{1}{\sqrt{2}}$ and $\sin\phi = \frac{1}{\sqrt{2}}$ and $\phi = \frac{\pi}{4}$:

$$\sin\theta\cos\phi + \cos\theta\sin\phi = 1 \rightarrow \sin(\theta + \phi) = 1$$

$$\theta + \phi = \frac{\pi}{2}$$

$$\theta + \frac{\pi}{4} = \frac{\pi}{2} \rightarrow \theta = \frac{\pi}{4}$$

38. $\sin\theta + \cos\theta = -\sqrt{2}$

Divide each side by $\sqrt{2}$: $\frac{1}{\sqrt{2}}\sin\theta + \frac{1}{\sqrt{2}}\cos\theta = -1$

Rewrite in the sum of two angles form where $\cos\phi = \frac{1}{\sqrt{2}}$ and $\sin\phi = \frac{1}{\sqrt{2}}$ and $\phi = \frac{\pi}{4}$:

$$\sin\theta\cos\phi + \cos\theta\sin\phi = -1 \rightarrow \sin(\theta + \phi) = -1$$

$$\theta + \phi = \frac{3\pi}{2}$$

$$\theta + \frac{\pi}{4} = \frac{3\pi}{2} \rightarrow \theta = \frac{5\pi}{4}$$

39. Use INTERSECT to solve:

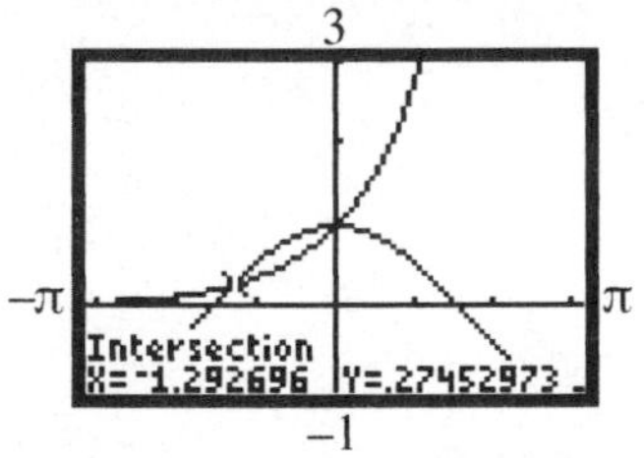

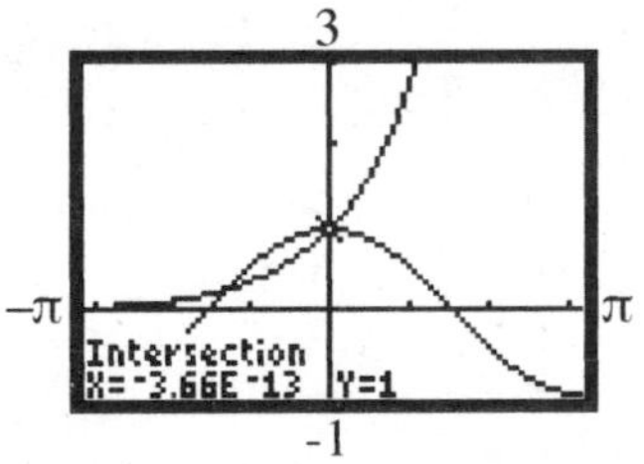

$x \approx -1.29, 0$

40. Use ZERO to solve:

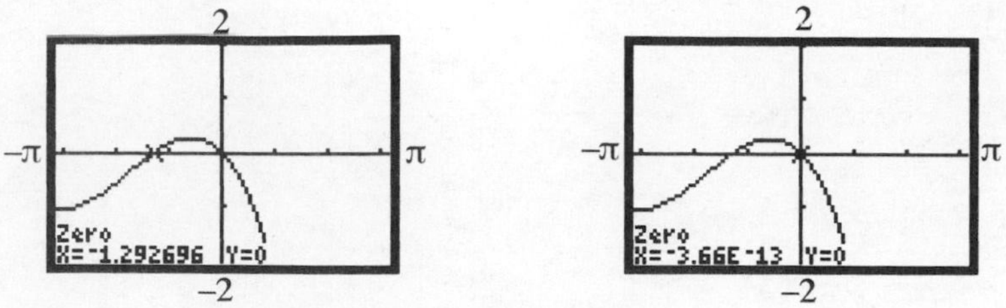

$x \approx -1.29, 0$

41. Use INTERSECT to solve:

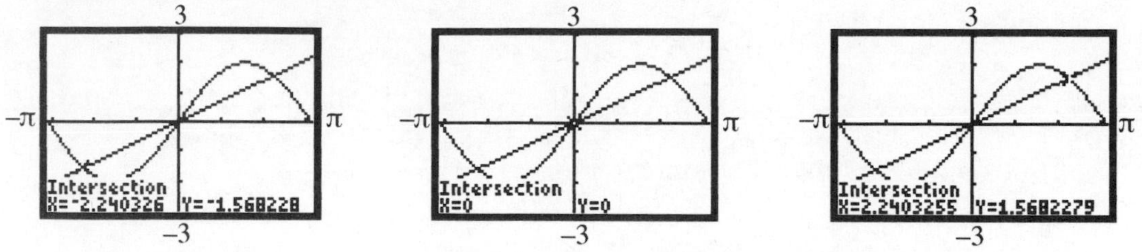

$x \approx -2.24, 0, 2.24$

42. Use ZERO to solve:

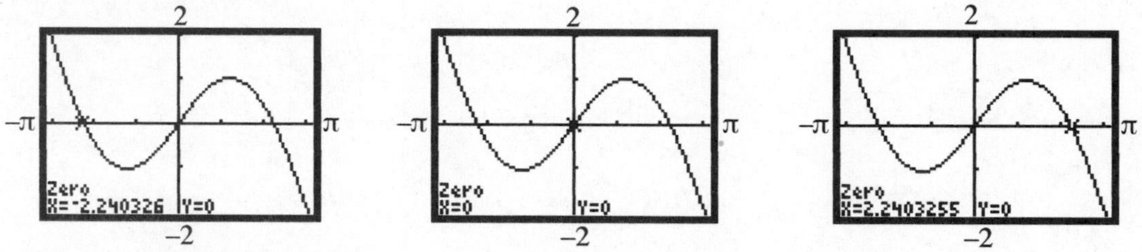

$x \approx -2.24, 0, 2.24$

43. Use INTERSECT to solve:

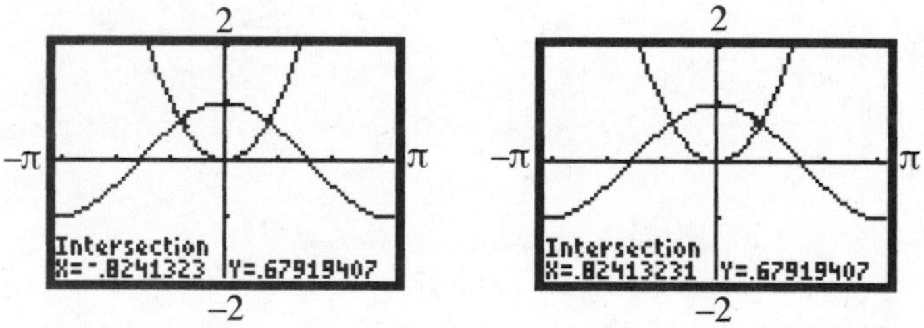

$x \approx -0.82, 0.82$

44. Use ZERO to solve:

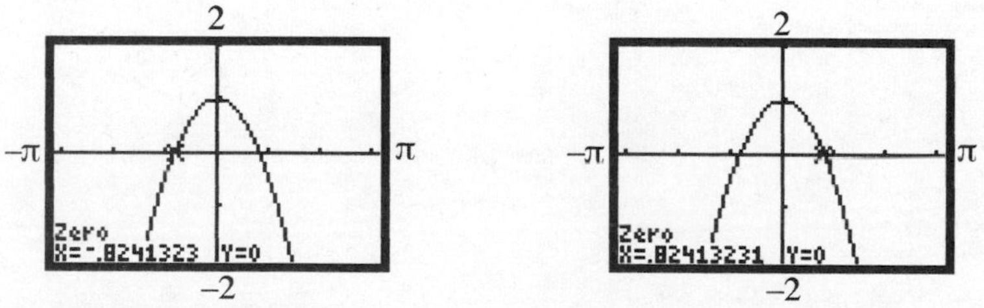

$x \approx -0.82, 0.82$

45. $x + 5\cos x = 0$
Find the intersection of
$y_1 = x + 5\cos x$ and $y_2 = 0$:

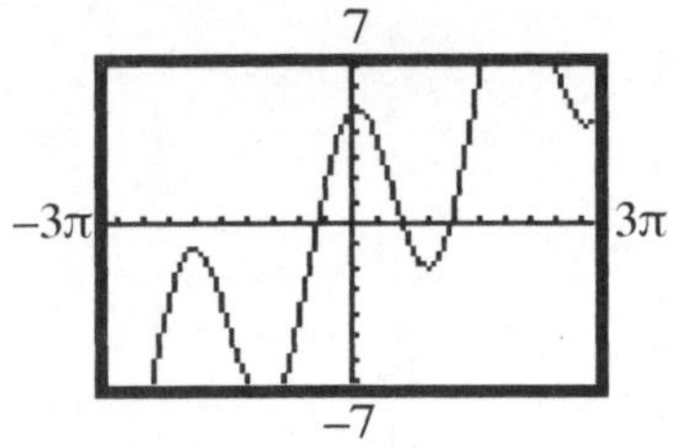

$x \approx -1.31, 1.98, 3.84$

46. $x - 4\sin x = 0$
Find the intersection of
$y_1 = x - 4\sin x$ and $y_2 = 0$:

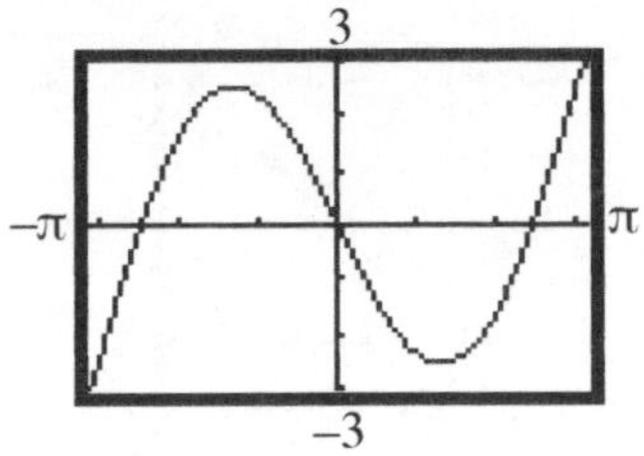

$x \approx -2.47, 0, 2.47$

47. $22x - 17\sin x = 3$
Find the intersection of
$y_1 = 22x - 17\sin x$ and $y_2 = 3$:

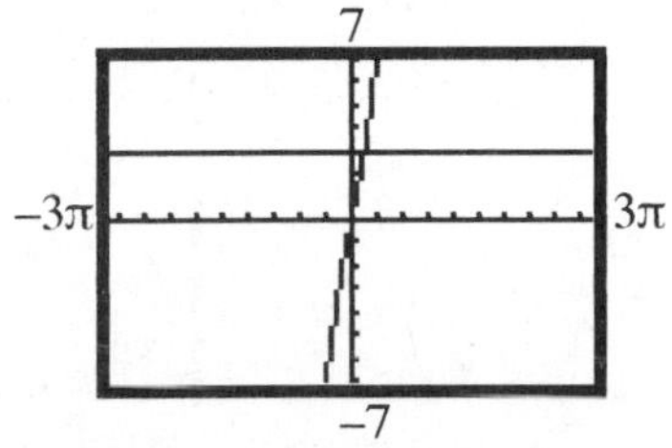

$x \approx 0.52$

48. $19x + 8\cos x = 2$
Find the intersection of
$y_1 = 19x + 8\cos x$ and $y_2 = 2$:

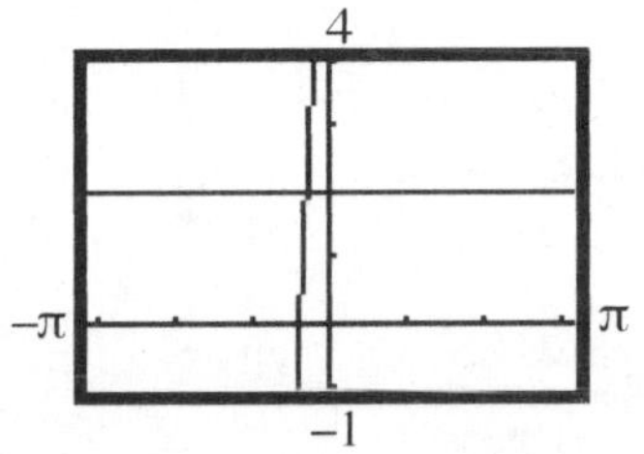

$x \approx -0.30$

49. $\sin x + \cos x = x$
Find the intersection of
$y_1 = \sin x + \cos x$ and $y_2 = x$:

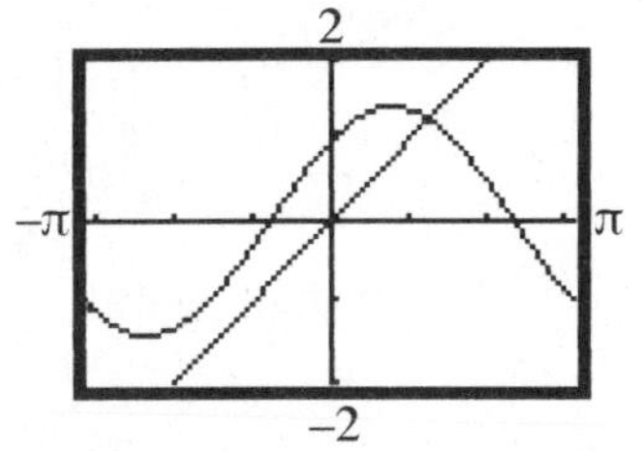

$x \approx 1.26$

50. $\sin x - \cos x = x$
Find the intersection of
$y_1 = \sin x - \cos x$ and $y_2 = x$:

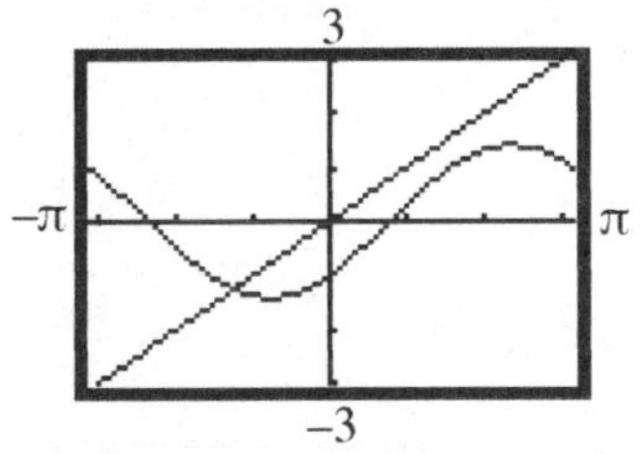

$x \approx -1.26$

51. $x^2 - 2\cos x = 0$
Find the intersection of
$y_1 = x^2 - 2\cos x$ and $y_2 = 0$:

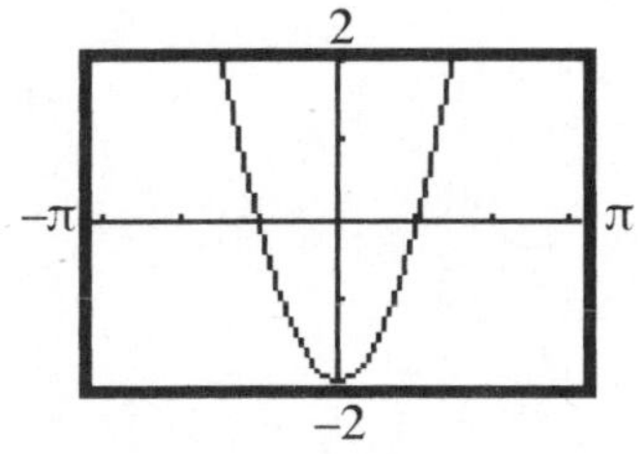

$x \approx -1.02, 1.02$

52. $x^2 + 3\sin x = 0$
Find the intersection of
$y_1 = x^2 + 3\sin x$ and $y_2 = 0$:

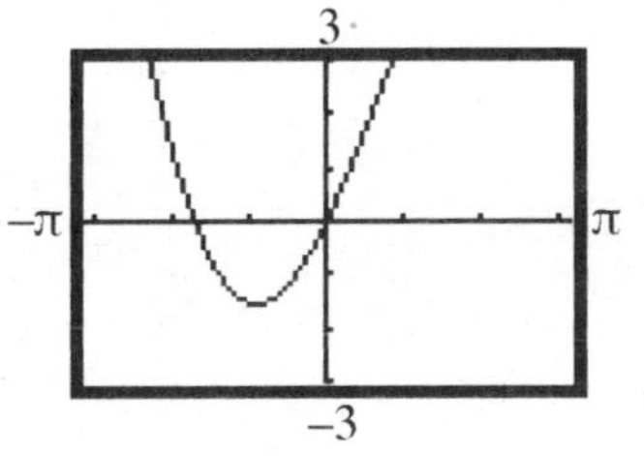

$x \approx -1.72, 0$

53. $x^2 - 2\sin 2x = 3x$
Find the intersection of
$y_1 = x^2 - 2\sin 2x$ and $y_2 = 3x$:

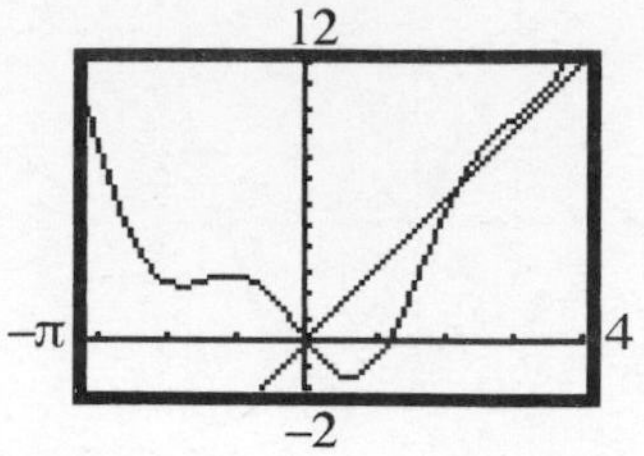

$x \approx 0, 2.15$

54. $x^2 = x + 3\cos(2x)$
Find the intersection of
$y_1 = x^2$ and $y_2 = x + 3\cos(2x)$:

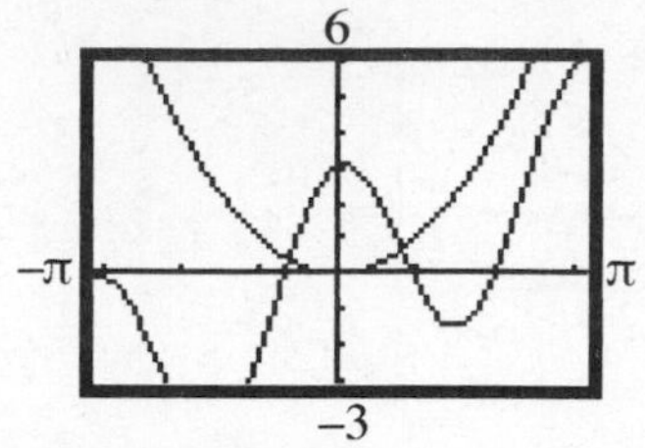

$x \approx -0.62, 0.81$

55. $6\sin x - e^x = 2,\ x > 0$
Find the intersection of
$y_1 = 6\sin x - e^x$ and $y_2 = 2$:

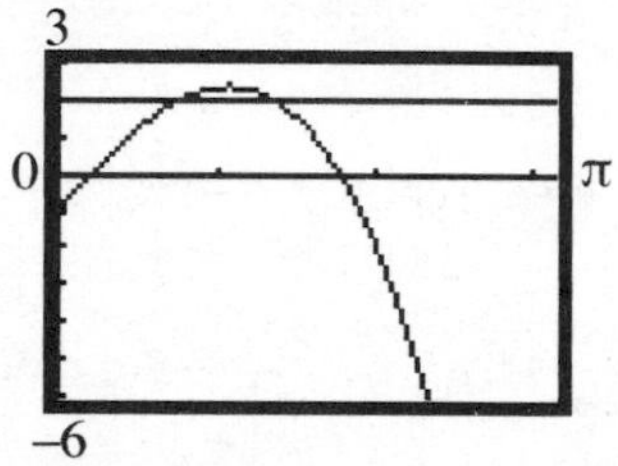

$x \approx 0.76, 1.35$

56. $4\cos(3x) - e^x = 1,\ x > 0$
Find the intersection of
$y_1 = 4\cos(3x) - e^x$ and $y_2 = 1$:

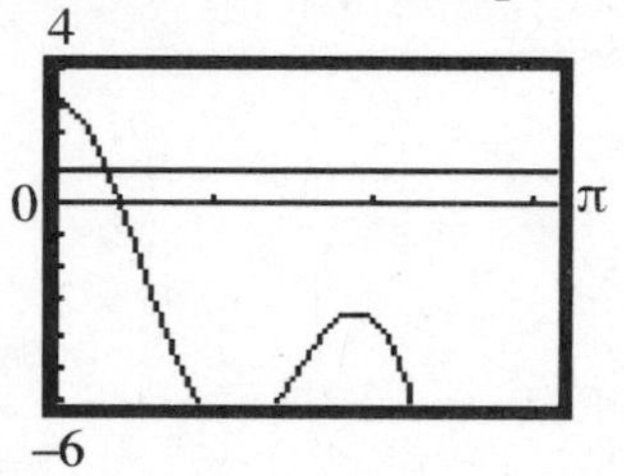

$x \approx 0.31$

57. (a) Solve: $\cos(2\theta) + \cos\theta = 0,\ 0° < \theta < 90°$

$$2\cos^2\theta - 1 + \cos\theta = 0 \rightarrow 2\cos^2\theta + \cos\theta - 1 = 0$$

$$(2\cos\theta - 1)(\cos\theta + 1) = 0$$

$$2\cos\theta - 1 = 0 \rightarrow \cos\theta = \frac{1}{2} \rightarrow \theta = 60°,\ 300°$$

$$\text{or } \cos\theta + 1 = 0 \rightarrow \cos\theta = -1 \rightarrow \theta = 180°$$

The solution is 60°.

(b) Solve: $\cos(2\theta) + \cos\theta = 0,\ 0° < \theta < 90°$

$$2\cos\left(\frac{3\theta}{2}\right)\cos\left(\frac{\theta}{2}\right) = 0 \rightarrow \cos\left(\frac{3\theta}{2}\right) = 0 \text{ or } \cos\left(\frac{\theta}{2}\right) = 0$$

$$\frac{3\theta}{2} = 90° \rightarrow \theta = 60°$$

$$\frac{3\theta}{2} = 270° \rightarrow \theta = 180°$$

$$\frac{\theta}{2} = 90° \rightarrow \theta = 180°$$

$$\frac{\theta}{2} = 270° \rightarrow \theta = 540°$$

The solution is 60°.

(c) $A(60°) = 16\sin 60°(\cos 60° + 1) = 16 \cdot \frac{\sqrt{3}}{2}\left(\frac{1}{2} + 1\right) = 12\sqrt{3}\text{ in}^2 \approx 20.78\text{ in}^2$

(d) Graph and use the MAXIMUM feature:

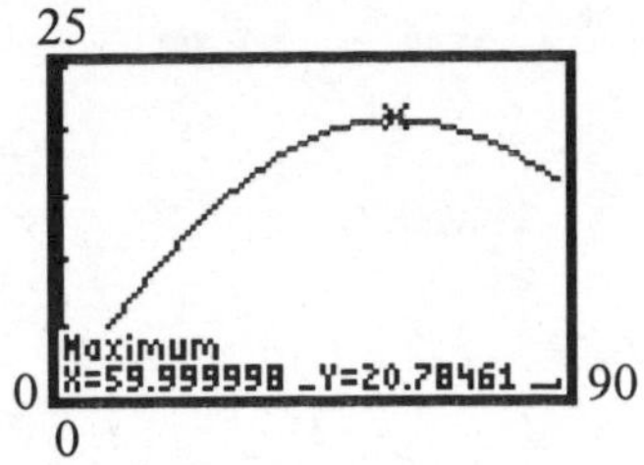

The maximum area is approximately 20.78 in^2 when the angle is 60°.

58. (a) $\sin(2\theta) + \cos(2\theta) = 0$

Divide each side by $\sqrt{2}$:

$$\frac{1}{\sqrt{2}}\sin(2\theta) + \frac{1}{\sqrt{2}}\cos(2\theta) = 0$$

Rewrite in the sum of two angles form where $\cos\phi = \frac{1}{\sqrt{2}}$ and $\sin\phi = \frac{1}{\sqrt{2}}$ and $\phi = \frac{\pi}{4}$:

$$\sin(2\theta)\cos\phi + \cos(2\theta)\sin\phi = 0 \to \sin(2\theta + \phi) = 0$$

$$2\theta + \phi = 0 + k\pi$$

$$2\theta + \frac{\pi}{4} = 0 + k\pi \to 2\theta = -\frac{\pi}{4} + k\pi$$

$$\theta = -\frac{\pi}{8} + \frac{k\pi}{2}$$

$$\theta = \frac{3\pi}{8} \quad \text{or} \quad 67.5°$$

(b) $\sin(2\theta) + \cos(2\theta) = 0$

$$\sin(2\theta) = -\cos(2\theta) \to \frac{\sin(2\theta)}{\cos(2\theta)} = -1$$

$$\tan(2\theta) = -1 \to 2\theta = \frac{3\pi}{4} \to \theta = \frac{3\pi}{8} \quad \text{or} \quad 67.5°$$

(c) $$R = \frac{32^2\sqrt{2}}{32}(\sin(2\cdot 67.5°) - \cos(2\cdot 67.5°) - 1) = 32\sqrt{2}(\sin(135°) - \cos(135°) - 1)$$

$$= 32\sqrt{2}\left(\frac{\sqrt{2}}{2} - \left(-\frac{\sqrt{2}}{2}\right) - 1\right) = 32\sqrt{2}(\sqrt{2} - 1) = 64 - 32\sqrt{2} \approx 18.75 \text{ feet}$$

(d) Graphing:

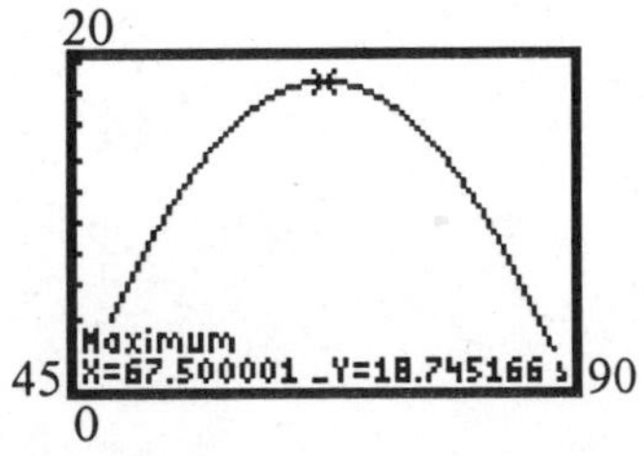

The angle that maximizes the distance is 67.5° and the maximum distance is 18.75 feet.

59. Graph:

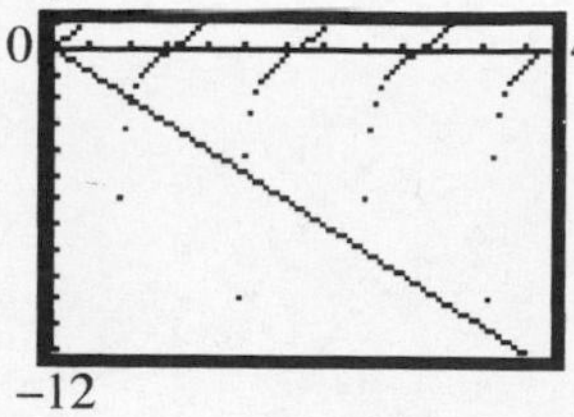

The first two positive solutions are 2.03 and 4.91.

60. (a) Let L be the length of the ladder with x and y being the lengths of the two parts in each hallway.

$$L = x + y$$

$$\cos\theta = \frac{3}{x} \quad \rightarrow \quad x = \frac{3}{\cos\theta} = 3\sec\theta$$

$$\sin\theta = \frac{4}{y} \quad \rightarrow \quad y = \frac{4}{\sin\theta} = 4\csc\theta$$

$$L(\theta) = 3\sec\theta + 4\csc\theta$$

(b) $3\sec\theta\tan\theta - 4\csc\theta\cot\theta = 0$

$$3\sec\theta\tan\theta = 4\csc\theta\cot\theta$$

$$\frac{\sec\theta\tan\theta}{\csc\theta\cot\theta} = \frac{4}{3} \rightarrow \tan^3\theta = \frac{4}{3} \rightarrow \tan\theta = \sqrt[3]{\frac{4}{3}} \approx 1.10064$$

$$\theta = 47.74°$$

(c) $L = 3\sec 47.74° + 4\csc 47.74° \approx 9.87$ feet

(d) Graphing:

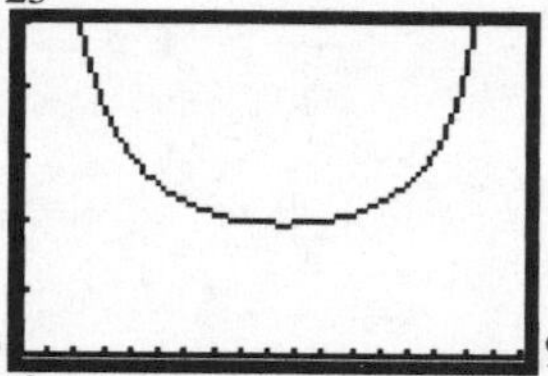

The graph shows a minimum, not a maximum.

61. (a) $107 = \dfrac{(34.8)^2 \sin 2\theta}{9.8}$

$$\sin(2\theta) = \frac{107(9.8)}{(34.8)^2} = 0.8659$$

$$2\theta = \sin^{-1} 0.8659 = 59.98° \text{ or } 120.02° \rightarrow \theta = 29.99° \text{ or } 60.01°$$

(b) Graph and use the MAXIMUM feature:

The maximum distance is 123.58 meters when the angle is 45°.

(c) Graph:

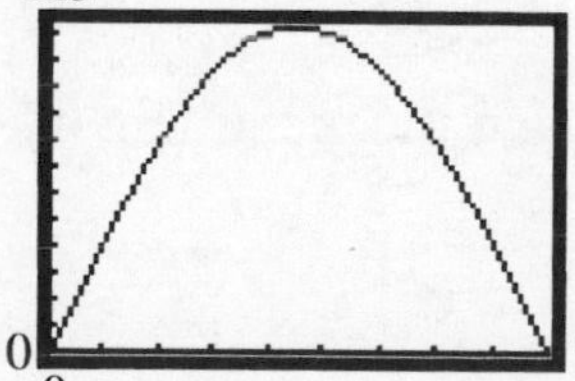

62. (a) $110 = \dfrac{40^2 \sin(2\theta)}{9.8}$

$\sin(2\theta) = \dfrac{110 \cdot 9.8}{40^2} \approx 0.67375$

$2\theta = 42.357^\circ$ or 137.643°

$\theta = 21.18^\circ$ or 68.82°

(b) The maximum distance is approximately 163.3 meter

(c) Graphing:

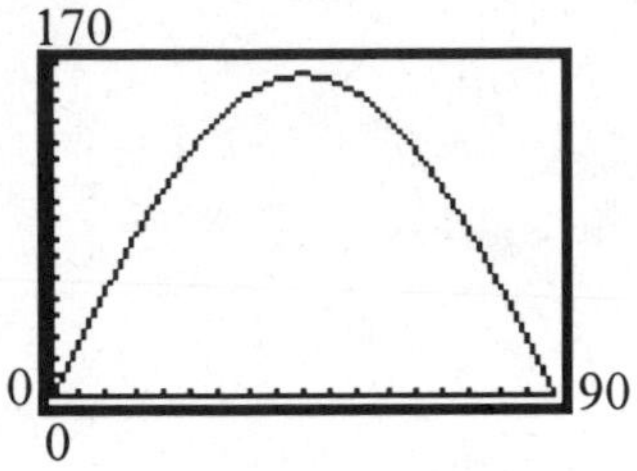

Chapter 8

Analytic Trigonometry

8.R Chapter Review

1. $\sin^{-1}(1)$

We are finding the angle θ, $-\frac{\pi}{2} \le \theta \le \frac{\pi}{2}$, whose sine equals 1.

$$\sin\theta = 1 \qquad -\frac{\pi}{2} \le \theta \le \frac{\pi}{2}$$

$$\theta = \frac{\pi}{2} \to \sin^{-1}(1) = \frac{\pi}{2}$$

2. $\cos^{-1}(0)$

We are finding the angle θ, $0 \le \theta \le \pi$, whose cosine equals 0.

$$\cos\theta = 0 \qquad 0 \le \theta \le \pi$$

$$\theta = \frac{\pi}{2} \to \cos^{-1}(0) = \frac{\pi}{2}$$

3. $\tan^{-1}(1)$

We are finding the angle θ, $-\frac{\pi}{2} < \theta < \frac{\pi}{2}$, whose tangent equals 1.

$$\tan\theta = 1 \qquad -\frac{\pi}{2} < \theta < \frac{\pi}{2}$$

$$\theta = \frac{\pi}{4} \to \tan^{-1}(1) = \frac{\pi}{4}$$

4. $\sin^{-1}\left(-\frac{1}{2}\right)$

We are finding the angle θ, $-\frac{\pi}{2} \le \theta \le \frac{\pi}{2}$, whose sine equals $-\frac{1}{2}$.

$$\sin\theta = -\frac{1}{2} \qquad -\frac{\pi}{2} \le \theta \le \frac{\pi}{2}$$

$$\theta = -\frac{\pi}{6} \to \sin^{-1}\left(-\frac{1}{2}\right) = -\frac{\pi}{6}$$

5. $\cos^{-1}\left(-\frac{\sqrt{3}}{2}\right)$

We are finding the angle θ, $0 \le \theta \le \pi$, whose cosine equals $-\frac{\sqrt{3}}{2}$.

$$\cos\theta = -\frac{\sqrt{3}}{2} \qquad 0 \le \theta \le \pi$$

$$\theta = \frac{5\pi}{6} \rightarrow \cos^{-1}\left(-\frac{\sqrt{3}}{2}\right) = \frac{5\pi}{6}$$

6. $\tan^{-1}\left(-\sqrt{3}\right)$

We are finding the angle θ, $-\frac{\pi}{2} < \theta < \frac{\pi}{2}$, whose tangent equals $-\sqrt{3}$.

$$\tan\theta = -\sqrt{3} \qquad -\frac{\pi}{2} < \theta < \frac{\pi}{2}$$

$$\theta = -\frac{\pi}{3} \rightarrow \tan^{-1}\left(-\sqrt{3}\right) = -\frac{\pi}{3}$$

7. $\sin\left(\cos^{-1}\left(\frac{\sqrt{2}}{2}\right)\right)$

Find the angle θ, $0 \le \theta \le \pi$, whose cosine equals $\frac{\sqrt{2}}{2}$.

$$\cos\theta = \frac{\sqrt{2}}{2} \qquad 0 \le \theta \le \pi$$

$$\theta = \frac{\pi}{4} \rightarrow \sin\left(\cos^{-1}\left(\frac{\sqrt{2}}{2}\right)\right) = \sin\left(\frac{\pi}{4}\right) = \frac{\sqrt{2}}{2}$$

8. $\cos\left(\sin^{-1}(0)\right)$

Find the angle θ, $-\frac{\pi}{2} \le \theta \le \frac{\pi}{2}$, whose sine equals 0.

$$\sin\theta = 0 \qquad -\frac{\pi}{2} \le \theta \le \frac{\pi}{2}$$

$$\theta = 0 \rightarrow \cos\left(\sin^{-1}(0)\right) = \cos(0) = 1$$

9. $\tan\left(\sin^{-1}\left(-\frac{\sqrt{3}}{2}\right)\right)$

Find the angle θ, $-\frac{\pi}{2} \le \theta \le \frac{\pi}{2}$, whose sine equals $-\frac{\sqrt{3}}{2}$.

$$\sin\theta = -\frac{\sqrt{3}}{2} \qquad -\frac{\pi}{2} \le \theta \le \frac{\pi}{2}$$

$$\theta = -\frac{\pi}{3} \rightarrow \tan\left(\sin^{-1}\left(-\frac{\sqrt{3}}{2}\right)\right) = \tan\left(-\frac{\pi}{3}\right) = -\sqrt{3}$$

10. $\tan\left(\cos^{-1}\left(-\frac{1}{2}\right)\right)$

Find the angle θ, $0 \le \theta \le \pi$, whose cosine equals $-\frac{1}{2}$.

$$\cos\theta = -\frac{1}{2} \qquad 0 \le \theta \le \pi$$

$$\theta = \frac{2\pi}{3} \to \tan\left(\cos^{-1}\left(-\frac{1}{2}\right)\right) = \tan\left(\frac{2\pi}{3}\right) = -\sqrt{3}$$

11. $\sec\left(\tan^{-1}\left(\frac{\sqrt{3}}{3}\right)\right)$

Find the angle θ, $-\frac{\pi}{2} < \theta < \frac{\pi}{2}$, whose tangent is $\frac{\sqrt{3}}{3}$

$$\tan\theta = \frac{\sqrt{3}}{3}, \qquad -\frac{\pi}{2} < \theta < \frac{\pi}{2}$$

$$\theta = \frac{\pi}{6} \to \sec\left(\tan^{-1}\left(\frac{\sqrt{3}}{3}\right)\right) = \sec\left(\frac{\pi}{6}\right) = \frac{2\sqrt{3}}{3}$$

12. $\csc\left(\sin^{-1}\left(\frac{\sqrt{3}}{2}\right)\right)$

Find the angle θ, $-\frac{\pi}{2} \le \theta \le \frac{\pi}{2}$, whose sine equals $\frac{\sqrt{3}}{2}$.

$$\sin\theta = \frac{\sqrt{3}}{2} \qquad -\frac{\pi}{2} \le \theta \le \frac{\pi}{2}$$

$$\theta = \frac{\pi}{3} \to \csc\left(\sin^{-1}\left(\frac{\sqrt{3}}{2}\right)\right) = \csc\left(\frac{\pi}{3}\right) = \frac{2\sqrt{3}}{3}$$

13. $\sin\left(\tan^{-1}\left(\frac{3}{4}\right)\right)$

Since $\tan\theta = \frac{3}{4}$, $-\frac{\pi}{2} < \theta < \frac{\pi}{2}$, let $x = 4$ and $y = 3$. Solve for r:

$$16 + 9 = r^2 \to r^2 = 25 \to r = 5$$

θ is in quadrant I.

$$\sin\left(\tan^{-1}\left(\frac{3}{4}\right)\right) = \sin\theta = \frac{y}{r} = \frac{3}{5}$$

14. $\cos\left(\sin^{-1}\left(\frac{3}{5}\right)\right)$

Since $\sin\theta = \frac{3}{5}$, $-\frac{\pi}{2} \le \theta \le \frac{\pi}{2}$, let $r = 5$ and $y = 3$. Solve for x:

$$x^2 + 9 = 25 \to x^2 = 16 \to x = \pm 4$$

Since θ is in quadrant I, $x = 4$

$$\cos\left(\sin^{-1}\left(\frac{3}{5}\right)\right)=\cos\theta=\frac{x}{r}=\frac{4}{5}$$

15. $\tan\left(\sin^{-1}\left(-\frac{4}{5}\right)\right)$

Since $\sin\theta=-\frac{4}{5}$, $-\frac{\pi}{2}\le\theta\le\frac{\pi}{2}$, let $y=-4$ and $r=5$. Solve for x:

$$x^2+16=25\rightarrow x^2=9\rightarrow x=\pm3$$

Since θ is in quadrant IV, $x=3$.

$$\tan\left(\sin^{-1}\left(-\frac{4}{5}\right)\right)=\tan\theta=\frac{y}{x}=\frac{-4}{3}=-\frac{4}{3}$$

16. $\tan\left(\cos^{-1}\left(-\frac{3}{5}\right)\right)$

Since $\cos\theta=-\frac{3}{5}$, $0\le\theta\le\pi$, let $x=-3$ and $r=5$. Solve for y:

$$9+y^2=25\rightarrow y^2=16\rightarrow y=\pm4$$

Since θ is in quadrant II, $y=4$.

$$\tan\left(\cos^{-1}\left(-\frac{3}{5}\right)\right)=\tan\theta=\frac{y}{x}=\frac{4}{-3}=-\frac{4}{3}$$

17. $\sin^{-1}\left(\cos\left(\frac{2\pi}{3}\right)\right)=\sin^{-1}\left(-\frac{1}{2}\right)=-\frac{\pi}{6}$

18. $\cos^{-1}\left(\tan\left(\frac{3\pi}{4}\right)\right)=\cos^{-1}(-1)=\pi$

19. $\tan^{-1}\left(\tan\left(\frac{7\pi}{4}\right)\right)=\tan^{-1}(-1)=-\frac{\pi}{4}$

20. $\cos^{-1}\left(\cos\left(\frac{7\pi}{6}\right)\right)=\cos^{-1}\left(-\frac{\sqrt{3}}{2}\right)=\frac{5\pi}{6}$

21. $\tan\theta\cot\theta-\sin^2\theta=\tan\theta\cdot\frac{1}{\tan\theta}-\sin^2\theta=1-\sin^2\theta=\cos^2\theta$

22. $\sin\theta\csc\theta-\sin^2\theta=\sin\theta\cdot\frac{1}{\sin\theta}-\sin^2\theta=1-\sin^2\theta=\cos^2\theta$

23. $\cos^2\theta(1+\tan^2\theta)=\cos^2\theta\cdot\sec^2\theta=\cos^2\theta\cdot\frac{1}{\cos^2\theta}=1$

24. $(1-\cos^2\theta)(1+\cot^2\theta)=\sin^2\theta\cdot\csc^2\theta=\sin^2\theta\cdot\frac{1}{\sin^2\theta}=1$

25. $4\cos^2\theta + 3\sin^2\theta = \cos^2\theta + 3\cos^2\theta + 3\sin^2\theta = \cos^2\theta + 3(\cos^2\theta + \sin^2\theta)$
$= \cos^2\theta + 3\cdot 1 = \cos^2\theta + 3 = 3 + \cos^2\theta$

26. $4\sin^2\theta + 2\cos^2\theta = 2\sin^2\theta + 2\sin^2\theta + 2\cos^2\theta = 2\sin^2\theta + 2(\sin^2\theta + \cos^2\theta)$
$= 2\sin^2\theta + 2\cdot 1 = 2(1-\cos^2\theta) + 2 = 2 - 2\cos^2\theta + 2 = 4 - 2\cos^2\theta$

27. $$\frac{1-\cos\theta}{\sin\theta} + \frac{\sin\theta}{1-\cos\theta} = \frac{(1-\cos\theta)^2 + \sin^2\theta}{\sin\theta(1-\cos\theta)} = \frac{1-2\cos\theta+\cos^2\theta+\sin^2\theta}{\sin\theta(1-\cos\theta)}$$
$$= \frac{1-2\cos\theta+1}{\sin\theta(1-\cos\theta)} = \frac{2-2\cos\theta}{\sin\theta(1-\cos\theta)} = \frac{2(1-\cos\theta)}{\sin\theta(1-\cos\theta)} = \frac{2}{\sin\theta} = 2\csc\theta$$

28. $$\frac{\sin\theta}{1+\cos\theta} + \frac{1+\cos\theta}{\sin\theta} = \frac{\sin^2\theta + (1+\cos\theta)^2}{\sin\theta(1+\cos\theta)} = \frac{\sin^2\theta + 1 + 2\cos\theta + \cos^2\theta}{\sin\theta(1+\cos\theta)}$$
$$= \frac{1+2\cos\theta+1}{\sin\theta(1+\cos\theta)} = \frac{2+2\cos\theta}{\sin\theta(1+\cos\theta)} = \frac{2(1+\cos\theta)}{\sin\theta(1+\cos\theta)} = \frac{2}{\sin\theta} = 2\csc\theta$$

29. $$\frac{\cos\theta}{\cos\theta-\sin\theta} = \frac{\cos\theta}{\cos\theta-\sin\theta}\cdot\frac{\left(\frac{1}{\cos\theta}\right)}{\left(\frac{1}{\cos\theta}\right)} = \frac{1}{\left(1-\frac{\sin\theta}{\cos\theta}\right)} = \frac{1}{1-\tan\theta}$$

30. $$1-\frac{\cos^2\theta}{1+\sin\theta} = \frac{1+\sin\theta-\cos^2\theta}{1+\sin\theta} = \frac{1+\sin\theta-(1-\sin^2\theta)}{1+\sin\theta} = \frac{\sin\theta+\sin^2\theta}{1+\sin\theta}$$
$$= \frac{\sin\theta(1+\sin\theta)}{1+\sin\theta} = \sin\theta$$

31. $$\frac{\csc\theta}{1+\csc\theta} = \frac{\left(\frac{1}{\sin\theta}\right)}{\left(1+\frac{1}{\sin\theta}\right)} = \frac{\left(\frac{1}{\sin\theta}\right)}{\left(\frac{\sin\theta+1}{\sin\theta}\right)} = \left(\frac{1}{1+\sin\theta}\right)\cdot\left(\frac{1-\sin\theta}{1-\sin\theta}\right) = \frac{1-\sin\theta}{1-\sin^2\theta} = \frac{1-\sin\theta}{\cos^2\theta}$$

32. $$\frac{1+\sec\theta}{\sec\theta} = \frac{\left(1+\frac{1}{\cos\theta}\right)}{\left(\frac{1}{\cos\theta}\right)} = \frac{\left(\frac{\cos\theta+1}{\cos\theta}\right)}{\left(\frac{1}{\cos\theta}\right)} = \left(\frac{1+\cos\theta}{1}\right)\cdot\left(\frac{1-\cos\theta}{1-\cos\theta}\right) = \frac{1-\cos^2\theta}{1-\cos\theta} = \frac{\sin^2\theta}{1-\cos\theta}$$

33. $$\csc\theta - \sin\theta = \frac{1}{\sin\theta} - \sin\theta = \frac{1-\sin^2\theta}{\sin\theta} = \frac{\cos^2\theta}{\sin\theta} = \cos\theta\cdot\frac{\cos\theta}{\sin\theta} = \cos\theta\cot\theta$$

34. $$\frac{\csc\theta}{1-\cos\theta} = \left(\frac{\left(\frac{1}{\sin\theta}\right)}{1-\cos\theta}\right)\cdot\left(\frac{1+\cos\theta}{1+\cos\theta}\right) = \left(\frac{1}{\sin\theta}\right)\cdot\left(\frac{1+\cos\theta}{1-\cos^2\theta}\right) = \frac{1+\cos\theta}{\sin\theta\sin^2\theta} = \frac{1+\cos\theta}{\sin^3\theta}$$

35. $\dfrac{1-\sin\theta}{\sec\theta} = \cos\theta(1-\sin\theta) = \cos\theta(1-\sin\theta)\cdot\dfrac{1+\sin\theta}{1+\sin\theta} = \dfrac{\cos\theta(1-\sin^2\theta)}{1+\sin\theta}$

$= \dfrac{\cos\theta(\cos^2\theta)}{1+\sin\theta} = \dfrac{\cos^3\theta}{1+\sin\theta}$

36. $\dfrac{1-\cos\theta}{1+\cos\theta} = \dfrac{\left(\dfrac{1-\cos\theta}{\sin\theta}\right)}{\left(\dfrac{1+\cos\theta}{\sin\theta}\right)} = \left(\dfrac{\csc\theta-\cot\theta}{\csc\theta+\cot\theta}\right)\cdot\left(\dfrac{\csc\theta-\cot\theta}{\csc\theta-\cot\theta}\right) = \dfrac{(\csc\theta-\cot\theta)^2}{\csc^2\theta-\cot^2\theta}$

$= \dfrac{(\csc\theta-\cot\theta)^2}{1} = (\csc\theta-\cot\theta)^2$

37. $\cot\theta-\tan\theta = \dfrac{\cos\theta}{\sin\theta}-\dfrac{\sin\theta}{\cos\theta} = \dfrac{\cos^2\theta-\sin^2\theta}{\sin\theta\cos\theta} = \dfrac{1-\sin^2\theta-\sin^2\theta}{\sin\theta\cos\theta} = \dfrac{1-2\sin^2\theta}{\sin\theta\cos\theta}$

38. $\dfrac{\left(2\sin^2\theta-1\right)^2}{\sin^4\theta-\cos^4\theta} = \dfrac{\left(-\left(1-2\sin^2\theta\right)\right)^2}{\left(\sin^2\theta-\cos^2\theta\right)\left(\sin^2\theta+\cos^2\theta\right)} = \dfrac{(-\cos(2\theta))^2}{-1\left(\cos^2\theta-\sin^2\theta\right)\cdot 1}$

$= \dfrac{\cos^2(2\theta)}{-\cos(2\theta)} = -\cos(2\theta) = -1\left(2\cos^2\theta-1\right) = 1-2\cos^2\theta$

39. $\dfrac{\cos(\alpha+\beta)}{\cos\alpha\sin\beta} = \dfrac{\cos\alpha\cos\beta-\sin\alpha\sin\beta}{\cos\alpha\sin\beta} = \dfrac{\cos\alpha\cos\beta}{\cos\alpha\sin\beta}-\dfrac{\sin\alpha\sin\beta}{\cos\alpha\sin\beta} = \cot\beta-\tan\alpha$

40. $\dfrac{\sin(\alpha-\beta)}{\sin\alpha\cos\beta} = \dfrac{\sin\alpha\cos\beta-\cos\alpha\sin\beta}{\sin\alpha\cos\beta} = \dfrac{\sin\alpha\cos\beta}{\sin\alpha\cos\beta}-\dfrac{\cos\alpha\sin\beta}{\sin\alpha\cos\beta} = 1-\cot\alpha\tan\beta$

41. $\dfrac{\cos(\alpha-\beta)}{\cos\alpha\cos\beta} = \dfrac{\cos\alpha\cos\beta+\sin\alpha\sin\beta}{\cos\alpha\cos\beta} = \dfrac{\cos\alpha\cos\beta}{\cos\alpha\cos\beta}+\dfrac{\sin\alpha\sin\beta}{\cos\alpha\cos\beta} = 1+\tan\alpha\tan\beta$

42. $\dfrac{\cos(\alpha+\beta)}{\sin\alpha\cos\beta} = \dfrac{\cos\alpha\cos\beta-\sin\alpha\sin\beta}{\sin\alpha\cos\beta} = \dfrac{\cos\alpha\cos\beta}{\sin\alpha\cos\beta}-\dfrac{\sin\alpha\sin\beta}{\sin\alpha\cos\beta} = \cot\alpha-\tan\beta$

43. $(1+\cos\theta)\left(\tan\left(\dfrac{\theta}{2}\right)\right) = (1+\cos\theta)\cdot\dfrac{\sin\theta}{1+\cos\theta} = \sin\theta$

44. $\sin\theta\tan\left(\dfrac{\theta}{2}\right) = \sin\theta\cdot\dfrac{1-\cos\theta}{\sin\theta} = 1-\cos\theta$

45. $2\cot\theta\cot(2\theta) = 2\cdot\dfrac{\cos\theta}{\sin\theta}\cdot\dfrac{\cos(2\theta)}{\sin(2\theta)} = \dfrac{2\cos\theta(\cos^2\theta-\sin^2\theta)}{(\sin\theta)2\sin\theta\cos\theta} = \dfrac{\cos^2\theta-\sin^2\theta}{\sin^2\theta}$

$= \cot^2\theta-1$

46. $2\sin(2\theta)\left(1-2\sin^2\theta\right) = 2\sin(2\theta)\cos(2\theta) = \sin(2(2\theta)) = \sin(4\theta)$

47. $1-8\sin^2\theta\cos^2\theta = 1-2(2\sin\theta\cos\theta)^2 = 1-2\sin^2(2\theta) = \cos(4\theta)$

48. $\dfrac{\sin(3\theta)\cos\theta-\cos(3\theta)\sin\theta}{\sin(2\theta)} = \dfrac{\sin(3\theta-\theta)}{\sin(2\theta)} = \dfrac{\sin(2\theta)}{\sin(2\theta)} = 1$

49. $\dfrac{\sin(2\theta)+\sin(4\theta)}{\cos(2\theta)+\cos(4\theta)} = \dfrac{2\sin(3\theta)\cos(-\theta)}{2\cos(3\theta)\cos(-\theta)} = \dfrac{\sin(3\theta)}{\cos(3\theta)} = \tan(3\theta)$

50. $\dfrac{\sin(2\theta)+\sin(4\theta)}{\sin(2\theta)-\sin(4\theta)} + \dfrac{\tan(3\theta)}{\tan\theta} = \dfrac{2\sin(3\theta)\cos(-\theta)}{2\sin(-\theta)\cos(3\theta)} + \dfrac{\tan(3\theta)}{\tan\theta}$

$= \tan(3\theta)\cot(-\theta) + \dfrac{\tan(3\theta)}{\tan\theta} = -\dfrac{\tan(3\theta)}{\tan\theta} + \dfrac{\tan(3\theta)}{\tan\theta} = 0$

51. $\dfrac{\cos(2\theta)-\cos(4\theta)}{\cos(2\theta)+\cos(4\theta)} - \tan\theta\tan(3\theta) = \dfrac{-2\sin(3\theta)\sin(-\theta)}{2\cos(3\theta)\cos(-\theta)} - \tan\theta\tan(3\theta)$

$= \dfrac{2\sin(3\theta)\sin\theta}{2\cos(3\theta)\cos\theta} - \tan\theta\tan(3\theta) = \tan(3\theta)\tan\theta - \tan\theta\tan(3\theta) = 0$

52. $\cos(2\theta)-\cos(10\theta) = -2\sin(6\theta)\sin(-4\theta) = 2\sin(6\theta)\sin(4\theta)$

$= \dfrac{\sin(4\theta)}{\cos(4\theta)}(2\sin 6\theta\cos 4\theta) = \tan 4\theta(\sin(10\theta)+\sin(2\theta))$

$= \tan(4\theta)(\sin(2\theta)+\sin(10\theta))$

53. $\sin(165^\circ) = \sin(120^\circ+45^\circ) = \sin(120^\circ)\cos(45^\circ)+\cos(120^\circ)\sin(45^\circ)$

$= \left(\dfrac{\sqrt{3}}{2}\right)\cdot\left(\dfrac{\sqrt{2}}{2}\right)+\left(-\dfrac{1}{2}\right)\cdot\left(\dfrac{\sqrt{2}}{2}\right) = \dfrac{1}{4}\left(\sqrt{6}-\sqrt{2}\right)$

54. $\tan(105^\circ) = \sin(60^\circ+45^\circ) = \dfrac{\tan(60^\circ)+\tan(45^\circ)}{1-\tan(60^\circ)\tan(45^\circ)} = \dfrac{\sqrt{3}+1}{1-\sqrt{3}\cdot 1} = \left(\dfrac{1+\sqrt{3}}{1-\sqrt{3}}\right)\cdot\left(\dfrac{1+\sqrt{3}}{1+\sqrt{3}}\right)$

$= \dfrac{1+2\sqrt{3}+3}{1-3} = \dfrac{4+2\sqrt{3}}{-2} = -2-\sqrt{3}$

55. $\cos\left(\dfrac{5\pi}{12}\right) = \cos\left(\dfrac{3\pi}{12}+\dfrac{2\pi}{12}\right) = \cos\left(\dfrac{\pi}{4}\right)\cos\left(\dfrac{\pi}{6}\right) - \sin\left(\dfrac{\pi}{4}\right)\sin\left(\dfrac{\pi}{6}\right) = \dfrac{\sqrt{2}}{2}\cdot\dfrac{\sqrt{3}}{2} - \dfrac{\sqrt{2}}{2}\cdot\dfrac{1}{2}$

$= \dfrac{1}{4}\left(\sqrt{6}-\sqrt{2}\right)$

56. $\sin\left(-\dfrac{\pi}{12}\right) = \sin\left(\dfrac{2\pi}{12}-\dfrac{3\pi}{12}\right) = \sin\left(\dfrac{\pi}{6}\right)\cos\left(\dfrac{\pi}{4}\right) - \cos\left(\dfrac{\pi}{6}\right)\sin\left(\dfrac{\pi}{4}\right) = \dfrac{1}{2}\cdot\dfrac{\sqrt{2}}{2} - \dfrac{\sqrt{3}}{2}\cdot\dfrac{\sqrt{2}}{2}$

$= \dfrac{\sqrt{2}-\sqrt{6}}{4}$

57. $\cos(80^\circ)\cos(20^\circ)+\sin(80^\circ)\sin(20^\circ) = \cos(80^\circ-20^\circ) = \cos(60^\circ) = \dfrac{1}{2}$

58. $\sin(70^\circ)\cos(40^\circ)-\cos(70^\circ)\sin(40^\circ)=\sin(70^\circ-40^\circ)=\sin(30^\circ)=\dfrac{1}{2}$

59. $$\tan\left(\frac{\pi}{8}\right)=\tan\left(\frac{\left(\frac{\pi}{4}\right)}{2}\right)=\sqrt{\frac{\left(1-\cos\left(\frac{\pi}{4}\right)\right)}{\left(1+\cos\left(\frac{\pi}{4}\right)\right)}}=\sqrt{\frac{\left(1-\frac{\sqrt{2}}{2}\right)}{\left(1+\frac{\sqrt{2}}{2}\right)}}=\sqrt{\left(\frac{2-\sqrt{2}}{2+\sqrt{2}}\right)\cdot\left(\frac{2-\sqrt{2}}{2-\sqrt{2}}\right)}$$
$$=\sqrt{\frac{6-4\sqrt{2}}{2}}=\sqrt{3-2\sqrt{2}}$$

60. $$\sin\left(\frac{5\pi}{8}\right)=\sin\left(\frac{\left(\frac{5\pi}{4}\right)}{2}\right)=\sqrt{\frac{\left(1-\cos\left(\frac{5\pi}{4}\right)\right)}{2}}=\sqrt{\frac{\left(1-\left(-\frac{\sqrt{2}}{2}\right)\right)}{2}}=\sqrt{\frac{2+\sqrt{2}}{4}}=\frac{\sqrt{2+\sqrt{2}}}{2}$$

61. $\sin\alpha=\dfrac{4}{5},\ 0<\alpha<\dfrac{\pi}{2};\qquad \sin\beta=\dfrac{5}{13},\ \dfrac{\pi}{2}<\beta<\pi$

$\cos\alpha=\dfrac{3}{5},\ \tan\alpha=\dfrac{4}{3},\ \cos\beta=-\dfrac{12}{13},\ \tan\beta=-\dfrac{5}{12},\quad 0<\dfrac{\alpha}{2}<\dfrac{\pi}{4},\quad \dfrac{\pi}{4}<\dfrac{\beta}{2}<\dfrac{\pi}{2}$

(a) $\sin(\alpha+\beta)=\sin\alpha\cos\beta+\cos\alpha\sin\beta=\left(\dfrac{4}{5}\right)\cdot\left(-\dfrac{12}{13}\right)+\left(\dfrac{3}{5}\right)\cdot\left(\dfrac{5}{13}\right)=\dfrac{-48+15}{65}=-\dfrac{33}{65}$

(b) $\cos(\alpha+\beta)=\cos\alpha\cos\beta-\sin\alpha\sin\beta=\left(\dfrac{3}{5}\right)\cdot\left(-\dfrac{12}{13}\right)-\left(\dfrac{4}{5}\right)\cdot\left(\dfrac{5}{13}\right)=\dfrac{-36-20}{65}=-\dfrac{56}{65}$

(c) $\sin(\alpha-\beta)=\sin\alpha\cos\beta-\cos\alpha\sin\beta=\left(\dfrac{4}{5}\right)\cdot\left(-\dfrac{12}{13}\right)-\left(\dfrac{3}{5}\right)\cdot\left(\dfrac{5}{13}\right)=\dfrac{-48-15}{65}=-\dfrac{63}{65}$

(d) $$\tan(\alpha+\beta)=\frac{\tan\alpha+\tan\beta}{1-\tan\alpha\tan\beta}=\frac{\left(\frac{4}{3}+\left(-\frac{5}{12}\right)\right)}{\left(1-\left(\frac{4}{3}\right)\cdot\left(-\frac{5}{12}\right)\right)}=\frac{\left(\frac{11}{12}\right)}{\left(\frac{14}{9}\right)}=\frac{11}{12}\cdot\frac{9}{14}=\frac{33}{56}$$

(e) $\sin(2\alpha)=2\sin\alpha\cos\alpha=2\cdot\dfrac{4}{5}\cdot\dfrac{3}{5}=\dfrac{24}{25}$

(f) $\cos(2\beta)=\cos^2\beta-\sin^2\beta=\left(-\dfrac{12}{13}\right)^2-\left(\dfrac{5}{13}\right)^2=\dfrac{144}{169}-\dfrac{25}{169}=\dfrac{119}{169}$

(g) $$\sin\left(\frac{\beta}{2}\right)=\sqrt{\frac{1-\cos\beta}{2}}=\sqrt{\frac{1-\left(-\frac{12}{13}\right)}{2}}=\sqrt{\frac{\left(\frac{25}{13}\right)}{2}}=\sqrt{\frac{25}{26}}=\frac{5}{\sqrt{26}}=\frac{5\sqrt{26}}{26}$$

(h) $$\cos\left(\frac{\alpha}{2}\right)=\sqrt{\frac{1+\cos\alpha}{2}}=\sqrt{\frac{\left(1+\frac{3}{5}\right)}{2}}=\sqrt{\frac{\left(\frac{8}{5}\right)}{2}}=\sqrt{\frac{4}{5}}=\frac{2}{\sqrt{5}}=\frac{2\sqrt{5}}{5}$$

62. $\cos\alpha = \frac{4}{5},\ 0<\alpha<\frac{\pi}{2};\qquad \cos\beta=\frac{5}{13},\ -\frac{\pi}{2}<\beta<0$

$\sin\alpha=\frac{3}{5},\ \tan\alpha=\frac{3}{4},\ \sin\beta=-\frac{12}{13},\ \tan\beta=-\frac{12}{5},\quad 0<\frac{\alpha}{2}<\frac{\pi}{4},\quad -\frac{\pi}{4}<\frac{\beta}{2}<0$

(a) $\sin(\alpha+\beta)=\sin\alpha\cos\beta+\cos\alpha\sin\beta=\left(\frac{3}{5}\right)\cdot\left(\frac{5}{13}\right)+\left(\frac{4}{5}\right)\cdot\left(-\frac{12}{13}\right)=\frac{15-48}{65}=-\frac{33}{65}$

(b) $\cos(\alpha+\beta)=\cos\alpha\cos\beta-\sin\alpha\sin\beta=\left(\frac{4}{5}\right)\cdot\left(\frac{5}{13}\right)-\left(\frac{3}{5}\right)\cdot\left(-\frac{12}{13}\right)=\frac{20+36}{65}=\frac{56}{65}$

(c) $\sin(\alpha-\beta)=\sin\alpha\cos\beta-\cos\alpha\sin\beta=\frac{3}{5}\cdot\frac{5}{13}-\frac{4}{5}\cdot\frac{-12}{13}=\frac{15+48}{65}=\frac{63}{65}$

(d) $\tan(\alpha+\beta)=\dfrac{\tan\alpha+\tan\beta}{1-\tan\alpha\tan\beta}=\dfrac{\left(\frac{3}{4}+\left(-\frac{12}{5}\right)\right)}{\left(1-\left(\frac{3}{4}\right)\cdot\left(-\frac{12}{5}\right)\right)}=\dfrac{\left(-\frac{33}{20}\right)}{\left(\frac{56}{20}\right)}=-\frac{33}{20}\cdot\frac{20}{56}=-\frac{33}{56}$

(e) $\sin(2\alpha)=2\sin\alpha\cos\alpha=2\cdot\frac{3}{5}\cdot\frac{4}{5}=\frac{24}{25}$

(f) $\cos(2\beta)=\cos^2\beta-\sin^2\beta=\left(\frac{5}{13}\right)^2-\left(\frac{-12}{13}\right)^2=\frac{25}{169}-\frac{144}{169}=-\frac{119}{169}$

(g) $\sin\left(\frac{\beta}{2}\right)=-\sqrt{\frac{1-\cos\beta}{2}}=-\sqrt{\frac{\left(1-\left(\frac{5}{13}\right)\right)}{2}}=-\sqrt{\frac{\left(\frac{8}{13}\right)}{2}}=-\sqrt{\frac{4}{13}}=-\frac{2}{\sqrt{13}}=-\frac{2\sqrt{13}}{13}$

(h) $\cos\left(\frac{\alpha}{2}\right)=\sqrt{\frac{1+\cos\alpha}{2}}=\sqrt{\frac{\left(1+\frac{4}{5}\right)}{2}}=\sqrt{\frac{\left(\frac{9}{5}\right)}{2}}=\sqrt{\frac{9}{10}}=\frac{3}{\sqrt{10}}=\frac{3\sqrt{10}}{10}$

63. $\sin\alpha=-\frac{3}{5},\ \pi<\alpha<\frac{3\pi}{2};\qquad \cos\beta=\frac{12}{13},\ \frac{3\pi}{2}<\beta<2\pi$

$\cos\alpha=-\frac{4}{5},\ \tan\alpha=\frac{3}{4},\ \sin\beta=-\frac{5}{13},\ \tan\beta=-\frac{5}{12},\quad \frac{\pi}{2}<\frac{\alpha}{2}<\frac{3\pi}{4},\quad \frac{3\pi}{4}<\frac{\beta}{2}<\pi$

(a) $\sin(\alpha+\beta)=\sin\alpha\cos\beta+\cos\alpha\sin\beta=\left(-\frac{3}{5}\right)\cdot\left(\frac{12}{13}\right)+\left(-\frac{4}{5}\right)\cdot\left(-\frac{5}{13}\right)=\frac{-36+20}{65}=-\frac{16}{65}$

(b) $\cos(\alpha+\beta)=\cos\alpha\cos\beta-\sin\alpha\sin\beta=\left(-\frac{4}{5}\right)\cdot\left(\frac{12}{13}\right)-\left(-\frac{3}{5}\right)\cdot\left(-\frac{5}{13}\right)=\frac{-48-15}{65}=-\frac{63}{65}$

(c) $\sin(\alpha-\beta)=\sin\alpha\cos\beta-\cos\alpha\sin\beta=\left(-\frac{3}{5}\right)\cdot\left(\frac{12}{13}\right)-\left(-\frac{4}{5}\right)\cdot\left(-\frac{5}{13}\right)=\frac{-36-20}{65}=-\frac{56}{65}$

(d) $\tan(\alpha+\beta)=\dfrac{\tan\alpha+\tan\beta}{1-\tan\alpha\tan\beta}=\dfrac{\left(\frac{3}{4}+\left(-\frac{5}{12}\right)\right)}{\left(1-\left(\frac{3}{4}\right)\cdot\left(-\frac{5}{12}\right)\right)}=\dfrac{\left(\frac{1}{3}\right)}{\left(\frac{21}{16}\right)}=\frac{1}{3}\cdot\frac{16}{21}=\frac{16}{63}$

(e) $\sin(2\alpha)=2\sin\alpha\cos\alpha=2\cdot\left(-\frac{3}{5}\right)\cdot\left(-\frac{4}{5}\right)=\frac{24}{25}$

(f) $\cos(2\beta)=\cos^2\beta-\sin^2\beta=\left(\frac{12}{13}\right)^2-\left(-\frac{5}{13}\right)^2=\frac{144}{169}-\frac{25}{169}=\frac{119}{169}$

(g) $\sin\left(\frac{\beta}{2}\right)=\sqrt{\frac{1-\cos\beta}{2}}=\sqrt{\frac{\left(1-\left(\frac{12}{13}\right)\right)}{2}}=\sqrt{\frac{\left(\frac{1}{13}\right)}{2}}=\sqrt{\frac{1}{26}}=\frac{1}{\sqrt{26}}=\frac{\sqrt{26}}{26}$

(h) $\cos\left(\frac{\alpha}{2}\right)=-\sqrt{\frac{1+\cos\alpha}{2}}=-\sqrt{\frac{\left(1+\left(-\frac{4}{5}\right)\right)}{2}}=-\sqrt{\frac{\left(\frac{1}{5}\right)}{2}}=-\sqrt{\frac{1}{10}}=-\frac{1}{\sqrt{10}}=-\frac{\sqrt{10}}{10}$

64. $\sin\alpha=-\frac{4}{5},\ -\frac{\pi}{2}<\alpha<0;\qquad \cos\beta=-\frac{5}{13},\ \frac{\pi}{2}<\beta<\pi$

$\cos\alpha=\frac{3}{5},\ \tan\alpha=-\frac{4}{3},\ \sin\beta=\frac{12}{13},\ \tan\beta=-\frac{12}{5},\quad -\frac{\pi}{4}<\frac{\alpha}{2}<0,\ \ \frac{\pi}{4}<\frac{\beta}{2}<\frac{\pi}{2}$

(a) $\sin(\alpha+\beta)=\sin\alpha\cos\beta+\cos\alpha\sin\beta=\left(-\frac{4}{5}\right)\cdot\left(-\frac{5}{13}\right)+\frac{3}{5}\cdot\frac{12}{13}=\frac{20+36}{65}=\frac{56}{65}$

(b) $\cos(\alpha+\beta)=\cos\alpha\cos\beta-\sin\alpha\sin\beta=\left(\frac{3}{5}\right)\cdot\left(-\frac{5}{13}\right)-\left(-\frac{4}{5}\right)\cdot\left(\frac{12}{13}\right)=\frac{-15+48}{65}=\frac{33}{65}$

(c) $\sin(\alpha-\beta)=\sin\alpha\cos\beta-\cos\alpha\sin\beta=\left(-\frac{4}{5}\right)\cdot\left(-\frac{5}{13}\right)-\left(\frac{3}{5}\right)\cdot\left(\frac{12}{13}\right)=\frac{20-36}{65}=-\frac{16}{65}$

(d) $\tan(\alpha+\beta)=\frac{\tan\alpha+\tan\beta}{1-\tan\alpha\tan\beta}=\frac{\left(-\frac{4}{3}+\left(-\frac{12}{5}\right)\right)}{\left(1-\left(-\frac{4}{3}\right)\cdot\left(-\frac{12}{5}\right)\right)}=\frac{\left(-\frac{56}{15}\right)}{\left(-\frac{33}{15}\right)}=\left(-\frac{56}{15}\right)\cdot\left(-\frac{15}{33}\right)=\frac{56}{33}$

(e) $\sin(2\alpha)=2\sin\alpha\cos\alpha=2\cdot\left(-\frac{4}{5}\right)\cdot\left(\frac{3}{5}\right)=-\frac{24}{25}$

(f) $\cos(2\beta)=\cos^2\beta-\sin^2\beta=\left(-\frac{5}{13}\right)^2-\left(\frac{12}{13}\right)^2=\frac{25}{169}-\frac{144}{169}=-\frac{119}{169}$

(g) $\sin\left(\frac{\beta}{2}\right)=\sqrt{\frac{1-\cos\beta}{2}}=\sqrt{\frac{\left(1-\left(-\frac{5}{13}\right)\right)}{2}}=\sqrt{\frac{\left(\frac{18}{13}\right)}{2}}=\sqrt{\frac{9}{13}}=\frac{3}{\sqrt{13}}=\frac{3\sqrt{13}}{13}$

(h) $\cos\left(\frac{\alpha}{2}\right)=\sqrt{\frac{1+\cos\alpha}{2}}=\sqrt{\frac{\left(1+\frac{3}{5}\right)}{2}}=\sqrt{\frac{\left(\frac{8}{5}\right)}{2}}=\sqrt{\frac{4}{5}}=\frac{2}{\sqrt{5}}=\frac{2\sqrt{5}}{5}$

65. $\tan\alpha=\frac{3}{4},\ \pi<\alpha<\frac{3\pi}{2};\qquad \tan\beta=\frac{12}{5},\ 0<\beta<\frac{\pi}{2}$

$\sin\alpha=-\frac{3}{5},\ \cos\alpha=-\frac{4}{5},\ \sin\beta=\frac{12}{13},\ \cos\beta=\frac{5}{13},\quad \frac{\pi}{2}<\frac{\alpha}{2}<\frac{3\pi}{4},\ \ 0<\frac{\beta}{2}<\frac{\pi}{4}$

(a) $\sin(\alpha+\beta)=\sin\alpha\cos\beta+\cos\alpha\sin\beta=\left(-\frac{3}{5}\right)\cdot\left(\frac{5}{13}\right)+\left(-\frac{4}{5}\right)\cdot\left(\frac{12}{13}\right)=\frac{-15-48}{65}=-\frac{63}{65}$

(b) $\cos(\alpha+\beta)=\cos\alpha\cos\beta-\sin\alpha\sin\beta=\left(-\frac{4}{5}\right)\cdot\left(\frac{5}{13}\right)-\left(-\frac{3}{5}\right)\cdot\left(\frac{12}{13}\right)=\frac{-20+36}{65}=\frac{16}{65}$

(c) $\sin(\alpha-\beta)=\sin\alpha\cos\beta-\cos\alpha\sin\beta=\left(-\frac{3}{5}\right)\cdot\left(\frac{5}{13}\right)-\left(-\frac{4}{5}\right)\cdot\left(\frac{12}{13}\right)=\frac{-15+48}{65}=\frac{33}{65}$

(d) $\tan(\alpha+\beta)=\dfrac{\tan\alpha+\tan\beta}{1-\tan\alpha\tan\beta}=\dfrac{\left(\frac{3}{4}+\left(\frac{12}{5}\right)\right)}{\left(1-\left(\frac{3}{4}\right)\cdot\left(\frac{12}{5}\right)\right)}=\dfrac{\left(\frac{15+48}{20}\right)}{\left(-\frac{4}{5}\right)}=\left(\frac{63}{20}\right)\cdot\left(-\frac{5}{4}\right)=-\frac{63}{16}$

(e) $\sin(2\alpha)=2\sin\alpha\cos\alpha=2\cdot\left(-\frac{3}{5}\right)\cdot\left(-\frac{4}{5}\right)=\frac{24}{25}$

(f) $\cos(2\beta)=\cos^2\beta-\sin^2\beta=\left(\frac{5}{13}\right)^2-\left(\frac{12}{13}\right)^2=\frac{25}{169}-\frac{144}{169}=-\frac{119}{169}$

(g) $\sin\left(\frac{\beta}{2}\right)=\sqrt{\dfrac{1-\cos\beta}{2}}=\sqrt{\dfrac{\left(1-\left(\frac{5}{13}\right)\right)}{2}}=\sqrt{\dfrac{\left(\frac{8}{13}\right)}{2}}=\sqrt{\frac{4}{13}}=\frac{2}{\sqrt{13}}=\frac{2\sqrt{13}}{13}$

(h) $\cos\left(\frac{\alpha}{2}\right)=-\sqrt{\dfrac{1+\cos\alpha}{2}}=-\sqrt{\dfrac{\left(1+\left(-\frac{4}{5}\right)\right)}{2}}=-\sqrt{\dfrac{\left(\frac{1}{5}\right)}{2}}=-\sqrt{\frac{1}{10}}=-\frac{1}{\sqrt{10}}=-\frac{\sqrt{10}}{10}$

66. $\tan\alpha=-\frac{4}{3},\ \frac{\pi}{2}<\alpha<\pi;\qquad \cot\beta=\frac{12}{5},\ \pi<\beta<\frac{3\pi}{2}$

$\sin\alpha=\frac{4}{5},\ \cos\alpha=-\frac{3}{5},\ \sin\beta=-\frac{5}{13},\ \cos\beta=-\frac{12}{13},\quad \frac{\pi}{4}<\frac{\alpha}{2}<\frac{\pi}{2},\quad \frac{\pi}{2}<\frac{\beta}{2}<\frac{3\pi}{4}$

(a) $\sin(\alpha+\beta)=\sin\alpha\cos\beta+\cos\alpha\sin\beta=\left(\frac{4}{5}\right)\cdot\left(-\frac{12}{13}\right)+\left(-\frac{3}{5}\right)\cdot\left(-\frac{5}{13}\right)=\frac{-48+15}{65}=-\frac{33}{65}$

(b) $\cos(\alpha+\beta)=\cos\alpha\cos\beta-\sin\alpha\sin\beta=\left(-\frac{3}{5}\right)\cdot\left(-\frac{12}{13}\right)-\left(\frac{4}{5}\right)\cdot\left(-\frac{5}{13}\right)=\frac{36+20}{65}=\frac{56}{65}$

(c) $\sin(\alpha-\beta)=\sin\alpha\cos\beta-\cos\alpha\sin\beta=\frac{4}{5}\cdot\frac{-12}{13}-\frac{-3}{5}\cdot\frac{-5}{13}=\frac{-48-15}{65}=-\frac{63}{65}$

(d) $\tan(\alpha+\beta)=\dfrac{\tan\alpha+\tan\beta}{1-\tan\alpha\tan\beta}=\dfrac{\left(-\frac{4}{3}+\frac{5}{12}\right)}{\left(1-\left(-\frac{4}{3}\right)\cdot\left(\frac{5}{12}\right)\right)}=\dfrac{\left(\frac{-16+5}{12}\right)}{\left(\frac{56}{36}\right)}=\left(-\frac{11}{12}\right)\cdot\left(\frac{36}{56}\right)=-\frac{33}{56}$

(e) $\sin(2\alpha)=2\sin\alpha\cos\alpha=2\cdot\left(\frac{4}{5}\right)\cdot\left(-\frac{3}{5}\right)=-\frac{24}{25}$

(f) $\cos(2\beta)=\cos^2\beta-\sin^2\beta=\left(\frac{-12}{13}\right)^2-\left(\frac{-5}{13}\right)^2=\frac{144}{169}-\frac{25}{169}=\frac{119}{169}$

(g) $\sin\left(\frac{\beta}{2}\right)=\sqrt{\dfrac{1-\cos\beta}{2}}=\sqrt{\dfrac{\left(1-\left(-\frac{12}{13}\right)\right)}{2}}=\sqrt{\dfrac{\left(\frac{25}{13}\right)}{2}}=\sqrt{\frac{25}{26}}=\frac{5}{\sqrt{26}}=\frac{5\sqrt{26}}{26}$

(h) $\cos\left(\frac{\alpha}{2}\right)=\sqrt{\dfrac{1+\cos\alpha}{2}}=\sqrt{\dfrac{\left(1+\left(-\frac{3}{5}\right)\right)}{2}}=\sqrt{\dfrac{\left(\frac{2}{5}\right)}{2}}=\sqrt{\frac{1}{5}}=\frac{1}{\sqrt{5}}=\frac{\sqrt{5}}{5}$

67. $\sec\alpha = 2,\ -\frac{\pi}{2} < \alpha < 0; \qquad \sec\beta = 3,\ \frac{3\pi}{2} < \beta < 2\pi$

$\sin\alpha = -\frac{\sqrt{3}}{2},\ \cos\alpha = \frac{1}{2},\ \tan\alpha = -\sqrt{3},\ \sin\beta = -\frac{2\sqrt{2}}{3},\ \cos\beta = \frac{1}{3},\ \tan\beta = -2\sqrt{2},$

$-\frac{\pi}{4} < \frac{\alpha}{2} < 0,\quad \frac{3\pi}{4} < \frac{\beta}{2} < \pi$

(a) $\sin(\alpha+\beta) = \sin\alpha\cos\beta + \cos\alpha\sin\beta = \left(-\frac{\sqrt{3}}{2}\right)\cdot\left(\frac{1}{3}\right) + \left(\frac{1}{2}\right)\cdot\left(-\frac{2\sqrt{2}}{3}\right) = \frac{-\sqrt{3}-2\sqrt{2}}{6}$

(b) $\cos(\alpha+\beta) = \cos\alpha\cos\beta - \sin\alpha\sin\beta = \left(\frac{1}{2}\right)\cdot\left(\frac{1}{3}\right) - \left(-\frac{\sqrt{3}}{2}\right)\cdot\left(-\frac{2\sqrt{2}}{3}\right) = \frac{1-2\sqrt{6}}{6}$

(c) $\sin(\alpha-\beta) = \sin\alpha\cos\beta - \cos\alpha\sin\beta = \left(-\frac{\sqrt{3}}{2}\right)\cdot\left(\frac{1}{3}\right) - \left(\frac{1}{2}\right)\cdot\left(-\frac{2\sqrt{2}}{3}\right) = \frac{-\sqrt{3}+2\sqrt{2}}{6}$

(d) $\tan(\alpha+\beta) = \frac{\tan\alpha + \tan\beta}{1-\tan\alpha\tan\beta} = \frac{\left(-\sqrt{3}+\left(-2\sqrt{2}\right)\right)}{\left(1-\left(-\sqrt{3}\right)\left(-2\sqrt{2}\right)\right)} = \left(\frac{-\sqrt{3}-2\sqrt{2}}{1-2\sqrt{6}}\right)\cdot\left(\frac{1+2\sqrt{6}}{1+2\sqrt{6}}\right)$

$= \frac{-9\sqrt{3}-8\sqrt{2}}{-23} = \frac{9\sqrt{3}+8\sqrt{2}}{23}$

(e) $\sin(2\alpha) = 2\sin\alpha\cos\alpha = 2\cdot\left(-\frac{\sqrt{3}}{2}\right)\cdot\left(\frac{1}{2}\right) = -\frac{\sqrt{3}}{2}$

(f) $\cos(2\beta) = \cos^2\beta - \sin^2\beta = \left(\frac{1}{3}\right)^2 - \left(\frac{-2\sqrt{2}}{3}\right)^2 = \frac{1}{9} - \frac{8}{9} = -\frac{7}{9}$

(g) $\sin\left(\frac{\beta}{2}\right) = \sqrt{\frac{1-\cos\beta}{2}} = \sqrt{\frac{1-\left(\frac{1}{3}\right)}{2}} = \sqrt{\frac{\left(\frac{2}{3}\right)}{2}} = \sqrt{\frac{1}{3}} = \frac{1}{\sqrt{3}} = \frac{\sqrt{3}}{3}$

(h) $\cos\left(\frac{\alpha}{2}\right) = \sqrt{\frac{1+\cos\alpha}{2}} = \sqrt{\frac{\left(1+\frac{1}{2}\right)}{2}} = \sqrt{\frac{\left(\frac{3}{2}\right)}{2}} = \sqrt{\frac{3}{4}} = \frac{\sqrt{3}}{2}$

68. $\csc\alpha = 2,\ \frac{\pi}{2} < \alpha < \pi; \qquad \sec\beta = -3,\ \frac{\pi}{2} < \beta < \pi$

$\sin\alpha = \frac{1}{2},\ \cos\alpha = -\frac{\sqrt{3}}{2},\ \tan\alpha = -\frac{\sqrt{3}}{3},\ \sin\beta = \frac{2\sqrt{2}}{3},\ \cos\beta = -\frac{1}{3},\ \tan\beta = -2\sqrt{2},$

$\frac{\pi}{4} < \frac{\alpha}{2} < \frac{\pi}{2},\quad \frac{\pi}{4} < \frac{\beta}{2} < \frac{\pi}{2}$

(a) $\sin(\alpha+\beta) = \sin\alpha\cos\beta + \cos\alpha\sin\beta = \left(\frac{1}{2}\right)\cdot\left(-\frac{1}{3}\right) + \left(-\frac{\sqrt{3}}{2}\right)\cdot\left(\frac{2\sqrt{2}}{3}\right) = \frac{-1-2\sqrt{6}}{6}$

(b) $\cos(\alpha+\beta) = \cos\alpha\cos\beta - \sin\alpha\sin\beta = \left(-\frac{\sqrt{3}}{2}\right)\cdot\left(-\frac{1}{3}\right) - \left(\frac{1}{2}\right)\cdot\left(\frac{2\sqrt{2}}{3}\right) = \frac{\sqrt{3}-2\sqrt{2}}{6}$

(c) $\sin(\alpha-\beta) = \sin\alpha\cos\beta - \cos\alpha\sin\beta = \left(\frac{1}{2}\right)\cdot\left(-\frac{1}{3}\right) - \left(-\frac{\sqrt{3}}{2}\right)\cdot\left(\frac{2\sqrt{2}}{3}\right) = \frac{-1+2\sqrt{6}}{6}$

(d) $\tan(\alpha+\beta)=\dfrac{\tan\alpha+\tan\beta}{1-\tan\alpha\tan\beta}=\dfrac{\left(-\frac{\sqrt{3}}{3}+\left(-2\sqrt{2}\right)\right)}{\left(1-\left(-\frac{\sqrt{3}}{3}\right)\left(-2\sqrt{2}\right)\right)}=\dfrac{\left(\frac{-\sqrt{3}-6\sqrt{2}}{3}\right)}{\left(\frac{3-2\sqrt{6}}{3}\right)}$

$=\left(\dfrac{-\sqrt{3}-6\sqrt{2}}{3-2\sqrt{6}}\right)\cdot\left(\dfrac{3+2\sqrt{6}}{3+2\sqrt{6}}\right)=\dfrac{-3\sqrt{3}-2\sqrt{18}-18\sqrt{2}-12\sqrt{12}}{9-24}$

$=\dfrac{-27\sqrt{3}-24\sqrt{2}}{-15}=\dfrac{9\sqrt{3}+8\sqrt{2}}{5}$

(e) $\sin(2\alpha)=2\sin\alpha\cos\alpha=2\cdot\left(\dfrac{1}{2}\right)\cdot\left(-\dfrac{\sqrt{3}}{2}\right)=-\dfrac{\sqrt{3}}{2}$

(f) $\cos(2\beta)=\cos^2\beta-\sin^2\beta=\left(\dfrac{-1}{3}\right)^2-\left(\dfrac{2\sqrt{2}}{3}\right)^2=\dfrac{1}{9}-\dfrac{8}{9}=-\dfrac{7}{9}$

(g) $\sin\left(\dfrac{\beta}{2}\right)=\sqrt{\dfrac{1-\cos\beta}{2}}=\sqrt{\dfrac{\left(1-\left(-\frac{1}{3}\right)\right)}{2}}=\sqrt{\dfrac{\left(\frac{4}{3}\right)}{2}}=\sqrt{\dfrac{4}{6}}=\dfrac{2}{\sqrt{6}}=\dfrac{2\sqrt{6}}{6}=\dfrac{\sqrt{6}}{3}$

(h) $\cos\left(\dfrac{\alpha}{2}\right)=\sqrt{\dfrac{1+\cos\alpha}{2}}=\sqrt{\dfrac{\left(1+\left(-\frac{\sqrt{3}}{2}\right)\right)}{2}}=\sqrt{\dfrac{\left(\frac{2-\sqrt{3}}{2}\right)}{2}}=\sqrt{\dfrac{2-\sqrt{3}}{4}}=\dfrac{\sqrt{2-\sqrt{3}}}{2}$

69. $\sin\alpha=-\dfrac{2}{3},\ \pi<\alpha<\dfrac{3\pi}{2};\qquad \cos\beta=-\dfrac{2}{3},\ \pi<\beta<\dfrac{3\pi}{2}$

$\cos\alpha=-\dfrac{\sqrt{5}}{3},\ \tan\alpha=\dfrac{2\sqrt{5}}{5},\ \sin\beta=-\dfrac{\sqrt{5}}{3},\ \tan\beta=\dfrac{\sqrt{5}}{2},\ \dfrac{\pi}{2}<\dfrac{\alpha}{2}<\dfrac{3\pi}{4},\ \dfrac{\pi}{2}<\dfrac{\beta}{2}<\dfrac{3\pi}{4}$

(a) $\sin(\alpha+\beta)=\sin\alpha\cos\beta+\cos\alpha\sin\beta=\left(-\dfrac{2}{3}\right)\cdot\left(-\dfrac{2}{3}\right)+\left(-\dfrac{\sqrt{5}}{3}\right)\cdot\left(-\dfrac{\sqrt{5}}{3}\right)=\dfrac{4+5}{9}=1$

(b) $\cos(\alpha+\beta)=\cos\alpha\cos\beta-\sin\alpha\sin\beta=\left(-\dfrac{\sqrt{5}}{3}\right)\cdot\left(-\dfrac{2}{3}\right)-\left(-\dfrac{2}{3}\right)\cdot\left(-\dfrac{\sqrt{5}}{3}\right)=\dfrac{2\sqrt{5}-2\sqrt{5}}{9}=0$

(c) $\sin(\alpha-\beta)=\sin\alpha\cos\beta-\cos\alpha\sin\beta=\left(-\dfrac{2}{3}\right)\cdot\left(-\dfrac{2}{3}\right)-\left(-\dfrac{\sqrt{5}}{3}\right)\cdot\left(-\dfrac{\sqrt{5}}{3}\right)=\dfrac{4-5}{9}=-\dfrac{1}{9}$

(d) $\tan(\alpha+\beta)=\dfrac{\tan\alpha+\tan\beta}{1-\tan\alpha\tan\beta}=\dfrac{\left(\frac{2\sqrt{5}}{5}+\frac{\sqrt{5}}{2}\right)}{\left(1-\left(\frac{2\sqrt{5}}{5}\right)\cdot\left(\frac{\sqrt{5}}{2}\right)\right)}=\dfrac{\left(\frac{4\sqrt{5}+5\sqrt{5}}{10}\right)}{\left(\frac{10-10}{10}\right)}=\dfrac{\left(\frac{9\sqrt{5}}{10}\right)}{0}$ Undefined

(e) $\sin(2\alpha)=2\sin\alpha\cos\alpha=2\cdot\left(-\dfrac{2}{3}\right)\cdot\left(-\dfrac{\sqrt{5}}{3}\right)=\dfrac{4\sqrt{5}}{9}$

(f) $\cos(2\beta)=\cos^2\beta-\sin^2\beta=\left(-\dfrac{2}{3}\right)^2-\left(-\dfrac{\sqrt{5}}{3}\right)^2=\dfrac{4}{9}-\dfrac{5}{9}=-\dfrac{1}{9}$

(g) $\sin\left(\frac{\beta}{2}\right)=\sqrt{\frac{1-\cos\beta}{2}}=\sqrt{\frac{\left(1-\left(-\frac{2}{3}\right)\right)}{2}}=\sqrt{\frac{\left(\frac{5}{3}\right)}{2}}=\sqrt{\frac{5}{6}}=\frac{\sqrt{30}}{6}$

(h) $\cos\left(\frac{\alpha}{2}\right)=-\sqrt{\frac{1+\cos\alpha}{2}}=-\sqrt{\frac{\left(1+\left(-\frac{\sqrt{5}}{3}\right)\right)}{2}}=-\sqrt{\frac{\left(\frac{3-\sqrt{5}}{3}\right)}{2}}=-\sqrt{\frac{3-\sqrt{5}}{6}}=-\frac{\sqrt{18-6\sqrt{5}}}{6}$

70. $\tan\alpha=-2,\ \frac{\pi}{2}<\alpha<\pi;\qquad \cot\beta=-2,\ \frac{\pi}{2}<\beta<\pi\qquad \tan\beta=-\frac{1}{2}$

$\sin\alpha=\frac{2}{\sqrt{5}},\ \cos\alpha=-\frac{1}{\sqrt{5}},\ \sin\beta=\frac{1}{\sqrt{5}},\ \cos\beta=-\frac{2}{\sqrt{5}},\quad \frac{\pi}{4}<\frac{\alpha}{2}<\frac{\pi}{2},\quad \frac{\pi}{4}<\frac{\beta}{2}<\frac{\pi}{2}$

(a) $\sin(\alpha+\beta)=\sin\alpha\cos\beta+\cos\alpha\sin\beta=\left(\frac{2}{\sqrt{5}}\right)\cdot\left(-\frac{2}{\sqrt{5}}\right)+\left(-\frac{1}{\sqrt{5}}\right)\cdot\left(\frac{1}{\sqrt{5}}\right)=\frac{-4-1}{5}=-\frac{5}{5}=-1$

(b) $\cos(\alpha+\beta)=\cos\alpha\cos\beta-\sin\alpha\sin\beta=\left(-\frac{1}{\sqrt{5}}\right)\cdot\left(-\frac{2}{\sqrt{5}}\right)-\left(\frac{2}{\sqrt{5}}\right)\cdot\left(\frac{1}{\sqrt{5}}\right)=\frac{2-2}{5}=0$

(c) $\sin(\alpha-\beta)=\sin\alpha\cos\beta-\cos\alpha\sin\beta=\left(\frac{2}{\sqrt{5}}\right)\cdot\left(-\frac{2}{\sqrt{5}}\right)-\left(-\frac{1}{\sqrt{5}}\right)\cdot\left(\frac{1}{\sqrt{5}}\right)=\frac{-4+1}{5}=-\frac{3}{5}$

(d) $\tan(\alpha+\beta)=\frac{\tan\alpha+\tan\beta}{1-\tan\alpha\tan\beta}=\frac{\left(-2+\left(-\frac{1}{2}\right)\right)}{\left(1-(-2)\cdot\left(-\frac{1}{2}\right)\right)}=\frac{\left(-\frac{5}{2}\right)}{0}=\text{undefined}$

(e) $\sin(2\alpha)=2\sin\alpha\cos\alpha=2\cdot\left(\frac{2}{\sqrt{5}}\right)\cdot\left(-\frac{1}{\sqrt{5}}\right)=-\frac{4}{5}$

(f) $\cos(2\beta)=\cos^2\beta-\sin^2\beta=\left(\frac{-2}{\sqrt{5}}\right)^2-\left(\frac{1}{\sqrt{5}}\right)^2=\frac{4}{5}-\frac{1}{5}=\frac{3}{5}$

(g) $\sin\left(\frac{\beta}{2}\right)=\sqrt{\frac{1-\cos\beta}{2}}=\sqrt{\frac{\left(1-\left(-\frac{2}{\sqrt{5}}\right)\right)}{2}}=\sqrt{\frac{\left(\frac{\sqrt{5}+2}{\sqrt{5}}\right)}{2}}=\sqrt{\frac{\sqrt{5}+2}{2\sqrt{5}}}=\sqrt{\frac{5+2\sqrt{5}}{10}}$

(h) $\cos\left(\frac{\alpha}{2}\right)=\sqrt{\frac{1+\cos\alpha}{2}}=\sqrt{\frac{\left(1+\left(-\frac{1}{\sqrt{5}}\right)\right)}{2}}=\sqrt{\frac{\left(\frac{\sqrt{5}-1}{\sqrt{5}}\right)}{2}}=\sqrt{\frac{\sqrt{5}-1}{2\sqrt{5}}}=\sqrt{\frac{5-\sqrt{5}}{10}}$

71. $\cos\left(\sin^{-1}\left(\frac{3}{5}\right)-\cos^{-1}\left(\frac{1}{2}\right)\right)$

Let $\alpha=\sin^{-1}\left(\frac{3}{5}\right)$ and $\beta=\cos^{-1}\left(\frac{1}{2}\right)$. α is in quadrant I; β is in quadrant I.

Then $\sin\alpha=\frac{3}{5},\ -\frac{\pi}{2}\le\alpha\le\frac{\pi}{2}$, and $\cos\beta=\frac{1}{2}, 0\le\beta\le\pi$.

$$\cos\alpha = \sqrt{1-\sin^2\alpha} = \sqrt{1-\left(\frac{3}{5}\right)^2} = \sqrt{1-\frac{9}{25}} = \sqrt{\frac{16}{25}} = \frac{4}{5}$$

$$\sin\beta = \sqrt{1-\cos^2\beta} = \sqrt{1-\left(\frac{1}{2}\right)^2} = \sqrt{1-\frac{1}{4}} = \sqrt{\frac{3}{4}} = \frac{\sqrt{3}}{2}$$

$$\cos\left(\sin^{-1}\left(\frac{3}{5}\right)-\cos^{-1}\left(\frac{1}{2}\right)\right) = \cos(\alpha-\beta) = \cos\alpha\cos\beta + \sin\alpha\sin\beta$$

$$= \left(\frac{4}{5}\right)\cdot\left(\frac{1}{2}\right) + \left(\frac{3}{5}\right)\cdot\left(\frac{\sqrt{3}}{2}\right) = \frac{4+3\sqrt{3}}{10}$$

72. $\sin\left(\cos^{-1}\left(\frac{5}{13}\right)-\cos^{-1}\left(\frac{4}{5}\right)\right)$

Let $\alpha = \cos^{-1}\left(\frac{5}{13}\right)$ and $\beta = \cos^{-1}\left(\frac{4}{5}\right)$. α is in quadrant I; β is in quadrant I.

Then $\cos\alpha = \frac{5}{13},\ 0 \le \alpha \le \pi$, and $\cos\beta = \frac{4}{5}, 0 \le \beta \le \pi$.

$$\sin\alpha = \sqrt{1-\cos^2\alpha} = \sqrt{1-\left(\frac{5}{13}\right)^2} = \sqrt{1-\frac{25}{169}} = \sqrt{\frac{144}{169}} = \frac{12}{13}$$

$$\sin\beta = \sqrt{1-\cos^2\beta} = \sqrt{1-\left(\frac{4}{5}\right)^2} = \sqrt{1-\frac{16}{25}} = \sqrt{\frac{9}{25}} = \frac{3}{5}$$

$$\sin\left(\cos^{-1}\left(\frac{5}{13}\right)-\cos^{-1}\left(\frac{4}{5}\right)\right) = \sin(\alpha-\beta) = \sin\alpha\cos\beta - \cos\alpha\sin\beta$$

$$= \left(\frac{12}{13}\right)\cdot\left(\frac{4}{5}\right) - \left(\frac{5}{13}\right)\cdot\left(\frac{3}{5}\right) = \frac{48-15}{65} = \frac{33}{65}$$

73. $\tan\left[\sin^{-1}\left(-\frac{1}{2}\right)-\tan^{-1}\left(\frac{3}{4}\right)\right]$

Let $\alpha = \sin^{-1}\left(-\frac{1}{2}\right)$ and $\beta = \tan^{-1}\left(\frac{3}{4}\right)$. α is in quadrant IV; β is in quadrant I.

Then $\sin\alpha = -\frac{1}{2},\ -\frac{\pi}{2} \le \alpha \le \frac{\pi}{2}$, and $\tan\beta = \frac{3}{4}, -\frac{\pi}{2} < \beta < \frac{\pi}{2}$.

$$\cos\alpha = \sqrt{1-\sin^2\alpha} = \sqrt{1-\left(-\frac{1}{2}\right)^2} = \sqrt{1-\frac{1}{4}} = \sqrt{\frac{3}{4}} = \frac{\sqrt{3}}{2};\quad \tan\alpha = -\frac{1}{\sqrt{3}} = -\frac{\sqrt{3}}{3}$$

$$\tan\left[\sin^{-1}\left(-\frac{1}{2}\right)-\tan^{-1}\left(\frac{3}{4}\right)\right]=\tan(\alpha-\beta)=\frac{\tan\alpha-\tan\beta}{1+\tan\alpha\tan\beta}=\frac{\left(-\frac{\sqrt{3}}{3}-\frac{3}{4}\right)}{\left(1+\left(-\frac{\sqrt{3}}{3}\right)\cdot\left(\frac{3}{4}\right)\right)}$$

$$=\frac{\left(\frac{-4\sqrt{3}-9}{12}\right)}{\left(1-\frac{3\sqrt{3}}{12}\right)}=\left(\frac{-9-4\sqrt{3}}{12-3\sqrt{3}}\right)\cdot\left(\frac{12+3\sqrt{3}}{12+3\sqrt{3}}\right)$$

$$=\frac{-144-75\sqrt{3}}{117}=\frac{-48-25\sqrt{3}}{39}$$

74. $\cos\left(\tan^{-1}(-1)+\cos^{-1}\left(-\frac{4}{5}\right)\right)$

Let $\alpha=\tan^{-1}(-1)$ and $\beta=\cos^{-1}\left(-\frac{4}{5}\right)$. α is in quadrant IV; β is in quadrant II.

Then $\tan\alpha=-1,\ -\frac{\pi}{2}<\alpha<\frac{\pi}{2}$, and $\cos\beta=-\frac{4}{5},\ 0\le\beta\le\pi$.

$$\sec\alpha=\sqrt{1+\tan^2\alpha}=\sqrt{1+(-1)^2}=\sqrt{2};\quad \cos\alpha=\frac{1}{\sqrt{2}}=\frac{\sqrt{2}}{2}$$

$$\sin\alpha=\sqrt{1-\cos^2\alpha}=\sqrt{1-\left(\frac{\sqrt{2}}{2}\right)^2}=\sqrt{1-\frac{1}{2}}=\sqrt{\frac{1}{2}}=\frac{\sqrt{2}}{2}$$

$$\sin\beta=\sqrt{1-\cos^2\beta}=\sqrt{1-\left(-\frac{4}{5}\right)^2}=\sqrt{1-\frac{16}{25}}=\sqrt{\frac{9}{25}}=\frac{3}{5}$$

$$\cos\left(\tan^{-1}(-1)+\cos^{-1}\left(-\frac{4}{5}\right)\right)=\cos(\alpha+\beta)=\cos\alpha\cos\beta-\sin\alpha\sin\beta$$

$$=\left(\frac{\sqrt{2}}{2}\right)\cdot\left(-\frac{4}{5}\right)+\left(\frac{\sqrt{2}}{2}\right)\cdot\left(\frac{3}{5}\right)=\frac{-4\sqrt{2}+3\sqrt{2}}{10}=-\frac{\sqrt{2}}{10}$$

75. $\sin\left[2\cos^{-1}\left(-\frac{3}{5}\right)\right]$

Let $\alpha=\cos^{-1}\left(-\frac{3}{5}\right)$. α is in quadrant II.

Then $\cos\alpha=-\frac{3}{5},\ 0\le\alpha\le\pi$.

$$\sin\alpha=\sqrt{1-\cos^2\alpha}=\sqrt{1-\left(-\frac{3}{5}\right)^2}=\sqrt{1-\frac{9}{25}}=\sqrt{\frac{16}{25}}=\frac{4}{5}$$

$$\sin\left[2\cos^{-1}\left(-\frac{3}{5}\right)\right]=\sin2\alpha=2\sin\alpha\cos\alpha=2\cdot\left(\frac{4}{5}\right)\cdot\left(-\frac{3}{5}\right)=-\frac{24}{25}$$

76. $\cos\left(2\tan^{-1}\left(\frac{4}{3}\right)\right)$

Let $\alpha = \tan^{-1}\left(\frac{4}{3}\right)$. α is in quadrant I.

Then $\tan\alpha = \frac{4}{3}$, $-\frac{\pi}{2} < \alpha < \frac{\pi}{2}$.

$$\sec\alpha = \sqrt{\tan^2\alpha + 1} = \sqrt{\left(\frac{4}{3}\right)^2 + 1} = \sqrt{\frac{16}{9} + 1} = \sqrt{\frac{25}{9}} = \frac{5}{3}; \quad \cos\alpha = \frac{3}{5}$$

$$\cos\left[2\tan^{-1}\left(\frac{4}{3}\right)\right] = \cos 2\alpha = 2\cos^2\alpha - 1 = 2\left(\frac{3}{5}\right)^2 - 1 = 2\cdot\left(\frac{9}{25}\right) - 1 = -\frac{7}{25}$$

77. $\cos\theta = \frac{1}{2}$

$\theta = \frac{\pi}{3} + 2k\pi$ or $\theta = \frac{5\pi}{3} + 2k\pi$, where k is any integer

The solutions on the interval $[0, 2\pi)$ are $\theta = \frac{\pi}{3}, \frac{5\pi}{3}$

78. $\sin\theta = -\frac{\sqrt{3}}{2}$

$\theta = \frac{4\pi}{3} + 2k\pi$ or $\theta = \frac{5\pi}{3} + 2k\pi$, where k is any integer

The solutions on the interval $[0, 2\pi)$ are $\theta = \frac{4\pi}{3}, \frac{5\pi}{3}$

79. $2\cos\theta + \sqrt{2} = 0 \rightarrow 2\cos\theta = -\sqrt{2} \rightarrow \cos\theta = -\frac{\sqrt{2}}{2}$

$\theta = \frac{3\pi}{4} + 2k\pi$ or $\theta = \frac{5\pi}{4} + 2k\pi$, k is any integer

The solutions on the interval $[0, 2\pi)$ are $\theta = \frac{3\pi}{4}, \frac{5\pi}{4}$.

80. $\tan\theta + \sqrt{3} = 0 \rightarrow \tan\theta = -\sqrt{3}$

$\theta = \frac{2\pi}{3} + k\pi$, k is any integer

The solutions on the interval $[0, 2\pi)$ are $\theta = \frac{2\pi}{3}, \frac{5\pi}{3}$.

81. $\sin(2\theta) + 1 = 0 \rightarrow \sin(2\theta) = -1$

$2\theta = \frac{3\pi}{2} + 2k\pi \rightarrow \theta = \frac{3\pi}{4} + k\pi$, where k is any integer

The solutions on the interval $[0, 2\pi)$ are $\theta = \frac{3\pi}{4}, \frac{7\pi}{4}$

82. $\cos(2\theta)=0$

$$2\theta=\frac{\pi}{2}+2k\pi \rightarrow \theta=\frac{\pi}{4}+k\pi$$
$$2\theta=\frac{3\pi}{2}+2k\pi \rightarrow \theta=\frac{3\pi}{4}+k\pi$$
, where k is any integer

The solutions on the interval $[0, 2\pi)$ are $\theta=\frac{\pi}{4},\frac{3\pi}{4},\frac{5\pi}{4},\frac{7\pi}{4}$

83. $\tan(2\theta)=0$

$2\theta=0+k\pi \rightarrow \theta=\frac{k\pi}{2}$, where k is any integer

The solutions on the interval $[0, 2\pi)$ are $\theta=0,\frac{\pi}{2},\pi,\frac{3\pi}{2}$.

84. $\sin(3\theta)=1$

$3\theta=\frac{\pi}{2}+2k\pi \rightarrow \theta=\frac{\pi}{6}+\frac{2k\pi}{3}$, where k is any integer

The solutions on the interval $[0, 2\pi)$ are $\theta=\frac{\pi}{6},\frac{5\pi}{6},\frac{3\pi}{2}$

85. $\sec^2\theta=4$

$$\sec\theta=\pm2 \rightarrow \cos\theta=\pm\frac{1}{2}$$

$\theta=\frac{\pi}{3}+k\pi$, where k is any integer

$\theta=\frac{2\pi}{3}+k\pi$, where k is any integer

The solutions on the interval $[0, 2\pi)$ are $\theta=\frac{\pi}{3},\frac{2\pi}{3},\frac{4\pi}{3},\frac{5\pi}{3}$

86. $\csc^2\theta=1$

$$\csc\theta=\pm1 \rightarrow \sin\theta=\pm1$$

$\theta=\frac{\pi}{2}+k\pi$, where k is any integer

The solutions on the interval $[0, 2\pi)$ are $\theta=\frac{\pi}{2},\frac{3\pi}{2}$

87.
$$\sin\theta=\tan\theta$$
$$\sin\theta=\frac{\sin\theta}{\cos\theta} \rightarrow \sin\theta\cos\theta=\sin\theta$$
$$\sin\theta\cos\theta-\sin\theta=0 \rightarrow \sin\theta(\cos\theta-1)=0$$
$$\cos\theta-1=0 \rightarrow \cos\theta=1 \rightarrow \theta=\pi$$
$$\text{or } \sin\theta=0 \rightarrow \theta=0$$
The solutions on the interval $[0, 2\pi)$ are $\theta=0,\pi$.

88. $\cos\theta = \sec\theta$

$$\cos\theta = \frac{1}{\cos\theta} \rightarrow \cos^2\theta = 1$$

$$\cos\theta = 1 \rightarrow \theta = 0$$

$$\text{or } \cos\theta = -1 \rightarrow \theta = \pi$$

The solutions on the interval $[0, 2\pi)$ are $\theta = 0, \pi$.

89. $\sin\theta + \sin(2\theta) = 0$

$$\sin\theta + 2\sin\theta\cos\theta = 0 \rightarrow \sin\theta(1 + 2\cos\theta) = 0$$

$$1 + 2\cos\theta = 0 \rightarrow \cos\theta = -\frac{1}{2} \rightarrow \theta = \frac{2\pi}{3}, \frac{4\pi}{3}$$

$$\text{or } \sin\theta = 0 \rightarrow \theta = 0, \pi$$

The solutions on the interval $[0, 2\pi)$ are $\theta = 0, \frac{2\pi}{3}, \pi, \frac{4\pi}{3}$.

90. $\cos(2\theta) = \sin\theta$

$$1 - 2\sin^2\theta = \sin\theta \rightarrow 2\sin^2\theta + \sin\theta - 1 = 0$$

$$(2\sin\theta - 1)(\sin\theta + 1) = 0$$

$$2\sin\theta - 1 = 0 \rightarrow \sin\theta = \frac{1}{2} \rightarrow \theta = \frac{\pi}{6}, \frac{5\pi}{6}$$

$$\text{or } \sin\theta + 1 = 0 \rightarrow \sin\theta = -1 \rightarrow \theta = \frac{3\pi}{2}$$

The solutions on the interval $[0, 2\pi)$ are $\theta = \frac{\pi}{6}, \frac{5\pi}{6}, \frac{3\pi}{2}$.

91. $\sin(2\theta) - \cos\theta - 2\sin\theta + 1 = 0$

$$2\sin\theta\cos\theta - \cos\theta - 2\sin\theta + 1 = 0 \rightarrow \cos\theta(2\sin\theta - 1) - 1(2\sin\theta - 1) = 0$$

$$(2\sin\theta - 1)(\cos\theta - 1) = 0$$

$$\sin\theta = \frac{1}{2} \rightarrow \theta = \frac{\pi}{6}, \frac{5\pi}{6}$$

$$\text{or } \cos\theta = 1 \rightarrow \theta = 0$$

The solutions on the interval $[0, 2\pi)$ are $\theta = 0, \frac{\pi}{6}, \frac{5\pi}{6}$.

92. $\sin(2\theta) - \sin\theta - 2\cos\theta + 1 = 0$

$$2\sin\theta\cos\theta - \sin\theta - 2\cos\theta + 1 = 0 \rightarrow \sin\theta(2\cos\theta - 1) - 1(2\cos\theta - 1) = 0$$

$$(2\cos\theta - 1)(\sin\theta - 1) = 0$$

$$\cos\theta = \frac{1}{2} \rightarrow \theta = \frac{\pi}{3}, \frac{5\pi}{3}$$

$$\text{or } \sin\theta = 1 \rightarrow \theta = \frac{\pi}{2}$$

The solutions on the interval $[0, 2\pi)$ are $\theta = \frac{\pi}{3}, \frac{\pi}{2}, \frac{5\pi}{3}$.

93. $2\sin^2\theta - 3\sin\theta + 1 = 0$

$(2\sin\theta - 1)(\sin\theta - 1) = 0$

$$2\sin\theta - 1 = 0 \rightarrow \sin\theta = \frac{1}{2} \rightarrow \theta = \frac{\pi}{6}, \frac{5\pi}{6}$$

$$\text{or } \sin\theta - 1 = 0 \rightarrow \sin\theta = 1 \rightarrow \theta = \frac{\pi}{2}$$

The solutions on the interval $[0, 2\pi)$ are $\theta = \frac{\pi}{6}, \frac{\pi}{2}, \frac{5\pi}{6}$.

94. $2\cos^2\theta + \cos\theta - 1 = 0$

$(2\cos\theta - 1)(\cos\theta + 1) = 0$

$$2\cos\theta - 1 = 0 \rightarrow \cos\theta = \frac{1}{2} \rightarrow \theta = \frac{\pi}{3}, \frac{5\pi}{3}$$

$$\text{or } \cos\theta + 1 = 0 \rightarrow \cos\theta = -1 \rightarrow \theta = \pi$$

The solutions on the interval $[0, 2\pi)$ are $\theta = \frac{\pi}{3}, \pi, \frac{5\pi}{3}$.

95. $4\sin^2\theta = 1 + 4\cos\theta$

$$4\left(1 - \cos^2\theta\right) = 1 + 4\cos\theta \rightarrow 4 - 4\cos^2\theta = 1 + 4\cos\theta$$

$4\cos^2\theta + 4\cos\theta - 3 = 0 \rightarrow (2\cos\theta - 1)(2\cos\theta + 3) = 0$

$$2\cos\theta - 1 = 0 \rightarrow \cos\theta = \frac{1}{2} \rightarrow \theta = \frac{\pi}{3}, \frac{5\pi}{3}$$

$$\text{or } 2\cos\theta + 3 = 0 \rightarrow \cos\theta = -\frac{3}{2}, \text{ which is impossible}$$

The solutions on the interval $[0, 2\pi)$ are $\theta = \frac{\pi}{3}, \frac{5\pi}{3}$.

96. $8 - 12\sin^2\theta = 4\cos^2\theta$

$8 - 12\sin^2\theta = 4\left(1 - \sin^2\theta\right) \rightarrow 8 - 12\sin^2\theta = 4 - 4\sin^2\theta$

$$4 = 8\sin^2\theta \rightarrow \sin^2\theta = \frac{4}{8}$$

$$\sin^2\theta = \frac{1}{2} \rightarrow \sin\theta = \pm\sqrt{\frac{1}{2}} = \pm\frac{\sqrt{2}}{2} \Rightarrow \theta = \frac{\pi}{4}, \frac{3\pi}{4}, \frac{5\pi}{4}, \frac{7\pi}{4}$$

The solutions on the interval $[0, 2\pi)$ are $\theta = \frac{\pi}{4}, \frac{3\pi}{4}, \frac{5\pi}{4}, \frac{7\pi}{4}$.

97. $\sin(2\theta) = \sqrt{2}\cos\theta$

$2\sin\theta\cos\theta = \sqrt{2}\cos\theta \rightarrow 2\sin\theta\cos\theta - \sqrt{2}\cos\theta = 0 \rightarrow \cos\theta\left(2\sin\theta - \sqrt{2}\right) = 0$

$$\cos\theta = 0 \rightarrow \theta = \frac{\pi}{2}, \frac{3\pi}{2}$$

$$\text{or } 2\sin\theta - \sqrt{2} = 0 \rightarrow \sin\theta = \frac{\sqrt{2}}{2} \rightarrow \theta = \frac{\pi}{4}, \frac{3\pi}{4}$$

The solutions on the interval $[0,2\pi)$ are $\theta=\frac{\pi}{4},\frac{\pi}{2},\frac{3\pi}{4},\frac{3\pi}{2}$.

98. $1+\sqrt{3}\cos\theta+\cos(2\theta)=0$

$$1+\sqrt{3}\cos\theta+2\cos^2(\theta)-1=0\rightarrow 2\cos^2(\theta)+\sqrt{3}\cos\theta=0\rightarrow\cos\theta\left(2\cos\theta+\sqrt{3}\right)=0$$

$$\cos\theta=0\rightarrow\theta=\frac{\pi}{2},\frac{3\pi}{2}$$

$$\text{or } 2\cos\theta+\sqrt{3}\rightarrow\cos\theta=-\frac{\sqrt{3}}{2}\rightarrow\theta=\frac{5\pi}{6},\frac{7\pi}{6}$$

The solutions on the interval $[0,2\pi)$ are $\theta=\frac{\pi}{2},\frac{5\pi}{6},\frac{7\pi}{6},\frac{3\pi}{2}$.

99. $\sin\theta-\cos\theta=1$

Divide each side by $\sqrt{2}$:

$$\frac{1}{\sqrt{2}}\sin\theta-\frac{1}{\sqrt{2}}\cos\theta=\frac{1}{\sqrt{2}}$$

Rewrite in the difference of two angles form where

$$\cos\phi=\frac{1}{\sqrt{2}} \text{ and } \sin\phi=\frac{1}{\sqrt{2}} \text{ and } \phi=\frac{\pi}{4}:$$

$$\sin\theta\cos\phi-\cos\theta\sin\phi=\frac{1}{\sqrt{2}}$$

$$\sin(\theta-\phi)=\frac{\sqrt{2}}{2}$$

$$\theta-\phi=\frac{\pi}{4} \text{ or } \theta-\phi=\frac{3\pi}{4}$$

$$\theta-\frac{\pi}{4}=\frac{\pi}{4} \text{ or } \theta-\frac{\pi}{4}=\frac{3\pi}{4}$$

$$\theta=\frac{\pi}{2} \text{ or } \theta=\pi$$

The solutions on the interval $[0, 2\pi)$ are $\theta=\frac{\pi}{2},\pi$.

100. $\sin\theta-\sqrt{3}\cos\theta=2$

$$\sin\theta-2=\sqrt{3}\cos\theta\rightarrow\sin^2\theta-4\sin\theta+4=3\cos^2\theta$$

$$\sin^2\theta-4\sin\theta+4=3\left(1-\sin^2\theta\right)\rightarrow\sin^2\theta-4\sin\theta+4=3-3\sin^2\theta$$

$$4\sin^2\theta-4\sin\theta+1=0\rightarrow(2\sin\theta-1)(2\sin\theta-1)=0$$

$$2\sin\theta-1=0\rightarrow\sin\theta=\frac{1}{2}\rightarrow\theta=\frac{\pi}{6},\frac{5\pi}{6}$$

The solutions on the interval $[0, 2\pi)$ are $\theta=\frac{\pi}{6},\frac{5\pi}{6}$.

101. $2x = 5\cos x$
Find the intersection of
$y_1 = 2x$ and $y_2 = 5\cos x$:

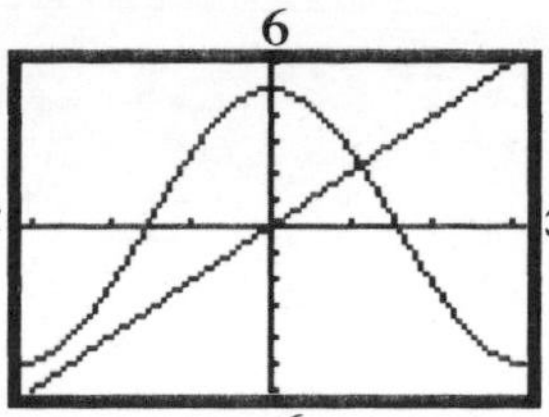

$x \approx 1.11$

102. $2x = 5\sin x$
Find the intersection of
$y_1 = 2x$ and $y_2 = 5\sin x$:

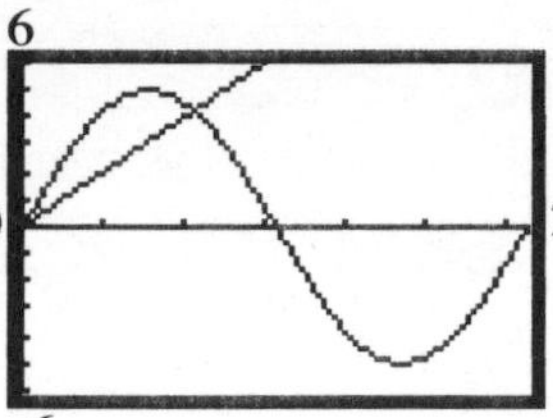

$x \approx 0, 2.13$

103. $2\sin x + 3\cos x = 4x$
Find the intersection of
$y_1 = 2\sin x + 3\cos x$ and $y_2 = 4x$:

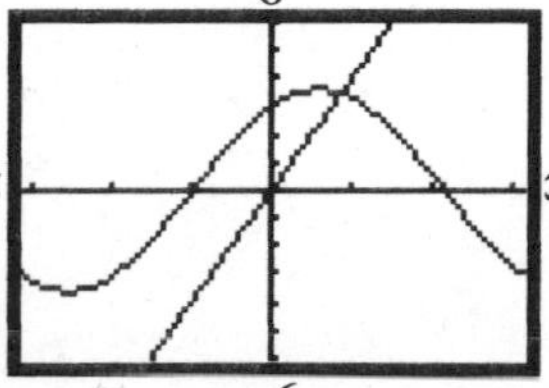

$x \approx 0.87$

104. $3\cos x + x = \sin x$
Find the intersection of
$y_1 = 3\cos x + x$ and $y_2 = \sin x$:

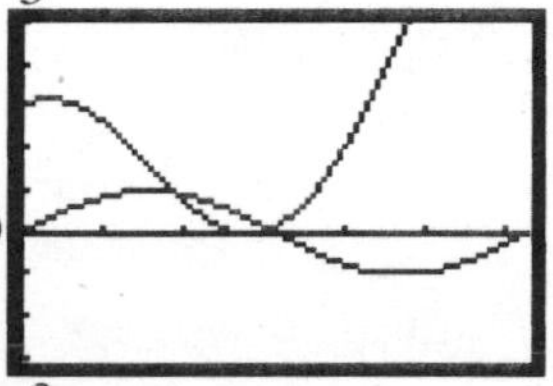

$x \approx 1.89, 3.07$

105. $\sin x = \ln x$
Find the intersection of
$y_1 = \sin x$ and $y_2 = \ln x$:

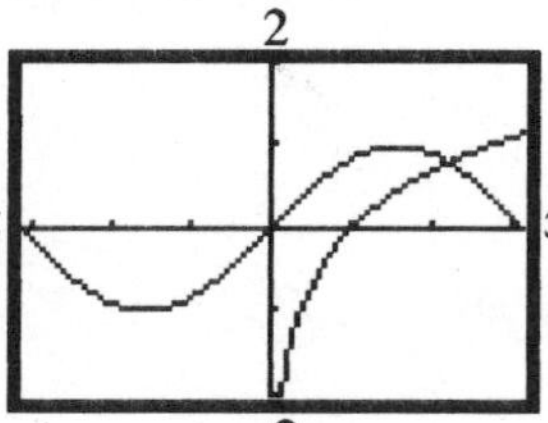

$x \approx 2.22$

106. $\sin x = e^{-x}$
Find the intersection of
$y_1 = \sin x$ and $y_2 = e^{-x}$:

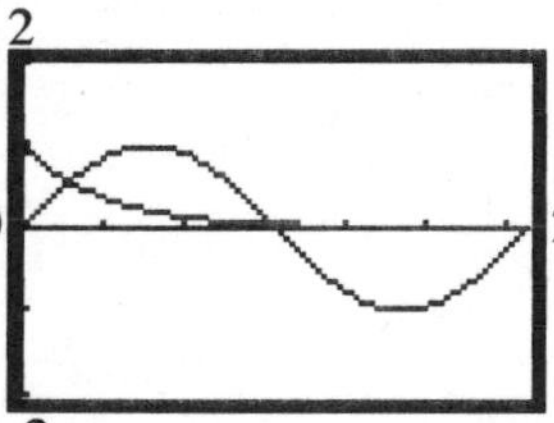

$x \approx 0.59, 3.10$

Chapter 9

Applications of Trigonometric Functions

9.1 Applications Involving Right Triangles

1. $b = 5,\ \beta = 20°$

$$\sin\beta = \frac{b}{c} \rightarrow \sin(20°) = \frac{5}{c} \rightarrow c = \frac{5}{\sin(20°)} \approx \frac{5}{0.3420} \approx 14.62$$

$$\tan\beta = \frac{b}{a} \rightarrow \tan(20°) = \frac{5}{a} \rightarrow a = \frac{5}{\tan(20°)} \approx \frac{5}{0.3640} \approx 13.74$$

$$\alpha = 90° - \beta = 90° - 20° = 70°$$

2. $b = 4,\ \beta = 10°$

$$\sin\beta = \frac{b}{c} \rightarrow \sin(10°) = \frac{4}{c} \rightarrow c = \frac{4}{\sin(10°)} \approx \frac{4}{0.1736} \approx 23.04$$

$$\tan\beta = \frac{b}{a} \rightarrow \tan(10°) = \frac{4}{a} \rightarrow a = \frac{4}{\tan(10°)} \approx \frac{4}{0.1763} \approx 22.69$$

$$\alpha = 90° - \beta = 90° - 10° = 80°$$

3. $a = 6,\ \beta = 40°$

$$\cos\beta = \frac{a}{c} \rightarrow \cos(40°) = \frac{6}{c} \rightarrow c = \frac{6}{\cos(40°)} \approx \frac{6}{0.7660} \approx 7.83$$

$$\tan\beta = \frac{b}{a} \rightarrow \tan(40°) = \frac{b}{6} \rightarrow b = 6\tan(40°) \approx 6 \cdot (0.8391) \approx 5.03$$

$$\alpha = 90° - \beta = 90° - 40° = 50°$$

4. $a = 7,\ \beta = 50°$

$$\cos\beta = \frac{a}{c} \rightarrow \cos(50°) = \frac{7}{c} \rightarrow c = \frac{7}{\cos(50°)} \approx \frac{7}{0.6428} \approx 10.89$$

$$\tan\beta = \frac{b}{a} \rightarrow \tan(50°) = \frac{b}{7} \rightarrow b = 7\tan(50°) \approx 7 \cdot (1.1918) \approx 8.34$$

$$\alpha = 90° - \beta = 90° - 50° = 40°$$

5. $b = 4,\ \alpha = 10^\circ$

$$\tan\alpha = \frac{a}{b} \rightarrow \tan(10^\circ) = \frac{a}{4} \rightarrow a = 4\tan(10^\circ) \approx 4 \cdot (0.1763) \approx 0.71$$

$$\cos\alpha = \frac{b}{c} \rightarrow \cos(10^\circ) = \frac{4}{c} \rightarrow c = \frac{4}{\cos(10^\circ)} \approx \frac{4}{0.9848} \approx 4.06$$

$$\beta = 90^\circ - \alpha = 90^\circ - 10^\circ = 80^\circ$$

6. $b = 6,\ \alpha = 20^\circ$

$$\tan\alpha = \frac{a}{b} \rightarrow \tan(20^\circ) = \frac{a}{6} \rightarrow a = 6\tan(20^\circ) \approx 6 \cdot (0.3640) \approx 2.18$$

$$\cos\alpha = \frac{b}{c} \rightarrow \cos(20^\circ) = \frac{6}{c} \rightarrow c = \frac{6}{\cos(20^\circ)} \approx \frac{6}{0.9397} \approx 6.39$$

$$\beta = 90^\circ - \alpha = 90^\circ - 20^\circ = 70^\circ$$

7. $a = 5,\ \alpha = 25^\circ$

$$\cot\alpha = \frac{b}{a} \rightarrow \cot(25^\circ) = \frac{b}{5} \rightarrow b = 5\cot(25^\circ) \approx 5 \cdot (2.1445) \approx 10.72$$

$$\csc\alpha = \frac{c}{a} \rightarrow \csc(25^\circ) = \frac{c}{5} \rightarrow c = 5\csc(25^\circ) \approx 5 \cdot (2.3662) \approx 11.83$$

$$\beta = 90^\circ - \alpha = 90^\circ - 25^\circ = 65^\circ$$

8. $a = 6,\ \alpha = 40^\circ$

$$\cot\alpha = \frac{a}{b} \rightarrow \cot(40^\circ) = \frac{b}{6} \rightarrow b = 6\cot(40^\circ) \approx 6 \cdot (1.1918) \approx 7.15$$

$$\csc\alpha = \frac{c}{a} \rightarrow \csc(45^\circ) = \frac{c}{6} \rightarrow c = 6\csc(40^\circ) \approx 6 \cdot (1.5557) \approx 9.33$$

$$\beta = 90^\circ - \alpha = 90^\circ - 40^\circ = 50^\circ$$

9. $c = 9,\ \beta = 20^\circ$

$$\sin\beta = \frac{b}{c} \rightarrow \sin(20^\circ) = \frac{b}{9} \rightarrow b = 9\sin(20^\circ) \approx 9 \cdot (0.3420) \approx 3.08$$

$$\cos\beta = \frac{a}{c} \rightarrow \cos(20^\circ) = \frac{a}{9} \rightarrow a = 9\cos(20^\circ) \approx 9 \cdot (0.9397) \approx 8.46$$

$$\alpha = 90^\circ - \alpha = 90^\circ - 20^\circ = 70^\circ$$

10. $c = 10,\ \alpha = 40^\circ$

$$\sin\alpha = \frac{a}{c} \rightarrow \sin(40^\circ) = \frac{a}{10} \rightarrow a = 10\sin(40^\circ) \approx 10 \cdot (0.6428) \approx 6.43$$

$$\cos\alpha = \frac{b}{c} \rightarrow \cos(40^\circ) = \frac{b}{10} \rightarrow b = 10\cos(40^\circ) \approx 10 \cdot (0.7660) \approx 7.66$$

$$\beta = 90^\circ - \alpha = 90^\circ - 40^\circ = 50^\circ$$

11. $a = 5,\ b = 3$

$c^2 = a^2 + b^2 = 5^2 + 3^2 = 25 + 9 = 34 \rightarrow c = \sqrt{34} \approx 5.83$

$\tan\alpha = \frac{a}{b} = \frac{5}{3} \approx 1.6667 \rightarrow \alpha \approx 59.0°$

$\beta = 90° - \alpha = 90° - 59.0° = 31.0°$

12. $a = 2,\ b = 8$

$c^2 = a^2 + b^2 = 2^2 + 8^2 = 4 + 64 = 68 \rightarrow c = \sqrt{68} \approx 8.25$

$\tan\alpha = \frac{a}{b} = \frac{2}{8} = 0.2500 \rightarrow \alpha \approx 14.0°$

$\beta = 90° - \alpha = 90° - 14.0° = 76.0°$

13. $a = 2,\ c = 5$

$c^2 = a^2 + b^2 \rightarrow b^2 = c^2 - a^2 = 5^2 - 2^2 = 25 - 4 = 21 \rightarrow b = \sqrt{21} \approx 4.58$

$\sin\alpha = \frac{a}{c} = \frac{2}{5} = 0.4000 \rightarrow \alpha \approx 23.6°$

$\beta = 90° - \alpha = 90° - 23.6° = 66.4°$

14. $b = 4,\ c = 6$

$c^2 = a^2 + b^2 \rightarrow a^2 = c^2 - b^2 = 6^2 - 4^2 = 36 - 16 = 20 \rightarrow a = \sqrt{20} \approx 4.47$

$\cos\alpha = \frac{b}{c} = \frac{4}{6} = 0.6667 \rightarrow \alpha \approx 48.2°$

$\beta = 90° - \alpha = 90° - 48.2° = 41.8°$

15. $c = 8,\ \alpha = 35°$

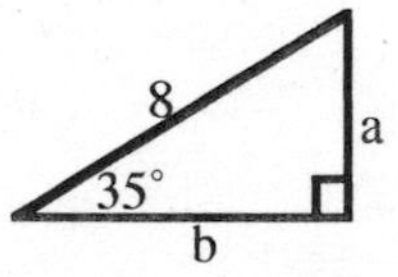

$\sin(35°) = \frac{a}{8} \rightarrow a = 8\sin(35°) \approx 8(0.5736) \approx 4.59$ in.

$\cos(35°) = \frac{b}{8} \rightarrow b = 8\cos(35°) \approx 8(0.8192) \approx 6.55$ in.

16. $c = 10,\ \alpha = 40°$

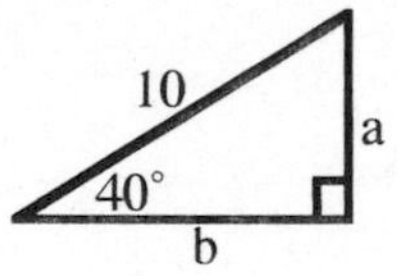

$\sin(40°) = \frac{a}{10} \rightarrow a = 10\sin(40°) \approx 10(0.6428) \approx 6.43$ cm.

$\cos(40°) = \frac{b}{10} \rightarrow b = 10\cos(40°) \approx 10(0.7660) \approx 7.66$ cm.

17. $\alpha = 25°,\ a = 5$

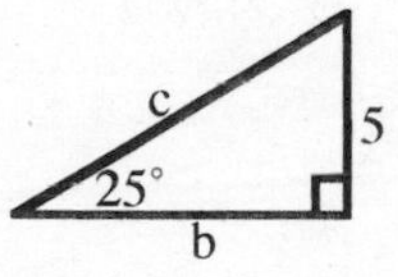

$\sin(25°) = \frac{5}{c} \rightarrow c = \frac{5}{\sin(25°)} \approx \frac{5}{0.4226} \approx 11.83$ in.

$\alpha = 25°,\ b = 5$

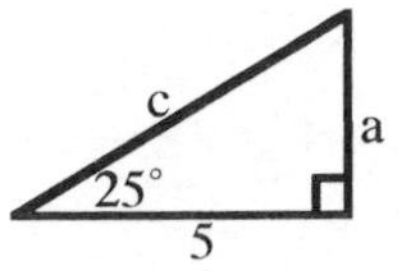

$$\cos(25°) = \frac{5}{c} \rightarrow c = \frac{5}{\cos(25°)} \approx \frac{5}{0.9063} \approx 5.52 \text{ in.}$$

18. $\alpha = \frac{\pi}{8},\ a = 3$

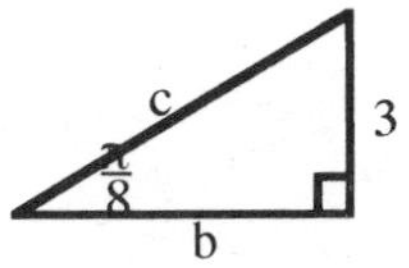

$$\sin\left(\frac{\pi}{8}\right) = \frac{3}{c} \rightarrow c = \frac{3}{\sin\left(\frac{\pi}{8}\right)} \approx \frac{3}{0.3827} \approx 7.84 \text{ m.}$$

$\alpha = \frac{\pi}{8},\ b = 3$

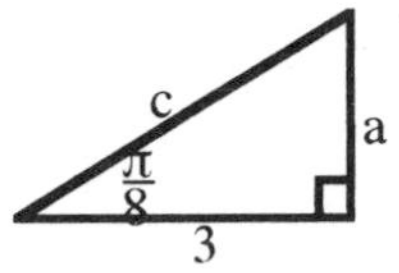

$$\cos\left(\frac{\pi}{8}\right) = \frac{3}{c} \rightarrow c = \frac{3}{\cos\left(\frac{\pi}{8}\right)} \approx \frac{3}{0.9239} \approx 3.25 \text{ m.}$$

19. $c = 5,\ a = 2$

$$\sin\alpha = \frac{2}{5} = 0.4000 \rightarrow \alpha \approx 23.6 \rightarrow \beta = 90° - \alpha = 90° - 23.6° \approx 66.4°$$

20. $c = 3,\ a = 1$

$$\sin\alpha = \frac{1}{3} \approx 0.3333 \rightarrow \alpha \approx 19.5 \rightarrow \beta = 90° - \alpha = 90° - 19.5° \approx 70.5°$$

21. $\tan(35°) = \frac{b}{100} \rightarrow b = 100\tan(35°) \approx 100(0.7002) \approx 70.02$ feet

22. $\tan(40°) = \frac{b}{100} \rightarrow b = 100\tan(40°) \approx 100(0.8391) \approx 83.91$ feet

23. $\tan(85.361°) = \frac{a}{80} \rightarrow a = 80\tan(85.361°) \approx 80(12.3239) \approx 985.91$ feet

24.

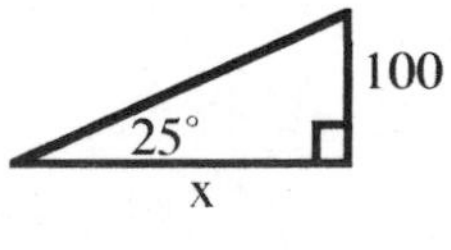

$$\tan(25°) = \frac{100}{x} \rightarrow x = \frac{100}{\tan(25°)} \approx \frac{100}{0.4663} \approx 214.45 \text{ feet}$$

25.

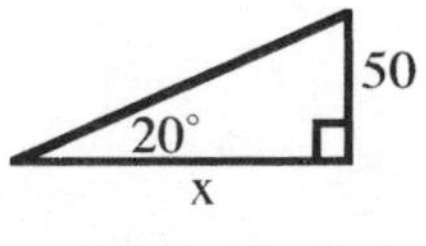

$$\tan(20°) = \frac{50}{x} \rightarrow x = \frac{50}{\tan(20°)} \approx \frac{50}{0.3640} \approx 137.37 \text{ meters}$$

26.

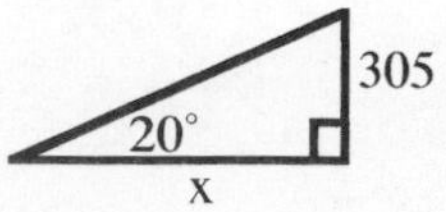

$$\tan(20°) = \frac{305}{x} \rightarrow x = \frac{305}{\tan(20°)} \approx \frac{305}{0.3640} \approx 837.98 \text{ feet}$$

27.

$$\sin(70°) = \frac{x}{22} \rightarrow x = 22\sin(70°) \approx 22(0.9397) \approx 20.67 \text{ feet}$$

28.

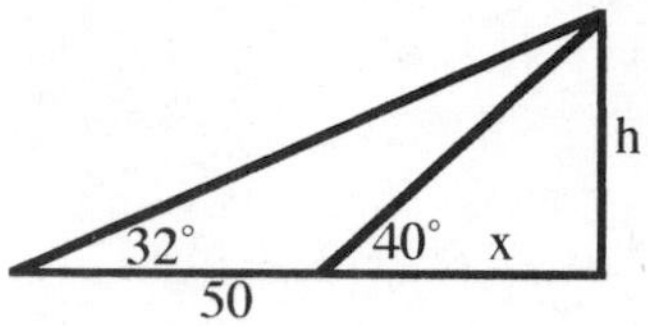

$$\tan(40°) = \frac{h}{x} \rightarrow x = \frac{h}{\tan(40°)}$$

$$\tan(32°) = \frac{h}{x+50} \rightarrow h = (x+50)\tan(32°) = \left(\frac{h}{\tan(40°)} + 50\right)\tan(32°)$$

$$h = \left(\frac{h}{0.8391} + 50\right)0.6249$$

$$h = 0.7447h + 31.245 \rightarrow 0.2553h = 31.245 \rightarrow h \approx 122.37$$

29. opposite side = 10 feet, adjacent side = 35 feet

$$\tan\theta = \frac{10}{35} \approx 0.2857 \rightarrow \theta = \tan^{-1}\left(\frac{10}{35}\right) \approx 15.9°$$

30.

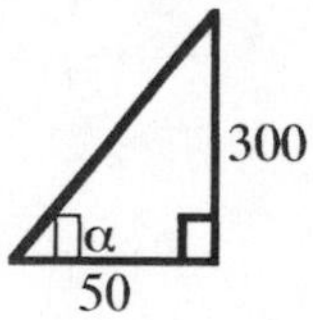

$$\tan\alpha = \frac{300}{50} = 6 \rightarrow \alpha = 80.5°$$

31. Let h represent the height of Lincoln's face.

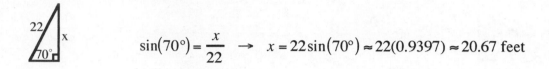

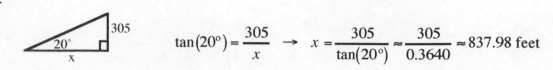

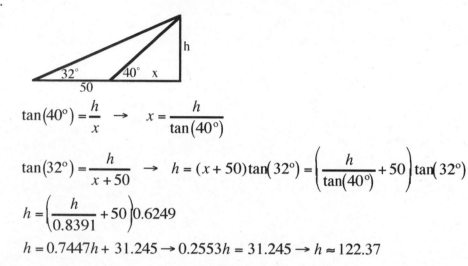

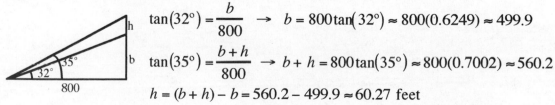

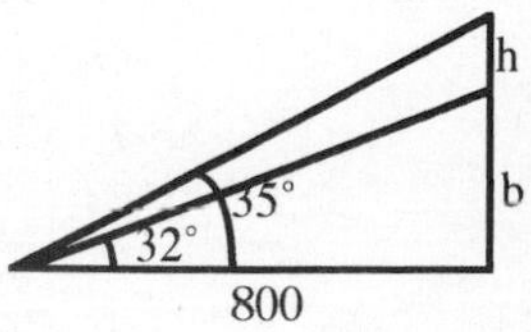

$$\tan(32°) = \frac{b}{800} \rightarrow b = 800\tan(32°) \approx 800(0.6249) \approx 499.9$$

$$\tan(35°) = \frac{b+h}{800} \rightarrow b+h = 800\tan(35°) \approx 800(0.7002) \approx 560.2$$

$$h = (b+h) - b = 560.2 - 499.9 \approx 60.27 \text{ feet}$$

32.

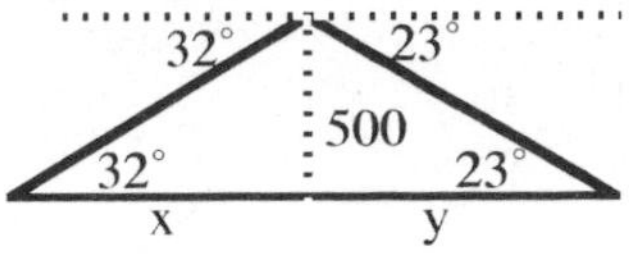

$$\tan(32°) = \frac{500}{x} \rightarrow x = \frac{500}{\tan(32°)}$$

$$\tan(23°) = \frac{500}{y} \rightarrow y = \frac{500}{\tan(23°)}$$

$$\text{Distance} = x + y = \frac{500}{\tan(32°)} + \frac{500}{\tan(23°)} \approx 1978.09 \text{ feet}$$

33.

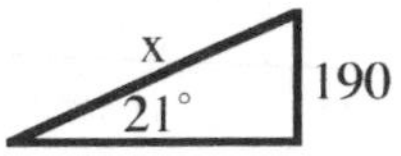

$$\sin(21°) = \frac{190}{x} \rightarrow x = \frac{190}{\sin(21°)} \approx \frac{190}{0.3584} \approx 530.18 \text{ ft.}$$

34.

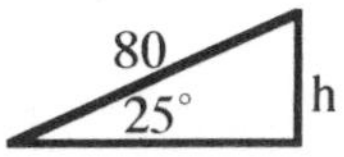

$$\sin(25°) = \frac{h}{80} \rightarrow h = 80\sin(25°) \approx 80(0.4226) \approx 33.81 \text{ ft.}$$

35.

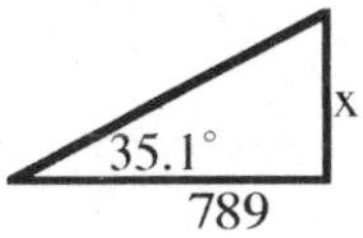

$$\tan(35.1°) = \frac{x}{789} \rightarrow x = 789\tan(35.1°) \approx 789(0.7028) \approx 554.52 \text{ ft}$$

36.

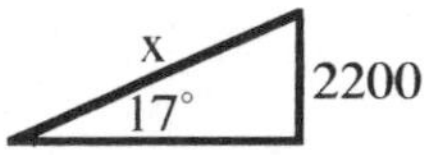

$$\sin 17° = \frac{2200}{x} \rightarrow x = \frac{2200}{\sin(17°)} \approx \frac{2200}{0.2924} \approx 7524.67 \text{ ft.}$$

37. (a) $\tan(15°) = \dfrac{30}{x} \rightarrow x = \dfrac{30}{\tan(15°)} \approx \dfrac{30}{0.2679} \approx 111.96$ feet

The truck is traveling at 111.96 ft/sec.

$$\frac{111.96 \text{ ft}}{\text{sec}} \cdot \frac{1 \text{ mile}}{5280 \text{ ft}} \cdot \frac{3600 \text{ sec}}{\text{hr}} \approx 76.34 \text{ mi / hr}$$

(b) $\tan(20°) = \dfrac{30}{x} \rightarrow x = \dfrac{30}{\tan(20°)} \approx \dfrac{30}{0.3640} \approx 82.42$ feet

The truck is traveling at 82.42 ft/sec.

$$\frac{82.42 \text{ ft}}{\text{sec}} \cdot \frac{1 \text{ mile}}{5280 \text{ ft}} \cdot \frac{3600 \text{ sec}}{\text{hr}} \approx 56.20 \text{ mi / hr}$$

(c) A ticket is issued for traveling at a speed of 60 mi/hr or more.

$$\frac{60 \text{ mi}}{\text{hr}} \cdot \frac{5280 \text{ ft}}{\text{mi}} \cdot \frac{1\text{hr}}{3600 \text{ sec}} = 88 \text{ ft / sec.}$$

If $\tan\theta < \frac{30}{88}$, the trooper should issue a ticket.

A ticket is issued if $\theta < 18.8°$.

38.

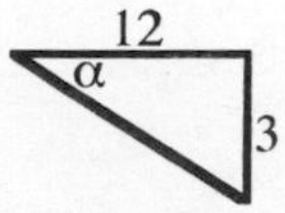

$$\tan\alpha = \frac{3}{12} = 0.25 \quad \rightarrow \quad \alpha \approx 14.0°$$

39. Find angle θ: (see the figure)

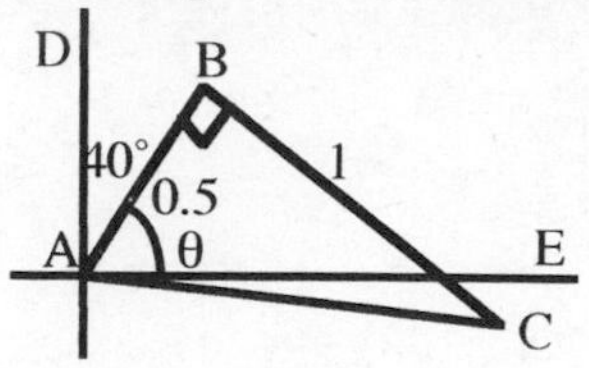

$$\tan\theta = \frac{1}{0.5} = 2 \quad \rightarrow \quad \theta = 63.4°$$
$$\angle DAC = 40° + 63.4° = 103.4°$$
$$\angle EAC = 103.4° - 90° = 13.4°$$

The bearing the control tower should use is S76.6˚E.

40. Find angle AMB and subtract from 80° to obtain θ.

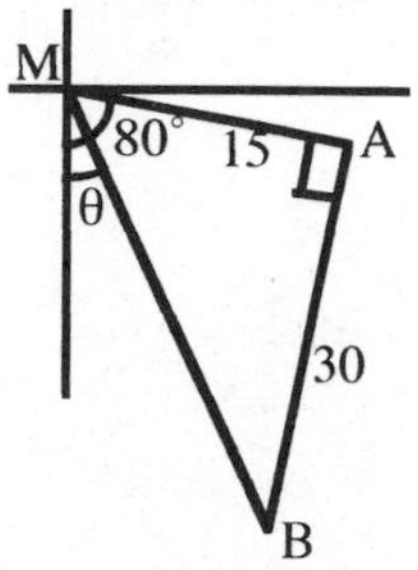

$$\tan\angle AMB = \frac{30}{15} = 2 \quad \rightarrow \quad \angle AMB = 63.4°$$
$$\theta = 80° - 63.4° = 16.6°$$

The bearing is S16.6° E.

41. $\tan\alpha = \dfrac{10-6}{15} = \dfrac{4}{15} \quad \rightarrow \quad \alpha = 14.9°$

42. The height of the beam above the wall is 46 – 20 = 26 feet.

$$\tan\theta = \frac{26}{10} = 2.6 \quad \rightarrow \quad \theta \approx 69°$$

43. The length of the highway $= x + y + z$

$$\sin(40°) = \frac{1}{x} \quad \rightarrow \quad x = \frac{1}{\sin(40°)} \approx 1.56 \text{ mi}$$

$$\sin(50°) = \frac{1}{z} \quad \rightarrow \quad z = \frac{1}{\sin(50°)} \approx 1.31 \text{ mi}$$

$$\tan(40°) = \frac{1}{a} \quad \rightarrow \quad a = \frac{1}{\tan(40°)} \approx 1.19 \text{ mi}$$

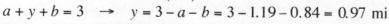

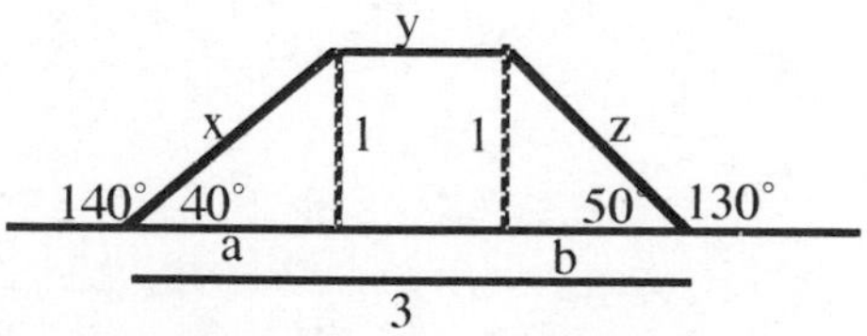

$$\tan(50°) = \frac{1}{b} \quad \rightarrow \quad b = \frac{1}{\tan(50°)} \approx 0.84 \text{ mi}$$

$$a + y + b = 3 \quad \rightarrow \quad y = 3 - a - b = 3 - 1.19 - 0.84 = 0.97 \text{ mi}$$

The length of the highway is: 1.56 + 0.97 + 1.31 = 3.83 miles.

44. (a) $\cos\left(\dfrac{\theta}{2}\right) = \dfrac{3960}{3960 + h}$

(b) $d = 3960\,\theta$

(c) $\cos\left(\frac{d}{7920}\right)=\frac{3960}{3960+h}$

(d) $\cos\left(\frac{2500}{7920}\right)=\frac{3960}{3960+h}$

$$0.9506=\frac{3960}{3960+h}$$

$$0.9506(3960+h)=3960\rightarrow 3764+0.9506h=3960\rightarrow 0.9506h=196$$

$$h\approx 206 \text{ miles}$$

(e) $\cos\left(\frac{d}{7920}\right)=\frac{3960}{3960+300}=\frac{3960}{4260}\approx 0.9296$

$$\frac{d}{7920}\approx 0.3775\rightarrow d\approx 2990 \text{ miles}$$

45. In order to see George's head and feet the camera must be x feet from George. Solve:

$$\tan(20°)=\frac{4}{x}\quad\rightarrow\quad x=\frac{4}{\tan(20°)}\approx 10.99 \text{ feet}$$

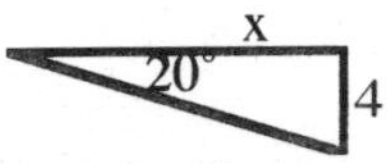

The camera will need to be moved back 1 foot to see George's feet.

46.

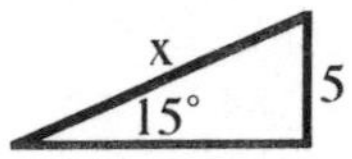

$$\sin(15°)=\frac{5}{x}\quad\rightarrow\quad x=\frac{5}{\sin(15°)}\approx\frac{5}{0.2588}\approx 19.32 \text{ ft.}$$

47. $\sin\theta=\frac{y}{1}=y;\qquad \cos\theta=\frac{x}{1}=x$

(a) $A=2xy=2\cos\theta\sin\theta$

(b) $2\cos\theta\sin\theta=2\sin\theta\cos\theta=\sin(2\theta)$

(c) The largest value of the sine function is 1. Solve:

$$\sin(2\theta)=1\rightarrow 2\theta=\frac{\pi}{2}\rightarrow\theta=\frac{\pi}{4}$$

(d) $x=\cos\left(\frac{\pi}{4}\right)=\frac{\sqrt{2}}{2}\qquad y=\sin\left(\frac{\pi}{4}\right)=\frac{\sqrt{2}}{2}$

The dimensions are $\sqrt{2}$ by $\frac{\sqrt{2}}{2}$.

48. Let b represent the base of the triangle.

$$\cos\left(\frac{\theta}{2}\right)=\frac{h}{s}\rightarrow h=s\cdot\cos\left(\frac{\theta}{2}\right)\qquad \sin\left(\frac{\theta}{2}\right)=\frac{\left(\frac{1}{2}b\right)}{s}\rightarrow b=2s\cdot\sin\left(\frac{\theta}{2}\right)$$

$$A=\frac{1}{2}b\cdot h=\frac{1}{2}\left(2s\cdot\sin\left(\frac{\theta}{2}\right)\right)\left(s\cdot\cos\left(\frac{\theta}{2}\right)\right)=s^2\cdot\sin\left(\frac{\theta}{2}\right)\cos\left(\frac{\theta}{2}\right)=\frac{1}{2}s^2\cdot\sin\theta$$

49. Find θ: (see figure)

$$\cos\theta = \frac{3960}{\left(3960 + \frac{362}{5280}\right)} \approx 0.99998269$$

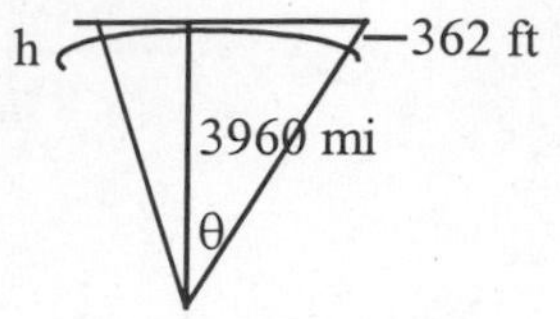

$$\theta \approx 0.00588439 \text{ radians}$$

Find the arc length from the base of the lighthouse to the horizon:

$s = r\theta = 3960(0.00588439) \approx 23.3$ miles

The distance from the ship to the horizon point is 40 – 23.3 = 16.7 miles.

$$\theta = \frac{s}{r} = \frac{16.7}{3960} \approx 0.00421717$$

If h is the height of the ship, $\cos(0.00421717) = \dfrac{3960}{3960 + h}$.

Solve for h:

$$(3960 + h)\cos(0.00421717) = 3960$$

$$h = \frac{3960}{\cos(0.00421717)} - 3960 \approx 0.0352 \text{ miles or } \approx 186 \text{ feet}$$

The ship would have to be 186 feet tall to see the lighthouse from 40 miles away.

The distance from the plane to the horizon point is 120 – 23.3 = 96.7 miles.

$$\theta = \frac{s}{r} = \frac{96.7}{3960} \approx 0.02441919$$

If h is the height of the plane, $\cos(0.02441919) = \dfrac{3960}{3960 + h}$.

Solve for h:

$$(3960 + h)\cos(0.02441919) = 3960$$

$$h = \frac{3960}{\cos(0.02441919)} - 3960 \approx 1.18 \text{ miles or } \approx 6230 \text{ feet}$$

A plane at an altitude of 6230 feet could see the lighthouse from 120 miles away. The brochure understates the distance from which the lighthouse can be seen.

Chapter 9

Applications of Trigonometric Functions

9.2 The Law of Sines

1. $c = 5,\ \beta = 45^\circ,\ \gamma = 95^\circ$

$\alpha = 180^\circ - \beta - \gamma = 180^\circ - 45^\circ - 95^\circ = 40^\circ$

$$\frac{\sin\alpha}{a} = \frac{\sin\gamma}{c} \rightarrow \frac{\sin(40^\circ)}{a} = \frac{\sin(95^\circ)}{5} \rightarrow a = \frac{5\sin(40^\circ)}{\sin(95^\circ)} \approx 3.23$$

$$\frac{\sin\beta}{b} = \frac{\sin\gamma}{c} \rightarrow \frac{\sin(45^\circ)}{b} = \frac{\sin(95^\circ)}{5} \rightarrow b = \frac{5\sin(45^\circ)}{\sin(95^\circ)} \approx 3.55$$

2. $c = 4,\ \alpha = 45^\circ,\ \beta = 40^\circ$

$\gamma = 180^\circ - \alpha - \beta = 180^\circ - 45^\circ - 40^\circ = 95^\circ$

$$\frac{\sin\alpha}{a} = \frac{\sin\gamma}{c} \rightarrow \frac{\sin(45^\circ)}{a} = \frac{\sin(95^\circ)}{4} \rightarrow a = \frac{4\sin(45^\circ)}{\sin(95^\circ)} \approx 2.84$$

$$\frac{\sin\beta}{b} = \frac{\sin\gamma}{c} \rightarrow \frac{\sin(40^\circ)}{b} = \frac{\sin(95^\circ)}{4} \rightarrow b = \frac{4\sin(40^\circ)}{\sin(95^\circ)} \approx 2.58$$

3. $b = 3,\ \alpha = 50^\circ,\ \gamma = 85^\circ$

$\beta = 180^\circ - \alpha - \gamma = 180^\circ - 50^\circ - 85^\circ = 45^\circ$

$$\frac{\sin\alpha}{a} = \frac{\sin\beta}{b} \rightarrow \frac{\sin(50^\circ)}{a} = \frac{\sin(45^\circ)}{3} \rightarrow a = \frac{3\sin(50^\circ)}{\sin(45^\circ)} \approx 3.25$$

$$\frac{\sin\gamma}{c} = \frac{\sin\beta}{b} \rightarrow \frac{\sin(85^\circ)}{c} = \frac{\sin(45^\circ)}{3} \rightarrow c = \frac{3\sin(85^\circ)}{\sin(45^\circ)} \approx 4.23$$

4. $b = 10,\ \beta = 30^\circ,\ \gamma = 125^\circ$

$\alpha = 180^\circ - \beta - \gamma = 180^\circ - 30^\circ - 125^\circ = 25^\circ$

$$\frac{\sin\alpha}{a} = \frac{\sin\beta}{b} \rightarrow \frac{\sin(25^\circ)}{a} = \frac{\sin(30^\circ)}{10} \rightarrow a = \frac{10\sin(25^\circ)}{\sin(30^\circ)} \approx 8.45$$

$$\frac{\sin\gamma}{c} = \frac{\sin\beta}{b} \rightarrow \frac{\sin(125^\circ)}{c} = \frac{\sin(30^\circ)}{10} \rightarrow c = \frac{10\sin(125^\circ)}{\sin(30^\circ)} \approx 16.38$$

5. $b=7,\ \alpha=40^\circ,\ \beta=45^\circ$

$\gamma=180^\circ-\alpha-\beta=180^\circ-40^\circ-45^\circ=95^\circ$

$$\frac{\sin\alpha}{a}=\frac{\sin\beta}{b} \to \frac{\sin(40^\circ)}{a}=\frac{\sin(45^\circ)}{7} \to a=\frac{7\sin(40^\circ)}{\sin(45^\circ)}\approx 6.36$$

$$\frac{\sin\gamma}{c}=\frac{\sin\beta}{b} \to \frac{\sin(95^\circ)}{c}=\frac{\sin(45^\circ)}{7} \to c=\frac{7\sin(95^\circ)}{\sin(45^\circ)}\approx 9.86$$

6. $c=5,\ \alpha=10^\circ,\ \beta=5^\circ$

$\gamma=180^\circ-\alpha-\beta=180^\circ-10^\circ-5^\circ=165^\circ$

$$\frac{\sin\alpha}{a}=\frac{\sin\gamma}{c} \to \frac{\sin(10^\circ)}{a}=\frac{\sin(165^\circ)}{5} \to a=\frac{5\sin(10^\circ)}{\sin(165^\circ)}\approx 3.35$$

$$\frac{\sin\beta}{b}=\frac{\sin\gamma}{c} \to \frac{\sin(5^\circ)}{b}=\frac{\sin(165^\circ)}{5} \to b=\frac{5\sin(5^\circ)}{\sin(165^\circ)}\approx 1.68$$

7. $b=2,\ \beta=40^\circ,\ \gamma=100^\circ$

$\alpha=180^\circ-\beta-\gamma=180^\circ-40^\circ-100^\circ=40^\circ$

$$\frac{\sin\alpha}{a}=\frac{\sin\beta}{b} \to \frac{\sin(40^\circ)}{a}=\frac{\sin(40^\circ)}{2} \to a=\frac{2\sin(40^\circ)}{\sin(40^\circ)}=2$$

$$\frac{\sin\gamma}{c}=\frac{\sin\beta}{b} \to \frac{\sin(100^\circ)}{c}=\frac{\sin(40^\circ)}{2} \to c=\frac{2\sin(100^\circ)}{\sin(40^\circ)}\approx 3.06$$

8. $b=6,\ \alpha=100^\circ,\ \beta=30^\circ$

$\gamma=180^\circ-\alpha-\beta=180^\circ-100^\circ-30^\circ=50^\circ$

$$\frac{\sin\alpha}{a}=\frac{\sin\beta}{b} \to \frac{\sin(100^\circ)}{a}=\frac{\sin(30^\circ)}{6} \to a=\frac{6\sin(100^\circ)}{\sin(30^\circ)}\approx 11.82$$

$$\frac{\sin\gamma}{c}=\frac{\sin\beta}{b} \to \frac{\sin(50^\circ)}{c}=\frac{\sin(30^\circ)}{6} \to c=\frac{6\sin(50^\circ)}{\sin(30^\circ)}\approx 9.19$$

9. $\alpha=40^\circ,\ \beta=20^\circ,\ a=2$

$\gamma=180^\circ-\alpha-\beta=180^\circ-40^\circ-20^\circ=120^\circ$

$$\frac{\sin\alpha}{a}=\frac{\sin\beta}{b} \to \frac{\sin(40^\circ)}{2}=\frac{\sin(20^\circ)}{b} \to b=\frac{2\sin(20^\circ)}{\sin(40^\circ)}\approx 1.06$$

$$\frac{\sin\gamma}{c}=\frac{\sin\alpha}{a} \to \frac{\sin(120^\circ)}{c}=\frac{\sin(40^\circ)}{2} \to c=\frac{2\sin(120^\circ)}{\sin(40^\circ)}\approx 2.69$$

10. $\alpha = 50°,\ \gamma = 20°,\ a = 3$
$\beta = 180° - \alpha - \gamma = 180° - 50° - 20° = 110°$
$$\frac{\sin\alpha}{a} = \frac{\sin\beta}{b} \rightarrow \frac{\sin(50°)}{3} = \frac{\sin(110°)}{b} \rightarrow b = \frac{3\sin(110°)}{\sin(50°)} \approx 3.68$$
$$\frac{\sin\gamma}{c} = \frac{\sin\alpha}{a} \rightarrow \frac{\sin(20°)}{c} = \frac{\sin(50°)}{3} \rightarrow c = \frac{3\sin(20°)}{\sin(50°)} \approx 1.34$$

11. $\beta = 70°,\ \gamma = 10°,\ b = 5$
$\alpha = 180° - \beta - \gamma = 180° - 70° - 10° = 100°$
$$\frac{\sin\alpha}{a} = \frac{\sin\beta}{b} \rightarrow \frac{\sin(100°)}{a} = \frac{\sin(70°)}{5} \rightarrow a = \frac{5\sin(100°)}{\sin(70°)} \approx 5.24$$
$$\frac{\sin\gamma}{c} = \frac{\sin\beta}{b} \rightarrow \frac{\sin(10°)}{c} = \frac{\sin(70°)}{5} \rightarrow c = \frac{5\sin(10°)}{\sin(70°)} \approx 0.92$$

12. $\alpha = 70°,\ \beta = 60°,\ c = 4$
$\gamma = 180° - \alpha - \beta = 180° - 70° - 60° = 50°$
$$\frac{\sin\alpha}{a} = \frac{\sin\gamma}{c} \rightarrow \frac{\sin(70°)}{a} = \frac{\sin(50°)}{4} \rightarrow a = \frac{4\sin(70°)}{\sin(50°)} \approx 4.91$$
$$\frac{\sin\beta}{b} = \frac{\sin\gamma}{c} \rightarrow \frac{\sin(60°)}{b} = \frac{\sin(50°)}{4} \rightarrow b = \frac{4\sin(60°)}{\sin(50°)} \approx 4.52$$

13. $\alpha = 110°,\ \gamma = 30°,\ c = 3$
$\beta = 180° - \alpha - \gamma = 180° - 110° - 30° = 40°$
$$\frac{\sin\alpha}{a} = \frac{\sin\gamma}{c} \rightarrow \frac{\sin(110°)}{a} = \frac{\sin(30°)}{3} \rightarrow a = \frac{3\sin(110°)}{\sin(30°)} \approx 5.64$$
$$\frac{\sin\gamma}{c} = \frac{\sin\beta}{b} \rightarrow \frac{\sin(30°)}{3} = \frac{\sin(40°)}{b} \rightarrow b = \frac{3\sin(40°)}{\sin(30°)} \approx 3.86$$

14. $\beta = 10°,\ \gamma = 100°,\ b = 2$
$\alpha = 180° - \beta - \gamma = 180° - 10° - 100° = 70°$
$$\frac{\sin\alpha}{a} = \frac{\sin\beta}{b} \rightarrow \frac{\sin(70°)}{a} = \frac{\sin(10°)}{2} \rightarrow a = \frac{2\sin(70°)}{\sin(10°)} \approx 10.82$$
$$\frac{\sin\gamma}{c} = \frac{\sin\beta}{b} \rightarrow \frac{\sin(100°)}{c} = \frac{\sin(10°)}{2} \rightarrow c = \frac{2\sin(100°)}{\sin(10°)} \approx 11.34$$

15. $\alpha = 40^\circ,\ \beta = 40^\circ,\ c = 2$

$\gamma = 180^\circ - \alpha - \beta = 180^\circ - 40^\circ - 40^\circ = 100^\circ$

$$\frac{\sin\alpha}{a} = \frac{\sin\gamma}{c} \rightarrow \frac{\sin(40^\circ)}{a} = \frac{\sin(100^\circ)}{2} \rightarrow a = \frac{2\sin(40^\circ)}{\sin(100^\circ)} \approx 1.31$$

$$\frac{\sin\beta}{b} = \frac{\sin\gamma}{c} \rightarrow \frac{\sin(40^\circ)}{b} = \frac{\sin(100^\circ)}{2} \rightarrow b = \frac{2\sin(40^\circ)}{\sin(100^\circ)} \approx 1.31$$

16. $\beta = 20^\circ,\ \gamma = 70^\circ,\ a = 1$

$\alpha = 180^\circ - \beta - \gamma = 180^\circ - 20^\circ - 70^\circ = 90^\circ$

$$\frac{\sin\alpha}{a} = \frac{\sin\beta}{b} \rightarrow \frac{\sin(90^\circ)}{1} = \frac{\sin(20^\circ)}{b} \rightarrow b = \frac{1\sin(20^\circ)}{\sin(90^\circ)} \approx 0.34$$

$$\frac{\sin\gamma}{c} = \frac{\sin\alpha}{a} \rightarrow \frac{\sin(70^\circ)}{c} = \frac{\sin(90^\circ)}{1} \rightarrow c = \frac{1\sin(70^\circ)}{\sin(90^\circ)} \approx 0.94$$

17. $a = 3,\ b = 2,\ \alpha = 50^\circ$

$$\frac{\sin\beta}{b} = \frac{\sin\alpha}{a} \rightarrow \frac{\sin\beta}{2} = \frac{\sin(50^\circ)}{3} \rightarrow \sin\beta = \frac{2\sin(50^\circ)}{3} \approx 0.5107$$

$\rightarrow \beta = 30.7^\circ$ or $\beta = 149.3^\circ$

The second value is discarded because $\alpha + \beta > 180^\circ$.

$\gamma = 180^\circ - \alpha - \beta = 180^\circ - 50^\circ - 30.7^\circ = 99.3^\circ$

$$\frac{\sin\gamma}{c} = \frac{\sin\alpha}{a} \rightarrow \frac{\sin(99.3^\circ)}{c} = \frac{\sin(50^\circ)}{3} \rightarrow c = \frac{3\sin(99.3^\circ)}{\sin(50^\circ)} \approx 3.86$$

One triangle: $\beta \approx 30.7^\circ,\ \gamma \approx 99.3^\circ,\ c \approx 3.86$

18. $b = 4,\ c = 3,\ \beta = 40^\circ$

$$\frac{\sin\beta}{b} = \frac{\sin\gamma}{c} \rightarrow \frac{\sin(40^\circ)}{4} = \frac{\sin\gamma}{3} \rightarrow \sin\gamma = \frac{3\sin(40^\circ)}{4} = 0.4821$$

$\rightarrow \gamma = 28.8^\circ$ or $\gamma = 151.2^\circ$

The second value is discarded because $\beta + \gamma > 180^\circ$.

$\alpha = 180^\circ - \beta - \gamma = 180^\circ - 40^\circ - 28.8^\circ = 111.2^\circ$

$$\frac{\sin\beta}{b} = \frac{\sin\alpha}{a} \rightarrow \frac{\sin(40^\circ)}{4} = \frac{\sin(111.2^\circ)}{a} \rightarrow a = \frac{4\sin(111.2^\circ)}{\sin(40^\circ)} \approx 5.80$$

One triangle: $\alpha \approx 111.2^\circ,\ \gamma \approx 28.8^\circ,\ a \approx 5.80$

19. $b = 5,\ c = 3,\ \beta = 100^\circ$

$$\frac{\sin\beta}{b} = \frac{\sin\gamma}{c} \rightarrow \frac{\sin(100^\circ)}{5} = \frac{\sin\gamma}{3} \rightarrow \sin\gamma = \frac{3\sin(100^\circ)}{5} = 0.5909$$

$\rightarrow \gamma = 36.2^\circ$ or $\gamma = 143.8^\circ$

The second value is discarded because $\beta + \gamma > 180^\circ$.

$\alpha = 180° - \beta - \gamma = 180° - 100° - 36.2° = 43.8°$

$\frac{\sin\beta}{b} = \frac{\sin\alpha}{a} \rightarrow \frac{\sin(100°)}{5} = \frac{\sin(43.8°)}{a} \rightarrow a = \frac{5\sin(43.8°)}{\sin(100°)} \approx 3.51$

One triangle: $\alpha \approx 43.8°$, $\gamma \approx 36.2°$, $a \approx 3.51$

20. $a = 2$, $c = 1$, $\alpha = 120°$

$\frac{\sin\gamma}{c} = \frac{\sin\alpha}{a} \rightarrow \frac{\sin\gamma}{1} = \frac{\sin(120°)}{2} \rightarrow \sin\gamma = \frac{1\sin(120°)}{2} = 0.4330$

$\rightarrow \gamma = 25.7°$ or $\gamma = 154.3°$

The second value is discarded because $\alpha + \gamma > 180°$.

$\beta = 180° - \alpha - \gamma = 180° - 120° - 25.7° = 34.3°$

$\frac{\sin\beta}{b} = \frac{\sin\alpha}{a} \rightarrow \frac{\sin(34.3°)}{b} = \frac{\sin(120°)}{2} \rightarrow b = \frac{2\sin(34.3°)}{\sin(120°)} \approx 1.30$

One triangle: $\beta \approx 34.3°$, $\gamma \approx 25.7°$, $b \approx 1.30$

21. $a = 4$, $b = 5$, $\alpha = 60°$

$\frac{\sin\beta}{b} = \frac{\sin\alpha}{a} \rightarrow \frac{\sin\beta}{5} = \frac{\sin(60°)}{4} \rightarrow \sin\beta = \frac{5\sin(60°)}{4} = 1.0825$

There is no angle β for which $\sin\beta > 1$. Therefore, there is no triangle with the given measurements.

22. $b = 2$, $c = 3$, $\beta = 40°$

$\frac{\sin\beta}{b} = \frac{\sin\gamma}{c} \rightarrow \frac{\sin(40°)}{2} = \frac{\sin\gamma}{3} \rightarrow \sin\gamma = \frac{3\sin(40°)}{2} = 0.9642$

$\rightarrow \gamma_1 = 74.6°$ or $\gamma_2 = 105.4°$

For both values, $\beta + \gamma < 180°$. Therefore, there are two triangles.

$\alpha_1 = 180° - \beta - \gamma_1 = 180° - 40° - 74.6° = 65.4°$

$\frac{\sin\beta}{b} = \frac{\sin\alpha_1}{a_1} \rightarrow \frac{\sin(40°)}{2} = \frac{\sin(65.4°)}{a_1} \rightarrow a_1 = \frac{2\sin(65.4°)}{\sin(40°)} \approx 2.83$

$\alpha_2 = 180° - \beta - \gamma_2 = 180° - 40° - 105.4° = 34.6°$

$\frac{\sin\beta}{b} = \frac{\sin\alpha_2}{a_2} \rightarrow \frac{\sin(40°)}{2} = \frac{\sin(34.6°)}{a_2} \rightarrow a_2 = \frac{2\sin(34.6°)}{\sin(40°)} \approx 1.77$

Two triangles: $\alpha_1 \approx 65.4°$, $\gamma_1 \approx 74.6°$, $a_1 \approx 2.83$
or $\alpha_2 \approx 34.6°$, $\gamma_2 \approx 105.4°$, $a_2 \approx 1.77$

23. $b = 4$, $c = 6$, $\beta = 20°$

$\frac{\sin\beta}{b} = \frac{\sin\gamma}{c} \rightarrow \frac{\sin(20°)}{4} = \frac{\sin\gamma}{6} \rightarrow \sin\gamma = \frac{6\sin(20°)}{4} \approx 0.5130$

$\rightarrow \gamma_1 = 30.9°$ or $\gamma_2 = 149.1°$

For both values, $\beta + \gamma < 180°$. Therefore, there are two triangles.

$\alpha_1 = 180° - \beta - \gamma_1 = 180° - 20° - 30.9° = 129.1°$

$$\frac{\sin\beta}{b} = \frac{\sin\alpha_1}{a_1} \rightarrow \frac{\sin(20°)}{4} = \frac{\sin(129.1°)}{a_1} \rightarrow a_1 = \frac{4\sin(129.1°)}{\sin(20°)} \approx 9.07$$

$\alpha_2 = 180° - \beta - \gamma_2 = 180° - 20° - 149.1° = 10.9°$

$$\frac{\sin\beta}{b} = \frac{\sin\alpha_2}{a_2} \rightarrow \frac{\sin(20°)}{4} = \frac{\sin(10.9°)}{a_2} \rightarrow a_2 = \frac{4\sin(10.9°)}{\sin(20°)} \approx 2.20$$

Two triangles: $\alpha_1 \approx 129.1°$, $\gamma_1 \approx 30.9°$, $a_1 \approx 9.08$
or $\alpha_2 \approx 10.9°$, $\gamma_2 \approx 149.1°$, $a_2 \approx 2.21$

24. $a = 3$, $b = 7$, $\alpha = 70°$

$$\frac{\sin\beta}{b} = \frac{\sin\alpha}{a} \rightarrow \frac{\sin\beta}{7} = \frac{\sin(70°)}{3} \rightarrow \sin\beta = \frac{7\sin(70°)}{3} \approx 2.1926$$

There is no angle β for which $\sin\beta > 1$. Therefore, there is no triangle with the given measurements.

25. $a = 2$, $c = 1$, $\gamma = 100°$

$$\frac{\sin\gamma}{c} = \frac{\sin\alpha}{a} \rightarrow \frac{\sin(100°)}{1} = \frac{\sin\alpha}{2} \rightarrow \sin\alpha = \frac{2\sin(100°)}{1} \approx 1.9696$$

There is no angle α for which $\sin\alpha > 1$. Therefore, there is no triangle with the given measurements.

26. $b = 4$, $c = 5$, $\beta = 95°$

$$\frac{\sin\gamma}{c} = \frac{\sin\beta}{b} \rightarrow \frac{\sin\gamma}{5} = \frac{\sin(95°)}{4} \rightarrow \sin\gamma = \frac{5\sin(95°)}{4} \approx 1.2452$$

There is no angle γ for which $\sin\gamma > 1$. Therefore, there is no triangle with the given measurements.

27. $a = 2$, $c = 1$, $\gamma = 25°$

$$\frac{\sin\alpha}{a} = \frac{\sin\gamma}{c} \rightarrow \frac{\sin\alpha}{2} = \frac{\sin(25°)}{1} \rightarrow \sin\alpha = \frac{2\sin(25°)}{1} \approx 0.8452$$

$$\rightarrow \alpha_1 = 57.7° \text{ or } \alpha_2 = 122.3°$$

For both values, $\alpha + \gamma < 180°$. Therefore, there are two triangles.

$\beta_1 = 180° - \alpha_1 - \gamma = 180° - 57.7° - 25° = 97.3°$

$$\frac{\sin\beta_1}{b_1} = \frac{\sin\gamma}{c} \rightarrow \frac{\sin(97.3°)}{b_1} = \frac{\sin(25°)}{1} \rightarrow b_1 = \frac{1\sin(97.3°)}{\sin(25°)} \approx 2.35$$

$\beta_2 = 180° - \alpha_2 - \gamma = 180° - 122.3° - 25° = 32.7°$

$$\frac{\sin\beta_2}{b_2} = \frac{\sin\gamma}{c} \rightarrow \frac{\sin(32.7°)}{b_2} = \frac{\sin(25°)}{1} \rightarrow b_2 = \frac{1\sin(32.7°)}{\sin(25°)} \approx 1.28$$

Two triangles: $\alpha_1 \approx 57.7°$, $\beta_1 \approx 97.3°$, $b_1 \approx 2.35$
or $\alpha_2 \approx 122.3°$, $\beta_2 \approx 32.7°$, $b_2 \approx 1.28$

28. $b = 4,\ c = 5,\ \beta = 40°$

$$\frac{\sin\beta}{b} = \frac{\sin\gamma}{c} \rightarrow \frac{\sin(40°)}{4} = \frac{\sin\gamma}{5} \rightarrow \sin\gamma = \frac{5\sin(40°)}{4} \approx 0.8035$$

$$\rightarrow \gamma_1 = 53.5° \text{ or } \gamma_2 = 126.5°$$

For both values, $\beta + \gamma < 180°$. Therefore, there are two triangles.

$\alpha_1 = 180° - \beta - \gamma_1 = 180° - 40° - 53.5° = 86.5°$

$$\frac{\sin\beta}{b} = \frac{\sin\alpha_1}{a_1} \rightarrow \frac{\sin(40°)}{4} = \frac{\sin(86.5°)}{a_1} \rightarrow a_1 = \frac{4\sin(86.5°)}{\sin(40°)} \approx 6.21$$

$\alpha_2 = 180° - \beta - \gamma_2 = 180° - 40° - 126.5° = 13.5°$

$$\frac{\sin\beta}{b} = \frac{\sin\alpha_2}{a_2} \rightarrow \frac{\sin(40°)}{4} = \frac{\sin(13.5°)}{a_2} \rightarrow a_2 = \frac{4\sin(13.5°)}{\sin(40°)} \approx 1.45$$

Two triangles: $\alpha_1 \approx 86.5°,\ \gamma_1 \approx 53.5°,\ a_1 \approx 6.21$
or $\alpha_2 \approx 13.5°,\ \gamma_2 \approx 126.5°,\ a_2 \approx 1.45$

29. (a) Find γ; then use the Law of Sines:

$\gamma = 180° - 60° - 55° = 65°$

$$\frac{\sin(55°)}{a} = \frac{\sin(65°)}{150} \rightarrow a = \frac{150\sin(55°)}{\sin(65°)} \approx 135.58 \text{ miles}$$

$$\frac{\sin(60°)}{b} = \frac{\sin(65°)}{150} \rightarrow b = \frac{150\sin(60°)}{\sin(65°)} \approx 143.3 \text{ miles}$$

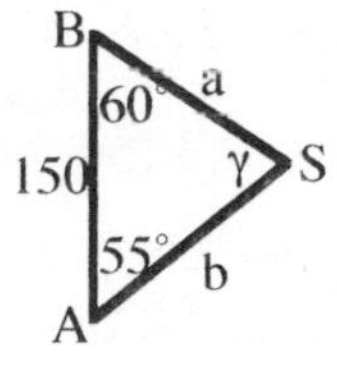

(b) $t = \frac{a}{r} = \frac{135.6}{200} \approx 0.68$ hours or ≈ 41 minutes

30. Find β; then use the Law of Sines:

$\beta = 180° - 40° - 50° = 90°$

$$\frac{\sin 50°}{c} = \frac{\sin(90°)}{100} \rightarrow c = \frac{100\sin(50°)}{\sin(90°)} \approx 76.6 \text{ feet}$$

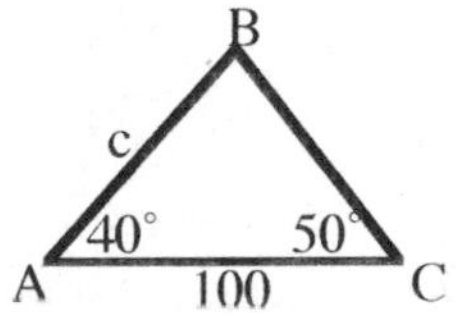

31. $\angle CAB = 180° - 25° = 155°$ $\angle ABC = 180° - 155° - 15° = 10°$

Let c represent the distance from A to B.

$$\frac{\sin(15°)}{c} = \frac{\sin(10°)}{1000} \rightarrow c = \frac{1000\sin(15°)}{\sin(10°)} \approx 1490.48 \text{ feet}$$

The length of the proposed ski lift is approximately 1490 feet.

32. Use the results of Problem 31 that the distance from A to B is 1490 feet.
Let h represent the distance from B to D.

$$\sin(25°) = \frac{h}{1490} \rightarrow h = 1490\sin(25°) \approx 1490(0.4226) \approx 629.9 \text{ feet}$$

33. Find the distance from B to the plane:

$\gamma = 180° - 40° - 35° = 105° \qquad (\gamma = \angle APB)$

$$\frac{\sin(40°)}{x} = \frac{\sin(105°)}{1000} \rightarrow x = \frac{1000\sin(40°)}{\sin(105°)} \approx 665.5 \text{ feet}$$

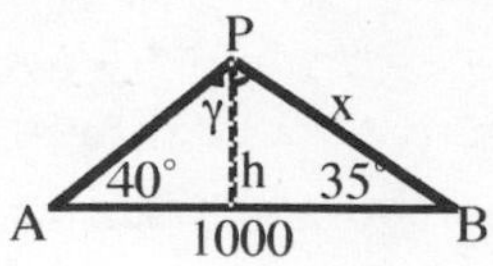

Find the height:

$$\sin(35°) = \frac{h}{x} = \frac{h}{665.5} \rightarrow h = (665.5)\sin(35°) \approx 381.69 \text{ feet}$$

The plane is 381.69 feet high.

34. Find the distance from C to the bridge:

$\gamma = 180° - 69.2° - 65.5° = 45.3° \qquad (\gamma = \angle ACB)$

$$\frac{\sin(65.5°)}{x} = \frac{\sin(45.3°)}{880} \rightarrow x = \frac{880\sin(65.5°)}{\sin(45.3°)} \approx 1127 \text{ feet}$$

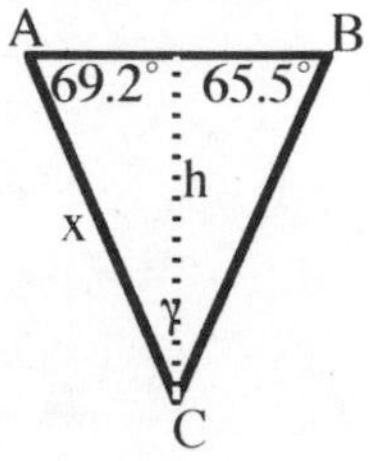

Find the height :

$$\sin(69.2°) = \frac{h}{x} = \frac{h}{1127} \rightarrow h = (1127)\sin(69.2°) \approx 1054.14 \text{ feet}$$

The bridge is 1054.14 feet high.

35. (a) $\angle ABC = 180° - 40° = 140°$

Find the angle at city C:

$$\frac{\sin C}{150} = \frac{\sin(140°)}{300} \rightarrow \sin C = \frac{150\sin(140°)}{300} \approx 0.3214 \rightarrow C \approx 18.7°$$

Find the angle at city A :

$A = 180° - 140° - 18.7° = 21.3°$

$$\frac{\sin(21.3°)}{y} = \frac{\sin(140°)}{300} \rightarrow y = \frac{300\sin(21.3°)}{\sin(140°)} \approx 169.18 \text{ miles}$$

The distance from city B to city C is approximately 169.18 miles.

(b) To find the angle to turn, subtract angle C from 180°:

$180° - 18.7° = 161.3°$

The pilot needs to turn through an angle of 161.3° to return to city A.

36. The time of the actual trip was:

$$t = \frac{50+70}{250} = \frac{120}{250} = 0.48 \text{ hour}$$

$a = 70,\ b = 50,\ \alpha = 10°$ Solve the triangle:

$$\frac{\sin(10°)}{70} = \frac{\sin\beta}{50} \rightarrow \sin\beta = \frac{50\sin(10°)}{70} \approx 0.1240$$

$\beta \approx 7.1°$

$\gamma = 180° - 10° - 7.1° = 162.9°$

$$\frac{\sin(10^\circ)}{70} = \frac{\sin(162.9^\circ)}{c} \rightarrow c = \frac{70\sin(162.9^\circ)}{\sin(10^\circ)} \approx 118.5$$

$$t = \frac{118.5}{250} \approx 0.474 \text{ hour}$$

The trip should have taken 0.474 hour but because of the incorrect course took 0.48 hour. Thus the trip took 0.006 hour or 0.36 minutes longer.

37. Find angle β $(\angle ACB)$:

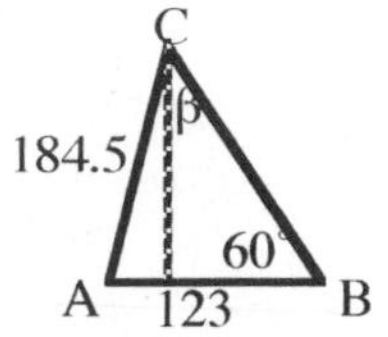

$$\frac{\sin\beta}{123} = \frac{\sin(60^\circ)}{184.5} \rightarrow \sin\beta = \frac{123\sin(60^\circ)}{184.5} \approx 0.5774$$

$$\beta \approx 35.3^\circ$$

$$\angle CAB = 180^\circ - 60^\circ - 35.3^\circ \approx 84.7^\circ$$

Find the perpendicular distance:

$$\sin(84.7^\circ) = \frac{h}{184.5} \rightarrow h = 184.5\sin(84.7^\circ) = 183.72 \text{ feet}$$

38. Let θ be $\angle AOP$.

$$\frac{\sin\theta`}{9} = \frac{\sin(15^\circ)}{3} \rightarrow \sin\theta = \frac{9\sin(15^\circ)}{3} \approx 0.7765$$

$$\theta \approx 51^\circ \text{ or } \theta \approx 180^\circ - 51^\circ = 129^\circ$$

$$A = 114^\circ \text{ or } A = 36^\circ$$

$$\frac{\sin(114^\circ)}{a} = \frac{\sin(15^\circ)}{3} \qquad \frac{\sin(36^\circ)}{a} = \frac{\sin(15^\circ)}{3}$$

$$a = \frac{3\sin(114^\circ)}{\sin(15^\circ)} \approx 10.6 \text{ inches} \quad \text{or} \quad a = \frac{3\sin(36^\circ)}{\sin(15^\circ)} \approx 6.8 \text{ inches}$$

The distance from the piston to the center of the crankshaft is either 6.8 inches or 10.6 inches.

39. $\alpha = 180^\circ - 140^\circ = 40^\circ$ $\quad \beta = 180^\circ - 135^\circ = 45^\circ$

$\gamma = 180^\circ - 40^\circ - 45^\circ = 95^\circ$

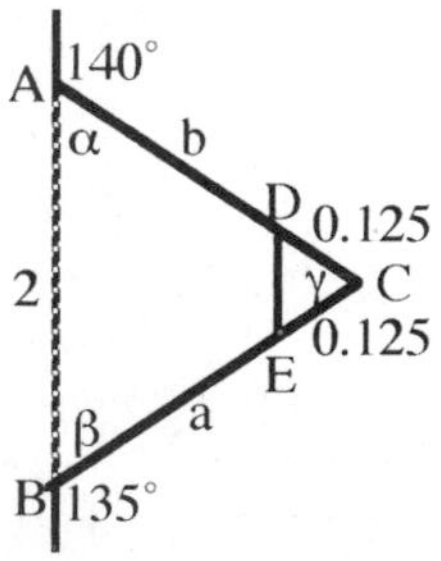

$$\frac{\sin(40^\circ)}{a} = \frac{\sin(95^\circ)}{2} \rightarrow a = \frac{2\sin(40^\circ)}{\sin 95^\circ} \approx 1.290 \text{ mi}$$

$$\frac{\sin(45^\circ)}{b} = \frac{\sin(95^\circ)}{2} \rightarrow b = \frac{2\sin(45^\circ)}{\sin(95^\circ)} \approx 1.420 \text{ mi}$$

$$\overline{BE} = 1.290 - 0.125 = 1.165 \text{ mi}$$

$$\overline{AD} = 1.420 - 0.125 = 1.295 \text{ mi}$$

$$\angle CDE = \angle CED = \frac{180^\circ - 95^\circ}{2} = 42.5^\circ$$

For the isosceles triangle, $\frac{\sin(95^\circ)}{DE} = \frac{\sin(42.5^\circ)}{0.125} \rightarrow DE = \frac{0.125\sin(95^\circ)}{\sin(42.5^\circ)} \approx 0.184$ miles

The length of the highway is $1.165 + 1.295 + 0.184 = 2.64$ miles.

40. From the diagram, $\angle ABC = 55°$ and $\angle BAC = 75°$ (where point C is the ship)

(a) Use the Law of Sines:

$$\frac{\sin(50°)}{3} = \frac{\sin(55°)}{x} \to x = \frac{3\sin(55°)}{\sin(50°)} \approx 3.21 \text{ miles}$$

(x is the distance from the ship to lighthouse A.)

(b) Use the Law of Sines:

$$\frac{\sin(50°)}{3} = \frac{\sin(75°)}{y} \to y = \frac{3\sin(75°)}{\sin(50°)} \approx 3.78 \text{ miles}$$

(y is the distance from the ship to lighthouse B.)

(c) Use the Law of Sines:

$$\frac{\sin(90°)}{3.2} = \frac{\sin(75°)}{z} \to z = \frac{3.2\sin(75°)}{\sin(90°)} \approx 3.1 \text{ miles}$$

(z is the distance from the ship to the shore.)

41. $\angle ABD = 180° - 30° = 150°$ $\quad \gamma = 180° - 150° - 20° = 10°$

$$\frac{\sin(150°)}{y} = \frac{\sin(10°)}{1} \to y = \frac{1\sin(150°)}{\sin(10°)} \approx 2.88 \text{ mi}$$

$$\frac{\sin\beta}{2.88} = \frac{\sin(20°)}{1} \to \sin\beta = \frac{2.88\sin(20°)}{1} \approx 0.9850$$

$$\beta \approx 80°$$

$\alpha = 180° - 80° - 30° = 70°$

$$\frac{\sin(70°)}{x} = \frac{\sin(30°)}{1} \to x = \frac{\sin(70°)}{\sin(30°)} \approx 1.88 \text{ mi}$$

The ship is about 1.88 miles from the harbor.

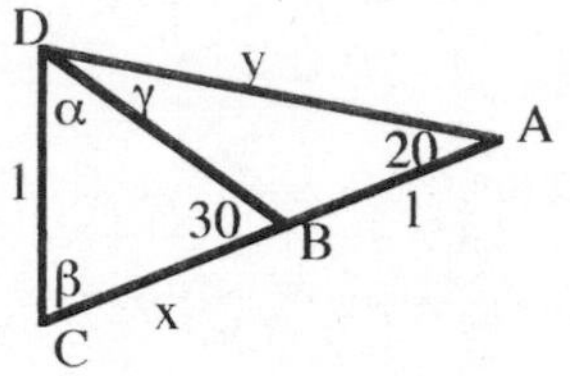

42. The tower forms an angle of 95° with the ground. Let x be the distance from the ranger to the tower.

$\angle ABC = 180° - 95° - 35° = 50°$

$$\frac{\sin(35°)}{100} = \frac{\sin(50°)}{x} \to x = \frac{100\sin(50°)}{\sin(35°)} \approx 133.6 \text{ feet}$$

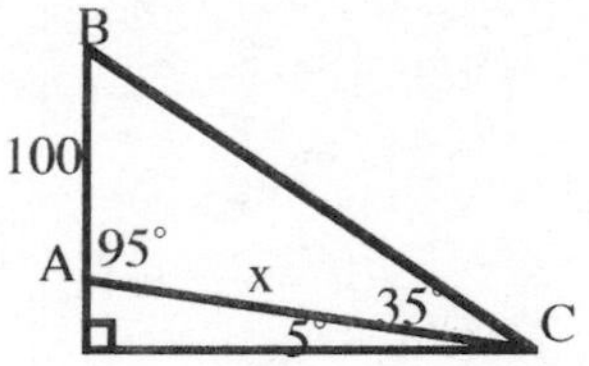

43. Using the Law of Sines:

$$\frac{\sin(46.27°)}{x} = \frac{\sin(90° - 46.27°)}{y + 100}$$

$$(y + 100)\sin(46.27°) = x\sin(43.73°)$$

$$y\sin(46.27°) + 100\sin(46.27°) = x\sin(43.73°)$$

$$y = \frac{x\sin(43.73°) - 100\sin(46.27°)}{\sin(46.27°)}$$

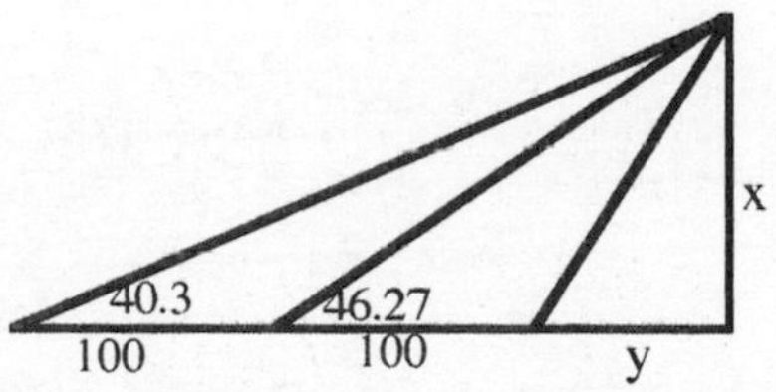

$$\frac{\sin(40.3^\circ)}{x}=\frac{\sin(90^\circ-40.3^\circ)}{y+200}$$

$$(y+200)\sin(40.3^\circ)=x\sin(49.7^\circ)$$

$$y\sin(40.3^\circ)+200\sin(40.3^\circ)=x\sin(49.7^\circ)$$

$$y=\frac{x\sin(49.7^\circ)-200\sin(40.3^\circ)}{\sin(40.3^\circ)}$$

Set the two equations equal to each other and solve:

$$\frac{x\sin(43.73^\circ)-100\sin(46.27^\circ)}{\sin(46.27^\circ)}=\frac{x\sin(49.7^\circ)-200\sin(40.3^\circ)}{\sin(40.3^\circ)}$$

$$x\sin(43.73^\circ)\cdot\sin(40.3^\circ)-100\sin(46.27^\circ)\cdot\sin(40.3^\circ)$$
$$=x\sin(49.7^\circ)\cdot\sin(46.27^\circ)-200\sin(40.3^\circ)\cdot\sin(46.27^\circ)$$

$$x\sin(43.73^\circ)\cdot\sin(40.3^\circ)-x\sin(49.7^\circ)\cdot\sin(46.27^\circ)$$
$$=100\sin(46.27^\circ)\cdot\sin(40.3^\circ)-200\sin(40.3^\circ)\cdot\sin(46.27^\circ)$$

$$x=\frac{100\sin(46.27^\circ)\cdot\sin(40.3^\circ)-200\sin(40.3^\circ)\cdot\sin(46.27^\circ)}{\sin(43.73^\circ)\cdot\sin(40.3^\circ)-\sin(49.7^\circ)\cdot\sin(46.27^\circ)}\approx 449.36\text{ feet}$$

44. Use the Law of Sines:

$$\frac{\sin(20^\circ)}{h}=\frac{\sin(70^\circ)}{x}\quad\rightarrow\quad x=\frac{h\sin(70^\circ)}{\sin(20^\circ)}$$

$$\frac{\sin(15^\circ)}{h}=\frac{\sin(75^\circ)}{x+700}\quad\rightarrow\quad x=\frac{h\sin(75^\circ)}{\sin(15^\circ)}-700$$

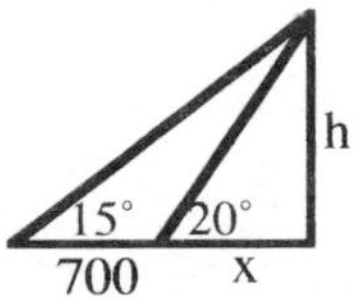

$$\frac{h\sin(70^\circ)}{\sin(20^\circ)}=\frac{h\sin(75^\circ)}{\sin(15^\circ)}-700$$

$$h\left(\frac{\sin(70^\circ)}{\sin(20^\circ)}-\frac{\sin(75^\circ)}{\sin(15^\circ)}\right)=-700\rightarrow h=\frac{-700}{\left(\frac{\sin(70^\circ)}{\sin(20^\circ)}-\frac{\sin(75^\circ)}{\sin(15^\circ)}\right)}\approx 710.97\text{ feet}$$

45. Using the Law of Sines:

$$\frac{\sin(30^\circ)}{h}=\frac{\sin(60^\circ)}{x}\quad\rightarrow\quad x=\frac{h\sin(60^\circ)}{\sin(30^\circ)}$$

$$\frac{\sin(20^\circ)}{h}=\frac{\sin(70^\circ)}{x+40}\quad\rightarrow\quad x=\frac{h\sin(70^\circ)}{\sin(20^\circ)}-40$$

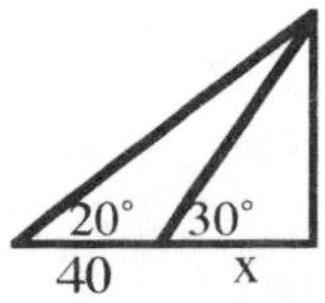

$$\frac{h\sin(60^\circ)}{\sin(30^\circ)}=\frac{h\sin(70^\circ)}{\sin(20^\circ)}-40$$

$$h\left(\frac{\sin(60^\circ)}{\sin(30^\circ)}-\frac{\sin(70^\circ)}{\sin(20^\circ)}\right)=-40\rightarrow h=\frac{-40}{\left(\frac{\sin(60^\circ)}{\sin(30^\circ)}-\frac{\sin(70^\circ)}{\sin(20^\circ)}\right)}\approx 39.39\text{ feet}$$

46. Using the Law of Sines:

$$\frac{\sin(162^\circ)}{x}=\frac{\sin(12^\circ)}{10}\rightarrow x=\frac{10\sin(162^\circ)}{\sin(12^\circ)}\approx 14.86 \text{ feet}$$

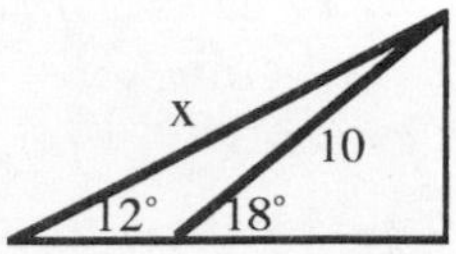

47. Find the distance from B to the helicopter:

$\gamma = 180^\circ - 40^\circ - 25^\circ = 115^\circ \qquad (\gamma = \angle APB)$

$$\frac{\sin(40^\circ)}{x}=\frac{\sin(115^\circ)}{100} \rightarrow x=\frac{100\sin(40^\circ)}{\sin(115^\circ)}\approx 70.9 \text{ feet}$$

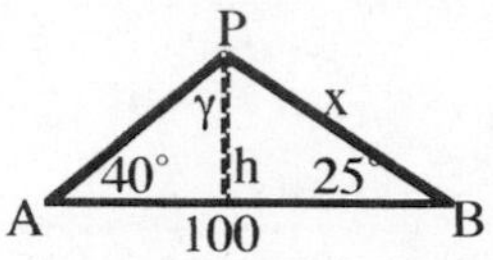

Find the height:

$$\sin(25^\circ)=\frac{h}{x}\approx\frac{h}{70.9} \rightarrow h\approx 70.9(\sin 25^\circ)\approx 29.97 \text{ feet}$$

The helicopter is about 30 feet high.

48. $$\frac{a+b}{c}=\frac{a}{c}+\frac{b}{c}=\frac{\sin\alpha}{\sin\gamma}+\frac{\sin\beta}{\sin\gamma}=\frac{\sin\alpha+\sin\beta}{\sin\gamma}=\frac{2\sin\left(\frac{\alpha+\beta}{2}\right)\cos\left(\frac{\alpha-\beta}{2}\right)}{2\sin\left(\frac{\gamma}{2}\right)\cos\left(\frac{\gamma}{2}\right)}$$

$$=\frac{\sin\left(\frac{\pi}{2}-\frac{\gamma}{2}\right)\cos\left(\frac{\alpha-\beta}{2}\right)}{\sin\left(\frac{\gamma}{2}\right)\cos\left(\frac{\gamma}{2}\right)}=\frac{\cos\left(\frac{\gamma}{2}\right)\cos\left(\frac{\alpha-\beta}{2}\right)}{\sin\left(\frac{\gamma}{2}\right)\cos\left(\frac{\gamma}{2}\right)}=\frac{\cos\left(\frac{1}{2}(\alpha-\beta)\right)}{\sin\left(\frac{1}{2}\gamma\right)}$$

49. $$\frac{a-b}{c}=\frac{a}{c}-\frac{b}{c}=\frac{\sin\alpha}{\sin\gamma}-\frac{\sin\beta}{\sin\gamma}=\frac{\sin\alpha-\sin\beta}{\sin\gamma}=\frac{2\sin\left(\frac{\alpha-\beta}{2}\right)\cos\left(\frac{\alpha+\beta}{2}\right)}{\sin\left(2\cdot\frac{\gamma}{2}\right)}$$

$$=\frac{2\sin\left(\frac{\alpha-\beta}{2}\right)\cos\left(\frac{\alpha+\beta}{2}\right)}{2\sin\left(\frac{\gamma}{2}\right)\cos\left(\frac{\gamma}{2}\right)}=\frac{\sin\left(\frac{\alpha-\beta}{2}\right)\cos\left(\frac{\pi}{2}-\frac{\gamma}{2}\right)}{\sin\left(\frac{\gamma}{2}\right)\cos\left(\frac{\gamma}{2}\right)}=\frac{\sin\left(\frac{\alpha-\beta}{2}\right)\sin\left(\frac{\gamma}{2}\right)}{\sin\left(\frac{\gamma}{2}\right)\cos\left(\frac{\gamma}{2}\right)}$$

$$=\frac{\sin\left(\frac{\alpha-\beta}{2}\right)}{\cos\left(\frac{\gamma}{2}\right)}=\frac{\sin\left(\frac{1}{2}(\alpha-\beta)\right)}{\cos\left(\frac{1}{2}\gamma\right)}$$

50. $$a=\frac{b\sin\alpha}{\sin\beta}=\frac{b\sin(180^\circ-(\beta+\gamma))}{\sin\beta}=\frac{b}{\sin\beta}\sin(\beta+\gamma)$$

$$=\frac{b}{\sin\beta}(\sin\beta\cos\gamma+\cos\beta\sin\gamma)=b\cos\gamma+\frac{b\sin\gamma}{\sin\beta}\cos\beta=b\cos\gamma+c\cos\beta$$

51. Derive the Law of Tangents:

$$\frac{a-b}{a+b}=\frac{\left(\frac{a-b}{c}\right)}{\left(\frac{a+b}{c}\right)}=\frac{\left(\frac{\sin\left(\frac{1}{2}(\alpha-\beta)\right)}{\cos\left(\frac{1}{2}\gamma\right)}\right)}{\left(\frac{\cos\left(\frac{1}{2}(\alpha-\beta)\right)}{\sin\left(\frac{1}{2}\gamma\right)}\right)}=\frac{\sin\left(\frac{1}{2}(\alpha-\beta)\right)}{\cos\left(\frac{1}{2}\gamma\right)}\cdot\frac{\sin\left(\frac{1}{2}\gamma\right)}{\cos\left(\frac{1}{2}(\alpha-\beta)\right)}=\tan\left(\frac{1}{2}(\alpha-\beta)\right)\tan\left(\frac{1}{2}\gamma\right)$$

$$=\tan\left(\frac{1}{2}(\alpha-\beta)\right)\tan\left(\frac{1}{2}(\pi-(\alpha+\beta))\right)=\tan\left(\frac{1}{2}(\alpha-\beta)\right)\tan\left(\frac{\pi}{2}-\left(\frac{\alpha+\beta}{2}\right)\right)$$

$$=\tan\left(\frac{1}{2}(\alpha-\beta)\right)\cot\left(\frac{\alpha+\beta}{2}\right)=\frac{\tan\left(\frac{1}{2}(\alpha-\beta)\right)}{\tan\left(\frac{1}{2}(\alpha+\beta)\right)}$$

52. $\sin\beta=\sin(\angle ABC)=\sin(\angle AB'C)=\frac{b}{2r}$

$$\frac{\sin\beta}{b}=\frac{1}{2r}$$

The result follows from the Law of Sines.

Chapter 9

Applications of Trigonometric Functions

9.3 The Law of Cosines

1. $a=2,\ c=4,\ \beta=45^\circ \qquad b^2=a^2+c^2-2ac\cos\beta$

$b^2=2^2+4^2-2\cdot 2\cdot 4\cos(45^\circ)=20-16\cdot\dfrac{\sqrt{2}}{2}=20-8\sqrt{2}\approx 8.6863$

$b\approx 2.95$

$a^2=b^2+c^2-2bc\cos\alpha \ \rightarrow\ 2bc\cos\alpha=b^2+c^2-a^2 \ \rightarrow\ \cos\alpha=\dfrac{b^2+c^2-a^2}{2bc}$

$\cos\alpha=\dfrac{2.95^2+4^2-2^2}{2(2.95)(4)}=\dfrac{20.6863}{23.6}\approx 0.8765\rightarrow\alpha\approx 28.7^\circ$

$c^2=a^2+b^2-2ab\cos\gamma \ \rightarrow\ \cos\gamma=\dfrac{a^2+b^2-c^2}{2ab}=\dfrac{2^2+2.95^2-4^2}{2(2)(2.95)}\approx -0.2794\rightarrow\gamma\approx 106.3^\circ$

2. $b=3,\ c=4,\ \alpha=30^\circ \qquad a^2=b^2+c^2-2bc\cos\alpha$

$a^2=3^2+4^2-2\cdot 3\cdot 4\cos(30^\circ)=25-24\cdot(0.8660)\approx 4.216$

$a\approx 2.05$

$c^2=a^2+b^2-2ab\cos\gamma \ \rightarrow\ \cos\gamma=\dfrac{a^2+b^2-c^2}{2ab}=\dfrac{2.05^2+3^2-4^2}{2(2.05)(3)}\approx -0.2274\rightarrow\gamma\approx 103.1^\circ$

$b^2=a^2+c^2-2ac\cos\beta \ \rightarrow\ \cos\beta=\dfrac{a^2+c^2-b^2}{2ac}=\dfrac{2.05^2+4^2-3^2}{2(2.05)(4)}\approx 0.6831\rightarrow\beta\approx 46.9^\circ$

3. $a=2,\ b=3,\ \gamma=95^\circ \qquad c^2=a^2+b^2-2ab\cos\gamma$

$c^2=2^2+3^2-2\cdot 2\cdot 3\cos(95^\circ)=13-12\cdot(-0.0872)\approx 14.0459$

$c\approx 3.75$

$a^2=b^2+c^2-2bc\cos\alpha \ \rightarrow\ \cos\alpha=\dfrac{b^2+c^2-a^2}{2bc}=\dfrac{3^2+3.75^2-2^2}{2(3)(3.75)}\approx 0.8472\rightarrow\alpha\approx 32.1^\circ$

$b^2=a^2+c^2-2ac\cos\beta \ \rightarrow\ \cos\beta=\dfrac{a^2+c^2-b^2}{2ac}=\dfrac{2^2+3.75^2-3^2}{2(2)(3.75)}\approx 0.6042\rightarrow\beta\approx 52.9^\circ$

4. $a = 2,\ c = 5,\ \beta = 20^\circ \qquad b^2 = a^2 + c^2 - 2ac\cos\beta$

$b^2 = 2^2 + 5^2 - 2\cdot 2\cdot 5\cos(20^\circ) = 29 - 20(0.9397) \approx 10.206$

$b \approx 3.19$

$a^2 = b^2 + c^2 - 2bc\cos\alpha \rightarrow 2bc\cos\alpha = b^2 + c^2 - a^2 \rightarrow \cos\alpha = \dfrac{b^2 + c^2 - a^2}{2bc}$

$\cos\alpha = \dfrac{3.19^2 + 5^2 - 2^2}{2(3.19)(5)} \approx 0.9773 \rightarrow \alpha \approx 12.4^\circ$

$c^2 = a^2 + b^2 - 2ab\cos\gamma \rightarrow \cos\gamma = \dfrac{a^2 + b^2 - c^2}{2ab} = \dfrac{2^2 + 3.19^2 - 5^2}{2(2)(3.19)} \approx -0.8483 \rightarrow \gamma \approx 148.0^\circ$

5. $a = 6,\ b = 5,\ c = 8$

$a^2 = b^2 + c^2 - 2bc\cos\alpha \rightarrow \cos\alpha = \dfrac{b^2 + c^2 - a^2}{2bc} = \dfrac{5^2 + 8^2 - 6^2}{2(5)(8)} \approx 0.6625 \rightarrow \alpha \approx 48.5^\circ$

$b^2 = a^2 + c^2 - 2ac\cos\beta \rightarrow \cos\beta = \dfrac{a^2 + c^2 - b^2}{2ac} = \dfrac{6^2 + 8^2 - 5^2}{2(6)(8)} \approx 0.7813 \rightarrow \beta = 38.6^\circ$

$c^2 = a^2 + b^2 - 2ab\cos\gamma \rightarrow \cos\gamma = \dfrac{a^2 + b^2 - c^2}{2ab} = \dfrac{6^2 + 5^2 - 8^2}{2(6)(5)} \approx -0.0500 \rightarrow \gamma = 92.9^\circ$

6. $a = 8,\ b = 5,\ c = 4$

$a^2 = b^2 + c^2 - 2bc\cos\alpha \rightarrow \cos\alpha = \dfrac{b^2 + c^2 - a^2}{2bc} = \dfrac{5^2 + 4^2 - 8^2}{2(5)(4)} \approx -0.5750 \rightarrow \alpha \approx 125.1^\circ$

$b^2 = a^2 + c^2 - 2ac\cos\beta \rightarrow \cos\beta = \dfrac{a^2 + c^2 - b^2}{2ac} = \dfrac{8^2 + 4^2 - 5^2}{2(8)(4)} \approx 0.8594 \rightarrow \beta \approx 30.8^\circ$

$c^2 = a^2 + b^2 - 2ab\cos\gamma \rightarrow \cos\gamma = \dfrac{a^2 + b^2 - c^2}{2ab} = \dfrac{8^2 + 5^2 - 4^2}{2(8)(5)} \approx 0.9125 \rightarrow \gamma = 24.1^\circ$

7. $a = 9,\ b = 6,\ c = 4$

$a^2 = b^2 + c^2 - 2bc\cos\alpha \rightarrow \cos\alpha = \dfrac{b^2 + c^2 - a^2}{2bc} = \dfrac{6^2 + 4^2 - 9^2}{2(6)(4)} \approx -0.6042 \rightarrow \alpha \approx 127.2^\circ$

$b^2 = a^2 + c^2 - 2ac\cos\beta \rightarrow \cos\beta = \dfrac{a^2 + c^2 - b^2}{2ac} = \dfrac{9^2 + 4^2 - 6^2}{2(9)(4)} \approx 0.8472 \rightarrow \beta = 32.1^\circ$

$c^2 = a^2 + b^2 - 2ab\cos\gamma \rightarrow \cos\gamma = \dfrac{a^2 + b^2 - c^2}{2ab} = \dfrac{9^2 + 6^2 - 4^2}{2(9)(6)} \approx 0.9352 \rightarrow \gamma = 20.7^\circ$

8. $a = 4,\ b = 3,\ c = 4$

$a^2 = b^2 + c^2 - 2bc\cos\alpha \rightarrow \cos\alpha = \dfrac{b^2 + c^2 - a^2}{2bc} = \dfrac{3^2 + 4^2 - 4^2}{2(3)(4)} \approx 0.3750 \rightarrow \alpha \approx 68.0^\circ$

$b^2 = a^2 + c^2 - 2ac\cos\beta \rightarrow \cos\beta = \dfrac{a^2 + c^2 - b^2}{2ac} = \dfrac{4^2 + 4^2 - 3^2}{2(4)(4)} \approx 0.7188 \rightarrow \beta = 44.0^\circ$

$$c^2 = a^2 + b^2 - 2ab\cos\gamma \rightarrow \cos\gamma = \frac{a^2+b^2-c^2}{2ab} = \frac{4^2+3^2-4^2}{2(4)(3)} \approx 0.3750 \rightarrow \gamma = 68.0°$$

9. $a = 3,\ b = 4,\ \gamma = 40°$

$c^2 = a^2 + b^2 - 2ab\cos\gamma$

$c^2 = 3^2 + 4^2 - 2\cdot 3\cdot 4\cos(40°) \approx 6.6149$

$c \approx 2.57$

$$a^2 = b^2 + c^2 - 2bc\cos\alpha \rightarrow \cos\alpha = \frac{b^2+c^2-a^2}{2bc} = \frac{4^2+2.57^2-3^2}{2(4)(2.57)} \approx 0.6617 \rightarrow \alpha \approx 48.6°$$

$$b^2 = a^2 + c^2 - 2ac\cos\beta \rightarrow \cos\beta = \frac{a^2+c^2-b^2}{2ac} = \frac{3^2+2.57^2-4^2}{2(3)(2.57)} \approx -0.0256 \rightarrow \beta \approx 91.4°$$

10. $a = 2,\ c = 1,\ \beta = 10°$

$b^2 = a^2 + c^2 - 2ac\cos\beta$

$b^2 = 2^2 + 1^2 - 2\cdot 2\cdot 1\cos(10°) \approx 1.0608$

$b \approx 1.03$

$$a^2 = b^2 + c^2 - 2bc\cos\alpha \rightarrow \cos\alpha = \frac{b^2+c^2-a^2}{2bc} = \frac{1.03^2+1^2-2^2}{2(1.03)(1)} \approx -0.9413 \rightarrow \alpha \approx 160.3°$$

$$c^2 = a^2 + b^2 - 2ab\cos\gamma \rightarrow \cos\gamma = \frac{a^2+b^2-c^2}{2ab} = \frac{2^2+1.03^2-1^2}{2(2)(1.03)} \approx 0.9857 \rightarrow \gamma = 9.7°$$

11. $b = 1,\ c = 3,\ \alpha = 80°$

$a^2 = b^2 + c^2 - 2bc\cos\alpha$

$a^2 = 1^2 + 3^2 - 2\cdot 1\cdot 3\cos(80°) \approx 8.9581$

$a \approx 2.99$

$$c^2 = a^2 + b^2 - 2ab\cos\gamma \rightarrow \cos\gamma = \frac{a^2+b^2-c^2}{2ab} = \frac{2.99^2+1^2-3^2}{2(2.99)(1)} \approx 0.1572 \rightarrow \gamma \approx 80.8°$$

$$b^2 = a^2 + c^2 - 2ac\cos\beta \rightarrow \cos\beta = \frac{a^2+c^2-b^2}{2ac} = \frac{2.99^2+3^2-1^2}{2(2.99)(3)} \approx 0.9443 \rightarrow \beta = 19.2°$$

12. $a = 6,\ b = 4,\ \gamma = 60°$

$c^2 = a^2 + b^2 - 2ab\cos\gamma$

$c^2 = 6^2 + 4^2 - 2\cdot 6\cdot 4\cos(60°) = 28$

$c \approx 5.29$

$$a^2 = b^2 + c^2 - 2bc\cos\alpha \rightarrow \cos\alpha = \frac{b^2+c^2-a^2}{2bc} = \frac{4^2+5.29^2-6^2}{2(4)(5.29)} \approx 0.1887 \rightarrow \alpha \approx 79.1°$$

$$b^2 = a^2 + c^2 - 2ac\cos\beta \rightarrow \cos\beta = \frac{a^2+c^2-b^2}{2ac} = \frac{6^2+5.29^2-4^2}{2(6)(5.29)} \approx 0.7559 \rightarrow \beta = 40.9°$$

13. $a = 3,\ c = 2,\ \beta = 110°$

$b^2 = a^2 + c^2 - 2ac\cos\beta$

$b^2 = 3^2 + 2^2 - 2\cdot 3\cdot 2\cos(110°) \approx 17.1042$

$b \approx 4.14$

$a^2 = b^2 + c^2 - 2bc\cos\alpha \rightarrow \cos\alpha = \dfrac{b^2 + c^2 - a^2}{2bc} = \dfrac{4.14^2 + 2^2 - 3^2}{2(4.14)(2)} \approx 0.7331 \rightarrow \alpha \approx 43.0°$

$c^2 = a^2 + b^2 - 2ab\cos\gamma \rightarrow \cos\gamma = \dfrac{a^2 + b^2 - c^2}{2ab} = \dfrac{3^2 + 4.14^2 - 2^2}{2(3)(4.14)} \approx 0.8913 \rightarrow \gamma \approx 27.0°$

14. $b = 4,\ c = 1,\ \alpha = 120°$

$a^2 = b^2 + c^2 - 2bc\cos\alpha$

$a^2 = 4^2 + 1^2 - 2\cdot 4\cdot 1\cos(120°) = 21$

$a \approx 4.58$

$c^2 = a^2 + b^2 - 2ab\cos\gamma \rightarrow \cos\gamma = \dfrac{a^2 + b^2 - c^2}{2ab} = \dfrac{4.58^2 + 4^2 - 1^2}{2(4.58)(4)} \approx 0.9819 \rightarrow \gamma \approx 10.9°$

$b^2 = a^2 + c^2 - 2ac\cos\beta \rightarrow \cos\beta = \dfrac{a^2 + c^2 - b^2}{2ac} = \dfrac{4.58^2 + 1^2 - 4^2}{2(4.58)(1)} \approx 0.6524 \rightarrow \beta \approx 49.3°$

15. $a = 2,\ b = 2,\ \gamma = 50°$

$c^2 = a^2 + b^2 - 2ab\cos\gamma$

$c^2 = 2^2 + 2^2 - 2\cdot 2\cdot 2\cos(50°) \approx 2.8577$

$c \approx 1.69$

$a^2 = b^2 + c^2 - 2bc\cos\alpha \rightarrow \cos\alpha = \dfrac{b^2 + c^2 - a^2}{2bc} = \dfrac{2^2 + 1.69^2 - 2^2}{2(2)(1.69)} \approx 0.4225 \rightarrow \alpha \approx 65.0°$

$b^2 = a^2 + c^2 - 2ac\cos\beta \rightarrow \cos\beta = \dfrac{a^2 + c^2 - b^2}{2ac} = \dfrac{2^2 + 1.69^2 - 2^2}{2(2)(1.69)} \approx 0.4225 \rightarrow \beta \approx 65.0°$

16. $a = 3,\ c = 2,\ \beta = 90°$

$b^2 = a^2 + c^2 - 2ac\cos\beta$

$b^2 = 3^2 + 2^2 - 2\cdot 3\cdot 2\cos(90°) = 13$

$b \approx 3.61$

$a^2 = b^2 + c^2 - 2bc\cos\alpha \rightarrow \cos\alpha = \dfrac{b^2 + c^2 - a^2}{2bc} = \dfrac{3.61^2 + 2^2 - 3^2}{2(3.61)(2)} \approx 0.5562 \rightarrow \alpha \approx 56.2°$

$c^2 = a^2 + b^2 - 2ab\cos\gamma \rightarrow \cos\gamma = \dfrac{a^2 + b^2 - c^2}{2ab} = \dfrac{3^2 + 3.61^2 - 2^2}{2(3)(3.61)} \approx 0.8325 \rightarrow \gamma \approx 33.6°$

17. $a = 12,\ b = 13,\ c = 5$

$a^2 = b^2 + c^2 - 2bc\cos\alpha \rightarrow \cos\alpha = \dfrac{b^2 + c^2 - a^2}{2bc} = \dfrac{13^2 + 5^2 - 12^2}{2(13)(5)} \approx 0.3846 \rightarrow \alpha \approx 67.4°$

$$b^2=a^2+c^2-2ac\cos\beta \;\rightarrow\; \cos\beta=\frac{a^2+c^2-b^2}{2ac}=\frac{12^2+5^2-13^2}{2(12)(5)}=0\rightarrow\beta=90^\circ$$

$$c^2=a^2+b^2-2ab\cos\gamma \;\rightarrow\; \cos\gamma=\frac{a^2+b^2-c^2}{2ab}=\frac{12^2+13^2-5^2}{2(12)(13)}\approx 0.9231\rightarrow\gamma\approx 22.6^\circ$$

18. $a=4,\; b=5,\; c=3$

$$a^2=b^2+c^2-2bc\cos\alpha \;\rightarrow\; \cos\alpha=\frac{b^2+c^2-a^2}{2bc}=\frac{5^2+3^2-4^2}{2(5)(3)}=0.6\rightarrow\alpha\approx 53.1^\circ$$

$$b^2=a^2+c^2-2ac\cos\beta \;\rightarrow\; \cos\beta=\frac{a^2+c^2-b^2}{2ac}=\frac{4^2+3^2-5^2}{2(4)(3)}=0\rightarrow\beta=90^\circ$$

$$c^2=a^2+b^2-2ab\cos\gamma \;\rightarrow\; \cos\gamma=\frac{a^2+b^2-c^2}{2ab}=\frac{4^2+5^2-3^2}{2(4)(5)}=0.8\rightarrow\gamma\approx 36.9^\circ$$

19. $a=2,\; b=2,\; c=2$

$$a^2=b^2+c^2-2bc\cos\alpha \;\rightarrow\; \cos\alpha=\frac{b^2+c^2-a^2}{2bc}=\frac{2^2+2^2-2^2}{2(2)(2)}=0.5\rightarrow\alpha=60^\circ$$

$$b^2=a^2+c^2-2ac\cos\beta \;\rightarrow\; \cos\beta=\frac{a^2+c^2-b^2}{2ac}=\frac{2^2+2^2-2^2}{2(2)(2)}=0.5\rightarrow\beta=60^\circ$$

$$c^2=a^2+b^2-2ab\cos\gamma \;\rightarrow\; \cos\gamma=\frac{a^2+b^2-c^2}{2ab}=\frac{2^2+2^2-2^2}{2(2)(2)}=0.5\rightarrow\gamma=60^\circ$$

20. $a=3,\; b=3,\; c=2$

$$a^2=b^2+c^2-2bc\cos\alpha \;\rightarrow\; \cos\alpha=\frac{b^2+c^2-a^2}{2bc}=\frac{3^2+2^2-3^2}{2(3)(2)}\approx 0.3333\rightarrow\alpha\approx 70.5^\circ$$

$$b^2=a^2+c^2-2ac\cos\beta \;\rightarrow\; \cos\beta=\frac{a^2+c^2-b^2}{2ac}=\frac{3^2+2^2-3^2}{2(3)(2)}\approx 0.3333\rightarrow\beta\approx 70.5^\circ$$

$$c^2=a^2+b^2-2ab\cos\gamma \;\rightarrow\; \cos\gamma=\frac{a^2+b^2-c^2}{2ab}=\frac{3^2+3^2-2^2}{2(3)(3)}\approx 0.7778\rightarrow\gamma\approx 38.9^\circ$$

21. $a=5,\; b=8,\; c=9$

$$a^2=b^2+c^2-2bc\cos\alpha \;\rightarrow\; \cos\alpha=\frac{b^2+c^2-a^2}{2bc}=\frac{8^2+9^2-5^2}{2(8)(9)}\approx 0.8333\rightarrow\alpha\approx 33.6^\circ$$

$$b^2=a^2+c^2-2ac\cos\beta \;\rightarrow\; \cos\beta=\frac{a^2+c^2-b^2}{2ac}=\frac{5^2+9^2-8^2}{2\cdot 5\cdot 9}\approx 0.4667\rightarrow\beta\approx 62.2^\circ$$

$$c^2=a^2+b^2-2ab\cos\gamma \;\rightarrow\; \cos\gamma=\frac{a^2+b^2-c^2}{2ab}=\frac{5^2+8^2-9^2}{2\cdot 5\cdot 8}=0.1000\rightarrow\gamma\approx 84.3^\circ$$

22. $a = 4,\ b = 3,\ c = 6$

$$a^2 = b^2 + c^2 - 2bc\cos\alpha \ \rightarrow\ \cos\alpha = \frac{b^2 + c^2 - a^2}{2bc} = \frac{3^2 + 6^2 - 4^2}{2(3)(6)} \approx 0.8056 \rightarrow \alpha \approx 36.3^\circ$$

$$b^2 = a^2 + c^2 - 2ac\cos\beta \ \rightarrow\ \cos\beta = \frac{a^2 + c^2 - b^2}{2ac} = \frac{4^2 + 6^2 - 3^2}{2(4)(6)} \approx 0.8958 \rightarrow \beta \approx 26.4^\circ$$

$$c^2 = a^2 + b^2 - 2ab\cos\gamma \ \rightarrow\ \cos\gamma = \frac{a^2 + b^2 - c^2}{2ab} = \frac{4^2 + 3^2 - 6^2}{2(4)(3)} \approx -0.4583 \rightarrow \gamma \approx 117.3^\circ$$

23. $a = 10,\ b = 8,\ c = 5$

$$a^2 = b^2 + c^2 - 2bc\cos\alpha \ \rightarrow\ \cos\alpha = \frac{b^2 + c^2 - a^2}{2bc} = \frac{8^2 + 5^2 - 10^2}{2(8)(5)} \approx -0.1375 \rightarrow \alpha \approx 97.9^\circ$$

$$b^2 = a^2 + c^2 - 2ac\cos\beta \ \rightarrow\ \cos\beta = \frac{a^2 + c^2 - b^2}{2ac} = \frac{10^2 + 5^2 - 8^2}{2(10)(5)} \approx 0.6100 \rightarrow \beta \approx 52.4^\circ$$

$$c^2 = a^2 + b^2 - 2ab\cos\gamma \ \rightarrow\ \cos\gamma = \frac{a^2 + b^2 - c^2}{2ab} = \frac{10^2 + 8^2 - 5^2}{2(10)(8)} \approx 0.8688 \rightarrow \gamma \approx 29.7^\circ$$

24. $a = 9,\ b = 7,\ c = 10$

$$a^2 = b^2 + c^2 - 2bc\cos\alpha \ \rightarrow\ \cos\alpha = \frac{b^2 + c^2 - a^2}{2bc} = \frac{7^2 + 10^2 - 9^2}{2(7)(10)} \approx 0.4857 \rightarrow \alpha \approx 60.9^\circ$$

$$b^2 = a^2 + c^2 - 2ac\cos\beta \ \rightarrow\ \cos\beta = \frac{a^2 + c^2 - b^2}{2ac} = \frac{9^2 + 10^2 - 7^2}{2(9)(10)} \approx 0.7333 \rightarrow \beta \approx 42.8^\circ$$

$$c^2 = a^2 + b^2 - 2ab\cos\gamma \ \rightarrow\ \cos\gamma = \frac{a^2 + b^2 - c^2}{2ab} = \frac{9^2 + 7^2 - 10^2}{2(9)(7)} \approx 0.2381 \rightarrow \gamma = 76.2^\circ$$

25. Find the third side of the triangle using the Law of Cosines:

$a = 50,\ b = 70,\ \gamma = 70^\circ$

$c^2 = a^2 + b^2 - 2ab\cos\gamma = 50^2 + 70^2 - 2 \cdot 50 \cdot 70\cos(70^\circ) \approx 5005.86 \rightarrow c \approx 70.75$

The houses are approximately 70.75 feet apart.

26. (a) The angle inside the triangle at Sarasota is $180^\circ - 50^\circ = 130^\circ$. Use the Law of Cosines to find the third side:

$a = 150,\ b = 100,\ \gamma = 130^\circ$

$c^2 = a^2 + b^2 - 2ab\cos\gamma = 150^2 + 100^2 - 2 \cdot 150 \cdot 100\cos(130^\circ) \approx 51783.63$

$c \approx 227.56$ miles

(b) Use the Law of Sines to find the angle inside the triangle at Orlando:

$$\frac{\sin\alpha}{150} = \frac{\sin(130^\circ)}{227.6} \rightarrow \sin\alpha = \frac{150\sin(130^\circ)}{227.6} \approx 0.5049 \rightarrow \alpha \approx 30.3^\circ$$

Since the angle of the triangle is 30.3°, the angle through which the pilot must turn is $180^\circ - 30.3^\circ = 149.7^\circ$.

27. (a) After 15 minutes, the plane would have flown $220(0.25) = 55$ miles.

Find the third side of the triangle:

$a = 55,\ b = 330,\ \gamma = 10^\circ$

$$c^2 = a^2 + b^2 - 2ab\cos\gamma = 55^2 + 330^2 - 2\cdot 55\cdot 330\cos(10^\circ) \approx 76176.48 \rightarrow c \approx 276$$

Find the measure of the angle opposite the 330 side:

$$\cos\beta = \frac{a^2 + c^2 - b^2}{2ac} = \frac{55^2 + 276^2 - 330^2}{2(55)(276)} \approx -0.9782 \rightarrow \beta \approx 168^\circ$$

The pilot should turn through an angle of 180° – 168° = 12°.

(b) If the total trip is to be done in 90 minutes, and 15 minutes were used already, then there are 75 minutes or 1.25 hours to complete the trip. The plane must travel 276 miles in 1.25 hours.

$$r = \frac{276}{1.25} = 220.8 \text{ miles/ hour}$$

The pilot must maintain a speed of 220.8 mi/hr to complete the whole trip in 90 minutes.

28. After 10 hours the ship will have traveled 150 nautical miles along its altered course. Use the Law of Cosines to find the distance from Barbados on the new course.

$a = 600,\ b = 150,\ \gamma = 20^\circ$

$$c^2 = a^2 + b^2 - 2ab\cos\gamma = 600^2 + 150^2 - 2\cdot 600\cdot 150\cos(20^\circ) \approx 213355.33$$

$c \approx 461.9$ nautical miles

(a) Use the Law of Cosines to find the angle opposite the side of 600:

$$\cos\alpha = \frac{b^2 + c^2 - a^2}{2bc}$$

$$\cos\beta = \frac{150^2 + 461.9^2 - 600^2}{2(150)(461.9)} \approx -0.8959 \rightarrow \beta \approx 153.6^\circ$$

The captain needs to turn the ship through an angle of 180° – 153.6° = 26.4°.

(b) $t = \dfrac{461.9}{15} \approx 30.8$ hours are required for the second leg of the trip. The total time for the trip will be 40.8 hours.

29. (a) Find x in the figure:

$$x^2 = 60.5^2 + 90^2 - 2(60.5)90\cos(45^\circ) \approx 4059.86$$

$x \approx 63.7$ feet

It is about 63.7 feet from the pitching rubber to first base.

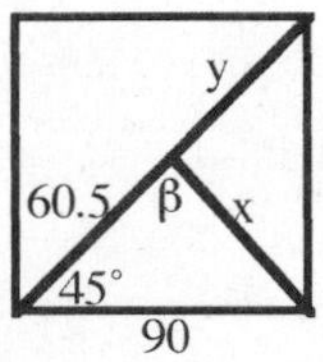

(b) Use the Pythagorean Theorem to find y in the figure:

$$90^2 + 90^2 = (60.5 + y)^2 \rightarrow 8100 + 8100 = (60.5 + y)^2$$

$$16200 = (60.5 + y)^2 \rightarrow 60.5 + y \approx 127.3 \rightarrow y \approx 66.8 \text{ feet}$$

It is about 66.8 feet from the pitching rubber to second base.

(c) Find β in the figure by using the Law of Cosines:

$$\cos\beta = \frac{60.5^2 + 63.7^2 - 90^2}{2(60.5)(63.7)} \approx -0.0496 \rightarrow \beta \approx 92.8^\circ$$

The pitcher needs to turn through an angle of 92.8° to face first base.

30. (a) Find x in the figure:

$$x^2 = 46^2 + 60^2 - 2(46)60\cos(45°) \approx 1812.77$$

$x \approx 42.6$ feet

It is about 42.58 feet from the pitching rubber to first base.

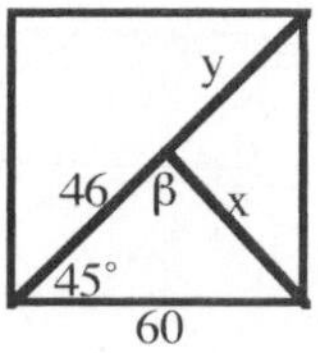

(b) Use the Pythagorean Theorem to find y in the figure:

$$60^2 + 60^2 = (46 + y)^2 \rightarrow 3600 + 3600 = (46 + y)^2$$

$$7200 = (46 + y)^2 \rightarrow 46 + y \approx 84.9 \rightarrow y \approx 38.85 \text{ feet}$$

It is about 38.9 feet from the pitching rubber to second base.

(c) Find β in the figure by using the Law of Cosines:

$$\cos\beta = \frac{46^2 + 42.6^2 - 60^2}{2(46)(42.6)} \approx 0.0844 \rightarrow \beta \approx 85.2°$$

The pitcher needs to turn through an angle of 85.2° to face first base.

31. (a) Find x by using the Law of Cosines:

$$x^2 = 500^2 + 100^2 - 2(500)100\cos(80°) \approx 242{,}635$$

$x \approx 492.6$ feet

The guy wire needs to be about 492.6 feet long.

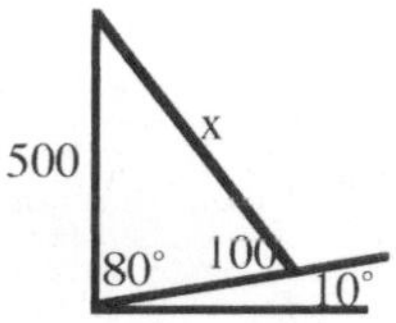

(b) Use the Pythagorean Theorem to find the value of y:

$$y^2 = 100^2 + 250^2 = 72500$$

$y = 269.3$ feet

The guy wire needs to be about 269.3 feet long.

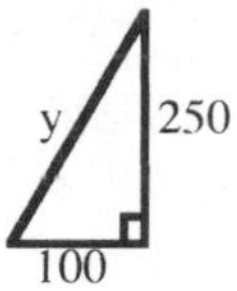

32. Find x by using the Law of Cosines:

$$x^2 = 500^2 + 100^2 - 2(500)100\cos(85°) \approx 251{,}284$$

$x \approx 501.28$ feet

The guy wire needs to be about 501.3 feet long.

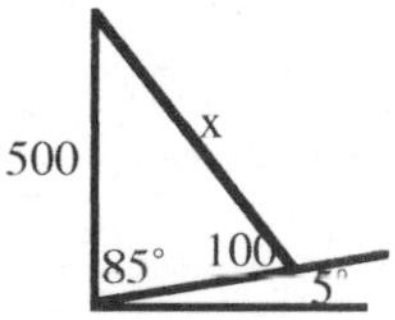

Find y by using the Law of Cosines:

$$y^2 = 500^2 + 100^2 - 2(500)100\cos(95°) \approx 268{,}716$$

$y \approx 518.38$ feet

The guy wire needs to be about 518.4 feet long.

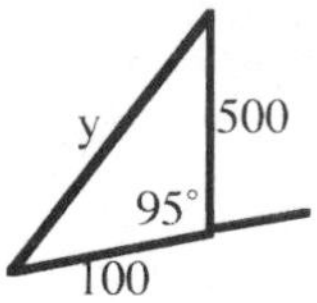

33. Find x by using the Law of Cosines:

$$x^2 = 400^2 + 90^2 - 2(400)90\cos(45°) \approx 117{,}188.3$$

$x \approx 342.3$ feet

It is approximately 342.3 feet from dead center to third base.

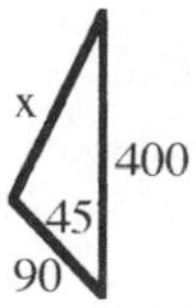

34. Find x by using the Law of Cosines:

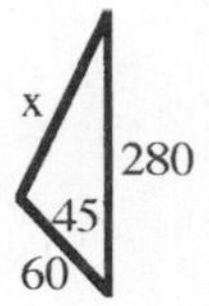

$$x^2 = 280^2 + 60^2 - 2(280)60\cos(45°) \approx 58{,}241.2$$

$$x \approx 241.33 \text{ feet}$$

It is approximately 241.3 feet from dead center to third base.

35. Use the Law of Cosines:

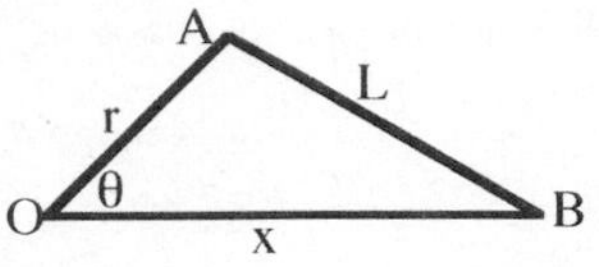

$$L^2 = x^2 + r^2 - 2xr\cos\theta$$

$$x^2 - 2xr\cos\theta + r^2 - L^2 = 0$$

$$x = \frac{2r\cos\theta + \sqrt{(2r\cos\theta)^2 - 4(1)(r^2 - L^2)}}{2(1)}$$

$$x = \frac{2r\cos\theta + \sqrt{4r^2\cos^2\theta - 4(r^2 - L^2)}}{2}$$

$$x = r\cos\theta + \sqrt{r^2\cos^2\theta + L^2 - r^2}$$

36. Use the Law of Cosines to find the length of side d:

$$d^2 = r^2 + r^2 - 2\cdot r\cdot r\cdot\cos\theta = 2r^2 - 2r^2\cos\theta = 2r^2(1-\cos\theta) = 4r^2\left(\frac{1-\cos\theta}{2}\right)$$

$$d = 2r\sqrt{\frac{1-\cos\theta}{2}} = 2r\sin\frac{\theta}{2}$$

Since $d < s$, and $s = r\theta$, we have $2r\sin\frac{\theta}{2} < r\theta$ or $\sin\frac{\theta}{2} < \frac{\theta}{2}$.

Therefore, $\sin\theta < \theta$ for any angle θ.

37. $$\cos\left(\frac{\gamma}{2}\right) = \sqrt{\frac{1+\cos\gamma}{2}} = \sqrt{\frac{\left(1 + \frac{a^2+b^2-c^2}{2ab}\right)}{2}} = \sqrt{\frac{2ab + a^2 + b^2 - c^2}{4ab}} = \sqrt{\frac{(a+b)^2 - c^2}{4ab}}$$

$$= \sqrt{\frac{(a+b+c)(a+b-c)}{4ab}} = \sqrt{\frac{2s(2s-c-c)}{4ab}} = \sqrt{\frac{4s(s-c)}{4ab}} = \sqrt{\frac{s(s-c)}{ab}}$$

38. $$\sin\left(\frac{\gamma}{2}\right) = \sqrt{\frac{1-\cos\gamma}{2}} = \sqrt{\frac{\left(1 - \frac{a^2+b^2-c^2}{2ab}\right)}{2}} = \sqrt{\frac{2ab - a^2 - b^2 + c^2}{4ab}}$$

$$= \sqrt{\frac{-(a^2 - 2ab + b^2 - c^2)}{4ab}} = \sqrt{\frac{-((a-b)^2 - c^2)}{4ab}} = \sqrt{\frac{-(a-b+c)(a-b-c)}{4ab}}$$

$$= \sqrt{\frac{(a-b+c)(b+c-a)}{4ab}} = \sqrt{\frac{(2s-2b)(2s-2a)}{4ab}} = \sqrt{\frac{4(s-b)(s-a)}{4ab}}$$

$$= \sqrt{\frac{(s-a)(s-b)}{ab}}$$

39. $$\frac{\cos\alpha}{a} + \frac{\cos\beta}{b} + \frac{\cos\gamma}{c} = \frac{b^2+c^2-a^2}{2bca} + \frac{a^2+c^2-b^2}{2acb} + \frac{a^2+b^2-c^2}{2abc}$$

$$= \frac{b^2+c^2-a^2+a^2+c^2-b^2+a^2+b^2-c^2}{2abc} = \frac{a^2+b^2+c^2}{2abc}$$

Chapter 9

Applications of Trigonometric Functions

9.4 The Area of a Triangle

1. $a = 2,\ c = 4,\ \beta = 45°$

   $A = \frac{1}{2}ac\sin\beta = \frac{1}{2}(2)(4)\sin(45°) \approx 2.83$

2. $b = 3,\ c = 4,\ \alpha = 30°$

   $A = \frac{1}{2}bc\sin\alpha = \frac{1}{2}(3)(4)\sin(30°) = 3$

3. $a = 2,\ b = 3,\ \gamma = 95°$

   $A = \frac{1}{2}ab\sin\gamma = \frac{1}{2}(2)(3)\sin(95°) \approx 2.99$

4. $a = 2,\ c = 5,\ \beta = 20°$

   $A = \frac{1}{2}ac\sin\beta = \frac{1}{2}(2)(5)\sin(20°) \approx 1.71$

5. $a = 6,\ b = 5,\ c = 8$

   $s = \frac{1}{2}(a + b + c) = \frac{1}{2}(6 + 5 + 8) = \frac{19}{2}$

   $A = \sqrt{s(s - a)(s - b)(s - c)} = \sqrt{\frac{19}{2}\left(\frac{7}{2}\right)\left(\frac{9}{2}\right)\left(\frac{3}{2}\right)} = \sqrt{\frac{3591}{16}} \approx 14.98$

6. $a = 8,\ b = 5,\ c = 4$

   $s = \frac{1}{2}(a + b + c) = \frac{1}{2}(8 + 5 + 4) = \frac{17}{2}$

   $A = \sqrt{s(s - a)(s - b)(s - c)} = \sqrt{\frac{17}{2}\left(\frac{1}{2}\right)\left(\frac{7}{2}\right)\left(\frac{9}{2}\right)} = \sqrt{\frac{1071}{16}} \approx 8.18$

7. $a = 9,\ b = 6,\ c = 4$

   $s = \frac{1}{2}(a + b + c) = \frac{1}{2}(9 + 6 + 4) = \frac{19}{2}$

   $A = \sqrt{s(s - a)(s - b)(s - c)} = \sqrt{\frac{19}{2}\left(\frac{1}{2}\right)\left(\frac{7}{2}\right)\left(\frac{11}{2}\right)} = \sqrt{\frac{1463}{16}} \approx 9.56$

8. $a = 4,\ b = 3,\ c = 4$

$$s = \frac{1}{2}(a+b+c) = \frac{1}{2}(4+3+4) = \frac{11}{2}$$

$$A = \sqrt{s(s-a)(s-b)(s-c)} = \sqrt{\frac{11}{2}\left(\frac{3}{2}\right)\left(\frac{5}{2}\right)\left(\frac{3}{2}\right)} = \sqrt{\frac{495}{16}} \approx 5.56$$

9. $a = 3,\ b = 4,\ \gamma = 40^\circ$

$$A = \frac{1}{2}ab\sin\gamma = \frac{1}{2}(3)(4)\sin(40^\circ) \approx 3.86$$

10. $a = 2,\ c = 1,\ \beta = 10^\circ$

$$A = \frac{1}{2}ac\sin\beta = \frac{1}{2}(2)(1)\sin(10^\circ) \approx 0.17$$

11. $b = 1,\ c = 3,\ \alpha = 80^\circ$

$$A = \frac{1}{2}bc\sin\alpha = \frac{1}{2}(1)(3)\sin(80^\circ) \approx 1.48$$

12. $a = 6,\ b = 4,\ \gamma = 60^\circ$

$$A = \frac{1}{2}ab\sin\gamma = \frac{1}{2}(6)(4)\sin(60^\circ) \approx 10.39$$

13. $a = 3,\ c = 2,\ \beta = 110^\circ$

$$A = \frac{1}{2}ac\sin\beta = \frac{1}{2}(3)(2)\sin(110^\circ) \approx 2.82$$

14. $b = 4,\ c = 1,\ \alpha = 120^\circ$

$$A = \frac{1}{2}bc\sin\alpha = \frac{1}{2}(4)(1)\sin(120^\circ) \approx 1.73$$

15. $a = 2,\ b = 2,\ \gamma = 50^\circ$

$$A = \frac{1}{2}ab\sin\gamma = \frac{1}{2}(2)(2)\sin(50^\circ) \approx 1.53$$

16. $a = 3,\ c = 2,\ \beta = 90^\circ$

$$A = \frac{1}{2}ac\sin\beta = \frac{1}{2}(3)(2)\sin(90^\circ) = 3$$

17. $a = 12,\ b = 13,\ c = 5$

$$s = \frac{1}{2}(a+b+c) = \frac{1}{2}(12+13+5) = 15$$

$$A = \sqrt{s(s-a)(s-b)(s-c)} = \sqrt{15(3)(2)(10)} = \sqrt{900} = 30$$

18. $a = 4,\ b = 5,\ c = 3$
$s = \frac{1}{2}(a+b+c) = \frac{1}{2}(4+5+3) = 6$
$A = \sqrt{s(s-a)(s-b)(s-c)} = \sqrt{6(2)(1)(3)} = \sqrt{36} = 6$

19. $a = 2,\ b = 2,\ c = 2$
$s = \frac{1}{2}(a+b+c) = \frac{1}{2}(2+2+2) = 3$
$A = \sqrt{s(s-a)(s-b)(s-c)} = \sqrt{3(1)(1)(1)} = \sqrt{3} \approx 1.73$

20. $a = 3,\ b = 3,\ c = 2$
$s = \frac{1}{2}(a+b+c) = \frac{1}{2}(3+3+2) = 4$
$A = \sqrt{s(s-a)(s-b)(s-c)} = \sqrt{4(1)(1)(2)} = \sqrt{8} \approx 2.83$

21. $a = 5,\ b = 8,\ c = 9$
$s = \frac{1}{2}(a+b+c) = \frac{1}{2}(5+8+9) = 11$
$A = \sqrt{s(s-a)(s-b)(s-c)} = \sqrt{11(6)(3)(2)} = \sqrt{396} \approx 19.90$

22. $a = 4,\ b = 3,\ c = 6$
$s = \frac{1}{2}(a+b+c) = \frac{1}{2}(4+3+6) = \frac{13}{2}$
$A = \sqrt{s(s-a)(s-b)(s-c)} = \sqrt{\frac{13}{2}\left(\frac{5}{2}\right)\left(\frac{7}{2}\right)\left(\frac{1}{2}\right)} = \sqrt{\frac{455}{16}} \approx 5.33$

23. $a = 10,\ b = 8,\ c = 5$
$s = \frac{1}{2}(a+b+c) = \frac{1}{2}(10+8+5) = \frac{23}{2}$
$A = \sqrt{s(s-a)(s-b)(s-c)} = \sqrt{\frac{23}{2}\left(\frac{3}{2}\right)\left(\frac{7}{2}\right)\left(\frac{13}{2}\right)} = \sqrt{\frac{6279}{16}} \approx 19.81$

24. $a = 9,\ b = 7,\ c = 10$
$s = \frac{1}{2}(a+b+c) = \frac{1}{2}(9+7+10) = 13$
$A = \sqrt{s(s-a)(s-b)(s-c)} = \sqrt{13(4)(6)(3)} = \sqrt{936} \approx 30.59$

25. Area of a sector $= \frac{1}{2}r^2\theta$ where θ is in radians.
$\theta = 70^\circ \cdot \frac{\pi}{180} = \frac{7\pi}{18}$
Area of the sector $= \frac{1}{2} \cdot 8^2 \cdot \frac{7\pi}{18} = \frac{112\pi}{9} \approx 39.10$ square feet
Area of the triangle $= \frac{1}{2} \cdot 8 \cdot 8\sin(70^\circ) = 32\sin(70^\circ) \approx 30.07$ square feet
Area of the segment $= 39.10 - 30.07 = 9.03$ square feet

26. Area of a sector $= \frac{1}{2}r^2\theta$ where θ is in radians.

$$\theta = 40^\circ \cdot \frac{\pi}{180} = \frac{2\pi}{9}$$

Area of the sector $= \frac{1}{2} \cdot 5^2 \cdot \frac{2\pi}{9} = \frac{25\pi}{9}$ square inches

Area of the triangle $= \frac{1}{2} \cdot 5 \cdot 5\sin(40^\circ) = \frac{25}{2}\sin(40^\circ)$ square inches

Area of the segment $= \frac{25\pi}{9} - \frac{25}{2}\sin(40^\circ) \approx 0.69$ square inches

27. Find the area of the lot using Heron's Formula:

$a = 100,\ b = 50,\ c = 75$

$$s = \frac{1}{2}(a+b+c) = \frac{1}{2}(100+50+75) = \frac{225}{2}$$

$$A = \sqrt{s(s-a)(s-b)(s-c)} = \sqrt{\frac{225}{2}\left(\frac{25}{2}\right)\left(\frac{125}{2}\right)\left(\frac{75}{2}\right)} = \sqrt{\frac{52{,}734{,}375}{16}} \approx 1815.46$$

The cost is \$3 times the area:

Cost = \$3(1815.46) = \$5446.38

28. Diameter of canvas is 24 feet; radius of canvas is 12 feet; angle is 260°.

Area of a sector $= \frac{1}{2}r^2\theta$ where θ is in radians.

$$\theta = 260^\circ \cdot \frac{\pi}{180} = \frac{13\pi}{9}$$

Area of the sector $= \frac{1}{2} \cdot 12^2 \cdot \frac{13\pi}{9} = \frac{936\pi}{9} = 104\pi \approx 326.73$ square feet

29. The area of the shaded region = the area of the semicircle – the area of the triangle.

Area of the semicircle $= \frac{1}{2}\pi r^2 = \frac{1}{2}\pi(4)^2 = 8\pi$ square centimeters

The triangle is a right triangle. Find the other leg:

$$6^2 + b^2 = 8^2 \ \rightarrow\ b^2 = 64 - 36 = 28 \ \rightarrow\ b = \sqrt{28} = 2\sqrt{7}$$

Area of the triangle $= \frac{1}{2} \cdot 6 \cdot 2\sqrt{7} = 6\sqrt{7}$ square centimeters

Area of the shaded region $= 8\pi - 6\sqrt{7} \approx 9.26$ square centimeters

30. The area of the shaded region = the area of the semicircle – the area of the triangle.

Area of the semicircle $= \frac{1}{2}\pi r^2 = \frac{1}{2}\pi(5)^2 = \frac{25}{2}\pi$ square inches

The triangle is a right triangle. Find the other leg:

$$8^2 + b^2 = 10^2 \ \rightarrow\ b^2 = 100 - 64 = 36 \ \rightarrow\ b = \sqrt{36} = 6$$

Area of the triangle $= \frac{1}{2} \cdot 8 \cdot 6 = 24$ square inches

Area of the shaded region $= 12.5\pi - 24 \approx 15.27$ square inches

31. Use the Law of Sines in the area of the triangle formula:

$$A = \frac{1}{2}ab\sin\gamma = \frac{1}{2}a\sin\gamma\left(\frac{a\sin\beta}{\sin\alpha}\right) = \frac{a^2\sin\beta\sin\gamma}{2\sin\alpha}$$

32. $A = \frac{1}{2}bc\sin\alpha = \frac{1}{2}b\sin\alpha\left(\frac{b\sin\gamma}{\sin\beta}\right) = \frac{b^2\sin\alpha\sin\gamma}{2\sin\beta}$

$$A = \frac{1}{2}ac\sin\beta = \frac{1}{2}c\sin\beta\left(\frac{c\sin\alpha}{\sin\gamma}\right) = \frac{c^2\sin\alpha\sin\beta}{2\sin\gamma}$$

33. $\alpha = 40°,\ \beta = 20°,\ a = 2 \qquad \gamma = 180° - \alpha - \beta = 180° - 40° - 20° = 120°$

$$A = \frac{a^2\sin\beta\sin\gamma}{2\sin\alpha} = \frac{2^2\sin(20°)\sin(120°)}{2\sin(40°)} \approx \frac{4(0.3420)(0.8660)}{2(0.6428)} \approx 0.92$$

34. $\alpha = 50°,\ \gamma = 20°,\ a = 3 \qquad \beta = 180° - \alpha - \gamma = 180° - 50° - 20° = 110°$

$$A = \frac{a^2\sin\beta\sin\gamma}{2\sin\alpha} = \frac{3^2\sin(110°)\sin(20°)}{2\sin(50°)} \approx \frac{9(0.9397)(0.3420)}{2(0.7660)} \approx 1.89$$

35. $\beta = 70°,\ \gamma = 10°,\ b = 5 \qquad \alpha = 180° - \beta - \gamma = 180° - 70° - 10° = 100°$

$$A = \frac{b^2\sin\alpha\sin\gamma}{2\sin\beta} = \frac{5^2\sin(100°)\sin(10°)}{2\sin(70°)} \approx \frac{25(0.9848)(0.1736)}{2(0.9397)} \approx 2.27$$

36. $\alpha = 70°,\ \beta = 60°,\ c = 4 \qquad \gamma = 180° - \alpha - \beta = 180° - 70° - 60° = 50°$

$$A = \frac{c^2\sin\alpha\sin\beta}{2\sin\gamma} = \frac{4^2\sin(70°)\sin(60°)}{2\sin(50°)} \approx \frac{16(0.9397)(0.8660)}{2(0.7660)} \approx 8.50$$

37. $\alpha = 110°,\ \gamma = 30°,\ c = 3 \qquad \beta = 180° - \alpha - \gamma = 180° - 110° - 30° = 40°$

$$A = \frac{c^2\sin\alpha\sin\beta}{2\sin\gamma} = \frac{3^2\sin(110°)\sin(40°)}{2\sin(30°)} \approx \frac{9(0.9397)(0.6428)}{2(0.5000)} \approx 5.44$$

38. $\beta = 10°,\ \gamma = 100°,\ b = 2 \qquad \alpha = 180° - \beta - \gamma = 180° - 10° - 100° = 70°$

$$A = \frac{b^2\sin\alpha\sin\gamma}{2\sin\beta} = \frac{2^2\sin(70°)\sin(100°)}{2\sin(10°)} \approx \frac{4(0.9397)(0.9848)}{2(0.1736)} \approx 10.66$$

39. The area is the sum of the area of a triangle and a sector.

Area of the triangle $= \frac{1}{2}r \cdot r\sin(\pi - \theta) = \frac{1}{2}r^2\sin(\pi - \theta)$

Area of the sector $= \frac{1}{2}r^2\theta$

$$A = \frac{1}{2}r^2\sin(\pi - \theta) + \frac{1}{2}r^2\theta = \frac{1}{2}r^2(\sin(\pi - \theta) + \theta)$$

$$= \frac{1}{2}r^2(\sin\pi\cos\theta - \cos\pi\sin\theta + \theta) = \frac{1}{2}r^2(0 + \sin\theta + \theta) = \frac{1}{2}r^2(\theta + \sin\theta)$$

40. Find the lengths of the diagonals of the polygon. Use the Law of Cosines:

$$x^2 = 35^2 + 80^2 - 2 \cdot 35 \cdot 80\cos(15°) \approx 2215.82 \rightarrow x \approx 47.07 \text{ feet}$$

The interior angle of the third triangle is: $180° - 100° = 80°$.

$y^2 = 45^2 + 20^2 - 2\cdot 45\cdot 20\cos(80°) \approx 2112.43 \rightarrow y \approx 45.96$ feet

Find the area of the three triangles.

$$s_1 = \frac{1}{2}(35+80+47.07) = 81.035$$

$$A_1 = \sqrt{81.035(81.035-35)(81.035-80)(81.035-47.07)} \approx 362.13 \text{ ft}^2$$

$$s_2 = \frac{1}{2}(40+46+47.07) = 66.535$$

$$A_2 = \sqrt{66.535(66.535-40)(66.535-46)(66.535-47.07)} \approx 840.06 \text{ ft}^2$$

$$s_3 = \frac{1}{2}(45+20+46) = 55.5$$

$$A_3 = \sqrt{55.5(55.5-45)(55.5-20)(55.5-46)} \approx 443.32 \text{ ft}^2$$

The approximate area of the lake is $362.13 + 840.06 + 443.32 = 1645.51 \text{ ft}^2$

41. The grazing area must be considered in sections. A_1 represents $\frac{3}{4}$ of a circle:

$$A_1 = \frac{3}{4}\pi(100)^2 = 7500\pi \approx 23{,}562 \text{ square feet}$$

Angles are needed to find A_2 and A_3: (see the figure)

In $\Delta ABC, \angle CBA = 45°, AB = 10, AC = 90$

Find $\angle BCA$:

$$\frac{\sin\angle CBA}{90} = \frac{\sin\angle BCA}{10} \rightarrow \frac{\sin(45°)}{90} = \frac{\sin\angle BCA}{10}$$

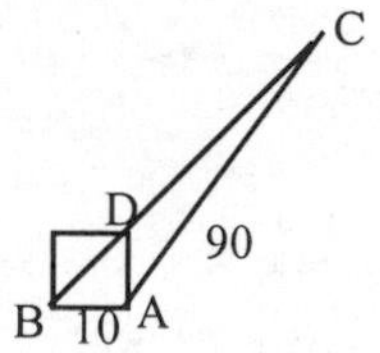

$$\sin\angle BCA = \frac{10\sin(45°)}{90} \approx 0.0786$$

$$\angle BCA \approx 4.5°$$

$$m\angle BAC = 180° - 45° - 4.5° = 130.5°$$

$$m\angle DAC = 130.5° - 90° = 40.5°$$

Area of $A_3 = \frac{1}{2}(10)(90)\sin(40.5°) \approx 292$ square feet

Area of sector $A_2 = \frac{1}{2}(90)^2\left(49.5°\cdot\frac{\pi}{180}\right) \approx 3499$ square feet

Since the cow can go in either direction around the barn, A_2 and A_3 must be doubled. Total grazing area is: $23{,}562 + 2(3499) + 2(292) = 31{,}144$ square feet

42. The grazing area must be considered in sections. A_1 represents $\frac{3}{4}$ of a circle:

$$A_1 = \frac{3}{4}\pi(100)^2 = 7500\pi \approx 23{,}562 \text{ square feet}$$

Angles are needed to find A_2 and A_3: (see the figure)

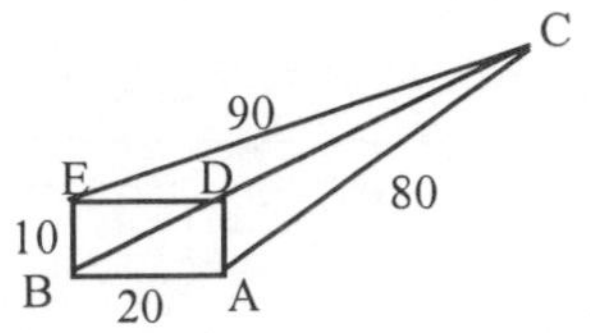

In $\Delta ABC, \tan\angle CBA = \frac{10}{20} \rightarrow \angle CBA = 26.6°$,

$AB = 20, AC = 80$

Find $\angle BCA$:

$$\frac{\sin\angle CBA}{80} = \frac{\sin\angle BCA}{20} \rightarrow \frac{\sin(26.6°)}{80} = \frac{\sin\angle BCA}{20}$$

$$\sin\angle BCA = \frac{20\sin(26.6°)}{80} \approx 0.1119$$

$$\angle BCA \approx 6.4°$$

$$m\angle BAC = 180° - 26.6° - 6.4° = 147°$$

$$m\angle DAC = 147° - 90° = 57°$$

Area of $A_3 = \frac{1}{2}(10)(80)\sin(57°) \approx 335.5$ square feet

Area of sector $A_2 = \frac{1}{2}(80)^2\left(33°\cdot\frac{\pi}{180}\right) \approx 1843.1$ square feet

There are similar areas on the opposite side of the barn. Calculate their areas.

Angles are needed to find A_4 and A_5: (see the figure)

In $\Delta EBC, \angle CBE = 90° - 26.6° = 63.4°, EB = 10, EC = 90$

Find $\angle BCE$:

$$\frac{\sin\angle CBE}{90} = \frac{\sin\angle BCE}{10} \rightarrow \frac{\sin(63.4°)}{90} = \frac{\sin\angle BCE}{10}$$

$$\sin\angle BCE = \frac{10\sin(63.4°)}{90} \approx 0.0994$$

$$\angle BCE \approx 5.7°$$

$$m\angle BEC = 180° - 63.4° - 5.7° = 110.9°$$

$$m\angle DEC = 110.9° - 90° = 20.9°$$

Area of $A_5 = \frac{1}{2}(20)(90)\sin 20.9° \approx 321.1$ square feet

Area of sector $A_4 = \frac{1}{2}(90)^2\left(69.1°\cdot\frac{\pi}{180}\right) \approx 4884.4$ square feet

Total grazing area is: $23{,}562 + 1843.1 + 335.5 + 4884.4 + 321.1 = 30{,}946.1 \text{ ft}^2$

43. $h_1 = \frac{2K}{a},\ h_2 = \frac{2K}{b},\ h_3 = \frac{2K}{c}$ where K is the area of the triangle.

$$\frac{1}{h_1} + \frac{1}{h_2} + \frac{1}{h_3} = \frac{a}{2K} + \frac{b}{2K} + \frac{c}{2K} = \frac{a+b+c}{2K} = \frac{2s}{2K} = \frac{s}{K}$$

44. From Problem 31, we have $A = \frac{a^2 \sin\beta\sin\gamma}{2\sin\alpha}$.

From Problem 43, we have $h = \frac{2K}{a}$ where K is the area of the triangle

$$\frac{a^2\sin\beta\sin\gamma}{2\sin\alpha} = K \rightarrow \frac{a\sin\beta\sin\gamma}{\sin\alpha} = \frac{2K}{a} = h$$

45. $h = \dfrac{a \sin\beta \sin\gamma}{\sin\alpha}$ where h is the altitude to side a.

In ΔOAB, c is opposite angle AOB. The two adjacent angles are $\dfrac{\alpha}{2}$ and $\dfrac{\beta}{2}$.

Then $r = \dfrac{c \cdot \sin\left(\dfrac{\alpha}{2}\right)\sin\left(\dfrac{\beta}{2}\right)}{\sin(\angle AOB)}$

$\angle AOB = \pi - \left(\dfrac{\alpha}{2} + \dfrac{\beta}{2}\right)$

$$\sin(\angle AOB) = \sin\left(\pi - \left(\frac{\alpha}{2} + \frac{\beta}{2}\right)\right) = \sin\left(\frac{\alpha}{2} + \frac{\beta}{2}\right) = \sin\left(\frac{\alpha+\beta}{2}\right) = \cos\left(\frac{\pi}{2} - \left(\frac{\alpha+\beta}{2}\right)\right)$$

$$= \cos\left(\frac{\pi - (\alpha+\beta)}{2}\right) = \cos\left(\frac{\gamma}{2}\right)$$

Thus, $r = \dfrac{c \cdot \sin\left(\dfrac{\alpha}{2}\right)\sin\left(\dfrac{\beta}{2}\right)}{\cos\left(\dfrac{\gamma}{2}\right)}$

46. $$\cot\left(\frac{\gamma}{2}\right) = \frac{\cos\left(\frac{\gamma}{2}\right)}{\sin\left(\frac{\gamma}{2}\right)} = \frac{\dfrac{c \cdot \sin\left(\frac{\alpha}{2}\right)\sin\left(\frac{\beta}{2}\right)}{r}}{\sqrt{\dfrac{(s-a)(s-b)}{ab}}} = \frac{c \cdot \sqrt{\dfrac{(s-b)(s-c)}{bc}}\sqrt{\dfrac{(s-a)(s-c)}{ac}}}{r\sqrt{\dfrac{(s-a)(s-b)}{ab}}}$$

$$= \frac{c\sqrt{s-b}\sqrt{s-c}\sqrt{s-a}\sqrt{s-c}\sqrt{a}\sqrt{b}}{r\sqrt{s-a}\sqrt{s-b}\sqrt{b}\sqrt{c}\sqrt{a}\sqrt{c}} = \frac{c(s-c)}{r \cdot c} = \frac{s-c}{r}$$

47. Use the result of Problem 46:

$$\cot\left(\frac{\alpha}{2}\right) + \cot\left(\frac{\beta}{2}\right) + \cot\left(\frac{\gamma}{2}\right) = \frac{s-a}{r} + \frac{s-b}{r} + \frac{s-c}{r} = \frac{s-a+s-b+s-c}{r}$$

$$= \frac{3s-(a+b+c)}{r} = \frac{3s-2s}{r} = \frac{s}{r}$$

48. The area of a triangle is $\dfrac{1}{2}bh$. Find the area of ΔABC by adding the areas of three triangles.

$K = \text{Area } \Delta AOB + \text{ Area } \Delta AOC + \text{ Area } \Delta BOC$

$$= \frac{1}{2}rc + \frac{1}{2}rb + \frac{1}{2}ra = \frac{1}{2}r(a+b+c) = rs$$

$rs = \sqrt{s(s-a)(s-b)(s-c)}$

$$r = \frac{\sqrt{s(s-a)(s-b)(s-c)}}{s} = \sqrt{\frac{(s-a)(s-b)(s-c)}{s}}$$

Chapter 9

Applications of Trigonometric Functions

9.5 Simple Harmonic Motion; Damped Motion

1. $d = -5\cos(\pi t)$

2. $d = -10\cos\left(\frac{2\pi}{3}t\right)$

3. $d = -6\cos(2t)$

4. $d = -4\cos(4t)$

5. $d = -5\sin(\pi t)$

6. $d = -10\sin\left(\frac{2\pi}{3}t\right)$

7. $d = -6\sin(2t)$

8. $d = -4\sin(4t)$

9. $d = 5\sin(3t)$
   (a) Simple harmonic
   (b) 5 meters
   (c) $\frac{2\pi}{3}$ seconds
   (d) $\frac{3}{2\pi}$ oscillation/second

10. $d = 4\sin(2t)$
   (a) Simple harmonic
   (b) 4 meters
   (c) π seconds
   (d) $\frac{1}{\pi}$ oscillation/second

11. $d = 6\cos(\pi t)$
   (a) Simple harmonic
   (b) 6 meters
   (c) 2 seconds
   (d) $\frac{1}{2}$ oscillation/second

12. $d = 5\cos\left(\frac{\pi}{2}t\right)$
   (a) Simple harmonic
   (b) 5 meters
   (c) 4 seconds
   (d) $\frac{1}{4}$ oscillation/second

13. $d = -3\sin\left(\frac{1}{2}t\right)$
   (a) Simple harmonic
   (b) 3 meters
   (c) 4π seconds
   (d) $\frac{1}{4\pi}$ oscillation/second

14. $d = -2\cos(2t)$
   (a) Simple harmonic
   (b) 2 meters
   (c) π second
   (d) $\frac{1}{\pi}$ oscillation/second

15. $d = 6 + 2\cos(2\pi t)$
   (a) Simple harmonic
   (b) 2 meters
   (c) 1 second
   (d) 1 oscillation/second

16. $d = 4 + 3\sin(\pi t)$
   (a) Simple harmonic
   (b) 3 meters
   (c) 2 second
   (d) $\frac{1}{2}$ oscillation/second

17. $d(t)=e^{-t/\pi}\cos(2t), \quad 0 \le t \le 2\pi$

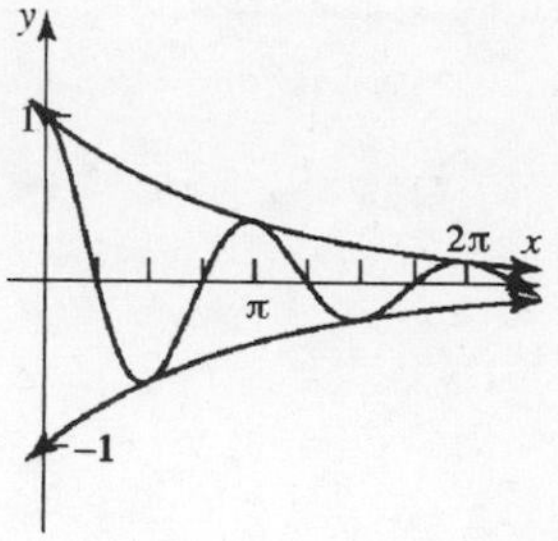

18. $d(t)=e^{-t/2\pi}\cos(2t), \quad 0 \le t \le 2\pi$

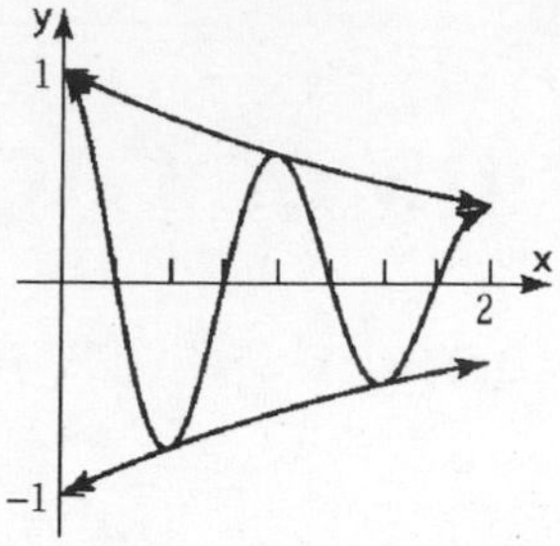

19. $d(t)=e^{-t/2\pi}\cos(t), \quad 0 \le t \le 2\pi$

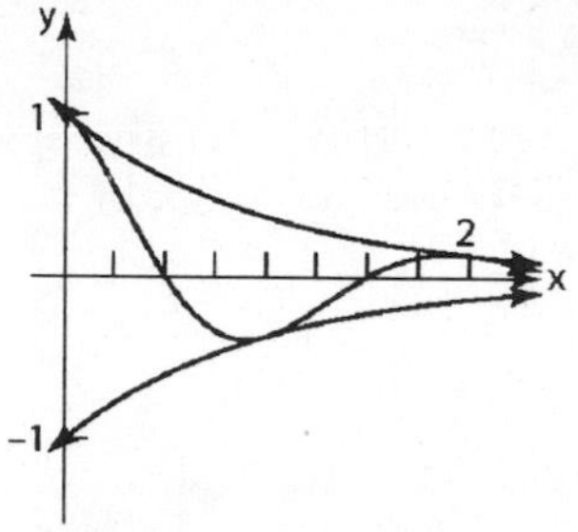

20. $d(t)=e^{-t/4\pi}\cos(t), \quad 0 \le t \le 2\pi$

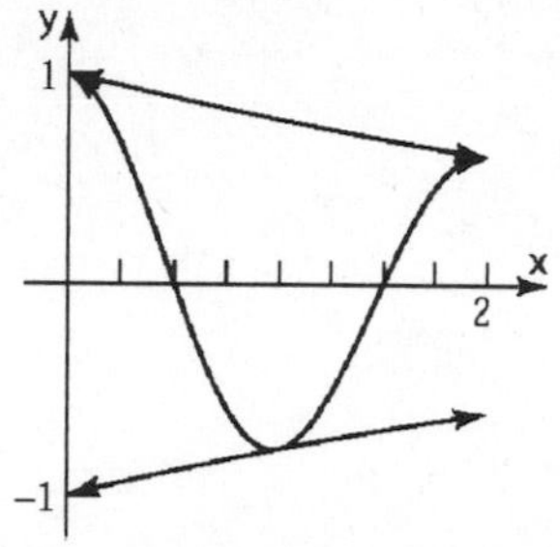

21. $f(x) = x + \cos x$

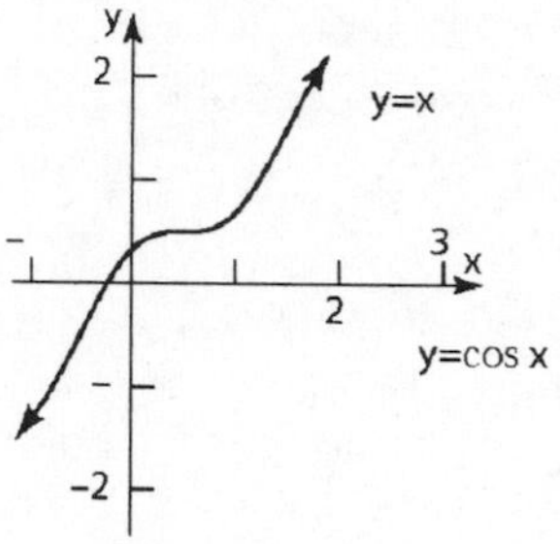

22. $f(x) = x + \cos(2x)$

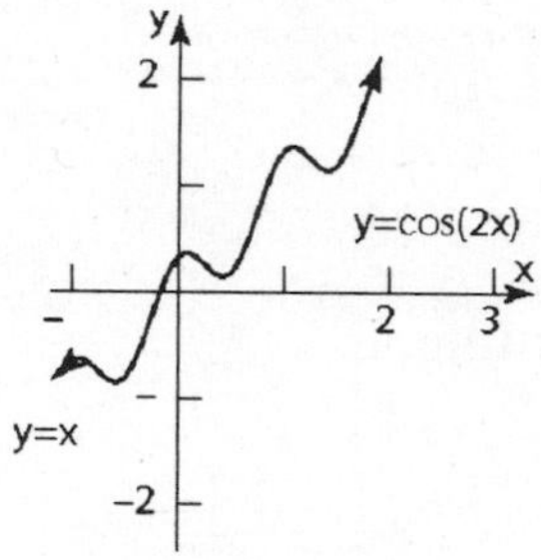

23. $f(x) = x - \sin x$

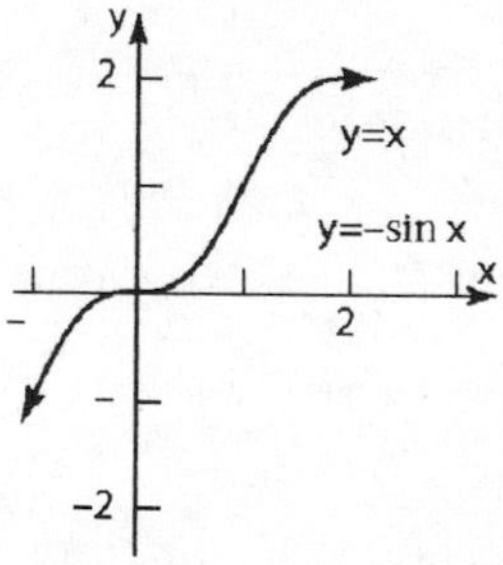

24. $f(x) = x - \cos x$

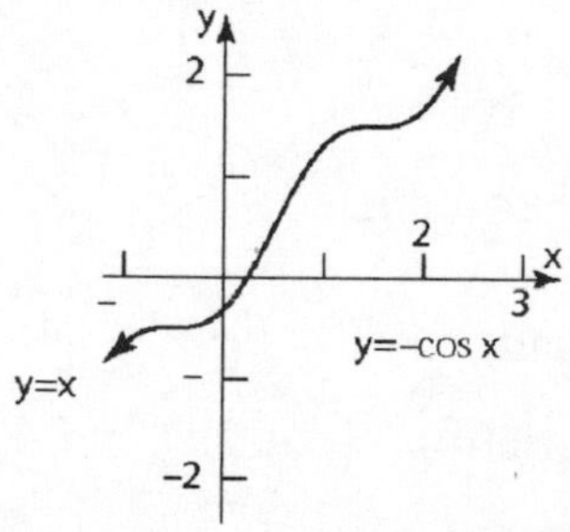

25. $f(x) = \sin x + \cos x$

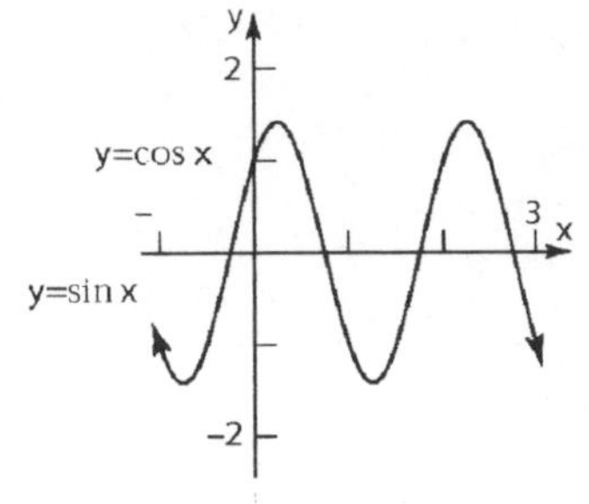

26. $f(x) = \sin(2x) + \cos x$

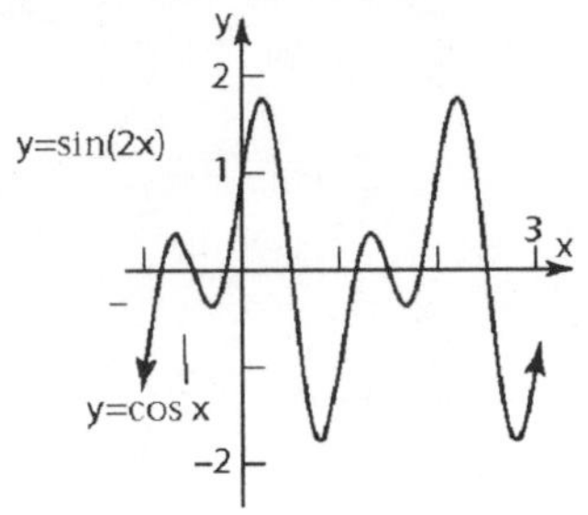

27. $f(x) = \sin x + \sin(2x)$

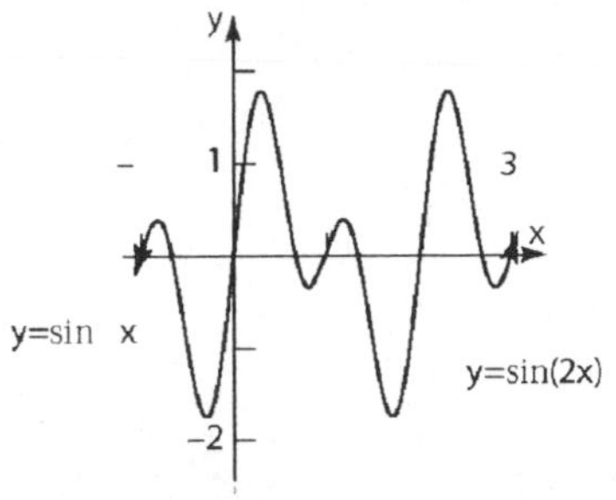

28. $f(x) = \cos(2x) + \cos x$

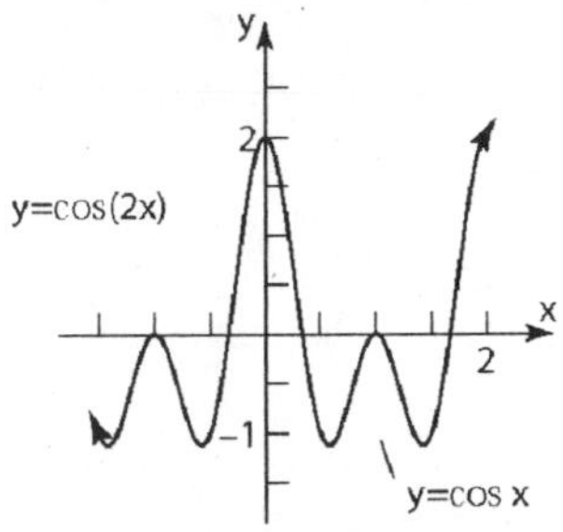

29. (a) Graph:

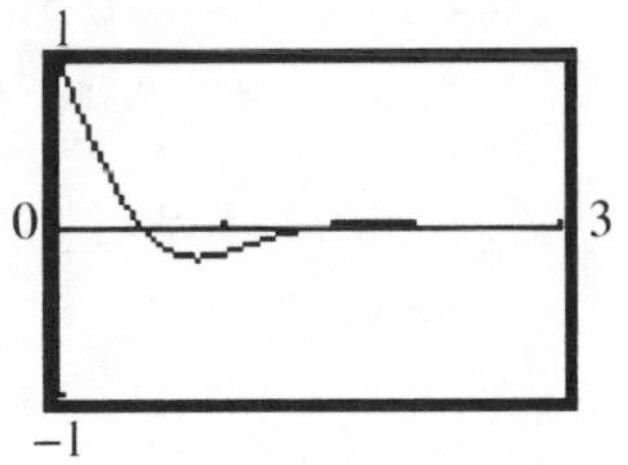

(b) The graph of V touches the graph of $y = e^{-1.9t}$ when $t = 0, 2$.
The graph of V touches the graph of $y = -e^{-1.9t}$ when $t = 1, 3$.

(c) To solve the inequality $-0.4 < e^{-t/3} \cdot \cos(\pi t) < 0.4$ on the interval $0 \le t \le 3$, we consider the graphs of $y = -0.4$; $y = e^{-t/3} \cdot \cos(\pi t)$; and $y = 0.4$.

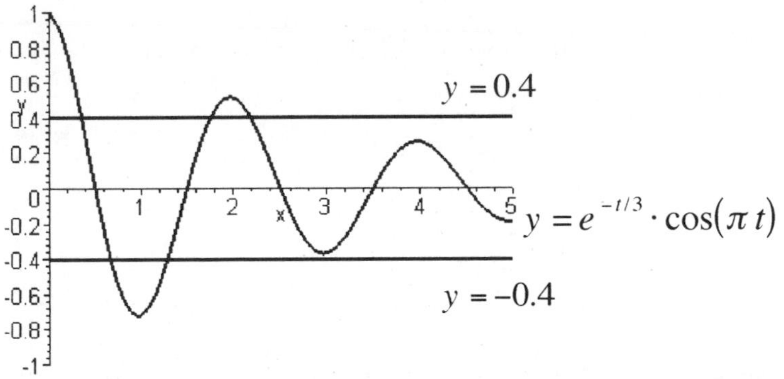

On the interval $0 \le t \le 3$, we can use the INTERSECT feature on a calculator to determine that $y = e^{-t/3} \cdot \cos(\pi t)$ intersects $y = 0.4$ when $t \approx 0.35$, $t \approx 1.75$ and $t \approx 2.19$, $y = e^{-t/3} \cdot \cos(\pi t)$ intersects $y = -0.4$ when $t \approx 0.67$ and $t \approx 1.28$ and the graph shows that $-0.4 < e^{-t/3} \cdot \cos(\pi t) < 0.4$ when $t = 3$. Therefore, the voltage V is between -0.4 and 0.4 on the intervals $0.35 < t < 0.67$, $1.28 < t < 1.75$ and $2.19 < t \le 3$.

30. (a) $f(x) = \frac{1}{2} \cdot \sin(2\pi x) + \frac{1}{4} \cdot \sin(4\pi x), \quad 0 \le x \le 2$

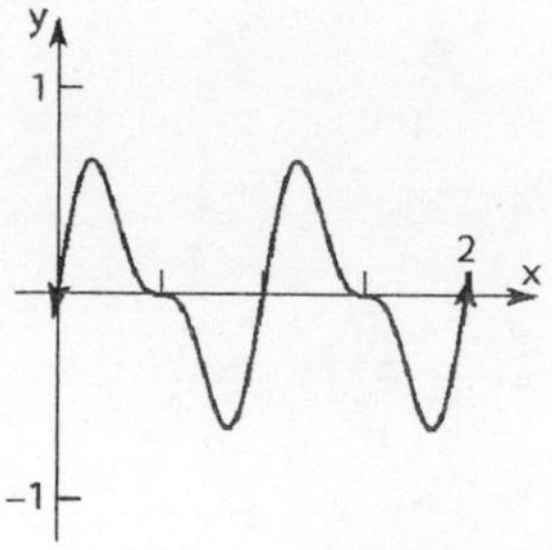

(b) $f(x) = \frac{1}{2} \cdot \sin(2\pi x) + \frac{1}{4} \cdot \sin(4\pi x) + \frac{1}{8} \cdot \sin(8\pi x), \quad 0 \le x \le 4$

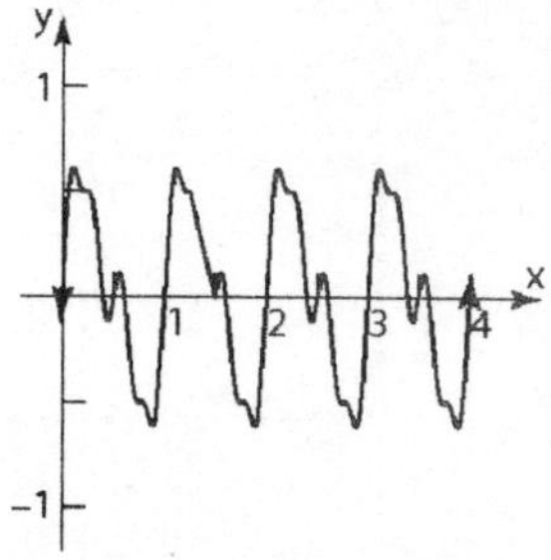

(c) $f(x) = \frac{1}{2} \cdot \sin(2\pi x) + \frac{1}{4} \cdot \sin(4\pi x) + \frac{1}{8} \cdot \sin(8\pi x) + \frac{1}{16} \cdot \sin(16\pi x), \; 0 \le x \le 4$

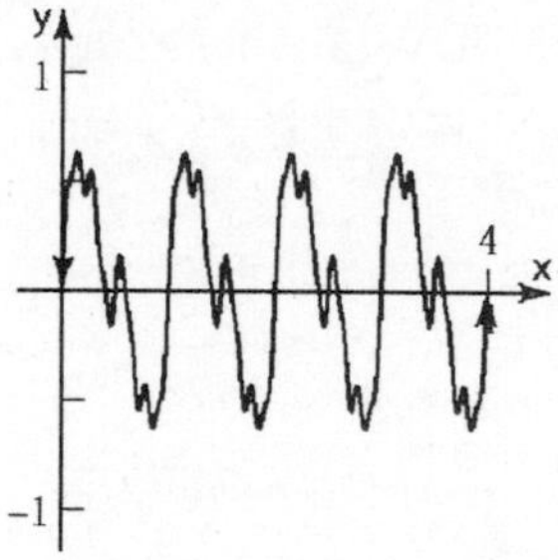

(d) $f(x) = \frac{1}{2} \cdot \sin(2\pi x) + \frac{1}{4} \cdot \sin(4\pi x) + \frac{1}{8} \cdot \sin(8\pi x)$

$+ \frac{1}{16} \cdot \sin(16\pi x) + \frac{1}{32} \cdot \sin(32\pi x), \quad 0 \le x \le 4$

31. $y = \sin(2\pi(852)t) + \sin(2\pi(1209)t)$

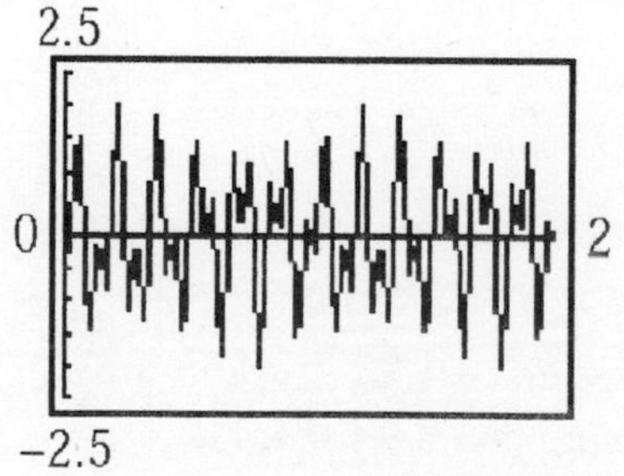

32. $y = \sin(2\pi(941)t) + \sin(2\pi(1209)t)$

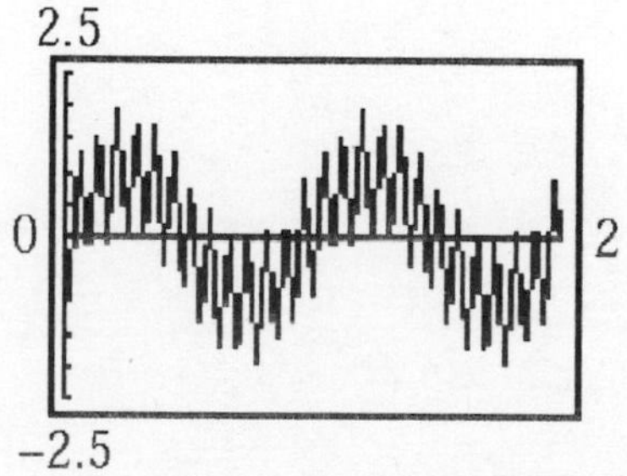

33. Graph $f(x) = \dfrac{\sin x}{x}$:

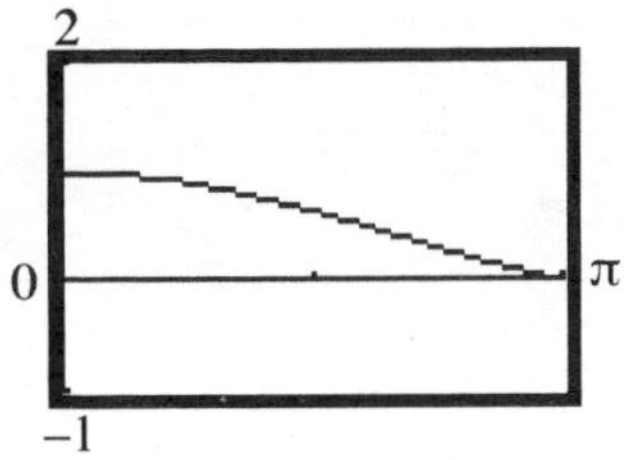

As x approaches 0, $\dfrac{\sin x}{x}$ approaches 1.

34. The graph will lie between the bounding curves $y = \pm x$, $y = \pm x^2$, $y = \pm x^3$, respectively, touching them at odd multiples of $\dfrac{\pi}{2}$. The x-intercepts of each graph are the multiples of π.

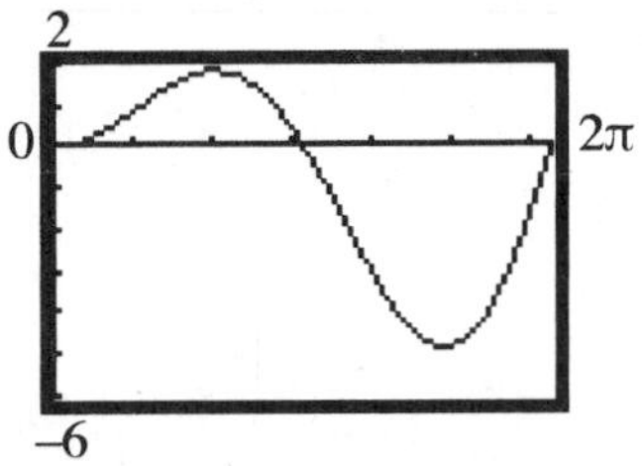

$y = x \sin x$

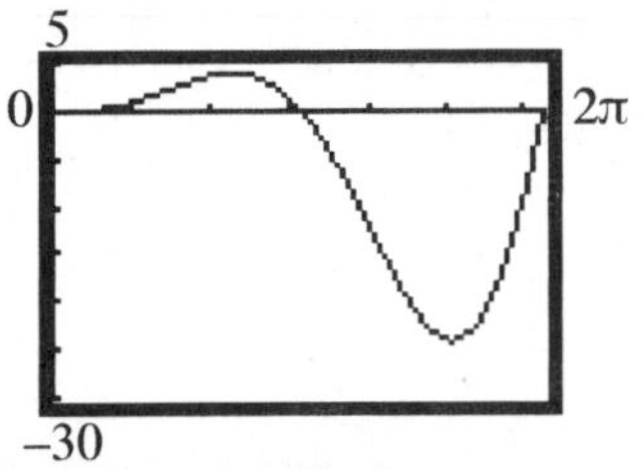

$y = x^2 \sin x$

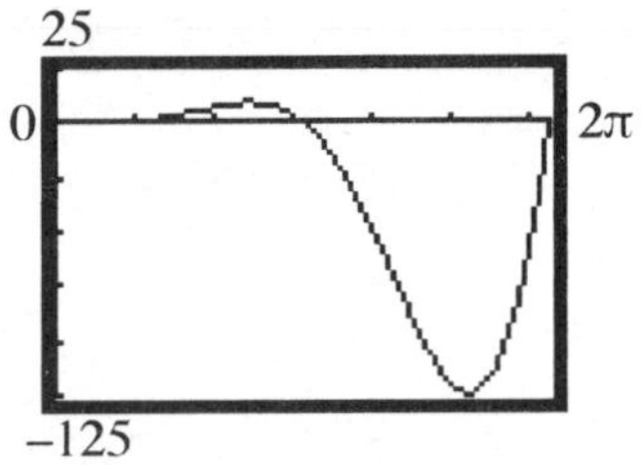

$y = x^3 \sin x$

35. Graphing:

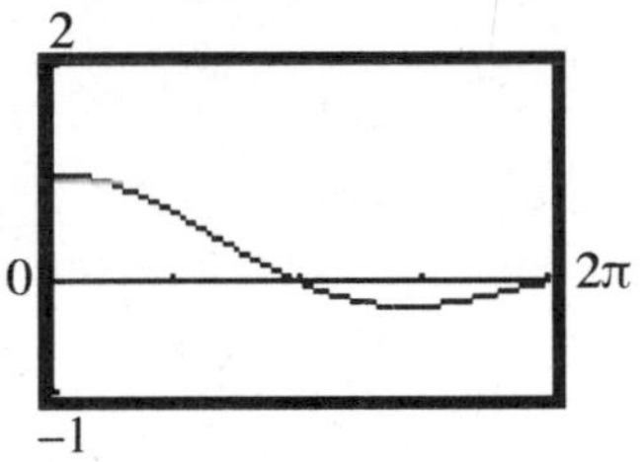

$y = \dfrac{1}{x} \sin x$

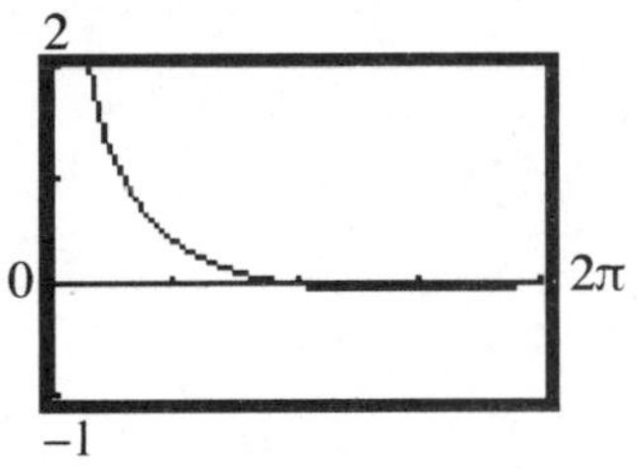

$y = \dfrac{1}{x^2} \sin x$

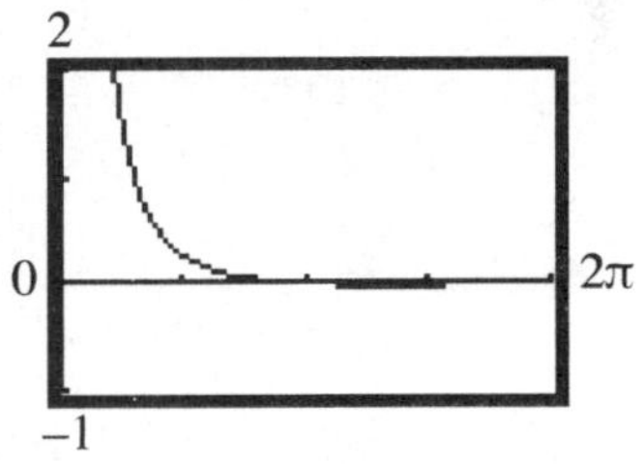

$y = \dfrac{1}{x^3} \sin x$

As x gets larger, the graph of $y = \dfrac{1}{x^n} \sin x$ gets closer to $y = 0$.

Chapter 9

Applications of Trigonometric Functions

9.R Chapter Review

1. $c = 10, \ \beta = 20°$

$$\sin\beta = \frac{b}{c} \ \rightarrow \ \sin(20°) = \frac{b}{10} \ \rightarrow \ b = 10\sin(20°) \approx 10(0.3420) \approx 3.42$$

$$\cos\beta = \frac{a}{c} \ \rightarrow \ \cos(20°) = \frac{a}{10} \ \rightarrow \ a = 10\cos(20°) \approx 10(0.9397) \approx 9.40$$

$$\alpha = 90° - \beta = 90° - 20° = 70°$$

2. $a = 5, \ \alpha = 35°$

$$\sin\alpha = \frac{a}{c} \ \rightarrow \ \sin(35°) = \frac{5}{c} \ \rightarrow \ c = \frac{5}{\sin(35°)} \approx \frac{5}{0.5736} \approx 8.72$$

$$\tan\alpha = \frac{a}{b} \ \rightarrow \ \tan(35°) = \frac{5}{b} \ \rightarrow \ b = \frac{5}{\tan(35°)} \approx \frac{5}{0.7002} \approx 7.14$$

$$\beta = 90° - \alpha = 90° - 35° = 55°$$

3. $b = 2, \ c = 5$

$$c^2 = a^2 + b^2 \ \rightarrow \ a^2 = c^2 - b^2 = 5^2 - 2^2 = 25 - 4 = 21 \ \rightarrow \ a = \sqrt{21} \approx 4.58$$

$$\sin\beta = \frac{b}{c} = \frac{2}{5} = 0.4000 \ \rightarrow \ \beta \approx 23.6°$$

$$\alpha = 90° - \beta = 90° - 23.6° = 66.4°$$

4. $b = 1, \ a = 3$

$$c^2 = a^2 + b^2 \ \rightarrow \ c^2 = 3^2 + 1^2 = 9 + 1 = 10 \ \rightarrow \ c = \sqrt{10} \approx 3.16$$

$$\tan\beta = \frac{b}{a} = \frac{1}{3} \approx 0.3333 \ \rightarrow \ \beta \approx 18.4°$$

$$\alpha = 90° - \beta = 90° - 18.4° = 71.6°$$

5. $\alpha = 50°, \ \beta = 30°, \ a = 1$

$$\gamma = 180° - \alpha - \beta = 180° - 50° - 30° = 100°$$

$$\frac{\sin\alpha}{a} = \frac{\sin\beta}{b} \ \rightarrow \ \frac{\sin(50°)}{1} = \frac{\sin(30°)}{b} \ \rightarrow \ b = \frac{1\sin(30°)}{\sin(50°)} \approx 0.65$$

$$\frac{\sin\gamma}{c} = \frac{\sin\alpha}{a} \ \rightarrow \ \frac{\sin(100°)}{c} = \frac{\sin(50°)}{1} \ \rightarrow \ c = \frac{1\sin(100°)}{\sin(50°)} \approx 1.29$$

6. $\alpha = 10°,\ \gamma = 40°,\ c = 2$

$\beta = 180° - \alpha - \gamma = 180° - 10° - 40° = 130°$

$$\frac{\sin\gamma}{c} = \frac{\sin\alpha}{a} \rightarrow \frac{\sin(40°)}{2} = \frac{\sin(10°)}{a} \rightarrow a = \frac{2\sin(10°)}{\sin(40°)} \approx 0.54$$

$$\frac{\sin\gamma}{c} = \frac{\sin\beta}{b} \rightarrow \frac{\sin(40°)}{2} = \frac{\sin(130°)}{b} \rightarrow b = \frac{2\sin(130°)}{\sin(40°)} \approx 2.38$$

7. $a = 5,\ c = 2,\ \alpha = 100°$

$$\frac{\sin\gamma}{c} = \frac{\sin\alpha}{a} \rightarrow \frac{\sin\gamma}{2} = \frac{\sin(100°)}{5} \rightarrow \sin\gamma = \frac{2\sin(100°)}{5} \approx 0.3939$$

$\rightarrow \gamma = 23.2°$ or $\gamma = 156.8°$

The second value is discarded because $\alpha + \gamma > 180°$.

$\beta = 180° - \alpha - \gamma = 180° - 100° - 23.2° = 56.8°$

$$\frac{\sin\beta}{b} = \frac{\sin\alpha}{a} \rightarrow \frac{\sin(56.8°)}{b} = \frac{\sin(100°)}{5} \rightarrow b = \frac{5\sin(56.8°)}{\sin(100°)} \approx 4.25$$

8. $a = 2,\ c = 5,\ \alpha = 60°$

$$\frac{\sin\gamma}{c} = \frac{\sin\alpha}{a} \rightarrow \frac{\sin\gamma}{5} = \frac{\sin(60°)}{2} \rightarrow \sin\gamma = \frac{5\sin(60°)}{2} \approx 2.1651$$

Since $\sin\gamma$ cannot be greater than 1, this is impossible. No triangle.

9. $a = 3,\ c = 1,\ \gamma = 110°$

$$\frac{\sin\gamma}{c} = \frac{\sin\alpha}{a} \rightarrow \frac{\sin(110°)}{1} = \frac{\sin\alpha}{3} \rightarrow \sin\alpha = \frac{3\sin(110°)}{1} \approx 2.8191$$

There is no angle α for which $\sin\alpha > 1$. Therefore, there is no triangle with the given measurements.

10. $a = 3,\ c = 1,\ \gamma = 20°$

$$\frac{\sin\gamma}{c} = \frac{\sin\alpha}{a} \rightarrow \frac{\sin(20°)}{1} = \frac{\sin\alpha}{3} \rightarrow \sin\alpha = \frac{3\sin(20°)}{1} \approx 1.0260$$

There is no angle α for which $\sin\alpha > 1$. Therefore, there is no triangle with the given measurements.

11. $a = 3,\ c = 1,\ \beta = 100°$

$$b^2 = a^2 + c^2 - 2ac\cos\beta = 3^2 + 1^2 - 2\cdot 3\cdot 1\cos(100°) \approx 11.0419 \rightarrow b \approx 3.32$$

$$a^2 = b^2 + c^2 - 2bc\cos\alpha \rightarrow \cos\alpha = \frac{b^2 + c^2 - a^2}{2bc} = \frac{3.32^2 + 1^2 - 3^2}{2(3.32)(1)} \approx 0.4552 \rightarrow \alpha \approx 62.8°$$

$$c^2 = a^2 + b^2 - 2ab\cos\gamma \rightarrow \cos\gamma = \frac{a^2 + b^2 - c^2}{2ab} = \frac{3^2 + 3.32^2 - 1^2}{2(3)(3.32)} \approx 0.9549 \rightarrow \gamma \approx 17.2°$$

12. $a = 3,\ b = 5,\ \beta = 80^\circ$

$$\frac{\sin\alpha}{a} = \frac{\sin\beta}{b} \rightarrow \frac{\sin\alpha}{3} = \frac{\sin(80^\circ)}{5} \rightarrow \sin\alpha = \frac{3\sin(80^\circ)}{5} \approx 0.5909$$

$$\rightarrow \alpha = 36.2^\circ \text{ or } \alpha = 143.8^\circ$$

The second value is discarded because $\alpha + \beta > 180^\circ$.

$\gamma = 180^\circ - \alpha - \beta = 180^\circ - 36.2^\circ - 80^\circ = 63.8^\circ$

$$\frac{\sin\gamma}{c} = \frac{\sin\beta}{b} \rightarrow \frac{\sin(63.8^\circ)}{c} = \frac{\sin(80^\circ)}{5} \rightarrow c = \frac{5\sin(63.8^\circ)}{\sin(80^\circ)} \approx 4.55$$

13. $a = 2,\ b = 3,\ c = 1$

$$a^2 = b^2 + c^2 - 2bc\cos\alpha \rightarrow \cos\alpha = \frac{b^2 + c^2 - a^2}{2bc} = \frac{3^2 + 1^2 - 2^2}{2(3)(1)} = 1.000 \rightarrow \alpha \approx 0^\circ$$

No triangle exists with an angle of 0°.

14. $a = 10,\ b = 7,\ c = 8$

$$a^2 = b^2 + c^2 - 2bc\cos\alpha \rightarrow \cos\alpha = \frac{b^2 + c^2 - a^2}{2bc} = \frac{7^2 + 8^2 - 10^2}{2(7)(8)} \approx 0.1161 \rightarrow \alpha \approx 83.3^\circ$$

$$b^2 = a^2 + c^2 - 2ac\cos\beta \rightarrow \cos\beta = \frac{a^2 + c^2 - b^2}{2ac} = \frac{10^2 + 8^2 - 7^2}{2(10)(8)} \approx 0.7188 \rightarrow \beta \approx 44.0^\circ$$

$\gamma = 180^\circ - \alpha - \beta \approx 180^\circ - 83.3^\circ - 44.0^\circ \approx 52.6^\circ$

15. $a = 1,\ b = 3,\ \gamma = 40^\circ$

$c^2 = a^2 + b^2 - 2ab\cos\gamma$

$c^2 = 1^2 + 3^2 - 2\cdot 1\cdot 3\cos(40^\circ) \approx 5.4037$

$c \approx 2.32$

$$a^2 = b^2 + c^2 - 2bc\cos\alpha \rightarrow \cos\alpha = \frac{b^2 + c^2 - a^2}{2bc} = \frac{3^2 + 2.32^2 - 1^2}{2(3)(2.32)} \approx 0.9614 \rightarrow \alpha \approx 16.1^\circ$$

$$b^2 = a^2 + c^2 - 2ac\cos\beta \rightarrow \cos\beta = \frac{a^2 + c^2 - b^2}{2ac} = \frac{1^2 + 2.32^2 - 3^2}{2(1)(2.32)} \approx -0.5641 \rightarrow \beta \approx 123.9^\circ$$

16. $a = 4,\ b = 1,\ \gamma = 100^\circ$

$c^2 = a^2 + b^2 - 2ab\cos\gamma$

$c^2 = 4^2 + 1^2 - 2\cdot 4\cdot 1\cos(100^\circ) \approx 18.3892$

$c \approx 4.29$

$$a^2 = b^2 + c^2 - 2bc\cos\alpha \rightarrow \cos\alpha = \frac{b^2 + c^2 - a^2}{2bc} = \frac{1^2 + 4.29^2 - 4^2}{2(1)(4.29)} \approx 0.3967 \rightarrow \alpha \approx 66.7^\circ$$

$$b^2 = a^2 + c^2 - 2ac\cos\beta \rightarrow \cos\beta = \frac{a^2 + c^2 - b^2}{2ac} = \frac{4^2 + 4.29^2 - 1^2}{2(4)(4.29)} \approx 0.9733 \rightarrow \beta \approx 13.3^\circ$$

17. $a = 5,\ b = 3,\ \alpha = 80°$

$$\frac{\sin\beta}{b}=\frac{\sin\alpha}{a} \rightarrow \frac{\sin\beta}{3}=\frac{\sin(80°)}{5} \rightarrow \sin\beta=\frac{3\sin(80°)}{5}\approx 0.5909$$

$$\rightarrow \beta=36.2° \text{ or } \beta=143.8°$$

The second value is discarded because $\alpha+\beta>180°$.

$\gamma=180°-\alpha-\beta=180°-80°-36.2°=63.8°$

$$\frac{\sin\gamma}{c}=\frac{\sin\alpha}{a} \rightarrow \frac{\sin(63.8°)}{c}=\frac{\sin(80°)}{5} \rightarrow c=\frac{5\sin(63.8°)}{\sin(80°)}\approx 4.55$$

18. $a = 2,\ b = 3,\ \alpha = 20°$

$$\frac{\sin\beta}{b}=\frac{\sin\alpha}{a} \rightarrow \frac{\sin\beta}{3}=\frac{\sin(20°)}{2} \rightarrow \sin\beta=\frac{3\sin(20°)}{2}\approx 0.5130$$

$$\rightarrow \beta_1=30.9° \text{ or } \beta_2=149.1°$$

For both values, $\alpha+\beta<180°$. Therefore, there are two triangles.

$\gamma_1=180°-\alpha-\beta_1=180°-20°-30.9°\approx 129.1°$

$$\frac{\sin\alpha}{a}=\frac{\sin\gamma_1}{c_1} \rightarrow \frac{\sin(20°)}{2}=\frac{\sin(129.1°)}{c_1} \rightarrow c_1=\frac{2\sin(129.1°)}{\sin(20°)}\approx 4.54$$

$\gamma_2=180°-\alpha-\beta_2=180°-20°-149.1°\approx 10.9°$

$$\frac{\sin\alpha}{a}=\frac{\sin\gamma_2}{c_2} \rightarrow \frac{\sin(20°)}{2}=\frac{\sin(10.9°)}{c_2} \rightarrow c_2=\frac{2\sin(10.9°)}{\sin(20°)}\approx 1.11$$

Two triangles: $\beta_1\approx 30.9°,\ \gamma_1\approx 129.1°,\ c_1\approx 4.54$

or $\beta_2\approx 149.1°,\ \gamma_2\approx 10.87°,\ c_2\approx 1.10$

19. $a=1,\ b=\frac{1}{2},\ c=\frac{4}{3}$

$$a^2=b^2+c^2-2bc\cos\alpha \rightarrow \cos\alpha=\frac{b^2+c^2-a^2}{2bc}=\frac{\left(\left(\frac{1}{2}\right)^2+\left(\frac{4}{3}\right)^2-1^2\right)}{2\left(\frac{1}{2}\right)\left(\frac{4}{3}\right)}\approx 0.7708 \rightarrow \alpha\approx 39.6°$$

$$b^2=a^2+c^2-2ac\cos\beta \rightarrow \cos\beta=\frac{a^2+c^2-b^2}{2ac}=\frac{\left(1^2+\left(\frac{4}{3}\right)^2-\left(\frac{1}{2}\right)^2\right)}{2(1)\left(\frac{4}{3}\right)}\approx 0.9479 \rightarrow \beta\approx 18.6°$$

$\gamma=180°-\alpha-\beta\approx 180°-39.6°-18.6°\approx 121.9°$

20. $a = 3,\ b = 2,\ c = 2$

$$a^2=b^2+c^2-2bc\cos\alpha \rightarrow \cos\alpha=\frac{b^2+c^2-a^2}{2bc}=\frac{2^2+2^2-3^2}{2(2)(2)}\approx -0.1250 \rightarrow \alpha\approx 97.2°$$

$b^2 = a^2 + c^2 - 2ac\cos\beta \rightarrow \cos\beta = \dfrac{a^2 + c^2 - b^2}{2ac} = \dfrac{3^2 + 2^2 - 2^2}{2(3)(2)} \approx 0.7500 \rightarrow \beta \approx 41.4°$

$\gamma = 180° - \alpha - \beta \approx 180° - 97.2° - 41.4° \approx 41.4°$

21. $a = 3,\ b = 4,\ \alpha = 10°$

$\dfrac{\sin\beta}{b} = \dfrac{\sin\alpha}{a} \rightarrow \dfrac{\sin\beta}{4} = \dfrac{\sin(10°)}{3} \rightarrow \sin\beta = \dfrac{4\sin(10°)}{3} \approx 0.2315$

$\rightarrow \beta_1 \approx 13.4°$ or $\beta_2 \approx 166.6°$

For both values, $\alpha + \beta < 180°$. Therefore, there are two triangles.

$\gamma_1 = 180° - \alpha - \beta_1 = 180° - 10° - 13.4° \approx 156.6°$

$\dfrac{\sin\alpha}{a} = \dfrac{\sin\gamma_1}{c_1} \rightarrow \dfrac{\sin(10°)}{3} = \dfrac{\sin(156.6°)}{c_1} \rightarrow c_1 = \dfrac{3\sin(156.6°)}{\sin(10°)} \approx 6.86$

$\gamma_2 = 180° - \alpha - \beta_2 = 180° - 10° - 166.6° \approx 3.4°$

$\dfrac{\sin\alpha}{a} = \dfrac{\sin\gamma_2}{c_2} \rightarrow \dfrac{\sin(10°)}{3} = \dfrac{\sin(3.4°)}{c_2} \rightarrow c_2 = \dfrac{3\sin(3.4°)}{\sin(10°)} \approx 1.02$

Two triangles: $\beta_1 \approx 13.4°,\ \gamma_1 \approx 156.6°,\ c_1 \approx 6.86$

or $\beta_2 \approx 166.6°,\ \gamma_2 \approx 3.4°,\ c_2 \approx 1.02$

22. $a = 4,\ \alpha = 20°,\ \beta = 100°$

$\gamma = 180° - \alpha - \beta = 180° - 20° - 100° = 60°$

$\dfrac{\sin\alpha}{a} = \dfrac{\sin\beta}{b} \rightarrow \dfrac{\sin(20°)}{4} = \dfrac{\sin(100°)}{b} \rightarrow b = \dfrac{4\sin(100°)}{\sin(20°)} \approx 11.52$

$\dfrac{\sin\gamma}{c} = \dfrac{\sin\alpha}{a} \rightarrow \dfrac{\sin(60°)}{c} = \dfrac{\sin(20°)}{4} \rightarrow c = \dfrac{4\sin(60°)}{\sin(20°)} \approx 10.13$

23. $b = 4,\ c = 5,\ \alpha = 70°$

$a^2 = b^2 + c^2 - 2bc\cos\alpha$

$a^2 = 4^2 + 5^2 - 2 \cdot 4 \cdot 5\cos(70°) \approx 27.3192$

$a \approx 5.23$

$c^2 = a^2 + b^2 - 2ab\cos\gamma \rightarrow \cos\gamma = \dfrac{a^2 + b^2 - c^2}{2ab} = \dfrac{5.23^2 + 4^2 - 5^2}{2(5.23)(4)} \approx 0.4386 \rightarrow \gamma \approx 64.0°$

$\beta = 180° - \alpha - \gamma = 180° - 70° - 64° \approx 46.0°$

24. $a = 1,\ b = 2,\ \gamma = 60°$

$c^2 = a^2 + b^2 - 2ab\cos\gamma$

$c^2 = 1^2 + 2^2 - 2 \cdot 1 \cdot 2\cos(60°) = 3$

$c \approx 1.73$

$a^2 = b^2 + c^2 - 2bc\cos\alpha \rightarrow \cos\alpha = \dfrac{b^2 + c^2 - a^2}{2bc} = \dfrac{2^2 + 1.73^2 - 1^2}{2(2)(1.73)} \approx 0.8660 \rightarrow \alpha \approx 30°$

$\beta = 180° - \alpha - \gamma = 180° - 30° - 60° = 90°$

25. $a = 2,\ b = 3,\ \gamma = 40^\circ$

$$A = \frac{1}{2}ab\sin\gamma = \frac{1}{2}(2)(3)\sin(40^\circ) \approx 1.93$$

26. $b = 5,\ c = 5,\ \alpha = 20^\circ$

$$A = \frac{1}{2}bc\sin\alpha = \frac{1}{2}(5)(5)\sin(20^\circ) \approx 4.28$$

27. $b = 4,\ c = 10,\ \alpha = 70^\circ$

$$A = \frac{1}{2}bc\sin\alpha = \frac{1}{2}(4)(10)\sin(70^\circ) \approx 18.79$$

28. $a = 2,\ b = 1,\ \gamma = 100^\circ$

$$A = \frac{1}{2}ab\sin\gamma = \frac{1}{2}(2)(1)\sin(100^\circ) \approx 0.98$$

29. $a = 4,\ b = 3,\ c = 5$

$$s = \frac{1}{2}(a + b + c) = \frac{1}{2}(4 + 3 + 5) = 6$$

$$A = \sqrt{s(s-a)(s-b)(s-c)} = \sqrt{6(2)(3)(1)} = \sqrt{36} = 6$$

30. $a = 10,\ b = 7,\ c = 8$

$$s = \frac{1}{2}(a + b + c) = \frac{1}{2}(10 + 7 + 8) = \frac{25}{2}$$

$$A = \sqrt{s(s-a)(s-b)(s-c)} = \sqrt{\frac{25}{2}\left(\frac{5}{2}\right)\left(\frac{11}{2}\right)\left(\frac{9}{2}\right)} = \sqrt{\frac{12375}{16}} \approx 27.81$$

31. $a = 4,\ b = 2,\ c = 5$

$$s = \frac{1}{2}(a + b + c) = \frac{1}{2}(4 + 2 + 5) = \frac{11}{2}$$

$$A = \sqrt{s(s-a)(s-b)(s-c)} = \sqrt{\frac{11}{2}\left(\frac{3}{2}\right)\left(\frac{7}{2}\right)\left(\frac{1}{2}\right)} = \sqrt{\frac{231}{16}} \approx 3.80$$

32. $a = 3,\ b = 2,\ c = 2$

$$s = \frac{1}{2}(a + b + c) = \frac{1}{2}(3 + 2 + 2) = \frac{7}{2}$$

$$A = \sqrt{s(s-a)(s-b)(s-c)} = \sqrt{\frac{7}{2}\left(\frac{1}{2}\right)\left(\frac{3}{2}\right)\left(\frac{3}{2}\right)} = \sqrt{\frac{63}{16}} \approx 1.98$$

33. $\alpha = 50^\circ,\ \beta = 30^\circ,\ a = 1$ $\qquad \gamma = 180^\circ - \alpha - \beta = 180^\circ - 50^\circ - 30^\circ = 100^\circ$

$$A = \frac{a^2\sin\beta\sin\gamma}{2\sin\alpha} = \frac{1^2\sin(30^\circ)\sin(100^\circ)}{2\sin(50^\circ)} \approx \frac{1(0.5000)(0.9848)}{2(0.7660)} \approx 0.32$$

34. $\alpha = 10°,\ \gamma = 40°,\ c = 3 \qquad \beta = 180° - \alpha - \gamma = 180° - 10° - 40° = 130°$

$$A = \frac{c^2 \sin\alpha \sin\beta}{2\sin\gamma} = \frac{3^2 \sin(10°)\sin(130°)}{2\sin(40°)} \approx \frac{9(0.1736)(0.7660)}{2(0.6428)} \approx 0.93$$

35. Use right triangle methods:

$$\tan(65°) = \frac{500}{b} \rightarrow b = \frac{500}{\tan(65°)} \approx 233.15$$

$$\tan(25°) = \frac{500}{a+b} \rightarrow a + b = \frac{500}{\tan(25°)} \approx 1072.25$$

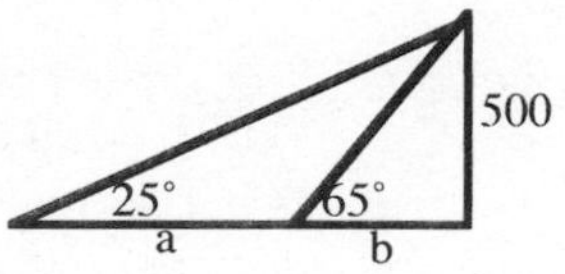

$a = 1072.25 - 233.15 = 839.1$ feet

The lake is approximately 839 feet long.

36. Use right triangle methods:

$$\tan(40°) = \frac{x}{200} \rightarrow x = 200\tan(40°) \approx 167.82$$

$$\tan(10°) = \frac{y}{200} \rightarrow y = 200\tan(10°) \approx 35.27$$

$d = 167.82 - 35.27 = 132.55$ feet

$$\text{speed} \approx \frac{132.55 \text{ feet}}{1 \text{ minute}} \cdot \frac{1 \text{ mile}}{5280 \text{ feet}} \cdot \frac{60 \text{ minutes}}{1 \text{ hour}} \approx 1.5 \text{ mi/hr}$$

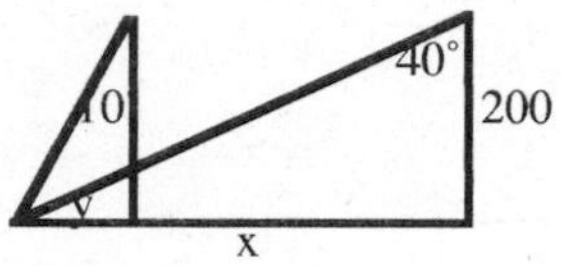

37. $\tan(25°) = \frac{b}{50} \rightarrow b = 50\tan(25°) \approx 50(0.4663) \approx 23.32$ feet

38. $\tan(25°) = \frac{h}{80} \rightarrow h = 80\tan(25°) \approx 80(0.4663) \approx 37.31$ feet

39. 1454 ft ≈ 0.2754 miles

$$\tan(5°) \approx \frac{0.2754}{a+1}$$

$$a + 1 = \frac{0.2754}{\tan(5°)} \approx 3.15 \rightarrow a \approx 2.15 \text{ miles}$$

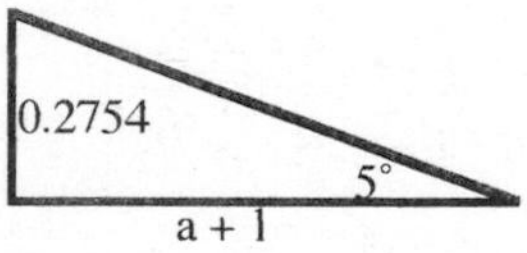

The boat is about 2.15 miles offshore.

40. $\sin\theta = \frac{900}{4100} \approx 0.2195 \rightarrow \theta \approx 12.7°$ The trail is inclined $-12.7°$ as seen from the hotel.

41. $\angle ABC = 180° - 20° = 160°$

Find the angle at city C:

$$\frac{\sin C}{100} = \frac{\sin(160°)}{300} \rightarrow \sin C = \frac{100\sin(160°)}{300} \approx 0.1140 \rightarrow C \approx 6.55°$$

Find the angle at city A:

$$A = 180° - 160° - 6.55° = 13.45°$$

$$\frac{\sin(13.45°)}{y} = \frac{\sin(160°)}{300} \rightarrow y = \frac{300\sin(13.45°)}{\sin(160°)} \approx 204.07 \text{ miles}$$

The distance from city B to city C is approximately 204 miles.

42. (a) The distance traveled is $420 \cdot \frac{1}{6} = 70$ miles.

Find the remaining distance to city B:

$$a^2 = 300^2 + 70^2 - 2(300)(70)\cos(5°) \approx 53059.82$$

$$a = 230.3 \text{ miles}$$

Find angle C:

$$\frac{\sin C}{300} = \frac{\sin(5°)}{230.3} \rightarrow \sin C = \frac{300\sin(5°)}{230.3} \approx 0.1135 \rightarrow C \approx 173.5°$$

The pilot should turn through an angle of 6.5° to correct the course.

(b) The time from city A to city B is $\frac{300}{420} = \frac{5}{7}$ hour. The time from city A to the point of the error is $\frac{1}{6}$ hour. The remaining part of the trip must be completed in $\frac{5}{7} - \frac{1}{6} = \frac{23}{42}$ hour. Calculate the rate:

$$r = \frac{230.3}{\left(\frac{23}{42}\right)} \approx 420.64 \text{ mi./hr.}$$

43. Draw a line perpendicular to the shore:

(a) $\angle ACB = 12° + 30° = 42°$

$\angle ABC = 90° - 30° = 60°$

$\angle CAB = 90° - 12° = 78°$

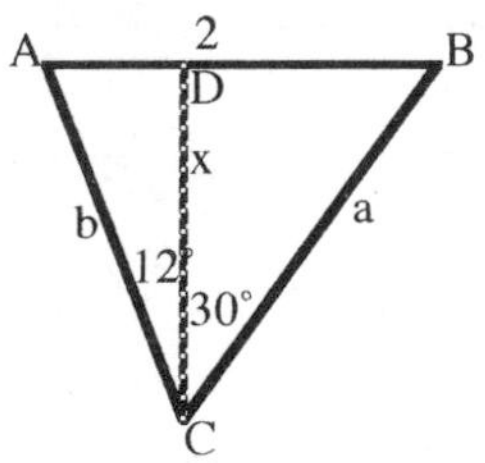

$$\frac{\sin(60°)}{b} = \frac{\sin(42°)}{2} \rightarrow b = \frac{2\sin(60°)}{\sin(42°)} \approx 2.59 \text{ miles}$$

(b) $$\frac{\sin(78°)}{a} = \frac{\sin(42°)}{2} \rightarrow a = \frac{2\sin(78°)}{\sin(42°)} \approx 2.92 \text{ miles}$$

(c) $\cos 12° = \frac{x}{2.59} \rightarrow x = 2.59\cos 12° \approx 2.53$ miles

44. $\alpha = 180° - 120° = 60° \quad \beta = 180° - 115° = 65°$
$\gamma = 180° - 60° - 65° = 55°$

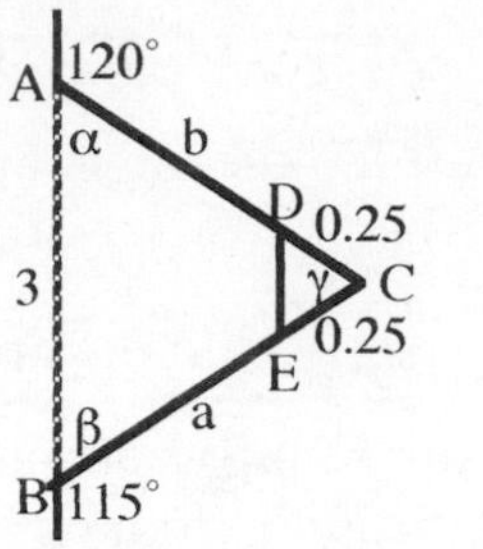

$$\frac{\sin(60°)}{a} = \frac{\sin(55°)}{3} \rightarrow a = \frac{3\sin(60°)}{\sin(55°)} \approx 3.17 \text{ mi}$$

$$\frac{\sin(65°)}{b} = \frac{\sin(55°)}{3} \rightarrow b = \frac{3\sin(65°)}{\sin(55°)} \approx 3.32 \text{ mi}$$

$\overline{BE} = 3.17 - 0.25 = 2.92$ mi

$\overline{AD} = 3.32 - 0.25 = 3.07$ mi

For the isosceles triangle,

$$\angle CDE = \angle CED = \frac{180° - 55°}{2} = 62.5°$$

$$\frac{\sin(55°)}{DE} = \frac{\sin(62.5°)}{0.25} \rightarrow DE = \frac{0.25\sin(55°)}{\sin(62.5°)} \approx 0.23 \text{ miles}$$

The length of the highway is $2.92 + 3.07 + 0.23 = 6.22$ miles.

45. (a) After 4 hours, the yacht would have sailed 18(4) = 72 miles.
Find the third side of the triangle determines the distance from the island:
$a = 72,\ b = 200,\ \gamma = 15°$

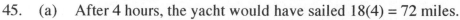

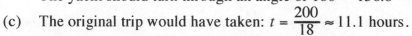

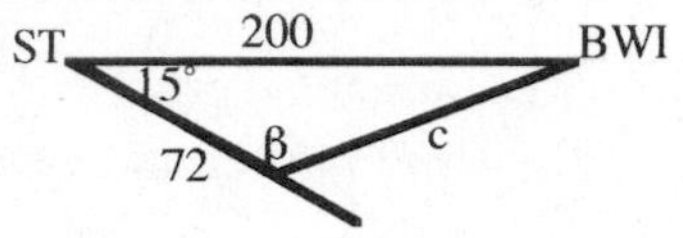

$$c^2 = a^2 + b^2 - 2ab\cos\gamma$$

$$c^2 = 72^2 + 200^2 - 2\cdot 72\cdot 200\cos(15°) \approx 17365.34$$

$c \approx 131.8$ miles

The yacht is about 131.8 miles from the island.

(b) Find the measure of the angle opposite the 200 side:

$$\cos\beta = \frac{a^2 + c^2 - b^2}{2ac} \rightarrow \cos\beta = \frac{72^2 + 131.8^2 - 200^2}{2(72)(131.8)} \approx -0.9192 \rightarrow \beta \approx 156.8°$$

The yacht should turn through an angle of 180° – 156.8° = 23.1° to correct its course.

(c) The original trip would have taken: $t = \dfrac{200}{18} \approx 11.1$ hours.

The actual trip takes: $t = 4 + \dfrac{131.8}{18} \approx 4 + 7.3 \approx 11.3$ hours.

The trip takes about 0.21 hour or 12 minutes longer.

46. Find the third side of the triangle using the Law of Cosines:
$a = 50,\ b = 60,\ \gamma = 80°$

$$c^2 = a^2 + b^2 - 2ab\cos\gamma = 50^2 + 60^2 - 2\cdot 50\cdot 60\cos(80°) \approx 5058.11$$

$c \approx 71.12$

The houses are approximately 71.12 feet apart.

47. Find the lengths of the two unknown sides of the middle triangle:

$$x^2 = 100^2 + 125^2 - 2(100)(125)\cos(50°) \approx 9555.31 \rightarrow x \approx 97.75 \text{ feet}$$

$$y^2 = 70^2 + 50^2 - 2(70)(50)\cos(100°) \approx 8615.54 \rightarrow y \approx 92.82 \text{ feet}$$

Find the areas of the three triangles:

$$A_1 = \frac{1}{2}(100)(125)\sin(50^\circ) \approx 4787.78 \text{ ft}^2$$

$$A_2 = \frac{1}{2}(50)(70)\sin(100^\circ) \approx 1723.41 \text{ ft}^2$$

$$s = \frac{1}{2}(50 + 97.75 + 92.82) = 120.285$$

$$A_3 = \sqrt{120.285(70.285)(22.535)(27.465)} \approx 2287.47$$

The approximate area of the lake is 4787.78 + 1723.41 + 2287.47 = 8798.67 sq.ft.

48. Construct a diagonal. Find the area of the first triangle and the length of the diagonal:

$$A_1 = \frac{1}{2}\cdot 50\cdot 100\cdot \sin(40^\circ) \approx 1606.97 \text{ ft}^2$$

$$d^2 = 50^2 + 100^2 - 2\cdot 50\cdot 100\cos(40^\circ) \approx 4839.56$$

$$d = 69.57 \text{ feet}$$

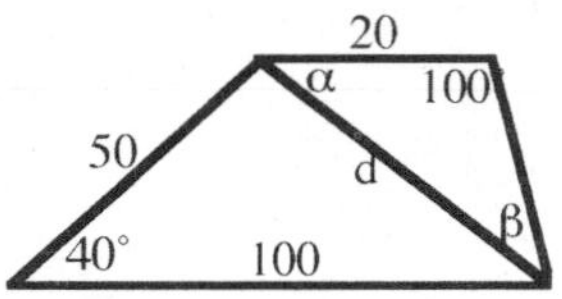

Use the Law of Sines to find β:

$$\frac{\sin\beta}{20} = \frac{\sin(100^\circ)}{69.57} \rightarrow \sin\beta = \frac{20\sin(100^\circ)}{69.57} \approx 0.2831 \rightarrow \beta \approx 16.4^\circ$$

$$\alpha = 180^\circ - 100^\circ - 16.4^\circ = 63.6^\circ$$

Find the area of the second triangle:

$$A_2 = \frac{1}{2}\cdot 20\cdot 69.57\cdot \sin(63.6^\circ) \approx 623.15 \text{ ft}^2$$

The cost of the parcel is: $\$100(1606.97 + 623.15) = \$223{,}012$

49. Area of the segment = area of the sector - area of the triangle.

$$\text{Area of sector} = \frac{1}{2}r^2\theta = \frac{1}{2}\cdot 6^2\left(50\cdot\frac{\pi}{180}\right) \approx 15.708 \text{ in}^2$$

$$\text{Area of triangle} = \frac{1}{2}ab\sin\theta = \frac{1}{2}\cdot 6\cdot 6\sin(50^\circ) \approx 13.789 \text{ in}^2$$

$$\text{Area of segment} = 15.708 - 13.789 = 1.92 \text{ in}^2$$

50. Find angle AMB and subtract from 80° to obtain θ.

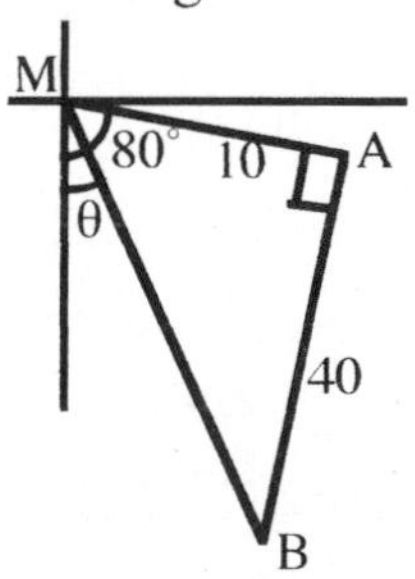

$$\tan\angle AMB = \frac{40}{10} = 4 \quad\rightarrow\quad \angle AMB \approx 76.0^\circ$$

$$\theta \approx 80^\circ - 76.0^\circ \approx 4.0^\circ$$

The bearing is S4.0°E.

51. Extend the tangent line until it meets a line extended through the centers of the pulleys. Label these extensions x and y. The distance between the points of tangency is z. Two similar triangles are formed. Therefore:

$\frac{24+y}{y}=\frac{6.5}{2.5}$

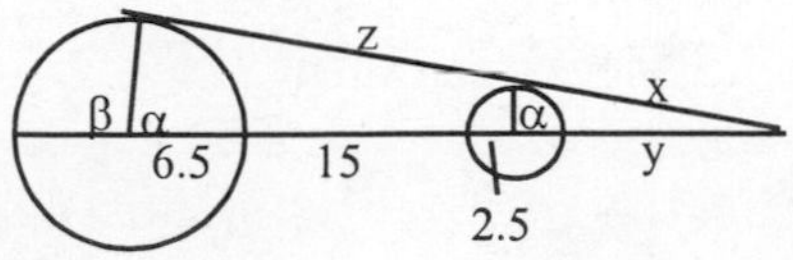

where $24+y$ is the hypotenuse of the larger triangle and y is the hypotenuse of the smaller triangle.

Solve for y:

$6.5y=2.5(24+y)\to 6.5y=60+2.5y\to 4y=60\to y=15$

Use the Pythagorean Theorem to find x:

$x^2+2.5^2=15^2\to x^2=225-6.25=218.75\to x\approx 14.79$

Use the Pythagorean Theorem to find z:

$(z+14.79)^2+6.5^2=(24+15)^2\to (z+14.79)^2=1521-42.25=1478.75$

$z+14.79=38.45\to z=23.66$

Find α:

$\cos\alpha=\frac{2.5}{15}\approx 0.1667 \quad\to\quad \alpha\approx 1.4033$ radians

$\beta=\pi-1.4033\approx 1.7383$ radians

The arc length on the larger pulley is: 6.5(1.7383) = 11.30 inches.
The arc length on the smaller pulley is 2.5(1.4033) = 3.51 inches.
The distance between the points of tangency is 23.66 inches.
The length of the belt is: 2(11.30 + 3.51 + 23.66) = 76.94 inches.

52. Find the lengths of x and 24 – x:

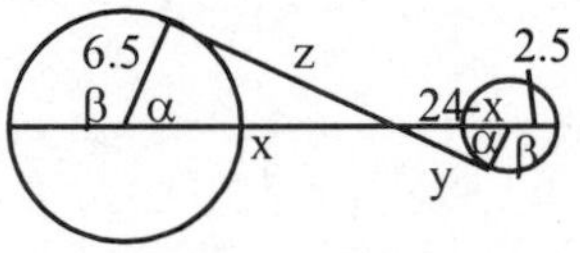

$\frac{6.5}{2.5}=\frac{x}{24-x}$

$2.5x=6.5(24-x)$

$2.5x=156-6.5x$

$9x=156\to x\approx 17.3\to 24-x=6.7$

$\cos\alpha=\frac{6.5}{17.3}\approx 0.376\to\alpha\approx 68.0°$

$\beta=180°-68.0°=112°$

$z=6.5\tan(68°)\approx 16.1$ in

$y=2.5\tan(68°)\approx 6.2$ in

The arc length on the larger pulley is: $6.5\left(112\cdot\frac{\pi}{180}\right)\approx 12.7$ inches.

The arc length on the smaller pulley is $2.5\left(112\cdot\frac{\pi}{180}\right)\approx 4.9$ inches.

The distance between the points of tangency is 16.1 + 6.2 = 22.3 inches.
The length of the belt is: 2(12.7 + 4.9 + 22.3) = 79.8 inches.

53. $d = 6\sin(2t)$
(a) Simple harmonic
(b) 6 feet
(c) π seconds
(d) $\frac{1}{\pi}$ oscillation/second

54. $d = 2\cos(4t)$
(a) Simple harmonic
(b) 2 feet
(c) $\frac{\pi}{2}$ seconds
(d) $\frac{2}{\pi}$ oscillation/second

55. $d = -2\cos(\pi t)$
(a) Simple harmonic
(b) 2 feet
(c) 2 seconds
(d) $\frac{1}{2}$ oscillation/second

56. $d = -3\sin\left(\frac{\pi}{2}t\right)$
(a) Simple harmonic
(b) 3 feet
(c) 4 seconds
(d) $\frac{1}{4}$ oscillation/second

57. $y = e^{-x/2\pi}\sin(2x), \quad 0 \le x \le 2\pi$

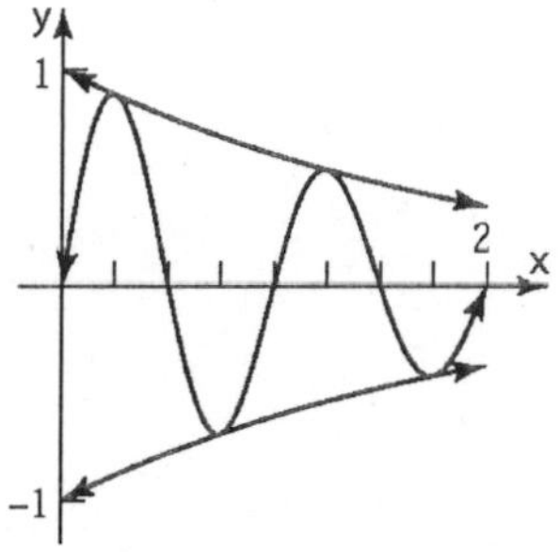

58. $y = e^{-x/3\pi}\cos(4x), \quad 0 \le x \le 2\pi$

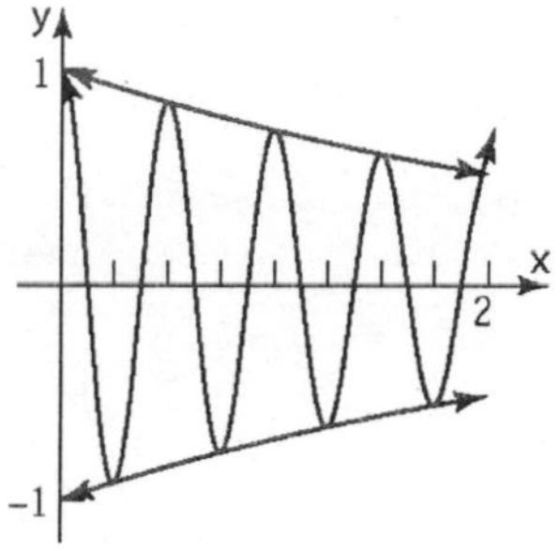

59. $y = x\cos(x), \quad 0 \le x \le 2\pi$

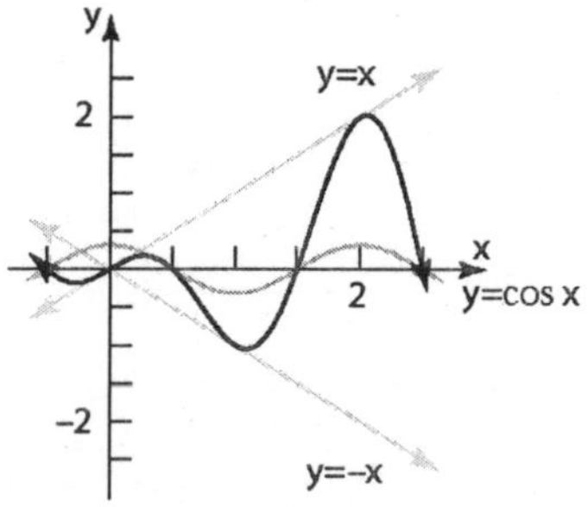

60. $y = x\sin(2x), \quad 0 \le x \le 2\pi$

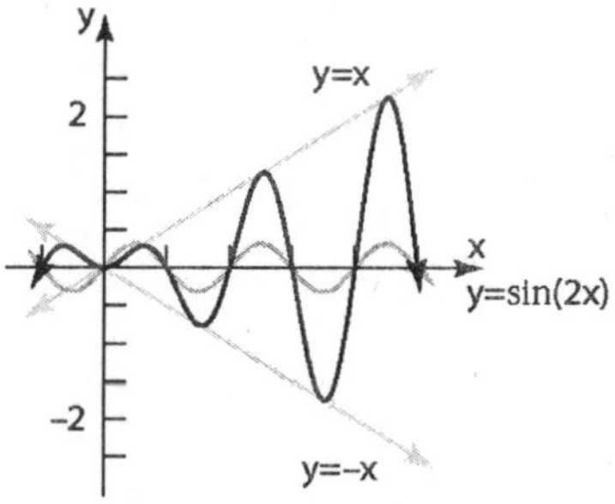

61. $y = 2\sin(x) + \cos(2x), \quad 0 \le x \le 2\pi$

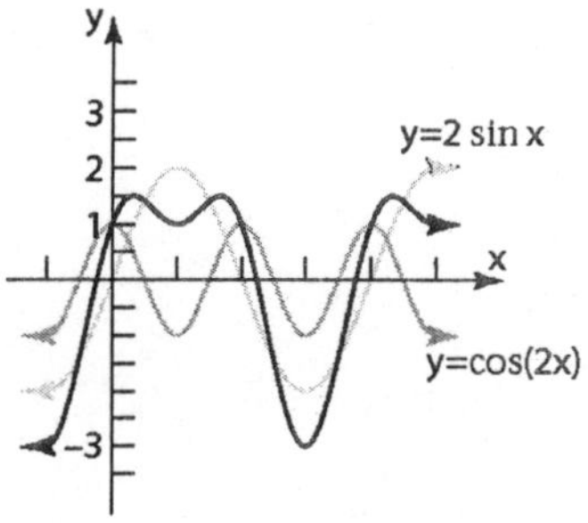

62. $y = 2\cos(2x) + \sin\left(\frac{x}{2}\right), \quad 0 \le x \le 2\pi$

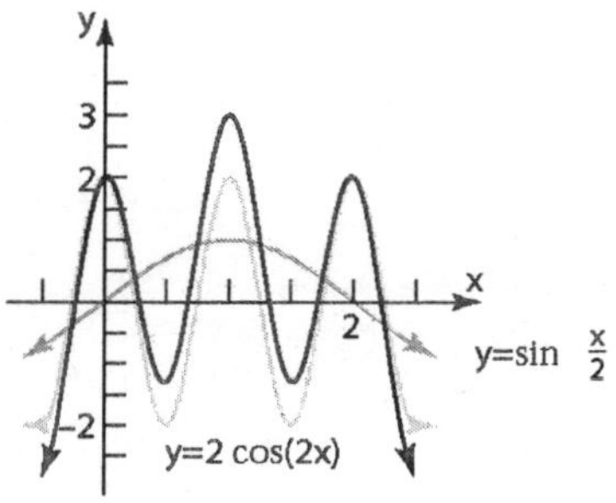

Chapter 10

Polar Coordinates; Vectors

10.1 Polar Coordinates

1. A	2. B	3. C	4. C
5. B	6. D	7. A	8. D

9. $(3, 90°)$

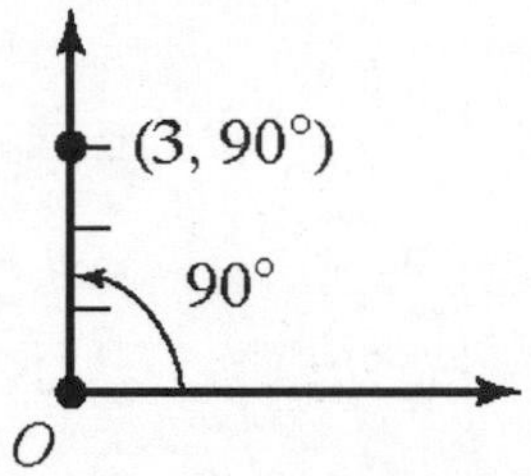

10. $(4, 270°)$

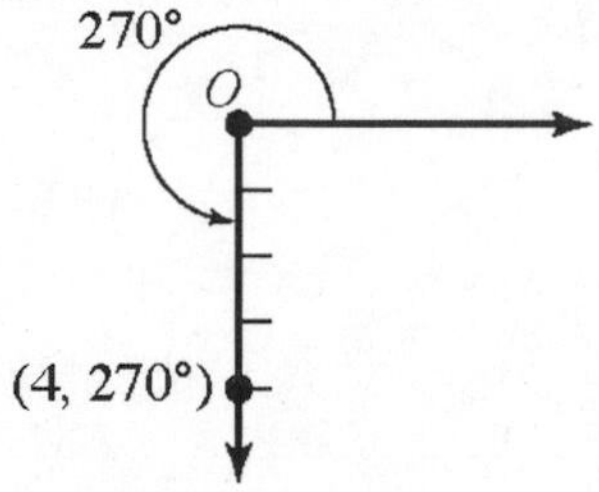

11. $(-2, 0)$

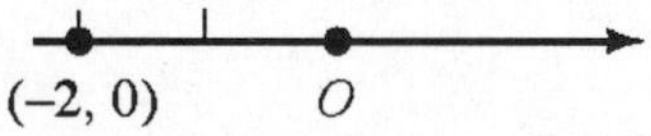

12. $(-3, \pi)$

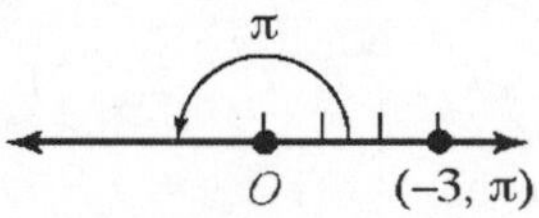

13. $\left(6, \frac{\pi}{6}\right)$

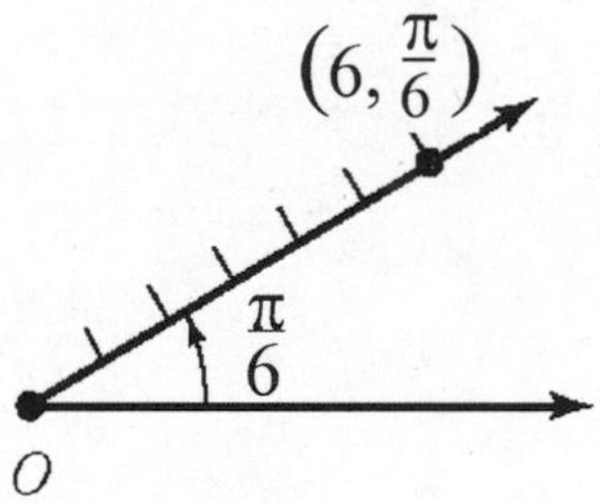

14. $\left(5, \frac{5\pi}{3}\right)$

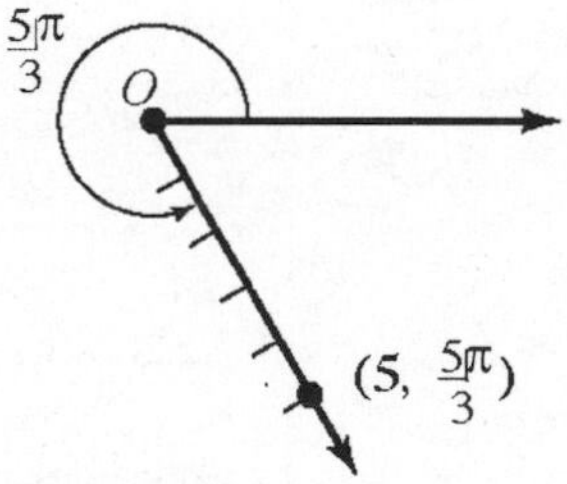

15. $(-2, 135°)$

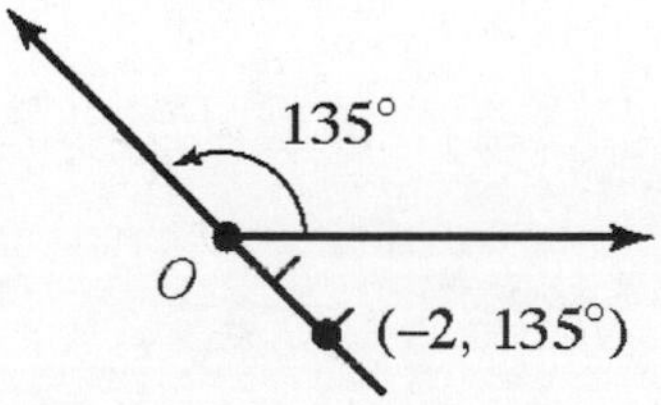

16. $(-3, 120°)$

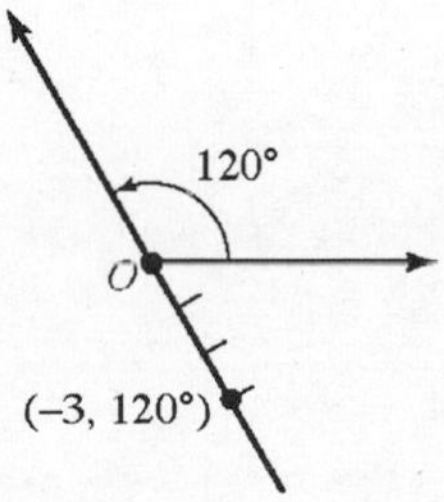

17. $\left(-1, -\frac{\pi}{3}\right)$

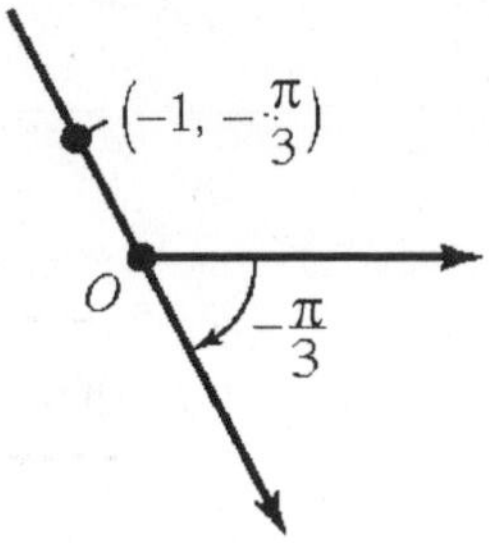

18. $\left(-3, -\frac{3\pi}{4}\right)$

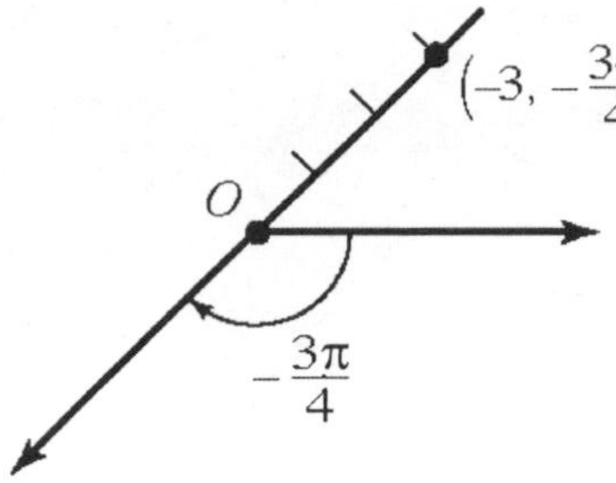

19. $(-2, -\pi)$

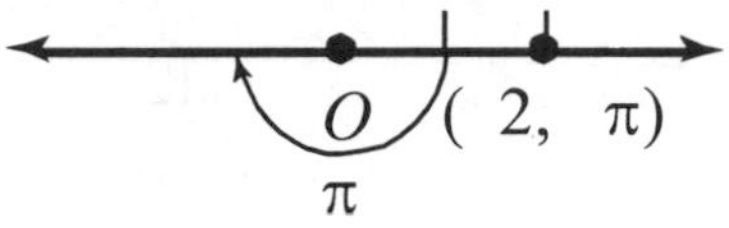

20. $\left(-3, -\frac{\pi}{2}\right)$

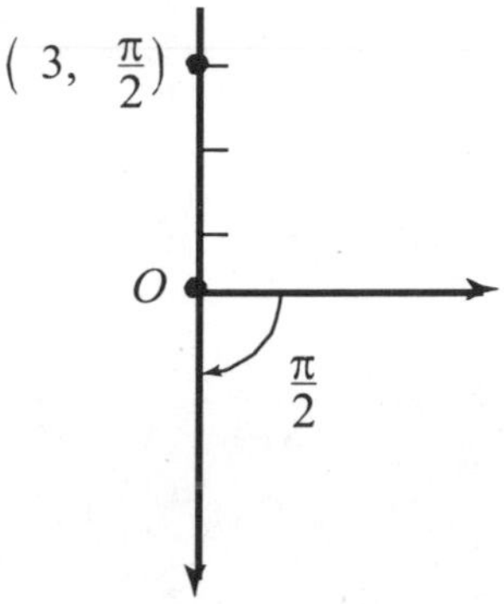

21. $\left(5, \frac{2\pi}{3}\right)$

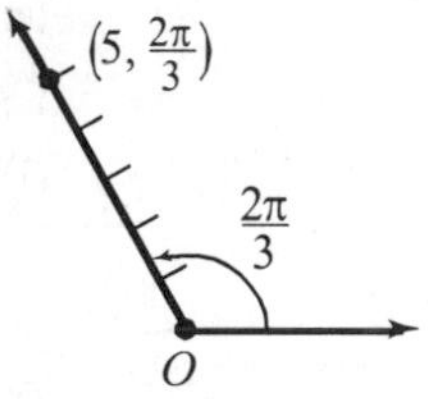

(a) $r > 0, \ -2\pi \le \theta < 0$ $\left(5, -\frac{4\pi}{3}\right)$

(b) $r < 0, \ 0 \le \theta < 2\pi$ $\left(-5, \frac{5\pi}{3}\right)$

(c) $r > 0, \ 2\pi \le \theta < 4\pi$ $\left(5, \frac{8\pi}{3}\right)$

22. $\left(4, \frac{3\pi}{4}\right)$

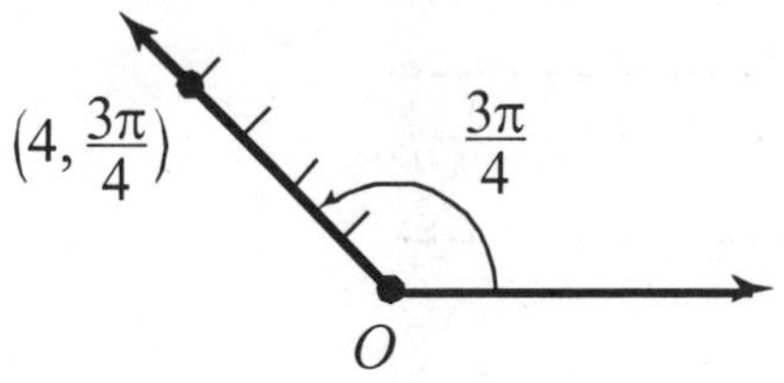

(a) $r > 0, \ -2\pi \le \theta < 0$ $\left(4, -\frac{5\pi}{4}\right)$

(b) $r < 0, \ 0 \le \theta < 2\pi$ $\left(-4, \frac{7\pi}{4}\right)$

(c) $r > 0, \ 2\pi \le \theta < 4\pi$ $\left(4, \frac{11\pi}{4}\right)$

23. $(-2, 3\pi)$

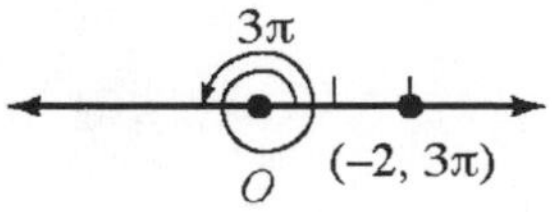

(a) $r > 0, \ -2\pi \le \theta < 0$ $(2, -2\pi)$

(b) $r < 0, \ 0 \le \theta < 2\pi$ $(-2, \pi)$

(c) $r > 0, \ 2\pi \le \theta < 4\pi$ $(2, 2\pi)$

24. $(-3, 4\pi)$

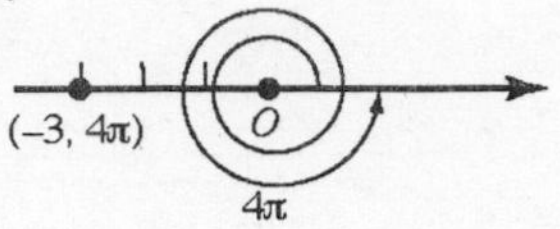

(a) $r > 0,\ -2\pi \le \theta < 0$ $(3, -\pi)$

(b) $r < 0,\ 0 \le \theta < 2\pi$ $(-3, 0)$

(c) $r > 0,\ 2\pi \le \theta < 4\pi$ $(3, 3\pi)$

25. $\left(1, \frac{\pi}{2}\right)$

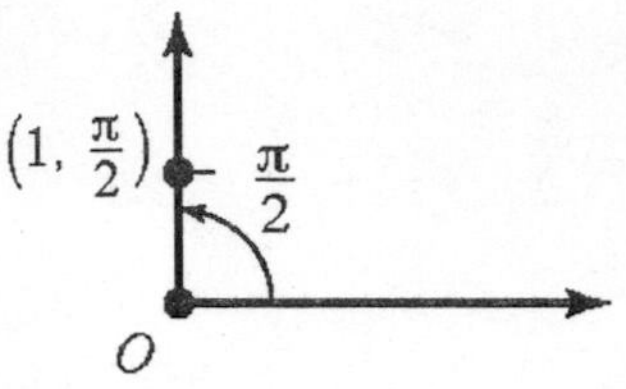

(a) $r > 0,\ -2\pi \le \theta < 0$ $\left(1, -\frac{3\pi}{2}\right)$

(b) $r < 0,\ 0 \le \theta < 2\pi$ $\left(-1, \frac{3\pi}{2}\right)$

(c) $r > 0,\ 2\pi \le \theta < 4\pi$ $\left(1, \frac{5\pi}{2}\right)$

26. $(2, \pi)$

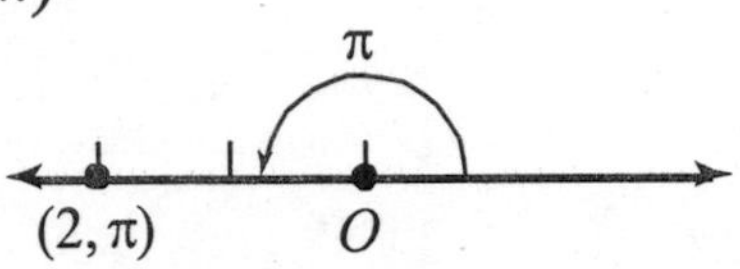

(a) $r > 0,\ -2\pi \le \theta < 0$ $(2, -\pi)$

(b) $r < 0,\ 0 \le \theta < 2\pi$ $(-2, 0)$

(c) $r > 0,\ 2\pi \le \theta < 4\pi$ $(2, 3\pi)$

27. $\left(-3, -\frac{\pi}{4}\right)$

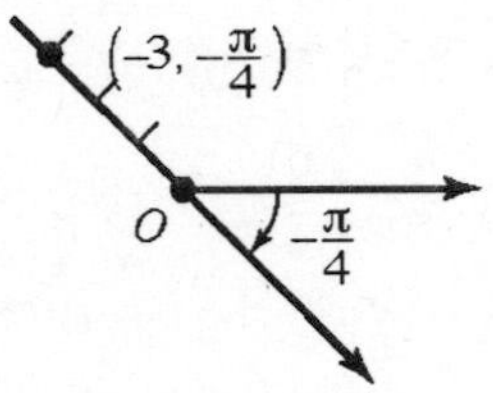

(a) $r > 0,\ -2\pi \le \theta < 0$ $\left(3, -\frac{5\pi}{4}\right)$

(b) $r < 0,\ 0 \le \theta < 2\pi$ $\left(-3, \frac{7\pi}{4}\right)$

(c) $r > 0,\ 2\pi \le \theta < 4\pi$ $\left(3, \frac{11\pi}{4}\right)$

28. $\left(-2, -\frac{2\pi}{3}\right)$

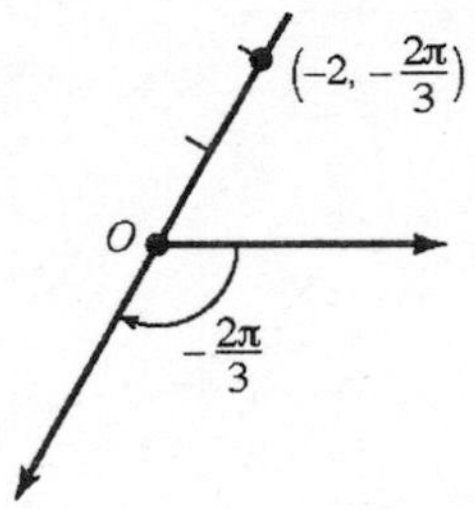

(a) $r > 0,\ -2\pi \le \theta < 0$ $\left(2, -\frac{5\pi}{3}\right)$

(b) $r < 0,\ 0 \le \theta < 2\pi$ $\left(-2, \frac{4\pi}{3}\right)$

(c) $r > 0,\ 2\pi \le \theta < 4\pi$ $\left(2, \frac{7\pi}{3}\right)$

29. $x = r\cos\theta = 3\cos\left(\frac{\pi}{2}\right) = 3 \cdot 0 = 0$

$y = r\sin\theta = 3\sin\left(\frac{\pi}{2}\right) = 3 \cdot 1 = 3$

The rectangular coordinates of the point $\left(3, \frac{\pi}{2}\right)$ are $(0, 3)$.

30. $x = r\cos\theta = 4\cos\left(\frac{3\pi}{2}\right) = 4\cdot 0 = 0$

$y = r\sin\theta = 4\sin\left(\frac{3\pi}{2}\right) = 4\cdot(-1) = -4$

The rectangular coordinates of the point $\left(4, \frac{3\pi}{2}\right)$ are $(0, -4)$.

31. $x = r\cos\theta = -2\cos(0) = -2\cdot 1 = -2$
$y = r\sin\theta = -2\sin(0) = -2\cdot 0 = 0$
The rectangular coordinates of the point $(-2, 0)$ are $(-2, 0)$.

32. $x = r\cos\theta = -3\cos(\pi) = -3(-1) = 3$
$y = r\sin\theta = -3\sin(\pi) = -3\cdot 0 = 0$
The rectangular coordinates of the point $(-3, \pi)$ are $(3, 0)$.

33. $x = r\cos\theta = 6\cos(150^\circ) = 6\cdot\left(-\frac{\sqrt{3}}{2}\right) = -3\sqrt{3}$

$y = r\sin\theta = 6\sin(150^\circ) = 6\cdot\frac{1}{2} = 3$

The rectangular coordinates of the point $(6, 150^\circ)$ are $\left(-3\sqrt{3}, 3\right)$

34. $x = r\cos\theta = 5\cos(300^\circ) = 5\cdot\frac{1}{2} = \frac{5}{2}$

$y = r\sin\theta = 5\sin(300^\circ) = 5\cdot\left(-\frac{\sqrt{3}}{2}\right) = -\frac{5\sqrt{3}}{2}$

The rectangular coordinates of the point $(5, 300^\circ)$ are $\left(\frac{5}{2}, -\frac{5\sqrt{3}}{2}\right)$.

35. $x = r\cos\theta = -2\cos\left(\frac{3\pi}{4}\right) = -2\cdot\left(-\frac{\sqrt{2}}{2}\right) = \sqrt{2}$

$y = r\sin\theta = -2\sin\left(\frac{3\pi}{4}\right) = -2\cdot\frac{\sqrt{2}}{2} = -\sqrt{2}$

The rectangular coordinates of the point $\left(-2, \frac{3\pi}{4}\right)$ are $\left(\sqrt{2}, -\sqrt{2}\right)$

36. $x = r\cos\theta = -3\cos\left(\frac{2\pi}{3}\right) = -3\cdot\left(-\frac{1}{2}\right) = \frac{3}{2}$

$y = r\sin\theta = -3\sin\left(\frac{2\pi}{3}\right) = -3\cdot\frac{\sqrt{3}}{2} = -\frac{3\sqrt{3}}{2}$

The rectangular coordinates of the point $\left(-3, \frac{2\pi}{3}\right)$ are $\left(\frac{3}{2}, -\frac{3\sqrt{3}}{2}\right)$.

37. $x = r\cos\theta = -1\cos\left(-\frac{\pi}{3}\right) = -1\cdot\frac{1}{2} = -\frac{1}{2}$

$y = r\sin\theta = -1\sin\left(-\frac{\pi}{3}\right) = -1\cdot\left(-\frac{\sqrt{3}}{2}\right) = \frac{\sqrt{3}}{2}$

The rectangular coordinates of the point $\left(-1, -\frac{\pi}{3}\right)$ are $\left(-\frac{1}{2}, \frac{\sqrt{3}}{2}\right)$.

38. $x = r\cos\theta = -3\cos\left(-\frac{3\pi}{4}\right) = -3\cdot\left(-\frac{\sqrt{2}}{2}\right) = \frac{3\sqrt{2}}{2}$

$y = r\sin\theta = -3\sin\left(-\frac{3\pi}{4}\right) = -3\cdot\left(-\frac{\sqrt{2}}{2}\right) = \frac{3\sqrt{2}}{2}$

The rectangular coordinates of the point $\left(-3, -\frac{3\pi}{4}\right)$ are $\left(\frac{3\sqrt{2}}{2}, \frac{3\sqrt{2}}{2}\right)$.

39. $x = r\cos\theta = -2\cos(-180^\circ) = -2\cdot -1 = 2$

$y = r\sin\theta = -2\sin(-180^\circ) = -2\cdot 0 = 0$

The rectangular coordinates of the point $(-2, -180^\circ)$ are $(2, 0)$.

40. $x = r\cos\theta = -3\cos(-90^\circ) = -3\cdot 0 = 0$

$y = r\sin\theta = -3\sin(-90^\circ) = -3\cdot(-1) = 3$

The rectangular coordinates of the point $(-3, -90^\circ)$ are $(0, 3)$.

41. $x = r\cos\theta = 7.5\cos(110^\circ) \approx 7.5(-0.3420) \approx -2.57$

$y = r\sin\theta = 7.5\sin(110^\circ) \approx 7.5(0.9397) \approx 7.05$

The rectangular coordinates of the point $(7.5, 110^\circ)$ are $(-2.57, 7.05)$.

42. $x = r\cos\theta = -3.1\cos(182^\circ) \approx -3.1(-0.9994) \approx 3.10$

$y = r\sin\theta = -3.1\sin(182^\circ) \approx -3.1(-0.0349) \approx 0.11$

The rectangular coordinates of the point $(-3.1, 182^\circ)$ are $(3.10, 0.11)$.

43. $x = r\cos\theta = 6.3\cos(3.8) \approx 6.3(-0.7910) \approx -4.98$

$y = r\sin\theta = 6.3\sin(3.8) \approx 6.3(-0.6119) \approx -3.85$

The rectangular coordinates of the point $(6.3, 3.8)$ are $(-4.98, -3.85)$.

44. $x = r\cos\theta = 8.1\cos(5.2) \approx 8.1(0.4685) \approx 3.79$
$y = r\sin\theta = 8.1\sin(5.2) \approx 8.1(-0.8835) \approx -7.16$
The rectangular coordinates of the point $(8.1, 5.2)$ are $(3.79, -7.16)$.

45. $r = \sqrt{x^2 + y^2} = \sqrt{3^2 + 0^2} = \sqrt{9} = 3 \qquad \theta = \tan^{-1}\left(\frac{y}{x}\right) = \tan^{-1}\left(\frac{0}{3}\right) = \tan^{-1}(0) = 0$
Polar coordinates of the point (3, 0) are (3, 0).

46. $r = \sqrt{x^2 + y^2} = \sqrt{0^2 + 2^2} = \sqrt{4} = 2 \qquad \theta = \tan^{-1}\left(\frac{y}{x}\right) = \tan^{-1}\left(\frac{2}{0}\right) = \frac{\pi}{2}$
Polar coordinates of the point (0, 2) are $\left(2, \frac{\pi}{2}\right)$.

47. $r = \sqrt{x^2 + y^2} = \sqrt{(-1)^2 + 0^2} = \sqrt{1} = 1 \qquad \theta = \tan^{-1}\left(\frac{y}{x}\right) = \tan^{-1}\left(\frac{0}{-1}\right) = \tan^{-1}(0) = 0$
The point lies on the negative x-axis thus $\theta = \pi$.
Polar coordinates of the point (–1, 0) are $(1, \pi)$.

48. $r = \sqrt{x^2 + y^2} = \sqrt{0^2 + (-2)^2} = \sqrt{4} = 2 \qquad \theta = \tan^{-1}\left(\frac{y}{x}\right) = \tan^{-1}\left(\frac{-2}{0}\right) = \frac{\pi}{2}$
The point lies on the negative y-axis thus $\theta = -\frac{\pi}{2}$.
Polar coordinates of the point (0, –2) are $\left(2, -\frac{\pi}{2}\right)$.

49. The point (1, –1) lies in quadrant IV.
$r = \sqrt{x^2 + y^2} = \sqrt{1^2 + (-1)^2} = \sqrt{2} \qquad \theta = \tan^{-1}\left(\frac{y}{x}\right) = \tan^{-1}\left(\frac{-1}{1}\right) = \tan^{-1}(-1) = -\frac{\pi}{4}$
Polar coordinates of the point $(1, -1)$ are $\left(\sqrt{2}, -\frac{\pi}{4}\right)$.

50. The point (–3, 3) lies in quadrant II.
$r = \sqrt{x^2 + y^2} = \sqrt{(-3)^2 + 3^2} = 3\sqrt{2} \qquad \theta = \tan^{-1}\left(\frac{y}{x}\right) = \tan^{-1}\left(\frac{3}{-3}\right) = \tan^{-1}(-1) = -\frac{\pi}{4}$
Polar coordinates of the point $(-3, 3)$ are $\left(3\sqrt{2}, \frac{3\pi}{4}\right)$.

51. The point $(\sqrt{3}, 1)$ lies in quadrant I.
$r = \sqrt{x^2 + y^2} = \sqrt{\left(\sqrt{3}\right)^2 + 1^2} = \sqrt{4} = 2 \qquad \theta = \tan^{-1}\left(\frac{y}{x}\right) = \tan^{-1}\left(\frac{1}{\sqrt{3}}\right) = \frac{\pi}{6}$
Polar coordinates of the point $(\sqrt{3}, 1)$ are $\left(2, \frac{\pi}{6}\right)$.

52. The point $\left(-2, -2\sqrt{3}\right)$ lies in quadrant III.

$$r=\sqrt{x^2+y^2}=\sqrt{(-2)^2+\left(-2\sqrt{3}\right)^2}=\sqrt{16}=4$$

$$\theta=\tan^{-1}\left(\frac{y}{x}\right)=\tan^{-1}\left(\frac{-2\sqrt{3}}{-2}\right)=\tan^{-1}\left(\sqrt{3}\right)=\frac{\pi}{3}$$

Polar coordinates of the point $\left(-2, -2\sqrt{3}\right)$ are $\left(4, \frac{4\pi}{3}\right)$.

53. The point (1.3, –2.1) lies in quadrant IV.

$$r=\sqrt{x^2+y^2}=\sqrt{1.3^2+(-2.1)^2}=\sqrt{6.1}\approx 2.47$$

$$\theta=\tan^{-1}\left(\frac{y}{x}\right)=\tan^{-1}\left(\frac{-2.1}{1.3}\right)\approx\tan^{-1}(-1.6154)\approx -1.02$$

Polar coordinates of the point $(1.3, -2.1)$ are $(2.47, -1.02)$.

54. The point (–0.8, –2.1) lies in quadrant III.

$$r=\sqrt{x^2+y^2}=\sqrt{(-0.8)^2+(-2.1)^2}=\sqrt{5.05}\approx 2.25$$

$$\theta=\tan^{-1}\left(\frac{y}{x}\right)=\tan^{-1}\left(\frac{-2.1}{-0.8}\right)\approx\tan^{-1}(2.625)\approx 1.21$$

$$\theta=\pi+1.21\approx 4.35$$

Polar coordinates of the point $(-0.8, -2.1)$ are $(2.25, 4.35)$.

55. The point (8.3, 4.2) lies in quadrant I.

$$r=\sqrt{x^2+y^2}=\sqrt{8.3^2+4.2^2}=\sqrt{86.53}\approx 9.30$$

$$\theta=\tan^{-1}\left(\frac{y}{x}\right)=\tan^{-1}\left(\frac{4.2}{8.3}\right)\approx\tan^{-1}(0.5060)\approx 0.47$$

Polar coordinates of the point $(8.3, 4.2)$ are $(9.30, 0.47)$.

56. The point (–2.3, 0.2) lies in quadrant II.

$$r=\sqrt{x^2+y^2}=\sqrt{(-2.3)^2+0.2^2}=\sqrt{5.33}\approx 2.31$$

$$\theta=\tan^{-1}\left(\frac{y}{x}\right)=\tan^{-1}\left(\frac{0.2}{-2.3}\right)\approx\tan^{-1}(-0.0870)\approx -0.09$$

$$\theta=\pi-0.09\approx 3.05$$

Polar coordinates of the point $(-2.3, 0.2)$ are $(2.31, 3.05)$.

57. $2x^2+2y^2=3$

$2\left(x^2+y^2\right)=3$

$2r^2=3\rightarrow r^2=\frac{3}{2}$

58. $x^2+y^2=x$

$r^2=r\cos\theta$

59. $$x^2 = 4y$$
$$(r\cos\theta)^2 = 4r\sin\theta$$
$$r^2\cos^2\theta - 4r\sin\theta = 0$$

60. $$y^2 = 2x$$
$$(r\sin\theta)^2 = 2r\cos\theta$$
$$r^2\sin^2\theta - 2r\cos\theta = 0$$

61. $$2xy = 1$$
$$2(r\cos\theta)(r\sin\theta) = 1$$
$$2r^2\sin\theta\cos\theta = 1 \to r^2\sin 2\theta = 1$$

62. $$4x^2y = 1$$
$$4(r\cos\theta)^2 r\sin\theta = 1$$
$$4r^2\cos^2\theta\, r\sin\theta = 1 \to 4r^3\cos^2\theta\sin\theta = 1$$

63. $$x = 4$$
$$r\cos\theta = 4$$

64. $$y = -3$$
$$r\sin\theta = -3$$

65. $$r = \cos\theta$$
$$r^2 = r\cos\theta$$
$$x^2 + y^2 = x \to x^2 - x + y^2 = 0$$

66. $$r = \sin\theta + 1$$
$$r^2 = r\sin\theta + r$$
$$x^2 + y^2 = y + \sqrt{x^2 + y^2}$$

67. $$r^2 = \cos\theta$$
$$r^3 = r\cos\theta$$
$$(x^2 + y^2)^{3/2} = x \to (x^2 + y^2)^{3/2} - x = 0$$

68. $$r = \sin\theta - \cos\theta$$
$$r^2 = r\sin\theta - r\cos\theta$$
$$x^2 + y^2 = y - x$$
$$x^2 + x + y^2 - y = 0$$

69. $$r = 2$$
$$\sqrt{x^2 + y^2} = 2 \to x^2 + y^2 = 4$$

70. $$r = 4$$
$$r^2 = 16 \to x^2 + y^2 = 16$$

71. $$r = \frac{4}{1 - \cos\theta}$$
$$r(1 - \cos\theta) = 4 \to r - r\cos\theta = 4$$
$$\sqrt{x^2 + y^2} - x = 4 \to \sqrt{x^2 + y^2} = x + 4$$
$$x^2 + y^2 = x^2 + 8x + 16$$
$$y^2 = 8(x + 2)$$

72. $$r = \frac{3}{3 - \cos\theta}$$
$$r(3 - \cos\theta) = 3 \to 3r - r\cos\theta = 3$$
$$3\sqrt{x^2 + y^2} - x = 3$$
$$3\sqrt{x^2 + y^2} = x + 3$$
$$9(x^2 + y^2) = x^2 + 6x + 9$$
$$9x^2 + 9y^2 = x^2 + 6x + 9$$
$$8x^2 - 6x + 9y^2 - 9 = 0$$

73. Rewrite the polar coordinates in rectangular form:
$$P_1 = (r_1, \theta_1) \quad \to \quad P_1 = (r_1\cos\theta_1, r_1\sin\theta_1)$$
$$P_2 = (r_2, \theta_2) \quad \to \quad P_2 = (r_2\cos\theta_2, r_2\sin\theta_2)$$
$$d = \sqrt{(r_2\cos\theta_2 - r_1\cos\theta_1)^2 + (r_2\sin\theta_2 - r_1\sin\theta_1)^2}$$
$$= \sqrt{r_2^2\cos^2\theta_2 - 2r_1r_2\cos\theta_2\cos\theta_1 + r_1^2\cos^2\theta_1 + r_2^2\sin^2\theta_2 - 2r_1r_2\sin\theta_2\sin\theta_1 + r_1^2\sin^2\theta_1}$$
$$= \sqrt{r_2^2(\cos^2\theta_2 + \sin^2\theta_2) + r_1^2(\cos^2\theta_1 + \sin^2\theta_1) - 2r_1r_2(\cos\theta_2\cos\theta_1 + \sin\theta_2\sin\theta_1)}$$
$$= \sqrt{r_2^2 + r_1^2 - 2r_1r_2\cos(\theta_2 - \theta_1)}$$

Chapter 10

Polar Coordinates; Vectors

10.2 Polar Equations and Graphs

1. $r = 4$
The equation is of the form $r = a,\ a > 0$.
It is a circle, center at the pole and radius 4.
Transform to rectangular form:
$$r = 4$$
$$r^2 = 16$$
$$x^2 + y^2 = 16$$

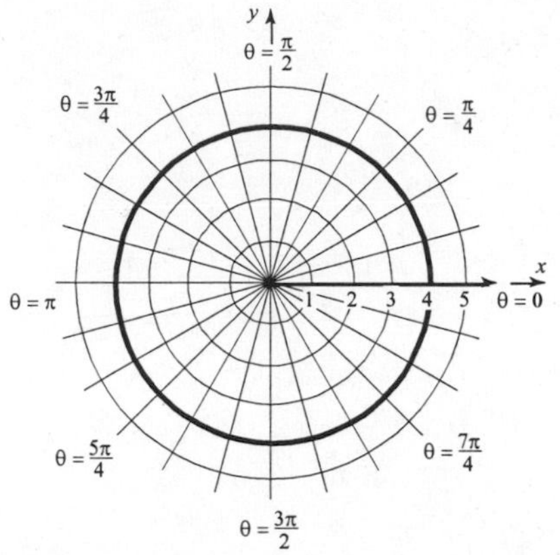

2. $r = 2$
The equation is of the form $r = a,\ a > 0$.
It is a circle, center at the pole and radius 2.
Transform to rectangular form:
$$r = 2$$
$$r^2 = 4$$
$$x^2 + y^2 = 4$$

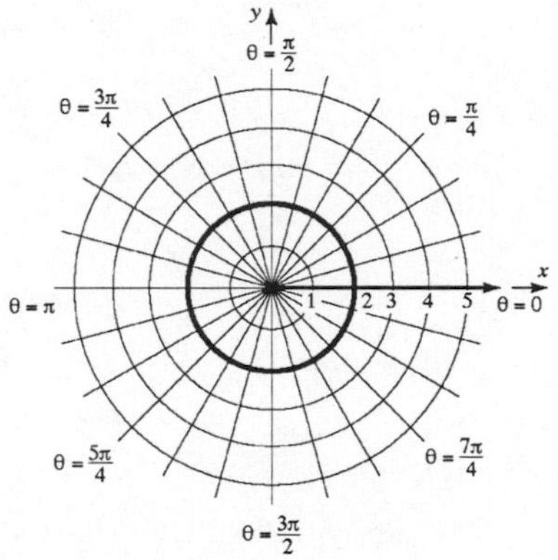

3. $\theta = \dfrac{\pi}{3}$
The equation is of the form $\theta = \alpha$. It is a line, passing through the pole at an angle of $\dfrac{\pi}{3}$.
Transform to rectangular form:
$$\theta = \frac{\pi}{3}$$
$$\tan\theta = \tan\left(\frac{\pi}{3}\right)$$
$$\frac{y}{x} = \sqrt{3} \rightarrow y = \sqrt{3}x$$

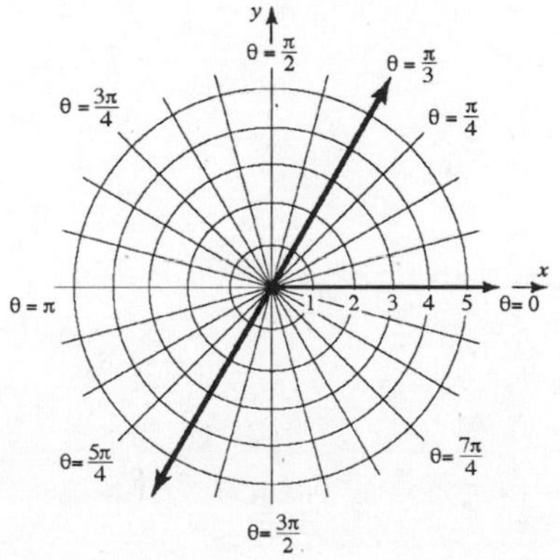

4. $\theta = -\dfrac{\pi}{4}$

The equation is of the form $\theta = \alpha$. It is a line, passing through the pole at an angle of $-\dfrac{\pi}{4}$.

Transform to rectangular form:

$$\theta = -\frac{\pi}{4}$$
$$\tan\theta = \tan\left(-\frac{\pi}{4}\right)$$
$$\frac{y}{x} = -1$$
$$y = -x$$

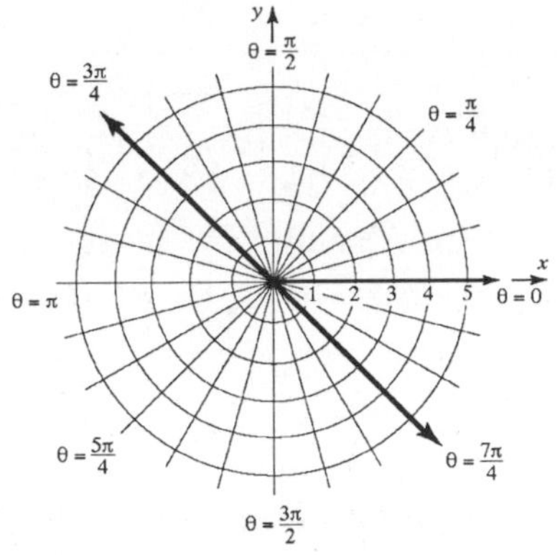

5. $r\sin\theta = 4$

The equation is of the form $r\sin\theta = b$. It is a horizontal line, 4 units above the pole.

Transform to rectangular form:

$$r\sin\theta = 4$$
$$y = 4$$

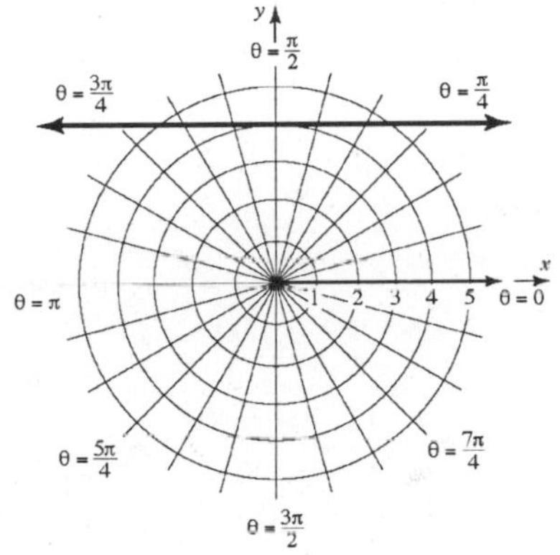

6. $r\cos\theta = 4$

The equation is of the form $r\cos\theta = a$. It is a vertical line, 4 units to the right of the pole.

Transform to rectangular form:

$$r\cos\theta = 4$$
$$x = 4$$

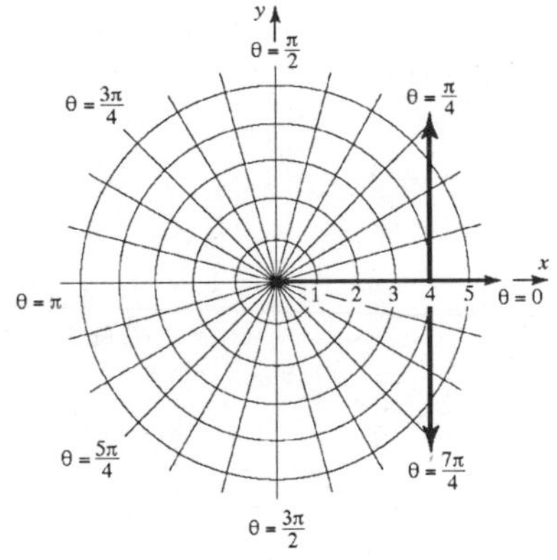

7. $r\cos\theta = -2$

The equation is of the form $r\cos\theta = a$. It is a vertical line, 2 units to the left of the pole.

Transform to rectangular form:

$$r\cos\theta = -2$$
$$x = -2$$

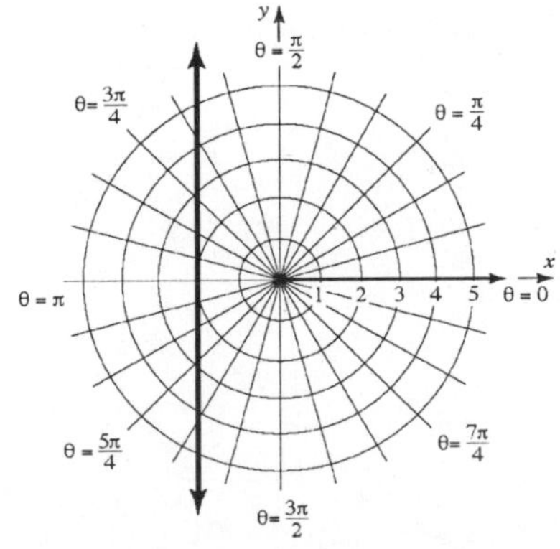

8. $r\sin\theta = -2$

The equation is of the form $r\sin\theta = b$. It is a horizontal line, 2 units below the pole.

Transform to rectangular form:

$$r\sin\theta = -2$$
$$y = -2$$

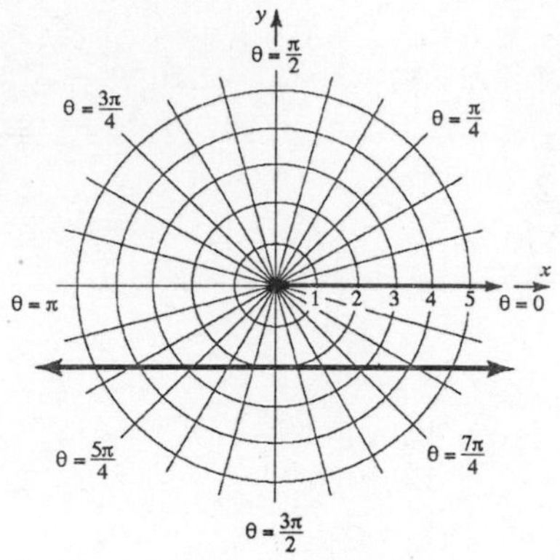

9. $r = 2\cos\theta$

The equation is of the form $r = 2a\cos\theta,\ a > 0$. It is a circle, passing through the pole, and center on the polar axis.

Transform to rectangular form:

$$r = 2\cos\theta$$
$$r^2 = 2r\cos\theta$$
$$x^2 + y^2 = 2x$$
$$x^2 - 2x + y^2 = 0$$
$$(x-1)^2 + y^2 = 1$$

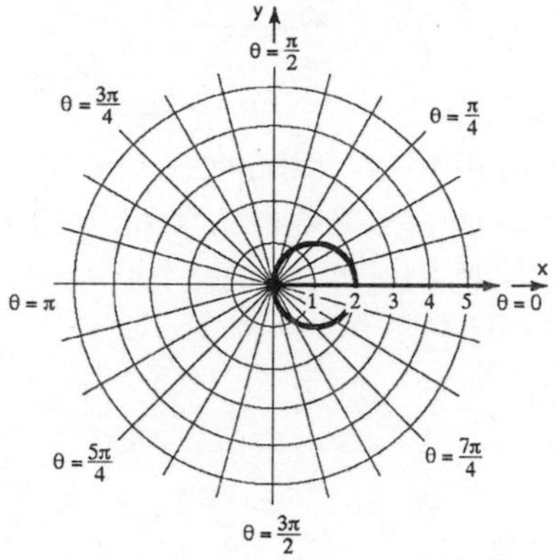

10. $r = 2\sin\theta$

The equation is of the form $r = 2a\sin\theta,\ a > 0$. It is a circle, passing through the pole, and center on the line $\theta = \frac{\pi}{2}$.

Transform to rectangular form:

$$r = 2\sin\theta$$
$$r^2 = 2r\sin\theta$$
$$x^2 + y^2 = 2y$$
$$x^2 + y^2 - 2y = 0$$
$$x^2 + (y-1)^2 = 1$$

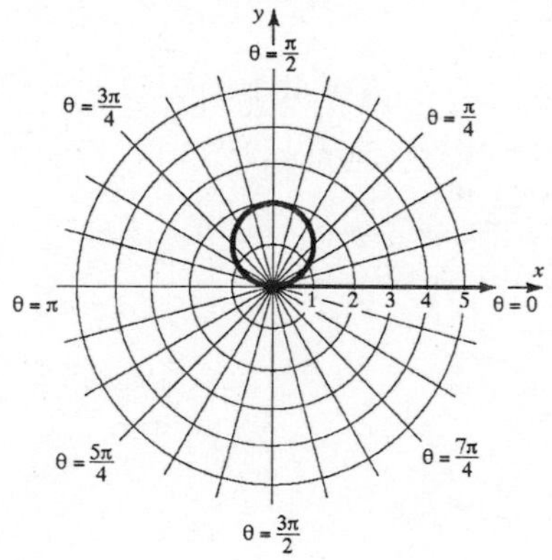

11. $r = -4\sin\theta$

The equation is of the form $r = 2a\sin\theta,\ a > 0$. It is a circle, passing through the pole, and center on the line $\theta = \dfrac{\pi}{2}$.

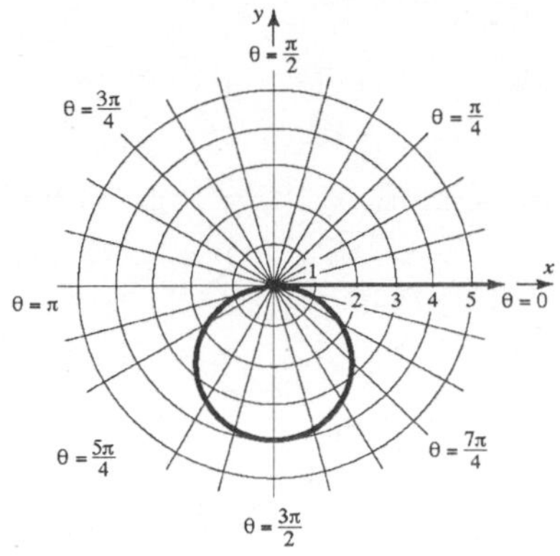

Transform to rectangular form:

$$r = -4\sin\theta$$
$$r^2 = -4r\sin\theta$$
$$x^2 + y^2 = -4y$$
$$x^2 + y^2 + 4y = 0$$
$$x^2 + (y+2)^2 = 4$$

12. $r = -4\cos\theta$

The equation is of the form $r = 2a\cos\theta,\ a > 0$. It is a circle, passing through the pole, and center on the polar axis.

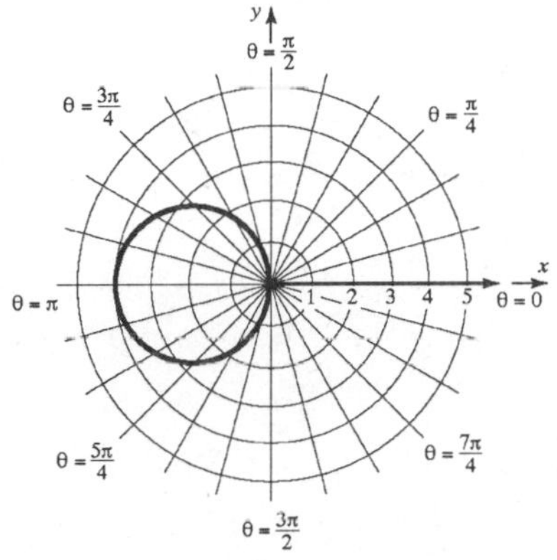

Transform to rectangular form:

$$r = -4\cos\theta$$
$$r^2 = -4r\cos\theta$$
$$x^2 + y^2 = -4x$$
$$x^2 + 4x + y^2 = 0$$
$$(x+2)^2 + y^2 = 4$$

13. $r\sec\theta = 4$

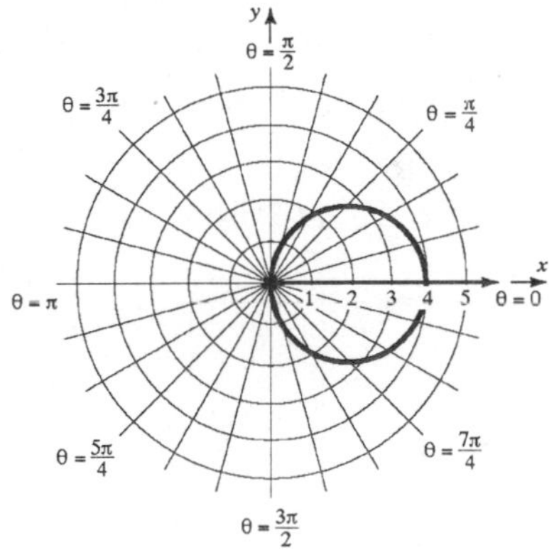

Transform to rectangular form:

$$r\sec\theta = 4$$
$$r \cdot \frac{1}{\cos\theta} = 4$$
$$r = 4\cos\theta$$
$$r^2 = 4r\cos\theta$$
$$x^2 + y^2 = 4x$$
$$x^2 - 4x + y^2 = 0$$
$$(x-2)^2 + y^2 = 4$$

The equation is a circle, passing through the pole, center on the polar axis and radius 2.

14. $r\csc\theta = 8$

Transform to rectangular form:

$$r\csc\theta = 8$$
$$r\cdot\frac{1}{\sin\theta} = 8$$
$$r = 8\sin\theta$$
$$r^2 = 8r\sin\theta$$
$$x^2 + y^2 = 8y$$
$$x^2 + y^2 - 8y = 0$$
$$x^2 + (y-4)^2 = 16$$

The equation is a circle, passing through the pole, center on the line $\theta = \frac{\pi}{2}$ and radius 4.

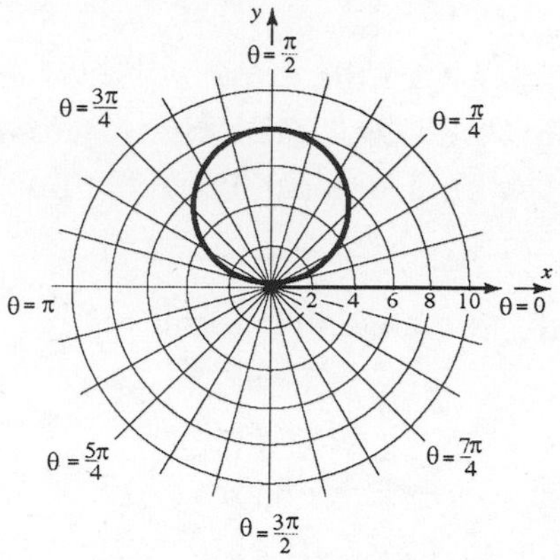

15. $r\csc\theta = -2$

Transform to rectangular form:

$$r\csc\theta = -2$$
$$r\cdot\frac{1}{\sin\theta} = -2$$
$$r = -2\sin\theta$$
$$r^2 = -2r\sin\theta$$
$$x^2 + y^2 = -2y$$
$$x^2 + y^2 + 2y = 0$$
$$x^2 + (y+1)^2 = 1$$

The equation is a circle, passing through the pole, center on the line $\theta = \frac{\pi}{2}$ and radius 1.

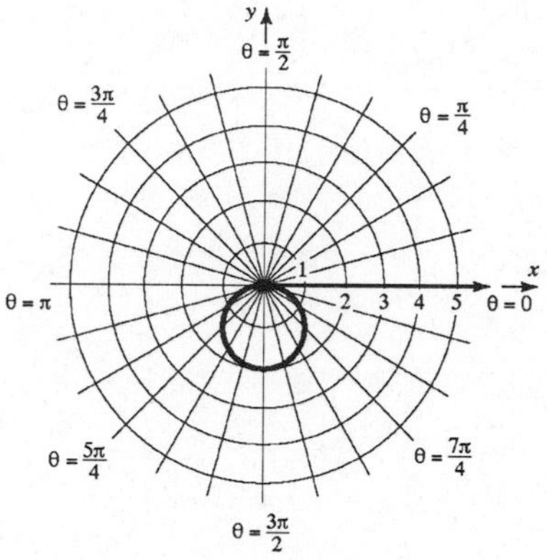

16. $r\sec\theta = -4$

Transform to rectangular form:

$$r\sec\theta = -4$$
$$r\cdot\frac{1}{\cos\theta} = -4$$
$$r = -4\cos\theta$$
$$r^2 = -4r\cos\theta$$
$$x^2 + y^2 = -4x$$
$$x^2 + 4x + y^2 = 0$$
$$(x+2)^2 + y^2 = 4$$

The equation is a circle, passing through the pole, center on the polar axis and radius 2.

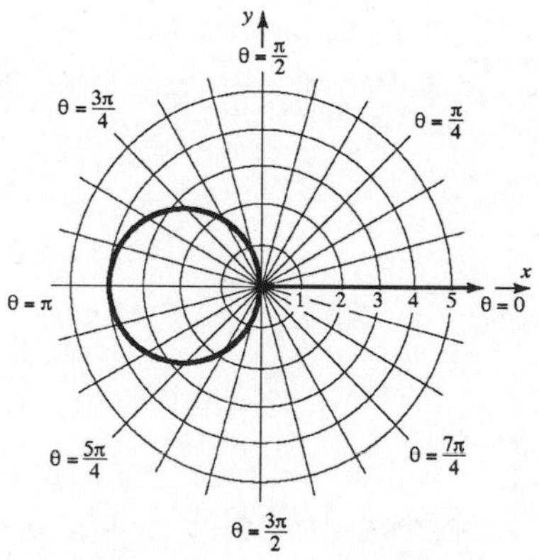

17. E
18. A
19. F
20. B
21. H
22. G
23. D
24. C

25. $r = 2 + 2\cos\theta$ The graph will be a cardioid. Check for symmetry:
Polar axis: Replace θ by $-\theta$. The result is $r = 2 + 2\cos(-\theta) = 2 + 2\cos\theta$.
The graph is symmetric with respect to the polar axis.

The line $\theta = \frac{\pi}{2}$: Replace θ by $\pi - \theta$.

$$r = 2 + 2\cos(\pi - \theta) = 2 + 2(\cos(\pi)\cos\theta + \sin(\pi)\sin\theta)$$
$$= 2 + 2(-\cos\theta + 0) = 2 - 2\cos\theta$$

The test fails.

The pole: Replace r by $-r$. $-r = 2 + 2\cos\theta$. The test fails.
Due to symmetry to the polar axis, assign values to θ from 0 to π.

θ	0	$\frac{\pi}{6}$	$\frac{\pi}{3}$	$\frac{\pi}{2}$	$\frac{2\pi}{3}$	$\frac{5\pi}{6}$	π
$r = 2 + 2\cos\theta$	4	$2 + \sqrt{3} \approx 3.7$	3	2	1	$2 - \sqrt{3} \approx 0.3$	0

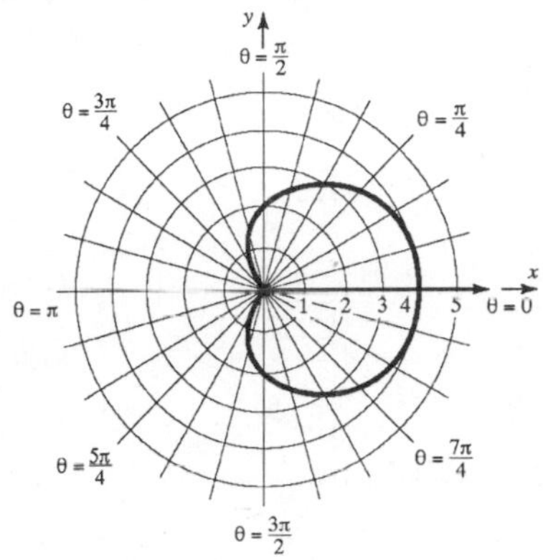

26. $r = 1 + \sin\theta$ The graph will be a cardioid. Check for symmetry:
Polar axis: Replace θ by $-\theta$. The result is $r = 1 + \sin(-\theta) = 1 - \sin\theta$.
The test fails.

The line $\theta = \frac{\pi}{2}$: Replace θ by $\pi - \theta$.

$$r = 1 + \sin(\pi - \theta) = 1 + (\sin(\pi)\cos\theta - \cos(\pi)\sin\theta)$$
$$= 1 + (0 + \sin\theta) = 1 + \sin\theta$$

The graph is symmetric with respect to the line $\theta = \frac{\pi}{2}$.

The pole: Replace r by $-r$. $-r = 1 + \sin\theta$. The test fails.
Due to symmetry to the line $\theta = \frac{\pi}{2}$, assign values to θ from $-\frac{\pi}{2}$ to $\frac{\pi}{2}$.

θ	$-\frac{\pi}{2}$	$-\frac{\pi}{3}$	$-\frac{\pi}{6}$	0	$\frac{\pi}{6}$	$\frac{\pi}{3}$	$\frac{\pi}{2}$
$r = 1 + \sin\theta$	0	$1 - \frac{\sqrt{3}}{2} \approx 0.1$	$\frac{1}{2}$	1	$\frac{3}{2}$	$1 + \frac{\sqrt{3}}{2} \approx 1.9$	2

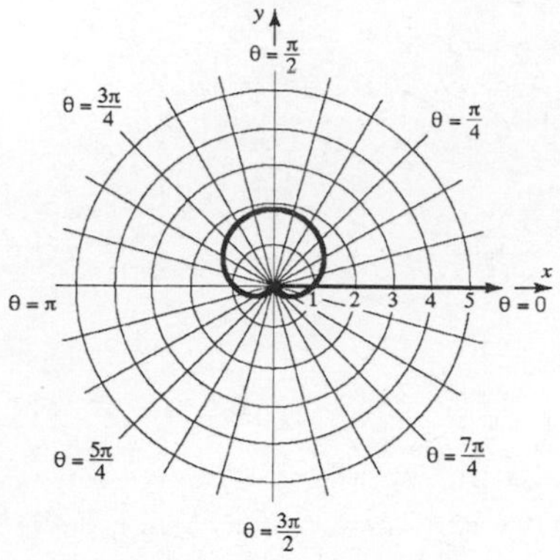

27. $r = 3 - 3\sin\theta$ The graph will be a cardioid. Check for symmetry:
Polar axis: Replace θ by $-\theta$. The result is $r = 3 - 3\sin(-\theta) = 3 + 3\sin\theta$.
The test fails.

The line $\theta = \frac{\pi}{2}$: Replace θ by $\pi - \theta$.

$$r = 3 - 3\sin(\pi - \theta) = 3 - 3(\sin(\pi)\cos\theta - \cos(\pi)\sin\theta)$$
$$= 3 - 3(0 + \sin\theta) = 3 - 3\sin\theta$$

The graph is symmetric with respect to the line $\theta = \frac{\pi}{2}$.

The pole: Replace r by $-r$. $-r = 3 - 3\sin\theta$. The test fails.

Due to symmetry to the line $\theta = \frac{\pi}{2}$, assign values to θ from $-\frac{\pi}{2}$ to $\frac{\pi}{2}$.

θ	$-\frac{\pi}{2}$	$-\frac{\pi}{3}$	$-\frac{\pi}{6}$	0	$\frac{\pi}{6}$	$\frac{\pi}{3}$	$\frac{\pi}{2}$
$r = 3 - 3\sin\theta$	6	$3 + \frac{3\sqrt{3}}{2} \approx 5.6$	$\frac{9}{2}$	3	$\frac{3}{2}$	$3 - \frac{3\sqrt{3}}{2} \approx 0.4$	0

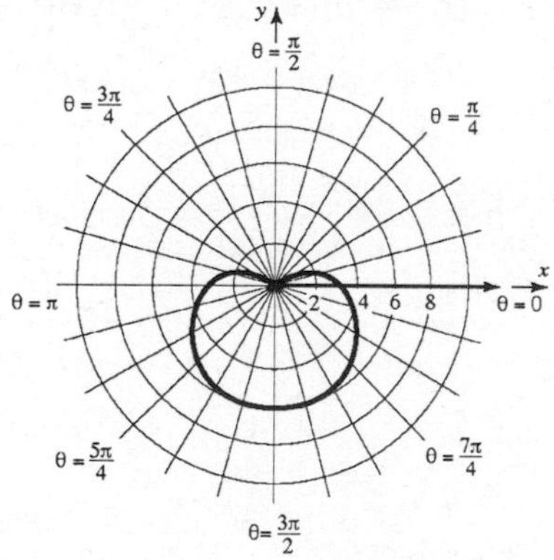

28. $r = 2 - 2\cos\theta$ The graph will be a cardioid. Check for symmetry:
Polar axis: Replace θ by $-\theta$. The result is $r = 2 - 2\cos(-\theta) = 2 - 2\cos\theta$.
The graph is symmetric with respect to the polar axis.

The linc $\theta = \frac{\pi}{2}$: Replace θ by $\pi - \theta$.

$$r = 2 - 2\cos(\pi - \theta) = 2 - 2(\cos(\pi)\cos\theta + \sin(\pi)\sin\theta)$$
$$= 2 - 2(-\cos\theta + 0) = 2 + 2\cos\theta$$

The test fails.

The pole: Replace r by $-r$. $-r = 2 - 2\cos\theta$. The test fails.
Due to symmetry to the polar axis, assign values to θ from 0 to π.

θ	0	$\frac{\pi}{6}$	$\frac{\pi}{3}$	$\frac{\pi}{2}$	$\frac{2\pi}{3}$	$\frac{5\pi}{6}$	π
$r = 2 - 2\cos\theta$	0	$2-\sqrt{3} \approx 0.3$	1	2	3	$2+\sqrt{3} \approx 3.7$	4

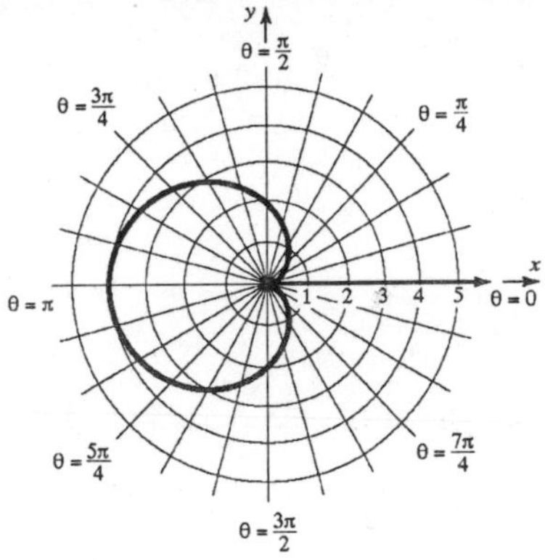

29. $r = 2 + \sin\theta$ The graph will be a limacon without an inner loop.
Check for symmetry:
Polar axis: Replace θ by $-\theta$. The result is $r = 2 + \sin(-\theta) = 2 - \sin\theta$.
The test fails.
The line $\theta = \frac{\pi}{2}$: Replace θ by $\pi - \theta$.

$$r = 2 + \sin(\pi - \theta) = 2 + (\sin(\pi)\cos\theta - \cos(\pi)\sin\theta)$$
$$= 2 + (0 + \sin\theta) = 2 + \sin\theta$$

The graph is symmetric with respect to the line $\theta = \frac{\pi}{2}$.
The pole: Replace r by $-r$. $-r = 2 + \sin\theta$. The test fails.
Due to symmetry to the line $\theta = \frac{\pi}{2}$, assign values to θ from $-\frac{\pi}{2}$ to $\frac{\pi}{2}$.

θ	$-\frac{\pi}{2}$	$-\frac{\pi}{3}$	$-\frac{\pi}{6}$	0	$\frac{\pi}{6}$	$\frac{\pi}{3}$	$\frac{\pi}{2}$
$r = 2 + \sin\theta$	1	$2-\frac{\sqrt{3}}{2} \approx 1.1$	$\frac{3}{2}$	2	$\frac{5}{2}$	$2+\frac{\sqrt{3}}{2} \approx 2.9$	3

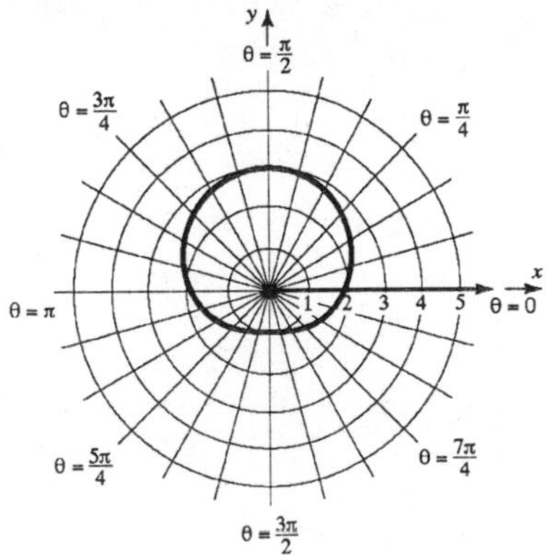

30. $r = 2 - \cos\theta$ The graph will be a limacon without an inner loop.
Check for symmetry:
Polar axis: Replace θ by $-\theta$. The result is $r = 2 - \cos(-\theta) = 2 - \cos\theta$.
The graph is symmetric with respect to the polar axis.
The line $\theta = \frac{\pi}{2}$: Replace θ by $\pi - \theta$.

$$r = 2 - \cos(\pi - \theta) = 2 - (\cos(\pi)\cos\theta + \sin(\pi)\sin\theta)$$
$$= 2 - (-\cos\theta + 0) = 2 + \cos\theta$$

The test fails.
The pole: Replace r by $-r$. $-r = 2 - \cos\theta$. The test fails.
Due to symmetry to the polar axis, assign values to θ from 0 to π.

θ	0	$\frac{\pi}{6}$	$\frac{\pi}{3}$	$\frac{\pi}{2}$	$\frac{2\pi}{3}$	$\frac{5\pi}{6}$	π
$r = 2 - \cos\theta$	1	$2 - \frac{\sqrt{3}}{2} \approx 1.1$	$\frac{3}{2}$	2	$\frac{5}{2}$	$2 + \frac{\sqrt{3}}{2} \approx 2.9$	3

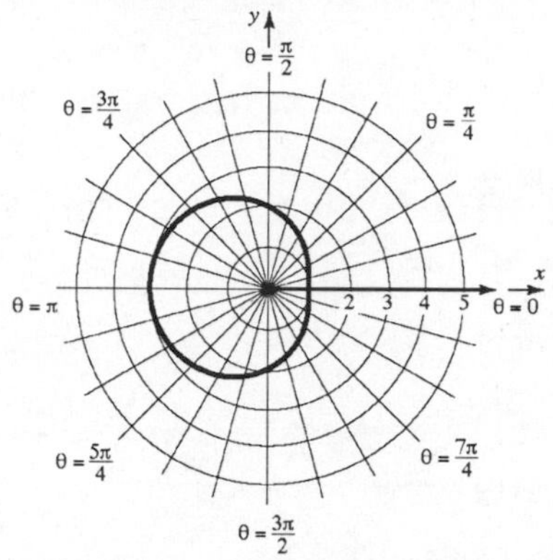

31. $r = 4 - 2\cos\theta$ The graph will be a limacon without an inner loop.
Check for symmetry:
Polar axis: Replace θ by $-\theta$. The result is $r = 4 - 2\cos(-\theta) = 4 - 2\cos\theta$.
The graph is symmetric with respect to the polar axis.
The line $\theta = \frac{\pi}{2}$: Replace θ by $\pi - \theta$.

$$r = 4 - 2\cos(\pi - \theta) = 4 - 2(\cos(\pi)\cos\theta + \sin(\pi)\sin\theta)$$
$$= 4 - 2(-\cos\theta + 0) = 4 + 2\cos\theta$$

The test fails.
The pole: Replace r by $-r$. $-r = 4 - 2\cos\theta$. The test fails.
Due to symmetry to the polar axis, assign values to θ from 0 to π.

θ	0	$\frac{\pi}{6}$	$\frac{\pi}{3}$	$\frac{\pi}{2}$	$\frac{2\pi}{3}$	$\frac{5\pi}{6}$	π
$r = 4 - 2\cos\theta$	2	$4 - \sqrt{3} \approx 2.3$	3	4	5	$4 + \sqrt{3} \approx 5.7$	6

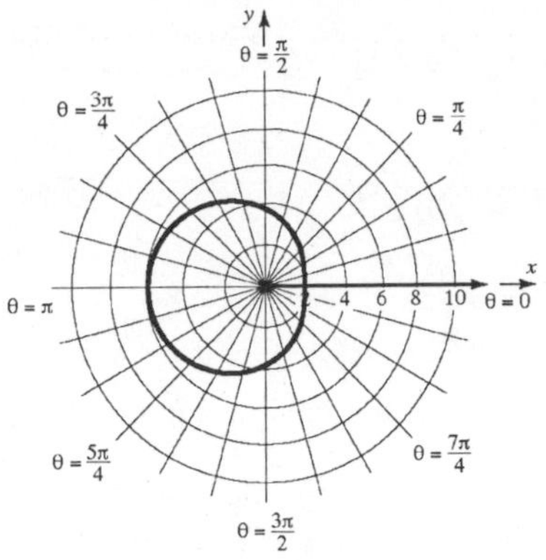

32. $r = 4 + 2\sin\theta$ The graph will be a limacon without an inner loop.
Check for symmetry:
Polar axis: Replace θ by $-\theta$. The result is $r = 4 + 2\sin(-\theta) = 4 - 2\sin\theta$.
The test fails.
The line $\theta = \frac{\pi}{2}$: Replace θ by $\pi - \theta$.

$$r = 4 + 2\sin(\pi - \theta) = 4 + 2(\sin(\pi)\cos\theta - \cos(\pi)\sin\theta)$$
$$= 4 + 2(0 + \sin\theta) = 4 + 2\sin\theta$$

The graph is symmetric with respect to the line $\theta = \frac{\pi}{2}$.
The pole: Replace r by $-r$. $-r = 4 + 2\sin\theta$. The test fails.
Due to symmetry to the line $\theta = \frac{\pi}{2}$, assign values to θ from $-\frac{\pi}{2}$ to $\frac{\pi}{2}$.

θ	$-\frac{\pi}{2}$	$-\frac{\pi}{3}$	$-\frac{\pi}{6}$	0	$\frac{\pi}{6}$	$\frac{\pi}{3}$	$\frac{\pi}{2}$
$r = 4 + 2\sin\theta$	2	$4 - \sqrt{3} \approx 2.3$	3	4	5	$4 + \sqrt{3} \approx 5.7$	6

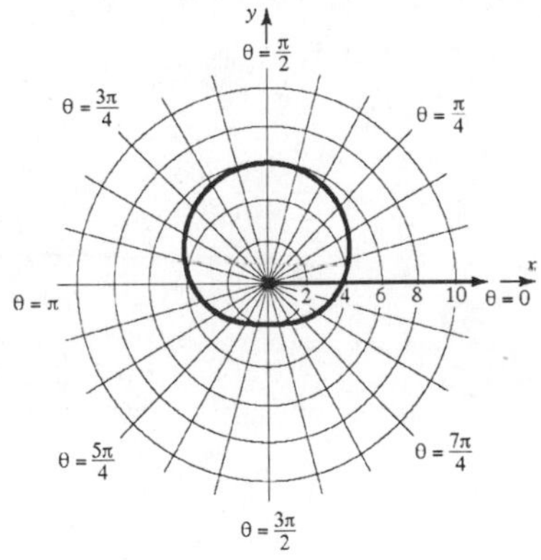

33. $r = 1 + 2\sin\theta$ The graph will be a limacon with an inner loop.
Check for symmetry:
Polar axis: Replace θ by $-\theta$. The result is $r = 1 + 2\sin(-\theta) = 1 - 2\sin\theta$.
The test fails.
The line $\theta = \frac{\pi}{2}$: Replace θ by $\pi - \theta$.

$$r = 1 + 2\sin(\pi - \theta) = 1 + 2(\sin(\pi)\cos\theta - \cos(\pi)\sin\theta)$$
$$= 1 + 2(0 + \sin\theta) = 1 + 2\sin\theta$$

The graph is symmetric with respect to the line $\theta = \frac{\pi}{2}$.

The pole: Replace r by $-r$. $-r = 1 + 2\sin\theta$. The test fails.

Due to symmetry to the line $\theta = \frac{\pi}{2}$, assign values to θ from $-\frac{\pi}{2}$ to $\frac{\pi}{2}$.

θ	$-\frac{\pi}{2}$	$-\frac{\pi}{3}$	$-\frac{\pi}{6}$	0	$\frac{\pi}{6}$	$\frac{\pi}{3}$	$\frac{\pi}{2}$
$r = 1 + 2\sin\theta$	-1	$1-\sqrt{3} \approx -0.7$	0	1	2	$1+\sqrt{3} \approx 2.7$	3

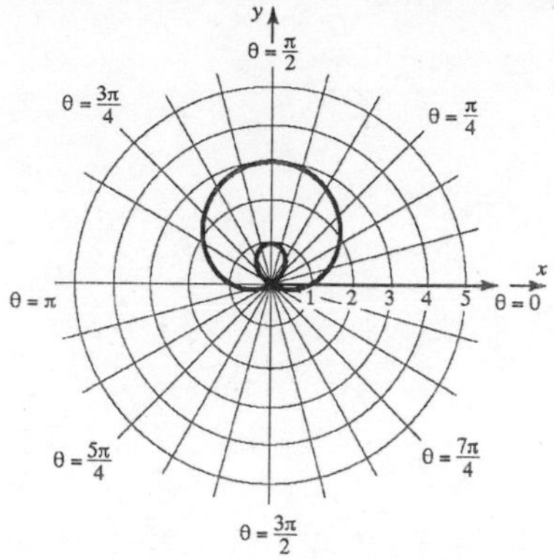

34. $r = 1 - 2\sin\theta$ The graph will be a limacon with an inner loop.
Check for symmetry:
Polar axis: Replace θ by $-\theta$. The result is $r = 1 - 2\sin(-\theta) = 1 + 2\sin\theta$.
The test fails.

The line $\theta = \frac{\pi}{2}$: Replace θ by $\pi - \theta$.

$$r = 1 - 2\sin(\pi - \theta) = 1 - 2(\sin(\pi)\cos\theta - \cos(\pi)\sin\theta)$$
$$= 1 - 2(0 + \sin\theta) = 1 - 2\sin\theta$$

The graph is symmetric with respect to the line $\theta = \frac{\pi}{2}$.

The pole: Replace r by $-r$. $-r = 1 - 2\sin\theta$. The test fails.

Due to symmetry to the line $\theta = \frac{\pi}{2}$, assign values to θ from $-\frac{\pi}{2}$ to $\frac{\pi}{2}$.

θ	$-\frac{\pi}{2}$	$-\frac{\pi}{3}$	$-\frac{\pi}{6}$	0	$\frac{\pi}{6}$	$\frac{\pi}{3}$	$\frac{\pi}{2}$
$r = 1 - 2\sin\theta$	3	$1+\sqrt{3} \approx 2.7$	2	1	0	$1-\sqrt{3} \approx -0.7$	-1

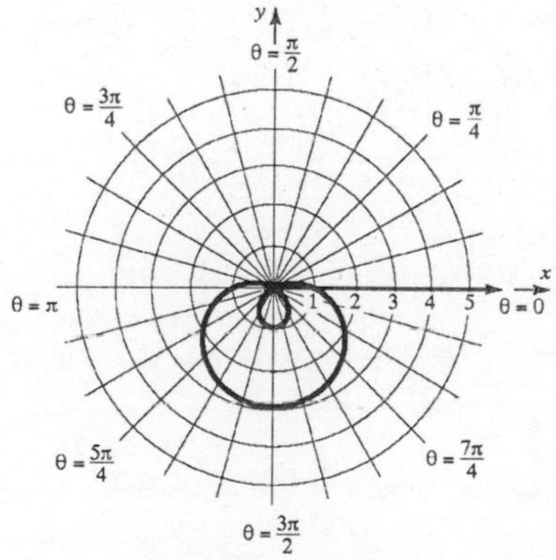

35. $r = 2 - 3\cos\theta$ The graph will be a limacon with an inner loop.
Check for symmetry:
Polar axis: Replace θ by $-\theta$. The result is $r = 2 - 3\cos(-\theta) = 2 - 3\cos\theta$.
The graph is symmetric with respect to the polar axis.
The line $\theta = \frac{\pi}{2}$: Replace θ by $\pi - \theta$.

$$r = 2 - 3\cos(\pi - \theta) = 2 - 3(\cos(\pi)\cos\theta + \sin(\pi)\sin\theta)$$
$$= 2 - 3(-\cos\theta + 0) = 2 + 3\cos\theta$$

The test fails.
The pole: Replace r by $-r$. $-r = 2 - 3\cos\theta$. The test fails.
Due to symmetry to the polar axis, assign values to θ from 0 to π.

θ	0	$\frac{\pi}{6}$	$\frac{\pi}{3}$	$\frac{\pi}{2}$	$\frac{2\pi}{3}$	$\frac{5\pi}{6}$	π
$r = 2 - 3\cos\theta$	-1	$2 - \frac{3\sqrt{3}}{2} \approx -0.6$	$\frac{1}{2}$	2	$\frac{7}{2}$	$2 + \frac{3\sqrt{3}}{2} \approx 4.6$	5

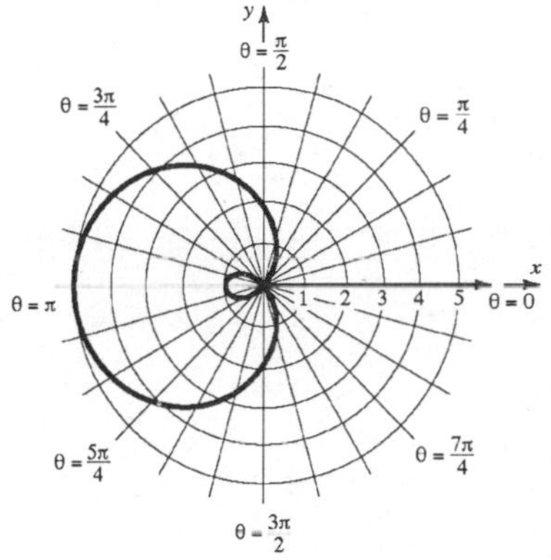

36. $r = 2 + 4\cos\theta$ The graph will be a limacon with an inner loop.
Check for symmetry:
Polar axis: Replace θ by $-\theta$. The result is $r = 2 + 4\cos(-\theta) = 2 + 4\cos\theta$.
The graph is symmetric with respect to the polar axis.
The line $\theta = \frac{\pi}{2}$: Replace θ by $\pi - \theta$.

$$r = 2 + 4\cos(\pi - \theta) = 2 + 4(\cos(\pi)\cos\theta + \sin(\pi)\sin\theta)$$
$$= 2 + 4(-\cos\theta + 0) = 2 - 4\cos\theta$$

The test fails.
The pole: Replace r by $-r$. $-r = 2 + 4\cos\theta$. The test fails.
Due to symmetry to the polar axis, assign values to θ from 0 to π.

θ	0	$\frac{\pi}{6}$	$\frac{\pi}{3}$	$\frac{\pi}{2}$	$\frac{2\pi}{3}$	$\frac{5\pi}{6}$	π
$r = 2 + 4\cos\theta$	6	$2 + 2\sqrt{3} \approx 5.5$	4	2	0	$2 - 2\sqrt{3} \approx -1.5$	-2

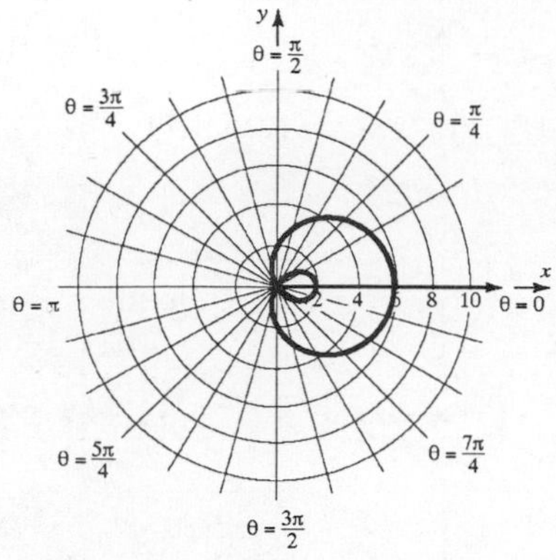

37. $r = 3\cos(2\theta)$ The graph will be a rose with four petals. Check for symmetry:

Polar axis: Replace θ by $-\theta$. $r = 3\cos(2(-\theta)) = 3\cos(-2\theta) = 3\cos(2\theta)$.

The graph is symmetric with respect to the polar axis.

The line $\theta = \frac{\pi}{2}$: Replace θ by $\pi - \theta$.

$$r = 3\cos(2(\pi - \theta)) = 3\cos(2\pi - 2\theta)$$
$$= 3(\cos(2\pi)\cos(2\theta) + \sin(2\pi)\sin(2\theta)) = 3(\cos 2\theta + 0) = 3\cos(2\theta)$$

The graph is symmetric with respect to the line $\theta = \frac{\pi}{2}$.

The pole: Since the graph is symmetric to both the polar axis and the line $\theta = \frac{\pi}{2}$, it is also symmetric to the pole.

Due to symmetry, assign values to θ from 0 to $\frac{\pi}{2}$.

θ	0	$\frac{\pi}{6}$	$\frac{\pi}{4}$	$\frac{\pi}{3}$	$\frac{\pi}{2}$
$r = 3\cos 2\theta$	3	$\frac{3}{2}$	0	$-\frac{3}{2}$	-3

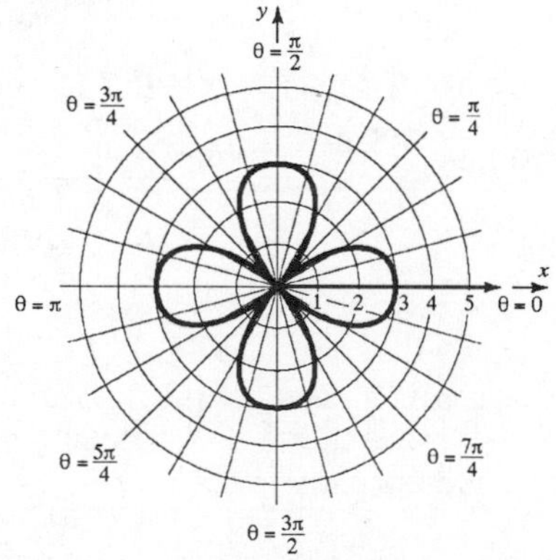

38. $r = 2\sin(3\theta)$ The graph will be a rose with three petals. Check for symmetry:

Polar axis: Replace θ by $-\theta$. $r = 2\sin(3(-\theta)) = 2\sin(-3\theta) = -2\sin(3\theta)$.

The test fails.

The line $\theta = \frac{\pi}{2}$: Replace θ by $\pi - \theta$.

$$r = 2\sin(3(\pi - \theta)) = 2\sin(3\pi - 3\theta)$$
$$= 2(\sin(3\pi)\cos(3\theta) - \cos(3\pi)\sin(3\theta)) = 2(0 + \sin(3\theta)) = 2\sin(3\theta)$$

The graph is symmetric with respect to the line $\theta = \frac{\pi}{2}$.

The pole: Replace r by $-r$. $-r = 2\sin(3\theta)$. The test fails.

Due to symmetry to the line $\theta = \frac{\pi}{2}$, assign values to θ from $-\frac{\pi}{2}$ to $\frac{\pi}{2}$.

θ	$-\frac{\pi}{2}$	$-\frac{\pi}{3}$	$-\frac{\pi}{4}$	$-\frac{\pi}{6}$	0	$\frac{\pi}{6}$	$\frac{\pi}{4}$	$\frac{\pi}{3}$	$\frac{\pi}{2}$
$r = 2\sin(3\theta)$	2	0	$-\sqrt{2} \approx -1.4$	-2	0	2	$\sqrt{2} \approx 1.4$	0	-2

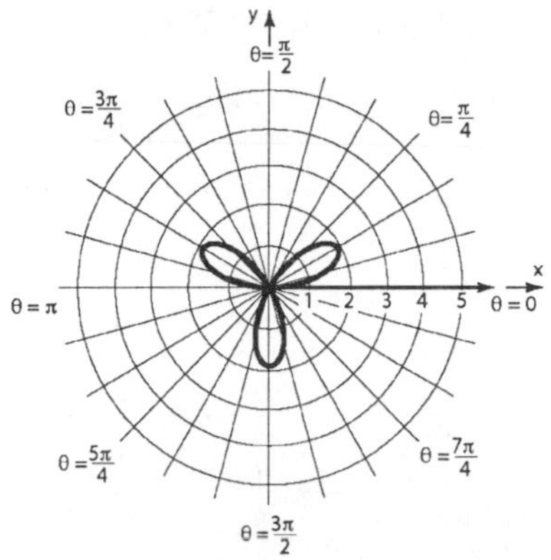

39. $r = 4\sin(5\theta)$ The graph will be a rose with five petals. Check for symmetry:

Polar axis: Replace θ by $-\theta$. $r = 4\sin(5(-\theta)) = 4\sin(-5\theta) = -4\sin(5\theta)$.

The test fails.

The line $\theta = \frac{\pi}{2}$: Replace θ by $\pi - \theta$.

$$r = 4\sin(5(\pi - \theta)) = 4\sin(5\pi - 5\theta)$$
$$= 4(\sin(5\pi)\cos(5\theta) - \cos(5\pi)\sin(5\theta)) = 4(0 + \sin(5\theta)) = 4\sin(5\theta)$$

The graph is symmetric with respect to the line $\theta = \frac{\pi}{2}$.

The pole: Replace r by $-r$. $-r = 4\sin(5\theta)$. The test fails.

Due to symmetry to the line $\theta = \frac{\pi}{2}$, assign values to θ from $-\frac{\pi}{2}$ to $\frac{\pi}{2}$.

θ	$-\frac{\pi}{2}$	$-\frac{\pi}{3}$	$-\frac{\pi}{4}$	$-\frac{\pi}{6}$	0	$\frac{\pi}{6}$	$\frac{\pi}{4}$	$\frac{\pi}{3}$	$\frac{\pi}{2}$
$r = 4\sin(5\theta)$	-4	$2\sqrt{3} \approx 3.5$	$-2\sqrt{2} \approx -2.8$	-2	0	2	$-2\sqrt{2} \approx -2.8$	$-2\sqrt{3} \approx -3.5$	4

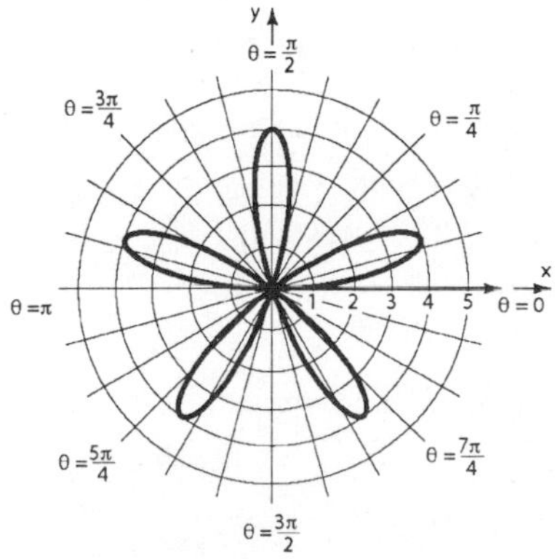

40. $r = 3\cos(4\theta)$ The graph will be a rose with eight petals. Check for symmetry:
Polar axis: Replace θ by $-\theta$. $r = 3\cos(4(-\theta)) = 3\cos(-4\theta) = 3\cos(4\theta)$.
The graph is symmetric with respect to the polar axis.
The line $\theta = \frac{\pi}{2}$: Replace θ by $\pi - \theta$.

$$r = 3\cos(4(\pi - \theta)) = 3\cos(4\pi - 4\theta)$$
$$= 3(\cos(4\pi)\cos(4\theta) + \sin(4\pi)\sin(4\theta) = 3(\cos 4\theta + 0) = 3\cos(4\theta)$$

The graph is symmetric with respect to the line $\theta = \frac{\pi}{2}$.
The pole: Since the graph is symmetric to both the polar axis and the line $\theta = \frac{\pi}{2}$, it is also symmetric to the pole.

Due to symmetry, assign values to θ from 0 to $\frac{\pi}{2}$.

θ	0	$\frac{\pi}{6}$	$\frac{\pi}{4}$	$\frac{\pi}{3}$	$\frac{\pi}{2}$
$r = 3\cos(4\theta)$	3	$-\frac{3}{2}$	-3	$-\frac{3}{2}$	3

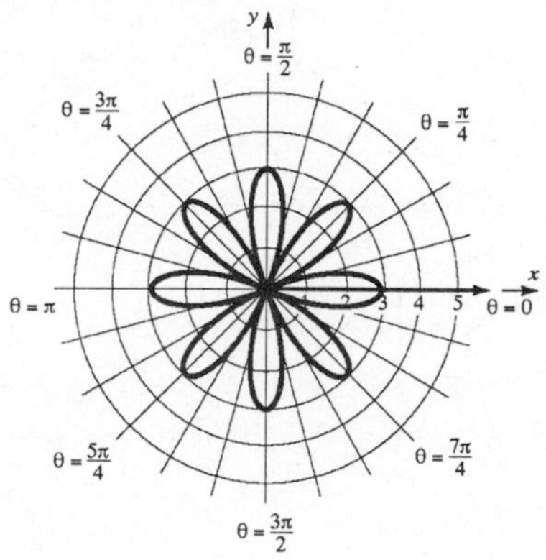

41. $r^2 = 9\cos(2\theta)$ The graph will be a lemniscate. Check for symmetry:
Polar axis: Replace θ by $-\theta$. $r^2 = 9\cos(2(-\theta)) = 9\cos(-2\theta) = 9\cos(2\theta)$.
The graph is symmetric with respect to the polar axis.
The line $\theta = \frac{\pi}{2}$: Replace θ by $\pi - \theta$.

$$r^2 = 9\cos(2(\pi - \theta)) = 9\cos(2\pi - 2\theta)$$
$$= 9(\cos(2\pi)\cos 2\theta + \sin(2\pi)\sin 2\theta) = 9(\cos 2\theta + 0) = 9\cos(2\theta)$$

The graph is symmetric with respect to the line $\theta = \frac{\pi}{2}$.
The pole: Since the graph is symmetric to both the polar axis and the line $\theta = \frac{\pi}{2}$, it is also symmetric to the pole.

Due to symmetry, assign values to θ from 0 to $\frac{\pi}{2}$.

θ	0	$\frac{\pi}{6}$	$\frac{\pi}{4}$	$\frac{\pi}{3}$	$\frac{\pi}{2}$
$r=\pm\sqrt{9\cos(2\theta)}$	± 3	$\pm\frac{3\sqrt{2}}{2}\approx\pm 2.1$	0	not defined	not defined

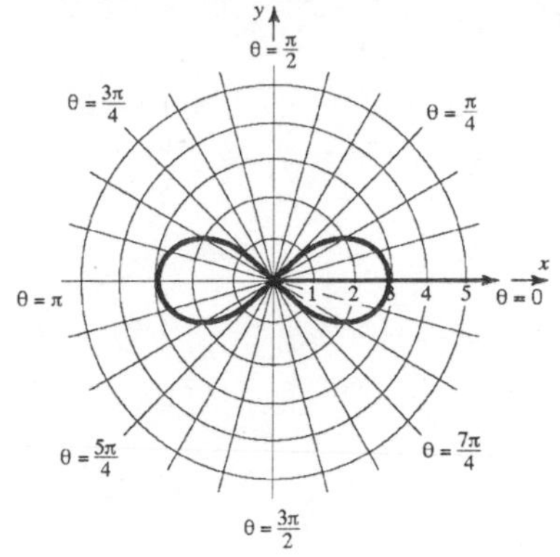

42. $r^2 = \sin(2\theta)$ The graph will be a lemniscate. Check for symmetry:
Polar axis: Replace θ by $-\theta$. $r^2 = \sin(2(-\theta)) = \sin(-2\theta) = -\sin(2\theta)$.
The test fails
The line $\theta = \frac{\pi}{2}$: Replace θ by $\pi - \theta$.

$$r^2 = \sin(2(\pi - \theta)) = \sin(2\pi - 2\theta)$$
$$= \sin(2\pi)\cos 2\theta - \cos(2\pi)\sin(2\theta) = 0 - \sin(2\theta) = -\sin(2\theta)$$

The test fails.
The pole: Replace r by $-r$. $(-r)^2 = \sin(2\theta) \rightarrow r^2 = \sin(2\theta)$.
The graph is symmetric to the pole.
Due to symmetry to the pole, assign values to θ from 0 to π.

θ	0	$\frac{\pi}{6}$	$\frac{\pi}{3}$	$\frac{\pi}{2}$	$\frac{2\pi}{3}$	$\frac{5\pi}{6}$	π
$r=\pm\sqrt{\sin(2\theta)}$	0	$\pm\sqrt{\frac{\sqrt{3}}{2}}$	$\pm\sqrt{\frac{\sqrt{3}}{2}}$	0	undefined	undefined	0

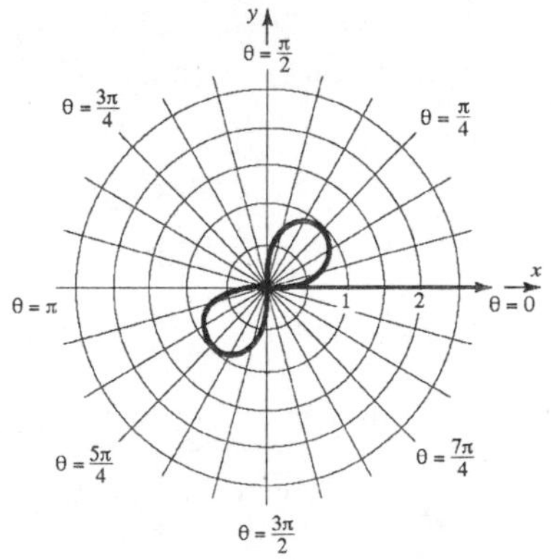

43. $r = 2^{\theta}$ The graph will be a spiral. Check for symmetry:
Polar axis: Replace θ by $-\theta$. $r = 2^{-\theta}$. The test fails.
The line $\theta = \frac{\pi}{2}$: Replace θ by $\pi - \theta$. $r = 2^{\pi-\theta}$. The test fails.

The pole: Replace r by $-r$. $-r = 2^{\theta}$. The test fails.

θ	$-\pi$	$-\frac{\pi}{2}$	$-\frac{\pi}{4}$	0	$\frac{\pi}{4}$	$\frac{\pi}{2}$	π	$\frac{3\pi}{2}$	2π
$r = 2^{\theta}$	0.1	0.3	0.6	1	1.7	3.0	8.8	26.2	77.9

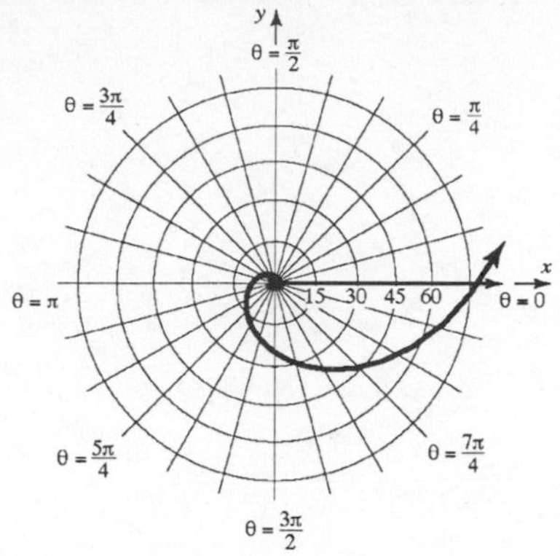

44. $r = 3^{\theta}$ The graph will be a spiral. Check for symmetry:
Polar axis: Replace θ by $-\theta$. $r = 3^{-\theta}$. The test fails.
The line $\theta = \frac{\pi}{2}$: Replace θ by $\pi - \theta$. $r = 3^{\pi-\theta}$. The test fails.
The pole: Replace r by $-r$. $-r = 3^{\theta}$. The test fails.

θ	$-\pi$	$-\frac{\pi}{2}$	$-\frac{\pi}{4}$	0	$\frac{\pi}{4}$	$\frac{\pi}{2}$	π	$\frac{3\pi}{2}$	2π
$r = 3^{\theta}$	0.03	0.2	0.4	1	2.4	5.6	31.5	177.2	995

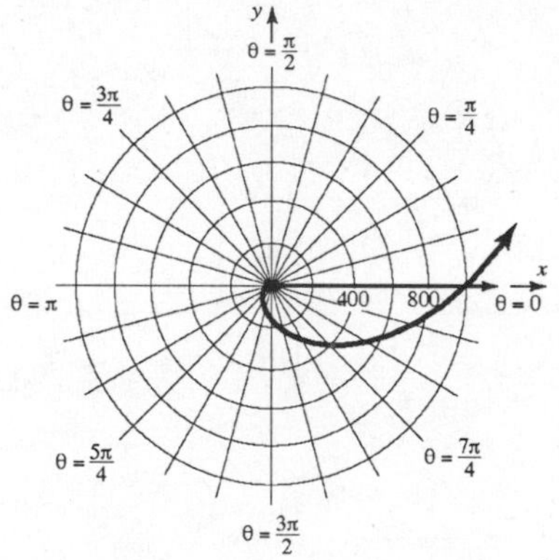

45. $r = 1 - \cos\theta$ The graph will be a cardioid. Check for symmetry:
Polar axis: Replace θ by $-\theta$. The result is $r = 1 - \cos(-\theta) = 1 - \cos\theta$.
The graph is symmetric with respect to the polar axis.
The line $\theta = \frac{\pi}{2}$: Replace θ by $\pi - \theta$.

$$r = 1 - \cos(\pi - \theta) = 1 - (\cos(\pi)\cos\theta + \sin(\pi)\sin\theta)$$
$$= 1 - (-\cos\theta + 0) = 1 + \cos\theta. \quad \text{The test fails}$$

The pole: Replace r by $-r$. $-r = 1 - \cos\theta$. The test fails.
Due to symmetry to the polar axis, assign values to θ from 0 to π.

θ	0	$\frac{\pi}{6}$	$\frac{\pi}{3}$	$\frac{\pi}{2}$	$\frac{2\pi}{3}$	$\frac{5\pi}{6}$	π
$r = 1 - \cos\theta$	0	$1 - \frac{\sqrt{3}}{2} \approx 0.1$	$\frac{1}{2}$	1	$\frac{3}{2}$	$1 + \frac{\sqrt{3}}{2} \approx 1.9$	2

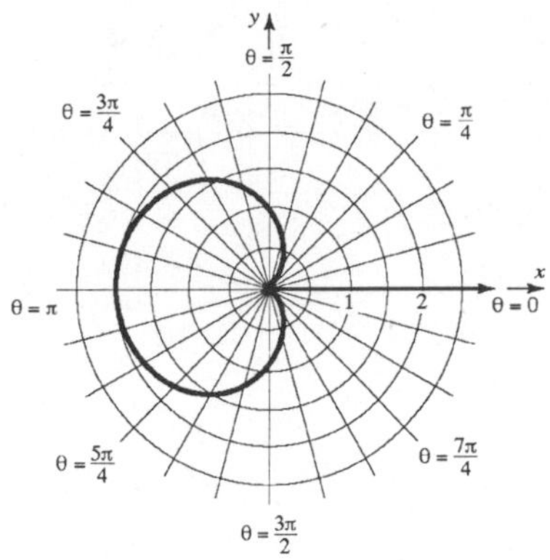

46. $r = 3 + \cos\theta$ The graph will be a limacon without an inner loop.
Check for symmetry:
Polar axis: Replace θ by $-\theta$. The result is $r = 3 + \cos(-\theta) = 3 + \cos\theta$.
The graph is symmetric with respect to the polar axis.
The line $\theta = \frac{\pi}{2}$: Replace θ by $\pi - \theta$.

$$r = 3 + \cos(\pi - \theta) = 3 + (\cos(\pi)\cos\theta + \sin(\pi)\sin\theta)$$
$$= 3 + (-\cos\theta + 0) = 3 - \cos\theta$$

The test fails.
The pole: Replace r by $-r$. $-r = 3 + \cos\theta$. The test fails.

Due to symmetry to the polar axis, assign values to θ from 0 to π.

θ	0	$\frac{\pi}{6}$	$\frac{\pi}{3}$	$\frac{\pi}{2}$	$\frac{2\pi}{3}$	$\frac{5\pi}{6}$	π
$r = 3 + \cos\theta$	4	$3 + \frac{\sqrt{3}}{2} \approx 3.9$	$\frac{7}{2}$	3	$\frac{5}{2}$	$3 - \frac{\sqrt{3}}{2} \approx 2.1$	2

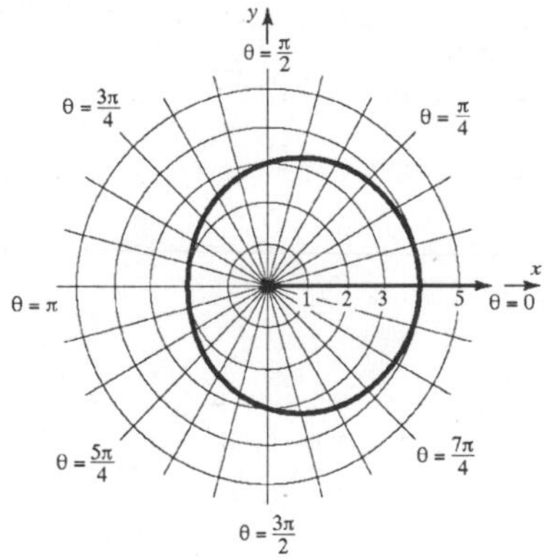

47. $r = 1 - 3\cos\theta$ The graph will be a limacon with an inner loop.
Check for symmetry:
Polar axis: Replace θ by $-\theta$. The result is $r = 1 - 3\cos(-\theta) = 1 - 3\cos\theta$.
The graph is symmetric with respect to the polar axis.
The line $\theta = \frac{\pi}{2}$: Replace θ by $\pi - \theta$.

$$r = 1 - 3\cos(\pi - \theta) = 1 - 3(\cos(\pi)\cos\theta + \sin(\pi)\sin\theta)$$
$$= 1 - 3(-\cos\theta + 0) = 1 + 3\cos\theta$$

The test fails.

The pole: Replace r by $-r$. $-r = 1 - 3\cos\theta$. The test fails.

Due to symmetry to the polar axis, assign values to θ from 0 to π.

θ	0	$\frac{\pi}{6}$	$\frac{\pi}{3}$	$\frac{\pi}{2}$	$\frac{2\pi}{3}$	$\frac{5\pi}{6}$	π
$r = 1 - 3\cos\theta$	-2	$1 - \frac{3\sqrt{3}}{2} \approx -1.6$	$-\frac{1}{2}$	1	$\frac{5}{2}$	$1 + \frac{3\sqrt{3}}{2} \approx 3.6$	4

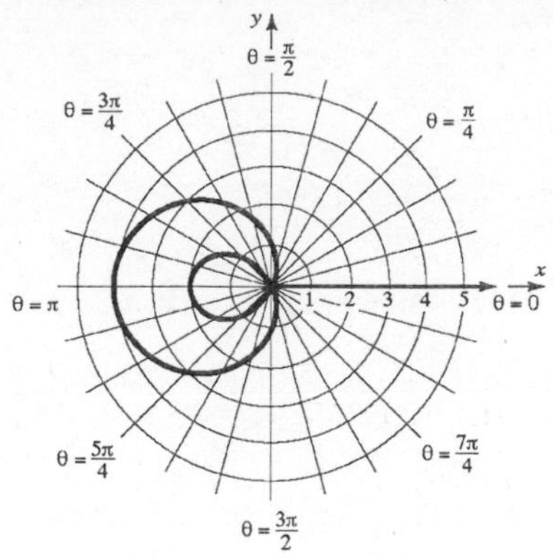

48. $r = 4\cos(3\theta)$ The graph will be a rose with three petals. Check for symmetry:

Polar axis: Replace θ by $-\theta$. $r = 4\cos(3(-\theta)) = 4\cos(-3\theta) = 4\cos(3\theta)$.

The graph is symmetric with respect to the polar axis.

The line $\theta = \frac{\pi}{2}$: Replace θ by $\pi - \theta$.

$$r = 4\cos(3(\pi - \theta)) = 4\cos(3\pi - 3\theta)$$
$$= 4(\cos(3\pi)\cos 3\theta + \sin(3\pi)\sin 3\theta) = 4(-\cos 3\theta + 0) = -4\cos(3\theta)$$

The test fails.

The pole: Replace r by $-r$. $-r = 4\cos(3\theta)$. The test fails.

Due to symmetry to the polar axis, assign values to θ from 0 to π.

θ	0	$\frac{\pi}{6}$	$\frac{\pi}{3}$	$\frac{\pi}{2}$	$\frac{2\pi}{3}$	$\frac{5\pi}{6}$	π
$r = 4\cos 3\theta$	4	0	-4	0	4	0	-4

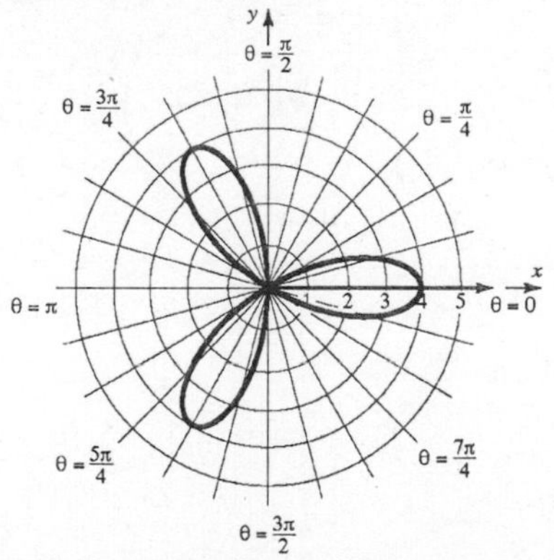

49. $r = \dfrac{2}{1 - \cos\theta}$ Check for symmetry:

Polar axis: Replace θ by $-\theta$. The result is $r = \dfrac{2}{1 - \cos(-\theta)} = \dfrac{2}{1 - \cos\theta}$.

The graph is symmetric with respect to the polar axis.

The line $\theta = \frac{\pi}{2}$: Replace θ by $\pi - \theta$.

$$r = \frac{2}{1-\cos(\pi-\theta)} = \frac{2}{1-(\cos(\pi)\cos\theta + \sin(\pi)\sin\theta)}$$

$$= \frac{2}{1-(-\cos\theta+0)} = \frac{2}{1+\cos\theta}$$

The test fails.

The pole: Replace r by $-r$. $-r = \frac{2}{1-\cos\theta}$. The test fails.

Due to symmetry to the polar axis, assign values to θ from 0 to π.

θ	0	$\frac{\pi}{6}$	$\frac{\pi}{3}$	$\frac{\pi}{2}$	$\frac{2\pi}{3}$	$\frac{5\pi}{6}$	π
$r = \frac{2}{1-\cos\theta}$	undefined	$\frac{2}{\left(1-\frac{\sqrt{3}}{2}\right)} \approx 14.9$	4	2	$\frac{4}{3}$	$\frac{2}{\left(1+\frac{\sqrt{3}}{2}\right)} \approx 1.1$	1

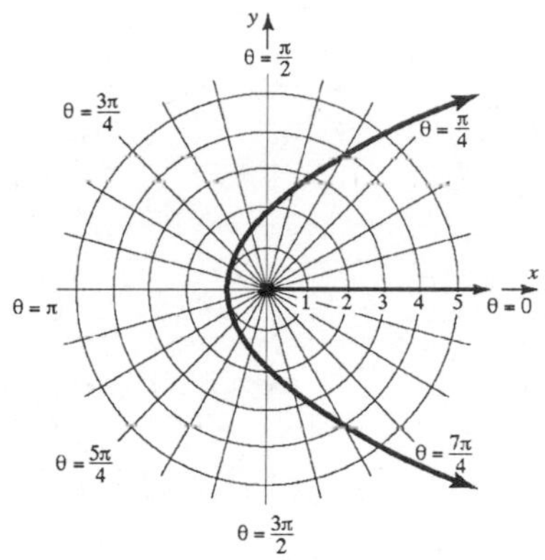

50. $r = \frac{2}{1-2\cos\theta}$ Check for symmetry:

Polar axis: Replace θ by $-\theta$. The result is $r = \frac{2}{1-2\cos(-\theta)} = \frac{2}{1-2\cos\theta}$.

The graph is symmetric with respect to the polar axis.

The line $\theta = \frac{\pi}{2}$: Replace θ by $\pi - \theta$.

$$r = \frac{2}{1-2\cos(\pi-\theta)} = \frac{2}{1-2(\cos(\pi)\cos\theta + \sin(\pi)\sin\theta)}$$

$$= \frac{2}{1-2(-\cos\theta+0)} = \frac{2}{1+2\cos\theta}$$

The test fails.

The pole: Replace r by $-r$. $-r = \frac{2}{1-2\cos\theta}$. The test fails.

Due to symmetry to the polar axis, assign values to θ from 0 to π.

θ	0	$\frac{\pi}{6}$	$\frac{\pi}{3}$	$\frac{\pi}{2}$	$\frac{2\pi}{3}$	$\frac{5\pi}{6}$	π
$r = \frac{2}{1-2\cos\theta}$	-2	$\frac{2}{1-\sqrt{3}} \approx -2.7$	undefined	2	1	$\frac{2}{1+\sqrt{3}} \approx 0.7$	$\frac{2}{3}$

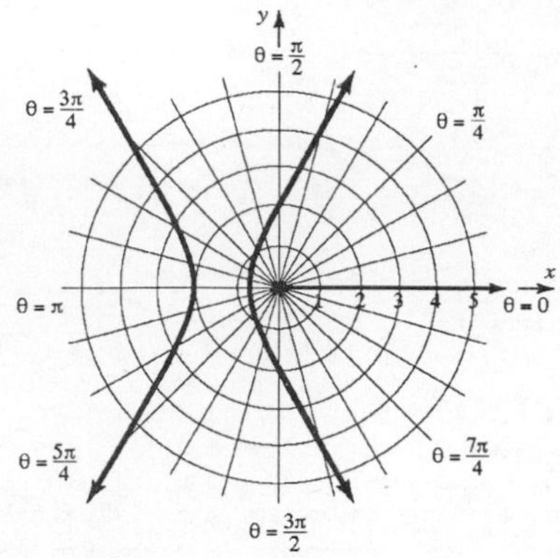

51. $r = \dfrac{1}{3-2\cos\theta}$ Check for symmetry:

Polar axis: Replace θ by $-\theta$. The result is $r = \dfrac{1}{3-2\cos(-\theta)} = \dfrac{1}{3-2\cos\theta}$.

The graph is symmetric with respect to the polar axis.

The line $\theta = \dfrac{\pi}{2}$: Replace θ by $\pi - \theta$.

$$r = \frac{1}{3-2\cos(\pi-\theta)} = \frac{1}{3-2(\cos(\pi)\cos\theta + \sin(\pi)\sin\theta)}$$

$$= \frac{1}{3-2(-\cos\theta+0)} = \frac{1}{3+2\cos\theta}$$

The test fails.

The pole: Replace r by $-r$. $-r = \dfrac{1}{3-2\cos\theta}$. The test fails.

Due to symmetry to the polar axis, assign values to θ from 0 to π.

θ	0	$\frac{\pi}{6}$	$\frac{\pi}{3}$	$\frac{\pi}{2}$	$\frac{2\pi}{3}$	$\frac{5\pi}{6}$	π
$r = \frac{1}{3-2\cos\theta}$	1	$\frac{1}{3-\sqrt{3}} \approx 0.8$	$\frac{1}{2}$	$\frac{1}{3}$	$\frac{1}{4}$	$\frac{1}{3+\sqrt{3}} \approx 0.2$	$\frac{1}{5}$

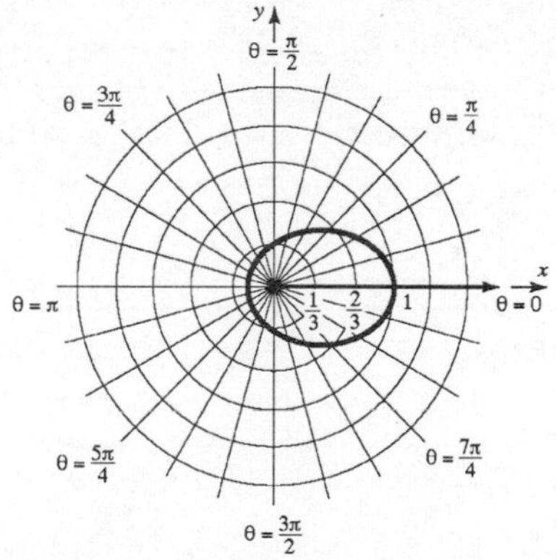

52. $r = \dfrac{1}{1-\cos\theta}$ Check for symmetry:

Polar axis: Replace θ by $-\theta$. The result is $r = \dfrac{1}{1-\cos(-\theta)} = \dfrac{1}{1-\cos\theta}$.

The graph is symmetric with respect to the polar axis.

The line $\theta = \dfrac{\pi}{2}$: Replace θ by $\pi - \theta$.

$$r = \frac{1}{1-\cos(\pi-\theta)} = \frac{1}{1-(\cos(\pi)\cos\theta+\sin(\pi)\sin\theta)}$$

$$= \frac{1}{1-(-\cos\theta+0)} = \frac{1}{1+\cos\theta}$$

The test fails.

The pole: Replace r by $-r$. $-r = \frac{1}{1-\cos\theta}$. The test fails.

Due to symmetry to the polar axis, assign values to θ from 0 to π.

θ	0	$\frac{\pi}{6}$	$\frac{\pi}{3}$	$\frac{\pi}{2}$	$\frac{2\pi}{3}$	$\frac{5\pi}{6}$	π
$r = \frac{2}{1-\cos\theta}$	undefined	$\frac{2}{\left(1-\frac{\sqrt{3}}{2}\right)} \approx 14.9$	4	2	$\frac{4}{3}$	$\frac{2}{\left(1+\frac{\sqrt{3}}{2}\right)} \approx 1.1$	1

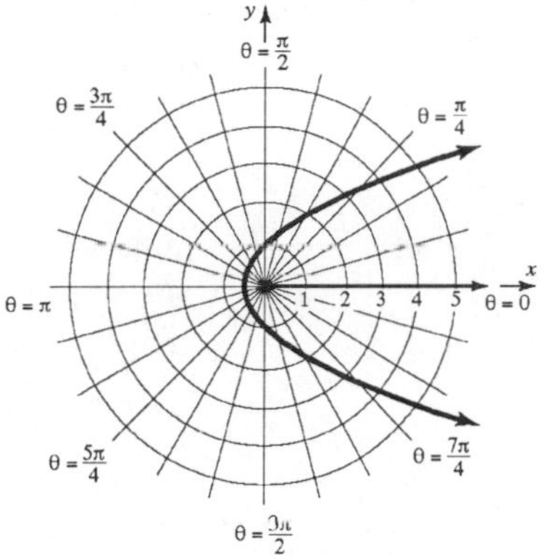

53. $r = \theta, \ \theta \geq 0$ Check for symmetry:

Polar axis: Replace θ by $-\theta$. $r = -\theta$. The test fails.

The line $\theta = \frac{\pi}{2}$: Replace θ by $\pi - \theta$. $r = \pi - \theta$. The test fails.

The pole: Replace r by $-r$. $-r = \theta$. The test fails.

θ	0	$\frac{\pi}{6}$	$\frac{\pi}{3}$	$\frac{\pi}{2}$	π	$\frac{3\pi}{2}$	2π
$r = \theta$	0	$\frac{\pi}{6} \approx 0.5$	$\frac{\pi}{3} \approx 1.0$	$\frac{\pi}{2} \approx 1.6$	$\pi \approx 3.1$	$\frac{3\pi}{2} \approx 4.7$	$2\pi \approx 6.3$

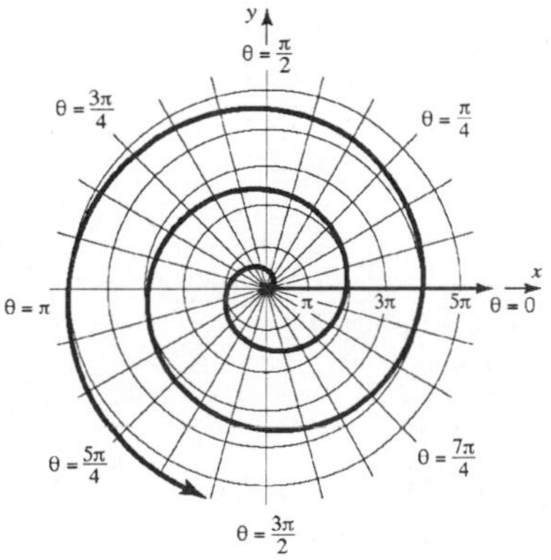

54. $r = \frac{3}{\theta}$ Check for symmetry:

Polar axis: Replace θ by $-\theta$. $r = \frac{3}{-\theta}$. The test fails.

The line $\theta = \frac{\pi}{2}$: Replace θ by $\pi - \theta$. $r = \frac{3}{\pi - \theta}$. The test fails.

The pole: Replace r by $-r$. $-r = \frac{3}{\theta}$. The test fails.

θ	0	$\frac{\pi}{6}$	$\frac{\pi}{3}$	$\frac{\pi}{2}$	π	$\frac{3\pi}{2}$	2π
$r = \frac{3}{\theta}$	undefined	$\frac{18}{\pi} \approx 5.7$	$\frac{9}{\pi} \approx 2.9$	$\frac{6}{\pi} \approx 1.9$	$\frac{3}{\pi} \approx 1.0$	$\frac{2}{\pi} \approx 0.6$	$\frac{3}{2\pi} \approx 0.5$

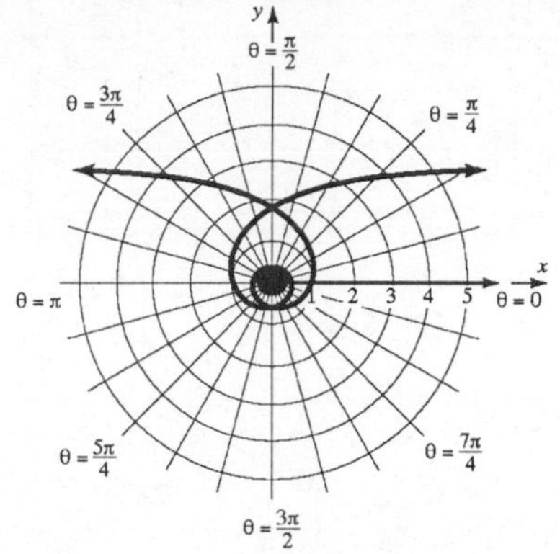

55. $r = \csc\theta - 2 = \frac{1}{\sin\theta} - 2, \quad 0 < \theta < \pi$ Check for symmetry:

Polar axis: Replace θ by $-\theta$. $r = \csc(-\theta) - 2 = -\csc\theta - 2$.
The test fails.

The line $\theta = \frac{\pi}{2}$: Replace θ by $\pi - \theta$.

$$r = \csc(\pi - \theta) - 2 = \frac{1}{\sin(\pi - \theta)} - 2$$

$$= \frac{1}{\sin(\pi)\cos\theta - \cos(\pi)\sin\theta} - 2 = \frac{1}{\sin\theta} - 2 = \csc\theta - 2$$

The graph is symmetric with respect to the line $\theta = \frac{\pi}{2}$.

The pole: Replace r by $-r$. $-r = \csc\theta - 2$. The test fails.

Due to symmetry, assign values to θ from 0 to $\frac{\pi}{2}$.

θ	0	$\frac{\pi}{6}$	$\frac{\pi}{4}$	$\frac{\pi}{3}$	$\frac{\pi}{2}$
$r = \csc\theta - 2$	not defined	0	$\sqrt{2} - 2 \approx -0.6$	$\frac{2\sqrt{3}}{3} - 2 \approx -0.8$	-1

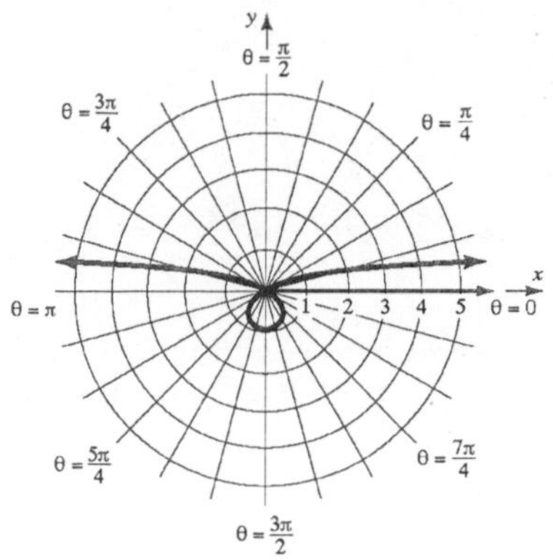

56. $r = \sin\theta\tan\theta$ Check for symmetry:

Polar axis: Replace θ by $-\theta$.

$$r = \sin(-\theta)\tan(-\theta) = (-\sin\theta)(-\tan\theta) = \sin\theta\tan\theta.$$

The graph is symmetric with respect to the polar axis.

The line $\theta = \frac{\pi}{2}$: Replace θ by $\pi - \theta$.

$$r = \sin(\pi-\theta)\tan(\pi-\theta) = (\sin(\pi)\cos\theta - \cos(\pi)\sin\theta)\left(\frac{\tan(\pi)-\tan\theta}{1+\tan(\pi)\tan\theta}\right)$$

$$= \sin\theta \cdot \frac{-\tan\theta}{1} = -\sin\theta\tan\theta$$

The test fails.

The pole: Replace r by $-r$. $-r = \sin\theta\tan\theta$. The test fails.

Due to symmetry to the polar axis, assign values to θ from 0 to π.

θ	0	$\frac{\pi}{6}$	$\frac{\pi}{3}$	$\frac{\pi}{2}$	$\frac{2\pi}{3}$	$\frac{5\pi}{6}$	π
$r = \sin\theta\tan\theta$	0	$\frac{1}{2}\cdot\frac{\sqrt{3}}{3} \approx 0.3$	$\frac{3}{2}$	undefined	$-\frac{3}{2}$	$\frac{1}{2}\cdot\left(-\frac{\sqrt{3}}{3}\right) \approx -0.3$	0

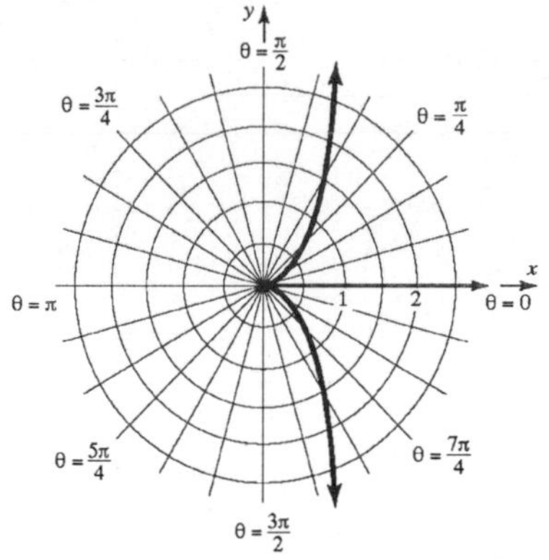

57. $r = \tan\theta,\ -\frac{\pi}{2} < \theta < \frac{\pi}{2}$ Check for symmetry:

Polar axis: Replace θ by $-\theta$. $r = \tan(-\theta) = -\tan\theta$. The test fails.

The line $\theta = \frac{\pi}{2}$: Replace θ by $\pi - \theta$.

$$r=\tan(\pi-\theta)=\frac{\tan(\pi)-\tan\theta}{1+\tan(\pi)\tan\theta}=\frac{-\tan\theta}{1}=-\tan\theta$$

The test fails.

The pole: Replace r by $-r$. $-r=\tan\theta$. The test fails.

θ	$-\frac{\pi}{3}$	$-\frac{\pi}{4}$	$-\frac{\pi}{6}$	0	$\frac{\pi}{6}$	$\frac{\pi}{4}$	$\frac{\pi}{3}$
$r=\tan\theta$	$-\sqrt{3}\approx-1.7$	-1	$-\frac{\sqrt{3}}{3}\approx-0.6$	0	$\frac{\sqrt{3}}{3}\approx 0.6$	1	$\sqrt{3}\approx 1.7$

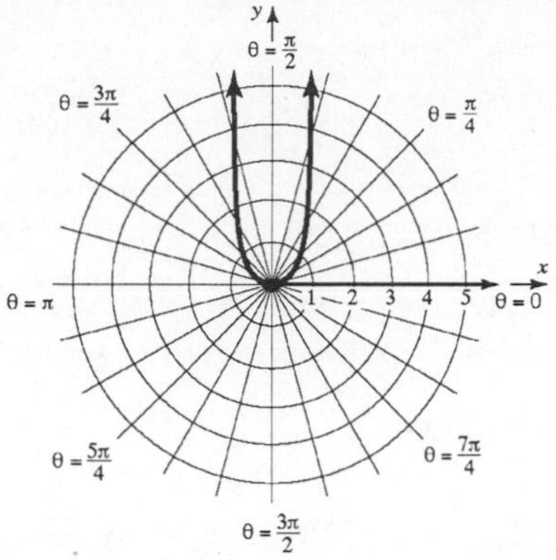

58. $r=\cos\left(\frac{\theta}{2}\right)$ Check for symmetry:

Polar axis: Replace θ by $-\theta$. $r=\cos\left(-\frac{\theta}{2}\right)=\cos\frac{\theta}{2}$.

The graph is symmetric to the polar axis.

The line $\theta=\frac{\pi}{2}$: Replace θ by $\pi-\theta$.

$$r=\cos\left(\frac{\pi-\theta}{2}\right)=\cos\left(\frac{\pi}{2}-\frac{\theta}{2}\right)=\cos\left(\frac{\pi}{2}\right)\cos\left(\frac{\theta}{2}\right)+\sin\left(\frac{\pi}{2}\right)\sin\left(\frac{\theta}{2}\right)=\sin\left(\frac{\theta}{2}\right)$$

The test fails.

The pole: Replace r by $-r$. $-r=\cos\frac{\theta}{2}$. The test fails.

Due to symmetry to the polar axis, assign values to θ from 0 to π.

θ	0	$\frac{\pi}{6}$	$\frac{\pi}{3}$	$\frac{\pi}{2}$	$\frac{2\pi}{3}$	$\frac{5\pi}{6}$	π
$r=\cos\left(\frac{\theta}{2}\right)$	1	0.97	$\frac{\sqrt{3}}{2}$	$\frac{\sqrt{2}}{2}$	$\frac{1}{2}$	0.26	0

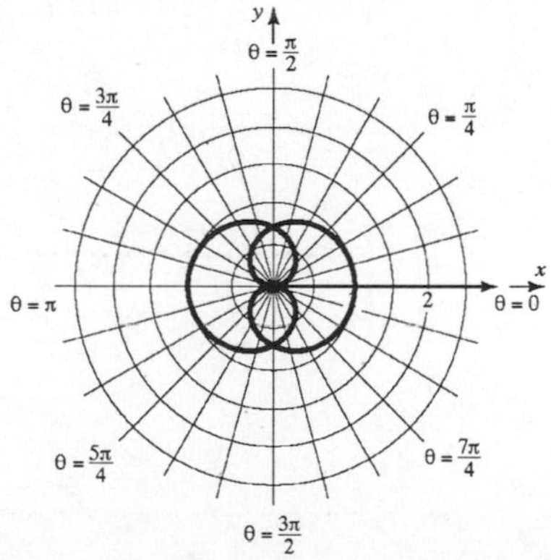

59. Convert the equation to rectangular form:

$r\sin\theta=a\rightarrow y=a$

The graph of $r\sin\theta=a$ is a horizontal line a units above the pole if $a>0$, and $|a|$ units below the pole, if $a<0$.

60. Convert the equation to rectangular form:

$$r\cos\theta = a \rightarrow x = a$$

The graph of $r\cos\theta = a$ is a vertical line a units to the right of the pole if $a > 0$, and $|a|$ units to the left of the pole, if $a < 0$.

61. Convert the equation to rectangular form:

$$r = 2a\sin\theta, a > 0$$

$$r^2 = 2ar\sin\theta$$

$$x^2 + y^2 = 2ay \rightarrow x^2 + y^2 - 2ay = 0 \rightarrow x^2 + (y-a)^2 = a^2$$

Circle: radius a, center at rectangular coordinates $(0, a)$.

62. Convert the equation to rectangular form:

$$r = -2a\sin\theta, a > 0$$

$$r^2 = -2ar\sin\theta$$

$$x^2 + y^2 = -2ay \rightarrow x^2 + y^2 + 2ay = 0 \rightarrow x^2 + (y+a)^2 = a^2$$

Circle: radius a, center at rectangular coordinates $(0, -a)$.

63. Convert the equation to rectangular form:

$$r = 2a\cos\theta, a > 0$$

$$r^2 = 2ar\cos\theta$$

$$x^2 + y^2 = 2ax \rightarrow x^2 - 2ax + y^2 = 0 \rightarrow (x-a)^2 + y^2 = a^2$$

Circle: radius a, center at rectangular coordinates $(a, 0)$.

64. Convert the equation to rectangular form:

$$r = -2a\cos\theta, a > 0$$

$$r^2 = -2ar\cos\theta$$

$$x^2 + y^2 = -2ax \rightarrow x^2 + 2ax + y^2 = 0 \rightarrow (x+a)^2 + y^2 = a^2$$

Circle: radius a, center at rectangular coordinates $(-a, 0)$.

65. (a) $r^2 = \cos\theta$: $r^2 = \cos(\pi - \theta) \rightarrow r^2 = -\cos\theta$ Test fails.
$(-r)^2 = \cos(-\theta) \rightarrow r^2 = \cos\theta$ New test works.

(b) $r^2 = \sin\theta$: $r^2 = \sin(\pi - \theta) \rightarrow r^2 = \sin\theta$ Test works.
$(-r)^2 = \sin(-\theta) \rightarrow r^2 = -\sin\theta$ New test fails.

66. Symmetry with respect to the pole: In a polar equation, replace θ by $\pi + \theta$. If an equivalent equation results, the graph is symmetric with respect to the pole.

(a) $r^2 = \sin\theta$: $r^2 = \sin(\pi + \theta) \rightarrow r^2 = -\sin\theta$ New test fails.
$(-r)^2 = \sin\theta \rightarrow r^2 = \sin\theta$ Test works.

(b) $r = \cos^2\theta$: $-r = \cos^2\theta$ Test fails.
$r = \cos^2(\pi + \theta) = (-\cos\theta)^2 = \cos^2\theta$ New test works.

Chapter 10

Polar Coordinates; Vectors

10.3 The Complex Plane; De Moivre's Theorem

1. $r = \sqrt{x^2 + y^2} = \sqrt{1^2 + 1^2} = \sqrt{2}$

   $\tan\theta = \dfrac{y}{x} = 1 \quad \rightarrow \quad \theta = 45°$

   The polar form of $z = 1 + i$ is

   $z = r(\cos\theta + i\sin\theta)$

   $= \sqrt{2}(\cos(45°) + i\sin(45°))$

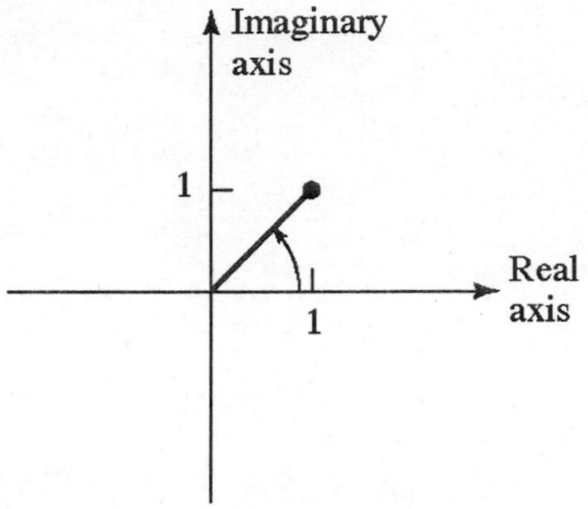

2. $r = \sqrt{x^2 + y^2} = \sqrt{(-1)^2 + 1^2} = \sqrt{2}$

   $\tan\theta = \dfrac{y}{x} = -1 \quad \rightarrow \quad \theta = 135°$

   The polar form of $z = -1 + i$ is

   $z = r(\cos\theta + i\sin\theta)$

   $= \sqrt{2}(\cos(135°) + i\sin(135°))$

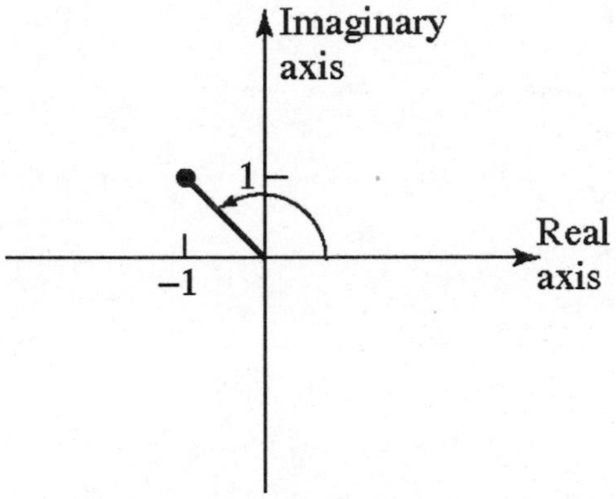

3. $r = \sqrt{x^2 + y^2} = \sqrt{(\sqrt{3})^2 + (-1)^2} = \sqrt{4} = 2$

   $\tan\theta = \dfrac{y}{x} = \dfrac{-1}{\sqrt{3}} = -\dfrac{\sqrt{3}}{3} \quad \rightarrow \quad \theta = 330°$

   The polar form of $z = \sqrt{3} - i$ is

   $z = r(\cos\theta + i\sin\theta)$

   $= 2(\cos(330°) + i\sin(330°))$

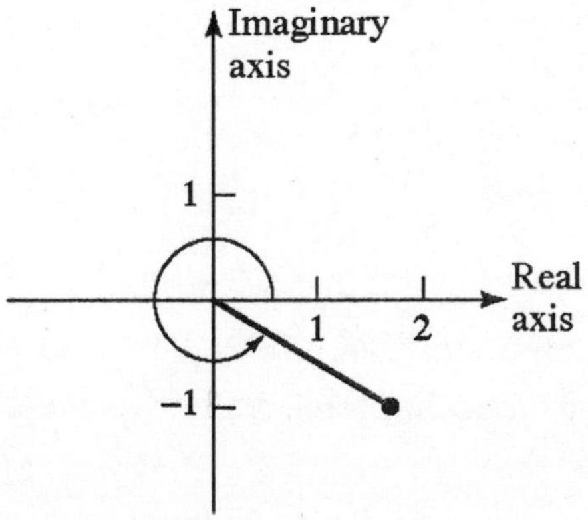

4. $r=\sqrt{x^2+y^2}=\sqrt{1^2+\left(-\sqrt{3}\right)^2}=\sqrt{4}=2$

$\tan\theta=\frac{y}{x}=\frac{-\sqrt{3}}{1}=-\sqrt{3} \quad\rightarrow\quad \theta=300°$

The polar form of $z=1-\sqrt{3}i$ is

$z=r(\cos\theta+i\sin\theta)$

$=2(\cos(300°)+i\sin(300°))$

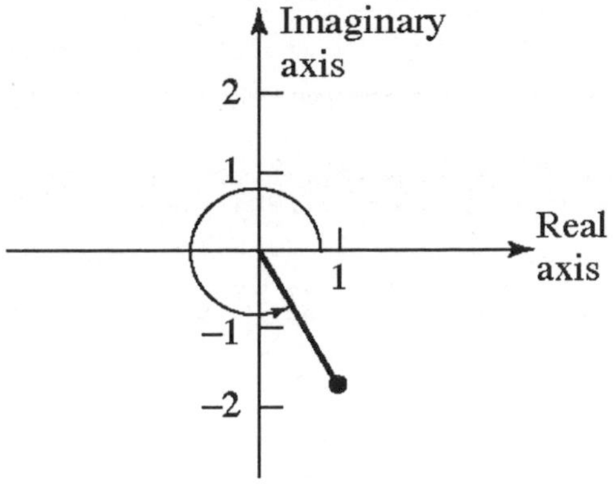

5. $r=\sqrt{x^2+y^2}=\sqrt{0^2+(-3)^2}=\sqrt{9}=3$

$\tan\theta=\frac{y}{x}=\frac{-3}{0}=\text{undefined}\rightarrow\theta=270°$

The polar form of $z=-3i$ is

$z=r(\cos\theta+i\sin\theta)$

$=3(\cos(270°)+i\sin(270°))$

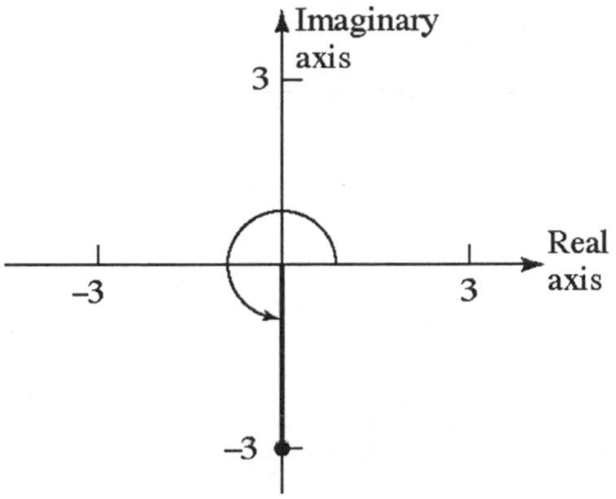

6. $r=\sqrt{x^2+y^2}=\sqrt{(-2)^2+0^2}=\sqrt{4}=2$

$\tan\theta=\frac{y}{x}=\frac{0}{-2}=0 \quad\rightarrow\quad \theta=180°$

The polar form of $z=-2$ is

$z=r(\cos\theta+i\sin\theta)$

$=2(\cos(180°)+i\sin(180°))$

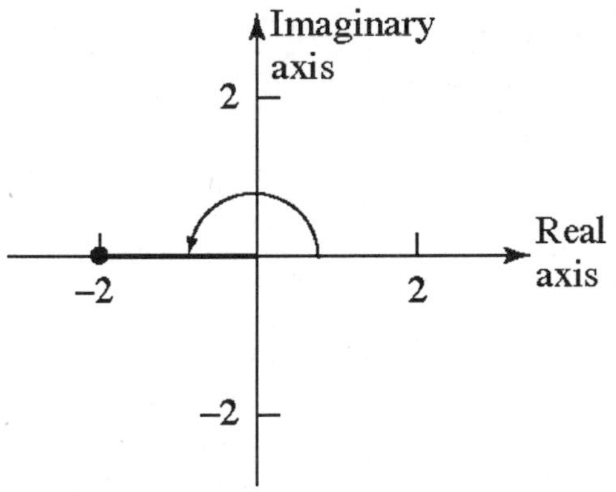

7. $r=\sqrt{x^2+y^2}=\sqrt{4^2+(-4)^2}=\sqrt{32}=4\sqrt{2}$

$\tan\theta=\frac{y}{x}=\frac{-4}{4}=-1 \quad\rightarrow\quad \theta=315°$

The polar form of $z=4-4i$ is

$z=r(\cos\theta+i\sin\theta)$

$=4\sqrt{2}(\cos(315°)+i\sin(315°))$

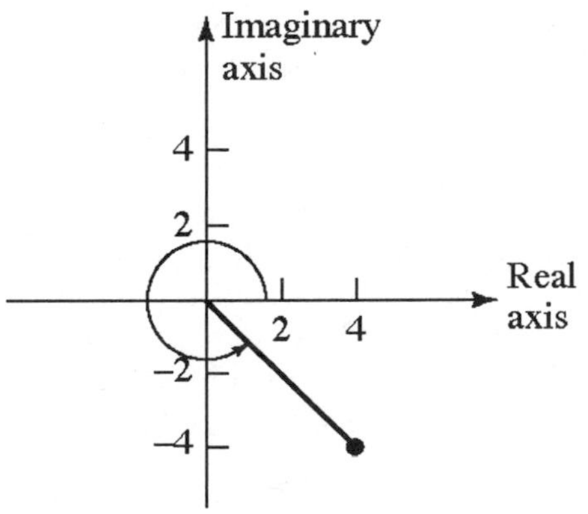

8. $r=\sqrt{x^2+y^2}=\sqrt{\left(9\sqrt{3}\right)^2+9^2}=\sqrt{324}=18$

$\tan\theta=\frac{y}{x}=\frac{9}{9\sqrt{3}}=\frac{\sqrt{3}}{3} \rightarrow \theta=30^\circ$

The polar form of $z=9\sqrt{3}+9i$ is

$z=r(\cos\theta+i\sin\theta)$

$=18(\cos(30^\circ)+i\sin(30^\circ))$

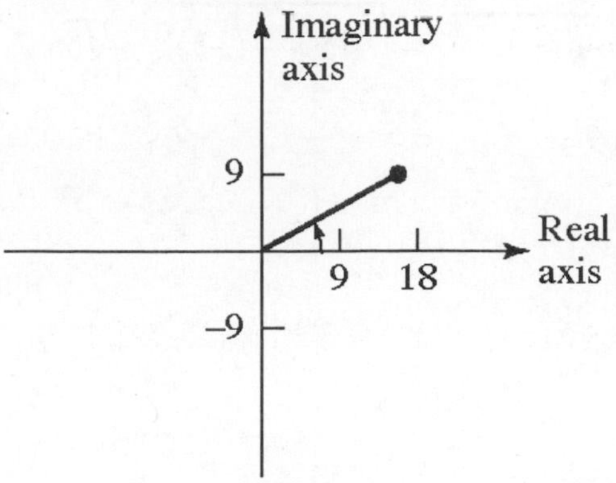

9. $r=\sqrt{x^2+y^2}=\sqrt{3^2+(-4)^2}=\sqrt{25}=5$

$\tan\theta=\frac{y}{x}=\frac{-4}{3} \rightarrow \theta\approx 306.9^\circ$

The polar form of $z=3-4i$ is

$z=r(\cos\theta+i\sin\theta)$

$=5(\cos(306.9^\circ)+i\sin(306.9^\circ))$

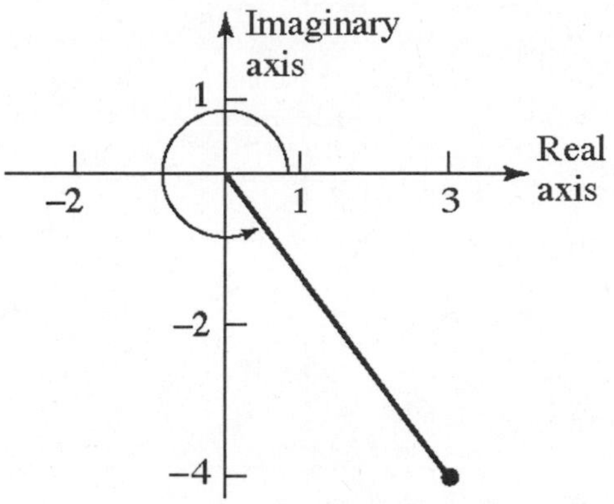

10. $r=\sqrt{x^2+y^2}=\sqrt{2^2+\left(\sqrt{3}\right)^2}=\sqrt{7}$

$\tan\theta=\frac{y}{x}=\frac{\sqrt{3}}{2} \rightarrow \theta\approx 40.9^\circ$

The polar form of $z=2+\sqrt{3}i$ is

$z=r(\cos\theta+i\sin\theta)$

$=\sqrt{7}(\cos(40.9^\circ)+i\sin(40.9^\circ))$

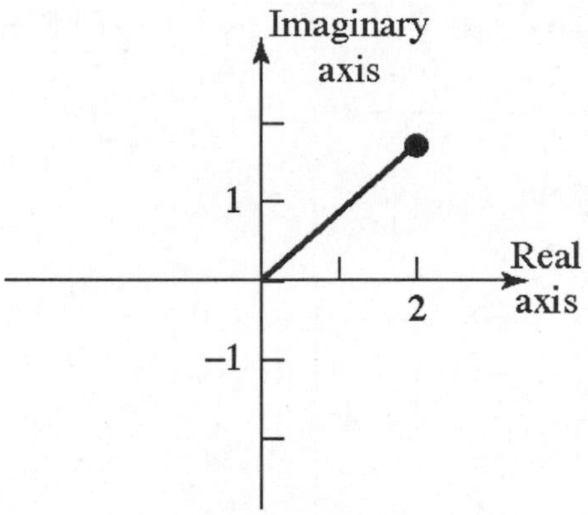

11. $r=\sqrt{x^2+y^2}=\sqrt{(-2)^2+3^2}=\sqrt{13}$

$\tan\theta=\frac{y}{x}=\frac{3}{-2}=-\frac{3}{2} \rightarrow \theta\approx 123.7^\circ$

The polar form of $z=-2+3i$ is

$z=r(\cos\theta+i\sin\theta)$

$=\sqrt{13}(\cos(123.7^\circ)+i\sin(123.7^\circ))$

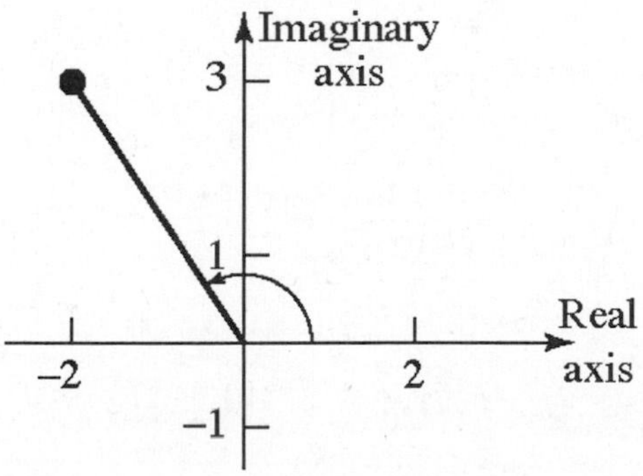

12. $r=\sqrt{x^2+y^2}=\sqrt{\left(\sqrt{5}\right)^2+(-1)^2}=\sqrt{6}$

$\tan\theta=\frac{y}{x}=\frac{-1}{\sqrt{5}}=-\frac{\sqrt{5}}{5} \quad \rightarrow \quad \theta\approx 335.9^\circ$

The polar form of $z=\sqrt{5}-i$ is

$z=r(\cos\theta+i\sin\theta)$

$=\sqrt{6}\left(\cos(335.9^\circ)+i\sin(335.9^\circ)\right)$

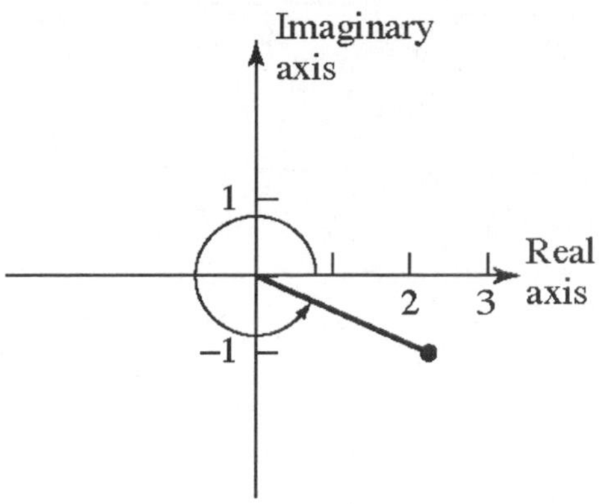

13. $2\left(\cos(120^\circ)+i\sin(120^\circ)\right)=2\left(-\frac{1}{2}+\frac{\sqrt{3}}{2}i\right)=-1+\sqrt{3}\,i$

14. $3\left(\cos(210^\circ)+i\sin(210^\circ)\right)=3\left(-\frac{\sqrt{3}}{2}-\frac{1}{2}i\right)=-\frac{3\sqrt{3}}{2}-\frac{3}{2}i$

15. $4\left(\cos\left(\frac{7\pi}{4}\right)+i\sin\left(\frac{7\pi}{4}\right)\right)=4\left(\frac{\sqrt{2}}{2}-\frac{\sqrt{2}}{2}i\right)=2\sqrt{2}-2\sqrt{2}\,i$

16. $2\left(\cos\left(\frac{5\pi}{6}\right)+i\sin\left(\frac{5\pi}{6}\right)\right)=2\left(-\frac{\sqrt{3}}{2}+\frac{1}{2}i\right)=-\sqrt{3}+i$

17. $3\left(\cos\left(\frac{3\pi}{2}\right)+i\sin\left(\frac{3\pi}{2}\right)\right)=3(0-1i)=-3i$

18. $4\left(\cos\left(\frac{\pi}{2}\right)+i\sin\left(\frac{\pi}{2}\right)\right)=4(0+1i)=4i$

19. $0.2\left(\cos(100^\circ)+i\sin(100^\circ)\right)\approx 0.2(-0.1736+0.9848i)=-0.0347+0.1970\,i$

20. $0.4\left(\cos(200^\circ)+i\sin(200^\circ)\right)\approx 0.4(-0.9397-0.3420i)=-0.3759-0.1368\,i$

21. $2\left(\cos\left(\frac{\pi}{18}\right)+i\sin\left(\frac{\pi}{18}\right)\right)\approx 2(0.9848+0.1736i)=1.9696+0.3472i$

22. $3\left(\cos\left(\frac{\pi}{10}\right)+i\sin\left(\frac{\pi}{10}\right)\right)\approx 3(0.9511+0.3090i)=2.8533+0.9270i$

23. $z\cdot w=2\left(\cos(40^\circ)+i\sin(40^\circ)\right)\cdot 4\left(\cos(20^\circ)+i\sin(20^\circ)\right)$

$=2\cdot 4\left(\cos(40^\circ+20^\circ)+i\sin(40^\circ+20^\circ)\right)=8\left(\cos(60^\circ)+i\sin(60^\circ)\right)$

$$\frac{z}{w}=\frac{2(\cos(40^\circ)+i\sin(40^\circ))}{4(\cos(20^\circ)+i\sin(20^\circ))}=\frac{2}{4}(\cos(40^\circ-20^\circ)+i\sin(40^\circ-20^\circ))$$
$$=\frac{1}{2}(\cos(20^\circ)+i\sin(20^\circ))$$

24. $z\cdot w=(\cos(120^\circ)+i\sin(120^\circ))\cdot(\cos(100^\circ)+i\sin(100^\circ))$
$$=(\cos(120^\circ+100^\circ)+i\sin(120^\circ+100^\circ))=\cos(220^\circ)+i\sin(220^\circ)$$
$$\frac{z}{w}=\frac{(\cos(120^\circ)+i\sin(120^\circ))}{(\cos(100^\circ)+i\sin(100^\circ))}=(\cos(120^\circ-100^\circ)+i\sin(120^\circ-100^\circ))$$
$$=\cos(20^\circ)+i\sin(20^\circ)$$

25. $z\cdot w=3(\cos(130^\circ)+i\sin(130^\circ))\cdot 4(\cos(270^\circ)+i\sin(270^\circ))$
$$=3\cdot4(\cos(130^\circ+270^\circ)+i\sin(130^\circ+270^\circ))=12(\cos(400^\circ)+i\sin(400^\circ))$$
$$=12(\cos(400^\circ-360^\circ)+i\sin(400^\circ-360^\circ))=12(\cos(40^\circ)+i\sin(40^\circ))$$
$$\frac{z}{w}=\frac{3(\cos(130^\circ)+i\sin(130^\circ))}{4(\cos(270^\circ)+i\sin(270^\circ))}=\frac{3}{4}(\cos(130^\circ-270^\circ)+i\sin(130^\circ-270^\circ))$$
$$=\frac{3}{4}(\cos(-140^\circ)+i\sin(-140^\circ))=\frac{3}{4}(\cos(220^\circ)+i\sin(220^\circ))$$

26. $z\cdot w=2(\cos(80^\circ)+i\sin(80^\circ))\cdot 6(\cos(200^\circ)+i\sin(200^\circ))$
$$=2\cdot6(\cos(80^\circ+200^\circ)+i\sin(80^\circ+200^\circ))=12(\cos 280^\circ+i\sin 280^\circ)$$
$$\frac{z}{w}=\frac{2(\cos(80^\circ)+i\sin(80^\circ))}{6(\cos(200^\circ)+i\sin(200^\circ))}=\frac{2}{6}(\cos(80^\circ-200^\circ)+i\sin(80^\circ-200^\circ))$$
$$=\frac{1}{3}(\cos(-120^\circ)+i\sin(-120^\circ))=\frac{1}{3}(\cos(240^\circ)+i\sin(240^\circ))$$

27. $z\cdot w=2\left(\cos\left(\frac{\pi}{8}\right)+i\sin\left(\frac{\pi}{8}\right)\right)\cdot 2\left(\cos\left(\frac{\pi}{10}\right)+i\sin\left(\frac{\pi}{10}\right)\right)=2\cdot2\left(\cos\left(\frac{\pi}{8}+\frac{\pi}{10}\right)+i\sin\left(\frac{\pi}{8}+\frac{\pi}{10}\right)\right)$
$$=4\left(\cos\left(\frac{9\pi}{40}\right)+i\sin\left(\frac{9\pi}{40}\right)\right)$$
$$\frac{z}{w}=\frac{2\left(\cos\left(\frac{\pi}{8}\right)+i\sin\left(\frac{\pi}{8}\right)\right)}{2\left(\cos\left(\frac{\pi}{10}\right)+i\sin\left(\frac{\pi}{10}\right)\right)}=\frac{2}{2}\left(\cos\left(\frac{\pi}{8}-\frac{\pi}{10}\right)+i\sin\left(\frac{\pi}{8}-\frac{\pi}{10}\right)\right)=\cos\left(\frac{\pi}{40}\right)+i\sin\left(\frac{\pi}{40}\right)$$

28. $z\cdot w=4\left(\cos\left(\frac{3\pi}{8}\right)+i\sin\left(\frac{3\pi}{8}\right)\right)\cdot 2\left(\cos\left(\frac{9\pi}{16}\right)+i\sin\left(\frac{9\pi}{16}\right)\right)$
$$=4\cdot2\left(\cos\left(\frac{3\pi}{8}+\frac{9\pi}{16}\right)+i\sin\left(\frac{3\pi}{8}+\frac{9\pi}{16}\right)\right)=8\left(\cos\left(\frac{15\pi}{16}\right)+i\sin\left(\frac{15\pi}{16}\right)\right)$$

$$\frac{z}{w}=\frac{4\left(\cos\left(\frac{3\pi}{8}\right)+i\sin\left(\frac{3\pi}{8}\right)\right)}{2\left(\cos\left(\frac{9\pi}{16}\right)+i\sin\left(\frac{9\pi}{16}\right)\right)}=\frac{4}{2}\left(\cos\left(\frac{3\pi}{8}-\frac{9\pi}{16}\right)+i\sin\left(\frac{3\pi}{8}-\frac{9\pi}{16}\right)\right)$$

$$=2\left(\cos\left(-\frac{3\pi}{16}\right)+i\sin\left(-\frac{3\pi}{16}\right)\right)=2\left(\cos\left(\frac{29\pi}{16}\right)+i\sin\left(\frac{29\pi}{16}\right)\right)$$

29. $z=2+2i \quad r=\sqrt{2^2+2^2}=\sqrt{8}=2\sqrt{2} \quad \tan\theta=\frac{2}{2}=1 \quad \theta=45^\circ$

$z=2\sqrt{2}\left(\cos(45^\circ)+i\sin(45^\circ)\right)$

$w=\sqrt{3}-i \quad r=\sqrt{\left(\sqrt{3}\right)^2+(-1)^2}=\sqrt{4}=2 \quad \tan\theta=\frac{-1}{\sqrt{3}}=-\frac{\sqrt{3}}{3} \quad \theta=330^\circ$

$w=2\left(\cos(330^\circ)+i\sin(330^\circ)\right)$

$$z\cdot w=2\sqrt{2}\left(\cos(45^\circ)+i\sin(45^\circ)\right)\cdot 2\left(\cos(330^\circ)+i\sin(330^\circ)\right)$$
$$=2\sqrt{2}\cdot 2\left(\cos(45^\circ+330^\circ)+i\sin(45^\circ+330^\circ)\right)=4\sqrt{2}\left(\cos(375^\circ)+i\sin(375^\circ)\right)$$
$$=4\sqrt{2}\left(\cos(375^\circ-360^\circ)+i\sin(375^\circ-360^\circ)\right)=4\sqrt{2}\left(\cos(15^\circ)+i\sin(15^\circ)\right)$$
$$\frac{z}{w}=\frac{2\sqrt{2}\left(\cos(45^\circ)+i\sin(45^\circ)\right)}{2\left(\cos(330^\circ)+i\sin(330^\circ)\right)}=\frac{2\sqrt{2}}{2}\left(\cos(45^\circ-330^\circ)+i\sin(45^\circ-330^\circ)\right)$$
$$=\sqrt{2}\left(\cos(-285^\circ)+i\sin(-285^\circ)\right)=\sqrt{2}\left(\cos(75^\circ)+i\sin(75^\circ)\right)$$

30. $z=1-i \quad r=\sqrt{1^2+(-1)^2}=\sqrt{2} \quad \tan\theta=\frac{-1}{1}=-1 \quad \theta=315^\circ$

$z=\sqrt{2}\left(\cos(315^\circ)+i\sin(315^\circ)\right)$

$w=1-\sqrt{3}i \quad r=\sqrt{1^2+\left(-\sqrt{3}\right)^2}=\sqrt{4}=2 \quad \tan\theta=\frac{-\sqrt{3}}{1}=-\sqrt{3} \quad \theta=300^\circ$

$w=2\left(\cos(300^\circ)+i\sin(300^\circ)\right)$

$$z\cdot w=\sqrt{2}\left(\cos(315^\circ)+i\sin(315^\circ)\right)\cdot 2\left(\cos(300^\circ)+i\sin(300^\circ)\right)$$
$$=\sqrt{2}\cdot 2\left(\cos((315^\circ)+(300^\circ))+i\sin(315^\circ+300^\circ)\right)=2\sqrt{2}\left(\cos 615^\circ+i\sin 615^\circ\right)$$
$$=2\sqrt{2}\left(\cos(615^\circ-360^\circ)+i\sin(615^\circ-360^\circ)\right)=2\sqrt{2}\left(\cos(255^\circ)+i\sin(255^\circ)\right)$$
$$\frac{z}{w}=\frac{\sqrt{2}\left(\cos 315^\circ+i\sin 315^\circ\right)}{2\left(\cos 300^\circ+i\sin 300^\circ\right)}=\frac{\sqrt{2}}{2}\left(\cos(315^\circ-300^\circ)+i\sin(315^\circ-300^\circ)\right)$$
$$=\frac{\sqrt{2}}{2}\left(\cos(15^\circ)+i\sin(15^\circ)\right)$$

31. $\left[4\left(\cos(40^\circ)+i\sin(40^\circ)\right)\right]^3=4^3\left(\cos(3\cdot 40^\circ)+i\sin(3\cdot 40^\circ)\right)=64\left(\cos(120^\circ)+i\sin(120^\circ)\right)$

$$=64\left(-\frac{1}{2}+\frac{\sqrt{3}}{2}i\right)=-32+32\sqrt{3}\,i$$

32. $\left[3\left(\cos(80°)+i\sin(80°)\right)\right]^3 = 3^3\left(\cos(3\cdot 80°)+i\sin(3\cdot 80°)\right) = 27\left(\cos(240°)+i\sin(240°)\right)$

$= 27\left(-\frac{1}{2}-\frac{\sqrt{3}}{2}\,i\right) = -\frac{27}{2}-\frac{27\sqrt{3}}{2}\,i$

33. $\left[2\left(\cos\left(\frac{\pi}{10}\right)+i\sin\left(\frac{\pi}{10}\right)\right)\right]^5 = 2^5\left(\cos\left(5\cdot\frac{\pi}{10}\right)+i\sin\left(5\cdot\frac{\pi}{10}\right)\right) = 32\left(\cos\left(\frac{\pi}{2}\right)+i\sin\left(\frac{\pi}{2}\right)\right)$

$= 32(0+1\,i) = 0+32\,i$

34. $\left[\sqrt{2}\left(\cos\left(\frac{5\pi}{16}\right)+i\sin\left(\frac{5\pi}{16}\right)\right)\right]^4 = \left(\sqrt{2}\right)^4\left(\cos\left(4\cdot\frac{5\pi}{16}\right)+i\sin\left(4\cdot\frac{5\pi}{16}\right)\right)$

$= 4\left(\cos\left(\frac{5\pi}{4}\right)+i\sin\left(\frac{5\pi}{4}\right)\right) = 4\left(-\frac{\sqrt{2}}{2}-\frac{\sqrt{2}}{2}\,i\right) = -2\sqrt{2}-2\sqrt{2}\,i$

35. $\left[\sqrt{3}\left(\cos(10°)+i\sin(10°)\right)\right]^6 = \sqrt{3}^6\left(\cos(6\cdot 10°)+i\sin(6\cdot 10°)\right) = 27\left(\cos(60°)+i\sin(60°)\right)$

$= 27\left(\frac{1}{2}+\frac{\sqrt{3}}{2}\,i\right) = \frac{27}{2}+\frac{27\sqrt{3}}{2}\,i$

36. $\left[\frac{1}{2}\cdot\left(\cos(72°)+i\sin(72°)\right)\right]^5 = \left(\frac{1}{2}\right)^5\cdot\left(\cos(5\cdot 72°)+i\sin(5\cdot 72°)\right)$

$= \frac{1}{32}\cdot\left(\cos(360°)+i\sin(360°)\right) = \frac{1}{32}\cdot(1+0\,i) = \frac{1}{32}$

37. $\left[\sqrt{5}\left(\cos\left(\frac{3\pi}{16}\right)+i\sin\left(\frac{3\pi}{16}\right)\right)\right]^4 = \left(\sqrt{5}\right)^4\left(\cos\left(4\cdot\frac{3\pi}{16}\right)+i\sin\left(4\cdot\frac{3\pi}{16}\right)\right)$

$= 25\left(\cos\left(\frac{3\pi}{4}\right)+i\sin\left(\frac{3\pi}{4}\right)\right) = 25\left(-\frac{\sqrt{2}}{2}+\frac{\sqrt{2}}{2}\,i\right) = -\frac{25\sqrt{2}}{2}+\frac{25\sqrt{2}}{2}\,i$

38. $\left[\sqrt{3}\left(\cos\left(\frac{5\pi}{18}\right)+i\sin\left(\frac{5\pi}{18}\right)\right)\right]^6 = \left(\sqrt{3}\right)^6\left(\cos\left(6\cdot\frac{5\pi}{18}\right)+i\sin\left(6\cdot\frac{5\pi}{18}\right)\right)$

$= 27\left(\cos\left(\frac{5\pi}{3}\right)+i\sin\left(\frac{5\pi}{3}\right)\right) = 27\left(\frac{1}{2}-\frac{\sqrt{3}}{2}\,i\right) = \frac{27}{2}-\frac{27\sqrt{3}}{2}\,i$

39. $1-i \qquad r=\sqrt{1^2+(-1)^2}=\sqrt{2} \qquad \tan\theta=\frac{-1}{1}=-1 \qquad \theta=\frac{7\pi}{4}$

$1-i=\sqrt{2}\left(\cos\left(\frac{7\pi}{4}\right)+i\sin\left(\frac{7\pi}{4}\right)\right)$

$(1-i)^5=\left[\sqrt{2}\left(\cos\left(\frac{7\pi}{4}\right)+i\sin\left(\frac{7\pi}{4}\right)\right)\right]^5 = \left(\sqrt{2}\right)^5\left(\cos\left(5\cdot\frac{7\pi}{4}\right)+i\sin\left(5\cdot\frac{7\pi}{4}\right)\right)$

$$= 4\sqrt{2}\left(\cos\left(\frac{35\pi}{4}\right) + i\sin\left(\frac{35\pi}{4}\right)\right) = 4\sqrt{2}\left(-\frac{\sqrt{2}}{2} + \frac{\sqrt{2}}{2}i\right) = -4 + 4i$$

40. $\sqrt{3} - i \quad r = \sqrt{(\sqrt{3})^2 + (-1)^2} = \sqrt{4} = 2 \quad \tan\theta = \frac{-1}{\sqrt{3}} = -\frac{\sqrt{3}}{3} \quad \theta = 330°$

$$\sqrt{3} - i = 2(\cos(330°) + i\sin(330°))$$

$$(\sqrt{3} - i)^6 = [2(\cos(330°) + i\sin(330°))]^6 = 2^6(\cos(6 \cdot 330°) + i\sin(6 \cdot 330°))$$

$$= 64(\cos(1980°) + i\sin(1980°)) = 64(-1 + 0i) = -64$$

41. $\sqrt{2} - i \quad r = \sqrt{(\sqrt{2})^2 + (-1)^2} = \sqrt{3} \quad \tan\theta = \frac{-1}{\sqrt{2}} = -\frac{\sqrt{2}}{2} \quad \theta \approx 324.7°$

$$\sqrt{2} - i \approx \sqrt{3}(\cos(324.7°) + i\sin(324.7°))$$

$$(\sqrt{2} - i)^6 \approx [\sqrt{3}(\cos(324.7°) + i\sin(324.7°))]^6 = (\sqrt{3})^6(\cos(6 \cdot 324.7°) + i\sin(6 \cdot 324.7°))$$

$$= 27(\cos(1948.2°) + i\sin(1948.2°)) \approx 27(-0.8499 + 0.5270\,i)$$

$$= -22.95 + 14.23\,i$$

42. $1 - \sqrt{5}i \quad r = \sqrt{1^2 + (-\sqrt{5})^2} = \sqrt{6} \quad \tan\theta = \frac{-\sqrt{5}}{1} = -\sqrt{5} \quad \theta \approx 294.1°$

$$1 - \sqrt{5}i \approx \sqrt{6}(\cos(294.1°) + i\sin(294.1°))$$

$$(1 - \sqrt{5}i)^8 \approx [\sqrt{6}(\cos(294.1°) + i\sin(294.1°))]^8 = (\sqrt{6})^8(\cos(8 \cdot 294.1°) + i\sin(8 \cdot 294.1°))$$

$$= 1296(\cos(2352.8°) + i\sin(2352.8°)) \approx 1296(-0.9751 - 0.2215\,i)$$

$$= -1263.7 - 287.1\,i$$

43. $1 + i \quad r = \sqrt{1^2 + 1^2} = \sqrt{2} \quad \tan\theta = \frac{1}{1} = 1 \quad \theta = 45°$

$$1 + i = \sqrt{2}(\cos 45° + i\sin 45°)$$

The three complex cube roots of $1 + i = \sqrt{2}(\cos(45°) + i\sin(45°))$ are:

$$z_k = \sqrt[3]{\sqrt{2}}\left[\cos\left(\frac{45°}{3} + \frac{360°k}{3}\right) + i\sin\left(\frac{45°}{3} + \frac{360°k}{3}\right)\right]$$

$$= \sqrt[6]{2}[\cos(15° + 120°k) + i\sin(15° + 120°k)]$$

$$z_0 = \sqrt[6]{2}[\cos(15° + 120° \cdot 0) + i\sin(15° + 120° \cdot 0)] = \sqrt[6]{2}(\cos(15°) + i\sin(15°))$$

$$z_1 = \sqrt[6]{2}[\cos(15° + 120° \cdot 1) + i\sin(15° + 120° \cdot 1)] = \sqrt[6]{2}(\cos(135°) + i\sin(135°))$$

$$z_2 = \sqrt[6]{2}[\cos(15° + 120° \cdot 2) + i\sin(15° + 120° \cdot 2)] = \sqrt[6]{2}(\cos(255°) + i\sin(255°))$$

44. $\sqrt{3} - i \quad r = \sqrt{(\sqrt{3})^2 + (-1)^2} = \sqrt{4} = 2 \quad \tan\theta = \frac{-1}{\sqrt{3}} = -\frac{\sqrt{3}}{3} \quad \theta = 330°$

$$\sqrt{3} - i = 2(\cos(330°) + i\sin(330°))$$

The four complex fourth roots of $\sqrt{3}-i = 2(\cos 330° + i\sin 330°)$ are:

$$z_k = \sqrt[4]{2}\left[\cos\left(\frac{330°}{4}+\frac{360°k}{4}\right)+i\sin\left(\frac{330°}{4}+\frac{360°k}{4}\right)\right]$$

$$= \sqrt[4]{2}\left[\cos(82.5°+90°k)+i\sin(82.5°+90°k)\right]$$

$$z_0 = \sqrt[4]{2}\left[\cos(82.5°+90°\cdot 0)+i\sin(82.5°+90°\cdot 0)\right] = \sqrt[4]{2}\left(\cos(82.5°)+i\sin(82.5°)\right)$$

$$z_1 = \sqrt[4]{2}\left[\cos(82.5°+90°\cdot 1)+i\sin(82.5°+90°\cdot 1)\right] = \sqrt[4]{2}\left(\cos(172.5°)+i\sin(172.5°)\right)$$

$$z_2 = \sqrt[4]{2}\left[\cos(82.5°+90°\cdot 2)+i\sin(82.5°+90°\cdot 2)\right] = \sqrt[4]{2}\left(\cos(262.5°)+i\sin(262.5°)\right)$$

$$z_3 = \sqrt[4]{2}\left[\cos(82.5°+90°\cdot 3)+i\sin(82.5°+90°\cdot 3)\right] = \sqrt[4]{2}\left(\cos(352.5°)+i\sin(352.5°)\right)$$

45. $4-4\sqrt{3}i \qquad r=\sqrt{4^2+\left(-4\sqrt{3}\right)^2}=\sqrt{64}=8 \qquad \tan\theta=\frac{-4\sqrt{3}}{4}=-\sqrt{3} \qquad \theta=300°$

$4-4\sqrt{3}i = 8\left(\cos(300°)+i\sin(300°)\right)$

The four complex fourth roots of $4-4\sqrt{3}i = 8\left(\cos(300°)+i\sin(300°)\right)$ are:

$$z_k = \sqrt[4]{8}\left[\cos\left(\frac{300°}{4}+\frac{360°k}{4}\right)+i\sin\left(\frac{300°}{4}+\frac{360°k}{4}\right)\right]$$

$$= \sqrt[4]{8}\left[\cos(75°+90°k)+i\sin(75°+90°k)\right]$$

$$z_0 = \sqrt[4]{8}\left[\cos(75°+90°\cdot 0)+i\sin(75°+90°\cdot 0)\right] = \sqrt[4]{8}\left(\cos(75°)+i\sin(75°)\right)$$

$$z_1 = \sqrt[4]{8}\left[\cos(75°+90°\cdot 1)+i\sin(75°+90°\cdot 1)\right] = \sqrt[4]{8}\left(\cos(165°)+i\sin(165°)\right)$$

$$z_2 = \sqrt[4]{8}\left[\cos(75°+90°\cdot 2)+i\sin(75°+90°\cdot 2)\right] = \sqrt[4]{8}\left(\cos(255°)+i\sin(255°)\right)$$

$$z_3 = \sqrt[4]{8}\left[\cos(75°+90°\cdot 3)+i\sin(75°+90°\cdot 3)\right] = \sqrt[4]{8}\left(\cos(345°)+i\sin(345°)\right)$$

46. $-8-8i \qquad r=\sqrt{(-8)^2+(-8)^2}=8\sqrt{2} \qquad \tan\theta=\frac{-8}{-8}=1 \qquad \theta=225°$

$-8-8i = 8\sqrt{2}\left(\cos(225°)+i\sin 225°\right)$

The three complex cube roots of $-8-8i = 8\sqrt{2}\left(\cos(225°)+i\sin(225°)\right)$ are:

$$z_k = \sqrt[3]{8\sqrt{2}}\left[\cos\left(\frac{225°}{3}+\frac{360°k}{3}\right)+i\sin\left(\frac{225°}{3}+\frac{360°k}{3}\right)\right]$$

$$= 2\sqrt[6]{2}\left[\cos(75°+120°k)+i\sin(75°+120°k)\right]$$

$$z_0 = 2\sqrt[6]{2}\left[\cos(75°+120°\cdot 0)+i\sin(75°+120°\cdot 0)\right] = 2\sqrt[6]{2}\left(\cos(75°)+i\sin(75°)\right)$$

$$z_1 = 2\sqrt[6]{2}\left[\cos(75°+120°\cdot 1)+i\sin(75°+120°\cdot 1)\right] = 2\sqrt[6]{2}\left(\cos(195°)+i\sin(195°)\right)$$

$$z_2 = 2\sqrt[6]{2}\left[\cos(75°+120°\cdot 2)+i\sin(75°+120°\cdot 2)\right] = 2\sqrt[6]{2}\left(\cos(315°)+i\sin(315°)\right)$$

47. $-16i \qquad r=\sqrt{0^2+(-16)^2}=\sqrt{256}=16 \qquad \tan\theta=\frac{-16}{0}=\text{undefined} \qquad \theta=270°$

$-16i = 16\left(\cos(270°)+i\sin(270°)\right)$

The four complex fourth roots of $-16i = 16(\cos 270° + i\sin 270°)$ are:

$$z_k = \sqrt[4]{16}\left[\cos\left(\frac{270°}{4}+\frac{360°k}{4}\right)+i\sin\left(\frac{270°}{4}+\frac{360°k}{4}\right)\right]$$
$$=2\left[\cos(67.5°+90°k)+i\sin(67.5°+90°k)\right]$$
$$z_0 = 2\left[\cos(67.5°+90°\cdot 0)+i\sin(67.5°+90°\cdot 0)\right]=2(\cos(67.5°)+i\sin(67.5°))$$
$$z_1 = 2\left[\cos(67.5°+90°\cdot 1)+i\sin(67.5°+90°\cdot 1)\right]=2(\cos(157.5°)+i\sin(157.5°))$$
$$z_2 = 2\left[\cos(67.5°+90°\cdot 2)+i\sin(67.5°+90°\cdot 2)\right]=2(\cos(247.5°)+i\sin(247.5°))$$
$$z_3 = 2\left[\cos(67.5°+90°\cdot 3)+i\sin(67.5°+90°\cdot 3)\right]=2(\cos(337.5°)+i\sin(337.5°))$$

48. -8 $\quad r=\sqrt{(-8)^2+0^2}=8 \quad \tan\theta=\frac{0}{-8}=0 \quad \theta=180°$

$-8=8(\cos(180°)+i\sin(180°))$

The three complex cube roots of $-8=8(\cos(180°)+i\sin(180°))$ are:

$$z_k = \sqrt[3]{8}\left[\cos\left(\frac{180°}{3}+\frac{360°k}{3}\right)+i\sin\left(\frac{180°}{3}+\frac{360°k}{3}\right)\right]$$
$$=2\left[\cos(60°+120°k)+i\sin(60°+120°k)\right]$$
$$z_0 = 2\left[\cos(60°+120°\cdot 0)+i\sin(60°+120°\cdot 0)\right]=2(\cos(60°)+i\sin(60°))$$
$$z_1 = 2\left[\cos(60°+120°\cdot 1)+i\sin(60°+120°\cdot 1)\right]=2(\cos(180°)+i\sin(180°))$$
$$z_2 = 2\left[\cos(60°+120°\cdot 2)+i\sin(60°+120°\cdot 2)\right]=2(\cos(300°)+i\sin(300°))$$

49. i $\quad r=\sqrt{0^2+1^2}=\sqrt{1}=1 \quad \tan\theta=\frac{1}{0}=\text{undefined} \quad \theta=90°$

$i=1(\cos(90°)+i\sin(90°))$

The five complex fifth roots of $i=1(\cos(90°)+i\sin(90°))$ are:

$$z_k = \sqrt[5]{1}\left[\cos\left(\frac{90°}{5}+\frac{360°k}{5}\right)+i\sin\left(\frac{90°}{5}+\frac{360°k}{5}\right)\right]$$
$$=1\left[\cos(18°+72°k)+i\sin(18°+72°k)\right]$$
$$z_0 = 1\left[\cos(18°+72°\cdot 0)+i\sin(18°+72°\cdot 0)\right]=\cos(18°)+i\sin(18°)$$
$$z_1 = 1\left[\cos(18°+72°\cdot 1)+i\sin(18°+72°\cdot 1)\right]=\cos(90°)+i\sin(90°)$$
$$z_2 = 1\left[\cos(18°+72°\cdot 2)+i\sin(18°+72°\cdot 2)\right]=\cos(162°)+i\sin(162°)$$
$$z_3 = 1\left[\cos(18°+72°\cdot 3)+i\sin(18°+72°\cdot 3)\right]=\cos(234°)+i\sin(234°)$$
$$z_4 = 1\left[\cos(18°+72°\cdot 4)+i\sin(18°+72°\cdot 4)\right]=\cos(306°)+i\sin(306°)$$

50. $-i$ $\quad r=\sqrt{0^2+(-1)^2}=\sqrt{1}=1 \quad \tan\theta=\frac{-1}{0}=\text{undefined} \quad \theta=270°$

$-i=1(\cos(270°)+i\sin(270°))$

The five complex fifth roots of $-i=1(\cos(270°)+i\sin(270°))$ are:

$$z_k = \sqrt[5]{1}\left[\cos\left(\frac{270^\circ}{5} + \frac{360^\circ k}{5}\right) + i\sin\left(\frac{270^\circ}{5} + \frac{360^\circ k}{5}\right)\right]$$
$$= 1\left[\cos(54^\circ + 72^\circ k) + i\sin(54^\circ + 72^\circ k)\right]$$
$$z_0 = 1\left[\cos(54^\circ + 72^\circ \cdot 0) + i\sin(54^\circ + 72^\circ \cdot 0)\right] = \cos(54^\circ) + i\sin(54^\circ)$$
$$z_1 = 1\left[\cos(54^\circ + 72^\circ \cdot 1) + i\sin(54^\circ + 72^\circ \cdot 1)\right] = \cos(126^\circ) + i\sin(126^\circ)$$
$$z_2 = 1\left[\cos(54^\circ + 72^\circ \cdot 2) + i\sin(54^\circ + 72^\circ \cdot 2)\right] = \cos(198^\circ) + i\sin(198^\circ)$$
$$z_3 = 1\left[\cos(54^\circ + 72^\circ \cdot 3) + i\sin(54^\circ + 72^\circ \cdot 3)\right] = \cos(270^\circ) + i\sin(270^\circ)$$
$$z_4 = 1\left[\cos(54^\circ + 72^\circ \cdot 4) + i\sin(54^\circ + 72^\circ \cdot 4)\right] = \cos(342^\circ) + i\sin(342^\circ)$$

51. $1 = 1 + 0i \qquad r = \sqrt{1^2 + 0^2} = \sqrt{1} = 1 \qquad \tan\theta = \frac{0}{1} = 0 \qquad \theta = 0^\circ$

$1 + 0i = 1(\cos(0^\circ) + i\sin(0^\circ))$

The four complex fourth roots of $1 + 0i = 1(\cos(0^\circ) + i\sin(0^\circ))$ are:

$$z_k = \sqrt[4]{1}\left[\cos\left(\frac{0^\circ}{4} + \frac{360^\circ k}{4}\right) + i\sin\left(\frac{0^\circ}{4} + \frac{360^\circ k}{4}\right)\right]$$
$$= 1\left[\cos(90^\circ k) + i\sin(90^\circ k)\right]$$
$$z_0 = \cos(90^\circ \cdot 0) + i\sin(90^\circ \cdot 0) = \cos(0^\circ) + i\sin(0^\circ) = 1 + 0i = 1$$
$$z_1 = \cos(90^\circ \cdot 1) + i\sin(90^\circ \cdot 1) = \cos(90^\circ) + i\sin(90^\circ) = 0 + 1i = i$$
$$z_2 = \cos(90^\circ \cdot 2) + i\sin(90^\circ \cdot 2) = \cos(180^\circ) + i\sin(180^\circ) = -1 + 0i = -1$$
$$z_3 = \cos(90^\circ \cdot 3) + i\sin(90^\circ \cdot 3) = \cos(270^\circ) + i\sin(270^\circ) = 0 - 1i = -i$$

The complex roots are: $1, i, -1, -i$.

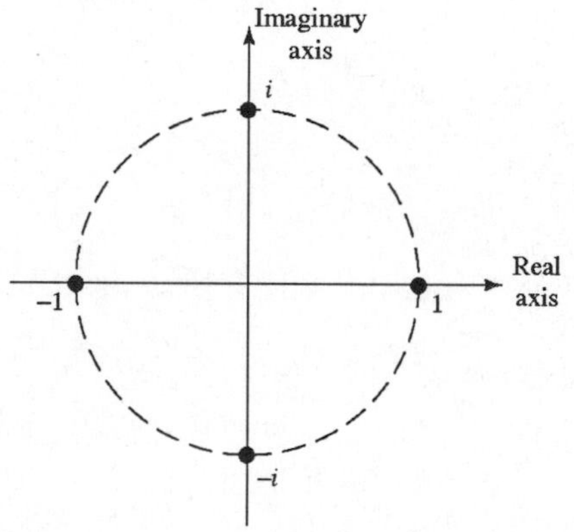

52. $1 = 1 + 0i \qquad r = \sqrt{1^2 + 0^2} = \sqrt{1} = 1 \qquad \tan\theta = \frac{0}{1} = 0 \qquad \theta = 0^\circ$

$1 + 0i = 1(\cos(0^\circ) + i\sin(0^\circ))$

The six complex sixth roots of $1 + 0i = 1(\cos 0^\circ + i\sin 0^\circ)$ are:

$$z_k = \sqrt[6]{1}\left[\cos\left(\frac{0^\circ}{6}+\frac{360^\circ k}{6}\right)+i\sin\left(\frac{0^\circ}{6}+\frac{360^\circ k}{6}\right)\right]$$
$$=1\left[\cos(60^\circ k)+i\sin(60^\circ k)\right]$$
$$z_0=\cos(60^\circ\cdot 0)+i\sin(60^\circ\cdot 0)=\cos(0^\circ)+i\sin(0^\circ)=1+0i=1$$
$$z_1=\cos(60^\circ\cdot 1)+i\sin(60^\circ\cdot 1)=\cos(60^\circ)+i\sin(60^\circ)=\frac{1}{2}+\frac{\sqrt{3}}{2}i$$
$$z_2=\cos(60^\circ\cdot 2)+i\sin(60^\circ\cdot 2)=\cos(120^\circ)+i\sin(120^\circ)=-\frac{1}{2}+\frac{\sqrt{3}}{2}i$$
$$z_3=\cos(60^\circ\cdot 3)+i\sin(60^\circ\cdot 3)=\cos(180^\circ)+i\sin(180^\circ)=-1+0i=-1$$
$$z_4=\cos(60^\circ\cdot 4)+i\sin(60^\circ\cdot 4)=\cos(240^\circ)+i\sin(240^\circ)=-\frac{1}{2}-\frac{\sqrt{3}}{2}i$$
$$z_5=\cos(60^\circ\cdot 5)+i\sin(60^\circ\cdot 5)=\cos(300^\circ)+i\sin(300^\circ)=\frac{1}{2}-\frac{\sqrt{3}}{2}i$$

The complex roots are: $1,\ \frac{1}{2}+\frac{\sqrt{3}}{2}i,\ -\frac{1}{2}+\frac{\sqrt{3}}{2}i,\ -1,\ -\frac{1}{2}-\frac{\sqrt{3}}{2}i,\ \frac{1}{2}-\frac{\sqrt{3}}{2}i$.

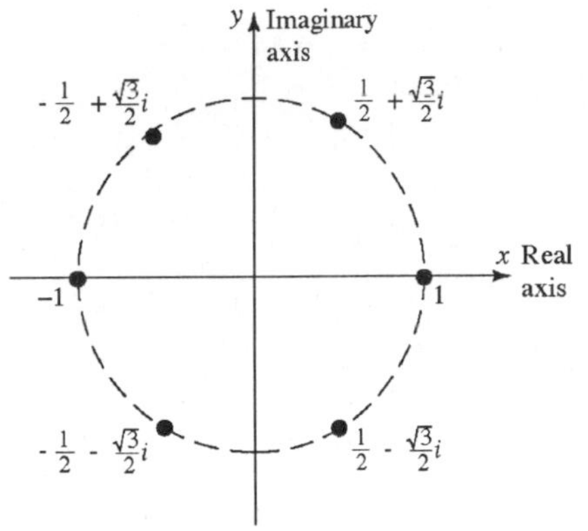

53. Let $w=r(\cos\theta+i\sin\theta)$ be a complex number. If $w\neq 0$, there are n distinct nth roots of w, given by the formula:

$$z_k=\sqrt[n]{r}\left(\cos\left(\frac{\theta}{n}+\frac{2k\pi}{n}\right)+i\sin\left(\frac{\theta}{n}+\frac{2k\pi}{n}\right)\right),\text{ where } k=0,1,2,\ldots,n-1$$

$$|z_k|=\sqrt[n]{r}\text{ for all }k$$

54. Since $|z_k|=\sqrt[n]{r}$ for all k, each of the complex nth roots lies on a circle with center at the origin and radius $\sqrt[n]{r}$.

55. Examining the formula for the distinct complex nth roots of the complex number $w=r(\cos\theta+i\sin\theta)$,

$$z_k=\sqrt[n]{r}\left(\cos\left(\frac{\theta}{n}+\frac{2k\pi}{n}\right)+i\sin\left(\frac{\theta}{n}+\frac{2k\pi}{n}\right)\right),\text{ where } k=0,1,2,\ldots,n-1$$

we see that the z_k are spaced apart by an angle of $\frac{2\pi}{n}$.

56. Let $z_1 = r_1(\cos\theta_1 + i\sin\theta_1)$ and $z_2 = r_2(\cos\theta_2 + i\sin\theta_2)$

$$\frac{z_1}{z_2} = \frac{r_1(\cos\theta_1 + i\sin\theta_1)}{r_2(\cos\theta_2 + i\sin\theta_2)} = \frac{r_1(\cos\theta_1 + i\sin\theta_1)}{r_2(\cos\theta_2 + i\sin\theta_2)} \cdot \frac{(\cos\theta_2 - i\sin\theta_2)}{(\cos\theta_2 - i\sin\theta_2)}$$

$$= \frac{r_1}{r_2} \cdot \frac{\cos\theta_1\cos\theta_2 - i\cos\theta_1\sin\theta_2 + i\sin\theta_1\cos\theta_2 + \sin\theta_1\sin\theta_2}{\cos^2\theta_2 + \sin^2\theta_2}$$

$$= \frac{r_1}{r_2} \cdot \frac{\cos\theta_1\cos\theta_2 + \sin\theta_1\sin\theta_2 + i(\sin\theta_1\cos\theta_2 - \cos\theta_1\sin\theta_2)}{1}$$

$$= \frac{r_1}{r_2}\left(\cos(\theta_1 - \theta_2) + i\sin(\theta_1 - \theta_2)\right)$$

Chapter 10

Polar Coordinates; Vectors

10.4 Vectors

1. $\mathbf{v} + \mathbf{w}$

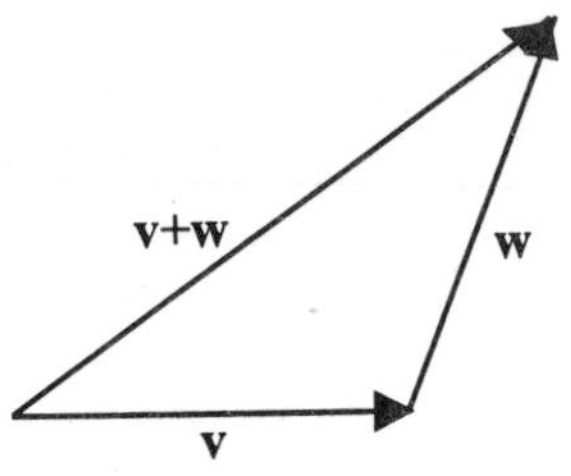

2. $\mathbf{u} + \mathbf{v}$

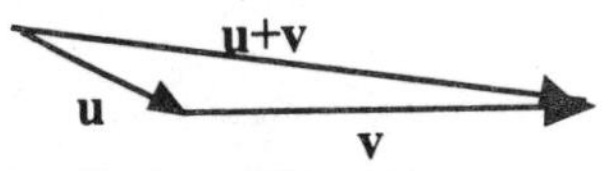

3. $3\mathbf{v}$

4. $4\mathbf{w}$

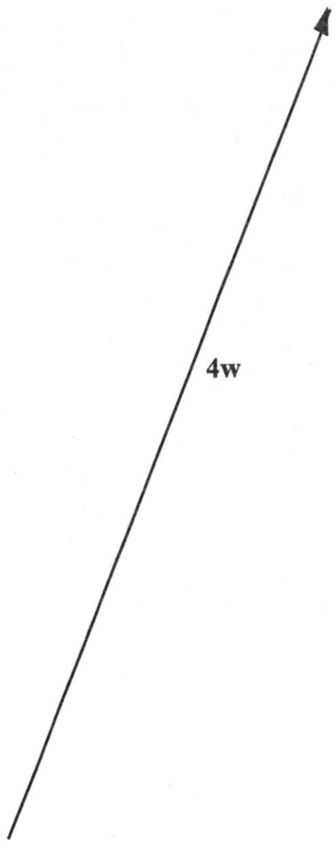

5. $\mathbf{v} - \mathbf{w}$

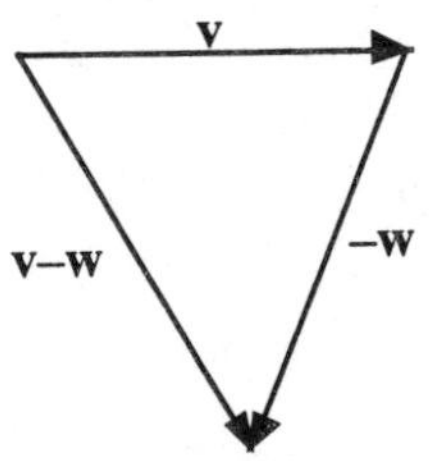

6. $\mathbf{u} - \mathbf{v}$

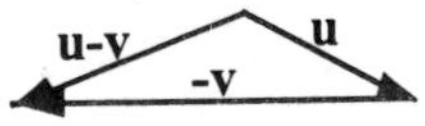

7. $\mathbf{3v + u - 2w}$

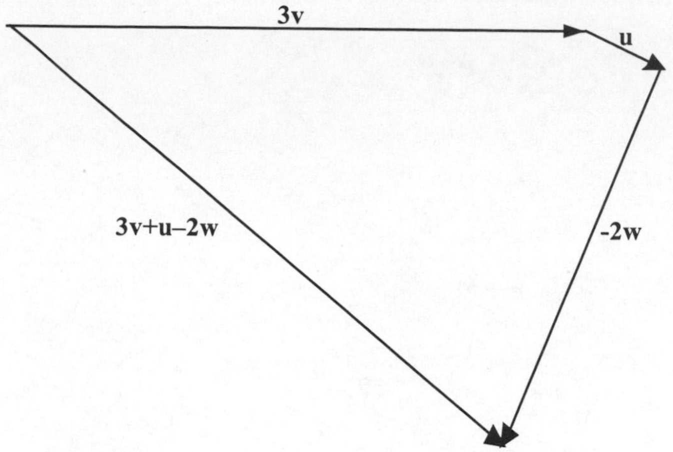

8. $\mathbf{2u - 3v + w}$

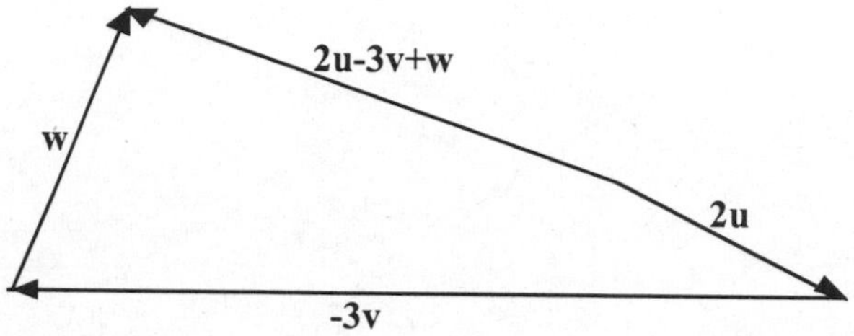

9. True

10. False $\mathbf{K + G = -F}$

11. False $\mathbf{C = -F + E - D}$

12. True

13. False $\mathbf{D - E = H + G}$

14. False $\mathbf{C + H = -G - F}$

15. True

16. True

17. If $\|\mathbf{v}\| = 4$, then $\|3\mathbf{v}\| = |3|\|\mathbf{v}\| = 3(4) = 12$.

18. If $\|\mathbf{v}\| = 2$, then $\|-4\mathbf{v}\| = |-4|\|\mathbf{v}\| = 4(2) = 8$.

19. $P = (0, 0), Q = (3, 4)$ $\quad \mathbf{v} = (3-0)\mathbf{i} + (4-0)\mathbf{j} = 3\mathbf{i} + 4\mathbf{j}$

20. $P = (0, 0), Q = (-3, -5)$ $\quad \mathbf{v} = (-3-0)\mathbf{i} + (-5-0)\mathbf{j} = -3\mathbf{i} - 5\mathbf{j}$

21. $P = (3, 2), Q = (5, 6)$ $\quad \mathbf{v} = (5-3)\mathbf{i} + (6-2)\mathbf{j} = 2\mathbf{i} + 4\mathbf{j}$

22. $P = (-3, 2), Q = (6, 5)$ $\quad \mathbf{v} = (6-(-3))\mathbf{i} + (5-2)\mathbf{j} = 9\mathbf{i} + 3\mathbf{j}$

23. $P = (-2, -1), Q = (6, -2)$ $\quad \mathbf{v} = (6-(-2))\mathbf{i} + (-2-(-1))\mathbf{j} = 8\mathbf{i} - \mathbf{j}$

24. $P = (-1, 4), Q = (6, 2)$ $\quad \mathbf{v} = (6-(-1))\mathbf{i} + (2-4)\mathbf{j} = 7\mathbf{i} - 2\mathbf{j}$

25. $P=(1,0), Q=(0,1)$ $\quad \mathbf{v}=(0-1)\mathbf{i}+(1-0)\mathbf{j}=-\mathbf{i}+\mathbf{j}$

26. $P=(1,1), Q=(2,2)$ $\quad \mathbf{v}=(2-1)\mathbf{i}+(2-1)\mathbf{j}=\mathbf{i}+\mathbf{j}$

27. For $\mathbf{v}=3\mathbf{i}-4\mathbf{j}$, $\|\mathbf{v}\|=\sqrt{3^2+(-4)^2}=\sqrt{25}=5$

28. For $\mathbf{v}=-5\mathbf{i}+12\mathbf{j}$, $\|\mathbf{v}\|=\sqrt{(-5)^2+12^2}=\sqrt{169}=13$

29. For $\mathbf{v}=\mathbf{i}-\mathbf{j}$, $\|\mathbf{v}\|=\sqrt{1^2+(-1)^2}=\sqrt{2}$

30. For $\mathbf{v}=-\mathbf{i}-\mathbf{j}$, $\|\mathbf{v}\|=\sqrt{(-1)^2+(-1)^2}=\sqrt{2}$

31. For $\mathbf{v}=-2\mathbf{i}+3\mathbf{j}$, $\|\mathbf{v}\|=\sqrt{(-2)^2+3^2}=\sqrt{13}$

32. For $\mathbf{v}=6\mathbf{i}+2\mathbf{j}$, $\|\mathbf{v}\|=\sqrt{6^2+2^2}=\sqrt{40}=2\sqrt{10}$

33. $\mathbf{v}=3\mathbf{i}-5\mathbf{j},\ \mathbf{w}=-2\mathbf{i}+3\mathbf{j}$

$$2\mathbf{v}+3\mathbf{w}=2(3\mathbf{i}-5\mathbf{j})+3(-2\mathbf{i}+3\mathbf{j})=6\mathbf{i}-10\mathbf{j}-6\mathbf{i}+9\mathbf{j}=-\mathbf{j}$$

34. $\mathbf{v}=3\mathbf{i}-5\mathbf{j},\ \mathbf{w}=-2\mathbf{i}+3\mathbf{j}$

$$3\mathbf{v}-2\mathbf{w}=3(3\mathbf{i}-5\mathbf{j})-2(-2\mathbf{i}+3\mathbf{j})=9\mathbf{i}-15\mathbf{j}+4\mathbf{i}-6\mathbf{j}=13\mathbf{i}-21\mathbf{j}$$

35. $\mathbf{v}=3\mathbf{i}-5\mathbf{j},\ \mathbf{w}=-2\mathbf{i}+3\mathbf{j}$

$$\|\mathbf{v}-\mathbf{w}\|=\|(3\mathbf{i}-5\mathbf{j})-(-2\mathbf{i}+3\mathbf{j})\|=\|5\mathbf{i}-8\mathbf{j}\|=\sqrt{5^2+(-8)^2}=\sqrt{89}$$

36. $\mathbf{v}=3\mathbf{i}-5\mathbf{j},\ \mathbf{w}=-2\mathbf{i}+3\mathbf{j}$

$$\|\mathbf{v}+\mathbf{w}\|=\|(3\mathbf{i}-5\mathbf{j})+(-2\mathbf{i}+3\mathbf{j})\|=\|\mathbf{i}-2\mathbf{j}\|=\sqrt{1^2+(-2)^2}=\sqrt{5}$$

37. $\mathbf{v}=3\mathbf{i}-5\mathbf{j},\ \mathbf{w}=-2\mathbf{i}+3\mathbf{j}$

$$\|\mathbf{v}\|-\|\mathbf{w}\|=\|3\mathbf{i}-5\mathbf{j}\|-\|-2\mathbf{i}+3\mathbf{j}\|=\sqrt{3^2+(-5)^2}-\sqrt{(-2)^2+3^2}=\sqrt{34}-\sqrt{13}$$

38. $\mathbf{v}=3\mathbf{i}-5\mathbf{j},\ \mathbf{w}=-2\mathbf{i}+3\mathbf{j}$

$$\|\mathbf{v}\|+\|\mathbf{w}\|=\|3\mathbf{i}-5\mathbf{j}\|+\|-2\mathbf{i}+3\mathbf{j}\|=\sqrt{3^2+(-5)^2}+\sqrt{(-2)^2+3^2}=\sqrt{34}+\sqrt{13}$$

39. $\mathbf{u}=\dfrac{\mathbf{v}}{\|\mathbf{v}\|}=\dfrac{5\mathbf{i}}{\|5\mathbf{i}\|}=\dfrac{5\mathbf{i}}{\sqrt{25+0}}=\dfrac{5\mathbf{i}}{5}=\mathbf{i}$

40. $\mathbf{u}=\dfrac{\mathbf{v}}{\|\mathbf{v}\|}=\dfrac{-3\mathbf{j}}{\|-3\mathbf{j}\|}=\dfrac{-3\mathbf{j}}{\sqrt{0+9}}=\dfrac{-3\mathbf{j}}{3}=-\mathbf{j}$

41. $\mathbf{u}=\dfrac{\mathbf{v}}{\|\mathbf{v}\|}=\dfrac{3\mathbf{i}-4\mathbf{j}}{\|3\mathbf{i}-4\mathbf{j}\|}=\dfrac{3\mathbf{i}-4\mathbf{j}}{\sqrt{3^2+(-4)^2}}=\dfrac{3\mathbf{i}-4\mathbf{j}}{\sqrt{25}}=\dfrac{3\mathbf{i}-4\mathbf{j}}{5}=\dfrac{3}{5}\mathbf{i}-\dfrac{4}{5}\mathbf{j}$

42. $\mathbf{u}=\dfrac{\mathbf{v}}{\|\mathbf{v}\|}=\dfrac{-5\mathbf{i}+12\mathbf{j}}{\|-5\mathbf{i}+12\mathbf{j}\|}=\dfrac{-5\mathbf{i}+12\mathbf{j}}{\sqrt{(-5)^2+12^2}}=\dfrac{-5\mathbf{i}+12\mathbf{j}}{\sqrt{169}}=\dfrac{-5\mathbf{i}+12\mathbf{j}}{13}=\dfrac{-5}{13}\mathbf{i}+\dfrac{12}{13}\mathbf{j}$

43. $\mathbf{u}=\dfrac{\mathbf{v}}{\|\mathbf{v}\|}=\dfrac{\mathbf{i}-\mathbf{j}}{\|\mathbf{i}-\mathbf{j}\|}=\dfrac{\mathbf{i}-\mathbf{j}}{\sqrt{1^2+(-1)^2}}=\dfrac{\mathbf{i}-\mathbf{j}}{\sqrt{2}}=\dfrac{1}{\sqrt{2}}\mathbf{i}-\dfrac{1}{\sqrt{2}}\mathbf{j}=\dfrac{\sqrt{2}}{2}\mathbf{i}-\dfrac{\sqrt{2}}{2}\mathbf{j}$

44. $\mathbf{u}=\dfrac{\mathbf{v}}{\|\mathbf{v}\|}=\dfrac{2\mathbf{i}-\mathbf{j}}{\|2\mathbf{i}-\mathbf{j}\|}=\dfrac{2\mathbf{i}-\mathbf{j}}{\sqrt{2^2+(-1)^2}}=\dfrac{2\mathbf{i}-\mathbf{j}}{\sqrt{5}}=\dfrac{2}{\sqrt{5}}\mathbf{i}-\dfrac{1}{\sqrt{5}}\mathbf{j}=\dfrac{2\sqrt{5}}{5}\mathbf{i}-\dfrac{\sqrt{5}}{5}\mathbf{j}$

45. Let $\mathbf{v}=a\mathbf{i}+b\mathbf{j}$. We want $\|\mathbf{v}\|=4$ and $a=2b$.

$\|\mathbf{v}\|=\sqrt{a^2+b^2}=\sqrt{(2b)^2+b^2}=\sqrt{5b^2}$

$\sqrt{5b^2}=4 \rightarrow 5b^2=16 \rightarrow b^2=\dfrac{16}{5} \rightarrow b=\pm\sqrt{\dfrac{16}{5}}=\pm\dfrac{4}{\sqrt{5}}=\pm\dfrac{4\sqrt{5}}{5}$

$a=2b=\pm\dfrac{8\sqrt{5}}{5}$

$\mathbf{v}=\dfrac{8\sqrt{5}}{5}\mathbf{i}+\dfrac{4\sqrt{5}}{5}\mathbf{j}$ or $\mathbf{v}=-\dfrac{8\sqrt{5}}{5}\mathbf{i}-\dfrac{4\sqrt{5}}{5}\mathbf{j}$

46. Let $\mathbf{v}=a\mathbf{i}+b\mathbf{j}$. We want $\|\mathbf{v}\|=3$ and $a=b$.

$\|\mathbf{v}\|=\sqrt{a^2+b^2}=\sqrt{b^2+b^2}=\sqrt{2b^2}$

$\sqrt{2b^2}=3 \rightarrow 2b^2=9 \rightarrow b^2=\dfrac{9}{2} \rightarrow b=\pm\sqrt{\dfrac{9}{2}}=\pm\dfrac{3}{\sqrt{2}}=\pm\dfrac{3\sqrt{2}}{2}$

$a=b=\pm\dfrac{3\sqrt{2}}{2}$

$\mathbf{v}=\dfrac{3\sqrt{2}}{2}\mathbf{i}+\dfrac{3\sqrt{2}}{2}\mathbf{j}$ or $\mathbf{v}=-\dfrac{3\sqrt{2}}{2}\mathbf{i}-\dfrac{3\sqrt{2}}{2}\mathbf{j}$

47. $\mathbf{v}=2\mathbf{i}-\mathbf{j},\ \mathbf{w}=x\mathbf{i}+3\mathbf{j}\qquad \|\mathbf{v}+\mathbf{w}\|=5$

$\|\mathbf{v}+\mathbf{w}\|=\|2\mathbf{i}-\mathbf{j}+x\mathbf{i}+3\mathbf{j}\|=\|(2+x)\mathbf{i}+2\mathbf{j}\|=\sqrt{(2+x)^2+2^2}$

$=\sqrt{x^2+4x+4+4}=\sqrt{x^2+4x+8}$

Solve for x:

$\sqrt{x^2+4x+8}=5 \rightarrow x^2+4x+8=25 \rightarrow x^2+4x-17=0$

$x=\dfrac{-4\pm\sqrt{16-4(1)(-17)}}{2(1)}=\dfrac{-4\pm\sqrt{84}}{2}=\dfrac{-4\pm2\sqrt{21}}{2}=-2\pm\sqrt{21}$

$x=-2+\sqrt{21}\approx2.58$ or $x=-2-\sqrt{21}\approx-6.58$

48. $P=(-3,1),\ Q=(x,4)\qquad \mathbf{v}=(x-(-3))\mathbf{i}+(4-1)\mathbf{j}=(x+3)\mathbf{i}+3\mathbf{j}$

$$\|\mathbf{v}\| = \sqrt{(x+3)^2 + 3^2} = \sqrt{x^2 + 6x + 9 + 9} = \sqrt{x^2 + 6x + 18}$$

$$\sqrt{x^2 + 6x + 18} = 5 \rightarrow x^2 + 6x + 18 = 25 \rightarrow x^2 + 6x - 7 = 0$$

$$(x+7)(x-1) = 0 \rightarrow x = -7 \text{ or } x = 1$$

49. $\|\mathbf{v}\| = 5, \quad \alpha = 60^\circ$

$$\mathbf{v} = \|\mathbf{v}\|(\cos\alpha\mathbf{i} + \sin\alpha\mathbf{j}) = 5(\cos(60^\circ)\mathbf{i} + \sin(60^\circ)\mathbf{j}) = 5\left(\frac{1}{2}\mathbf{i} + \frac{\sqrt{3}}{2}\mathbf{j}\right) = \frac{5}{2}\mathbf{i} + \frac{5\sqrt{3}}{2}\mathbf{j}$$

50. $\|\mathbf{v}\| = 8, \quad \alpha = 45^\circ$

$$\mathbf{v} = \|\mathbf{v}\|(\cos\alpha\mathbf{i} + \sin\alpha\mathbf{j}) = 8(\cos(45^\circ)\mathbf{i} + \sin(45^\circ)\mathbf{j}) = 8\left(\frac{\sqrt{2}}{2}\mathbf{i} + \frac{\sqrt{2}}{2}\mathbf{j}\right) = 4\sqrt{2}\mathbf{i} + 4\sqrt{2}\mathbf{j}$$

51. $\|\mathbf{v}\| = 14, \quad \alpha = 120^\circ$

$$\mathbf{v} = \|\mathbf{v}\|(\cos\alpha\mathbf{i} + \sin\alpha\mathbf{j}) = 14(\cos(120^\circ)\mathbf{i} + \sin(120^\circ)\mathbf{j}) = 14\left(-\frac{1}{2}\mathbf{i} + \frac{\sqrt{3}}{2}\mathbf{j}\right) = -7\mathbf{i} + 7\sqrt{3}\mathbf{j}$$

52. $\|\mathbf{v}\| = 3, \quad \alpha = 240^\circ$

$$\mathbf{v} = \|\mathbf{v}\|(\cos\alpha\mathbf{i} + \sin\alpha\mathbf{j}) = 3(\cos(240^\circ)\mathbf{i} + \sin(240^\circ)\mathbf{j}) = 3\left(-\frac{1}{2}\mathbf{i} - \frac{\sqrt{3}}{2}\mathbf{j}\right) = -\frac{3}{2}\mathbf{i} - \frac{3\sqrt{3}}{2}\mathbf{j}$$

53. $\|\mathbf{v}\| = 25, \quad \alpha = 330^\circ$

$$\mathbf{v} = \|\mathbf{v}\|(\cos\alpha\mathbf{i} + \sin\alpha\mathbf{j}) = 25(\cos(330^\circ)\mathbf{i} + \sin(330^\circ)\mathbf{j}) = 25\left(\frac{\sqrt{3}}{2}\mathbf{i} - \frac{1}{2}\mathbf{j}\right) = \frac{25\sqrt{3}}{2}\mathbf{i} - \frac{25}{2}\mathbf{j}$$

54. $\|\mathbf{v}\| = 15, \quad \alpha = 315^\circ$

$$\mathbf{v} = \|\mathbf{v}\|(\cos\alpha\mathbf{i} + \sin\alpha\mathbf{j}) = 15(\cos 315^\circ\mathbf{i} + \sin 315^\circ\,\mathbf{j}) = 15\left(\frac{\sqrt{2}}{2}\mathbf{i} - \frac{\sqrt{2}}{2}\mathbf{j}\right)$$

$$= \frac{15\sqrt{2}}{2}\mathbf{i} - \frac{15\sqrt{2}}{2}\mathbf{j}$$

55. $\mathbf{F} = 40(\cos(30^\circ)\mathbf{i} + \sin(30^\circ)\mathbf{j}) = 40\left(\frac{\sqrt{3}}{2}\mathbf{i} + \frac{1}{2}\mathbf{j}\right) = 20\sqrt{3}\mathbf{i} + 20\mathbf{j}$

56. $\mathbf{F} = 100(\cos(20^\circ)\mathbf{i} + \sin(20^\circ)\mathbf{j}) \approx 100(0.9397\mathbf{i} + 0.3420\mathbf{j}) = 93.97\mathbf{i} + 34.20\mathbf{j}$

57. $\mathbf{F}_1 = 40(\cos(30^\circ)\mathbf{i} + \sin(30^\circ)\mathbf{j}) = 40\left(\frac{\sqrt{3}}{2}\mathbf{i} + \frac{1}{2}\mathbf{j}\right) = 20\sqrt{3}\mathbf{i} + 20\mathbf{j}$

$$\mathbf{F}_2 = 60(\cos(-45^\circ)\mathbf{i} + \sin(-45^\circ)\mathbf{j}) = 60\left(\frac{\sqrt{2}}{2}\mathbf{i} - \frac{\sqrt{2}}{2}\mathbf{j}\right) = 30\sqrt{2}\,\mathbf{i} - 30\sqrt{2}\mathbf{j}$$

$$\mathbf{F}_1 + \mathbf{F}_2 = 20\sqrt{3}\,\mathbf{i} + 20\mathbf{j} + 30\sqrt{2}\,\mathbf{i} - 30\sqrt{2}\,\mathbf{j} = \left(20\sqrt{3} + 30\sqrt{2}\right)\mathbf{i} + \left(20 - 30\sqrt{2}\right)\mathbf{j}$$

58. $\mathbf{F}_1 = 30(\cos(45°)\mathbf{i} + \sin(45°)\mathbf{j}) = 30\left(\frac{\sqrt{2}}{2}\mathbf{i} + \frac{\sqrt{2}}{2}\mathbf{j}\right) = 15\sqrt{2}\,\mathbf{i} + 15\sqrt{2}\,\mathbf{j}$

$\mathbf{F}_2 = 70(\cos(120°)\mathbf{i} + \sin(120°)\mathbf{j}) = 70\left(-\frac{1}{2}\mathbf{i} + \frac{\sqrt{3}}{2}\mathbf{j}\right) = -35\mathbf{i} + 35\sqrt{3}\mathbf{j}$

$\mathbf{F}_1 + \mathbf{F}_2 = 15\sqrt{2}\,\mathbf{i} + 15\sqrt{2}\,\mathbf{j} + (-35)\mathbf{i} + 35\sqrt{3}\mathbf{j} = \left(15\sqrt{2} - 35\right)\mathbf{i} + \left(15\sqrt{2} + 35\sqrt{3}\right)\mathbf{j}$

59. Let $\mathbf{F}_1$ be the tension on the left cable and $\mathbf{F}_2$ be the tension on the right cable. Let $\mathbf{F}_3$ represent the force of the weight of the box.

$\mathbf{F}_1 = \|\mathbf{F}_1\|(\cos(155°)\mathbf{i} + \sin(155°)\mathbf{j}) \approx \|\mathbf{F}_1\|(-0.9063\mathbf{i} + 0.4226\mathbf{j})$

$\mathbf{F}_2 = \|\mathbf{F}_2\|(\cos(40°)\mathbf{i} + \sin(40°)\mathbf{j}) \approx \|\mathbf{F}_2\|(0.7660\mathbf{i} + 0.6428\mathbf{j})$

$\mathbf{F}_3 = -1000\mathbf{j}$

For equilibrium, the sum of the force vectors must be zero.

$\mathbf{F}_1 + \mathbf{F}_2 + \mathbf{F}_3 = -0.9063\|\mathbf{F}_1\|\mathbf{i} + 0.4226\|\mathbf{F}_1\|\mathbf{j} + 0.7660\|\mathbf{F}_2\|\mathbf{i} + 0.6428\|\mathbf{F}_2\|\mathbf{j} - 1000\mathbf{j}$

$= \left(-0.9063\|\mathbf{F}_1\| + 0.7660\|\mathbf{F}_2\|\right)\mathbf{i} + \left(0.4226\|\mathbf{F}_1\| + 0.6428\|\mathbf{F}_2\| - 1000\right)\mathbf{j} = 0$

Set the **i** and **j** components equal to zero and solve:

$$\begin{cases} -0.9063\|\mathbf{F}_1\| + 0.7660\|\mathbf{F}_2\| = 0 \rightarrow \|\mathbf{F}_2\| = \dfrac{0.9063}{0.7660}\|\mathbf{F}_1\| = 1.1832\|\mathbf{F}_1\| \\ 0.4226\|\mathbf{F}_1\| + 0.6428\|\mathbf{F}_2\| - 1000 = 0 \end{cases}$$

$0.4226\|\mathbf{F}_1\| + 0.6428(1.1832\|\mathbf{F}_1\|) - 1000 = 0 \rightarrow 1.1832\|\mathbf{F}_1\| = 1000$

$\|\mathbf{F}_1\| = 845.2$ pounds

$\|\mathbf{F}_2\| = 1.1832(845.2) = 1000$ pounds

The tension in the left cable is about 845.2 pounds and the tension in the right cable is about 1000 pounds.

60. Let $\mathbf{F}_1$ be the tension on the left cable and $\mathbf{F}_2$ be the tension on the right cable. Let $\mathbf{F}_3$ represent the force of the weight of the box.

$\mathbf{F}_1 = \|\mathbf{F}_1\|(\cos(145°)\mathbf{i} + \sin(145°)\mathbf{j}) \approx \|\mathbf{F}_1\|(-0.8192\mathbf{i} + 0.5736\mathbf{j})$

$\mathbf{F}_2 = \|\mathbf{F}_2\|(\cos(50°)\mathbf{i} + \sin(50°)\mathbf{j}) \approx \|\mathbf{F}_2\|(0.6428\mathbf{i} + 0.7660\mathbf{j})$

$\mathbf{F}_3 = -800\mathbf{j}$

For equilibrium, the sum of the force vectors must be zero.

$\mathbf{F}_1 + \mathbf{F}_2 + \mathbf{F}_3 = -0.8192\|\mathbf{F}_1\|\mathbf{i} + 0.5736\|\mathbf{F}_1\|\mathbf{j} + 0.6428\|\mathbf{F}_2\|\mathbf{i} + 0.7660\|\mathbf{F}_2\|\mathbf{j} - 800\mathbf{j}$

$= \left(-0.8192\|\mathbf{F}_1\| + 0.6428\|\mathbf{F}_2\|\right)\mathbf{i} + \left(0.5736\|\mathbf{F}_1\| + 0.7660\|\mathbf{F}_2\| - 800\right)\mathbf{j} = 0$

Set the **i** and **j** components equal to zero and solve:

$$\begin{cases} -0.8192\|\mathbf{F}_1\| + 0.6428\|\mathbf{F}_2\| = 0 \rightarrow \|\mathbf{F}_2\| = \dfrac{0.8192}{0.6428}\|\mathbf{F}_1\| = 1.2744\|\mathbf{F}_1\| \\ 0.5736\|\mathbf{F}_1\| + 0.7660\|\mathbf{F}_2\| - 800 = 0 \end{cases}$$

$0.5736\|\mathbf{F}_1\| + 0.7660(1.2744\|\mathbf{F}_1\|) - 800 = 0 \rightarrow 1.5498\|\mathbf{F}_1\| = 800$

$\|\mathbf{F}_1\| = 516.2$ pounds; $\|\mathbf{F}_2\| = 1.2744(516.2) = 657.8$ pounds

The tension in the left cable is about 516.2 pounds and the tension in the right cable is about 657.8 pounds.

61. Let $\mathbf{F}_1$ be the tension on the left end of the rope and $\mathbf{F}_2$ be the tension on the right end of the rope. Let $\mathbf{F}_3$ represent the force of the weight of the tightrope walker.

$$\mathbf{F}_1 = \|\mathbf{F}_1\|(\cos(175.8°)\mathbf{i} + \sin(175.8°)\mathbf{j}) \approx \|\mathbf{F}_1\|(-0.9973\mathbf{i} + 0.0732\mathbf{j})$$

$$\mathbf{F}_2 = \|\mathbf{F}_2\|(\cos(3.7°)\mathbf{i} + \sin(3.7°)\mathbf{j}) \approx \|\mathbf{F}_2\|(0.9979\mathbf{i} + 0.0645\mathbf{j})$$

$$\mathbf{F}_3 = -150\mathbf{j}$$

For equilibrium, the sum of the force vectors must be zero.

$$\mathbf{F}_1 + \mathbf{F}_2 + \mathbf{F}_3 = -0.9973\|\mathbf{F}_1\|\mathbf{i} + 0.0732\|\mathbf{F}_1\|\mathbf{j} + 0.9979\|\mathbf{F}_2\|\mathbf{i} + 0.0645\|\mathbf{F}_2\|\mathbf{j} - 150\mathbf{j}$$

$$= (-0.9973\|\mathbf{F}_1\| + 0.9979\|\mathbf{F}_2\|)\mathbf{i} + (0.0732\|\mathbf{F}_1\| + 0.0645\|\mathbf{F}_2\| - 150)\mathbf{j} = 0$$

Set the $\mathbf{i}$ and $\mathbf{j}$ components equal to zero and solve:

$$\begin{cases} -0.9973\|\mathbf{F}_1\| + 0.9979\|\mathbf{F}_2\| = 0 \quad \rightarrow \quad \|\mathbf{F}_2\| = \dfrac{0.9973}{0.9979}\|\mathbf{F}_1\| = 0.9994\|\mathbf{F}_1\| \\ 0.0732\|\mathbf{F}_1\| + 0.0645\|\mathbf{F}_2\| - 150 = 0 \end{cases}$$

$$0.0732\|\mathbf{F}_1\| + 0.0645(0.9994\|\mathbf{F}_1\|) - 150 = 0 \rightarrow 0.1377\|\mathbf{F}_1\| = 150$$

$\|\mathbf{F}_1\| = 1089.3$ pounds; $\|\mathbf{F}_2\| = 0.9994(1089.3) = 1088.6$ pounds

The tension in the left end of the rope is about 1089.3 pounds and the tension in the right end of the rope is about 1088.6 pounds.

62. Let $\mathbf{F}_1$ be the tension on the left end of the rope and $\mathbf{F}_2$ be the tension on the right end of the rope. Let $\mathbf{F}_3$ represent the force of the weight of the tightrope walker.

$$\mathbf{F}_1 = \|\mathbf{F}_1\|(\cos(176.2°)\mathbf{i} + \sin(176.2°)\mathbf{j}) \approx \|\mathbf{F}_1\|(-0.9978\mathbf{i} + 0.0663\mathbf{j})$$

$$\mathbf{F}_2 = \|\mathbf{F}_2\|(\cos(2.6°)\mathbf{i} + \sin(2.6°)\mathbf{j}) \approx \|\mathbf{F}_2\|(0.9990\mathbf{i} + 0.0454\mathbf{j})$$

$$\mathbf{F}_3 = -135\mathbf{j}$$

For equilibrium, the sum of the force vectors must be zero.

$$\mathbf{F}_1 + \mathbf{F}_2 + \mathbf{F}_3 = -0.9978\|\mathbf{F}_1\|\mathbf{i} + 0.0663\|\mathbf{F}_1\|\mathbf{j} + 0.9990\|\mathbf{F}_2\|\mathbf{i} + 0.0454\|\mathbf{F}_2\|\mathbf{j} - 135\mathbf{j}$$

$$= (-0.9978\|\mathbf{F}_1\| + 0.9990\|\mathbf{F}_2\|)\mathbf{i} + (0.0663\|\mathbf{F}_1\| + 0.0454\|\mathbf{F}_2\| - 135)\mathbf{j} = 0$$

Set the $\mathbf{i}$ and $\mathbf{j}$ components equal to zero and solve:

$$\begin{cases} -0.9978\|\mathbf{F}_1\| + 0.9990\|\mathbf{F}_2\| = 0 \quad \rightarrow \quad \|\mathbf{F}_2\| = \dfrac{0.9978}{0.9990}\|\mathbf{F}_1\| = 0.9988\|\mathbf{F}_1\| \\ 0.0663\|\mathbf{F}_1\| + 0.0454\|\mathbf{F}_2\| - 135 = 0 \end{cases}$$

$$0.0663\|\mathbf{F}_1\| + 0.0454(0.9988\|\mathbf{F}_1\|) - 135 = 0 \rightarrow 0.1116\|\mathbf{F}_1\| = 135$$

$\|\mathbf{F}_1\| = 1209.7$ pounds; $\|\mathbf{F}_2\| = 0.9988(1209.7) = 1208.2$ pounds

The tension in the left end of the rope is about 1209.7 pounds and the tension in the right end of the rope is about 1208.2 pounds.

63. The given forces are:

$$\mathbf{F}_1 = -3\mathbf{i};\quad \mathbf{F}_2 = -\mathbf{i} + 4\,\mathbf{j};\quad \mathbf{F}_3 = 4\mathbf{i} - 2\mathbf{j};\quad \mathbf{F}_4 = -4\,\mathbf{j}$$

A vector $\mathbf{x} = a\,\mathbf{i} + b\,\mathbf{j}$ needs to be added for equilibrium. Find vector $\mathbf{x} = a\,\mathbf{i} + b\,\mathbf{j}$:

$$\begin{aligned}
\mathbf{F}_1 + \mathbf{F}_2 + \mathbf{F}_3 + \mathbf{F}_4 + \mathbf{x} &= \mathbf{0} \\
-3\mathbf{i} + (-\mathbf{i} + 4\,\mathbf{j}) + (4\mathbf{i} - 2\,\mathbf{j}) + (-4\,\mathbf{j}) + (a\mathbf{i} + b\,\mathbf{j}) &= \mathbf{0} \\
0\mathbf{i} - 2\,\mathbf{j} + (a\mathbf{i} + b\,\mathbf{j}) &= \mathbf{0} \\
a\mathbf{i} + (-2 + b)\,\mathbf{j} &= \mathbf{0} \\
a &= 0 \\
-2 + b &= 0 \quad \rightarrow \quad b = 2
\end{aligned}$$

Therefore, $\mathbf{x} = 2\,\mathbf{j}$.

Chapter 10

Polar Coordinates; Vectors

10.5 The Dot Product

1. $\mathbf{v} = \mathbf{i} - \mathbf{j}, \quad \mathbf{w} = \mathbf{i} + \mathbf{j}$

 (a) $\mathbf{v} \bullet \mathbf{w} = 1(1) + (-1)(1) = 1 - 1 = 0$

 (b) $\cos\theta = \dfrac{\mathbf{v} \bullet \mathbf{w}}{\|\mathbf{v}\|\|\mathbf{w}\|} = \dfrac{0}{\sqrt{1^2 + (-1)^2}\sqrt{1^2 + 1^2}} = \dfrac{0}{\sqrt{2}\sqrt{2}} = \dfrac{0}{2} = 0 \quad \rightarrow \quad \theta = 90^\circ$

 (c) The vectors are orthogonal.

2. $\mathbf{v} = \mathbf{i} + \mathbf{j}, \quad \mathbf{w} = -\mathbf{i} + \mathbf{j}$

 (a) $\mathbf{v} \bullet \mathbf{w} = 1(-1) + 1(1) = -1 + 1 = 0$

 (b) $\cos\theta = \dfrac{\mathbf{v} \bullet \mathbf{w}}{\|\mathbf{v}\|\|\mathbf{w}\|} = \dfrac{0}{\sqrt{1^2 + 1^2}\sqrt{(-1)^2 + 1^2}} = \dfrac{0}{\sqrt{2}\sqrt{2}} = \dfrac{0}{2} = 0 \quad \rightarrow \quad \theta = 90^\circ$

 (c) The vectors are orthogonal.

3. $\mathbf{v} = 2\mathbf{i} + \mathbf{j}, \quad \mathbf{w} = \mathbf{i} + 2\mathbf{j}$

 (a) $\mathbf{v} \bullet \mathbf{w} = 2(1) + 1(2) = 2 + 2 = 4$

 (b) $\cos\theta = \dfrac{\mathbf{v} \bullet \mathbf{w}}{\|\mathbf{v}\|\|\mathbf{w}\|} = \dfrac{4}{\sqrt{2^2 + 1^2}\sqrt{1^2 + 2^2}} = \dfrac{4}{\sqrt{5}\sqrt{5}} = \dfrac{4}{5} = 0.8 \quad \rightarrow \quad \theta \approx 36.87^\circ$

 (c) The vectors are neither parallel nor orthogonal.

4. $\mathbf{v} = 2\mathbf{i} + 2\mathbf{j}, \quad \mathbf{w} = \mathbf{i} + 2\mathbf{j}$

 (a) $\mathbf{v} \bullet \mathbf{w} = 2(1) + 2(2) = 2 + 4 = 6$

 (b) $\cos\theta = \dfrac{\mathbf{v} \bullet \mathbf{w}}{\|\mathbf{v}\|\|\mathbf{w}\|} = \dfrac{6}{\sqrt{2^2 + 2^2}\sqrt{1^2 + 2^2}} = \dfrac{6}{2\sqrt{2}\sqrt{5}} = \dfrac{3}{\sqrt{10}} = \dfrac{3\sqrt{10}}{10}$

 $\theta \approx 18.43^\circ$

 (c) The vectors are neither parallel nor orthogonal.

5. $\mathbf{v} = \sqrt{3}\mathbf{i} - \mathbf{j}, \quad \mathbf{w} = \mathbf{i} + \mathbf{j}$

 (a) $\mathbf{v} \bullet \mathbf{w} = \sqrt{3}(1) + (-1)(1) = \sqrt{3} - 1$

 (b) $\cos\theta = \dfrac{\mathbf{v} \bullet \mathbf{w}}{\|\mathbf{v}\|\|\mathbf{w}\|} = \dfrac{\sqrt{3} - 1}{\sqrt{\left(\sqrt{3}\right)^2 + (-1)^2}\sqrt{1^2 + 1^2}} = \dfrac{\sqrt{3} - 1}{\sqrt{4}\sqrt{2}} = \dfrac{\sqrt{3} - 1}{2\sqrt{2}} = \dfrac{\sqrt{6} - \sqrt{2}}{4}$

 $\theta \approx 75^\circ$

 (c) The vectors are neither parallel nor orthogonal.

6. $\mathbf{v} = \mathbf{i} + \sqrt{3}\mathbf{j}, \quad \mathbf{w} = \mathbf{i} - \mathbf{j}$
   (a) $\mathbf{v} \bullet \mathbf{w} = 1(1) + \sqrt{3}(-1) = 1 - \sqrt{3}$
   (b) $\cos\theta = \dfrac{\mathbf{v} \bullet \mathbf{w}}{\|\mathbf{v}\|\|\mathbf{w}\|} = \dfrac{1-\sqrt{3}}{\sqrt{1^2 + (\sqrt{3})^2}\sqrt{1^2 + (-1)^2}} = \dfrac{1-\sqrt{3}}{\sqrt{4}\sqrt{2}} = \dfrac{1-\sqrt{3}}{2\sqrt{2}} = \dfrac{\sqrt{2}-\sqrt{6}}{4}$

   $\theta \approx 105°$
   (c) The vectors are neither parallel nor orthogonal.

7. $\mathbf{v} = 3\mathbf{i} + 4\mathbf{j}, \quad \mathbf{w} = 4\mathbf{i} + 3\mathbf{j}$
   (a) $\mathbf{v} \bullet \mathbf{w} = 3(4) + 4(3) = 12 + 12 = 24$
   (b) $\cos\theta = \dfrac{\mathbf{v} \bullet \mathbf{w}}{\|\mathbf{v}\|\|\mathbf{w}\|} = \dfrac{24}{\sqrt{3^2+4^2}\sqrt{4^2+3^2}} = \dfrac{24}{\sqrt{25}\sqrt{25}} = \dfrac{24}{25} = 0.96 \rightarrow \theta \approx 16.26°$
   (c) The vectors are neither parallel nor orthogonal.

8. $\mathbf{v} = 3\mathbf{i} - 4\mathbf{j}, \quad \mathbf{w} = 4\mathbf{i} - 3\mathbf{j}$
   (a) $\mathbf{v} \bullet \mathbf{w} = 3(4) + (-4)(-3) = 12 + 12 = 24$
   (b) $\cos\theta = \dfrac{\mathbf{v} \bullet \mathbf{w}}{\|\mathbf{v}\|\|\mathbf{w}\|} = \dfrac{24}{\sqrt{3^2+(-4)^2}\sqrt{4^2+(-3)^2}} = \dfrac{24}{\sqrt{25}\sqrt{25}} = \dfrac{24}{25} = 0.96$

   $\theta \approx 16.26°$
   (c) The vectors are neither parallel nor orthogonal.

9. $\mathbf{v} = 4\mathbf{i}, \quad \mathbf{w} = \mathbf{j}$
   (a) $\mathbf{v} \bullet \mathbf{w} = 4(0) + 0(1) = 0 + 0 = 0$
   (b) $\cos\theta = \dfrac{\mathbf{v} \bullet \mathbf{w}}{\|\mathbf{v}\|\|\mathbf{w}\|} = \dfrac{0}{\sqrt{4^2+0^2}\sqrt{0^2+1^2}} = \dfrac{0}{4 \cdot 1} = \dfrac{0}{4} = 0 \rightarrow \theta = 90°$
   (c) The vectors are orthogonal.

10. $\mathbf{v} = \mathbf{i}, \quad \mathbf{w} = -3\mathbf{j}$
   (a) $\mathbf{v} \bullet \mathbf{w} = 1(0) + 0(-3) = 0 + 0 = 0$
   (b) $\cos\theta = \dfrac{\mathbf{v} \bullet \mathbf{w}}{\|\mathbf{v}\|\|\mathbf{w}\|} = \dfrac{0}{\sqrt{1^2+0^2}\sqrt{0^2+(-3)^2}} = \dfrac{0}{1 \cdot 3} = \dfrac{0}{3} = 0 \rightarrow \theta = 90°$
   (c) The vectors are orthogonal.

11. $\mathbf{v} = \mathbf{i} - a\mathbf{j}, \quad \mathbf{w} = 2\mathbf{i} + 3\mathbf{j}$
   Two vectors are orthogonal if the dot product is zero. Solve for a:
   $\mathbf{v} \bullet \mathbf{w} = 1(2) + (-a)(3) = 2 - 3a$

   $2 - 3a = 0 \rightarrow 3a = 2 \rightarrow a = \dfrac{2}{3}$

12. $\mathbf{v} = \mathbf{i} + \mathbf{j}, \quad \mathbf{w} = \mathbf{i} + b\mathbf{j}$
   Two vectors are orthogonal if the dot product is zero. Solve for b:
   $\mathbf{v} \bullet \mathbf{w} = 1(1) + 1(b) = 1 + b$
   $1 + b = 0 \rightarrow b = -1$

13. $\mathbf{v} = 2\mathbf{i} - 3\mathbf{j}, \quad \mathbf{w} = \mathbf{i} - \mathbf{j}$

$$\mathbf{v}_1 = \text{proj}_{\mathbf{w}}\mathbf{v} = \frac{\mathbf{v} \bullet \mathbf{w}}{(\|\mathbf{w}\|)^2}\mathbf{w} = \frac{2(1)+(-3)(-1)}{\left(\sqrt{1^2+(-1)^2}\right)^2}(\mathbf{i}-\mathbf{j}) = \frac{5}{2}(\mathbf{i}-\mathbf{j}) = \frac{5}{2}\mathbf{i} - \frac{5}{2}\mathbf{j}$$

$$\mathbf{v}_2 = \mathbf{v} - \mathbf{v}_1 = (2\mathbf{i} - 3\mathbf{j}) - \left(\frac{5}{2}\mathbf{i} - \frac{5}{2}\mathbf{j}\right) = -\frac{1}{2}\mathbf{i} - \frac{1}{2}\mathbf{j}$$

14. $\mathbf{v} = -3\mathbf{i} + 2\mathbf{j}, \quad \mathbf{w} = 2\mathbf{i} + \mathbf{j}$

$$\mathbf{v}_1 = \text{proj}_{\mathbf{w}}\mathbf{v} = \frac{\mathbf{v} \bullet \mathbf{w}}{(\|\mathbf{w}\|)^2}\mathbf{w} = \frac{-3(2)+2(1)}{\left(\sqrt{2^2+1^2}\right)^2}(2\mathbf{i}+\mathbf{j}) = -\frac{4}{5}(2\mathbf{i}+\mathbf{j}) = -\frac{8}{5}\mathbf{i} - \frac{4}{5}\mathbf{j}$$

$$\mathbf{v}_2 = \mathbf{v} - \mathbf{v}_1 = (-3\mathbf{i} + 2\mathbf{j}) - \left(-\frac{8}{5}\mathbf{i} - \frac{4}{5}\mathbf{j}\right) = -\frac{7}{5}\mathbf{i} + \frac{14}{5}\mathbf{j}$$

15. $\mathbf{v} = \mathbf{i} - \mathbf{j}, \quad \mathbf{w} = \mathbf{i} + 2\mathbf{j}$

$$\mathbf{v}_1 = \text{proj}_{\mathbf{w}}\mathbf{v} = \frac{\mathbf{v} \bullet \mathbf{w}}{(\|\mathbf{w}\|)^2}\mathbf{w} = \frac{1(1)+(-1)(2)}{\left(\sqrt{1^2+2^2}\right)^2}(\mathbf{i}+2\mathbf{j}) = -\frac{1}{5}(\mathbf{i}+2\mathbf{j}) = -\frac{1}{5}\mathbf{i} - \frac{2}{5}\mathbf{j}$$

$$\mathbf{v}_2 = \mathbf{v} - \mathbf{v}_1 = (\mathbf{i} - \mathbf{j}) - \left(-\frac{1}{5}\mathbf{i} - \frac{2}{5}\mathbf{j}\right) = \frac{6}{5}\mathbf{i} - \frac{3}{5}\mathbf{j}$$

16. $\mathbf{v} = 2\mathbf{i} - \mathbf{j}, \quad \mathbf{w} = \mathbf{i} - 2\mathbf{j}$

$$\mathbf{v}_1 = \text{proj}_{\mathbf{w}}\mathbf{v} = \frac{\mathbf{v} \bullet \mathbf{w}}{(\|\mathbf{w}\|)^2}\mathbf{w} = \frac{2(1)+(-1)(-2)}{\left(\sqrt{1^2+(-2)^2}\right)^2}(\mathbf{i}-2\mathbf{j}) = \frac{4}{5}(\mathbf{i}-2\mathbf{j}) = \frac{4}{5}\mathbf{i} - \frac{8}{5}\mathbf{j}$$

$$\mathbf{v}_2 = \mathbf{v} - \mathbf{v}_1 = (2\mathbf{i} - \mathbf{j}) - \left(\frac{4}{5}\mathbf{i} - \frac{8}{5}\mathbf{j}\right) = \frac{6}{5}\mathbf{i} + \frac{3}{5}\mathbf{j}$$

17. $\mathbf{v} = 3\mathbf{i} + \mathbf{j}, \quad \mathbf{w} = -2\mathbf{i} - \mathbf{j}$

$$\mathbf{v}_1 = \text{proj}_{\mathbf{w}}\mathbf{v} = \frac{\mathbf{v} \bullet \mathbf{w}}{(\|\mathbf{w}\|)^2}\mathbf{w} = \frac{3(-2)+1(-1)}{\left(\sqrt{(-2)^2+(-1)^2}\right)^2}(-2\mathbf{i}-\mathbf{j}) = -\frac{7}{5}(-2\mathbf{i}-\mathbf{j}) = \frac{14}{5}\mathbf{i} + \frac{7}{5}\mathbf{j}$$

$$\mathbf{v}_2 = \mathbf{v} - \mathbf{v}_1 = (3\mathbf{i} + \mathbf{j}) - \left(\frac{14}{5}\mathbf{i} + \frac{7}{5}\mathbf{j}\right) = \frac{1}{5}\mathbf{i} - \frac{2}{5}\mathbf{j}$$

18. $\mathbf{v} = \mathbf{i} - 3\mathbf{j}, \quad \mathbf{w} = 4\mathbf{i} - \mathbf{j}$

$$\mathbf{v}_1 = \text{proj}_{\mathbf{w}}\mathbf{v} = \frac{\mathbf{v} \bullet \mathbf{w}}{(\|\mathbf{w}\|)^2}\mathbf{w} = \frac{1(4)+(-3)(-1)}{\left(\sqrt{4^2+(-1)^2}\right)^2}(4\mathbf{i}-\mathbf{j}) = \frac{7}{17}(4\mathbf{i}-\mathbf{j}) = \frac{28}{17}\mathbf{i} - \frac{7}{17}\mathbf{j}$$

$$\mathbf{v}_2 = \mathbf{v} - \mathbf{v}_1 = (\mathbf{i} - 3\mathbf{j}) - \left(\frac{28}{17}\mathbf{i} - \frac{7}{17}\mathbf{j}\right) = -\frac{11}{17}\mathbf{i} - \frac{44}{17}\mathbf{j}$$

19. Let $\mathbf{v}_a$ = the velocity of the plane in still air.
$\mathbf{v}_w$ = the velocity of the wind.
$\mathbf{v}_g$ = the velocity of the plane relative to the ground.
$\mathbf{v}_g = \mathbf{v}_a + \mathbf{v}_w$

$$\mathbf{v}_a = 550(\cos(225°)\mathbf{i} + \sin(225°)\mathbf{j}) = 550\left(-\frac{\sqrt{2}}{2}\mathbf{i} - \frac{\sqrt{2}}{2}\mathbf{j}\right) = -275\sqrt{2}\,\mathbf{i} - 275\sqrt{2}\,\mathbf{j}$$

$$\mathbf{v}_w = 80\mathbf{i}$$

$$\mathbf{v}_g = \mathbf{v}_a + \mathbf{v}_w = -275\sqrt{2}\,\mathbf{i} - 275\sqrt{2}\,\mathbf{j} + 80\mathbf{i} = \left(80 - 275\sqrt{2}\right)\mathbf{i} - 275\sqrt{2}\,\mathbf{j}$$

The speed of the plane relative to the ground is:

$$\|\mathbf{v}_g\| = \sqrt{\left(80 - 275\sqrt{2}\right)^2 + \left(-275\sqrt{2}\right)^2} = \sqrt{6400 - 44000\sqrt{2} + 151250 + 151250}$$
$$= \sqrt{246674.6} \approx 496.7 \text{ miles per hour}$$

To find the direction, find the angle between $\mathbf{v}_g$ and a convenient vector such as due south, $-\mathbf{j}$.

$$\cos\theta = \frac{\mathbf{v}_g \bullet -\mathbf{j}}{\|\mathbf{v}_g\|\|-\mathbf{j}\|} = \frac{\left(80 - 275\sqrt{2}\right)\cdot 0 + \left(-275\sqrt{2}\right)(-1)}{496.7\sqrt{0^2 + (-1)^2}} = \frac{275\sqrt{2}}{496.7} \approx 0.7829$$

$$\theta \approx 38.5°$$

The plane is traveling with a ground speed of about 496.7 miles per hour in a direction of 38.5° west of south.

20. Let $\mathbf{v}_a$ = the velocity of the plane in still air.
$\mathbf{v}_w$ = the velocity of the wind.
$\mathbf{v}_g$ = the velocity of the plane relative to the ground.
$\mathbf{v}_g = \mathbf{v}_a + \mathbf{v}_w$
$\mathbf{v}_a = 250(\cos\alpha\,\mathbf{i} + \sin\alpha\,\mathbf{j})$

$$\mathbf{v}_w = 40\left(\frac{\mathbf{i} - \mathbf{j}}{\|\mathbf{i} - \mathbf{j}\|}\right) = 40\left(\frac{\mathbf{i} - \mathbf{j}}{\sqrt{1+1}}\right) = \frac{40}{\sqrt{2}}(\mathbf{i} - \mathbf{j})$$

$$\mathbf{v}_g = \mathbf{v}_a + \mathbf{v}_w = 250\cos\alpha\,\mathbf{i} + 250\sin\alpha\,\mathbf{j} + 20\sqrt{2}\,\mathbf{i} - 20\sqrt{2}\,\mathbf{j} = a\mathbf{i}$$

Examining the $\mathbf{j}$ components:

$$250\sin\alpha - 20\sqrt{2} = 0 \rightarrow 250\sin\alpha = 20\sqrt{2}$$

$$\sin\alpha = \frac{20\sqrt{2}}{250} \approx 0.1131 \rightarrow \alpha \approx 6.5°$$

The heading of the plane should be N83.5°E.
Examining the $\mathbf{i}$ components:

$$250\cos(6.5°)\mathbf{i} + 20\sqrt{2}\,\mathbf{i} = a\mathbf{i}$$

$$276.7 = a$$

The speed of the plane relative to the ground is 276.7 miles per hour.

21. Let the positive x-axis point downstream, so that the velocity of the current is $\mathbf{v}_c = 3\mathbf{i}$.
Let $\mathbf{v}_w$ = the velocity of the boat in the water.
Let $\mathbf{v}_g$ = the velocity of the boat relative to the land.
Then $\mathbf{v}_g = \mathbf{v}_w + \mathbf{v}_c$
The speed of the boat is $\|\mathbf{v}_w\| = 20$; we need to find the direction.

Let $\mathbf{v}_w = a\mathbf{i} + b\mathbf{j}$ so $\|\mathbf{v}_w\| = \sqrt{a^2 + b^2} = 20 \rightarrow a^2 + b^2 = 400$.

Let $\mathbf{v}_g = k\mathbf{j}$.

Since $\mathbf{v}_g = \mathbf{v}_w + \mathbf{v}_c$, $k\mathbf{j} = a\mathbf{i} + b\mathbf{j} + 3\mathbf{i} \rightarrow k\mathbf{j} = (a+3)\mathbf{i} + b\mathbf{j}$

$a + 3 = 0$ and $k = b \rightarrow a = -3$

$a^2 + b^2 = 400 \rightarrow 9 + b^2 = 400 \rightarrow b^2 = 391 \rightarrow k = b \approx 19.77$

$\mathbf{v}_w = -3\mathbf{i} + 19.77\mathbf{j}$ and $\mathbf{v}_g = 19.77\mathbf{j}$

Find the angle between $\mathbf{v}_w$ and $\mathbf{j}$:

$$\cos\theta = \frac{\mathbf{v}_w \bullet \mathbf{j}}{\|\mathbf{v}_w\|\|\mathbf{j}\|} = \frac{-3\cdot 0 + 19.77(1)}{20\sqrt{0^2 + 1^2}} = \frac{19.77}{20} \approx 0.9885$$

$\theta \approx 8.7°$

The heading of the boat needs to be 8.7° upstream.
The velocity of the boat directly across the river is 19.77 kilometers per hour. The time to cross the river is: $t = \dfrac{0.5}{19.77} \approx 0.025$ hours or $t \approx 1.5$ minutes.

22. Let the positive x-axis point downstream, so that the velocity of the current is $\mathbf{v}_c = 5\mathbf{i}$.
Let $\mathbf{v}_w$ = the velocity of the boat in the water.
Let $\mathbf{v}_g$ = the velocity of the boat relative to the land.
Then $\mathbf{v}_g = \mathbf{v}_w + \mathbf{v}_c$
The speed of the boat is $\|\mathbf{v}_w\| = 20$; we need to find the direction.

Let $\mathbf{v}_w = a\mathbf{i} + b\mathbf{j}$ so $\|\mathbf{v}_w\| = \sqrt{a^2 + b^2} = 20 \rightarrow a^2 + b^2 = 400$.

Let $\mathbf{v}_g = k\mathbf{j}$.

Since $\mathbf{v}_g = \mathbf{v}_w + \mathbf{v}_c$, $k\mathbf{j} = a\mathbf{i} + b\mathbf{j} + 5\mathbf{i} \rightarrow k\mathbf{j} = (a+5)\mathbf{i} + b\mathbf{j}$

$a + 5 = 0$ and $k = b \rightarrow a = -5$

$a^2 + b^2 = 400 \rightarrow 25 + b^2 = 400 \rightarrow b^2 = 375 \rightarrow k = b \approx 19.36$

$\mathbf{v}_w = -5\mathbf{i} + 19.36\mathbf{j}$ and $\mathbf{v}_g = 19.36\mathbf{j}$

Find the angle between $\mathbf{v}_w$ and $\mathbf{j}$:

$$\cos\theta = \frac{\mathbf{v}_w \bullet \mathbf{j}}{\|\mathbf{v}_w\|\|\mathbf{j}\|} = \frac{-5\cdot 0 + 19.36(1)}{20\sqrt{0^2 + 1^2}} = \frac{19.36}{20} \approx 0.9680$$

$\theta \approx 14.5°$

The heading of the boat needs to be 14.5° upstream.
The velocity of the boat directly across the river is 19.36 kilometers per hour. The time to cross the river is: $t = \dfrac{0.5}{19.36} \approx 0.026$ hours or $t \approx 1.56$ minutes.

23. Split the force into the components going down the hill and perpendicular to the hill.

$\mathbf{F}_d = \mathbf{F}\sin(8°) = 5300\sin(8°)$
$= 5300(0.1392) \approx 738$ pounds

$\mathbf{F}_p = \mathbf{F}\cos(8°) = 5300\cos(8°)$
$= 5300(0.9903) \approx 5249$ pounds

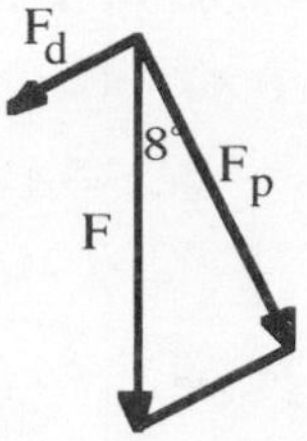

The force required to keep the car from rolling down the hill is about 738 pounds. The force perpendicular to the hill is approximately 5249 pounds.

24. Split the force into the components going down the hill and perpendicular to the hill.

$\mathbf{F}_d = \mathbf{F}\sin(10°) = 4500\sin(10°)$
$= 4500(0.1736) \approx 781.2$ pounds

$\mathbf{F}_p = \mathbf{F}\cos(10°) = 4500\cos(10°)$
$= 4500(0.9848) \approx 4431.6$ pounds

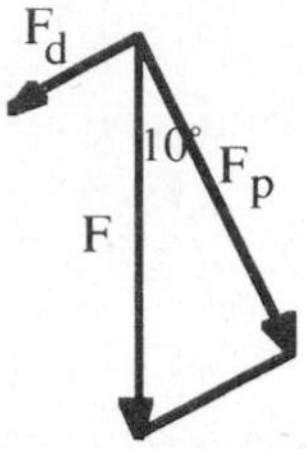

The force required to keep the car from rolling down the hill is about 781.2 pounds. The force perpendicular to the hill is approximately 4431.6 pounds.

25. Let $\mathbf{v}_a$ = the velocity of the plane in still air.
$\mathbf{v}_w$ = the velocity of the wind.
$\mathbf{v}_g$ = the velocity of the plane relative to the ground.
$\mathbf{v}_g = \mathbf{v}_a + \mathbf{v}_w$

$$\mathbf{v}_a = 500(\cos(45°)\mathbf{i} + \sin(45°)\mathbf{j}) = 500\left(\frac{\sqrt{2}}{2}\mathbf{i} + \frac{\sqrt{2}}{2}\mathbf{j}\right) = 250\sqrt{2}\,\mathbf{i} + 250\sqrt{2}\,\mathbf{j}$$

$$\mathbf{v}_w = 60(\cos(120°)\mathbf{i} + \sin(120°)\mathbf{j}) = 60\left(-\frac{1}{2}\mathbf{i} + \frac{\sqrt{3}}{2}\mathbf{j}\right) = -30\mathbf{i} + 30\sqrt{3}\,\mathbf{j}$$

$$\mathbf{v}_g = \mathbf{v}_a + \mathbf{v}_w = 250\sqrt{2}\,\mathbf{i} + 250\sqrt{2}\,\mathbf{j} - 30\mathbf{i} + 30\sqrt{3}\,\mathbf{j}$$
$$= \left(-30 + 250\sqrt{2}\right)\mathbf{i} + \left(250\sqrt{2} + 30\sqrt{3}\right)\mathbf{j}$$

The speed of the plane relative to the ground is:

$$\|\mathbf{v}_g\| = \sqrt{\left(-30 + 250\sqrt{2}\right)^2 + \left(250\sqrt{2} + 30\sqrt{3}\right)^2}$$
$$= \sqrt{269129.1} \approx 518.8 \text{ kilometers per hour}$$

To find the direction, find the angle between $\mathbf{v}_g$ and a convenient vector such as due north, $\mathbf{j}$.

$$\cos\theta = \frac{\mathbf{v}_g \cdot \mathbf{j}}{\|\mathbf{v}_g\|\|\mathbf{j}\|} = \frac{\left(-30 + 250\sqrt{2}\right)\cdot 0 + \left(250\sqrt{2} + 30\sqrt{3}\right)(1)}{518.8\sqrt{0^2 + 1^2}} = \frac{250\sqrt{2} + 30\sqrt{3}}{518.8}$$
$$= \frac{405.5}{518.8} \approx 0.7816 \quad \rightarrow \quad \theta \approx 38.6°$$

The plane is traveling with a ground speed of about 518.8 kilometers per hour in a direction of 38.6° east of north.

26. Let $\mathbf{v}_a$ = the velocity of the plane in still air.

$\mathbf{v}_w$ = the velocity of the wind.

$\mathbf{v}_g$ = the velocity of the plane relative to the ground.

$$\mathbf{v}_g = \mathbf{v}_a + \mathbf{v}_w$$

$$\mathbf{v}_a = 600(\cos(60°)\mathbf{i} - \sin(60°)\mathbf{j}) = 600\left(\frac{1}{2}\mathbf{i} - \frac{\sqrt{3}}{2}\mathbf{j}\right) = 300\mathbf{i} - 300\sqrt{3}\,\mathbf{j}$$

$$\mathbf{v}_w = 40(\cos(45°)\mathbf{i} - \sin(45°)\mathbf{j}) = 40\left(\frac{\sqrt{2}}{2}\mathbf{i} - \frac{\sqrt{2}}{2}\mathbf{j}\right) = 20\sqrt{2}\,\mathbf{i} - 20\sqrt{2}\,\mathbf{j}$$

$$\mathbf{v}_g = \mathbf{v}_a + \mathbf{v}_w = 300\mathbf{i} - 300\sqrt{3}\,\mathbf{j} + 20\sqrt{2}\,\mathbf{i} - 20\sqrt{2}\,\mathbf{j}$$

$$= \left(300 + 20\sqrt{2}\right)\mathbf{i} + \left(-300\sqrt{3} - 20\sqrt{2}\right)\mathbf{j}$$

The speed of the plane relative to the ground is:

$$\|\mathbf{v}_g\| = \sqrt{\left(300 + 20\sqrt{2}\right)^2 + \left(-300\sqrt{3} - 20\sqrt{2}\right)^2}$$

$$= \sqrt{407964} \approx 639 \text{ kilometers per hour}$$

To find the direction, find the angle between $\mathbf{v}_g$ and a convenient vector such as due north, $\mathbf{j}$.

$$\cos\theta = \frac{\mathbf{v}_g \bullet \mathbf{j}}{\|\mathbf{v}_g\|\|\mathbf{j}\|} = \frac{\left(300 + 20\sqrt{2}\right)\cdot 0 + \left(-300\sqrt{3} - 20\sqrt{2}\right)(1)}{639\sqrt{0^2 + 1^2}} = \frac{-300\sqrt{3} - 20\sqrt{2}}{639}$$

$$= \frac{-547.9}{639} \approx -0.8574$$

$$\theta \approx 149°$$

The plane is traveling with a ground speed of about 639 kilometers per hour in a direction of 31° east of south.

27. Let the positive x-axis point downstream, so that the velocity of the current is $\mathbf{v}_c = 3\mathbf{i}$.

Let $\mathbf{v}_w$ = the velocity of the boat in the water.

Let $\mathbf{v}_g$ = the velocity of the boat relative to the land.

Then $\mathbf{v}_g = \mathbf{v}_w + \mathbf{v}_c$

The speed of the boat is $\|\mathbf{v}_w\| = 20$; its direction is directly across the river, so

Let $\mathbf{v}_w = 20\mathbf{j}$.

$$\mathbf{v}_g = \mathbf{v}_w + \mathbf{v}_c = 20\mathbf{j} + 3\mathbf{i} = 3\mathbf{i} + 20\mathbf{j}$$

Let $\|\mathbf{v}_g\| = \sqrt{3^2 + 20^2} = \sqrt{409} \approx 20.2$ miles per hour

Find the angle between $\mathbf{v}_g$ and $\mathbf{j}$:

$$\cos\theta = \frac{\mathbf{v}_g \bullet \mathbf{j}}{\|\mathbf{v}_g\|\|\mathbf{j}\|} = \frac{3\cdot 0 + 20(1)}{20.2\sqrt{0^2 + 1^2}} = \frac{20}{20.2} \approx 0.9901$$

$$\theta \approx 8.1°$$

The heading of the boat will be 8.1° downstream.

28. Let the positive x-axis point downstream, so that the velocity of the current is $\mathbf{v}_c = 4\mathbf{i}$.
Let $\mathbf{v}_w$ = the velocity of the boat in the water.
Let $\mathbf{v}_g$ = the velocity of the boat relative to the land.
Then $\mathbf{v}_g = \mathbf{v}_w + \mathbf{v}_c$
The speed of the boat is $\|\mathbf{v}_w\| = 10$; its direction is directly across the river, so

Let $\mathbf{v}_w = 10\mathbf{j}$.

$\mathbf{v}_g = \mathbf{v}_w + \mathbf{v}_c = 10\mathbf{j} + 4\mathbf{i} = 4\mathbf{i} + 10\mathbf{j}$

Let $\|\mathbf{v}_g\| = \sqrt{4^2 + 10^2} = \sqrt{116} \approx 10.8$ miles per hour

Find the angle between $\mathbf{v}_g$ and $\mathbf{j}$:

$$\cos\theta = \frac{\mathbf{v}_g \cdot \mathbf{j}}{\|\mathbf{v}_g\|\|\mathbf{j}\|} = \frac{4\cdot 0 + 10(1)}{10.8\sqrt{0^2 + 1^2}} = \frac{10}{10.8} \approx 0.9259$$

$\theta \approx 22.2°$

The heading of the boat will be 22.2° downstream.

29. $\mathbf{F} = 3(\cos(60°)\mathbf{i} + \sin(60°)\mathbf{j}) = 3\left(\frac{1}{2}\mathbf{i} + \frac{\sqrt{3}}{2}\mathbf{j}\right) = \frac{3}{2}\mathbf{i} + \frac{3\sqrt{3}}{2}\mathbf{j}$

$W = \mathbf{F} \cdot AB = \left(\frac{3}{2}\mathbf{i} + \frac{3\sqrt{3}}{2}\mathbf{j}\right) \cdot 2\mathbf{i} = \frac{3}{2}(2) + \frac{3\sqrt{3}}{2}\cdot 0 = 3$ foot - pounds

30. $\mathbf{F} = 1(\cos(45°)\mathbf{i} + \sin(45°)\mathbf{j}) = 1\left(\frac{\sqrt{2}}{2}\mathbf{i} + \frac{\sqrt{2}}{2}\mathbf{j}\right) = \frac{\sqrt{2}}{2}\mathbf{i} + \frac{\sqrt{2}}{2}\mathbf{j}$

$W = \mathbf{F} \cdot AB = \left(\frac{\sqrt{2}}{2}\mathbf{i} + \frac{\sqrt{2}}{2}\mathbf{j}\right) \cdot 5\mathbf{i} = \frac{\sqrt{2}}{2}(5) + \frac{\sqrt{2}}{2}\cdot 0 = \frac{5\sqrt{2}}{2}$ foot - pounds

31. $\mathbf{F} = 20(\cos(30°)\mathbf{i} + \sin(30°)\mathbf{j}) = 20\left(\frac{\sqrt{3}}{2}\mathbf{i} + \frac{1}{2}\mathbf{j}\right) = 10\sqrt{3}\mathbf{i} + 10\mathbf{j}$

$W = \mathbf{F} \cdot AB = (10\sqrt{3}\mathbf{i} + 10\mathbf{j}) \cdot 100\mathbf{i} = 10\sqrt{3}(100) + 10\cdot 0 = 1732$ foot- pounds

32. $W = \mathbf{F} \cdot AB \qquad W = 2, \quad AB = 4\mathbf{i}$
$\mathbf{F} = \cos\alpha\,\mathbf{i} - \sin\alpha\,\mathbf{j}$

$2 = (\cos\alpha\,\mathbf{i} - \sin\alpha\,\mathbf{j}) \cdot 4\mathbf{i} \rightarrow 2 = 4\cos\alpha \rightarrow \frac{1}{2} = \cos\alpha \rightarrow \alpha = 60°$

33. Let $\mathbf{u} = a_1\mathbf{i} + b_1\mathbf{j}, \quad \mathbf{v} = a_2\mathbf{i} + b_2\mathbf{j}, \quad \mathbf{w} = a_3\mathbf{i} + b_3\mathbf{j}$

$$\begin{aligned}\mathbf{u}\cdot(\mathbf{v}+\mathbf{w}) &= (a_1\mathbf{i} + b_1\mathbf{j})\cdot(a_2\mathbf{i} + b_2\mathbf{j} + a_3\mathbf{i} + b_3\mathbf{j}) = (a_1\mathbf{i} + b_1\mathbf{j})\cdot(a_2\mathbf{i} + a_3\mathbf{i} + b_2\mathbf{j} + b_3\mathbf{j})\\ &= (a_1\mathbf{i} + b_1\mathbf{j})\cdot((a_2 + a_3)\mathbf{i} + (b_2 + b_3)\mathbf{j}) = a_1(a_2 + a_3) + b_1(b_2 + b_3)\\ &= a_1a_2 + a_1a_3 + b_1b_2 + b_1b_3 = a_1a_2 + b_1b_2 + a_1a_3 + b_1b_3\\ &= (a_1\mathbf{i} + b_1\mathbf{j})\cdot(a_2\mathbf{i} + b_2\mathbf{j}) + (a_1\mathbf{i} + b_1\mathbf{j})\cdot(a_3\mathbf{i} + b_3\mathbf{j}) = \mathbf{u}\cdot\mathbf{v} + \mathbf{u}\cdot\mathbf{w}\end{aligned}$$

34. $\mathbf{0} = 0\mathbf{i} + 0\mathbf{j}$ and $\mathbf{v} = a\mathbf{i} + b\mathbf{j}$. $\mathbf{0}\cdot\mathbf{v} = 0\cdot a + 0\cdot b = 0$

35. Let $\mathbf{v} = a\mathbf{i} + b\mathbf{j}$.

Since $\mathbf{v}$ is a unit vector, $\|\mathbf{v}\| = \sqrt{a^2 + b^2} = 1$ or $a^2 + b^2 = 1$

If α is the angle between $\mathbf{v}$ and $\mathbf{i}$, then $\cos\alpha = \dfrac{\mathbf{v} \bullet \mathbf{i}}{\|\mathbf{v}\|\|\mathbf{i}\|}$ or $\cos\alpha = \dfrac{(a\mathbf{i} + b\mathbf{j}) \bullet \mathbf{i}}{1 \cdot 1} = a$.

$$a^2 + b^2 = 1$$

$$\cos^2\alpha + b^2 = 1 \rightarrow b^2 = 1 - \cos^2\alpha \rightarrow b^2 = \sin^2\alpha \rightarrow b = \sin\alpha$$

Thus, $\mathbf{v} = \cos\alpha\ \mathbf{i} + \sin\alpha\ \mathbf{j}$

36. If $\mathbf{v} = a_1\mathbf{i} + b_1\mathbf{j} = \cos\alpha\,\mathbf{i} + \sin\alpha\,\mathbf{j}$ and $\mathbf{w} = a_2\mathbf{i} + b_2\mathbf{j} = \cos\beta\,\mathbf{i} + \sin\beta\,\mathbf{j}$, then

$$\cos(\alpha - \beta) = \mathbf{v} \bullet \mathbf{w} = a_1a_2 + b_1b_2 = \cos\alpha\cos\beta + \sin\alpha\sin\beta$$

37. Let $\mathbf{v} = a\mathbf{i} + b\mathbf{j}$.

$$\text{proj}_{\mathbf{i}}\mathbf{v} = \frac{\mathbf{v} \bullet \mathbf{i}}{(\|\mathbf{i}\|)^2}\mathbf{i} = \frac{(a\mathbf{i} + b\mathbf{j}) \bullet \mathbf{i}}{\left(\sqrt{1^2 + 0^2}\right)^2}\mathbf{i} = \frac{a(1) + b(0)}{1^2}\mathbf{i} = a\mathbf{i}$$

$\mathbf{v} \bullet \mathbf{i} = a, \quad \mathbf{v} \bullet \mathbf{j} = b,$

$\mathbf{v} = (\mathbf{v} \bullet \mathbf{i})\mathbf{i} + (\mathbf{v} \bullet \mathbf{j})\mathbf{j}$

38. (a) Let $\mathbf{u} = a_1\mathbf{i} + b_1\mathbf{j}$ and $\mathbf{v} = a_2\mathbf{i} + b_2\mathbf{j}$

$$\begin{aligned}(\mathbf{u} + \mathbf{v}) \bullet (\mathbf{u} - \mathbf{v}) &= ((a_1 + a_2)\mathbf{i} + (b_1 + b_2)\mathbf{j}) \bullet ((a_1 - a_2)\mathbf{i} + (b_1 - b_2)\mathbf{j}) \\ &= (a_1 + a_2)(a_1 - a_2) + (b_1 + b_2)(b_1 - b_2) = a_1^2 - a_2^2 + b_1^2 - b_2^2 \\ &= (a_1^2 + b_1^2) - (a_2^2 + b_2^2)\end{aligned}$$

Since the vectors have the same magnitudes and these two quantities represent the squares of the magnitudes of each, the difference is 0 and the vectors are orthogonal.

(b) Because the vectors $\mathbf{u}$ and $\mathbf{v}$ are radii of the circle, we know they have the same magnitude. Since $\mathbf{u} + \mathbf{v}$ and $\mathbf{u} - \mathbf{v}$ are sides of the angle inscribed in the semicircle and we know that they are orthogonal (part a), then this angle must be a right angle.

39. $$(\mathbf{v} - \alpha\mathbf{w}) \bullet \mathbf{w} = \mathbf{v} \bullet \mathbf{w} - \alpha\mathbf{w} \bullet \mathbf{w} = \mathbf{v} \bullet \mathbf{w} - \alpha(\|\mathbf{w}\|)^2 = \mathbf{v} \bullet \mathbf{w} - \frac{\mathbf{v} \bullet \mathbf{w}}{(\|\mathbf{w}\|)^2}(\|\mathbf{w}\|)^2 = 0$$

Therefore the vectors are orthogonal.

40. $$\begin{aligned}&(\|\mathbf{w}\|\mathbf{v} + \|\mathbf{v}\|\mathbf{w}) \bullet (\|\mathbf{w}\|\mathbf{v} - \|\mathbf{v}\|\mathbf{w}) \\ &= (\|\mathbf{w}\|)^2\mathbf{v} \bullet \mathbf{v} - \|\mathbf{w}\|\|\mathbf{v}\|\mathbf{v} \bullet \mathbf{w} + \|\mathbf{w}\|\|\mathbf{v}\|\mathbf{v} \bullet \mathbf{w} - (\|\mathbf{v}\|)^2\mathbf{w} \bullet \mathbf{w} \\ &= (\|\mathbf{w}\|)^2\mathbf{v} \bullet \mathbf{v} - (\|\mathbf{v}\|)^2\mathbf{w} \bullet \mathbf{w} = (\|\mathbf{w}\|)^2(\|\mathbf{v}\|)^2 - (\|\mathbf{v}\|)^2(\|\mathbf{w}\|)^2 = 0\end{aligned}$$

41. If $\mathbf{F}$ is orthogonal to $\mathbf{AB}$, then $W = \mathbf{F} \bullet \mathbf{AB} = (\mathbf{i} + \mathbf{j})(\mathbf{i} - \mathbf{j}) = 1 \cdot 1 + 1(-1) = 0$

42. $$\begin{aligned}(\|u + v\|)^2 - (\|u - v\|)^2 &= (u + v) \bullet (u + v) - (u - v) \bullet (u - v) \\ &= (u \bullet u + u \bullet v + v \bullet u + v \bullet v) - (u \bullet u - u \bullet v - v \bullet u + v \bullet v) \\ &= 2(u \bullet v) + 2(u \bullet v) = 4(u \bullet v)\end{aligned}$$

Chapter 10

Polar Coordinates; Vectors

10.R Chapter Review

1. $\left(3, \frac{\pi}{6}\right)$

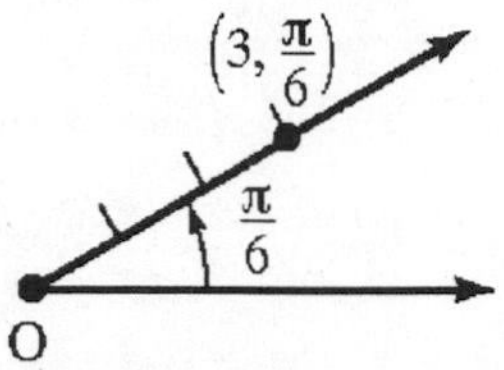

$x = 3\cos\left(\frac{\pi}{6}\right) = \frac{3\sqrt{3}}{2}$

$y = 3\sin\left(\frac{\pi}{6}\right) = \frac{3}{2}$

$\left(\frac{3\sqrt{3}}{2}, \frac{3}{2}\right)$

2. $\left(4, \frac{2\pi}{3}\right)$

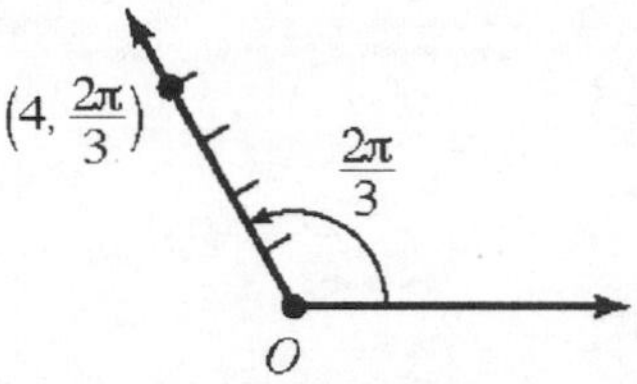

$x = 4\cos\left(\frac{2\pi}{3}\right) = -2$

$y = 4\sin\left(\frac{2\pi}{3}\right) = 2\sqrt{3}$

$\left(-2, 2\sqrt{3}\right)$

3. $\left(-2, \frac{4\pi}{3}\right)$

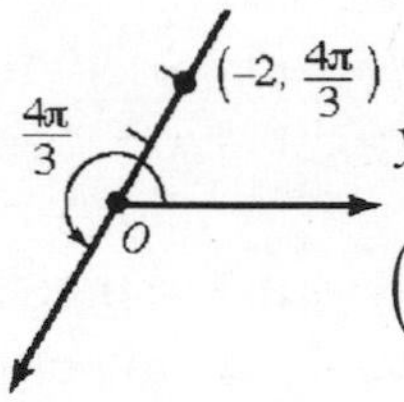

$x = -2\cos\left(\frac{4\pi}{3}\right) = 1$

$y = -2\sin\left(\frac{4\pi}{3}\right) = \sqrt{3}$

$\left(1, \sqrt{3}\right)$

4. $\left(-1, \frac{5\pi}{4}\right)$

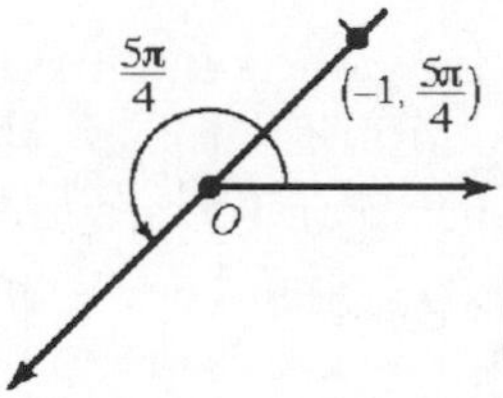

$x = -1\cos\left(\frac{5\pi}{4}\right) = \frac{\sqrt{2}}{2}$

$y = -1\sin\left(\frac{5\pi}{4}\right) = \frac{\sqrt{2}}{2}$

$\left(\frac{\sqrt{2}}{2}, \frac{\sqrt{2}}{2}\right)$

5. $\left(-3, -\frac{\pi}{2}\right)$

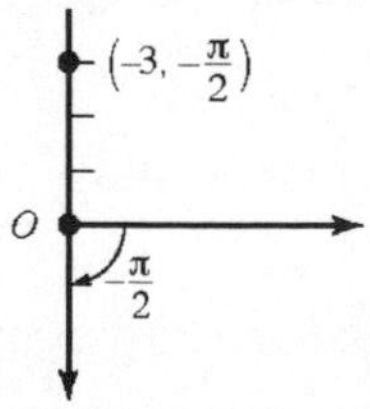

$x = -3\cos\left(-\frac{\pi}{2}\right) = 0$

$y = -3\sin\left(-\frac{\pi}{2}\right) = 3$

$(0, 3)$

6. $\left(-4, -\frac{\pi}{4}\right)$

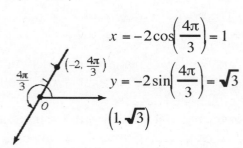

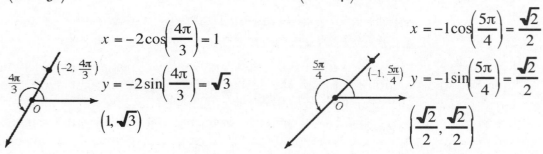

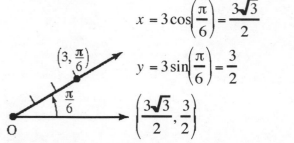

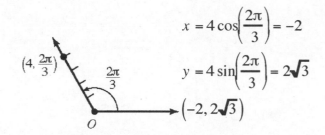

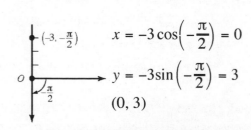

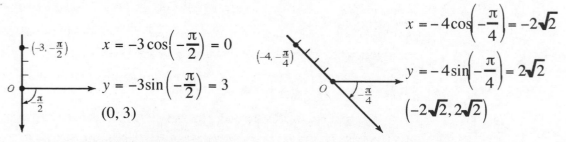

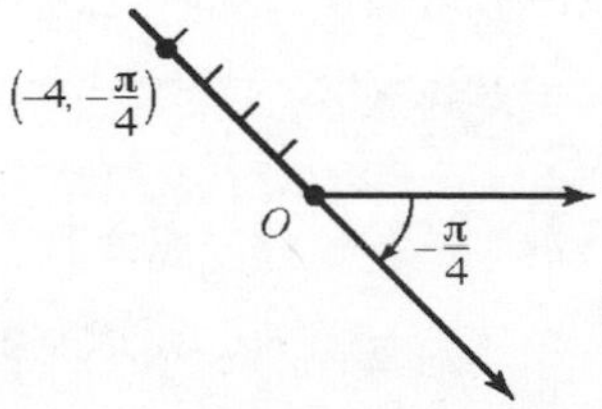

$x = -4\cos\left(-\frac{\pi}{4}\right) = -2\sqrt{2}$

$y = -4\sin\left(-\frac{\pi}{4}\right) = 2\sqrt{2}$

$\left(-2\sqrt{2}, 2\sqrt{2}\right)$

7. The point $(-3, 3)$ lies in quadrant II.

$r = \sqrt{x^2 + y^2} = \sqrt{(-3)^2 + 3^2} = 3\sqrt{2}$ $\quad \theta = \tan^{-1}\left(\frac{y}{x}\right) = \tan^{-1}\left(\frac{3}{-3}\right) = \tan^{-1}(-1) = -\frac{\pi}{4}$

Polar coordinates of the point $(-3, 3)$ are $\left(-3\sqrt{2}, -\frac{\pi}{4}\right)$ or $\left(3\sqrt{2}, \frac{3\pi}{4}\right)$.

8. The point (1, –1) lies in quadrant IV.

$r=\sqrt{x^2+y^2}=\sqrt{1^2+(-1)^2}=\sqrt{2}\qquad \theta=\tan^{-1}\left(\frac{y}{x}\right)=\tan^{-1}\left(\frac{-1}{1}\right)=\tan^{-1}(-1)=-\frac{\pi}{4}$

Polar coordinates of the point $(1,-1)$ are $\left(\sqrt{2},-\frac{\pi}{4}\right)$ and $\left(-\sqrt{2},\frac{3\pi}{4}\right)$.

9. The point (0, –2) lies on the negative y-axis.

$r=\sqrt{x^2+y^2}=\sqrt{0^2+(-2)^2}=2\qquad \theta=\tan^{-1}\left(\frac{y}{x}\right)=\tan^{-1}\left(\frac{-2}{0}\right)=-\frac{\pi}{2}$

Polar coordinates of the point $(0,-2)$ are $\left(2,-\frac{\pi}{2}\right)$ or $\left(-2,\frac{\pi}{2}\right)$.

10. The point (2, 0) lies on the positive x-axis.

$r=\sqrt{x^2+y^2}=\sqrt{2^2+0^2}=\sqrt{4}=2\qquad \theta=\tan^{-1}\left(\frac{y}{x}\right)=\tan^{-1}\left(\frac{0}{2}\right)=\tan^{-1}0=0$

Polar coordinates of the point (2, 0) are (2, 0) and $(-2,\pi)$.

11. The point (3, 4) lies in quadrant I.

$r=\sqrt{x^2+y^2}=\sqrt{3^2+4^2}=5\qquad \theta=\tan^{-1}\left(\frac{y}{x}\right)=\tan^{-1}\left(\frac{4}{3}\right)\approx 0.93$

Polar coordinates of the point $(3, 4)$ are $(5, 0.93)$ or $(-5, 4.07)$.

12. The point (–5, 12) lies in quadrant II.

$r=\sqrt{x^2+y^2}=\sqrt{(-5)^2+12^2}=13\qquad \theta=\tan^{-1}\left(\frac{y}{x}\right)=\tan^{-1}\left(\frac{12}{-5}\right)\approx -1.18$

Polar coordinates of the point $(-5, 12)$ are $(13, 1.96)$ or $(-13, 5.10)$.

13.
$$\begin{aligned}3x^2+3y^2&=6y\\ x^2+y^2&=2y\\ r^2&=2r\sin\theta\\ r^2-2r\sin\theta&=0\end{aligned}$$

14.
$$\begin{aligned}2x^2-2y^2&=5y\\ 2r^2\cos^2\theta-2r^2\sin^2\theta&=5r\sin\theta\\ 2r^2(\cos^2\theta-\sin^2\theta)&=5r\sin\theta\\ 2r\cos(2\theta)&=5\sin\theta\end{aligned}$$

15.
$$\begin{aligned}2x^2-y^2&=\frac{y}{x}\\ 2x^2+2y^2-3y^2&=\frac{y}{x}\\ 2(x^2+y^2)-3y^2&=\frac{y}{x}\\ 2r^2-3(r\sin\theta)^2&=\tan\theta\\ 2r^2-3r^2\sin^2\theta-\tan\theta&=0\\ r^2(2-3\sin\theta)-\tan\theta&=0\end{aligned}$$

16.
$$\begin{aligned}x^2+2y^2&=\frac{y}{x}\\ 2x^2+2y^2-x^2&=\frac{y}{x}\\ 2(x^2+y^2)-x^2&=\frac{y}{x}\\ 2r^2-(r\cos\theta)^2&=\tan\theta\\ 2r^2-r^2\cos^2\theta-\tan\theta&=0\\ r^2(2-\cos^2\theta)-\tan\theta&=0\end{aligned}$$

17. $x(x^2+y^2)=4$
$r\cos\theta(r^2)=4$
$r^3\cos\theta=4$

18. $y(x^2-y^2)=3$
$r\sin\theta(r^2\cos^2\theta-r^2\sin^2\theta)=3$
$r^3\sin\theta(\cos^2\theta-\sin^2\theta)=3$
$r^3\sin\theta\cos(2\theta)=3$

19. $r=2\sin\theta$
$r^2=2r\sin\theta$
$x^2+y^2=2y$
$x^2+y^2-2y=0$

20. $3r=\sin\theta$
$3r^2=r\sin\theta$
$3(x^2+y^2)=y$
$3x^2+3y^2-y=0$

21. $r=5$
$r^2=25$
$x^2+y^2=25$

22. $\theta=\frac{\pi}{4}$
$\tan\theta=\tan\left(\frac{\pi}{4}\right)$
$\frac{y}{x}=1$
$y=x$

23. $r\cos\theta+3r\sin\theta=6$
$x+3y=6$

24. $r^2\tan\theta=1$
$(x^2+y^2)\left(\frac{y}{x}\right)=1$
$x^2y+y^3=x$
$y^3+x^2y-x=0$

25. $r=4\cos\theta$ The graph will be a circle. Check for symmetry:
Polar axis: Replace θ by $-\theta$. The result is $r=4\cos(-\theta)=4\cos\theta$.
The graph is symmetric with respect to the polar axis.
The line $\theta=\frac{\pi}{2}$: Replace θ by $\pi-\theta$.
$$r=4\cos(\pi-\theta)=4(\cos(\pi)\cos\theta+\sin(\pi)\sin\theta)$$
$$=4(-\cos\theta+0)=-4\cos\theta$$
The test fails.
The pole: Replace r by $-r$. $-r=4\cos\theta$. The test fails.
Due to symmetry to the polar axis, assign values to θ from 0 to π.

θ	0	$\frac{\pi}{6}$	$\frac{\pi}{3}$	$\frac{\pi}{2}$	$\frac{2\pi}{3}$	$\frac{5\pi}{6}$	π
$r=4\cos\theta$	4	$2\sqrt{3}\approx 3.5$	2	0	-2	$-2\sqrt{3}\approx -3.5$	-4

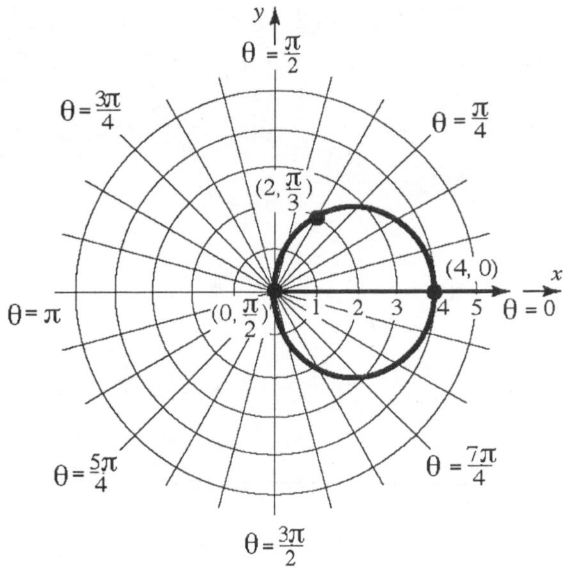

26. $r = 3\sin\theta$ The graph will be a circle. Check for symmetry:

Polar axis: Replace θ by $-\theta$. The result is $r = 3\sin(-\theta) = -3\sin\theta$. The test fails.

The line $\theta = \frac{\pi}{2}$: Replace θ by $\pi - \theta$.

$$r = 3\sin(\pi - \theta) = 3(\sin(\pi)\cos\theta - \cos(\pi)\sin\theta)$$
$$= 3(0 + \sin\theta) = 3\sin\theta$$

The graph is symmetric with respect to the line $\theta = \frac{\pi}{2}$.

The pole: Replace r by $-r$. $-r = 3\sin\theta$. The test fails.

Due to symmetry to the line $\theta = \frac{\pi}{2}$, assign values to θ from $-\frac{\pi}{2}$ to $\frac{\pi}{2}$.

θ	$-\frac{\pi}{2}$	$-\frac{\pi}{3}$	$-\frac{\pi}{6}$	0	$\frac{\pi}{6}$	$\frac{\pi}{3}$	$\frac{\pi}{2}$
$r = 3\sin\theta$	-3	$-\frac{3\sqrt{3}}{2} \approx -2.6$	$-\frac{3}{2}$	0	$\frac{3}{2}$	$\frac{3\sqrt{3}}{2} \approx 2.6$	3

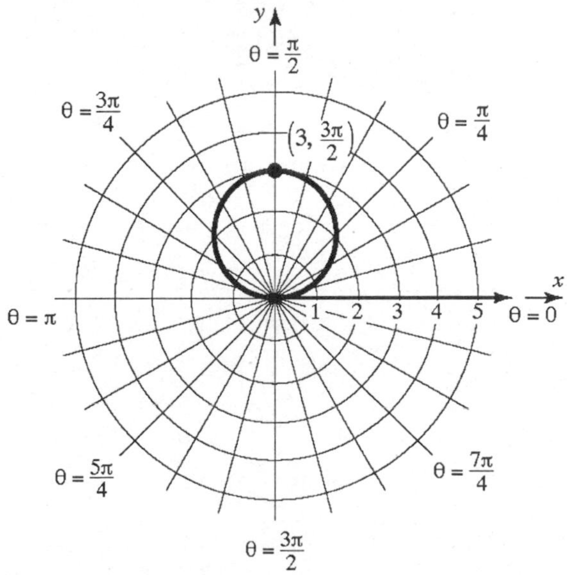

27. $r = 3 - 3\sin\theta$ The graph will be a cardioid. Check for symmetry:
Polar axis: Replace θ by $-\theta$. The result is $r = 3 - 3\sin(-\theta) = 3 + 3\sin\theta$.
The test fails.

The line $\theta = \frac{\pi}{2}$: Replace θ by $\pi - \theta$.

$$r = 3 - 3\sin(\pi - \theta) = 3 - 3(\sin(\pi)\cos\theta - \cos(\pi)\sin\theta)$$
$$= 3 - 3(0 + \sin\theta) = 3 - 3\sin\theta$$

The graph is symmetric with respect to the line $\theta = \frac{\pi}{2}$.

The pole: Replace r by $-r$. $-r = 3 - 3\sin\theta$. The test fails.

Due to symmetry to the line $\theta = \frac{\pi}{2}$, assign values to θ from $-\frac{\pi}{2}$ to $\frac{\pi}{2}$.

θ	$-\frac{\pi}{2}$	$-\frac{\pi}{3}$	$-\frac{\pi}{6}$	0	$\frac{\pi}{6}$	$\frac{\pi}{3}$	$\frac{\pi}{2}$
$r = 3 - 3\sin\theta$	6	$3 + \frac{3\sqrt{3}}{2} \approx 5.6$	$\frac{9}{2}$	3	$\frac{3}{2}$	$3 - \frac{3\sqrt{3}}{2} \approx 0.4$	0

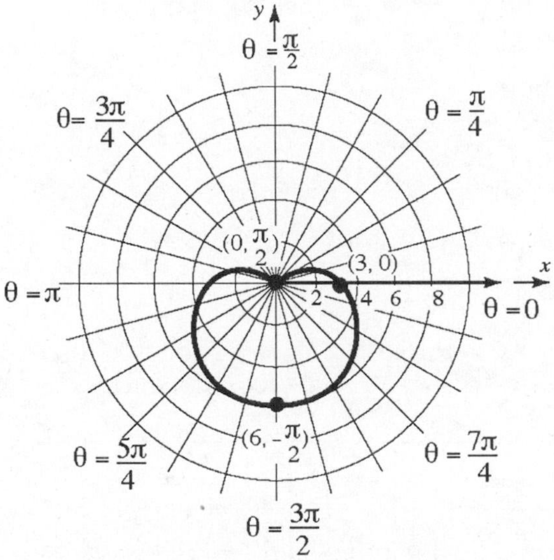

28. $r = 2 + \cos\theta$ The graph will be a limacon without an inner loop.
Check for symmetry:
Polar axis: Replace θ by $-\theta$. The result is $r = 2 + \cos(-\theta) = 2 + \cos\theta$.
The graph is symmetric with respect to the polar axis.

The line $\theta = \frac{\pi}{2}$: Replace θ by $\pi - \theta$.

$$r = 2 + \cos(\pi - \theta) = 2 + (\cos(\pi)\cos\theta + \sin(\pi)\sin\theta)$$
$$= 2 + (-\cos\theta + 0) = 2 - \cos\theta$$

The test fails.

The pole: Replace r by $-r$. $-r = 2 + \cos\theta$. The test fails.

Due to symmetry to the polar axis, assign values to θ from 0 to π.

θ	0	$\frac{\pi}{6}$	$\frac{\pi}{3}$	$\frac{\pi}{2}$	$\frac{2\pi}{3}$	$\frac{5\pi}{6}$	π
$r = 2 + \cos\theta$	3	$2 + \frac{\sqrt{3}}{2} \approx 2.9$	$\frac{5}{2}$	2	$\frac{3}{2}$	$2 - \frac{\sqrt{3}}{2} \approx 1.1$	1

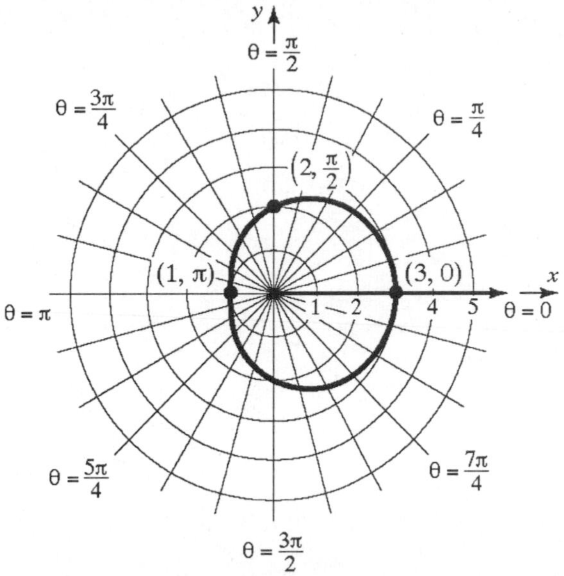

29. $r = 4 - \cos\theta$ The graph will be a limacon without an inner loop.
Check for symmetry:
Polar axis: Replace θ by $-\theta$. The result is $r = 4 - \cos(-\theta) = 4 - \cos\theta$.
The graph is symmetric with respect to the polar axis.
The line $\theta = \frac{\pi}{2}$: Replace θ by $\pi - \theta$.

$$r = 4 - \cos(\pi - \theta) = 4 - (\cos(\pi)\cos\theta + \sin(\pi)\sin\theta)$$
$$= 4 - (-\cos\theta + 0) = 4 + \cos\theta$$

The test fails.
The pole: Replace r by $-r$. $-r = 4 - \cos\theta$. The test fails.
Due to symmetry to the polar axis, assign values to θ from 0 to π.

θ	0	$\frac{\pi}{6}$	$\frac{\pi}{3}$	$\frac{\pi}{2}$	$\frac{2\pi}{3}$	$\frac{5\pi}{6}$	π
$r = 4 - \cos\theta$	3	$4 - \frac{\sqrt{3}}{2} \approx 3.1$	$\frac{7}{2}$	4	$\frac{9}{2}$	$4 + \frac{\sqrt{3}}{2} \approx 4.9$	5

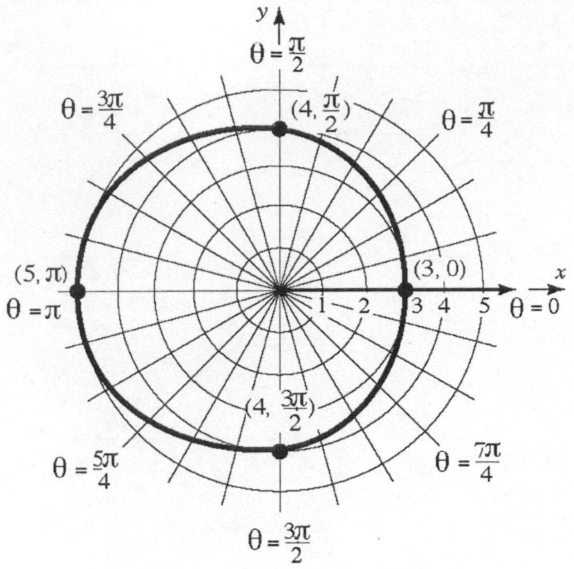

30. $r = 1 - 2\sin\theta$ The graph will be a limacon with an inner loop.
Check for symmetry:
Polar axis: Replace θ by $-\theta$. The result is $r = 1 - 2\sin(-\theta) = 1 + 2\sin\theta$.
The test fails.
The line $\theta = \frac{\pi}{2}$: Replace θ by $\pi - \theta$.

$$r = 1 - 2\sin(\pi - \theta) = 1 - 2(\sin(\pi)\cos\theta - \cos(\pi)\sin\theta)$$
$$= 1 - 2(0 + \sin\theta) = 1 - 2\sin\theta$$

The graph is symmetric with respect to the line $\theta = \frac{\pi}{2}$.
The pole: Replace r by $-r$. $-r = 1 - 2\sin\theta$. The test fails.
Due to symmetry to the line $\theta = \frac{\pi}{2}$, assign values to θ from $-\frac{\pi}{2}$ to $\frac{\pi}{2}$.

θ	$-\frac{\pi}{2}$	$-\frac{\pi}{3}$	$-\frac{\pi}{6}$	0	$\frac{\pi}{6}$	$\frac{\pi}{3}$	$\frac{\pi}{2}$
$r = 1 - 2\sin\theta$	3	$1+\sqrt{3} \approx 2.7$	2	1	0	$1-\sqrt{3} \approx -0.7$	-1

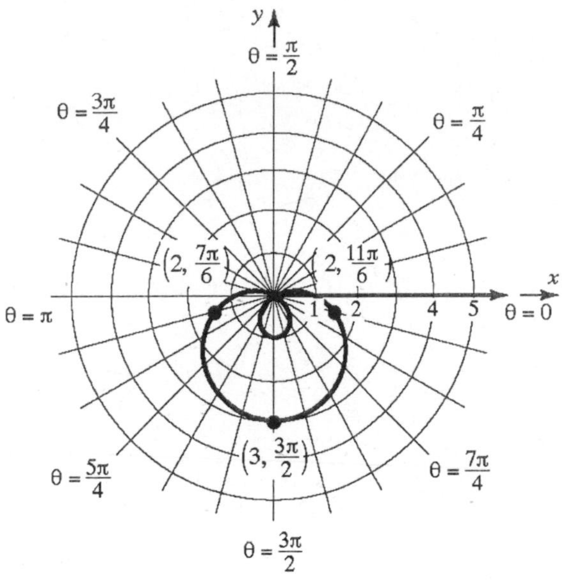

31. $r = \sqrt{x^2 + y^2} = \sqrt{(-1)^2 + (-1)^2} = \sqrt{2}$

$\tan\theta = \frac{y}{x} = \frac{-1}{-1} = 1 \quad \rightarrow \quad \theta = 225^\circ$

The polar form of $z = -1 - i$ is $z = r(\cos\theta + i\sin\theta) = \sqrt{2}(\cos(225^\circ) + i\sin(225^\circ))$.

32. $r = \sqrt{x^2 + y^2} = \sqrt{\left(-\sqrt{3}\right)^2 + 1^2} = \sqrt{4} = 2$

$\tan\theta = \frac{y}{x} = \frac{1}{-\sqrt{3}} = -\frac{\sqrt{3}}{3} \quad \rightarrow \quad \theta = 150^\circ$

The polar form of $z = -\sqrt{3} + i$ is $z = r(\cos\theta + i\sin\theta) = 2(\cos(150^\circ) + i\sin(150^\circ))$.

33. $r = \sqrt{x^2 + y^2} = \sqrt{4^2 + (-3)^2} = \sqrt{25} = 5$

$\tan\theta = \frac{y}{x} = -\frac{3}{4} \quad \rightarrow \quad \theta \approx 323.1^\circ$

The polar form of $z = 4 - 3i$ is $z = r(\cos\theta + i\sin\theta) = 5(\cos(323.1^\circ) + i\sin(323.1^\circ))$.

34. $r = \sqrt{x^2 + y^2} = \sqrt{3^2 + (-2)^2} = \sqrt{13}$

$\tan\theta = \frac{y}{x} = -\frac{2}{3} \quad \rightarrow \quad \theta \approx 326.3^\circ$

The polar form of $z = 3 - 2i$ is $z = r(\cos\theta + i\sin\theta) = \sqrt{13}(\cos(326.3^\circ) + i\sin(326.3^\circ))$.

35. $2(\cos(150^\circ) + i\sin(150^\circ)) = 2\left(-\frac{\sqrt{3}}{2} + \frac{1}{2}i\right) = -\sqrt{3} + i$

36. $3(\cos(60^\circ) + i\sin(60^\circ)) = 3\left(\frac{1}{2} + \frac{\sqrt{3}}{2}i\right) = \frac{3}{2} + \frac{3\sqrt{3}}{2}i$

37. $3\left(\cos\left(\frac{2\pi}{3}\right)+i\sin\left(\frac{2\pi}{3}\right)\right)=3\left(-\frac{1}{2}+\frac{\sqrt{3}}{2}i\right)=-\frac{3}{2}+\frac{3\sqrt{3}}{2}i$

38. $4\left(\cos\left(\frac{3\pi}{4}\right)+i\sin\left(\frac{3\pi}{4}\right)\right)=4\left(-\frac{\sqrt{2}}{2}+\frac{\sqrt{2}}{2}i\right)=-2\sqrt{2}+2\sqrt{2}\,i$

39. $0.1(\cos(350^\circ)+i\sin(350^\circ))\approx 0.1(0.9848-0.1736i)=0.0985-0.0174i$

40. $0.5(\cos(160^\circ)+i\sin(160^\circ))\approx 0.5(-0.9397+0.3420i)=-0.4699+0.1710i$

41. $z\cdot w=(\cos(80^\circ)+i\sin(80^\circ))\cdot(\cos(50^\circ)+i\sin(50^\circ))$
$=1\cdot 1(\cos(80^\circ+50^\circ)+i\sin(80^\circ+50^\circ))=\cos(130^\circ)+i\sin(130^\circ)$
$\frac{z}{w}=\frac{(\cos(80^\circ)+i\sin(80^\circ))}{(\cos(50^\circ)+i\sin(50^\circ))}=\frac{1}{1}(\cos(80^\circ-50^\circ)+i\sin(80^\circ-50^\circ))$
$=\cos(30^\circ)+i\sin(30^\circ)$

42. $z\cdot w=(\cos(205^\circ)+i\sin(205^\circ))\cdot(\cos(85^\circ)+i\sin(85^\circ))$
$=1\cdot 1(\cos(205^\circ+85^\circ)+i\sin(205^\circ+85^\circ))=\cos(290^\circ)+i\sin(290^\circ)$
$\frac{z}{w}=\frac{(\cos(205^\circ)+i\sin(205^\circ))}{(\cos(85^\circ)+i\sin(85^\circ))}=\frac{1}{1}(\cos(205^\circ-85^\circ)+i\sin(205^\circ-85^\circ))$
$=\cos(120^\circ)+i\sin(120^\circ)$

43. $z\cdot w=3\left(\cos\left(\frac{9\pi}{5}\right)+i\sin\left(\frac{9\pi}{5}\right)\right)\cdot 2\left(\cos\frac{\pi}{5}+i\sin\frac{\pi}{5}\right)=3\cdot 2\left(\cos\left(\frac{9\pi}{5}+\frac{\pi}{5}\right)+i\sin\left(\frac{9\pi}{5}+\frac{\pi}{5}\right)\right)$
$=6\cdot(\cos(2\pi)+i\sin(2\pi))=6(\cos(0)+i\sin(0))$
$\frac{z}{w}=\frac{3\cdot\left(\cos\left(\frac{9\pi}{5}\right)+i\sin\left(\frac{9\pi}{5}\right)\right)}{2\cdot\left(\cos\left(\frac{\pi}{5}\right)+i\sin\left(\frac{\pi}{5}\right)\right)}=\frac{3}{2}\left(\cos\left(\frac{9\pi}{5}-\frac{\pi}{5}\right)+i\sin\left(\frac{9\pi}{5}-\frac{\pi}{5}\right)\right)=\frac{3}{2}\left(\cos\left(\frac{8\pi}{5}\right)+i\sin\left(\frac{8\pi}{5}\right)\right)$

44. $z\cdot w=2\cdot\left(\cos\left(\frac{5\pi}{3}\right)+i\sin\left(\frac{5\pi}{3}\right)\right)\cdot 3\cdot\left(\cos\left(\frac{\pi}{3}\right)+i\sin\left(\frac{\pi}{3}\right)\right)=2\cdot 3\left(\cos\left(\frac{5\pi}{3}+\frac{\pi}{3}\right)+i\sin\left(\frac{5\pi}{3}+\frac{\pi}{3}\right)\right)$
$=6\cdot(\cos(2\pi)+i\sin(2\pi))=6\cdot(\cos(0)+i\sin(0))$
$\frac{z}{w}=\frac{2\cdot\left(\cos\left(\frac{5\pi}{3}\right)+i\sin\left(\frac{5\pi}{3}\right)\right)}{3\cdot\left(\cos\left(\frac{\pi}{3}\right)+i\sin\left(\frac{\pi}{3}\right)\right)}=\frac{2}{3}\cdot\left(\cos\left(\frac{5\pi}{3}-\frac{\pi}{3}\right)+i\sin\left(\frac{5\pi}{3}-\frac{\pi}{3}\right)\right)=\frac{2}{3}\cdot\left(\cos\frac{4\pi}{3}+i\sin\frac{4\pi}{3}\right)$

45. $z\cdot w=5(\cos(10^\circ)+i\sin(10^\circ))\cdot(\cos(355^\circ)+i\sin(355^\circ))$

$$= 5 \cdot 1(\cos(10° + 355°) + i\sin(10° + 355°)) = 5 \cdot (\cos(365°) + i\sin(365°))$$
$$= 5 \cdot (\cos(5°) + i\sin(5°))$$
$$\frac{z}{w} = \frac{5(\cos(10°) + i\sin(10°))}{(\cos(355°) + i\sin(355°))} = \frac{5}{1}(\cos(10° - 355°) + i\sin(10° - 355°))$$
$$= 5 \cdot (\cos(-345°) + i\sin(-345°)) = 5 \cdot (\cos(15°) + i\sin(15°))$$

46. $z \cdot w = 4 \cdot (\cos(50°) + i\sin(50°)) \cdot (\cos(340°) + i\sin(340°))$
$$= 4 \cdot 1(\cos(50° + 340°) + i\sin(50° + 340°)) = 4 \cdot (\cos(390°) + i\sin(390°))$$
$$= 4 \cdot (\cos(30°) + i\sin(30°))$$
$$\frac{z}{w} = \frac{4(\cos(50°) + i\sin 50°)}{(\cos(340°) + i\sin(340°))} = \frac{4}{1}(\cos(50° - 340°) + i\sin(50° - 340°))$$
$$= 4 \cdot (\cos(-290°) + i\sin(-290°)) = 4 \cdot (\cos(70°) + i\sin(70°))$$

47. $[3(\cos(20°) + i\sin(20°))]^3 = 3^3(\cos(3 \cdot 20°) + i\sin(3 \cdot 20°)) = 27(\cos(60°) + i\sin(60°))$
$$= 27\left(\frac{1}{2} + \frac{\sqrt{3}}{2}\,i\right) = \frac{27}{2} + \frac{27\sqrt{3}}{2}\,i$$

48. $[2(\cos(50°) + i\sin(50°))]^3 = 2^3(\cos(3 \cdot 50°) + i\sin(3 \cdot 50°)) = 8 \cdot (\cos(150°) + i\sin(150°))$
$$= 8\left(-\frac{\sqrt{3}}{2} + \frac{1}{2}\,i\right) = -4\sqrt{3} + 4\,i$$

49. $\left[\sqrt{2} \cdot \left(\cos\left(\frac{5\pi}{8}\right) + i\sin\left(\frac{5\pi}{8}\right)\right)\right]^4 = \left(\sqrt{2}\right)^4\left(\cos\left(4 \cdot \frac{5\pi}{8}\right) + i\sin\left(4 \cdot \frac{5\pi}{8}\right)\right)$
$$= 4 \cdot \left(\cos\left(\frac{5\pi}{2}\right) + i\sin\left(\frac{5\pi}{2}\right)\right) = 4(0 + 1\,i) = 4i$$

50. $\left[2 \cdot \left(\cos\left(\frac{5\pi}{16}\right) + i\sin\left(\frac{5\pi}{16}\right)\right)\right]^4 = 2^4 \cdot \left(\cos\left(4 \cdot \frac{5\pi}{16}\right) + i\sin\left(4 \cdot \frac{5\pi}{16}\right)\right)$
$$= 16 \cdot \left(\cos\left(\frac{5\pi}{4}\right) + i\sin\left(\frac{5\pi}{4}\right)\right) = 16 \cdot \left(-\frac{\sqrt{2}}{2} - \frac{\sqrt{2}}{2}\,i\right) = -8\sqrt{2} - 8\sqrt{2}\,i$$

51. $1 - \sqrt{3}\,i \qquad r = \sqrt{1^2 + \left(-\sqrt{3}\right)^2} = 2 \qquad \tan\theta = \frac{-\sqrt{3}}{1} = -\sqrt{3} \qquad \theta = 300°$
$$1 - \sqrt{3}\,i = 2(\cos(300°) + i\sin(300°))$$
$$\left(1 - \sqrt{3}\,i\right)^6 = [2(\cos(300°) + i\sin(300°))]^6 = 2^6 \cdot (\cos(6 \cdot 300°) + i\sin(6 \cdot 300°))$$
$$= 64 \cdot (\cos(1800°) + i\sin(1800°)) = 64 \cdot (\cos(0°) + i\sin(0°))$$
$$= 64 + 0\,i = 64$$

52. $2-2i \qquad r=\sqrt{2^2+(-2)^2}=2\sqrt{2} \qquad \tan\theta=\frac{-2}{2}=-1 \qquad \theta=315°$

$$2-2i=2\sqrt{2}\cdot(\cos(315°)+i\sin(315°))$$

$$(2-2i)^8=\left[2\sqrt{2}\cdot(\cos(315°)+i\sin(315°))\right]^8=\left(2\sqrt{2}\right)^8\cdot(\cos(8\cdot 315°)+i\sin(8\cdot 315°))$$

$$=4096\cdot(\cos(2520°)+i\sin(2520°))=4096\cdot(\cos(0°)+i\sin(0°))$$

$$=4096(1+0i)=4096$$

53. $3+4i \qquad r=\sqrt{3^2+4^2}=5 \qquad \tan\theta=\frac{4}{3} \qquad \theta\approx 53.1°$

$$3+4i=5\cdot(\cos(53.1°)+i\sin(53.1°))$$

$$(3+4i)^4=\left[5^4\cdot(\cos(4\cdot 53.1°)+i\sin(4\cdot 53.1°))\right]^4=625\cdot(\cos(212.4°)+i\sin(212.4°))$$

$$\approx 625\cdot(-0.8443+i(-0.5358))=-527.7-334.9i$$

54. $1-2i \qquad r=\sqrt{1^2+(-2)^2}=\sqrt{5} \qquad \tan\theta=\frac{-2}{1}=-2 \qquad \theta\approx 296.6°$

$$1-2i=\sqrt{5}\cdot(\cos(296.6°)+i\sin(296.6°))$$

$$(1-2i)^4=\left[\left(\sqrt{5}\right)^4\cdot(\cos(4\cdot 296.6°)+i\sin(4\cdot 296.6°))\right]$$

$$=25\cdot(\cos(1186.4°)+i\sin(1186.4°))$$

$$\approx 25\cdot(-0.2823+i(0.9593))=-7.0575+23.9825i$$

55. $27+0i \qquad r=\sqrt{27^2+0^2}=27 \qquad \tan\theta=\frac{0}{27}=0 \qquad \theta=0°$

$$27+0i=27(\cos(0°)+i\sin(0°))$$

The three complex cube roots of $27=27(\cos 0°+i\sin 0°)$ are:

$$z_k=\sqrt[3]{27}\cdot\left[\cos\left(\frac{0°}{3}+\frac{360°\cdot k}{3}\right)+i\sin\left(\frac{0°}{3}+\frac{360°\cdot k}{3}\right)\right]$$

$$=3[\cos(120°k)+i\sin(120°\cdot k)]$$

$$z_0=3[\cos(120°\cdot 0)+i\sin(120°\cdot 0)]=3\cdot(\cos(0°)+i\sin(0°))=3$$

$$z_1=3[\cos(120°\cdot 1)+i\sin(120°\cdot 1)]=3\cdot(\cos(120°)+i\sin(120°))=-\frac{3}{2}+\frac{3\sqrt{3}}{2}i$$

$$z_2=3[\cos(120°\cdot 2)+i\sin(120°\cdot 2)]=3\cdot(\cos(240°)+i\sin(240°))=-\frac{3}{2}-\frac{3\sqrt{3}}{2}i$$

56. $-16 \qquad r=\sqrt{(-16)^2+0^2}=\sqrt{256}=16 \qquad \tan\theta=\frac{0}{-16}=0 \qquad \theta=180°$

$$-16=16\cdot(\cos(180°)+i\sin(180°))$$

The four complex fourth roots of $-16=16\cdot(\cos(180°)+i\sin(180°))$ are:

$$z_k = \sqrt[4]{16}\left[\cos\left(\frac{180^\circ}{4} + \frac{360^\circ \cdot k}{4}\right) + i\sin\left(\frac{180^\circ}{4} + \frac{360^\circ \cdot k}{4}\right)\right]$$
$$= 2\left[\cos(45^\circ + 90^\circ k) + i\sin(45^\circ + 90^\circ \cdot k)\right]$$
$$z_0 = 2\left[\cos(45^\circ + 90^\circ \cdot 0) + i\sin(45^\circ + 90^\circ \cdot 0)\right] = 2\cdot(\cos(45^\circ) + i\sin(45^\circ)) = \sqrt{2} + \sqrt{2}\,i$$
$$z_1 = 2\left[\cos(45^\circ + 90^\circ \cdot 1) + i\sin(45^\circ + 90^\circ \cdot 1)\right] = 2\cdot(\cos(135^\circ) + i\sin(135^\circ)) = -\sqrt{2} + \sqrt{2}\,i$$
$$z_2 = 2\left[\cos(45^\circ + 90^\circ \cdot 2) + i\sin(45^\circ + 90^\circ \cdot 2)\right] = 2\cdot(\cos(225^\circ) + i\sin(225^\circ)) = -\sqrt{2} - \sqrt{2}\,i$$
$$z_3 = 2\left[\cos(45^\circ + 90^\circ \cdot 3) + i\sin(45^\circ + 90^\circ \cdot 3)\right] = 2\cdot(\cos(315^\circ) + i\sin(315^\circ)) = \sqrt{2} - \sqrt{2}\,i$$

57. $P = (1, -2), Q = (3, -6) \qquad \mathbf{v} = (3-1)\mathbf{i} + (-6-(-2))\mathbf{j} = 2\mathbf{i} - 4\mathbf{j}$
$\|\mathbf{v}\| = \sqrt{2^2 + (-4)^2} = \sqrt{20} = 2\sqrt{5}$

58. $P = (-3, 1), Q = (4, -2) \qquad \mathbf{v} = (4-(-3))\mathbf{i} + (-2-1)\mathbf{j} = 7\mathbf{i} - 3\mathbf{j}$
$\|\mathbf{v}\| = \sqrt{7^2 + (-3)^2} = \sqrt{58}$

59. $P = (0, -2), Q = (-1, 1) \qquad \mathbf{v} = (-1-0)\mathbf{i} + (1-(-2))\mathbf{j} = -1\mathbf{i} + 3\mathbf{j}$
$\|\mathbf{v}\| = \sqrt{(-1)^2 + 3^2} = \sqrt{10}$

60. $P = (3, -4), Q = (-2, 0) \qquad \mathbf{v} = (-2-3)\mathbf{i} + (0-(-4))\mathbf{j} = -5\mathbf{i} + 4\mathbf{j}$
$\|\mathbf{v}\| = \sqrt{(-5)^2 + 4^2} = \sqrt{41}$

61. $\mathbf{v} = -2\mathbf{i} + \mathbf{j},\ \mathbf{w} = 4\mathbf{i} - 3\mathbf{j}$
$4\mathbf{v} - 3\mathbf{w} = 4(-2\mathbf{i} + \mathbf{j}) - 3(4\mathbf{i} - 3\mathbf{j}) = -8\mathbf{i} + 4\mathbf{j} - 12\mathbf{i} + 9\mathbf{j} = -20\mathbf{i} + 13\mathbf{j}$

62. $\mathbf{v} = -2\mathbf{i} + \mathbf{j},\ \mathbf{w} = 4\mathbf{i} - 3\mathbf{j}$
$-\mathbf{v} + 2\mathbf{w} = -(-2\mathbf{i} + \mathbf{j}) + 2(4\mathbf{i} - 3\mathbf{j}) = 2\mathbf{i} - \mathbf{j} + 8\mathbf{i} - 6\mathbf{j} = 10\mathbf{i} - 7\mathbf{j}$

63. $\mathbf{v} = -2\mathbf{i} + \mathbf{j}$
$\|\mathbf{v}\| = \|-2\mathbf{i} + \mathbf{j}\| = \sqrt{(-2)^2 + 1^2} = \sqrt{5}$

64. $\mathbf{v} = -2\mathbf{i} + \mathbf{j},\ \mathbf{w} = 4\mathbf{i} - 3\mathbf{j}$
$\|\mathbf{v} + \mathbf{w}\| = \|(-2\mathbf{i} + \mathbf{j}) + (4\mathbf{i} - 3\mathbf{j})\| = \|2\mathbf{i} - 2\mathbf{j}\| = \sqrt{2^2 + (-2)^2} = \sqrt{8} = 2\sqrt{2}$

65. $\mathbf{v} = -2\mathbf{i} + \mathbf{j},\ \mathbf{w} = 4\mathbf{i} - 3\mathbf{j}$
$\|\mathbf{v}\| + \|\mathbf{w}\| = \|-2\mathbf{i} + \mathbf{j}\| + \|4\mathbf{i} - 3\mathbf{j}\| = \sqrt{(-2)^2 + 1^2} + \sqrt{4^2 + (-3)^2} = \sqrt{5} + 5$

66. $\mathbf{v} = -2\mathbf{i} + \mathbf{j},\ \mathbf{w} = 4\mathbf{i} - 3\mathbf{j}$
$\|2\mathbf{v}\| - 3\|\mathbf{w}\| = \|2(-2\mathbf{i} + \mathbf{j})\| - 3\|4\mathbf{i} - 3\mathbf{j}\| = \|-4\mathbf{i} + 2\mathbf{j}\| - 3\|4\mathbf{i} - 3\mathbf{j}\|$
$= \sqrt{(-4)^2 + 2^2} - 3\sqrt{4^2 + (-3)^2} = \sqrt{20} - 3\cdot 5 = 2\sqrt{5} - 15$

67. $\mathbf{u}=\dfrac{\mathbf{v}}{\|\mathbf{v}\|}=\dfrac{-2\mathbf{i}+\mathbf{j}}{\|-2\mathbf{i}+\mathbf{j}\|}=\dfrac{-2\mathbf{i}+\mathbf{j}}{\sqrt{(-2)^2+1^2}}=\dfrac{-2\mathbf{i}+\mathbf{j}}{\sqrt{5}}=-\dfrac{2\sqrt{5}}{5}\mathbf{i}+\dfrac{\sqrt{5}}{5}\mathbf{j}$

68. $\mathbf{u}=\dfrac{-\mathbf{w}}{\|\mathbf{w}\|}=\dfrac{-(4\mathbf{i}-3\mathbf{j})}{\|4\mathbf{i}-3\mathbf{j}\|}=\dfrac{-4\mathbf{i}+3\mathbf{j}}{\sqrt{4^2+(-3)^2}}=\dfrac{-4\mathbf{i}+3\mathbf{j}}{\sqrt{25}}=-\dfrac{4}{5}\mathbf{i}+\dfrac{3}{5}\mathbf{j}$

69. $\mathbf{v}=-2\mathbf{i}+\mathbf{j},\quad \mathbf{w}=4\mathbf{i}-3\mathbf{j}$

$\mathbf{v}\bullet\mathbf{w}=-2(4)+1(-3)=-8-3=-11$

$\cos\theta=\dfrac{\mathbf{v}\bullet\mathbf{w}}{\|\mathbf{v}\|\|\mathbf{w}\|}=\dfrac{-11}{\sqrt{(-2)^2+1^2}\sqrt{4^2+(-3)^2}}=\dfrac{-11}{\sqrt{5}\cdot 5}=\dfrac{-11}{5\sqrt{5}}\approx-0.9839$

$\theta\approx 169.7^\circ$

70. $\mathbf{v}=3\mathbf{i}-\mathbf{j},\quad \mathbf{w}=\mathbf{i}+\mathbf{j}$

$\mathbf{v}\bullet\mathbf{w}=3\cdot 1+(-1)(1)=3-1=2$

$\cos\theta=\dfrac{\mathbf{v}\bullet\mathbf{w}}{\|\mathbf{v}\|\|\mathbf{w}\|}=\dfrac{2}{\sqrt{3^2+(-1)^2}\sqrt{1^2+1^2}}=\dfrac{2}{\sqrt{10}\sqrt{2}}=\dfrac{1}{\sqrt{5}}\approx 0.4472$

$\theta\approx 63.4^\circ$

71. $\mathbf{v}=\mathbf{i}-3\mathbf{j},\quad \mathbf{w}=-\mathbf{i}+\mathbf{j}$

$\mathbf{v}\bullet\mathbf{w}=1(-1)+(-3)(1)=-1-3=-4$

$\cos\theta=\dfrac{\mathbf{v}\bullet\mathbf{w}}{\|\mathbf{v}\|\|\mathbf{w}\|}=\dfrac{-4}{\sqrt{1^2+(-3)^2}\sqrt{(-1)^2+1^2}}=\dfrac{-4}{\sqrt{10}\sqrt{2}}=\dfrac{-2}{\sqrt{5}}\approx-0.8944$

$\theta\approx 153.4^\circ$

72. $\mathbf{v}=\mathbf{i}+4\mathbf{j},\quad \mathbf{w}=3\mathbf{i}-2\mathbf{j}$

$\mathbf{v}\bullet\mathbf{w}=1(3)+(4)(-2)=3-8=-5$

$\cos\theta=\dfrac{\mathbf{v}\bullet\mathbf{w}}{\|\mathbf{v}\|\|\mathbf{w}\|}=\dfrac{-5}{\sqrt{1^2+4^2}\sqrt{3^2+(-2)^2}}=\dfrac{-5}{\sqrt{17}\sqrt{13}}=\dfrac{-5}{\sqrt{221}}\approx-0.3363$

$\theta\approx 109.7^\circ$

73. $\text{proj}_{\mathbf{w}}\mathbf{v}=\dfrac{\mathbf{v}\bullet\mathbf{w}}{\|\mathbf{w}\|^2}\mathbf{w}=\dfrac{(2\mathbf{i}+3\mathbf{j})\bullet(3\mathbf{i}+\mathbf{j})}{\sqrt{3^2+1^2}^{\,2}}(3\mathbf{i}+\mathbf{j})=\dfrac{2\cdot 3+3\cdot 1}{10}(3\mathbf{i}+\mathbf{j})=\dfrac{27}{10}\mathbf{i}+\dfrac{9}{10}\mathbf{j}$

74. $\text{proj}_{\mathbf{w}}\mathbf{v}=\dfrac{\mathbf{v}\bullet\mathbf{w}}{\|\mathbf{w}\|^2}\mathbf{w}=\dfrac{(-\mathbf{i}+2\mathbf{j})\bullet(3\mathbf{i}-\mathbf{j})}{\sqrt{3^2+(-1)^2}^{\,2}}(3\mathbf{i}-\mathbf{j})=\dfrac{-1\cdot 3+2(-1)}{10}(3\mathbf{i}-\mathbf{j})$

$=\dfrac{-15}{10}\mathbf{i}+\dfrac{5}{10}\mathbf{j}=-\dfrac{3}{2}\mathbf{i}+\dfrac{1}{2}\mathbf{j}$

75. Let the positive x-axis point downstream, so that the velocity of the current is $\mathbf{v}_c=2\mathbf{i}$.
Let $\mathbf{v}_w$ = the velocity of the swimmer in the water.
Let $\mathbf{v}_g$ = the velocity of the swimmer relative to the land.
Then $\mathbf{v}_g=\mathbf{v}_w+\mathbf{v}_c$
The speed of the swimmer is $\|\mathbf{v}_w\|=5$; its direction is directly across the river, so

Let $\mathbf{v}_w = 5\mathbf{j}$.
$\mathbf{v}_g = \mathbf{v}_w + \mathbf{v}_c = 5\mathbf{j} + 2\mathbf{i} = 2\mathbf{i} + 5\mathbf{j}$
Let $\|\mathbf{v}_g\| = \sqrt{2^2 + 5^2} = \sqrt{29} \approx 5.4$ miles per hour .

Since the river is 1 mile wide, it takes the swimmer 0.2 hours to cross the river. The swimmer will end up (0.2)(2) = 0.4 miles downstream.

76. Let $\mathbf{v}_a$ = the velocity of the plane in still air.
$\mathbf{v}_w$ = the velocity of the wind.
$\mathbf{v}_g$ = the velocity of the plane relative to the ground.
$\mathbf{v}_g = \mathbf{v}_a + \mathbf{v}_w$
$\mathbf{v}_a = 500\,\mathbf{j}$
$$\mathbf{v}_w = 60\left(\frac{\sqrt{2}}{2}\mathbf{i} - \frac{\sqrt{2}}{2}\mathbf{j}\right) = 30\sqrt{2}\,\mathbf{i} - 30\sqrt{2}\,\mathbf{j}$$
$$\mathbf{v}_g = \mathbf{v}_a + \mathbf{v}_w = 500\,\mathbf{j} + 30\sqrt{2}\,\mathbf{i} - 30\sqrt{2}\,\mathbf{j} = \left(30\sqrt{2}\right)\mathbf{i} + \left(500 - 30\sqrt{2}\right)\mathbf{j}$$
The speed of the plane relative to the ground is:
$$\|\mathbf{v}_g\| = \sqrt{\left(30\sqrt{2}\right)^2 + \left(500 - 30\sqrt{2}\right)^2} = \sqrt{1800 + 250000 - 30000\sqrt{2} + 1800}$$
$$= \sqrt{211{,}173.6} \approx 459.5 \text{ miles per hour}$$
To find the direction, find the angle between $\mathbf{v}_g$ and a convenient vector such as due north, $\mathbf{j}$.
$$\cos\theta = \frac{\mathbf{v}_g \bullet \mathbf{j}}{\|\mathbf{v}_g\|\|-\mathbf{j}\|} = \frac{\left(30\sqrt{2}\right)\cdot 0 + \left(500 - 30\sqrt{2}\right)(1)}{459.5\sqrt{0^2 + 1^2}} = \frac{500 - 30\sqrt{2}}{459.5} \approx 0.9958$$
$\theta \approx 5.3°$
The plane is traveling with a ground speed of about 459.5 miles per hour in a direction of 5.3° east of north.

77. Let $\mathbf{F}_1$ be the tension on the left cable and $\mathbf{F}_2$ be the tension on the right cable.
Let $\mathbf{F}_3$ represent the force of the weight of the box.
$$\mathbf{F}_1 = \|\mathbf{F}_1\|\left(\cos(140°)\mathbf{i} + \sin(140°)\mathbf{j}\right) \approx \|\mathbf{F}_1\|\left(-0.7660\mathbf{i} + 0.6428\mathbf{j}\right)$$
$$\mathbf{F}_2 = \|\mathbf{F}_2\|\left(\cos(30°)\mathbf{i} + \sin(30°)\mathbf{j}\right) \approx \|\mathbf{F}_2\|\left(0.8660\mathbf{i} + 0.5000\mathbf{j}\right)$$
$\mathbf{F}_3 = -2000\mathbf{j}$
For equilibrium, the sum of the force vectors must be zero.
$$\mathbf{F}_1 + \mathbf{F}_2 + \mathbf{F}_3 = -0.7660\|\mathbf{F}_1\|\mathbf{i} + 0.6428\|\mathbf{F}_1\|\mathbf{j} + 0.8660\|\mathbf{F}_2\|\mathbf{i} + 0.5000\|\mathbf{F}_2\|\mathbf{j} - 2000\mathbf{j}$$
$$= \left(-0.7660\|\mathbf{F}_1\| + 0.8660\|\mathbf{F}_2\|\right)\mathbf{i} + \left(0.6428\|\mathbf{F}_1\| + 0.5000\|\mathbf{F}_2\| - 2000\right)\mathbf{j}$$
$$= 0$$
Set the **i** and **j** components equal to zero and solve:
$$\begin{cases} -0.7660\|\mathbf{F}_1\| + 0.8660\|\mathbf{F}_2\| = 0 \rightarrow \|\mathbf{F}_2\| = \dfrac{0.7660}{0.8660}\|\mathbf{F}_1\| = 0.8845\|\mathbf{F}_1\| \\ 0.6428\|\mathbf{F}_1\| + 0.5000\|\mathbf{F}_2\| - 2000 = 0 \end{cases}$$

$$0.6428\|\mathbf{F}_1\| + 0.5000(0.8845\|\mathbf{F}_1\|) - 2000 = 0$$

$$1.0851\|\mathbf{F}_1\| = 2000 \rightarrow \|\mathbf{F}_1\| \approx 1843 \text{ pounds}$$

$$\|\mathbf{F}_2\| = 0.8845(1843) = 1630 \text{ pounds}$$

The tension in the left cable is about 1843 pounds and the tension in the right cable is about 1630 pounds.

78. Consider the diagram

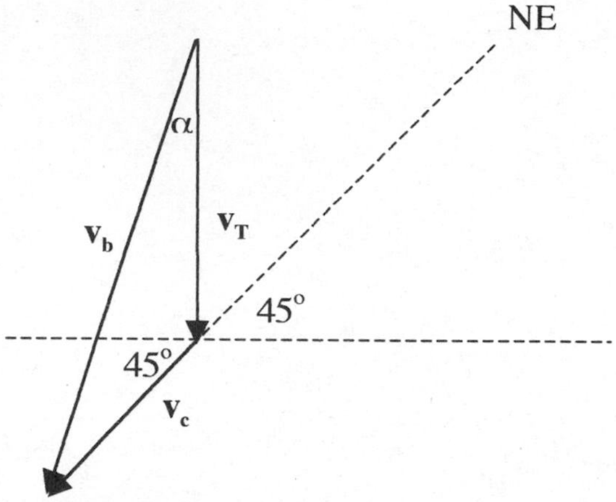

Let $\mathbf{v}_T$ represent the vector associated with the true velocity of the boat.

$$\|\mathbf{v}_c\| = 11 \Rightarrow \mathbf{v}_T = 0\cdot\mathbf{i} - 11\cdot\mathbf{j}$$

Let $\mathbf{v}_c$ represent the vector associated with the velocity of the current.

$$\|\mathbf{v}_c\| = 3 \Rightarrow \mathbf{v}_c = -\frac{\sqrt{3}}{2}\cdot\mathbf{i} - \frac{\sqrt{3}}{2}\cdot\mathbf{j}$$

Therefore, the velocity of the boat relative to the water is given by

$$\mathbf{v}_b = \mathbf{v}_T + \mathbf{v}_c$$

Let θ = the angle formed by $\mathbf{v}_T$ and $\mathbf{v}_c$.

From the diagram, we can see that $\theta = 135°$.

We can use the Law of Cosines to find the length of $\mathbf{v}_b$.

$$\|\mathbf{v}_b\|^2 = \|\mathbf{v}_T\|^2 + \|\mathbf{v}_c\|^2 - 2\cdot\|\mathbf{v}_T\|\cdot\|\mathbf{v}_c\|\cos(\theta)$$

$$\|\mathbf{v}_b\|^2 = 11^2 + 3^2 - 2\cdot 11\cdot 3\cos(135°) = 121 + 9 - 66\cdot\cos(135°) \approx 176.669$$

$$\|\mathbf{v}_b\| \approx \sqrt{176.669} \approx 13.2917$$

So the boat's speed relative to the water is approximately 13.29 mph.

The boat's direction is given by angle α in the diagram.

Using the Law of Sines yields

$$\frac{\sin\alpha}{3} = \frac{\sin(135°)}{\|\mathbf{v}_b\|} \rightarrow \|\mathbf{v}_b\|\cdot\sin\alpha = 3\cdot\sin(135°)$$

$$\sin\alpha = \frac{3\cdot\sin(135°)}{\|\mathbf{v}_b\|} \approx \frac{3\cdot\sin(135°)}{13.2917} \approx 0.1596$$

$$\alpha \approx \sin^{-1}(0.1596) \approx 9.18°$$

Therefore, the boat is headed approximately 9.18° west of south.

79. Let the positive x-axis point downstream, so that the velocity of the current is $\mathbf{v}_c = 5\mathbf{i}$.
Let $\mathbf{v}_w$ = the velocity of the boat in the water.
Let $\mathbf{v}_L$ = the velocity of the boat relative to the land.
Then $\mathbf{v}_L = \mathbf{v}_w + \mathbf{v}_c$
The speed of the boat is $\|\mathbf{v}_w\| = 15$; we need to find the direction.

Let $\mathbf{v}_w = a\mathbf{i} + b\mathbf{j}$ so $\|\mathbf{v}_w\| = \sqrt{a^2 + b^2} = 15 \rightarrow a^2 + b^2 = 225$.
Let $\mathbf{v}_L = k\mathbf{j}$.

Since $\mathbf{v}_L = \mathbf{v}_w + \mathbf{v}_c$, $k\mathbf{j} = a\mathbf{i} + b\mathbf{j} + 5\mathbf{i} \rightarrow k\mathbf{j} = (a+5)\mathbf{i} + b\mathbf{j}$
$a + 5 = 0$ and $k = b \rightarrow a = -5$

$$a^2 + b^2 = 225 \rightarrow 25 + b^2 = 225 \rightarrow b^2 = 200 \rightarrow k = b = \sqrt{200}$$

$$\mathbf{v}_w = -5\mathbf{i} + \sqrt{200}\mathbf{j} \text{ and } \mathbf{v}_L = \sqrt{200}\mathbf{j}$$

Find the angle between $\mathbf{v}_w$ and $\mathbf{v}_L$:

$$\cos\theta = \frac{\mathbf{v}_w \cdot \mathbf{v}_L}{\|\mathbf{v}_w\|\|\mathbf{v}_L\|} = \frac{-5\cdot 0 + \left(\sqrt{200}\right)^2}{(15)\left(\sqrt{200}\right)} = \frac{200}{15\sqrt{200}} = \frac{\sqrt{200}}{15} \approx 0.9428$$

$$\theta = \cos^{-1}\left(\frac{\sqrt{200}}{15}\right) \approx 19.47^\circ$$

The heading of the boat needs to be 19.47° upstream, in other words, the boat should head at an angle of $\alpha = 70.53^\circ$ to the shore.

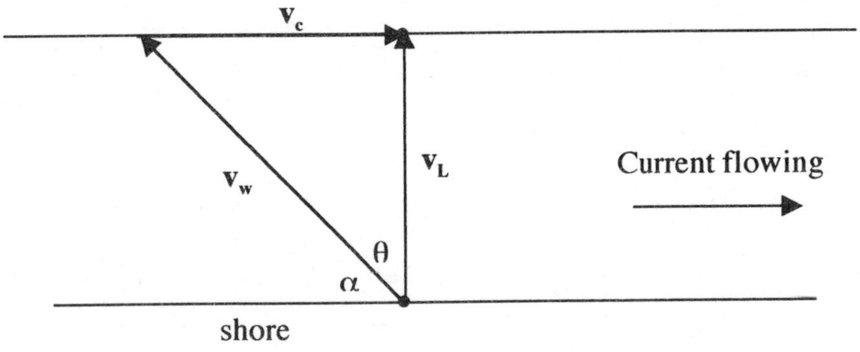

Analytic Geometry

11.2 The Parabola

1. B 2. G 3. E 4. D

5. H 6. A 7. C 8. F

9. The focus is (4, 0) and the vertex is (0, 0). Both lie on the horizontal line $y = 0$. $a = 4$ and since (4, 0) is to the right of (0, 0), the parabola opens to the right. The equation of the parabola is:

$$y^2 = 4ax$$
$$y^2 = 4 \cdot 4 \cdot x$$
$$y^2 = 16x$$

Letting $x = 4$, we find $y^2 = 64$ or $y = \pm 8$.
The points (4, 8) and (4, –8) define the latus rectum.

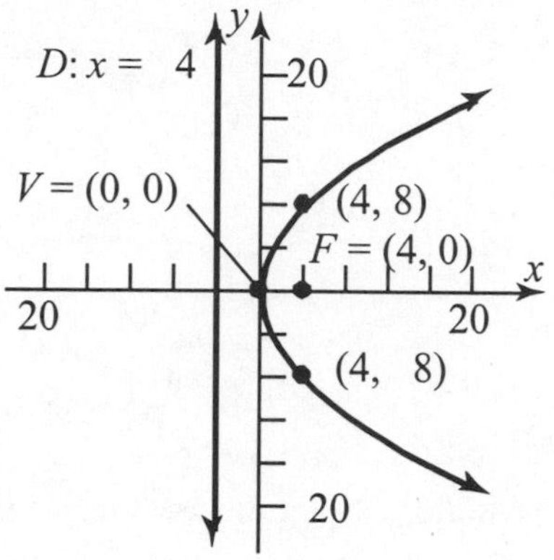

10. The focus is (0, 2) and the vertex is (0, 0). Both lie on the vertical line $x = 0$. $a = 2$ and since (0, 2) is above (0, 0), the parabola opens up The equation of the parabola is:

$$x^2 = 4ay$$
$$x^2 = 4 \cdot 2 \cdot y$$
$$x^2 = 8y$$

Letting $y = 2$, we find $x^2 = 16$ or $x = \pm 4$.
The points (–4, 2) and (4, 2) define the latus rectum.

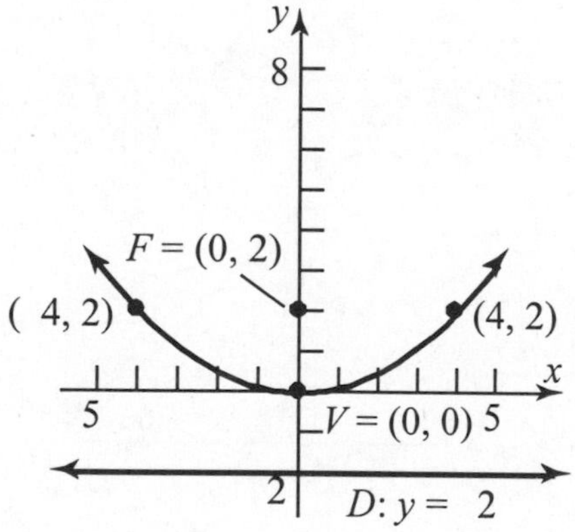

11. The focus is (0, –3) and the vertex is (0, 0). Both lie on the vertical line $x = 0$. $a = 3$ and since (0, –3) is below (0, 0), the parabola opens down. The equation of the parabola is:

$$x^2 = -4ay$$
$$x^2 = -4 \cdot 3 \cdot y$$
$$x^2 = -12y$$

Letting $y = -3$, we find $x^2 = 36$ or $x = \pm 6$. The points (6, 3) and (6, –3) define the latus rectum.

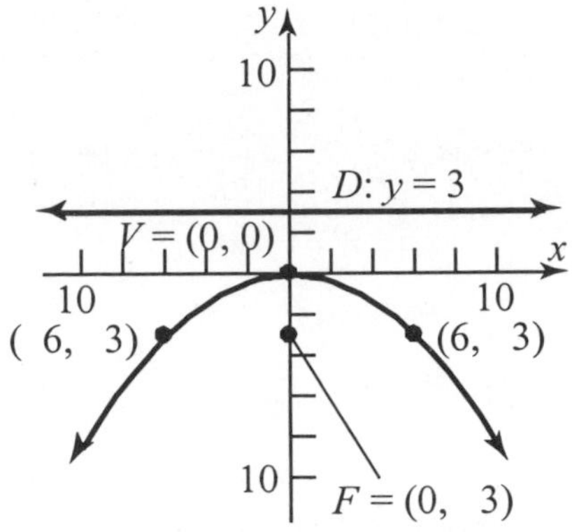

12. The focus is (–4, 0) and the vertex is (0, 0). Both lie on the horizontal line $y = 0$. $a = 4$ and since (–4, 0) is to the left of (0, 0), the parabola opens to the left. The equation of the parabola is:

$$y^2 = -4ax$$
$$y^2 = -4 \cdot 4 \cdot x$$
$$y^2 = -16x$$

Letting $x = -4$, we find $y^2 = 64$ or $y = \pm 8$. The points (–4, 8) and (–4, –8) define the latus rectum.

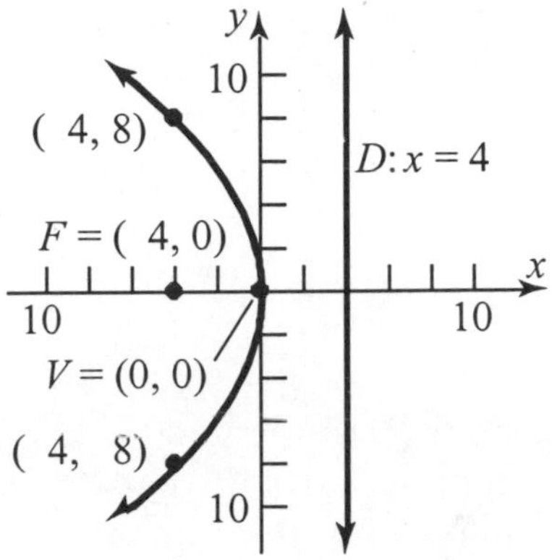

13. The focus is (–2, 0) and the directrix is $x = 2$. The vertex is (0, 0). $a = 2$ and since (–2, 0) is to the left of (0, 0), the parabola opens to the left. The equation of the parabola is:

$$y^2 = -4ax$$
$$y^2 = -4 \cdot 2 \cdot x$$
$$y^2 = -8x$$

Letting $x = -2$, we find $y^2 = 16$ or $y = \pm 4$. The points (–2, 4) and (–2, –4) define the latus rectum.

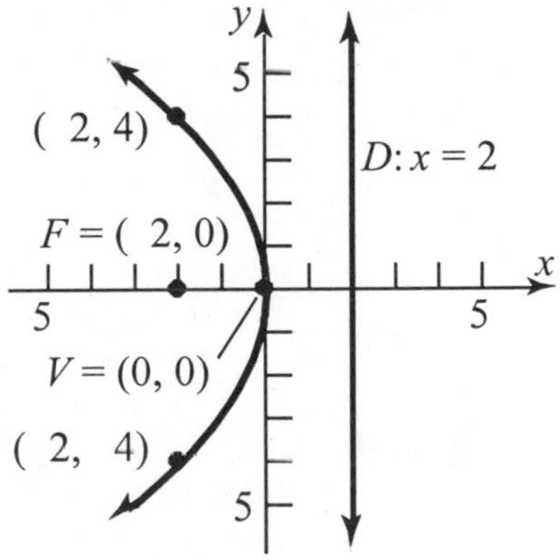

14. The focus is (0, –1) and the directrix is $y = 1$. The vertex is (0, 0). $a = 1$ and since (0, –1) is below (0, 0), the parabola opens down. The equation of the parabola is:

$$x^2 = -4ay$$
$$x^2 = -4 \cdot 1 \cdot y$$
$$x^2 = -4y$$

Letting $y = -1$, we find $x^2 = 4$ or $x = \pm 2$. The points (–2, –1) and (2, –1) define the latus rectum.

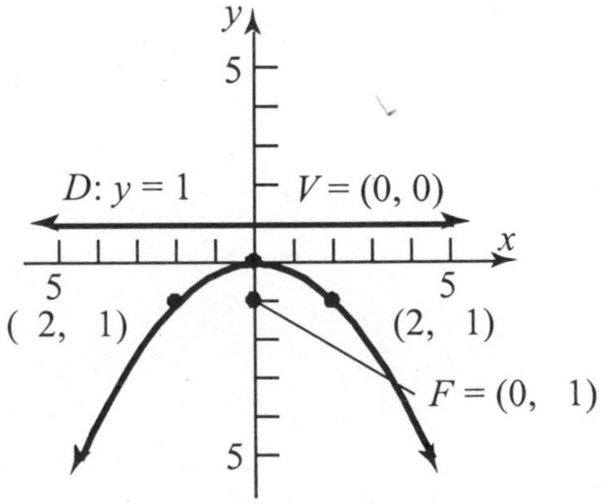

15. The directrix is $y=-\frac{1}{2}$ and the vertex is (0, 0). The focus is $\left(0,\frac{1}{2}\right)$. $a=\frac{1}{2}$ and since $\left(0,\frac{1}{2}\right)$ is above (0, 0), the parabola opens up. The equation of the parabola is:

$$x^2=4ay$$

$$x^2=4\cdot\frac{1}{2}\cdot y \rightarrow x^2=2y$$

Letting $y=\frac{1}{2}$, we find $x^2=1$ or $x=\pm 1$.

The points $\left(1,\frac{1}{2}\right)$ and $\left(-1,\frac{1}{2}\right)$ define the latus rectum.

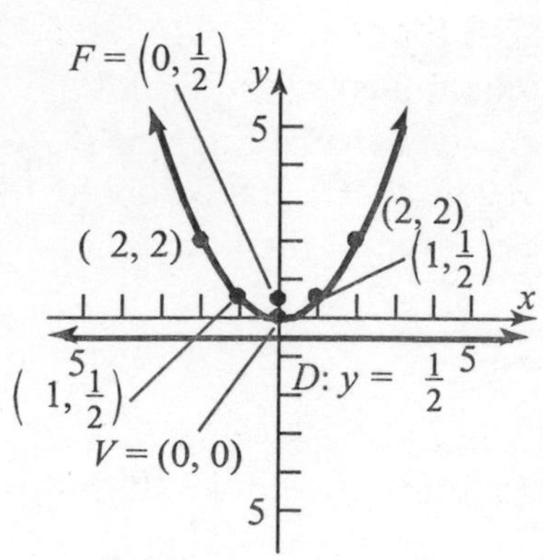

16. The directrix is $x=-\frac{1}{2}$ and the vertex is (0, 0). The focus is $\left(\frac{1}{2},0\right)$. $a=\frac{1}{2}$ and since $\left(\frac{1}{2},0\right)$ is to the right of (0, 0), the parabola opens to the right. The equation of the parabola is:

$$y^2=4ax$$

$$y^2=4\cdot\frac{1}{2}\cdot x \rightarrow y^2=2x$$

Letting $x=\frac{1}{2}$, we find $y^2=1$ or $y=\pm 1$. The points $\left(\frac{1}{2},-1\right)$ and $\left(\frac{1}{2},1\right)$ define the latus rectum.

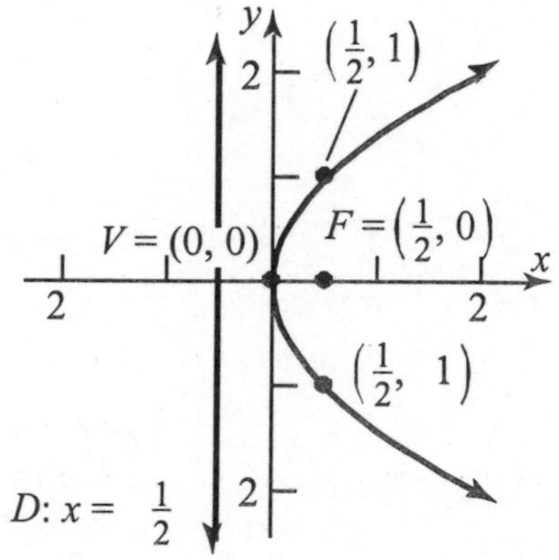

17. The focus is (2, –5) and the vertex is (2, –3). Both lie on the vertical line $x = 2$. $a = 2$ and since (2, –5) is below (2, –3), the parabola opens down. The equation of the parabola is:

$$(x-h)^2=-4a(y-k)$$

$$(x-2)^2=-4\cdot 2\cdot(y-(-3))$$

$$(x-2)^2=-8(y+3)$$

Letting $y=-5$, we find $(x-2)^2=16$ or $x-2=\pm 4$. So, $x=6$ or $x=-2$. The points (6, –5) and (–2, –5) define the latus rectum.

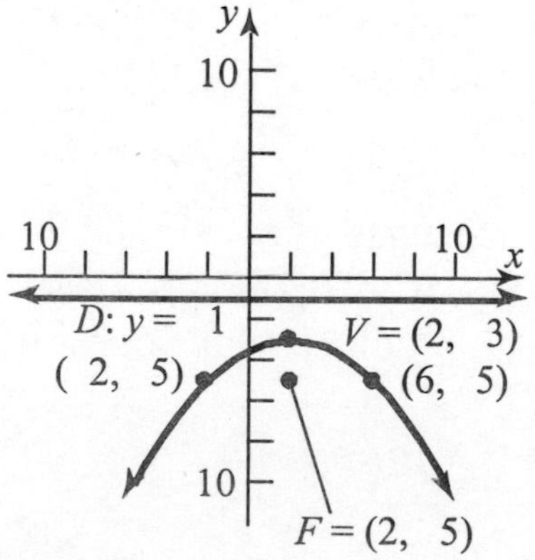

18. The focus is (6, –2) and the vertex is (4, –2). Both lie on the horizontal line $y=-2$. $a=2$ and since (6,–2) is to the right of (4, –2), the parabola opens to the right. The equation of the parabola is:

$$(y-k)^2 = 4a(x-h)$$
$$(y-(-2))^2 = 4\cdot 2\cdot(x-4)$$
$$(y+2)^2 = 8(x-4)$$

Letting $x=6$, we find $(y+2)^2=16$ or $y+2=\pm 4$. So, $y=-6$ or $y=2$. The points (6, –6) and (6, 2) define the latus rectum.

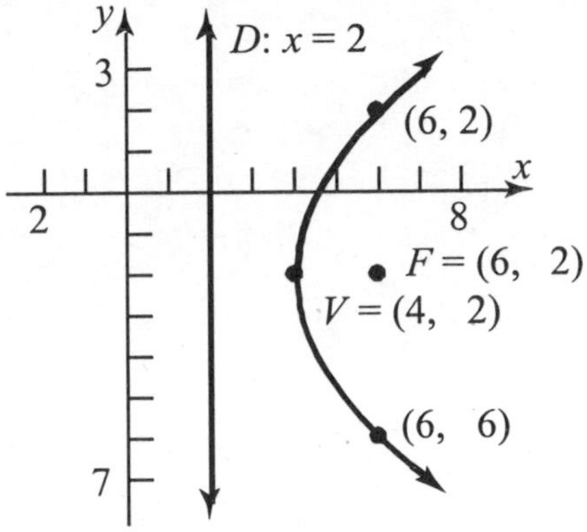

19. Vertex: (0,0). Since the axis of symmetry is vertical, the parabola opens up or down. Since (2, 3) is above (0, 0), the parabola opens up. The equation has the form $x^2 = 4ay$. Substitute the coordinates of (2, 3) into the equation to find a:

$$2^2 = 4a\cdot 3$$
$$4 = 12a \rightarrow a = \frac{1}{3}$$

The equation of the parabola is: $x^2 = \frac{4}{3}y$.

The focus is $\left(0,\frac{1}{3}\right)$. Letting $y=\frac{1}{3}$,

we find $x^2 = \frac{4}{9}$ or $x = \pm\frac{2}{3}$. The points $\left(\frac{2}{3},\frac{1}{3}\right)$ and $\left(-\frac{2}{3},\frac{1}{3}\right)$ define the latus rectum.

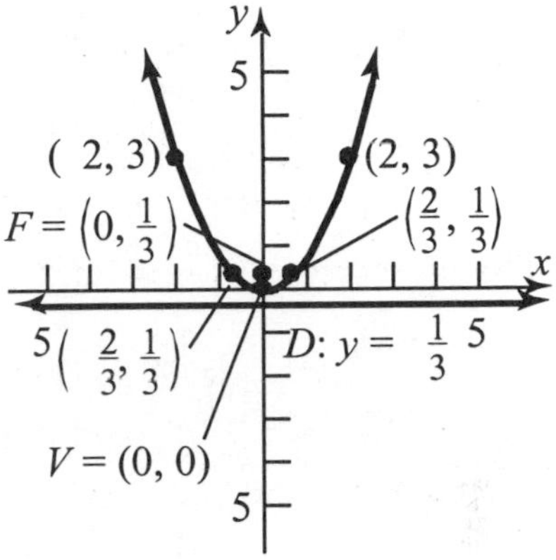

20. Vertex: (0,0). Since the axis of symmetry is horizontal, the parabola opens left or right. Since (2, 3) is to the right of (0, 0), the parabola opens to the right. The equation has the form $y^2 = 4ax$. Substitute the coordinates of (2, 3) into the equation to find a:

$$3^2 = 4a \cdot 2$$

$$9 = 8a \rightarrow a = \frac{9}{8}$$

The equation of the parabola is: $y^2 = \frac{9}{2}x$.

The focus is $\left(\frac{9}{8}, 0\right)$. Letting $x = \frac{9}{8}$, we find $y^2 = \frac{81}{16}$ or $y = \pm\frac{9}{4}$.

The points $\left(\frac{9}{8}, \frac{9}{4}\right)$ and $\left(\frac{9}{8}, -\frac{9}{4}\right)$ define the latus rectum.

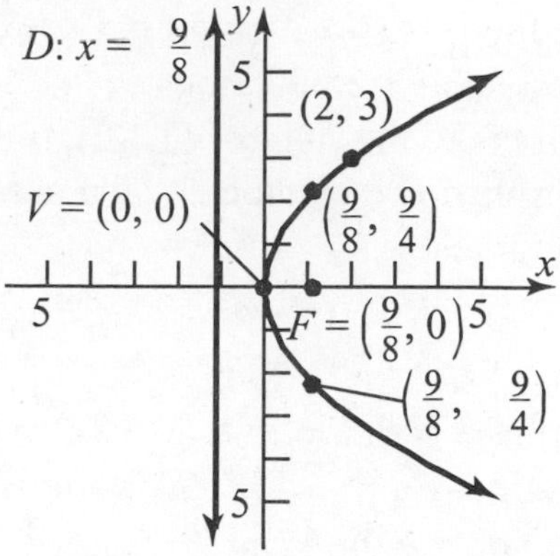

21. The directrix is $y = 2$ and the focus is (–3, 4). This is a vertical case, so the vertex is (–3, 3). $a = 1$ and since (–3, 4) is above $y = 2$, the parabola opens up. The equation of the parabola is:

$$(x - h)^2 = 4a(y - k)$$

$$(x - (-3))^2 = 4 \cdot 1 \cdot (y - 3)$$

$$(x + 3)^2 = 4(y - 3)$$

Letting $y = 4$, we find $(x + 3)^2 = 4$ or $x + 3 = \pm 2$. So, $x = -1$ or $x = -5$. The points (–1, 4) and (–5, 4) define the latus rectum.

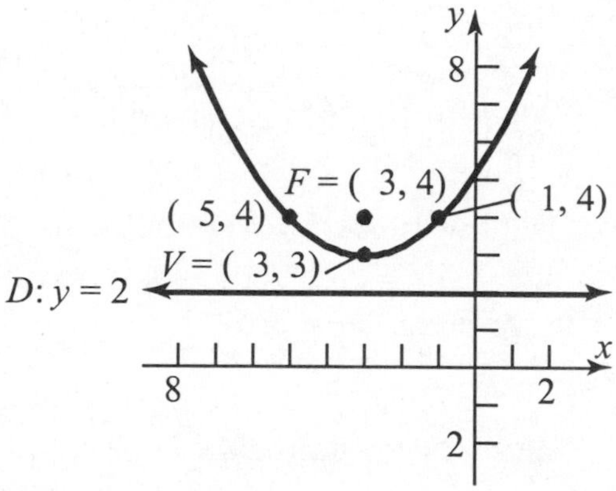

22. The directrix is $x = -4$ and the focus is (2, 4). This is a horizontal case, so the vertex is (–1, 4). $a = 3$ and since (2, 4) is to the right of $x = -4$, the parabola opens to the right. The equation of the parabola is:

$$(y - k)^2 = 4a(x - h)$$

$$(y - 4)^2 = 4 \cdot 3 \cdot (x - (-1))$$

$$(y - 4)^2 = 12(x + 1)$$

Letting $x = 2$, we find $(y - 4)^2 = 36$ or $y - 4 = \pm 6$. So, $y = -2$ or $y = 10$. The points (2, –2) and (2, 10) define the latus rectum.

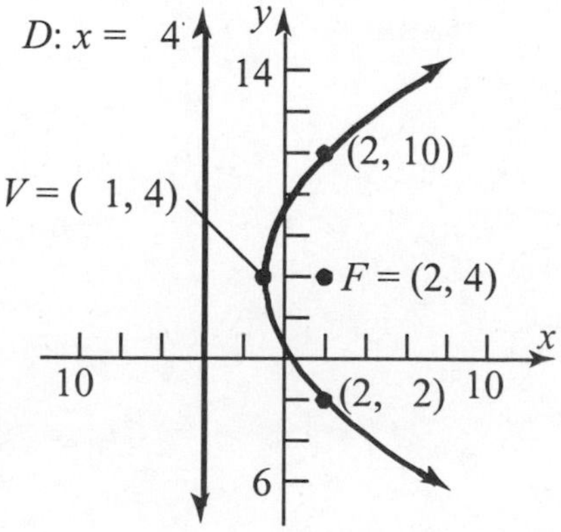

23. The directrix is $x = 1$ and the focus is $(-3, -2)$. This is a horizontal case, so the vertex is $(-1, -2)$. $a = 2$ and since $(-3, -2)$ is to the left of $x = 1$, the parabola opens to the left. The equation of the parabola is:

$$(y-k)^2 = -4a(x-h)$$
$$(y-(-2))^2 = -4\cdot 2\cdot(x-(-1))$$
$$(y+2)^2 = -8(x+1)$$

Letting $x = -3$, we find $(y+2)^2 = 16$ or $y+2 = \pm 4$. So, $y = 2$ or $y = -6$. The points $(-3, 2)$ and $(-3, -6)$ define the latus rectum.

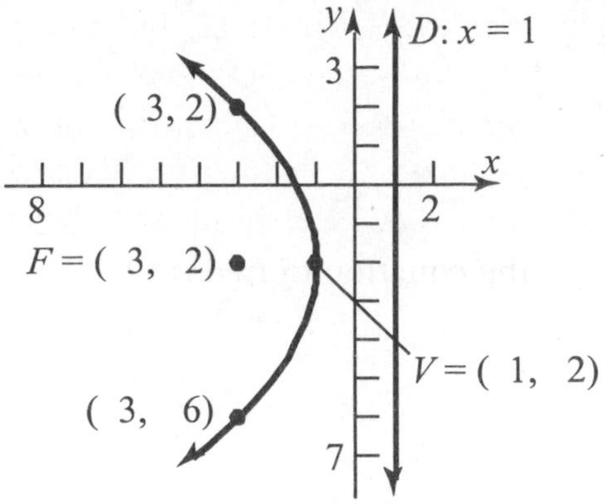

24. The directrix is $y = -2$ and the focus is $(-4, 4)$. This is a vertical case, so the vertex is $(-4, 1)$. $a = 3$ and since $(-4, 4)$ is above $y = -2$, the parabola opens up. The equation of the parabola is:

$$(x-h)^2 = 4a(y-k)$$
$$(x-(-4))^2 = 4\cdot 3\cdot(y-1)$$
$$(x+4)^2 = 12(y-1)$$

Letting $y = 4$, we find $(x+4)^2 = 36$ or $x+4 = \pm 6$. So, $x = -10$ or $x = 2$. The points $(-10, 4)$ and $(2, 4)$ define the latus rectum.

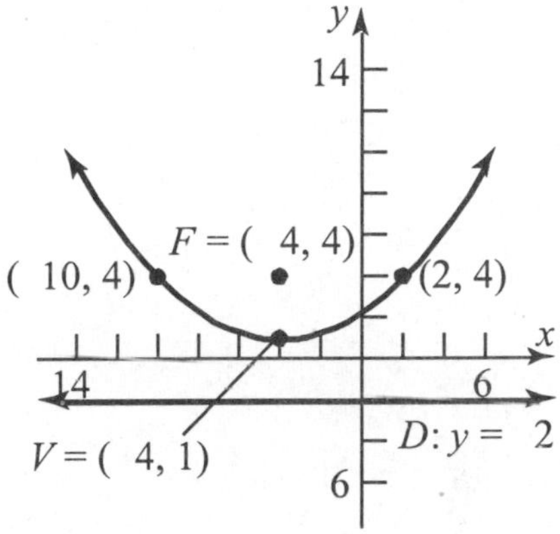

25. The equation $x^2 = 4y$ is in the form $x^2 = 4ay$ where $4a = 4$ or $a = 1$. Thus, we have:

Vertex: $(0, 0)$
Focus: $(0, 1)$
Directrix: $y = -1$

To graph, enter: $y_1 = x^2 / 4$

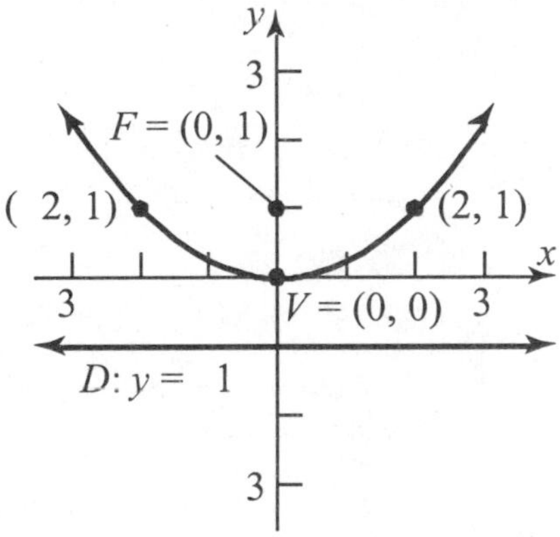

26. The equation $y^2 = 8x$ is in the form $y^2 = 4ax$ where $4a = 8$ or $a = 2$. Thus, we have:

Vertex: $(0, 0)$
Focus: $(2, 0)$
Directrix: $x = -2$

To graph, enter: $y_1 = \sqrt{8x}$; $y_2 = -\sqrt{8x}$

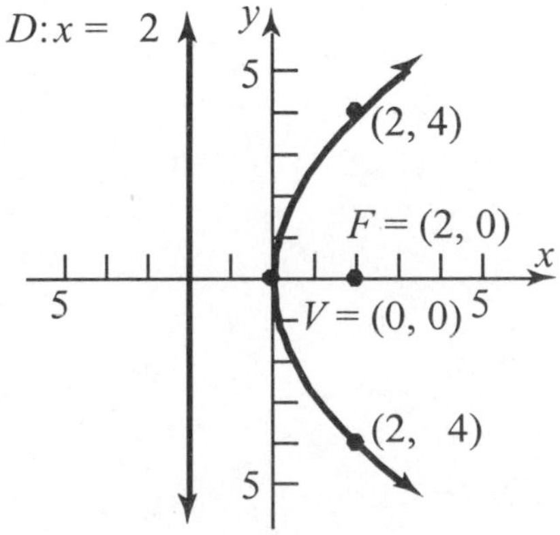

27. The equation $y^2 = -16x$ is in the form $y^2 = -4ax$ where $-4a = -16$ or $a = 4$. Thus, we have:

Vertex: (0, 0)
Focus: (–4, 0)
Directrix: $x = 4$

To graph, enter: $y_1 = \sqrt{-16x}$; $y_2 = -\sqrt{-16x}$

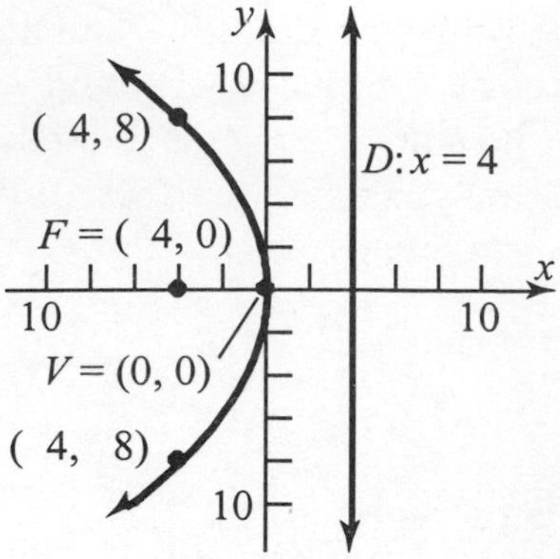

28. The equation $x^2 = -4y$ is in the form $x^2 = -4ay$ where $-4a = -4$ or $a = 1$. Thus, we have:

Vertex: (0, 0)
Focus: (0, –1)
Directrix: $y = 1$

To graph, enter: $y_1 = x^2 / (-4)$

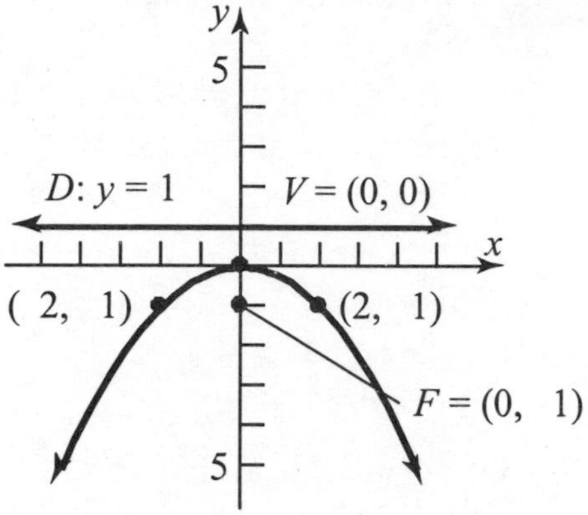

29. The equation $(y-2)^2 = 8(x+1)$ is in the form $(y-k)^2 = 4a(x-h)$ where $4a = 8$ or $a = 2$, $h = -1$, and $k = 2$. Thus, we have:

Vertex: (–1, 2)
Focus: (1, 2)
Directrix: $x = -3$

To graph, enter:

$y_1 = 2 + \sqrt{8(x+1)}$; $y_2 = 2 - \sqrt{8(x+1)}$

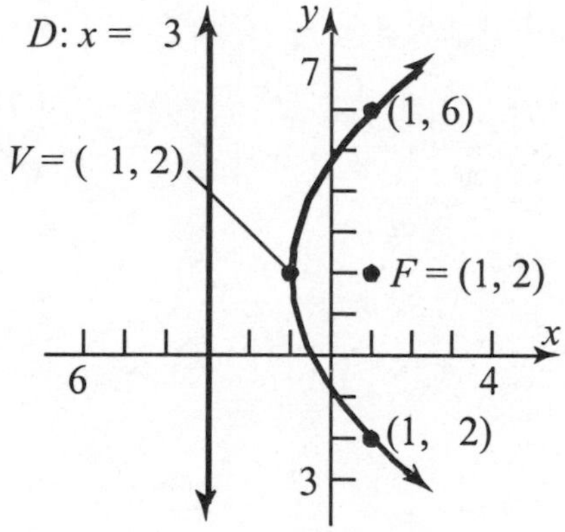

30. The equation $(x+4)^2 = 16(y+2)$ is in the form $(x-h)^2 = 4a(y-k)$ where $4a = 16$ or $a = 4$, $h = -4$, and $k = -2$. Thus, we have:

Vertex: (–4, –2)
Focus: (–4, 2)
Directrix: $y = -6$

To graph, enter:

$y_1 = -2 + (x+4)^2 / 16$

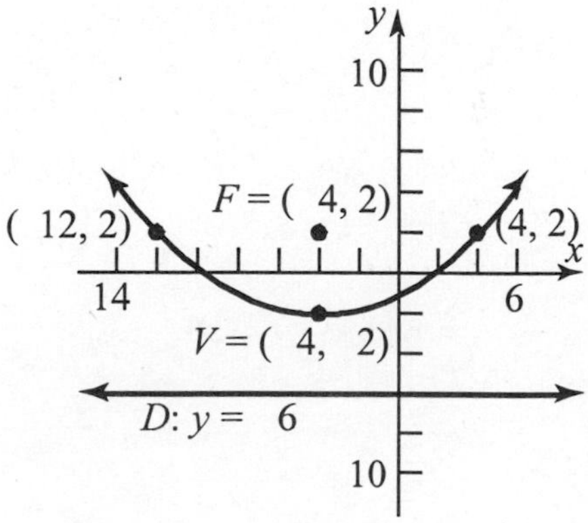

31. The equation $(x-3)^2 = -(y+1)$ is in the form $(x-h)^2 = -4a(y-k)$ where $-4a = -1$ or $a = \frac{1}{4}$, $h = 3$, and $k = -1$. Thus, we have:

Vertex: $(3, -1)$

Focus: $\left(3, -\frac{5}{4}\right)$

Directrix: $y = -\frac{3}{4}$

To graph, enter: $y_1 = -1 - (x-3)^2$

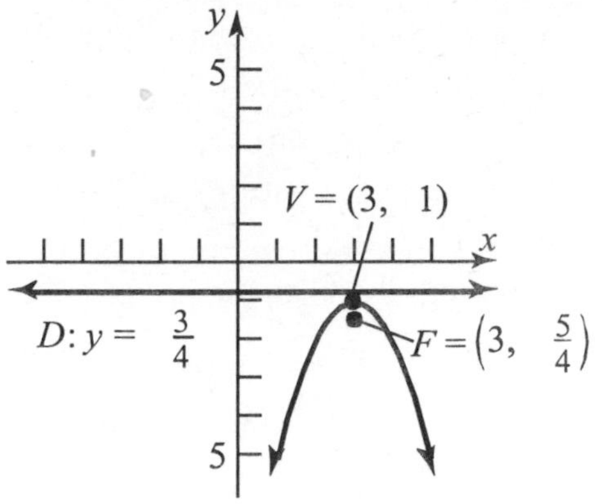

32. The equation $(y+1)^2 = -4(x-2)$ is in the form $(y-k)^2 = -4a(x-h)$ where $-4a = -4$ or $a = 1$, $h = 2$, and $k = -1$. Thus, we have:

Vertex: $(2, -1)$

Focus: $(1, -1)$

Directrix: $x = 3$

To graph, enter:

$y_1 = -1 + \sqrt{-4(x-2)}$;

$y_2 = -1 - \sqrt{-4(x-2)}$

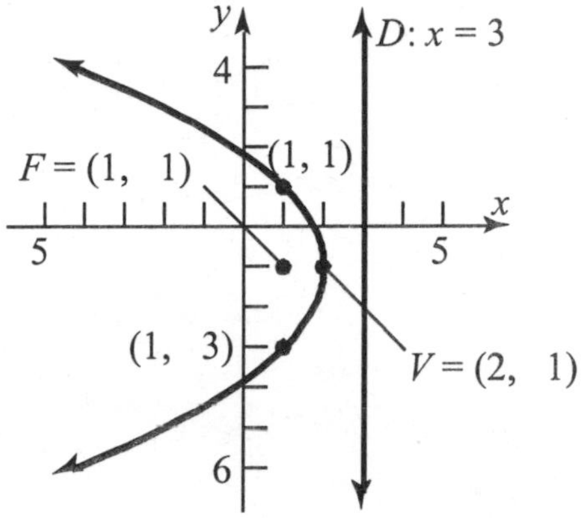

33. The equation $(y+3)^2 = 8(x-2)$ is in the form $(y-k)^2 = 4a(x-h)$ where $4a = 8$ or $a = 2$, $h = 2$, and $k = -3$. Thus, we have:

Vertex: $(2, -3)$

Focus: $(4, -3)$

Directrix: $x = 0$

To graph, enter:

$y_1 = -3 + \sqrt{8(x-2)}$; $y_2 = -3 - \sqrt{8(x-2)}$

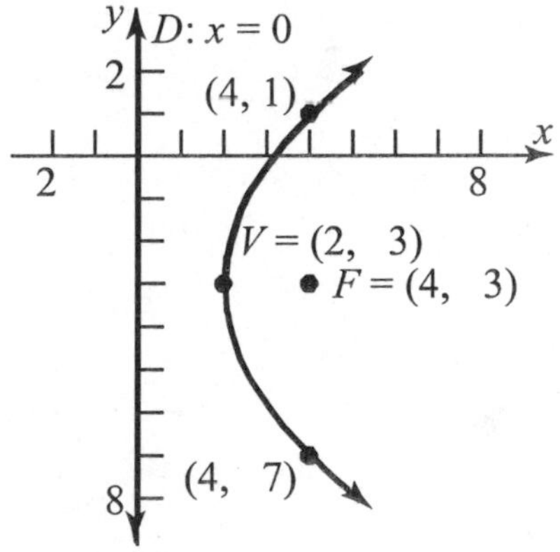

34. The equation $(x-2)^2 = 4(y-3)$ is in the form $(x-h)^2 = 4a(y-k)$ where $4a = 4$ or $a = 1$, $h = 2$, and $k = 3$. Thus, we have:

Vertex: $(2, 3)$

Focus: $(2, 4)$

Directrix: $y = 2$

To graph, enter: $y_1 = 3 + (x-2)^2 / 4$

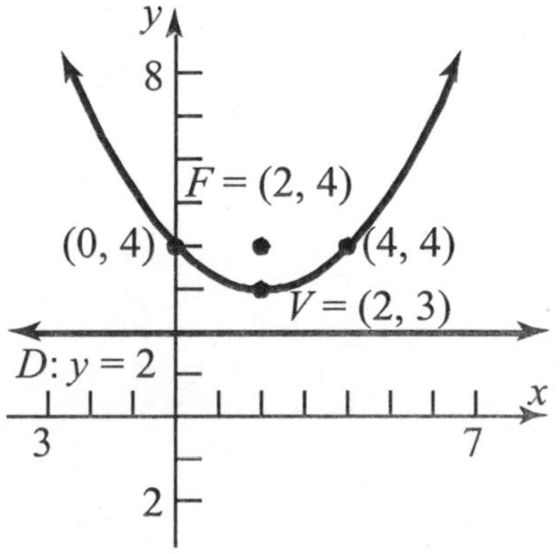

35. Complete the square to put in standard form:

$$y^2 - 4y + 4x + 4 = 0$$
$$y^2 - 4y + 4 = -4x$$
$$(y-2)^2 = -4x$$

The equation is in the form $(y-k)^2 = -4a(x-h)$ where $-4a = -4$ or $a = 1$, $h = 0$, and $k = 2$.

Thus, we have:

Vertex: $(0, 2)$
Focus: $(-1, 2)$
Directrix: $x = 1$

To graph, enter: $y_1 = 2 + \sqrt{-4x}$; $y_2 = 2 - \sqrt{-4x}$

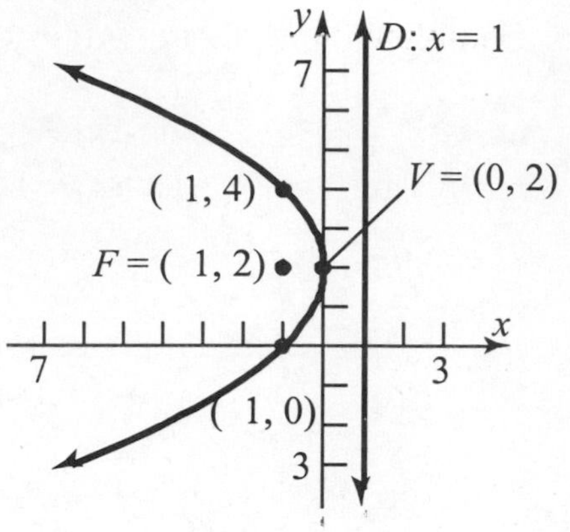

36. Complete the square to put in standard form:

$$x^2 + 6x - 4y + 1 = 0$$
$$x^2 + 6x + 9 = 4y - 1 + 9$$
$$(x+3)^2 = 4(y+2)$$

The equation is in the form $(x-h)^2 = 4a(y-k)$ where $4a = 4$ or $a = 1$, $h = -3$, and $k = -2$.

Thus, we have:

Vertex: $(-3, -2)$
Focus: $(-3, -1)$
Directrix: $y = -3$

To graph, enter: $y_1 = -2 + (x+3)^2 / 4$

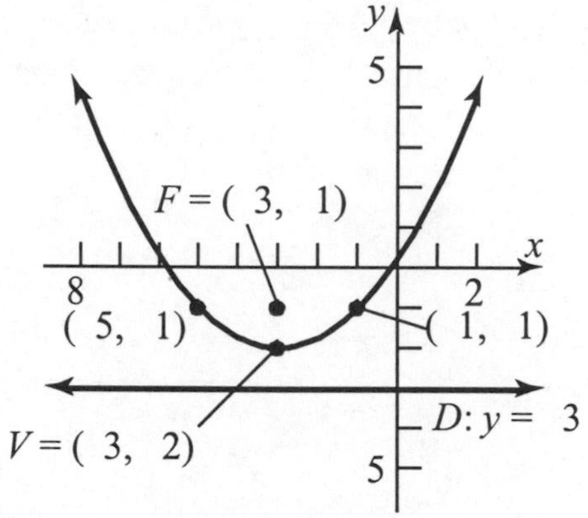

37. Complete the square to put in standard form:

$$x^2 + 8x = 4y - 8$$
$$x^2 + 8x + 16 = 4y - 8 + 16$$
$$(x+4)^2 = 4(y+2)$$

The equation is in the form $(x-h)^2 = 4a(y-k)$ where $4a = 4$ or $a = 1$, $h = -4$, and $k = -2$.

Thus, we have:

Vertex: $(-4, -2)$
Focus: $(-4, -1)$
Directrix: $y = -3$

To graph, enter: $y_1 = -2 + (x+4)^2 / 4$

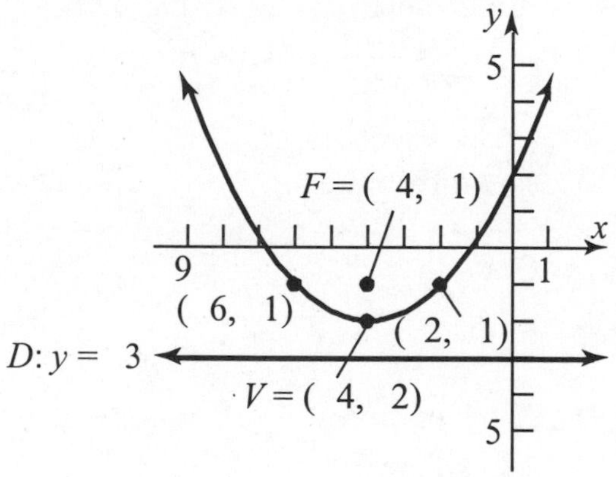

38. Complete the square to put in standard form:

$$y^2 - 2y = 8x - 1$$
$$y^2 - 2y + 1 = 8x - 1 + 1$$
$$(y-1)^2 = 8x$$

The equation is in the form $(y-k)^2 = 4a(x-h)$ where $4a = 8$ or $a = 2$, $h = 0$, and $k = 1$.
Thus, we have:

Vertex: (0, 1)
Focus: (2, 1)
Directrix: $x = -2$

To graph, enter: $y_1 = 1 + \sqrt{8x}$; $y_1 = 1 - \sqrt{8x}$

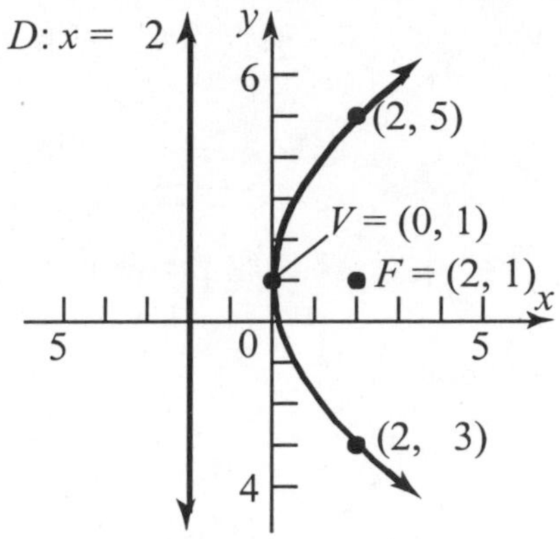

39. Complete the square to put in standard form:

$$y^2 + 2y - x = 0$$
$$y^2 + 2y + 1 = x + 1$$
$$(y+1)^2 = x + 1$$

The equation is in the form

$(y-k)^2 = 4a(x-h)$ where $4a = 1$ or $a = \frac{1}{4}$, $h = -1$, and $k = -1$.
Thus, we have:

Vertex: (–1, –1)
Focus: $\left(-\frac{3}{4}, -1\right)$
Directrix: $x = -\frac{5}{4}$

To graph, enter:
$y_1 = -1 + \sqrt{x+1}$; $y_2 = -1 - \sqrt{x+1}$

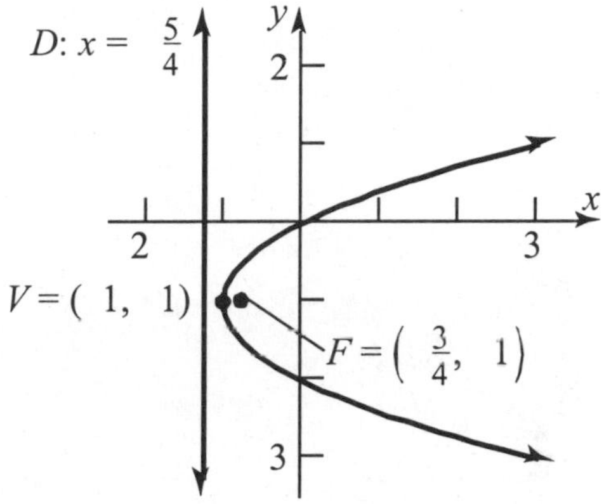

40. Complete the square to put in standard form:

$$x^2 - 4x = 2y$$
$$x^2 - 4x + 4 = 2y + 4$$
$$(x-2)^2 = 2(y+2)$$

The equation is in the form

$(x-h)^2 = 4a(y-k)$ where $4a = 2$ or $a = \frac{1}{2}$, $h = 2$, and $k = -2$. Thus, we have:

Vertex: (2, –2)
Focus: $\left(2, -\frac{3}{2}\right)$
Directrix: $y = -\frac{5}{2}$

To graph, enter: $y_1 = -2 + (x-2)^2 / 2$

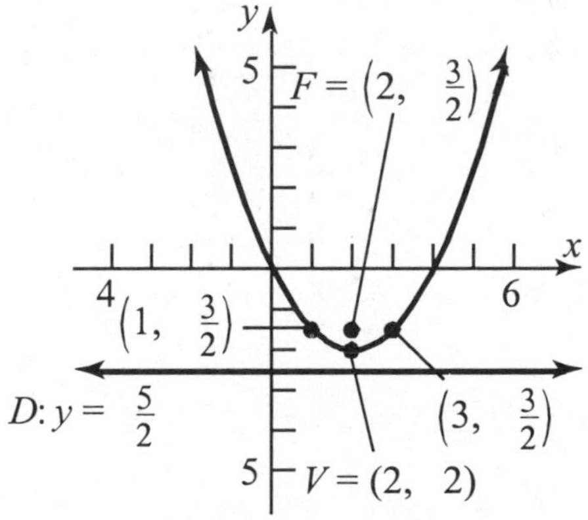

41. Complete the square to put in standard form:

$$x^2 - 4x = y + 4$$
$$x^2 - 4x + 4 = y + 4 + 4$$
$$(x-2)^2 = y + 8$$

The equation is in the form $(x-h)^2 = 4a(y-k)$ where $4a = 1$ or $a = \frac{1}{4}$, $h = 2$, and $k = -8$. Thus, we have:

Vertex: $(2, -8)$

Focus: $\left(2, -\frac{31}{4}\right)$

Directrix: $y = -\frac{33}{4}$

To graph, enter: $y_1 = -8 + (x-2)^2$

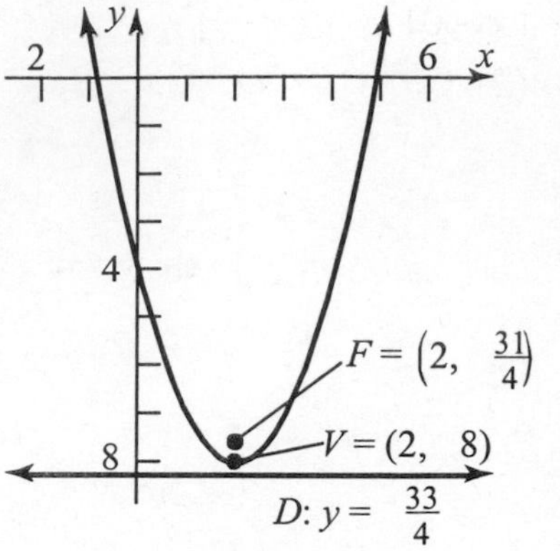

42. Complete the square to put in standard form:

$$y^2 + 12y = -x + 1$$
$$y^2 + 12y + 36 = -x + 1 + 36$$
$$(y+6)^2 = -(x-37)$$

The equation is in the form $(y-k)^2 = -4a(x-h)$ where $-4a = -1$ or $a = \frac{1}{4}$, $h = 37$, and $k = -6$. Thus, we have:

Vertex: $(37, -6)$

Focus: $\left(\frac{147}{4}, -6\right)$

Directrix: $x = \frac{149}{4}$

To graph, enter:

$y_1 = -6 + \sqrt{-(x-37)}$; $y_2 = -6 - \sqrt{-(x-37)}$

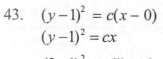

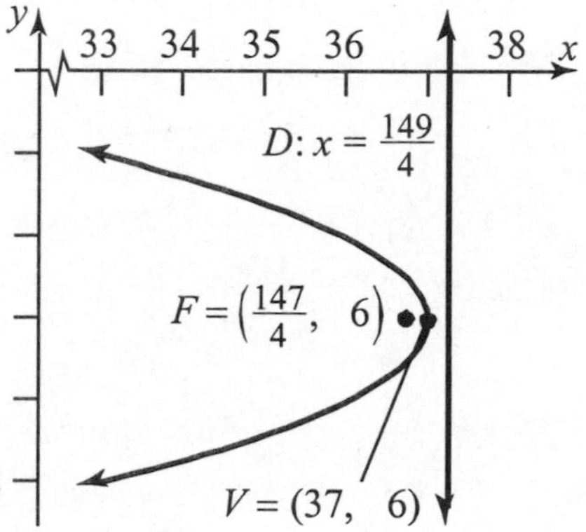

43. $(y-1)^2 = c(x-0)$

$(y-1)^2 = cx$

$(2-1)^2 = c(1) \rightarrow 1 = c$

$(y-1)^2 = x$

44. $(x-1)^2 = c(y-2)$

$(2-1)^2 = c(1-2)$

$1 = -c \rightarrow c = -1$

$(x-1)^2 = -(y-2)$

45. $(y-1)^2 = c(x-2)$

$(0-1)^2 = c(1-2)$

$1 = -c \rightarrow c = -1$

$(y-1)^2 = -(x-2)$

46. $(x-0)^2 = c(y-(-1))$

$x^2 = c(y+1)$

$2^2 = c(0+1) \rightarrow 4 = c$

$x^2 = 4(y+1)$

47. $(x-0)^2 = c(y-1)$
$(2-0)^2 = c(2-1) \rightarrow 4 = c$
$x^2 = 4(y-1)$

48. $(x-1)^2 = c(y-(-1))$
$(0-1)^2 = c(1+1) \rightarrow 1 = 2c \rightarrow c = \frac{1}{2}$
$(x-1)^2 = \frac{1}{2}(y+1)$

49. $(y-0)^2 = c(x-(-2))$
$y^2 = c(x+2)$
$1^2 = c(0+2) \rightarrow 1 = 2c \rightarrow c = \frac{1}{2}$
$y^2 = \frac{1}{2}(x+2)$

50. $(y-0)^2 = c(x-1)$
$(1-0)^2 = c(0-1)$
$1 = -c \rightarrow c = -1$
$y^2 = -(x-1)$

51. Set up the problem so that the vertex of the parabola is at (0, 0) and it opens up. Then the equation of the parabola has the form: $x^2 = 4ay$. Since the parabola is 10 feet across and 4 feet deep, the points (5, 4) and (–5, 4) are on the parabola.
Substitute and solve for a:
$$5^2 = 4a(4) \rightarrow 25 = 16a \rightarrow a = \frac{25}{16}$$
a is the distance from the vertex to the focus. Thus, the receiver (located at the focus) is $\frac{25}{16} = 1.5625$ feet, or 18.75 inches from the base of the dish, along the axis of the parabola.

52. Set up the problem so that the vertex of the parabola is at (0, 0) and it opens up. Then the equation of the parabola has the form: $x^2 = 4ay$. Since the parabola is 6 feet across and 2 feet deep, the points (3, 2) and (–3, 2) are on the parabola.
Substitute and solve for a:
$$3^2 = 4a(2) \rightarrow 9 = 8a \rightarrow a = \frac{9}{8}$$
a is the distance from the vertex to the focus. Thus, the receiver (located at the focus) is $\frac{9}{8} = 1.125$ feet, or 13.5 inches from the base of the dish, along the axis of the parabola.

53. Set up the problem so that the vertex of the parabola is at (0, 0) and it opens up. Then the equation of the parabola has the form: $x^2 = 4ay$. Since the parabola is 4 inches across and 1 inch deep, the points (2, 1) and (–2, 1) are on the parabola.
Substitute and solve for a: $2^2 = 4a(1) \rightarrow 4 = 4a \rightarrow a = 1$, a is the distance from the vertex to the focus. Thus, the bulb (located at the focus) should be 1 inch, from the vertex.

54. Set up the problem so that the vertex of the parabola is at (0, 0) and it opens up. Then the equation of the parabola has the form: $x^2 = 4ay$. Since the focus is 1 inch from the vertex and the depth is 2 inches, $a = 1$ and the points $(x, 2)$ and $(-x, 2)$ are on the parabola.
Substitute and solve for x:
$$x^2 = 4(1)(2) \rightarrow x^2 = 8 \rightarrow x = \pm 2\sqrt{2}$$

The diameter of the headlight is $4\sqrt{2}$ inches.

55. Set up the problem so that the vertex of the parabola is at (0, 0) and it opens up. Then the equation of the parabola has the form: $x^2 = cy$.
The point (300, 80) is a point on the parabola.
Solve for c and find the equation:

$$300^2 = c(80) \rightarrow c = 1125$$

$$x^2 = 1125y$$

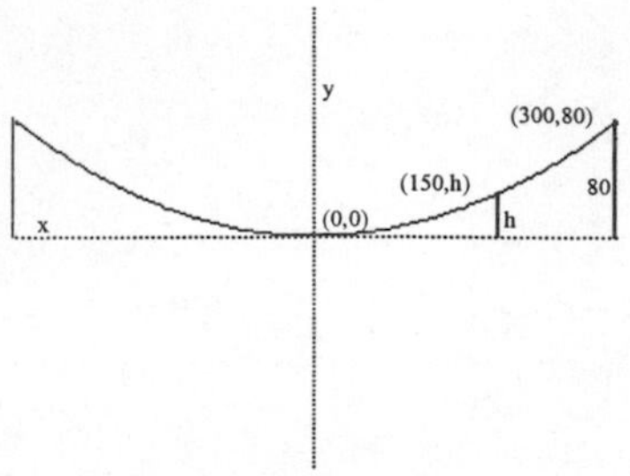

Since the height of the cable, 150 feet from the center, is to be found, the point (150, h) is a point on the parabola. Solve for h:

$$150^2 = 1125h \rightarrow 22500 = 1125h \rightarrow h = 20$$

The height of the cable, 150 feet from the center, is 20 feet.

56. Set up the problem so that the vertex of the parabola is at (0, 10) and it opens up. Then the equation of the parabola has the form: $x^2 = c(y-10)$.
The point (200, 100) is a point on the parabola.
Solve for c and find the equation:

$$200^2 = c(100-10)$$

$$40000 = 90c \rightarrow c = 444.44$$

$$x^2 = 444.44(y-10)$$

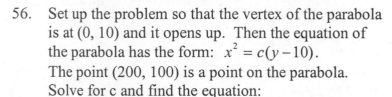

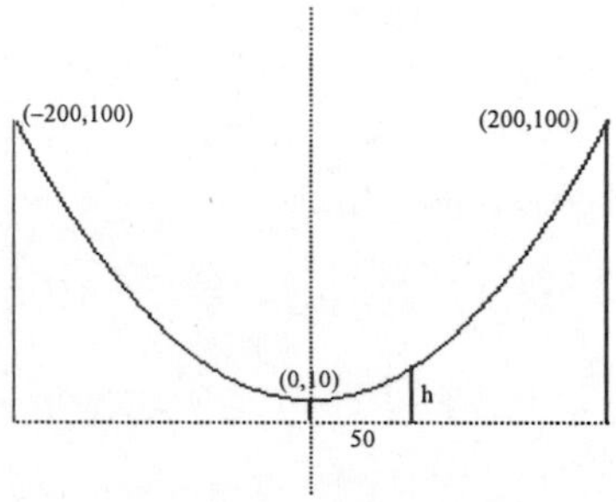

Since the height of the cable, 50 feet from the center, is to be found, the point (50, h) is a point on the parabola. Solve for h:

$$50^2 = 444.44(h-10) \rightarrow 2500 = 444.44h - 4444.4$$

$$444.44h = 6944.4 \rightarrow h = 15.625$$

The height of the cable, 50 feet from the center, is 15.625 feet.

57. Set up the problem so that the vertex of the parabola is at (0, 0) and it opens up. Then the equation of the parabola has the form: $x^2 = 4ay$. a is the distance from the vertex to the focus (where the source is located), so $a = 2$. Since the opening is 5 feet across, there is a point (2.5, y) on the parabola. Solve for y:

$$x^2 = 8y \rightarrow 2.5^2 = 8y \rightarrow 6.25 = 8y \rightarrow y = 0.78125 \text{ feet}$$

The depth of the searchlight should be 0.78125 feet.

58. Set up the problem so that the vertex of the parabola is at (0, 0) and it opens up. Then the equation of the parabola has the form: $x^2 = 4ay$. a is the distance from the vertex to the focus (where the source is located), so $a = 2$. Since the depth is 4 feet, there is a point (x, 4) on the parabola. Solve for x:

$$x^2 = 8y \rightarrow x^2 = 8 \cdot 4 \rightarrow x^2 = 32 \rightarrow x = \pm 4\sqrt{2}$$

The width of the opening of the searchlight should be $8\sqrt{2}$ feet.

59. Set up the problem so that the vertex of the parabola is at (0, 0) and it opens up. Then the equation of the parabola has the form: $x^2 = 4ay$. Since the parabola is 20 feet across and 6 feet deep, the points (10, 6) and (–10, 6) are on the parabola.
Substitute and solve for a:

$$10^2 = 4a(6) \to 100 = 24a \to a \approx 4.17 \text{ feet}$$

The heat source will be concentrated 4.17 feet from the base, along the axis of symmetry.

60. Set up the problem so that the vertex of the parabola is at (0, 0) and it opens up. Then the equation of the parabola has the form: $x^2 = 4ay$. Since the parabola is 4 inches across and 3 feet deep, the points (2, 36) and (–2, 36) are on the parabola.
Substitute and solve for a:

$$2^2 = 4a(36) \to 4 = 144a \to a = \frac{1}{36} \approx 0.0278 \text{ inches}$$

The collected light will be concentrated 0.0278 inches from the vertex, along the axis of symmetry.

61. Set up the problem so that the vertex of the parabola is at (0, 0) and it opens down. Then the equation of the parabola has the form: $x^2 = cy$.
The point (60, –25) is a point on the parabola.
Solve for c and find the equation:

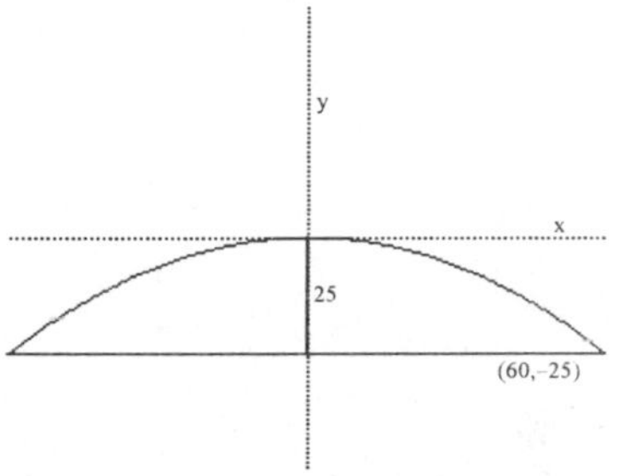

$$60^2 = c(-25) \to c = -144$$

$$x^2 = -144y$$

To find the height of the bridge, 10 feet from the center, the point (10, y) is a point on the parabola. Solve for y:

$$10^2 = -144y \to 100 = -144y \to y = -0.69$$

The height of the bridge, 10 feet from the center, is 25 – 0.69 = 24.31 feet.
To find the height of the bridge, 30 feet from the center, the point (30, y) is a point on the parabola. Solve for y:

$$30^2 = -144y \to 900 = -144y \to y = -6.25$$

The height of the bridge, 30 feet from the center, is 25 – 6.25 = 18.75 feet.
To find the height of the bridge, 50 feet from the center, the point (50, y) is a point on the parabola. Solve for y:

$$50^2 = -144y \to 2500 = -144y \to y = -17.36$$

The height of the bridge, 50 feet from the center, is 25 – 17.36 = 7.64 feet.

62. Set up the problem so that the vertex of the parabola is at (0, 0) and it opens down. Then the equation of the parabola has the form: $x^2 = cy$.
The points (50, –h) and (40, –h+10) are points on the parabola. Substitute and solve for c and h:

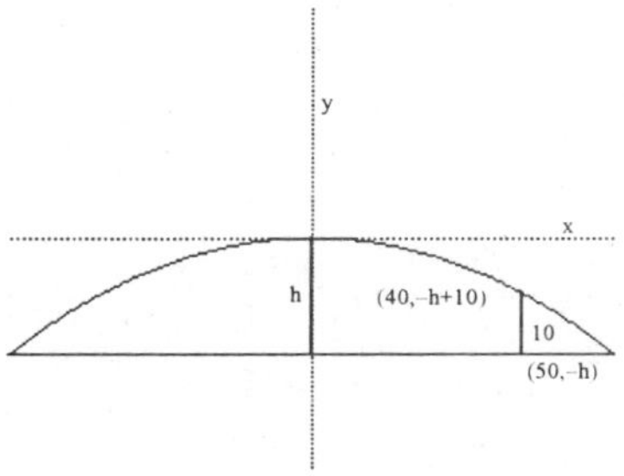

$$50^2 = c(-h) \qquad 40^2 = c(-h+10)$$

$$ch = -2500 \qquad 1600 = -ch + 10c$$

$$1600 = -(-2500) + 10c \to -900 = 10c \to c = -90$$

$$-90h = -2500 \to h = 27.78$$

The height of the bridge at the center is 27.78 feet.

63. $Ax^2 + Ey = 0 \quad A \neq 0,\ E \neq 0$

$$Ax^2 = -Ey \to x^2 = \frac{-E}{A}y$$

This is the equation of a parabola with vertex at (0, 0) and axis of symmetry being the y-axis. The focus is $\left(0, \frac{-E}{4A}\right)$. The directrix is $y = \frac{E}{4A}$.

64. $Cy^2 + Dx = 0 \quad C \neq 0,\ D \neq 0$

$$Cy^2 = -Dx \to y^2 = \frac{-D}{C}x$$

This is the equation of a parabola with vertex at (0, 0) and axis of symmetry being the x-axis. The focus is $\left(\frac{-D}{4C}, 0\right)$. The directrix is $x = \frac{D}{4C}$.

65. $Ax^2 + Dx + Ey + F = 0 \quad A \neq 0$

(a) If $E \neq 0$, then:

$$Ax^2 + Dx = -Ey - F \to A\left(x^2 + \frac{D}{A}x + \frac{D^2}{4A^2}\right) = -Ey - F + \frac{D^2}{4A}$$

$$\left(x + \frac{D}{2A}\right)^2 = \frac{1}{A}\left(-Ey - F + \frac{D^2}{4A}\right) \to \left(x + \frac{D}{2A}\right)^2 = \frac{-E}{A}\left(y + \frac{F}{E} - \frac{D^2}{4AE}\right)$$

$$\left(x + \frac{D}{2A}\right)^2 = \frac{-E}{A}\left(y - \frac{D^2 - 4AF}{4AE}\right)$$

This is the equation of a parabola whose vertex is $\left(\frac{-D}{2A}, \frac{D^2 - 4AF}{4AE}\right)$.

(b) If $E = 0$, then

$$Ax^2 + Dx + F = 0 \to x = \frac{-D \pm \sqrt{D^2 - 4AF}}{2A}$$

If $D^2 - 4AF = 0$, then $x = \frac{-D}{2A}$ is a vertical line.

(c) If $E = 0$, then

$$Ax^2 + Dx + F = 0 \to x = \frac{-D \pm \sqrt{D^2 - 4AF}}{2A}$$

If $D^2 - 4AF > 0$,

then $x = \frac{-D + \sqrt{D^2 - 4AF}}{2A}$ or $x = \frac{-D - \sqrt{D^2 - 4AF}}{2A}$ are two vertical lines.

(d) If $E = 0$, then

$$Ax^2 + Dx + F = 0 \to x = \frac{-D \pm \sqrt{D^2 - 4AF}}{2A}$$

If $D^2 - 4AF < 0$, there is no real solution. The graph contains no points.

66. $Cy^2 + Dx + Ey + F = 0 \qquad C \neq 0$

(a) If $D \neq 0$, then:

$$Cy^2 + Ey = -Dx - F \rightarrow C\left(y^2 + \frac{E}{C}y + \frac{E^2}{4C^2}\right) = -Dx - F + \frac{E^2}{4C}$$

$$\left(y + \frac{E}{2C}\right)^2 = \frac{1}{C}\left(-Dx - F + \frac{E^2}{4C}\right)$$

$$\left(y + \frac{E}{2C}\right)^2 = \frac{-D}{C}\left(x + \frac{F}{D} - \frac{E^2}{4CD}\right) \rightarrow \left(y + \frac{E}{2C}\right)^2 = \frac{-D}{C}\left(x - \frac{E^2 - 4CF}{4CD}\right)$$

This is the equation of a parabola whose vertex is $\left(\frac{-E}{2C}, \frac{E^2 - 4CF}{4CD}\right)$.

(b) If $D = 0$, then

$$Cy^2 + Ey + F = 0 \rightarrow y = \frac{-E \pm \sqrt{E^2 - 4CF}}{2C}$$

If $E^2 - 4CF = 0$, then $y = \frac{-E}{2C}$ is a horizontal line.

(c) If $D = 0$, then

$$Cy^2 + Ey + F = 0 \rightarrow y = \frac{-E \pm \sqrt{E^2 - 4CF}}{2C}$$

If $E^2 - 4CF > 0$,

then $y = \frac{-E + \sqrt{E^2 - 4CF}}{2C}$ or $y = \frac{-E - \sqrt{E^2 - 4CF}}{2C}$ are two horizontal lines.

(d) If $D = 0$, then

$$Cy^2 + Ey + F = 0 \rightarrow x = \frac{-E \pm \sqrt{E^2 - 4CF}}{2C}$$

If $E^2 - 4CF < 0$, there is no real solution. The graph contains no points.

Analytic Geometry

11.3 The Ellipse

1. C 2. D 3. B 4. A

5. $\dfrac{x^2}{25}+\dfrac{y^2}{4}=1$

The center of the ellipse is at the origin.
$a=5,\ b=2$. The vertices are (5, 0) and (–5, 0).
Find the value of c:

$$c^2=a^2-b^2=25-4=21\rightarrow c=\sqrt{21}$$

The foci are $\left(\sqrt{21},0\right)$ and $\left(-\sqrt{21},0\right)$.
To graph, enter:
$y_1=2\sqrt{(1-x^2/25)};\ y_1=-2\sqrt{(1-x^2/25)}$

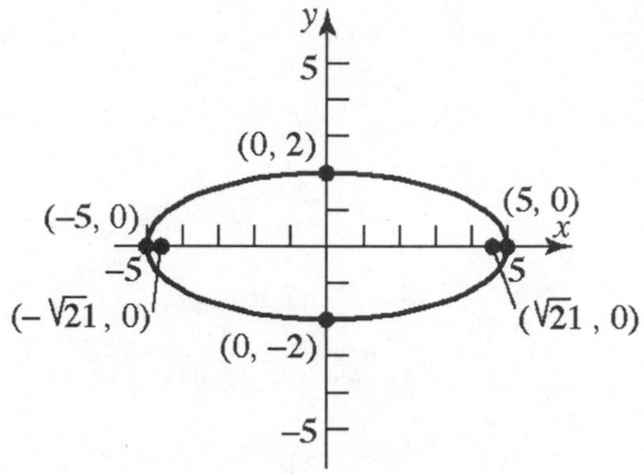

6. $\dfrac{x^2}{9}+\dfrac{y^2}{4}=1$

The center of the ellipse is at the origin.
$a=3,\ b=2$. The vertices are (3, 0) and (–3, 0).
Find the value of c:

$$c^2=a^2-b^2=9-4=5\rightarrow c=\sqrt{5}$$

The foci are $\left(\sqrt{5},0\right)$ and $\left(-\sqrt{5},0\right)$.
To graph, enter:
$y_1=2\sqrt{(1-x^2/9)};\ y_1=-2\sqrt{(1-x^2/9)}$

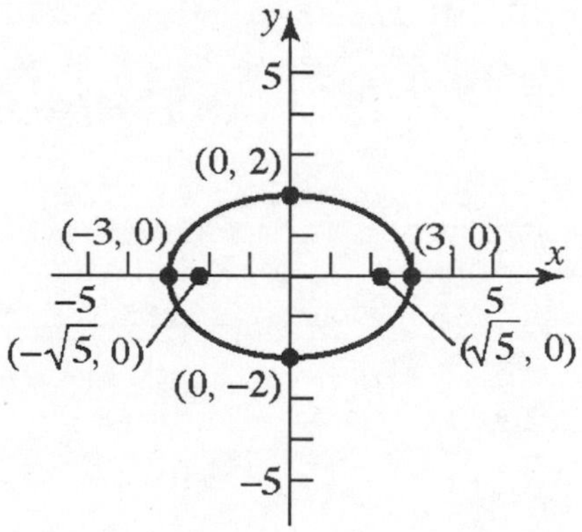

7. $\frac{x^2}{9}+\frac{y^2}{25}=1$

The center of the ellipse is at the origin.

$a=5,\ b=3$. The vertices are (0, 5) and (0, –5).

Find the value of c:

$$c^2=a^2-b^2=25-9=16$$

$$c=4$$

The foci are (0, 4) and (0, –4).

To graph, enter:

$y_1=5\sqrt{(1-x^2/9)};\ y_1=-5\sqrt{(1-x^2/9)}$

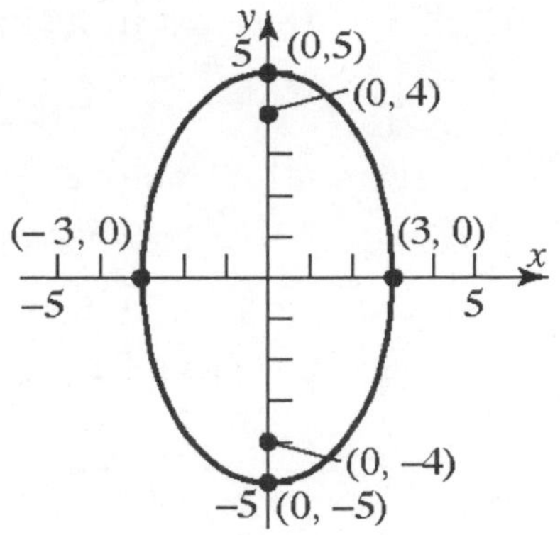

8. $x^2+\frac{y^2}{16}=1$

The center of the ellipse is at the origin.

$a=4,\ b=1$. The vertices are (0, 4) and (0, –4).

Find the value of c:

$$c^2=a^2-b^2=16-1=15$$

$$c=\sqrt{15}$$

The foci are $\left(0, \sqrt{15}\right)$ and $\left(0, -\sqrt{15}\right)$

To graph, enter: $y_1=4\sqrt{(1-x^2)};\ y_1=-4\sqrt{(1-x^2)}$

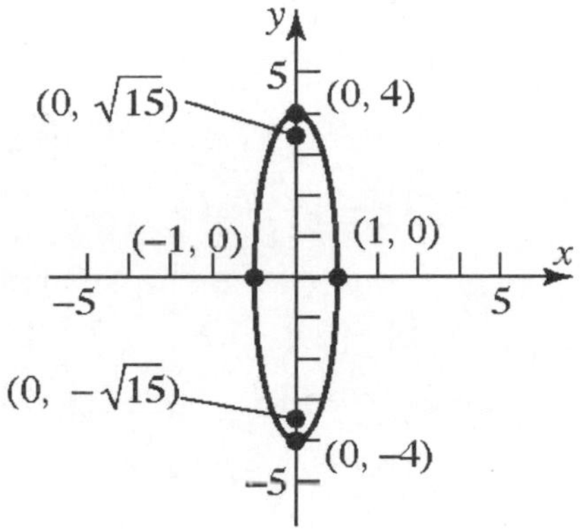

9. $4x^2+y^2=16$

Divide by 16 to put in standard form:

$$\frac{4x^2}{16}+\frac{y^2}{16}=\frac{16}{16}\ \rightarrow\ \frac{x^2}{4}+\frac{y^2}{16}=1$$

The center of the ellipse is at the origin.

$a=4,\ b=2$. The vertices are (0, 4) and (0, –4).

Find the value of c:

$$c^2=a^2-b^2=16-4=12$$

$$c=\sqrt{12}=2\sqrt{3}$$

The foci are $\left(0, 2\sqrt{3}\right)$ and $\left(0, -2\sqrt{3}\right)$.

To graph, enter:

$y_1=\sqrt{(16-4x^2)};\ y_1=-\sqrt{(16-4x^2)}$

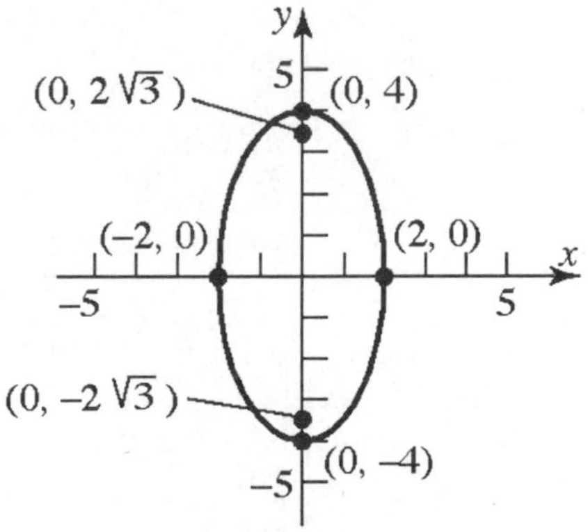

10. $x^2 + 9y^2 = 18$

Divide by 18 to put in standard form:

$$\frac{x^2}{18} + \frac{9y^2}{18} = \frac{18}{18} \rightarrow \frac{x^2}{18} + \frac{y^2}{2} = 1$$

The center of the ellipse is at the origin.

$a = 3\sqrt{2},\ b = \sqrt{2}$. The vertices are $(3\sqrt{2}, 0)$ and $(-3\sqrt{2}, 0)$. Find the value of c:

$$c^2 = a^2 - b^2 = 18 - 2 = 16$$

$$c = 4$$

The foci are (4, 0) and (–4, 0).

To graph, enter:

$y_1 = \sqrt{(18 - x^2)}\ / 3;\ y_1 = -\sqrt{(18 - x^2)}\ / 3$

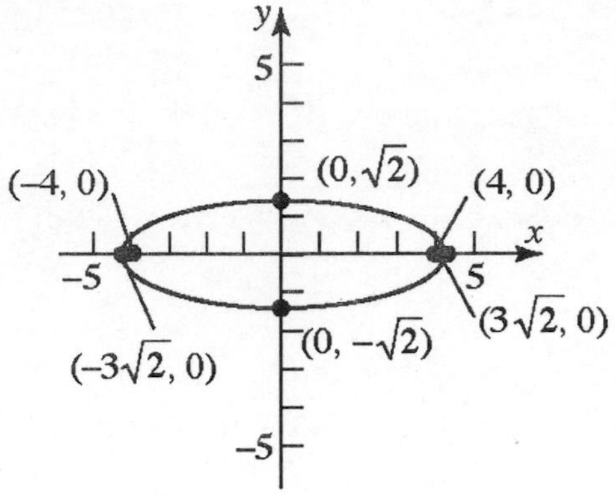

11. $4y^2 + x^2 = 8$

Divide by 8 to put in standard form:

$$\frac{4y^2}{8} + \frac{x^2}{8} = \frac{8}{8} \rightarrow \frac{x^2}{8} + \frac{y^2}{2} = 1$$

The center of the ellipse is at the origin.

$a = \sqrt{8} = 2\sqrt{2},\ b = \sqrt{2}$. The vertices are $(2\sqrt{2}, 0)$ and $(-2\sqrt{2}, 0)$. Find the value of c:

$$c^2 = a^2 - b^2 = 8 - 2 = 6$$

$$c = \sqrt{6}$$

The foci are $(\sqrt{6}, 0)$ and $(-\sqrt{6}, 0)$.

To graph, enter:

$y_1 = \sqrt{(2 - x^2 / 4)};\ y_1 = -\sqrt{(2 - x^2 / 4)}$

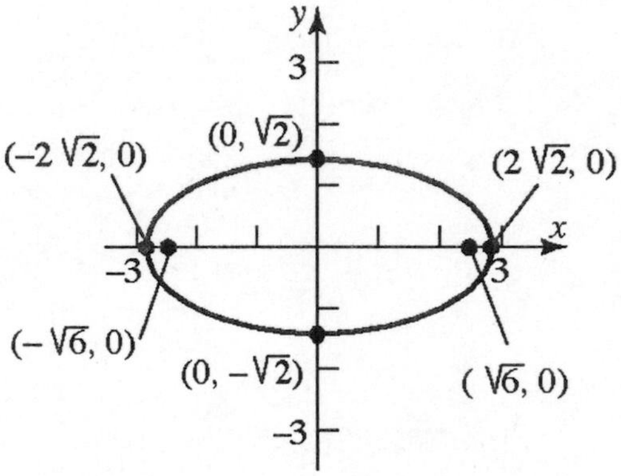

12. $4y^2 + 9x^2 = 36$

Divide by 36 to put in standard form:

$$\frac{4y^2}{36} + \frac{9x^2}{36} = \frac{36}{36} \rightarrow \frac{x^2}{4} + \frac{y^2}{9} = 1$$

The center of the ellipse is at the origin.

$a = 3,\ b = 2$. The vertices are (0, 3) and (0, –3).

Find the value of c:

$$c^2 = a^2 - b^2 = 9 - 4 = 5$$

$$c = \sqrt{5}$$

The foci are $(0, \sqrt{5})$ and $(0, -\sqrt{5})$.

To graph, enter:

$y_1 = \sqrt{((36 - 9x^2)/ 4)};\ y_1 = -\sqrt{((36 - 9x^2)/ 4)}$

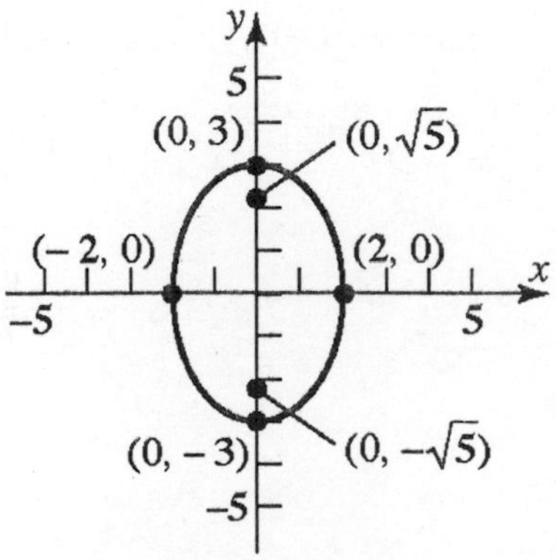

13. $x^2 + y^2 = 16$
This is the equation of a circle whose center is at (0, 0) and radius = 4.
To graph, enter: $y_1 = \sqrt{(16 - x^2)}$; $y_1 = -\sqrt{(16 - x^2)}$

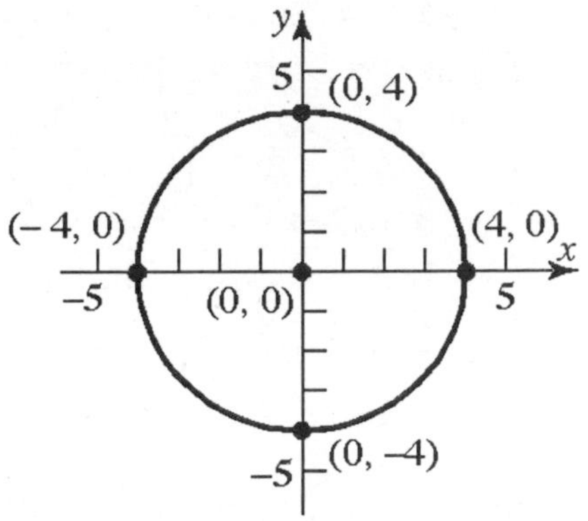

14. $x^2 + y^2 = 4$
This is the equation of a circle whose center is at (0, 0) and radius = 2.
To graph, enter: $y_1 = \sqrt{(4 - x^2)}$; $y_1 = -\sqrt{(4 - x^2)}$

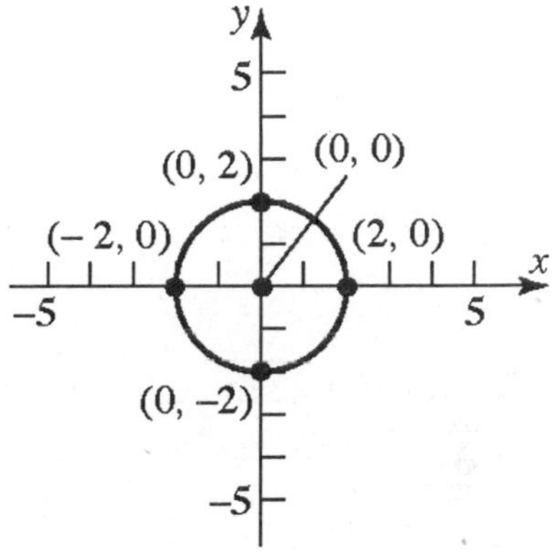

15. Center: (0, 0); Focus: (3, 0); Vertex: (5, 0);
Major axis is the x-axis; $a = 5$; $c = 3$. Find b:

$$b^2 = a^2 - c^2 = 25 - 9 = 16$$
$$b = 4$$

Write the equation: $\frac{x^2}{25} + \frac{y^2}{16} = 1$

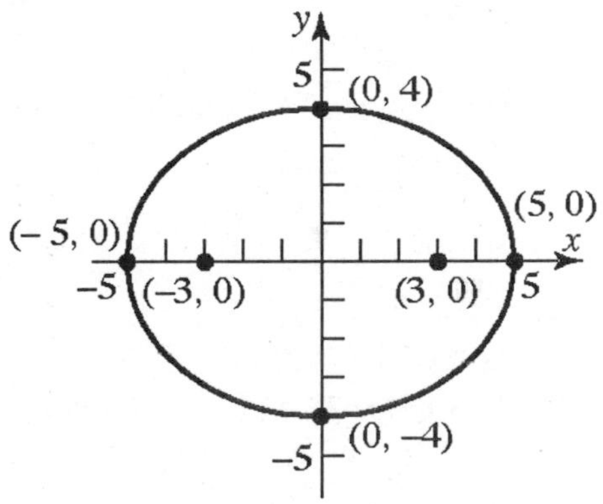

16. Center: (0, 0); Focus: (−1, 0); Vertex: (3, 0);
Major axis is the x-axis; $a = 3$; $c = 1$. Find b:

$$b^2 = a^2 - c^2 = 9 - 1 = 8$$
$$b = 2\sqrt{2}$$

Write the equation: $\frac{x^2}{9} + \frac{y^2}{8} = 1$

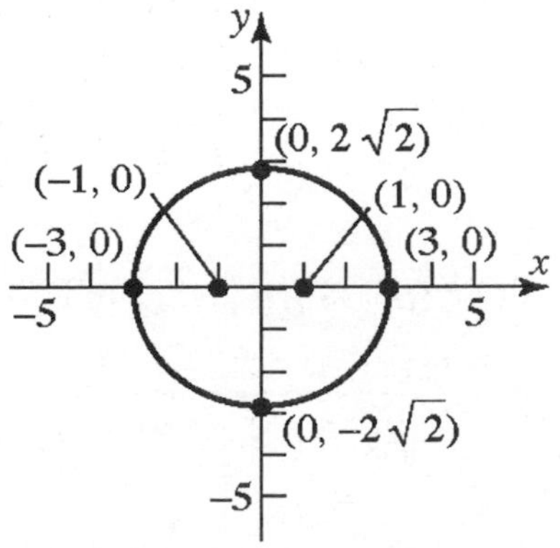

17. Center: (0, 0); Focus: (0, –4); Vertex: (0, 5);
Major axis is the y-axis; $a = 5$; $c = 4$. Find b:

$$b^2 = a^2 - c^2 = 25 - 16 = 9$$
$$b = 3$$

Write the equation: $\frac{x^2}{9} + \frac{y^2}{25} = 1$

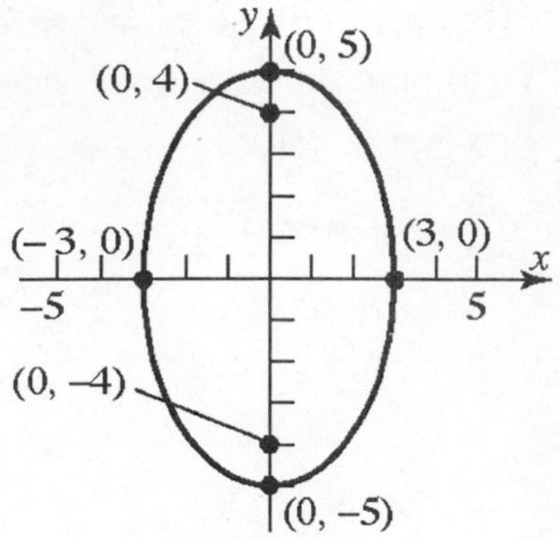

18. Center: (0, 0); Focus: (0, 1); Vertex: (0, –2);
Major axis is the y-axis; $a = 2$; $c = 1$. Find b:

$$b^2 = a^2 - c^2 = 4 - 1 = 3$$
$$b = \sqrt{3}$$

Write the equation: $\frac{x^2}{3} + \frac{y^2}{4} = 1$

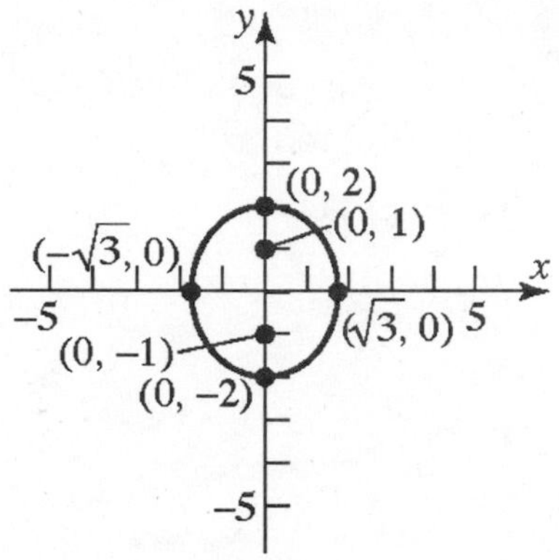

19. Foci: (±2, 0); Length of major axis is 6.
Center: (0, 0); Major axis is the x-axis;
$a = 3$; $c = 2$. Find b:

$$b^2 = a^2 - c^2 = 9 - 4 = 5$$
$$b = \sqrt{5}$$

Write the equation: $\frac{x^2}{9} + \frac{y^2}{5} = 1$

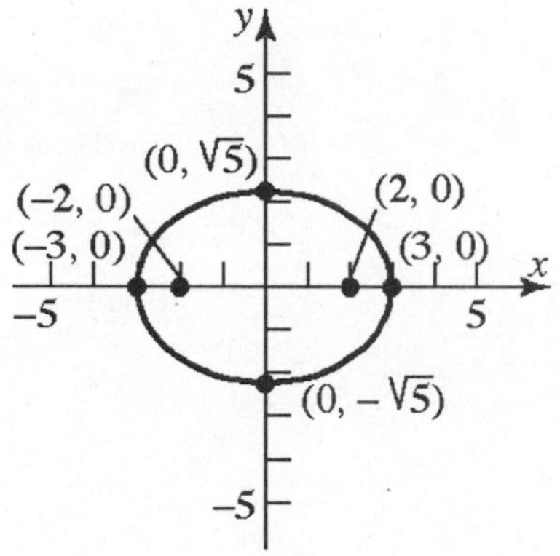

20. Focus: (0, –4); Vertices: (0, ±8).
Center: (0, 0); Major axis is the y-axis;
$a = 8$; $c = 4$. Find b:

$$b^2 = a^2 - c^2 = 64 - 16 = 48$$
$$b = 4\sqrt{3}$$

Write the equation: $\frac{x^2}{48} + \frac{y^2}{64} = 1$

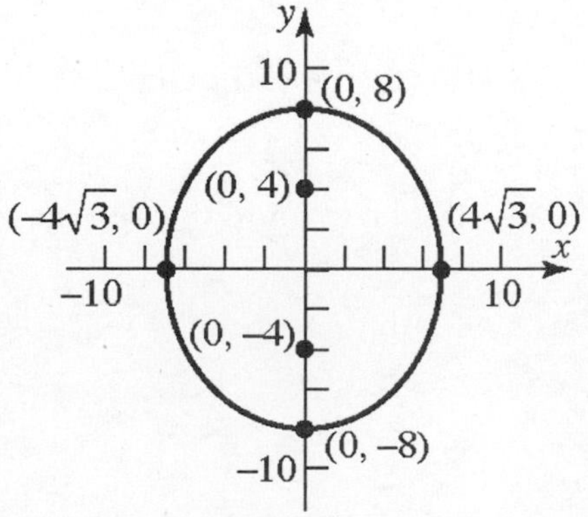

21. Foci: (0, ±3); x-intercepts are ±2. Center: (0, 0); Major axis is the y-axis; $c = 3$; $b = 2$. Find a:

$$a^2 = b^2 + c^2 = 4 + 9 = 13$$

$$a = \sqrt{13}$$

Write the equation: $\frac{x^2}{4} + \frac{y^2}{13} = 1$

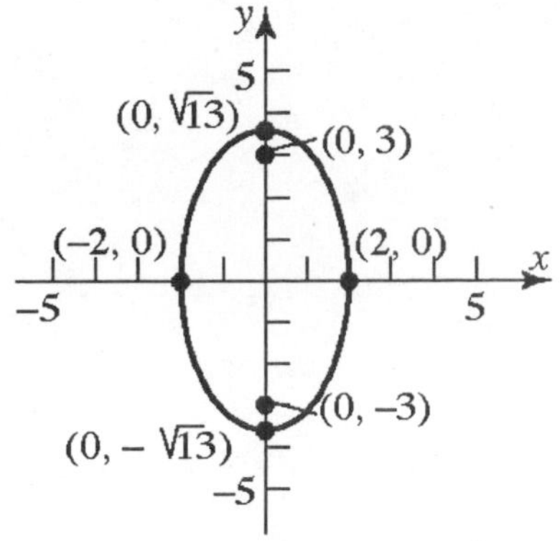

22. Foci: (0, ±2); length of the major axis is 8. Center: (0, 0); Major axis is the y-axis; $a = 4$; $c = 2$. Find b:

$$b^2 = a^2 - c^2 = 16 - 4 = 12$$

$$b = 2\sqrt{3}$$

Write the equation: $\frac{x^2}{12} + \frac{y^2}{16} = 1$

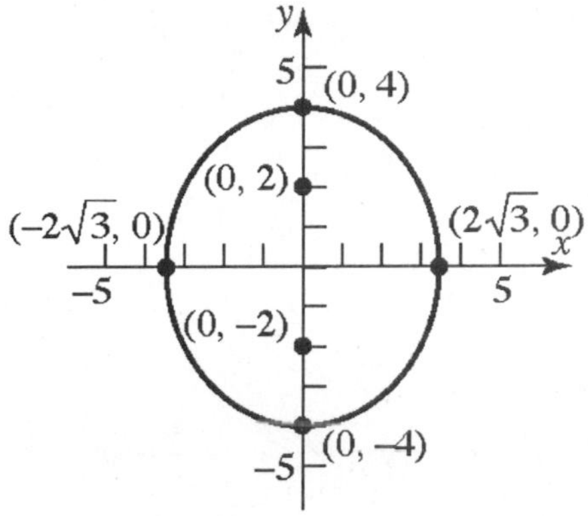

23. Center: (0, 0); Vertex: (0, 4); $b = 1$; Major axis is the y-axis; $a = 4$; $b = 1$.

Write the equation: $\frac{x^2}{1} + \frac{y^2}{16} = 1$

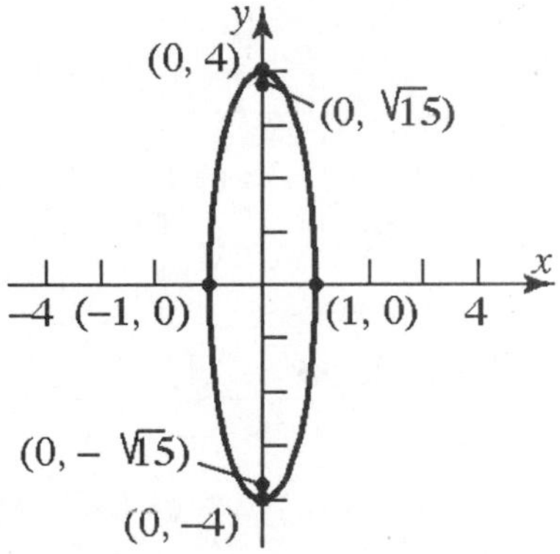

24. Vertices: (±5, 0); $c = 2$; Major axis is the x-axis; $a = 5$; Find b:

$$b^2 = a^2 - c^2 = 25 - 4 = 21$$

$$b = \sqrt{21}$$

Write the equation: $\frac{x^2}{25} + \frac{y^2}{21} = 1$

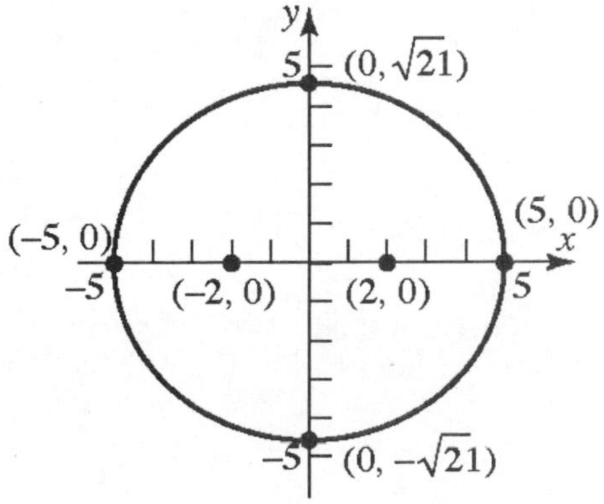

25. $\frac{(x+1)^2}{4} + \frac{(y-1)^2}{1} = 1$

26. $\frac{(x+1)^2}{1} + \frac{(y+1)^2}{4} = 1$

27. $\dfrac{(x-1)^2}{1}+\dfrac{y^2}{4}=1$

28. $\dfrac{x^2}{4}+\dfrac{(y-1)^2}{1}=1$

29. The equation $\dfrac{(x-3)^2}{4}+\dfrac{(y+1)^2}{9}=1$ is in the form $\dfrac{(x-h)^2}{b^2}+\dfrac{(y-k)^2}{a^2}=1$ (major axis parallel to the y-axis) where $a=3,\ b=2,\ h=3,$ and $k=-1$.
Solving for c:

$c^2=a^2-b^2=9-4=5\rightarrow c=\sqrt{5}$

Thus, we have:

Center: $(3,-1)$

Foci: $\left(3,-1+\sqrt{5}\right),\ \left(3,-1-\sqrt{5}\right)$

Vertices: $(3, 2), (3, -4)$

To graph, enter: $y_1=-1+3\sqrt{1-(x-3)^2/4}$;

$y_2=-1-3\sqrt{1-(x-3)^2/4}$

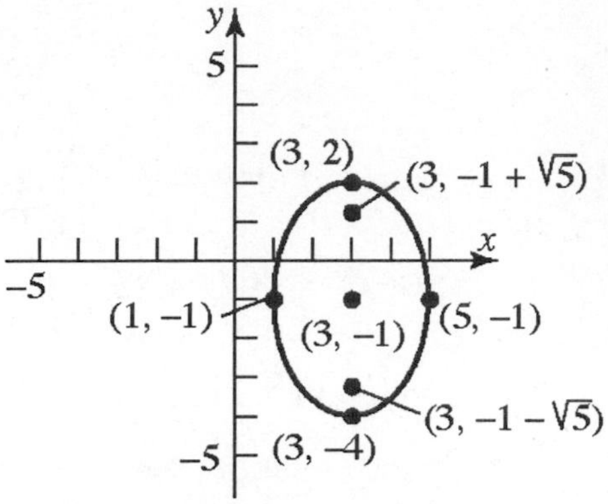

30. The equation $\dfrac{(x+4)^2}{9}+\dfrac{(y+2)^2}{4}=1$ is in the form $\dfrac{(x-h)^2}{a^2}+\dfrac{(y-k)^2}{b^2}=1$ (major axis parallel to the x-axis) where $a=3,\ b=2,\ h=-4,$ and $k=-2$.
Solving for c:

$c^2=a^2-b^2=9-4=5\rightarrow c=\sqrt{5}$

Thus, we have:

Center: $(-4,-2)$

Foci: $\left(-4+\sqrt{5},-2\right)\ \left(-4-\sqrt{5},-2\right)$

Vertices: $(-7, -2), (-1, -2)$

To graph, enter:

$y_1=-2+2\sqrt{1-(x+4)^2/9}$;

$y_2=-2-2\sqrt{1-(x+4)^2/9}$

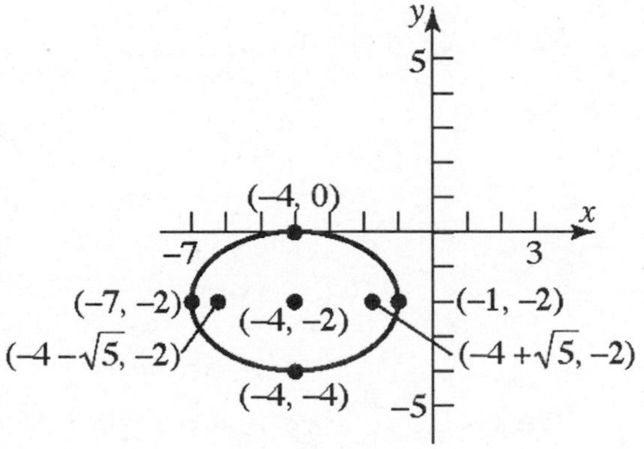

31. Divide by 16 to put the equation in standard form:

$$(x+5)^2+4(y-4)^2=16\rightarrow\frac{(x+5)^2}{16}+\frac{4(y-4)^2}{16}=\frac{16}{16}\rightarrow\frac{(x+5)^2}{16}+\frac{(y-4)^2}{4}=1$$

The equation is in the form $\dfrac{(x-h)^2}{a^2}+\dfrac{(y-k)^2}{b^2}=1$ (major axis parallel to the x-axis) where $a=4,\ b=2,\ h=-5,$ and $k=4$.
Solving for c:

$c^2=a^2-b^2=16-4=12\rightarrow c=\sqrt{12}=2\sqrt{3}$

Thus, we have:

Center: $(-5, 4)$

Foci: $\left(-5-2\sqrt{3},4\right), \left(-5+2\sqrt{3},4\right)$

Vertices: $(-9, 4)$, $(-1, 4)$

To graph, enter:

$y_1 = 4 + 2\sqrt{1-(x+5)^2/16}$;

$y_2 = 4 - 2\sqrt{1-(x+5)^2/16}$

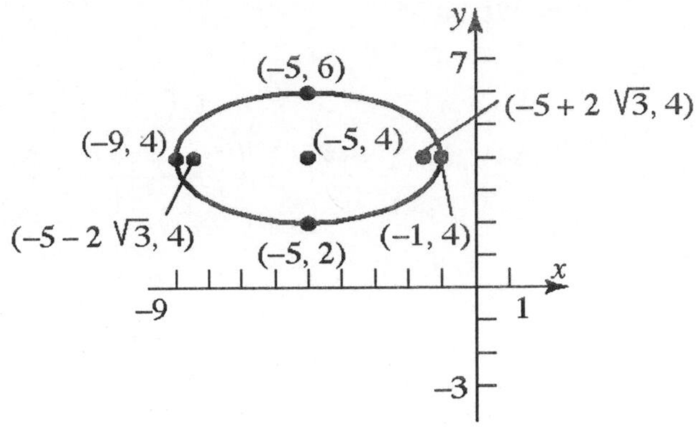

32. Divide by 18 to put the equation in standard form:

$$9(x-3)^2+(y+2)^2=18 \to \frac{9(x-3)^2}{18}+\frac{(y+2)^2}{18}=\frac{18}{18} \to \frac{(x-3)^2}{2}+\frac{(y+2)^2}{18}=1$$

The equation is in the form $\frac{(x-h)^2}{b^2}+\frac{(y-k)^2}{a^2}=1$ (major axis parallel to the y-axis) where $a=3\sqrt{2}$, $b=\sqrt{2}$, $h=3$, and $k=-2$.

Solving for c:

$c^2=a^2-b^2=18-2=16 \to c=4$

Thus, we have:

Center: $(3, -2)$

Foci: $(3, 2)$, $(3, -6)$

Vertices: $\left(3, -2+3\sqrt{2}\right)$ $\left(3, -2-3\sqrt{2}\right)$

To graph, enter: $y_1=-2+\sqrt{18-9(x-3)^2}$;

$y_2=-2-\sqrt{18-9(x-3)^2}$

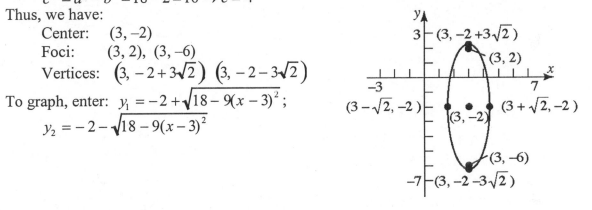

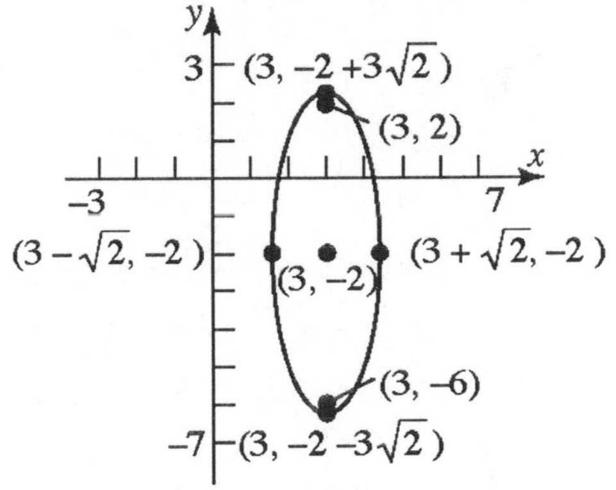

33. Complete the square to put the equation in standard form:

$$x^2+4x+4y^2-8y+4=0$$

$$(x^2+4x+4)+4(y^2-2y+1)=-4+4+4 \to (x+2)^2+4(y-1)^2=4$$

$$\frac{(x+2)^2}{4}+\frac{4(y-1)^2}{4}=\frac{4}{4} \to \frac{(x+2)^2}{4}+\frac{(y-1)^2}{1}=1$$

The equation is in the form $\frac{(x-h)^2}{a^2}+\frac{(y-k)^2}{b^2}=1$ (major axis parallel to the x-axis) where $a=2$, $b=1$, $h=-2$, and $k=1$.

Solving for c:

$c^2=a^2-b^2=4-1=3 \to c=\sqrt{3}$

Thus, we have:

Center: (–2, 1)

Foci: $\left(-2-\sqrt{3},1\right),\ \left(-2+\sqrt{3},1\right)$

Vertices: (–4, 1), (0, 1)

To graph, enter: $y_1 = 1+\sqrt{1-(x+2)^2/4}$;

$y_2 = 1-\sqrt{1-(x+2)^2/4}$

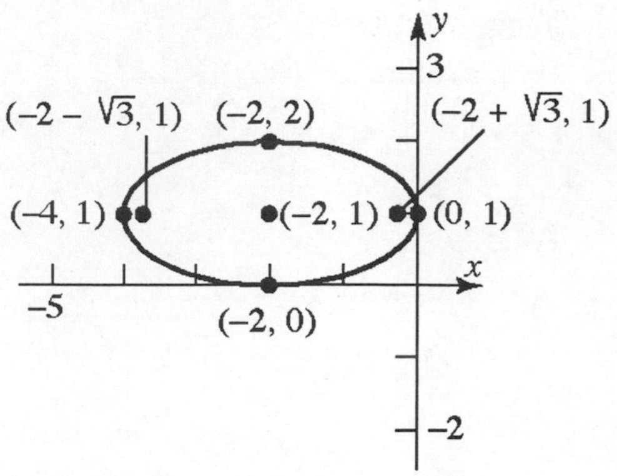

34. Complete the square to put the equation in standard form:

$$x^2+3y^2-12y+9=0 \rightarrow x^2+3(y^2-4y+4)=-9+12$$

$$x^2+3(y-2)^2=3 \rightarrow \frac{x^2}{3}+\frac{3(y-2)^2}{3}=\frac{3}{3} \rightarrow \frac{x^2}{3}+\frac{(y-2)^2}{1}=1$$

The equation is in the form $\frac{(x-h)^2}{a^2}+\frac{(y-k)^2}{b^2}=1$ (major axis parallel to the x-axis) where $a=\sqrt{3},\ b=1,\ h=0,$ and $k=2$.

Solving for c:

$c^2=a^2-b^2=3-1=2 \rightarrow c=\sqrt{2}$

Thus, we have:

Center: (0, 2)

Foci: $\left(-\sqrt{2},2\right),\ \left(\sqrt{2},2\right)$

Vertices: $\left(-\sqrt{3},2\right),\ \left(\sqrt{3},2\right)$

To graph, enter: $y_1 = 2+\sqrt{1-x^2/3}$;

$y_2 = 2-\sqrt{1-x^2/3}$

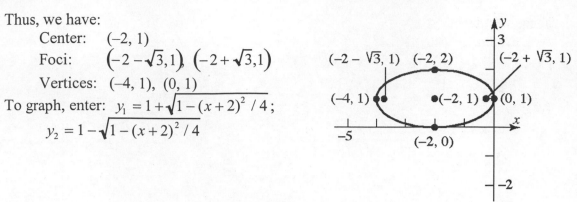

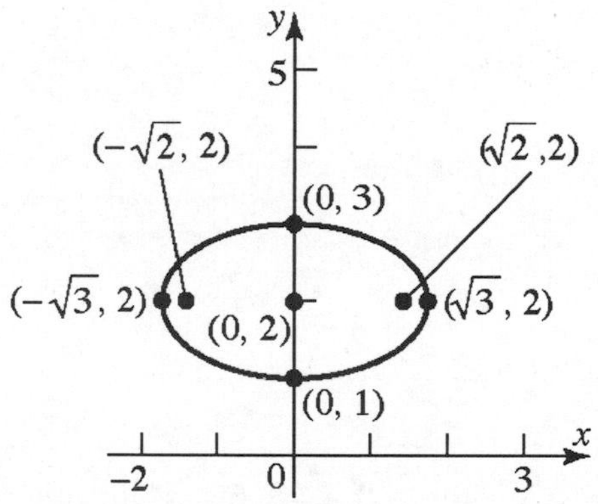

35. Complete the square to put the equation in standard form:

$$2x^2+3y^2-8x+6y+5=0 \rightarrow 2(x^2-4x)+3(y^2+2y)=-5$$

$$2(x^2-4x+4)+3(y^2+2y+1)=-5+8+3 \rightarrow 2(x-2)^2+3(y+1)^2=6$$

$$\frac{2(x-2)^2}{6}+\frac{3(y+1)^2}{6}=\frac{6}{6} \rightarrow \frac{(x-2)^2}{3}+\frac{(y+1)^2}{2}=1$$

The equation is in the form $\frac{(x-h)^2}{a^2}+\frac{(y-k)^2}{b^2}=1$ (major axis parallel to the x-axis) where $a=\sqrt{3},\ b=\sqrt{2},\ h=2,$ and $k=-1$.

Solving for c:

$c^2=a^2-b^2=3-2=1 \quad \rightarrow \quad c=1$

Thus, we have:

Center: $(2, -1)$

Foci: $(1, -1)$, $(3, -1)$

Vertices: $\left(2-\sqrt{3}, -1\right)$, $\left(2+\sqrt{3}, -1\right)$

To graph, enter: $y_1 = -1 + \sqrt{2 - 2(x-2)^2 / 3}$;

$y_2 = -1 - \sqrt{2 - 2(x-2)^2 / 3}$

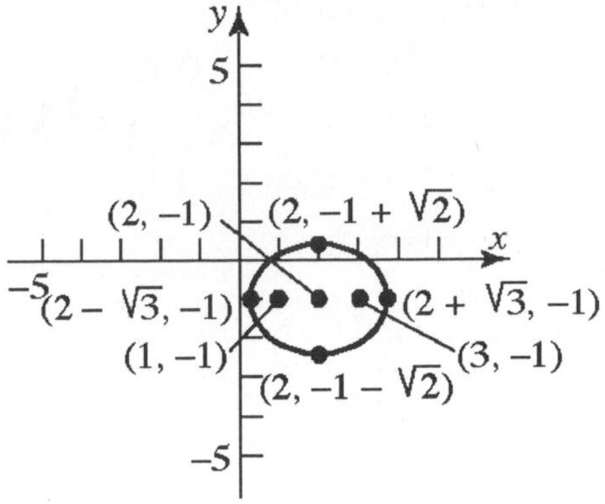

36. Complete the square to put the equation in standard form:

$$4x^2 + 3y^2 + 8x - 6y = 5 \rightarrow 4(x^2 + 2x) + 3(y^2 - 2y) = 5$$

$$4(x^2 + 2x + 1) + 3(y^2 - 2y + 1) = 5 + 4 + 3 \rightarrow 4(x+1)^2 + 3(y-1)^2 = 12$$

$$\frac{4(x+1)^2}{12} + \frac{3(y-1)^2}{12} = \frac{12}{12} \rightarrow \frac{(x+1)^2}{3} + \frac{(y-1)^2}{4} = 1$$

The equation is in the form $\frac{(x-h)^2}{b^2} + \frac{(y-k)^2}{a^2} = 1$ (major axis parallel to the y-axis) where $a = 2$, $b = \sqrt{3}$, $h = -1$, and $k = 1$.

Solving for c:

$c^2 = a^2 - b^2 = 4 - 3 = 1 \rightarrow c = 1$

Thus, we have:

Center: $(-1, 1)$

Foci: $(-1, 0)$, $(-1, 2)$

Vertices: $(-1, -1)$, $(-1, 3)$

To graph, enter: $y_1 = 1 + 2\sqrt{1 - (x+1)^2 / 3}$;

$y_2 = 1 - 2\sqrt{1 - (x+1)^2 / 3}$

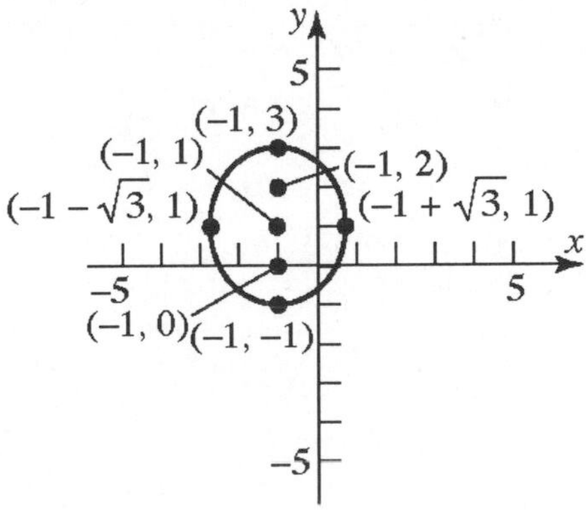

37. Complete the square to put the equation in standard form:

$$9x^2 + 4y^2 - 18x + 16y - 11 = 0 \rightarrow 9(x^2 - 2x) + 4(y^2 + 4y) = 11$$

$$9(x^2 - 2x + 1) + 4(y^2 + 4y + 4) = 11 + 9 + 16 \rightarrow 9(x-1)^2 + 4(y+2)^2 = 36$$

$$\frac{9(x-1)^2}{36} + \frac{4(y+2)^2}{36} = \frac{36}{36} \rightarrow \frac{(x-1)^2}{4} + \frac{(y+2)^2}{9} = 1$$

The equation is in the form $\frac{(x-h)^2}{b^2} + \frac{(y-k)^2}{a^2} = 1$ (major axis parallel to the y-axis) where $a = 3$, $b = 2$, $h = 1$, and $k = -2$.

Solving for c:

$c^2 = a^2 - b^2 = 9 - 4 = 5 \rightarrow c = \sqrt{5}$

Thus, we have:

Center: (1,–2)

Foci: $\left(1,-2+\sqrt{5}\right)$, $\left(1,-2-\sqrt{5}\right)$

Vertices: (1, 1), (1, –5)

To graph, enter: $y_1=-2+3\sqrt{1-(x-1)^2/4}$;

$y_2=-2-3\sqrt{1-(x-1)^2/4}$

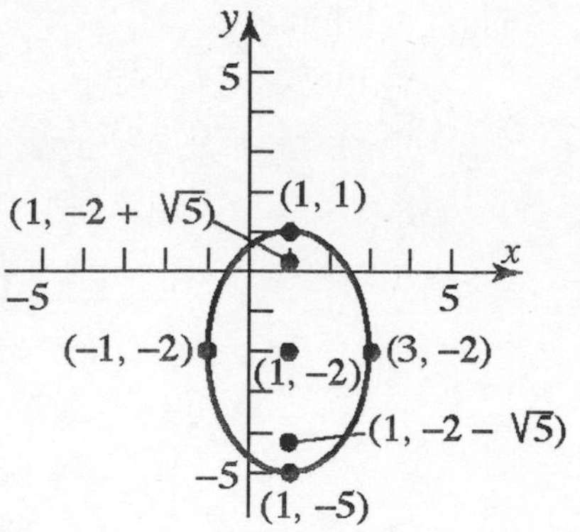

38. Complete the square to put the equation in standard form:

$$x^2+9y^2+6x-18y+9=0\to(x^2+6x)+9(y^2-2y)=-9$$

$$(x^2+6x+9)+9(y^2-2y+1)=-9+9+9\to(x+3)^2+9(y-1)^2=9$$

$$\frac{(x+3)^2}{9}+\frac{9(y-1)^2}{9}=\frac{9}{9}\to\frac{(x+3)^2}{9}+\frac{(y-1)^2}{1}=1$$

The equation is in the form $\frac{(x-h)^2}{a^2}+\frac{(y-k)^2}{b^2}=1$ (major axis parallel to the x-axis) where $a=3,\ b=1,\ h=-3$, and $k=1$.

Solving for c:

$c^2=a^2-b^2=9-1=8\to c=2\sqrt{2}$

Thus, we have:

Center: (–3, 1))

Foci: $\left(-3+2\sqrt{2},1\right)$, $\left(-3-2\sqrt{2},1\right)$

Vertices: (0, 1), (–6, 1)

To graph, enter:

$y_1=1+\sqrt{1-(x+3)^2/9}$;

$y_2=1-\sqrt{1-(x+3)^2/9}$

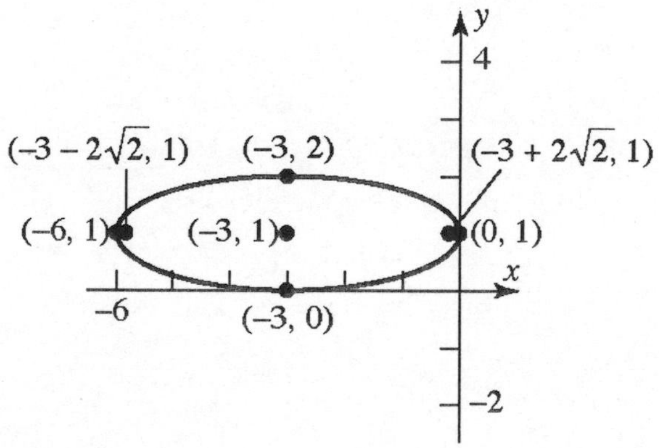

39. Complete the square to put the equation in standard form:

$$4x^2+y^2+4y=0\to4x^2+y^2+4y+4=4$$

$$4x^2+(y+2)^2=4\to\frac{4x^2}{4}+\frac{(y+2)^2}{4}=\frac{4}{4}\to\frac{x^2}{1}+\frac{(y+2)^2}{4}=1$$

The equation is in the form $\frac{(x-h)^2}{b^2}+\frac{(y-k)^2}{a^2}=1$ (major axis parallel to the y-axis) where $a=2,\ b=1,\ h=0$, and $k=-2$.

Solving for c:

$c^2=a^2-b^2=4-1=3\ \to\ c=\sqrt{3}$

Thus, we have:

Center: (0,–2)

Foci: $\left(0,-2+\sqrt{3}\right), \left(0,-2-\sqrt{3}\right)$

Vertices: (0, 0), (0, –4)

To graph, enter: $y_1=-2+2\sqrt{1-x^2}$;

$y_2=-2-2\sqrt{1-x^2}$

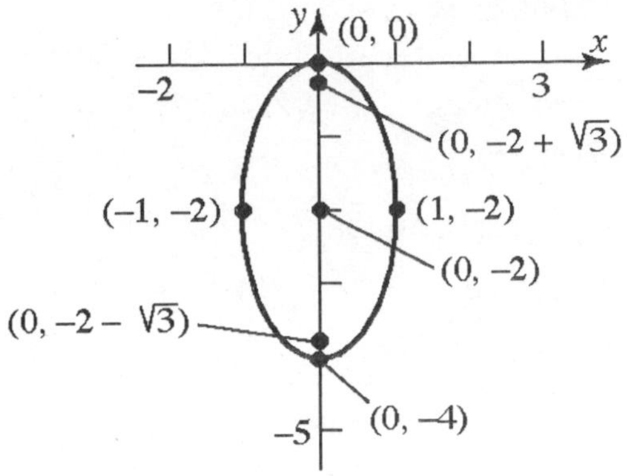

40. Complete the square to put the equation in standard form:

$$9x^2+y^2-18x=0\rightarrow 9(x^2-2x+1)+y^2=9$$

$$9(x-1)^2+y^2=9\rightarrow \frac{9(x-1)^2}{9}+\frac{y^2}{9}=\frac{9}{9}\rightarrow \frac{(x-1)^2}{1}+\frac{y^2}{9}=1$$

The equation is in the form $\frac{(x-h)^2}{b^2}+\frac{(y-k)^2}{a^2}=1$ (major axis parallel to the y-axis) where $a=3,\ b=1,\ h=1$, and $k=0$.

Solving for c:

$c^2=a^2-b^2=9-1=8 \ \rightarrow \ c=2\sqrt{2}$

Thus, we have:

Center: (1, 0)

Foci: $\left(1,2\sqrt{2}\right), \left(1,-2\sqrt{2}\right)$

Vertices: (1, 3), (1, –3)

To graph, enter: $y_1=3\sqrt{1-(x-1)^2}$;

$y_2=-3\sqrt{1-(x-1)^2}$

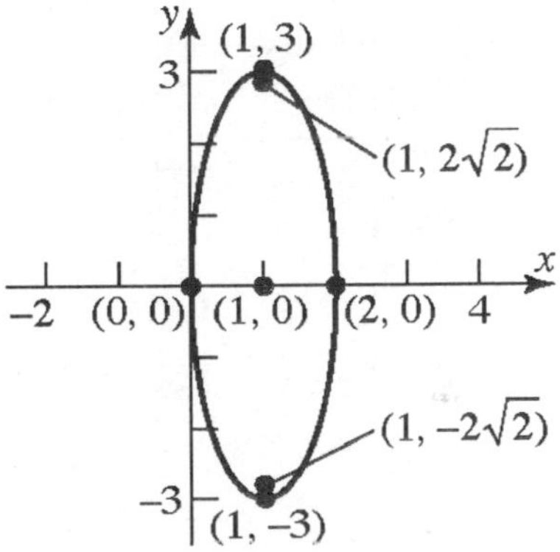

41. Center: (2, –2); Vertex: (7, –2); Focus: (4, –2); Major axis parallel to the x-axis; $a=5$; $c=2$.

Find b:

$b^2=a^2-c^2=25-4=21$

$b=\sqrt{21}$

Write the equation:

$\frac{(x-2)^2}{25}+\frac{(y+2)^2}{21}=1$

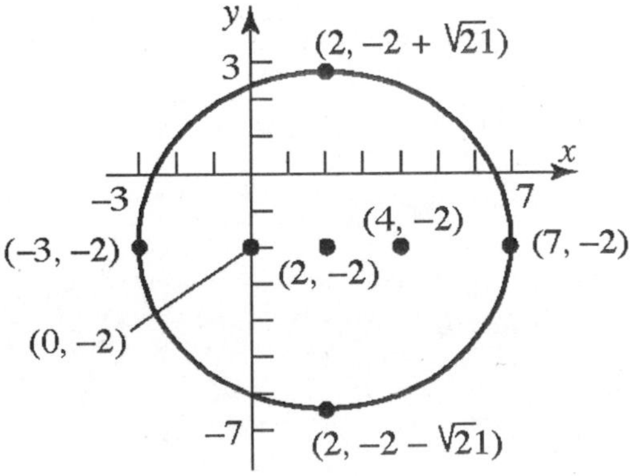

42. Center: $(-3, 1)$; Vertex: $(-3, 3)$; Focus: $(-3, 0)$; Major axis parallel to the y-axis; $a = 2$; $c = 1$.
Find b:

$$b^2 = a^2 - c^2 = 4 - 1 = 3$$
$$b = \sqrt{3}$$

Write the equation: $\dfrac{(x+3)^2}{3} + \dfrac{(y-1)^2}{4} = 1$

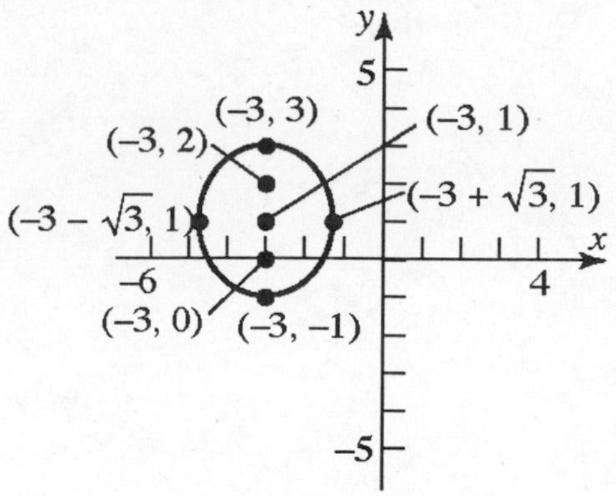

43. Vertices: $(4, 3)$, $(4, 9)$; Focus: $(4, 8)$; Center: $(4, 6)$; Major axis parallel to the y-axis; $a = 3$; $c = 2$.
Find b:

$$b^2 = a^2 - c^2 = 9 - 4 = 5$$
$$b = \sqrt{5}$$

Write the equation: $\dfrac{(x-4)^2}{5} + \dfrac{(y-6)^2}{9} = 1$

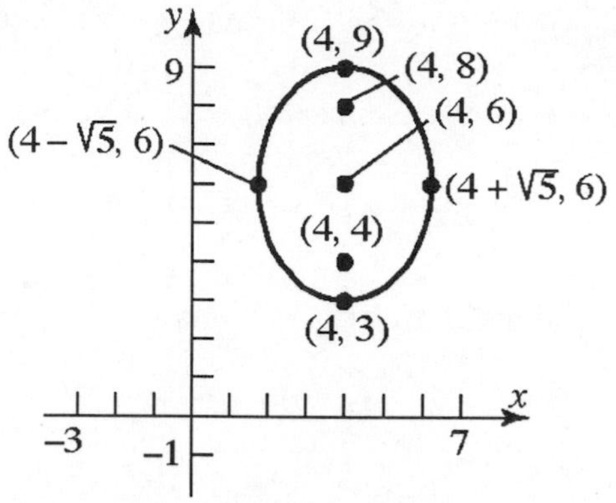

44. Foci: $(1, 2)$, $(-3, 2)$; Vertex: $(-4, 2)$; Center: $(-1, 2)$; Major axis parallel to the x-axis; $a = 3$; $c = 2$. Find b:

$$b^2 = a^2 - c^2 = 9 - 4 = 5$$
$$b = \sqrt{5}$$

Write the equation: $\dfrac{(x+1)^2}{9} + \dfrac{(y-2)^2}{5} = 1$

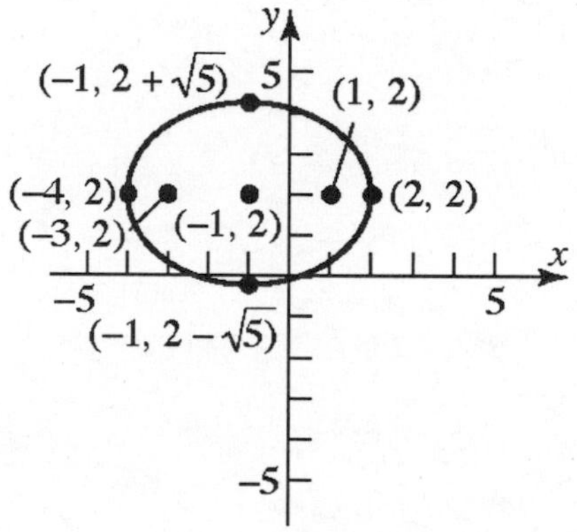

45. Foci: $(5, 1)$, $(-1, 1)$; length of the major axis $= 8$; Center: $(2, 1)$; Major axis parallel to the x-axis; $a = 4$; $c = 3$. Find b:

$$b^2 = a^2 - c^2 = 16 - 9 = 7$$
$$b = \sqrt{7}$$

Write the equation: $\dfrac{(x-2)^2}{16} + \dfrac{(y-1)^2}{7} = 1$

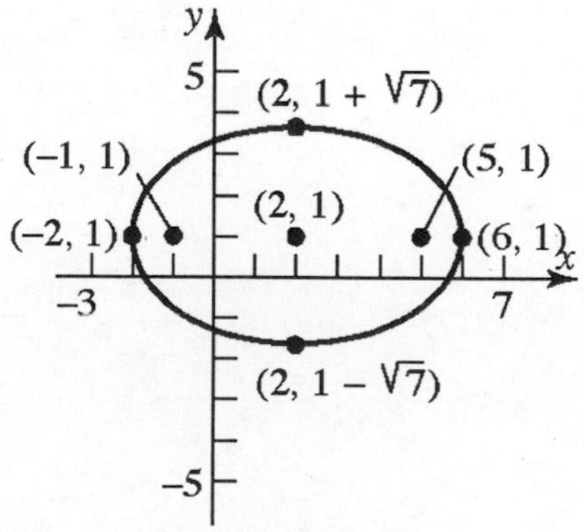

46. Vertices: $(2, 5), (2, -1)$; $c = 2$;
Center: $(2, 2)$; Major axis parallel to the y-axis;
$a = 3$; $c = 2$. Find b:
$$b^2 = a^2 - c^2 = 9 - 4 = 5$$
$$b = \sqrt{5}$$
Write the equation: $\dfrac{(x-2)^2}{5} + \dfrac{(y-2)^2}{9} = 1$

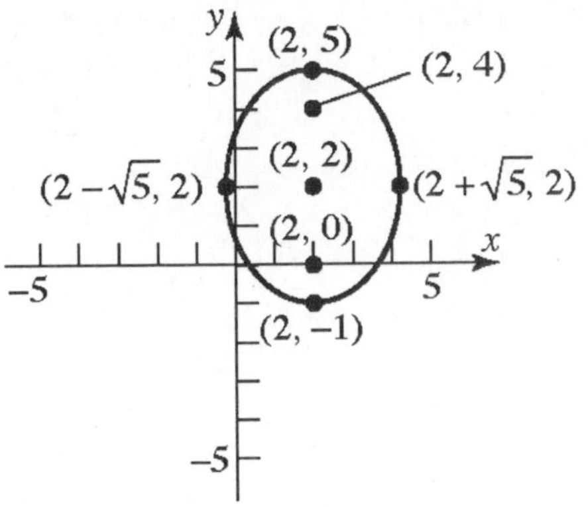

47. Center: $(1, 2)$; Focus: $(4, 2)$; contains the point $(1, 3)$; Major axis parallel to the x-axis; $c = 3$.
The equation has the form:
$$\frac{(x-1)^2}{a^2} + \frac{(y-2)^2}{b^2} = 1$$
Since the point $(1, 3)$ is on the curve:
$$\frac{0}{a^2} + \frac{1}{b^2} = 1$$
$$\frac{1}{b^2} = 1 \rightarrow b^2 = 1 \rightarrow b = 1$$
Find a:
$$a^2 = b^2 + c^2 = 1 + 9 = 10 \rightarrow a = \sqrt{10}$$
Write the equation: $\dfrac{(x-1)^2}{10} + \dfrac{(y-2)^2}{1} = 1$

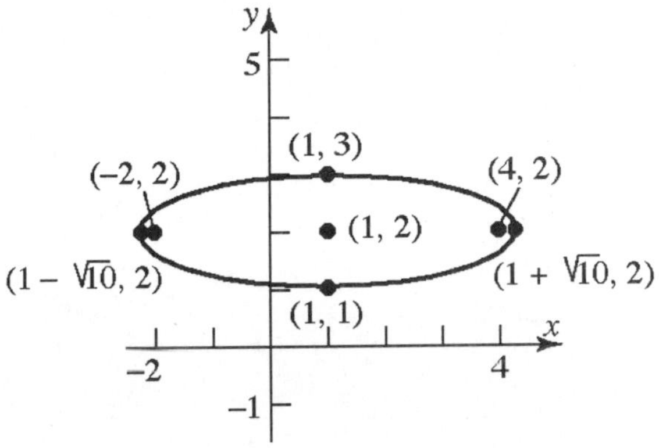

48. Center: $(1, 2)$; Focus: $(1, 4)$; contains the point $(2, 2)$; Major axis parallel to the y-axis; $c = 2$.
The equation has thc form:
$$\frac{(x-1)^2}{b^2} + \frac{(y-2)^2}{a^2} = 1$$
Since the point $(2, 2)$ is on the curve:
$$\frac{1}{b^2} + \frac{0}{a^2} = 1$$
$$\frac{1}{b^2} = 1 \rightarrow b^2 = 1 \rightarrow b = 1$$
Find a:
$$a^2 = b^2 + c^2 = 1 + 4 = 5 \rightarrow a = \sqrt{5}$$
Write the equation: $\dfrac{(x-1)^2}{1} + \dfrac{(y-2)^2}{5} = 1$

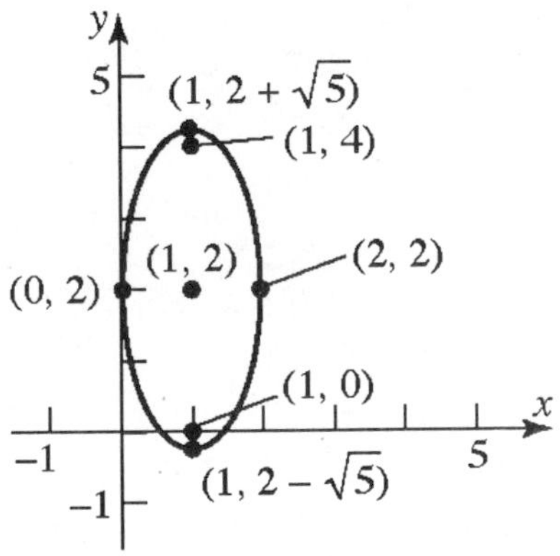

49. Center: (1, 2); Vertex: (4, 2); contains the point (1, 3); Major axis parallel to the x-axis; $a = 3$.
The equation has the form:
$$\frac{(x-1)^2}{a^2}+\frac{(y-2)^2}{b^2}=1$$
Since the point (1, 3) is on the curve:
$$\frac{0}{9}+\frac{1}{b^2}=1$$
$$\frac{1}{b^2}=1 \rightarrow b^2=1 \rightarrow b=1$$
Write the equation: $\dfrac{(x-1)^2}{9}+\dfrac{(y-2)^2}{1}=1$

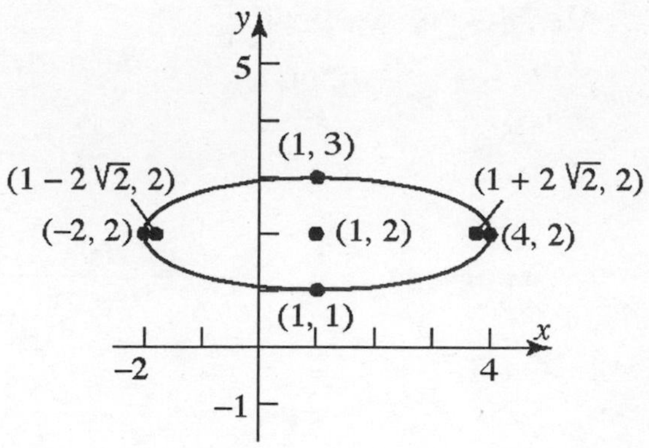

50. Center: (1, 2); Vertex: (1, 4); contains the point (2, 2); Major axis parallel to the y-axis; $a = 2$.
The equation has the form:
$$\frac{(x-1)^2}{b^2}+\frac{(y-2)^2}{a^2}=1$$
Since the point (2, 2) is on the curve:
$$\frac{1}{b^2}+\frac{0}{a^2}=1$$
$$\frac{1}{b^2}=1 \rightarrow b^2=1 \rightarrow b=1$$
Write the equation: $\dfrac{(x-1)^2}{1}+\dfrac{(y-2)^2}{4}=1$

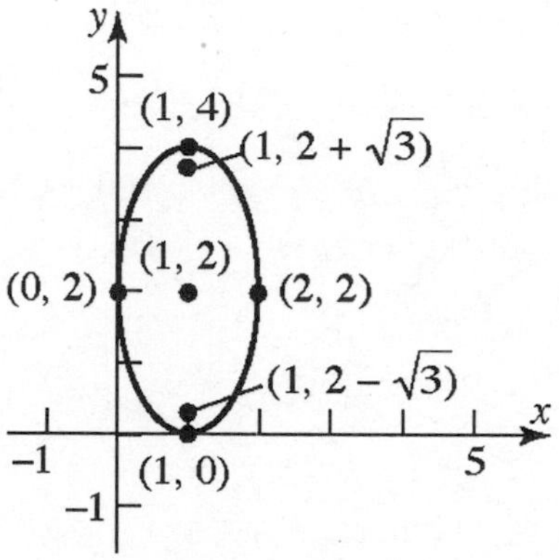

51. Rewrite the equation:
$$y=\sqrt{16-4x^2}$$
$$y^2=16-4x^2, \quad y \ge 0$$
$$4x^2+y^2=16, \quad y \ge 0$$
$$\frac{x^2}{4}+\frac{y^2}{16}=1, \quad y \ge 0$$

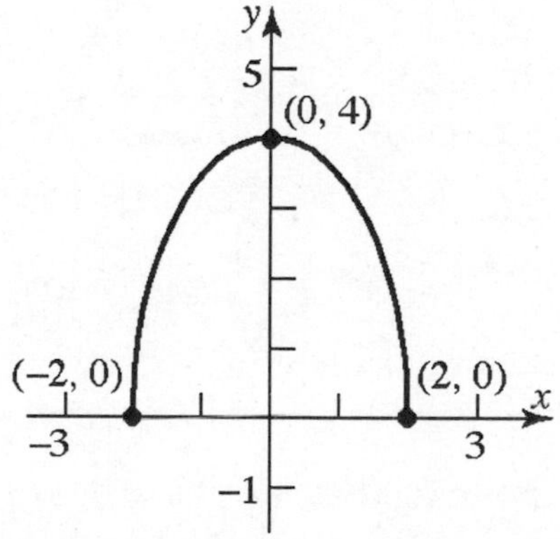

52. Rewrite the equation:

$$y = \sqrt{9 - 9x^2}$$
$$y^2 = 9 - 9x^2, \quad y \ge 0$$
$$9x^2 + y^2 = 9, \quad y \ge 0$$
$$\frac{x^2}{1} + \frac{y^2}{9} = 1, \quad y \ge 0$$

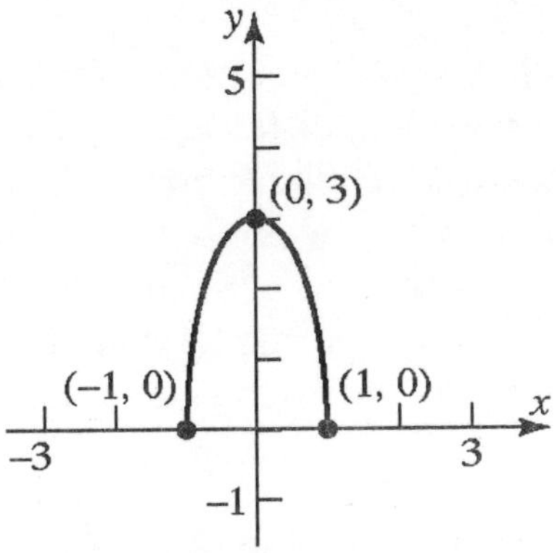

53. Rewrite the equation:

$$y = -\sqrt{64 - 16x^2}$$
$$y^2 = 64 - 16x^2, \quad y \le 0$$
$$16x^2 + y^2 = 64, \quad y \le 0$$
$$\frac{x^2}{4} + \frac{y^2}{64} = 1, \quad y \le 0$$

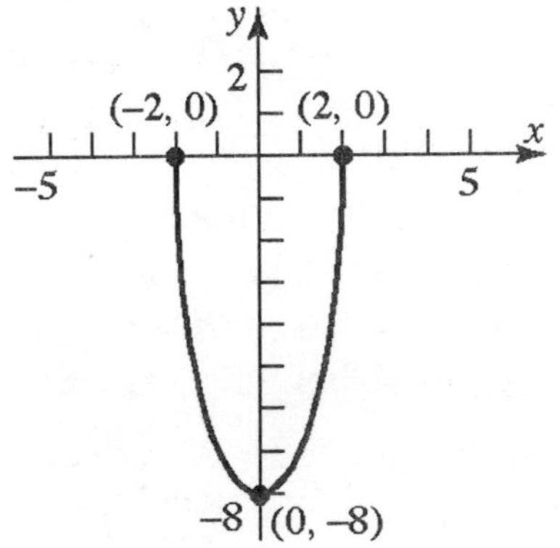

54. Rewrite the equation:

$$y = -\sqrt{4 - 4x^2}$$
$$y^2 = 4 - 4x^2, \quad y \le 0$$
$$4x^2 + y^2 = 4, \quad y \le 0$$
$$\frac{x^2}{1} + \frac{y^2}{4} = 1, \quad y \le 0$$

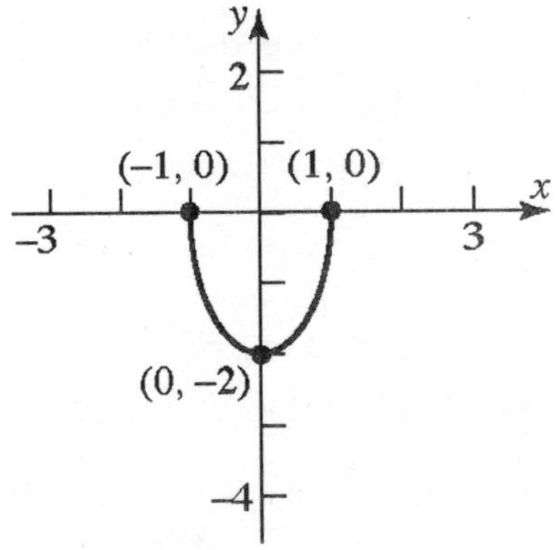

55. The center of the ellipse is (0, 0). The length of the major axis is 20, so $a = 10$. The length of half the minor axis is 6, so $b = 6$. The ellipse is situated with its major axis on the x-axis. The equation is: $\frac{x^2}{100} + \frac{y^2}{36} = 1$.

56. The center of the ellipse is (0, 0). The length of the major axis is 30, so $a = 15$. The length of half the minor axis is 10, so $b = 10$. The ellipse is situated with its major axis on the x-axis. The equation is: $\frac{x^2}{225} + \frac{y^2}{100} = 1$.
The roadway is 12 feet above the axis of the ellipse.
At the center ($x = 0$), the roadway is 2 feet above the arch.
At a point 5 feet either side of the center, evaluate the equation at $x = 5$:

$$\frac{5^2}{225}+\frac{y^2}{100}=1 \rightarrow \frac{y^2}{100}=1-\frac{25}{225}=\frac{200}{225} \rightarrow y=10\sqrt{\frac{200}{225}}\approx 9.43$$

The vertical distance from the roadway to the arch is $12-9.43\approx 2.57$ feet.

At a point 10 feet either side of the center, evaluate the equation at $x=10$:

$$\frac{10^2}{225}+\frac{y^2}{100}=1 \rightarrow \frac{y^2}{100}=1-\frac{100}{225}=\frac{125}{225} \rightarrow y=10\sqrt{\frac{125}{225}}\approx 7.45$$

The vertical distance from the roadway to the arch is $12-7.45\approx 4.55$ feet.

At a point 15 feet either side of the center, the roadway is 12 feet above the arch.

57. Assume that the half ellipse formed by the gallery is centered at (0, 0). Since the hall is 100 feet long, $2a=100$ or $a=50$. The distance from the center to the foci is 25 feet, so $c=25$. Find the height of the gallery which is b:

$$b^2=a^2-c^2=2500-625=1875 \rightarrow b=\sqrt{1875}\approx 43.3$$

The ceiling will be 43.3 feet high in the center.

58. Assume that the half ellipse formed by the gallery is centered at (0, 0). Since the distance between the foci is 100 feet and Jim is 6 feet from the nearest wall, the length of the gallery is 112 feet. $2a=112$ or $a=56$. The distance from the center to the foci is 50 feet, so $c=50$. Find the height of the gallery which is b:

$$b^2=a^2-c^2=3136-2500=636 \rightarrow b=\sqrt{636}\approx 25.2$$

The ceiling will be 25.2 feet high in the center.

59. Place the semielliptical arch so that the x-axis coincides with the water and the y-axis passes through the center of the arch. Since the bridge has a span of 120 feet, the length of the major axis is 120, or $2a=120$ or $a=60$. The maximum height of the bridge is 25 feet, so $b=25$. The equation is: $\frac{x^2}{3600}+\frac{y^2}{625}=1$.

The height 10 feet from the center:

$$\frac{10^2}{3600}+\frac{y^2}{625}=1 \rightarrow \frac{y^2}{625}=1-\frac{100}{3600} \rightarrow y^2=625\cdot\frac{3500}{3600} \rightarrow y\approx 24.65 \text{ feet}$$

The height 30 feet from the center:

$$\frac{30^2}{3600}+\frac{y^2}{625}=1 \rightarrow \frac{y^2}{625}=1-\frac{900}{3600} \rightarrow y^2=625\cdot\frac{2700}{3600} \rightarrow y\approx 21.65 \text{ feet}$$

The height 50 feet from the center:

$$\frac{50^2}{3600}+\frac{y^2}{625}=1 \rightarrow \frac{y^2}{625}=1-\frac{2500}{3600} \rightarrow y^2=625\cdot\frac{1100}{3600} \rightarrow y\approx 13.82 \text{ feet}$$

60. Place the semielliptical arch so that the x-axis coincides with the water and the y-axis passes through the center of the arch. Since the bridge has a span of 100 feet, the length of the major axis is 100, or $2a=100$ or $a=50$. Let h be the maximum height of the bridge. The equation is: $\frac{x^2}{2500}+\frac{y^2}{h^2}=1$.

The height of the arch 40 feet from the center is 10 feet. So (40, 10) is a point on the ellipse. Substitute and solve for h:

$$\frac{40^2}{2500}+\frac{10^2}{h^2}=1 \rightarrow \frac{10^2}{h^2}=1-\frac{1600}{2500}=\frac{9}{25} \rightarrow 9h^2=2500 \rightarrow h=\frac{50}{3}\approx 16.67$$

The height of the arch at its center is 16.67 feet.

61. Place the semielliptical arch so that the x-axis coincides with the major axis and the y-axis passes through the center of the arch. Since the ellipse is 40 feet wide, the length of the major axis is 40, or $2a = 40$ or $a = 20$. The height is 15 feet at the center, so $b = 15$. The equation is: $\frac{x^2}{400} + \frac{y^2}{225} = 1$.
The height 10 feet either side of the center:
$$\frac{10^2}{400} + \frac{y^2}{225} = 1 \rightarrow \frac{y^2}{225} = 1 - \frac{100}{400} \rightarrow y^2 = 225 \cdot \frac{3}{4} \rightarrow y \approx 12.99 \text{ feet}$$
The height 20 feet either side of the center:
$$\frac{20^2}{400} + \frac{y^2}{225} = 1 \rightarrow \frac{y^2}{225} = 1 - \frac{400}{400} \rightarrow y^2 = 225 \cdot 0 \rightarrow y \approx 0 \text{ feet}$$

62. Place the semielliptical arch so that the x-axis coincides with the major axis and the y-axis passes through the center of the arch. Since the height of the arch at the center is 20 feet, $b = 20$. The length of the major axis is to be found, so it is necessary to solve for a. The equation is: $\frac{x^2}{a^2} + \frac{y^2}{400} = 1$.
The height of the arch 28 feet from the center is to be 13 feet, so the point (28, 13) is on the ellipse. Substitute and solve for a:
$$\frac{28^2}{a^2} + \frac{13^2}{400} = 1 \rightarrow \frac{784}{a^2} = 1 - \frac{169}{400} = \frac{231}{400} \rightarrow 231a^2 = 313600 \rightarrow a^2 = 1357.6 \rightarrow a = 36.8$$
The span of the bridge is 73.6 feet.

63. Since the mean distance is 93 million miles, $a = 93$ million. The length of the major axis is 186 million. The perihelion is 186 million – 94.5 million = 91.5 million miles. The distance from the center of the ellipse to the sun (focus) is 93 million – 91.5 million = 1.5 million miles; therefore, $c = 1.5$ million. Find b:
$$b^2 = a^2 - c^2 = (93 \times 10^6)^2 - (1.5 \times 10^6)^2 = 8.64675 \times 10^{15} \rightarrow b = 92.99 \times 10^6$$
The equation of the orbit is: $\frac{x^2}{(93 \times 10^6)^2} + \frac{y^2}{(92.99 \times 10^6)^2} = 1$.

64. Since the mean distance is 142 million miles, $a = 142$ million. The length of the major axis is 284 million. The aphelion is 284 million – 128.5 million = 155.5 million miles. The distance from the center of the ellipse to the sun (focus) is 142 million – 128.5 million = 13.5 million miles; therefore, $c = 13.5$ million. Find b:
$$b^2 = a^2 - c^2 = (142 \times 10^6)^2 - (13.5 \times 10^6)^2 = 1.9982 \times 10^{16} \rightarrow b = 141.4 \times 10^6$$
The equation of the orbit is: $\frac{x^2}{(142 \times 10^6)^2} + \frac{y^2}{(141.4 \times 10^6)^2} = 1$.

65. The mean distance is 507 million – 23.2 million = 483.8 million miles.
The perihelion is 483.8 million – 23.2 million = 460.6 million miles.
Since $a = 483.8 \times 10^6$ and $c = 23.2 \times 10^6$, we can find b:
$$b^2 = a^2 - c^2 = (483.8 \times 10^6)^2 - (23.2 \times 10^6)^2 = 2.335242 \times 10^{17} \rightarrow b = 483.2 \times 10^6$$

The equation of the orbit of Jupiter is: $\dfrac{x^2}{(483.8\times 10^6)^2}+\dfrac{y^2}{(483.2\times 10^6)^2}=1$.

66. The mean distance is 4551 million + 897.5 million = 5448.5 million miles.
The aphelion is 5448.5 million + 897.5 million = 6346 million miles.
Since $a = 5448.5\times 10^6$ and $c = 897.5\times 10^6$, we can find b:

$$b^2 = a^2 - c^2 = (5448.5\times 10^6)^2 - (897.5\times 10^6)^2 = 2.88806\times 10^{19}$$

$$b = 5374.1\times 10^6$$

The equation of the orbit of Pluto is: $\dfrac{x^2}{(5448.5\times 10^6)^2}+\dfrac{y^2}{(5374.1\times 10^6)^2}=1$.

67. If the x-axis is placed along the 100 foot length and the y-axis is placed along the 50 foot length, the equation for the ellipse is: $\dfrac{x^2}{50^2}+\dfrac{y^2}{25^2}=1$.
Find y when x = 40:

$$\frac{40^2}{50^2}+\frac{y^2}{25^2}=1\rightarrow\frac{y^2}{625}=1-\frac{1600}{2500}\rightarrow y^2=625\cdot\frac{9}{25}\rightarrow y\approx 15 \text{ feet}$$

The width 10 feet from the side is 30 feet.

68. If the x-axis is placed along the 80 foot length and the y-axis is placed along the 40 foot width, the equation for the ellipse is: $\dfrac{x^2}{40^2}+\dfrac{y^2}{20^2}=1$.
Find y when x = 30:

$$\frac{30^2}{40^2}+\frac{y^2}{20^2}=1\rightarrow\frac{y^2}{400}=1-\frac{900}{1600}\rightarrow y^2=400\cdot\frac{7}{16}=175\rightarrow y\approx 13.2 \text{ feet}$$

The width 10 feet from the side is 26.4 feet.

69. (a) Put the equation in standard ellipse form:

$$Ax^2+Cy^2+F=0 \qquad A\neq 0,\ C\neq 0,\ F\neq 0$$

$$Ax^2+Cy^2=-F$$

$$\frac{Ax^2}{-F}+\frac{Cy^2}{-F}=1$$

$$\frac{x^2}{(-F/A)}+\frac{y^2}{(-F/C)}=1 \qquad \text{where } -F/A \text{ and } -F/C \text{ are positive}$$

This is the equation of an ellipse with center at (0, 0).

(b) If $A = C$, the equation becomes:

$$Ax^2+Ay^2=-F\ \rightarrow\ x^2+y^2=\frac{-F}{A}$$

This is the equation of a circle with center at (0, 0) and radius of $\sqrt{\dfrac{-F}{A}}$.

70. Complete the square on the given equation:

$$Ax^2 + Cy^2 + Dx + Ey + F = 0, \qquad A \neq 0,\ C \neq 0$$

$$A\left(x^2 + \frac{D}{A}x\right) + C\left(y^2 + \frac{E}{C}y\right) = -F$$

$$A\left(x^2 + \frac{D}{A}x + \frac{D^2}{4A^2}\right) + C\left(y^2 + \frac{E}{C}y + \frac{E^2}{4C^2}\right) = \frac{D^2}{4A^2} + \frac{E^2}{4C^2} - F$$

$$A\left(x + \frac{D}{2A}\right)^2 + C\left(y + \frac{E}{2C}\right)^2 = \frac{D^2}{4A^2} + \frac{E^2}{4C^2} - F$$

(a) If $\frac{D^2}{4A^2} + \frac{E^2}{4C^2} - F$ is of the same sign as A (and C), this is the equation of an ellipse whose center is $\left(\frac{-D}{2A}, \frac{-E}{2C}\right)$.

(b) If $\frac{D^2}{4A^2} + \frac{E^2}{4C^2} - F = 0$, the graph is a single point $\left(\frac{-D}{2A}, \frac{-E}{2C}\right)$.

(c) If $\frac{D^2}{4A^2} + \frac{E^2}{4C^2} - F$ is of the opposite sign as A (and C), this graph contains no points since the left side has the opposite sign of the right side.

71. Answers will vary.

Chapter 11

Analytic Geometry

11.4 The Hyperbola

1. B 2. C 3. A 4. D

5. Center: (0, 0); Focus: (3, 0); Vertex: (1, 0);
Transverse axis is the x-axis; $a = 1$; $c = 3$.
Find b:
$$b^2 = c^2 - a^2 = 9 - 1 = 8$$
$$b = \sqrt{8} = 2\sqrt{2}$$
Write the equation: $\frac{x^2}{1} - \frac{y^2}{8} = 1$
To graph, enter:
$y_1 = \sqrt{8(x^2 - 1)}$; $y_2 = -\sqrt{8(x^2 - 1)}$

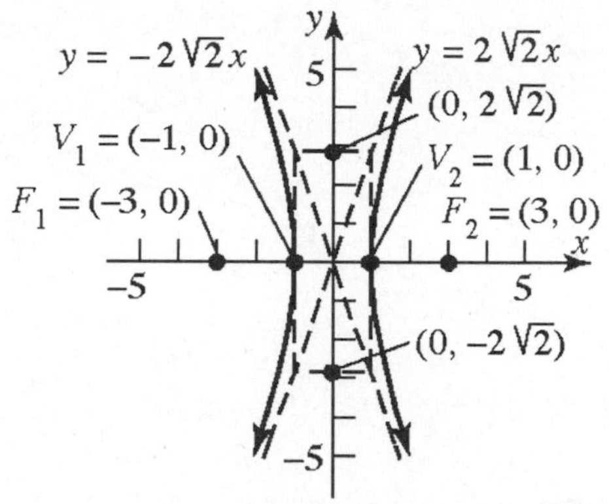

6. Center: (0, 0); Focus: (0, 5); Vertex: (0, 3);
Transverse axis is the y-axis; $a = 3$; $c = 5$.
Find b:
$$b^2 = c^2 - a^2 = 25 - 9 = 16$$
$$b = 4$$
Write the equation: $\frac{y^2}{9} - \frac{x^2}{16} = 1$
To graph, enter:
$y_1 = 3\sqrt{1 + x^2/16}$; $y_2 = -3\sqrt{1 + x^2/16}$

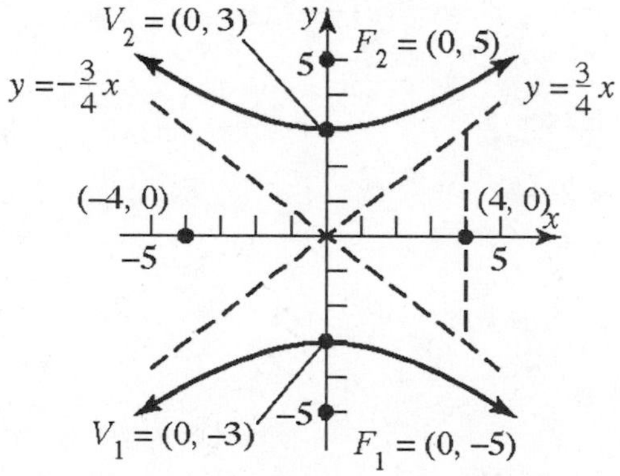

7. Center: (0, 0); Focus: (0, –6); Vertex: (0, 4)
Transverse axis is the y-axis; $a = 4$; $c = 6$.
Find b:
$$b^2 = c^2 - a^2 = 36 - 16 = 20$$
$$b = \sqrt{20} = 2\sqrt{5}$$
Write the equation: $\frac{y^2}{16} - \frac{x^2}{20} = 1$
To graph, enter:
$y_1 = 4\sqrt{1 + x^2/20}$; $y_2 = -4\sqrt{1 + x^2/20}$

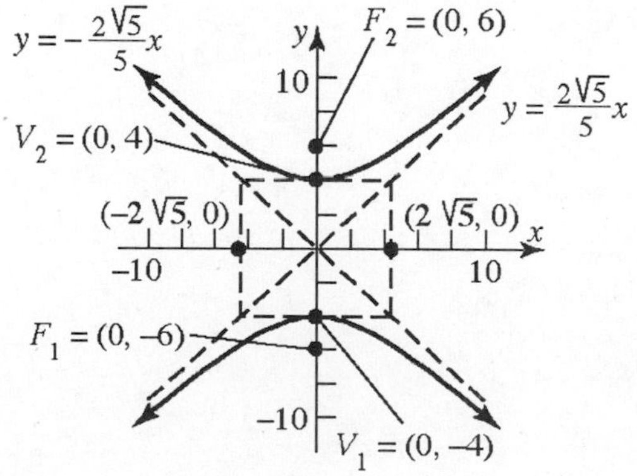

8. Center: (0, 0); Focus: (–3, 0); Vertex: (2, 0)
Transverse axis is the x-axis; $a = 2$; $c = 3$.
Find b:

$$b^2 = c^2 - a^2 = 9 - 4 = 5$$
$$b = \sqrt{5}$$

Write the equation: $\frac{x^2}{4} - \frac{y^2}{5} = 1$

To graph, enter:

$$y_1 = \sqrt{5(x^2/4 - 1)};\ y_2 = -\sqrt{5(x^2/4 - 1)}$$

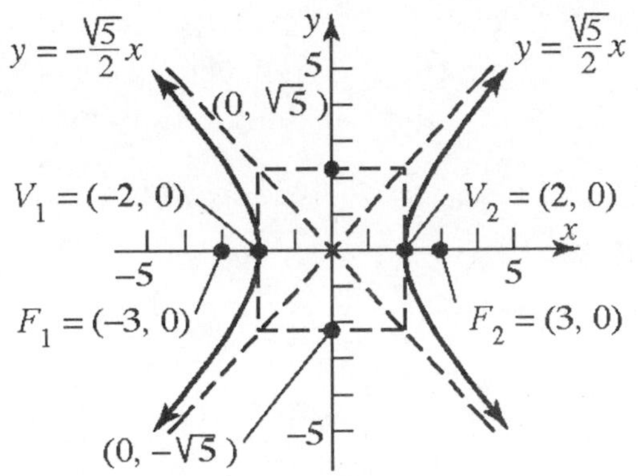

9. Foci: (–5, 0), (5, 0); Vertex: (3, 0)
Center: (0, 0); Transverse axis is the x-axis; $a = 3$; $c = 5$. Find b:

$$b^2 = c^2 - a^2 = 25 - 9 = 16 \rightarrow b = 4$$

Write the equation: $\frac{x^2}{9} - \frac{y^2}{16} = 1$

To graph, enter:

$$y_1 = 4\sqrt{x^2/9 - 1};\ y_2 = -4\sqrt{x^2/9 - 1}$$

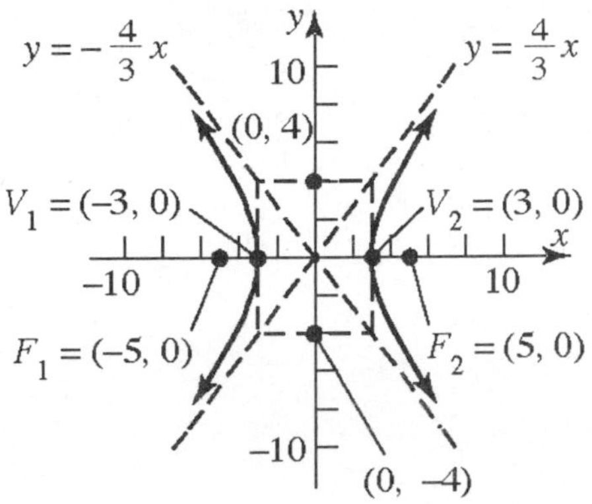

10. Focus: (0, 6); Vertices: (0, –2), (0, 2)
Center: (0, 0); Transverse axis is the y-axis; $a = 2$; $c = 6$. Find b:

$$b^2 = c^2 - a^2 = 36 - 4 = 32 \rightarrow b = 4\sqrt{2}$$

Write the equation: $\frac{y^2}{4} - \frac{x^2}{32} = 1$

To graph, enter:

$$y_1 = 2\sqrt{x^2/32 + 1};\ y_2 = -2\sqrt{x^2/32 + 1}$$

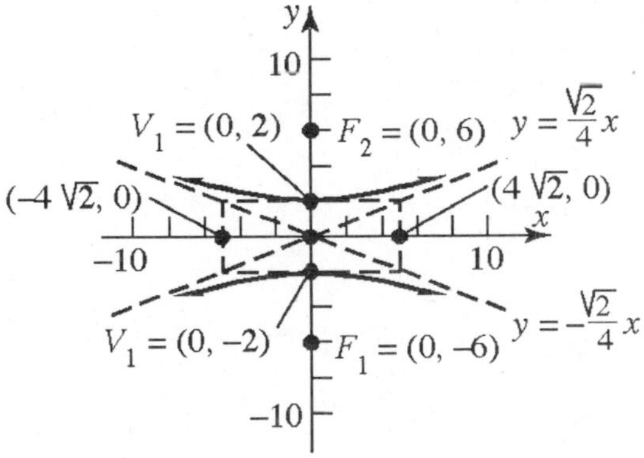

11. Vertices: (0, –6), (0, 6); Asymptote: $y = 2x$;
Center: (0, 0); Transverse axis is the y-axis; $a = 6$. Find b using the slope of the asymptote:

$$\frac{a}{b} = \frac{6}{b} = 2 \rightarrow 2b = 6 \rightarrow b = 3$$

Write the equation: $\frac{y^2}{36} - \frac{x^2}{9} = 1$

To graph, enter:

$$y_1 = 6\sqrt{1 + x^2/9};\ y_2 = -6\sqrt{1 + x^2/9}$$

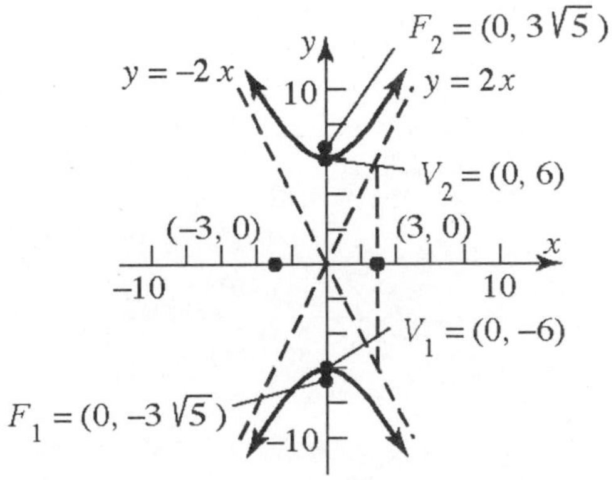

12. Vertices: (–4, 0), (4, 0); Asymptote: $y = 2x$; Center: (0, 0); Transverse axis is the x-axis; $a = 4$. Find b using the slope of the asymptote:

$$\frac{b}{a} = \frac{b}{4} = 2 \rightarrow b = 8$$

Write the equation: $\frac{x^2}{16} - \frac{y^2}{64} = 1$

To graph, enter:

$$y_1 = 8\sqrt{x^2/16 - 1};\ y_2 = -8\sqrt{x^2/16 - 1}$$

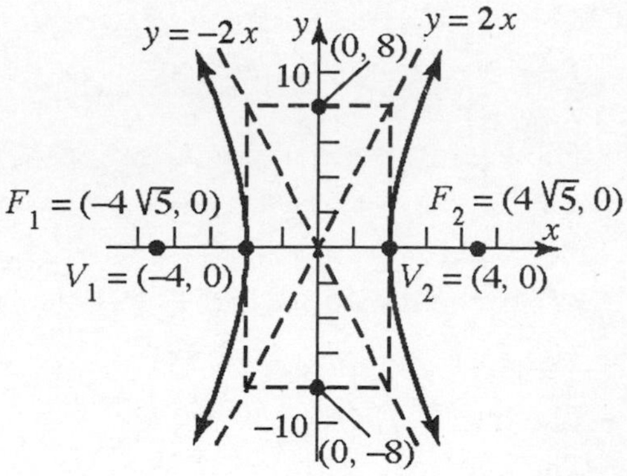

13. Foci: (–4, 0), (4, 0); Asymptote: $y = -x$; Center: (0, 0); Transverse axis is the x-axis; $c = 4$. Using the slope of the asymptote:

$$-\frac{b}{a} = -1 \rightarrow -b = -a \rightarrow b = a$$

Find b:

$$b^2 = c^2 - a^2 \rightarrow a^2 + b^2 = c^2 \qquad (c = 4)$$

$$b^2 + b^2 = 16 \rightarrow 2b^2 = 16 \rightarrow b^2 = 8$$

$$b = \sqrt{8} = 2\sqrt{2}$$

$$a = \sqrt{8} = 2\sqrt{2} \qquad (a = b)$$

Write the equation: $\frac{x^2}{8} - \frac{y^2}{8} = 1$

To graph, enter:

$$y_1 = \sqrt{x^2 - 8};\ y_2 = -\sqrt{x^2 - 8}$$

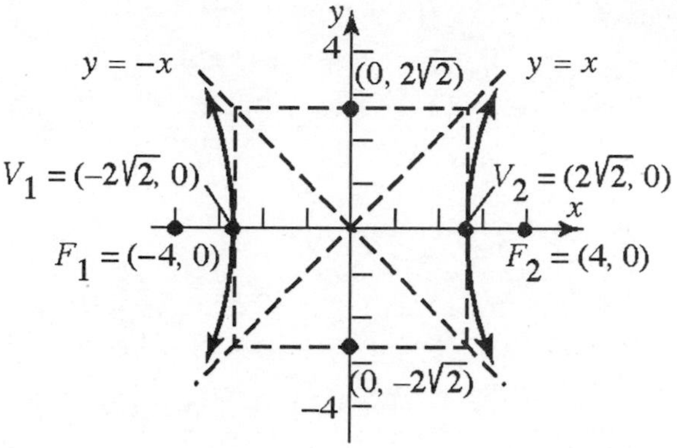

14. Foci: (0, –2), (0, 2); Asymptote: $y = -x$; Center: (0, 0); Transverse axis is the y-axis; $c = 2$. Using the slope of the asymptote:

$$-\frac{a}{b} = -1 \rightarrow -b = -a \rightarrow b = a$$

Find b:

$$b^2 = c^2 - a^2$$

$$a^2 + b^2 = c^2 \qquad (c = 2)$$

$$b^2 + b^2 = 4 \rightarrow 2b^2 = 4$$

$$b^2 = 2 \rightarrow b = \sqrt{2}$$

$$a = \sqrt{2} \qquad (a = b)$$

Write the equation: $\frac{y^2}{2} - \frac{x^2}{2} = 1$

To graph, enter:

$$y_1 = \sqrt{x^2 + 2};\ y_2 = -\sqrt{x^2 + 2}$$

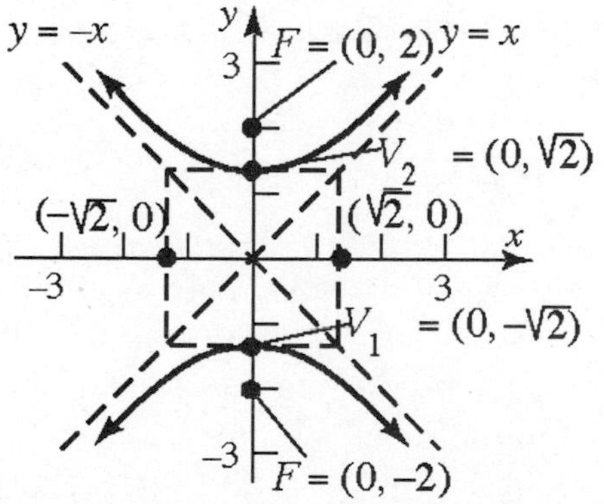

15. $\frac{x^2}{25} - \frac{y^2}{9} = 1$

The center of the hyperbola is at (0, 0).
$a = 5,\ b = 3$. The vertices are (5, 0) and (–5, 0). Find the value of c:
$c^2 = a^2 + b^2 = 25 + 9 = 34 \rightarrow c = \sqrt{34}$
The foci are $(\sqrt{34}, 0)$ and $(-\sqrt{34}, 0)$.
The transverse axis is $y = 0$.
The asymptotes are
$y = \frac{3}{5}x$ and $y = -\frac{3}{5}x$.
To graph, enter:
$y_1 = 3\sqrt{(x^2/25 - 1)};\ y_2 = -3\sqrt{(x^2/25 - 1)}$

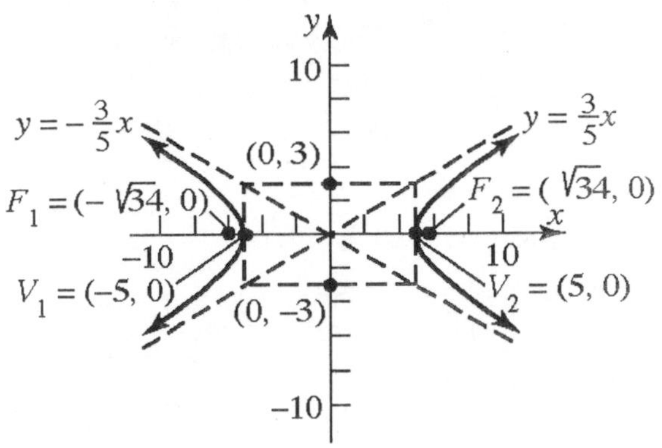

16. $\frac{y^2}{16} - \frac{x^2}{4} = 1$

The center of the hyperbola is at (0, 0).
$a = 4,\ b = 2$. The vertices are (0, 4) and (0, –4). Find the value of c:
$$c^2 = a^2 + b^2 = 16 + 4 = 20$$
$$c = \sqrt{20} = 2\sqrt{5}$$
The foci are $(0, 2\sqrt{5})$ and $(0, -2\sqrt{5})$.
The transverse axis is $x = 0$.
The asymptotes are $y = 2x$ and $y = -2x$.
To graph, enter:
$y_1 = 4\sqrt{(x^2/4 + 1)};\ y_2 = -4\sqrt{(x^2/4 + 1)}$

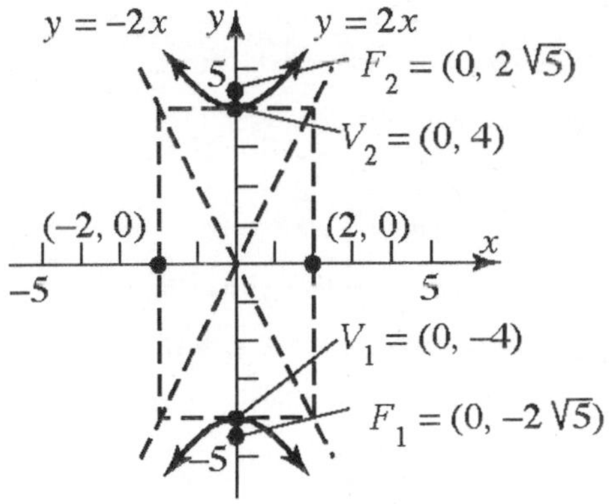

17. $4x^2 - y^2 = 16$

Divide both sides by 16 to put in standard form: $\frac{4x^2}{16} - \frac{y^2}{16} = \frac{16}{16} \rightarrow \frac{x^2}{4} - \frac{y^2}{16} = 1$

The center of the hyperbola is at (0, 0).
$a = 2,\ b = 4$. The vertices are (2, 0) and (–2, 0). Find the value of c:
$$c^2 = a^2 + b^2 = 4 + 16 = 20$$
$$c = \sqrt{20} = 2\sqrt{5}$$
The foci are $(2\sqrt{5}, 0)$ and $(-2\sqrt{5}, 0)$.
The transverse axis is $y = 0$.
The asymptotes are $y = 2x$ and $y = -2x$.
To graph, enter:
$y_1 = 4\sqrt{(x^2/4 - 1)};\ y_2 = -4\sqrt{(x^2/4 - 1)}$

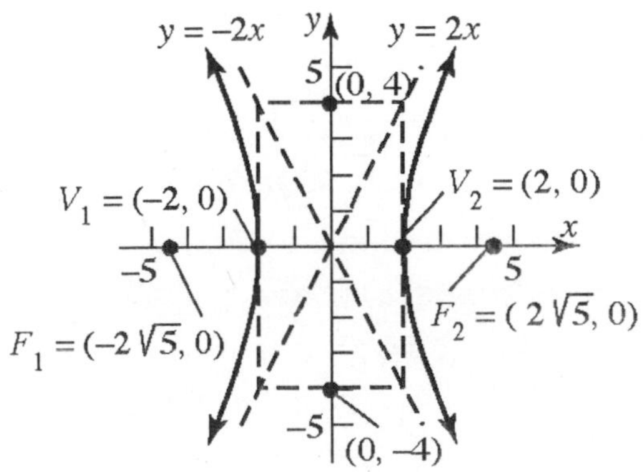

18. $y^2 - 4x^2 = 16$

Divide both sides by 16 to put in standard form: $\frac{y^2}{16} - \frac{4x^2}{16} = \frac{16}{16} \rightarrow \frac{y^2}{16} - \frac{x^2}{4} = 1$

The center of the hyperbola is at (0, 0).
$a = 4,\ b = 2$. The vertices are (0, 4) and (0, –4). Find the value of c:

$$c^2 = a^2 + b^2 = 16 + 4 = 20$$
$$c = \sqrt{20} = 2\sqrt{5}$$

The foci are $\left(0,\ 2\sqrt{5}\right)$ and $\left(0,\ -2\sqrt{5}\right)$.
The transverse axis is $x = 0$.
The asymptotes are $y = 2x$ and $y = -2x$.
To graph, enter:
$y_1 = 4\sqrt{(x^2/4+1)};\ y_2 = -4\sqrt{(x^2/4+1)}$

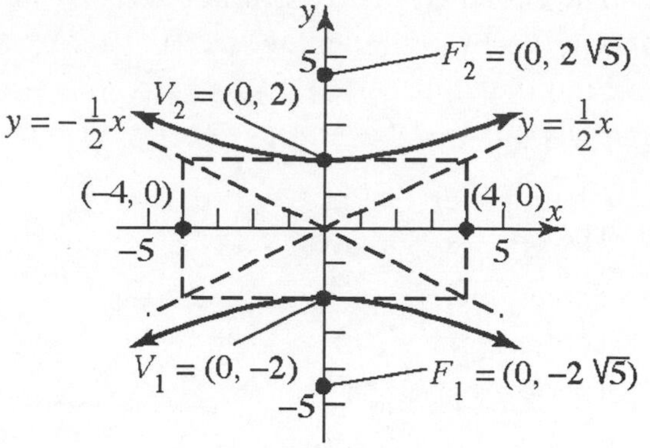

19. $y^2 - 9x^2 = 9$

Divide both sides by 9 to put in standard form: $\frac{y^2}{9} - \frac{9x^2}{9} = \frac{9}{9} \rightarrow \frac{y^2}{9} - \frac{x^2}{1} = 1$

The center of the hyperbola is at (0, 0).
$a = 3,\ b = 1$. The vertices are (0, 3) and (0, –3). Find the value of c:

$$c^2 = a^2 + b^2 = 9 + 1 = 10$$
$$c = \sqrt{10}$$

The foci are $\left(0, \sqrt{10}\right)$ and $\left(0, -\sqrt{10}\right)$.
The transverse axis is $x = 0$.
The asymptotes are $y = 3x$ and $y = -3x$.
To graph, enter:
$y_1 = \sqrt{(9x^2+9)};\ y_2 = -\sqrt{(9x^2+9)}$

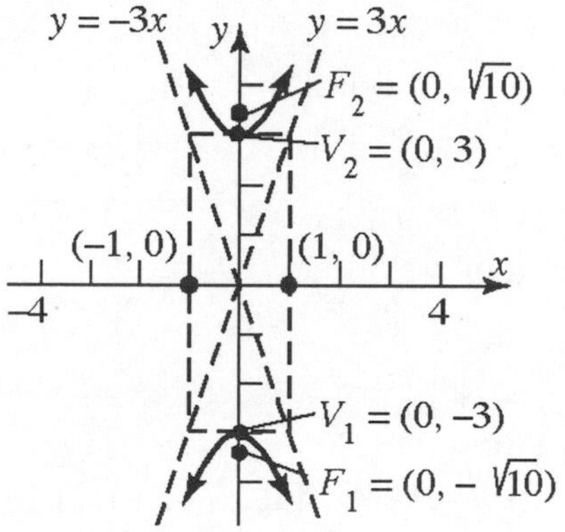

20. $x^2 - y^2 = 4$

Divide both sides by 4 to put in standard form: $\frac{x^2}{4} - \frac{y^2}{4} = \frac{4}{4} \rightarrow \frac{x^2}{4} - \frac{y^2}{4} = 1$

The center of the hyperbola is at (0, 0).
$a = 2,\ b = 2$. The vertices are (2, 0) and (–2, 0). Find the value of c:

$$c^2 = a^2 + b^2 = 4 + 4 = 8$$
$$c = \sqrt{8} = 2\sqrt{2}$$

The foci are $\left(2\sqrt{2}, 0\right)$ and $\left(-2\sqrt{2}, 0\right)$.
The transverse axis is $y = 0$.
The asymptotes are $y = x$ and $y = -x$.
To graph, enter:
$y_1 = \sqrt{(x^2-4)};\ y_2 = -\sqrt{(x^2-4)}$

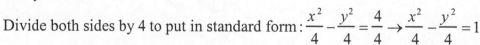

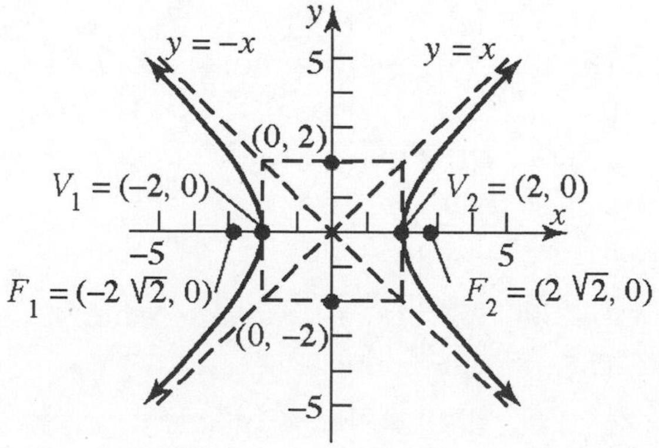

21. $y^2 - x^2 = 25$

Divide both sides by 25 to put in standard form: $\dfrac{y^2}{25} - \dfrac{x^2}{25} = 1$

The center of the hyperbola is at (0, 0).

$a = 5,\ b = 5$. The vertices are (0, 5) and (0, –5).

Find the value of c:

$$c^2 = a^2 + b^2 = 25 + 25 = 50$$

$$c = \sqrt{50} = 5\sqrt{2}$$

The foci are $\left(0, 5\sqrt{2}\right)$ and $\left(0, -5\sqrt{2}\right)$.

The transverse axis is $x = 0$.

The asymptotes are $y = x$ and $y = -x$.

To graph, enter:

$y_1 = \sqrt{(x^2 + 25)};\ y_2 = -\sqrt{(x^2 + 25)}$

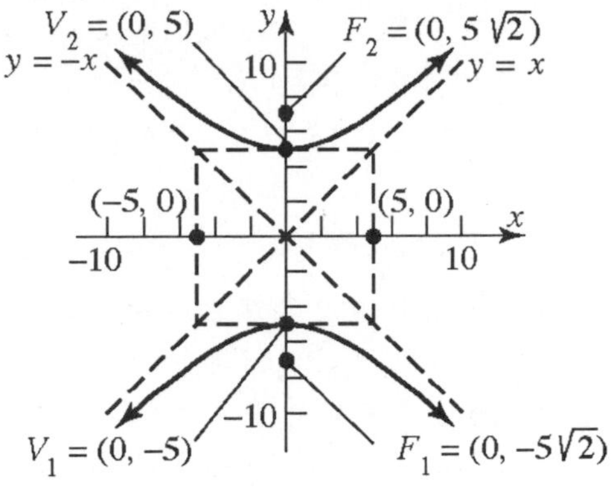

22. $2x^2 - y^2 = 4$

Divide both sides by 4 to put in standard form: $\dfrac{x^2}{2} - \dfrac{y^2}{4} = 1$

The center of the hyperbola is at (0, 0).

$a = \sqrt{2},\ b = 2$. The vertices are $\left(\sqrt{2}, 0\right)$ and $\left(-\sqrt{2}, 0\right)$. Find the value of c:

$$c^2 = a^2 + b^2 = 2 + 4 = 6$$

$$c = \sqrt{6}$$

The foci are $\left(\sqrt{6}, 0\right)$ and $\left(-\sqrt{6}, 0\right)$.

The transverse axis is $y = 0$.

The asymptotes are $y = \sqrt{2}x$ and $y = -\sqrt{2}\,x$.

To graph, enter:

$y_1 = \sqrt{(2x^2 - 4)};\ y_2 = -\sqrt{(2x^2 - 4)}$

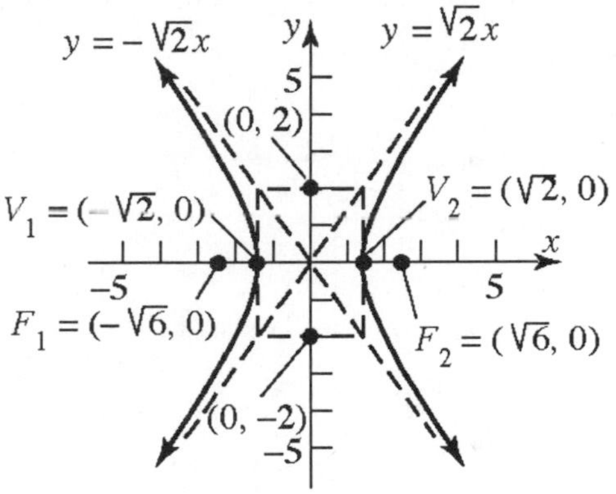

23. $x^2 - y^2 = 1$

24. $y^2 - x^2 = 1$

25. $\dfrac{y^2}{36} - \dfrac{x^2}{9} = 1$

26. $\dfrac{x^2}{4} - \dfrac{y^2}{16} = 1$

27. Center: $(4, -1)$; Focus: $(7, -1)$;
Vertex: $(6, -1)$; Transverse axis is parallel to the x-axis; $a = 2$; $c = 3$.
Find b:
$$b^2 = c^2 - a^2 = 9 - 4 = 5 \rightarrow b = \sqrt{5}$$
Write the equation:
$$\frac{(x-4)^2}{4} - \frac{(y+1)^2}{5} = 1$$

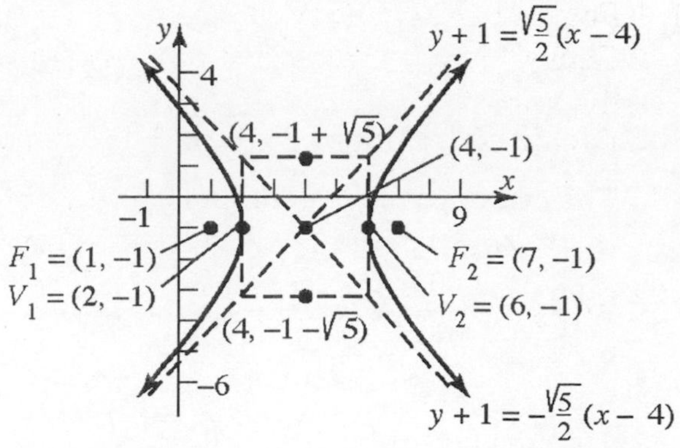

28. Center: $(-3, 1)$; Focus: $(-3, 6)$;
Vertex: $(-3, 4)$; Transverse axis is parallel to the y-axis; $a = 3$; $c = 5$.
Find b:
$$b^2 = c^2 - a^2 = 25 - 9 = 16 \rightarrow b = 4$$
Write the equation:
$$\frac{(y-1)^2}{9} - \frac{(x+3)^2}{16} = 1$$

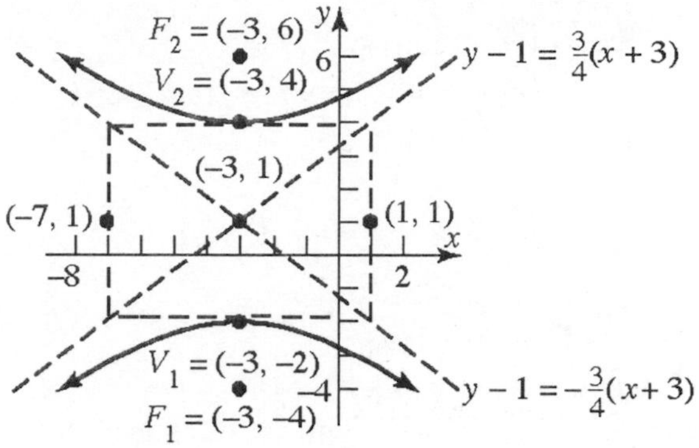

29. Center: $(-3, -4)$;
Focus: $(-3, -8)$;
Vertex: $(-3, -2)$;
Transverse axis is parallel to the y-axis; $a = 2$; $c = 4$.
Find b:
$$b^2 = c^2 - a^2 = 16 - 4 = 12$$
$$b = \sqrt{12} = 2\sqrt{3}$$
Write the equation:
$$\frac{(y+4)^2}{4} - \frac{(x+3)^2}{12} = 1$$

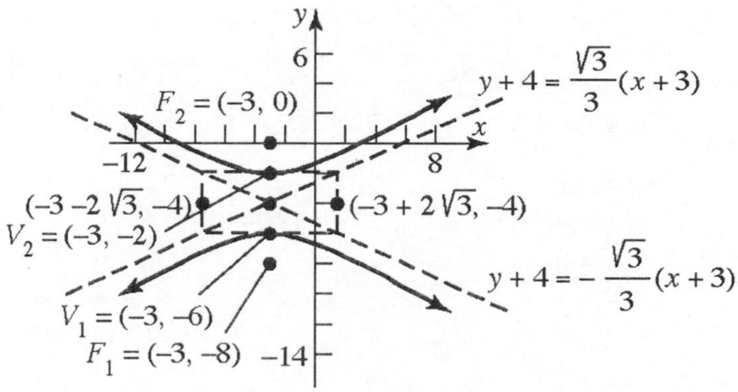

30. Center: $(1, 4)$; Focus: $(-2, 4)$;
Vertex: $(0, 4)$; Transverse axis is parallel to the x-axis; $a = 1$; $c = 3$.
Find b:
$$b^2 = c^2 - a^2 = 9 - 1 = 8$$
$$b = \sqrt{8} = 2\sqrt{2}$$
Write the equation: $\dfrac{(x-1)^2}{1} - \dfrac{(y-4)^2}{8} = 1$

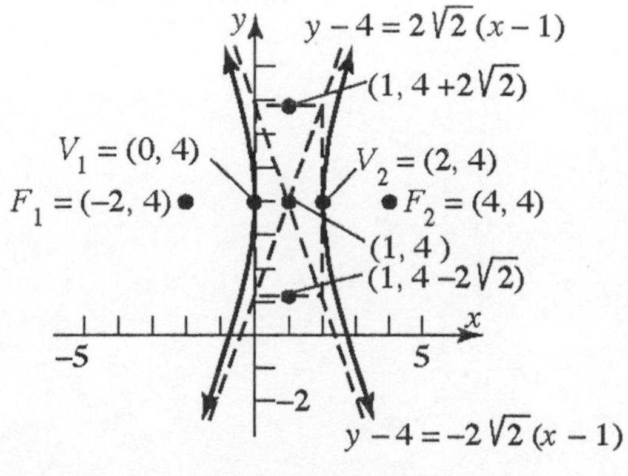

31. Foci: (3, 7), (7, 7); Vertex: (6, 7);
Center: (5, 7); Transverse axis is parallel to the x-axis; $a = 1$; $c = 2$.
Find b:
$$b^2 = c^2 - a^2 = 4 - 1 = 3$$
$$b = \sqrt{3}$$
Write the equation: $\frac{(x-5)^2}{1} - \frac{(y-7)^2}{3} = 1$

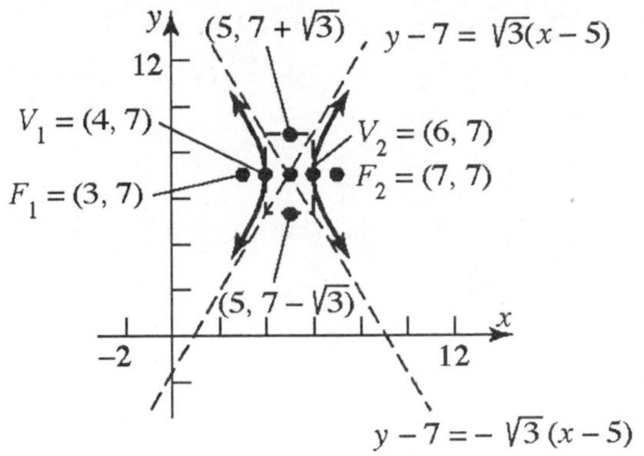

32. Focus: (−4, 0);
Vertices: (−4, 4), (−4, 2);
Center: (−4, 3); Transverse axis is parallel to the y-axis;
$a = 1$; $c = 3$. Find b:
$$b^2 = c^2 - a^2 = 9 - 1 = 8$$
$$b = \sqrt{8} = 2\sqrt{2}$$
Write the equation:
$$\frac{(y-3)^2}{1} - \frac{(x+4)^2}{8} = 1$$

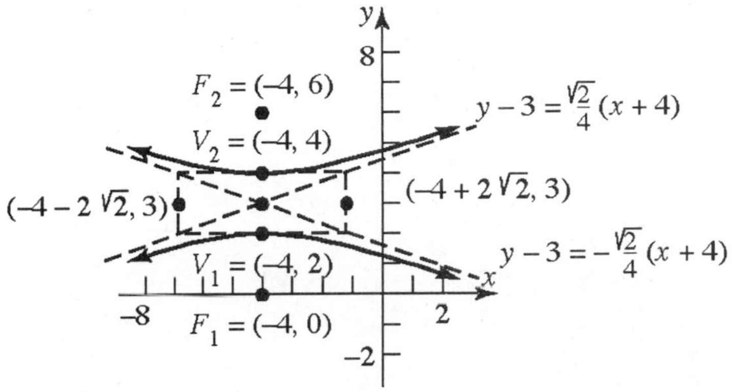

33. Vertices: (−1, −1), (3, −1);
Center: (1, −1); Transverse axis is parallel to the x-axis;
$a = 2$.
Asymptote: $\frac{x-1}{2} = \frac{y+1}{3}$
Using the slope of the asymptote:
$$\frac{b}{a} = \frac{b}{2} = \frac{3}{2} \rightarrow b = 3$$
Write the equation:
$$\frac{(x-1)^2}{4} - \frac{(y+1)^2}{9} = 1$$

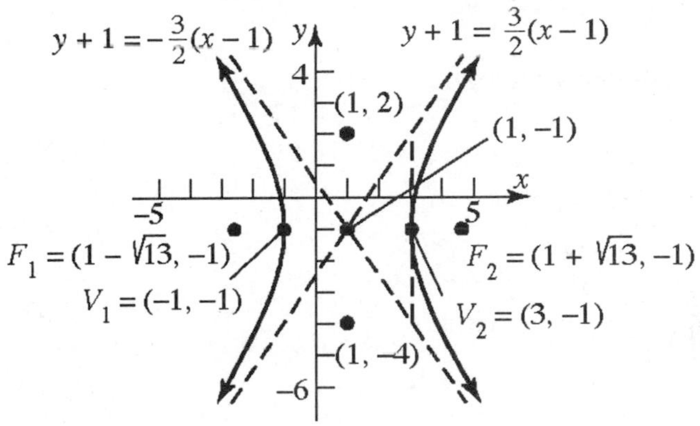

34. Vertices: (1, –3), (1, 1); Center: (1, –1); Transverse axis is parallel to the y-axis; $a = 2$.

Asymptote: $\frac{x-1}{2} = \frac{y+1}{3}$

Using the slope of the asymptote:

$$\frac{a}{b} = \frac{2}{b} = \frac{3}{2} \rightarrow 3b = 4 \rightarrow b = \frac{4}{3}$$

Write the equation:

$$\frac{(y+1)^2}{4} - \frac{(x-1)^2}{\left(\frac{16}{9}\right)} = 1$$

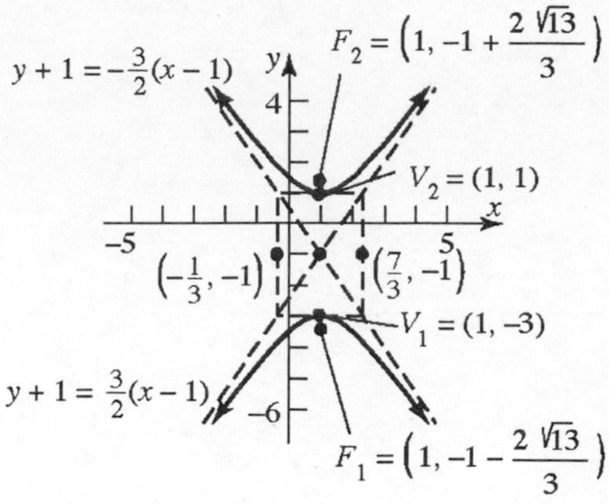

35. $\frac{(x-2)^2}{4} - \frac{(y+3)^2}{9} = 1$

The center of the hyperbola is at (2, –3). $a = 2$, $b = 3$. The vertices are (0, –3) and (4, –3). Find the value of c:

$$c^2 = a^2 + b^2 = 4 + 9 = 13 \rightarrow c = \sqrt{13}$$

Foci: $\left(2 - \sqrt{13}, -3\right)$ and $\left(2 + \sqrt{13}, -3\right)$.

Transverse axis: $y = -3$.

Asymptotes:

$$y + 3 = \frac{3}{2}(x-2);\ y + 3 = -\frac{3}{2}(x-2).$$

To graph, enter:

$$y_1 = -3 + 3\sqrt{((x-2)^2/4 - 1)};$$

$$y_2 = -3 - 3\sqrt{((x-2)^2/4 - 1)}$$

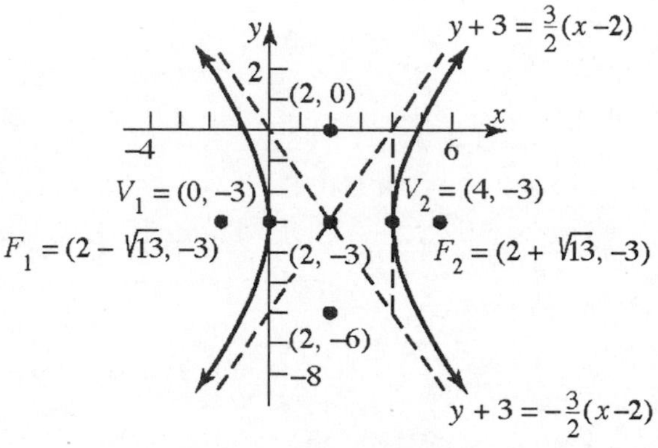

36. $\frac{(y+3)^2}{4} - \frac{(x-2)^2}{9} = 1$

The center of the hyperbola is at (2, –3). $a = 2$, $b = 3$.

The vertices are (2, –1) and (2, –5).

Find the value of c:

$$c^2 = a^2 + b^2 = 4 + 9 = 13$$

$$c = \sqrt{13}$$

Foci:

$\left(2, -3 - \sqrt{13}\right)$ and $\left(2, -3 + \sqrt{13}\right)$

Transverse axis: $x = 2$.

Asymptotes:

$$y + 3 = \frac{2}{3}(x-2);\ y + 3 = -\frac{2}{3}(x-2).$$

To graph, enter:

$$y_1 = -3 + 2\sqrt{((x-2)^2/9 + 1)};$$

$$y_2 = -3 - 2\sqrt{((x-2)^2/9 + 1)}$$

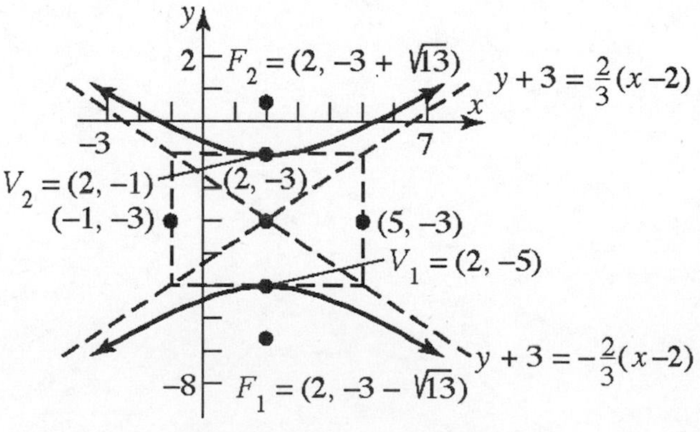

37. $(y-2)^2 - 4(x+2)^2 = 4$

Divide both sides by 4 to put in standard form: $\dfrac{(y-2)^2}{4} - \dfrac{(x+2)^2}{1} = 1$

The center of the hyperbola is at (–2, 2).
$a = 2$, $b = 1$. The vertices are (–2, 4) and (–2, 0). Find the value of c:

$$c^2 = a^2 + b^2 = 4 + 1 = 5 \rightarrow c = \sqrt{5}$$

Foci: $\left(-2, 2-\sqrt{5}\right)$ and $\left(-2, 2+\sqrt{5}\right)$.

Transverse axis: $x = -2$.

Asymptotes:
$y-2 = 2(x+2)$; $y-2 = -2(x+2)$.

To graph, enter: $y_1 = 2 + 2\sqrt{((x+2)^2 + 1)}$;
$y_2 = 2 - 2\sqrt{((x+2)^2 + 1)}$

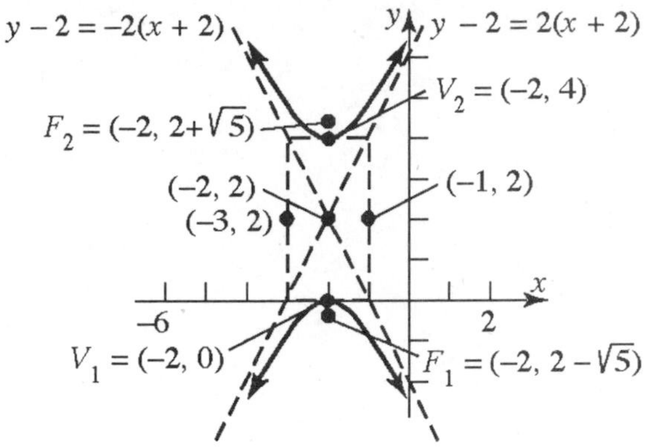

38. $(x+4)^2 - 9(y-3)^2 = 9$

Divide both sides by 9 to put in standard form: $\dfrac{(x+4)^2}{9} - \dfrac{(y-3)^2}{1} = 1$

The center of the hyperbola is at (–4, 3). $a = 3$, $b = 1$.
The vertices are (–7, 3) and (–1, 3). Find the value of c:

$$c^2 = a^2 + b^2 = 9 + 1 = 10$$

$$c = \sqrt{10}$$

Foci: $\left(-4-\sqrt{10}, 3\right)$ and $\left(-4+\sqrt{10}, 3\right)$.

Transverse axis: $y = 3$.

Asymptotes: $y-3 = \frac{1}{3}(x+4)$, $y-3 = -\frac{1}{3}(x+4)$.

To graph, enter: $y_1 = 3 + \sqrt{((x+4)^2/9 - 1)}$;
$y_2 = 3 - \sqrt{((x+4)^2/9 - 1)}$

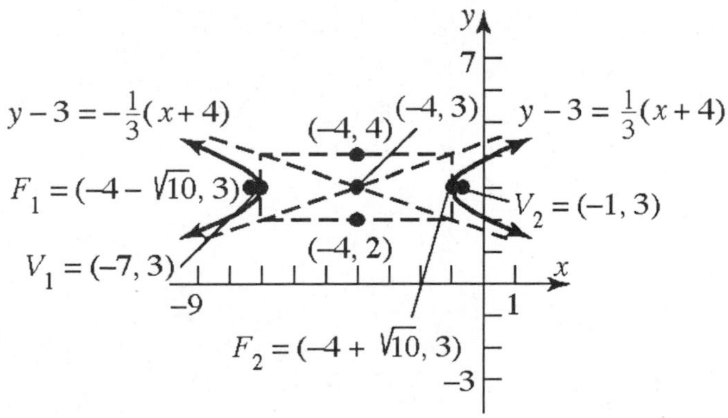

39. $(x+1)^2-(y+2)^2=4$

Divide both sides by 4 to put in standard form: $\dfrac{(x+1)^2}{4}-\dfrac{(y+2)^2}{4}=1$

The center of the hyperbola is at $(-1,-2)$. $a=2,\ b=2$.

The vertices are $(-3,-2)$ and $(1,-2)$.

Find the value of c:

$$c^2=a^2+b^2=4+4=8\rightarrow c=\sqrt{8}=2\sqrt{2}$$

Foci: $\left(-1-2\sqrt{2},-2\right)$ and $\left(-1+2\sqrt{2},-2\right)$.

Transverse axis: $y=-2$.

Asymptotes: $y+2=x+1,\ y+2=-(x+1)$.

To graph, enter: $y_1=-2+2\sqrt{((x+1)^2/4-1)}$; $y_2=-2-2\sqrt{((x+1)^2/4-1)}$

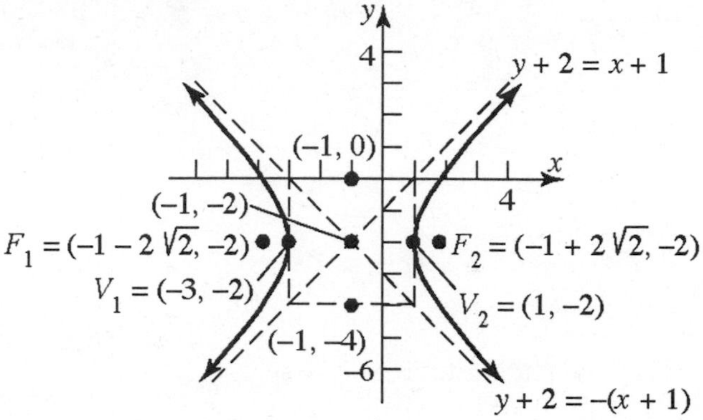

40. $(y-3)^2-(x+2)^2=4$

Divide both sides by 4 to put in standard form: $\dfrac{(y-3)^2}{4}-\dfrac{(x+2)^2}{4}=1$

The center of the hyperbola is at $(-2, 3)$. $a=2,\ b=2$.

The vertices are $(-2, 5)$ and $(-2, 1)$.

Find the value of c:

$$c^2=a^2+b^2=4+4=8\rightarrow c=\sqrt{8}=2\sqrt{2}$$

Foci: $\left(-2, 3-2\sqrt{2}\right)$ and $\left(-2, 3+2\sqrt{2}\right)$.

Transverse axis: $x=-2$.

Asymptotes: $y-3=x+2,\ y-3=-(x+2)$.

To graph, enter: $y_1=3+2\sqrt{((x+2)^2/4+1)}$; $y_2=3-2\sqrt{((x+2)^2/4+1)}$

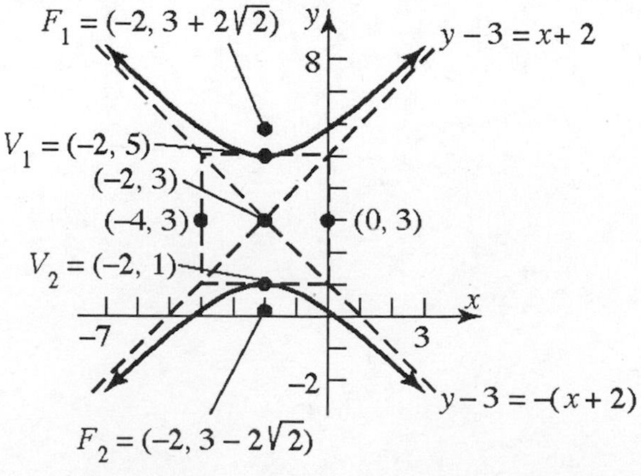

41. Complete the square to put in standard form:

$$x^2 - y^2 - 2x - 2y - 1 = 0$$
$$(x^2 - 2x + 1) - (y^2 + 2y + 1) = 1 + 1 - 1$$
$$(x-1)^2 - (y+1)^2 = 1$$

The center of the hyperbola is at $(1, -1)$. $a = 1$, $b = 1$.
The vertices are $(0, -1)$ and $(2, -1)$.
Find the value of c:

$$c^2 = a^2 + b^2 = 1 + 1 = 2$$
$$c = \sqrt{2}$$

Foci: $\left(1-\sqrt{2},-1\right)$ and $\left(1+\sqrt{2},-1\right)$.
Transverse axis: $y = -1$.
Asymptotes:
$y+1 = x-1$, $y+1 = -(x-1)$.
To graph, enter:
$y_1 = -1 + \sqrt{((x-1)^2 - 1)}$;
$y_2 = -1 - \sqrt{((x-1)^2 - 1)}$

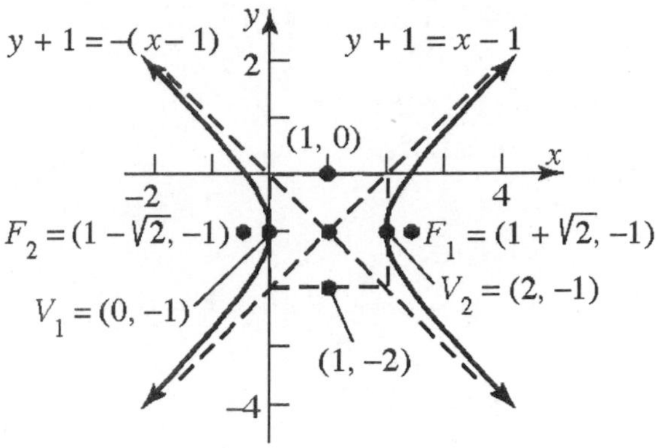

42. Complete the square to put in standard form:

$$y^2 - x^2 - 4y + 4x - 1 = 0$$
$$(y^2 - 4y + 4) - (x^2 - 4x + 4) = 1 + 4 - 4$$
$$(y-2)^2 - (x-2)^2 = 1$$

The center of the hyperbola is at $(2, 2)$. $a = 1$, $b = 1$.
The vertices are $(2, 1)$ and $(2, 3)$.
Find the value of c:

$$c^2 = a^2 + b^2 = 1 + 1 = 2$$
$$c = \sqrt{2}$$

Foci: $\left(2, 2-\sqrt{2}\right)$ and $\left(2, 2+\sqrt{2}\right)$.
Transverse axis: $x = 2$.
Asymptotes:
$y-2 = x-2$, $y-2 = -(x-2)$.
To graph, enter:
$y_1 = 2 + \sqrt{((x-2)^2 + 1)}$;
$y_2 = 2 - \sqrt{((x-2)^2 + 1)}$

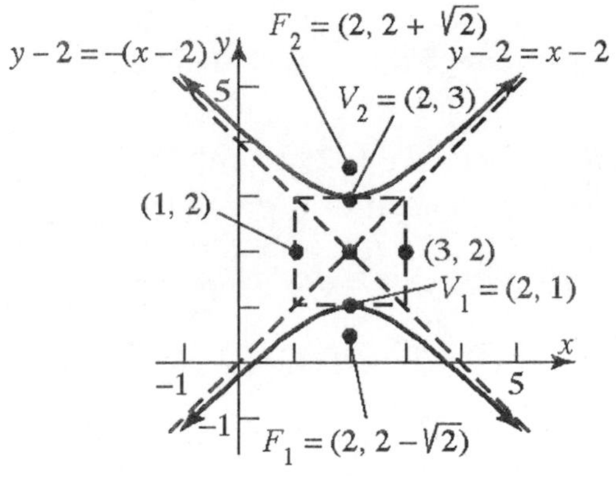

43. Complete the square to put in standard form:

$$y^2 - 4x^2 - 4y - 8x - 4 = 0$$
$$(y^2 - 4y + 4) - 4(x^2 + 2x + 1) = 4 + 4 - 4$$
$$(y-2)^2 - 4(x+1)^2 = 4$$
$$\frac{(y-2)^2}{4} - \frac{(x+1)^2}{1} = 1$$

The center of the hyperbola is at $(-1, 2)$. $a = 2$, $b = 1$.
The vertices are $(-1, 4)$ and $(-1, 0)$.
Find the value of c:

$c^2 = a^2 + b^2 = 4 + 1 = 5$

$c = \sqrt{5}$

Foci: $\left(-1, 2 - \sqrt{5}\right)$ and $\left(-1, 2 + \sqrt{5}\right)$.
Transverse axis: $x = -1$.
Asymptotes:
$y - 2 = 2(x+1)$, $y - 2 = -2(x+1)$.
To graph, enter:
$y_1 = 2 + 2\sqrt{((x+1)^2 + 1)}$;
$y_2 = 2 - 2\sqrt{((x+1)^2 + 1)}$

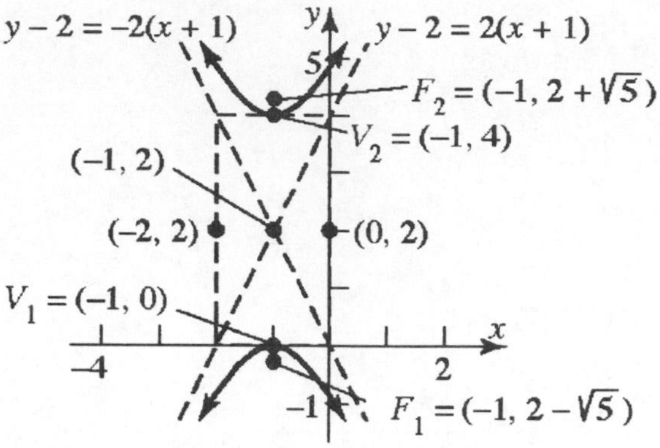

44. Complete the square to put in standard form:

$$2x^2 - y^2 + 4x + 4y - 4 = 0$$
$$2(x^2 + 2x + 1) - (y^2 - 4y + 4) = 4 + 2 - 4$$
$$2(x+1)^2 - (y-2)^2 = 2$$
$$\frac{(x+1)^2}{1} - \frac{(y-2)^2}{2} = 1$$

The center of the hyperbola is at $(-1, 2)$. $a = 1$, $b = \sqrt{2}$.
The vertices are $(-2, 2)$ and $(0, 2)$.
Find the value of c:

$c^2 = a^2 + b^2 = 1 + 2 = 3$

$c = \sqrt{3}$

Foci: $\left(-1 - \sqrt{3}, 2\right)$ and $\left(-1 + \sqrt{3}, 2\right)$.
Transverse axis: $y = 2$.
Asymptotes:
$y - 2 = \sqrt{2}(x+1)$, $y - 2 = -\sqrt{2}(x+1)$

.

To graph, enter:
$y_1 = 2 + \sqrt{2}\sqrt{((x+1)^2 - 1)}$;
$y_2 = 2 - \sqrt{2}\sqrt{((x+1)^2 - 1)}$

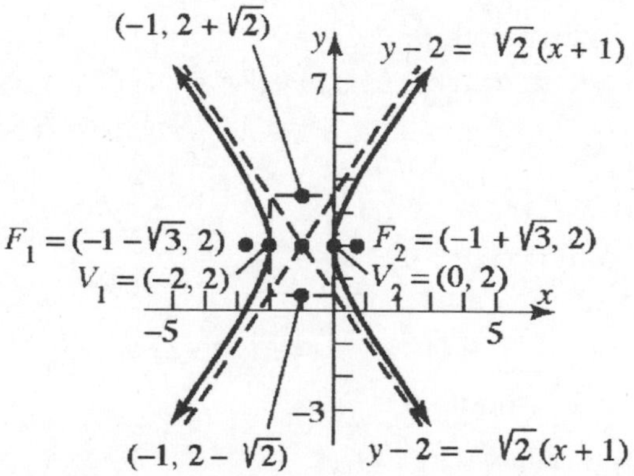

45. Complete the square to put in standard form:

$$4x^2 - y^2 - 24x - 4y + 16 = 0 \rightarrow 4(x^2 - 6x + 9) - (y^2 + 4y + 4) = -16 + 36 - 4$$

$$4(x-3)^2 - (y+2)^2 = 16 \rightarrow \frac{(x-3)^2}{4} - \frac{(y+2)^2}{16} = 1$$

The center of the hyperbola is at $(3, -2)$. $a = 2$, $b = 4$.

The vertices are $(1, -2)$ and $(5, -2)$.

Find the value of c:

$$c^2 = a^2 + b^2 = 4 + 16 = 20$$

$$c = \sqrt{20} = 2\sqrt{5}$$

Foci:

$\left(3 - 2\sqrt{5}, -2\right)$ and $\left(3 + 2\sqrt{5}, -2\right)$.

Transverse axis: $y = -2$.

Asymptotes:

$y + 2 = 2(x - 3)$, $y + 2 = -2(x - 3)$.

To graph, enter:

$y_1 = -2 + 4\sqrt{((x-3)^2 / 4 - 1)}$;

$y_2 = -2 - 4\sqrt{((x-3)^2 / 4 - 1)}$

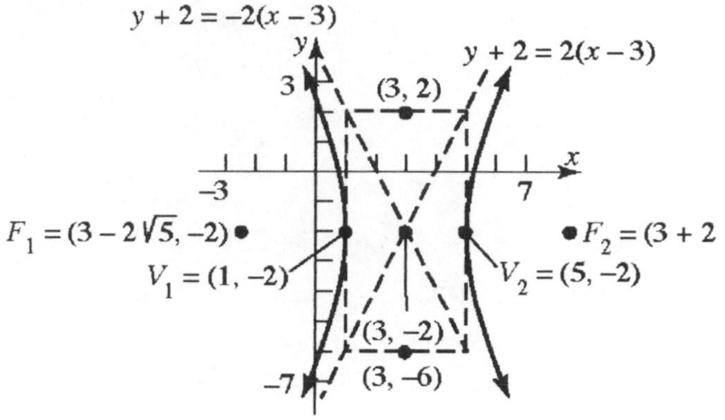

46. Complete the square to put in standard form:

$$2y^2 - x^2 + 2x + 8y + 3 = 0 \rightarrow 2(y^2 + 4y + 4) - (x^2 - 2x + 1) = -3 + 8 - 1$$

$$2(y+2)^2 - (x-1)^2 = 4 \rightarrow \frac{(y+2)^2}{2} - \frac{(x-1)^2}{4} = 1$$

The center of the hyperbola is at $(1, -2)$. $a = \sqrt{2}$, $b = 2$.

The vertices are $\left(1, -2 - \sqrt{2}\right)$ and $\left(1, -2 + \sqrt{2}\right)$

Find the value of c:

$$c^2 = a^2 + b^2 = 2 + 4 = 6 \rightarrow c = \sqrt{6}$$

Foci: $\left(1, -2 - \sqrt{6}\right)$ and $\left(1, -2 + \sqrt{6}\right)$.

Transverse axis: $x = 1$.

Asymptotes: $y + 2 = \frac{\sqrt{2}}{2}(x - 1)$, $y + 2 = -\frac{\sqrt{2}}{2}(x - 1)$

To graph, enter: $y_1 = -2 + \sqrt{2}\sqrt{((x-1)^2 / 4 + 1)}$; $y_2 = -2 - \sqrt{2}\sqrt{((x-1)^2 / 4 + 1)}$

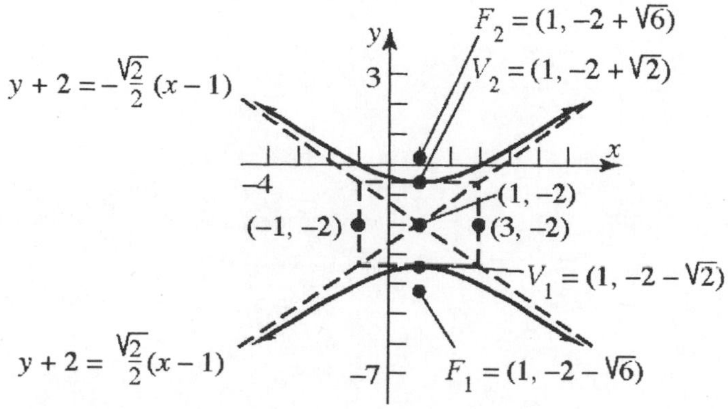

47. Complete the square to put in standard form:

$$y^2 - 4x^2 - 16x - 2y - 19 = 0 \rightarrow (y^2 - 2y + 1) - 4(x^2 + 4x + 4) = 19 + 1 - 16$$

$$(y-1)^2 - 4(x+2)^2 = 4 \rightarrow \frac{(y-1)^2}{4} - \frac{(x+2)^2}{1} = 1$$

The center of the hyperbola is at $(-2, 1)$. $a = 2$, $b = 1$. The vertices are $(-2, 3)$ and $(-2, -1)$. Find the value of c:

$$c^2 = a^2 + b^2 = 4 + 1 = 5$$

$$c = \sqrt{5}$$

Foci: $\left(-2, 1-\sqrt{5}\right)$ and $\left(-2, 1+\sqrt{5}\right)$.

Transverse axis: $x = -2$.

Asymptotes:

$y - 1 = 2(x+2); y - 1 = -2(x+2)$.

To graph, enter:

$y_1 = 1 + 2\sqrt{((x+2)^2 + 1)}$;

$y_2 = 1 - 2\sqrt{((x+2)^2 + 1)}$

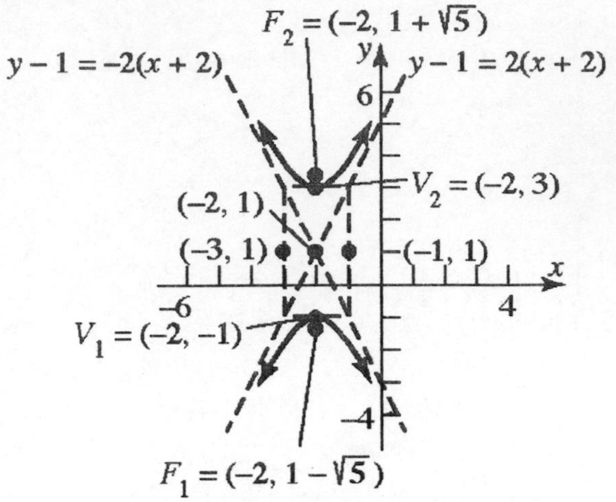

48. Complete the square to put in standard form:

$$x^2 - 3y^2 + 8x - 6y + 4 = 0 \rightarrow (x^2 + 8x + 16) - 3(y^2 + 2y + 1) = -4 + 16 - 3$$

$$(x+4)^2 - 3(y+1)^2 = 9 \rightarrow \frac{(x+4)^2}{9} - \frac{(y+1)^2}{3} = 1$$

The center of the hyperbola is at $(-4, -1)$. $a = 3$, $b = \sqrt{3}$. The vertices are $(-7, -1)$ and $(-1, -1)$.

Find the value of c:

$$c^2 = a^2 + b^2 = 9 + 3 = 12 \rightarrow c = \sqrt{12} = 2\sqrt{3}$$

Foci: $\left(-4 - 2\sqrt{3}, -1\right)$ and $\left(-4 + 2\sqrt{3}, -1\right)$.

Transverse axis: $y = -1$.

Asymptotes: $y + 1 = \frac{\sqrt{3}}{3}(x+4); y + 1 = -\frac{\sqrt{3}}{3}(x+4)$

To graph, enter: $y_1 = -1 + \sqrt{3}\sqrt{((x+4)^2/9 - 1)}$; $y_2 = -1 - \sqrt{3}\sqrt{((x+4)^2/9 - 1)}$

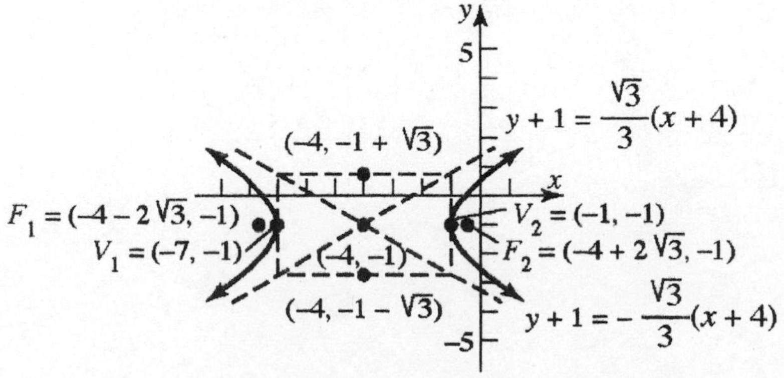

49. Rewrite the equation:

$$y = \sqrt{16+4x^2}$$
$$y^2 = 16+4x^2, \quad y \ge 0$$
$$y^2 - 4x^2 = 16, \quad y \ge 0$$
$$\frac{y^2}{16} - \frac{x^2}{4} = 1, \quad y \ge 0$$

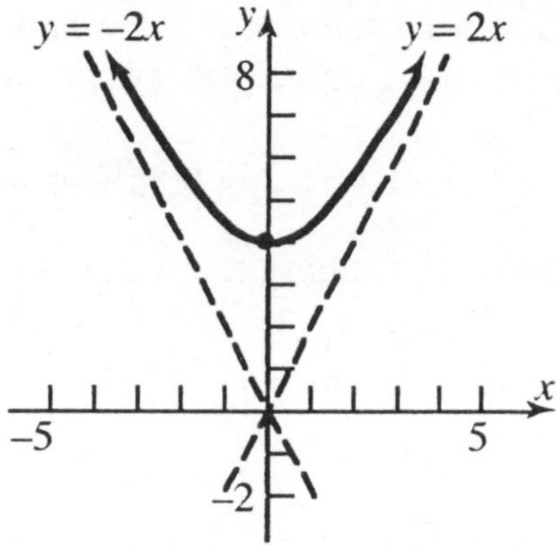

50. Rewrite the equation:

$$y = -\sqrt{9+9x^2}$$
$$y^2 = 9+9x^2, \quad y \le 0$$
$$y^2 - 9x^2 = 9, \quad y \le 0$$
$$\frac{y^2}{9} - \frac{x^2}{1} = 1, \quad y \le 0$$

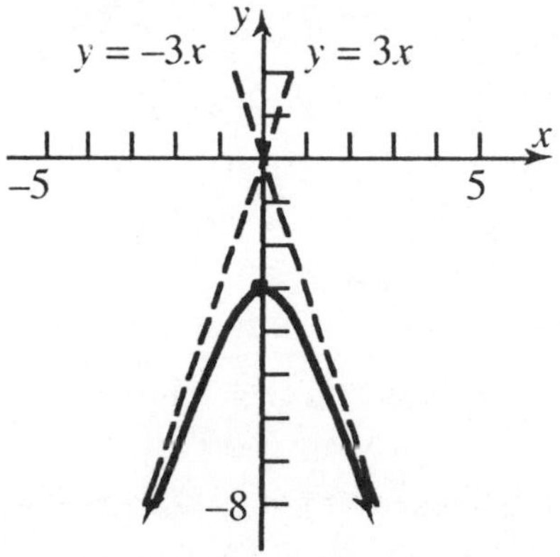

51. Rewrite the equation:

$$y = -\sqrt{-25+x^2}$$
$$y^2 = -25+x^2, \quad y \le 0$$
$$x^2 - y^2 = 25, \quad y \le 0$$
$$\frac{x^2}{25} - \frac{y^2}{25} = 1, \quad y \le 0$$

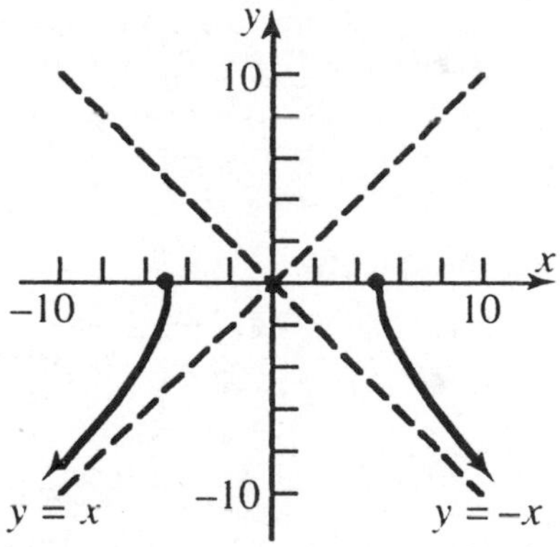

52. Rewrite the equation:

$$y = \sqrt{-1+x^2}$$
$$y^2 = -1+x^2, \quad y \ge 0$$
$$x^2 - y^2 = 1, \quad y \ge 0$$

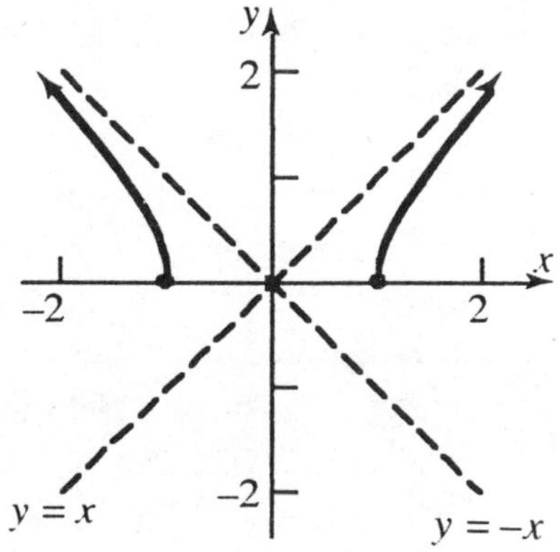

53. (a) Set up a coordinate system so that the two stations lie on the x-axis and the origin is midway between them. The ship lies on a hyperbola whose foci are the locations of the two stations. Since the time difference is 0.00038 seconds and the speed of the signal is 186,000 miles per second, the difference in the distances of the ships from each station is:

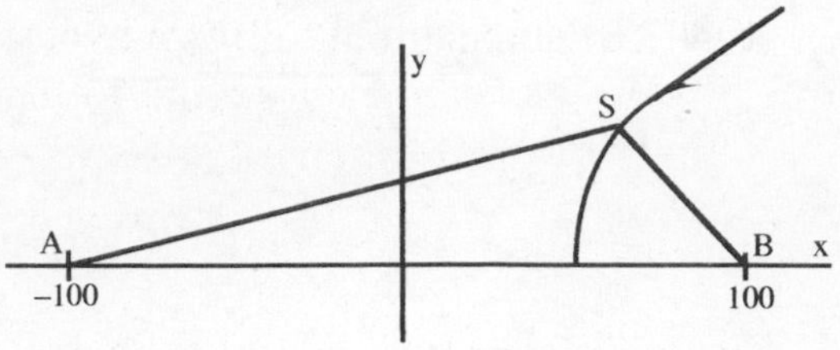

$$\text{distance} = (186{,}000)(0.00038) \approx 70.68 \text{ miles}$$

The difference of the distances from the ship to each station, 70.68, equals $2a$, so $a = 35.34$ and the vertex of the corresponding hyperbola is at $(35.34, 0)$. Since the focus is at (100, 0), following this hyperbola, the ship would reach shore 64.66 miles from the master station.

(b) The ship should follow a hyperbola with a vertex at (80, 0). For this hyperbola, $a = 80$, so the constant difference of the distances from the ship to each station is 160. The time difference the ship should look for is:

$$\text{time} = \frac{160}{186{,}000} \approx 0.00086 \text{ seconds}$$

(c) Find the equation of the hyperbola with vertex at (80, 0) and a focus at (100, 0). The form of the equation of the hyperbola is:

$$\frac{x^2}{a^2} - \frac{y^2}{b^2} = 1 \quad \text{where } a = 80.$$

Since $c = 100$ and $b^2 = c^2 - a^2 \rightarrow b^2 = 100^2 - 80^2 = 3600$.

The equation of the hyperbola is: $\frac{x^2}{6400} - \frac{y^2}{3600} = 1$.

Since the ship is 50 miles off shore, we have $y = 50$. Solve the equation for x:

$$\frac{x^2}{6400} - \frac{50^2}{3600} = 1 \rightarrow \frac{x^2}{6400} = 1 + \frac{2500}{3600} = \frac{61}{36} \rightarrow x^2 = 6400 \cdot \frac{61}{36}$$

$$x \approx 104 \text{ miles}$$

The ship's location is (104, 50).

54. (a) Set up a coordinate system so that the two stations lie on the x-axis and the origin is midway between them. The ship lies on a hyperbola whose foci are the locations of the two stations. Since the time difference is 0.00032 seconds and the speed of the signal is 186,000 miles per second, the difference in the distances of the ships from each station is:

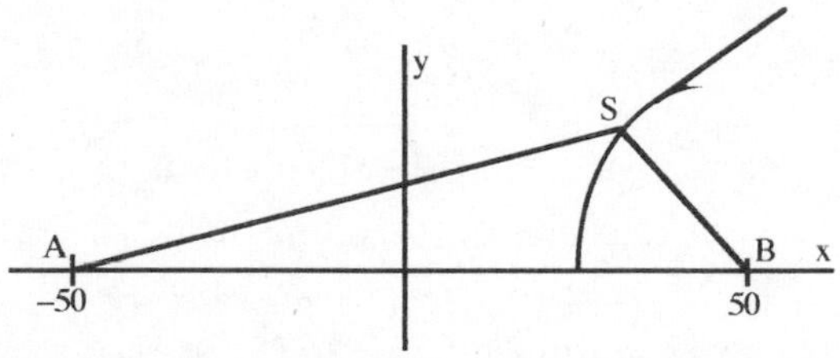

$$\text{distance} = (186{,}000)(0.00032) = 59.52 \text{ miles}$$

The difference of the distances from the ship to each station, 59.52, equals $2a$, so $a = 29.76$ and the vertex of the corresponding hyperbola is at $(29.76, 0)$. Since the focus is at (50, 0), following this hyperbola, the ship would reach shore 20.24 miles from the master station.

(b) The ship should follow a hyperbola with a vertex at (40, 0). For this hyperbola, $a = 40$, so the constant difference of the distances from the ship to each station is 80. The time difference the ship should look for is:

$$\text{time} = \frac{80}{186{,}000} \approx 0.00043 \text{ seconds}$$

(c) Find the equation of the hyperbola with vertex at (40, 0) and a focus at (50, 0). The form of the equation of the hyperbola is:

$$\frac{x^2}{a^2} - \frac{y^2}{b^2} = 1 \quad \text{where } a = 40.$$

Since $c = 50$ and $b^2 = c^2 - a^2 \rightarrow b^2 = 50^2 - 40^2 = 900$.

The equation of the hyperbola is: $\frac{x^2}{1600} - \frac{y^2}{900} = 1$.

Since the ship is 20 miles off shore, we have $y = 20$. Solve the equation for x:

$$\frac{x^2}{1600} - \frac{20^2}{900} = 1 \rightarrow \frac{x^2}{1600} = 1 + \frac{400}{900} = \frac{13}{9} \rightarrow x^2 = 1600 \cdot \frac{13}{9}$$

$$x \approx 48 \text{ miles}$$

The ship's location is (48, 20).

55. (a) Set up a rectangular coordinate system so that the two devices lie on the x-axis and the origin is midway between them. The devices serve as foci to the hyperbola so $c = \frac{2000}{2} = 1000$. Since the explosion occurs 200 feet from point B, the vertex of the hyperbola is (800, 0); therefore, $a = 800$. Finding b:

$$b^2 = c^2 - a^2 \rightarrow b^2 = 1000^2 - 800^2 = 360000 \rightarrow b = 600$$

The equation of the hyperbola is:

$$\frac{x^2}{800^2} - \frac{y^2}{600^2} = 1$$

If $x = 1000$, find y:

$$\frac{1000^2}{800^2} - \frac{y^2}{600^2} = 1 \rightarrow \frac{y^2}{600^2} = \frac{1000^2}{800^2} - 1 = \frac{600^2}{800^2} \rightarrow y^2 = 600^2 \cdot \frac{600^2}{800^2}$$

$$y = 450 \text{ feet}$$

The second detonation should take place 450 feet north of point B.

56. Answers will vary.

57. If the eccentricity is close to 1, then $c \approx a$ and $b \approx 0$. When b is close to 0, the hyperbola is very narrow, because the slopes of the asymptotes are close to 0.
If the eccentricity is very large, then c is much larger than a and b is very large. The result is a hyperbola that is very wide.

58. If $a = b$, then $c^2 = a^2 + a^2 = 2a^2$

Thus, $\frac{c^2}{a^2} = 2$ or $\frac{c}{a} = \sqrt{2}$

The eccentricity of an equilateral hyperbola is $\sqrt{2}$.

59. $\dfrac{x^2}{4} - y^2 = 1 \quad (a = 2,\ b = 1)$
is a hyperbola with horizontal transverse axis, centered at (0, 0) and has asymptotes: $y = \pm\dfrac{1}{2}x$

$y^2 - \dfrac{x^2}{4} = 1 \quad (a = 1,\ b = 2)$
is a hyperbola with vertical transverse axis, centered at (0, 0) and has asymptotes: $y = \pm\dfrac{1}{2}x$
Since the two hyperbolas have the same asymptotes, they are conjugate.

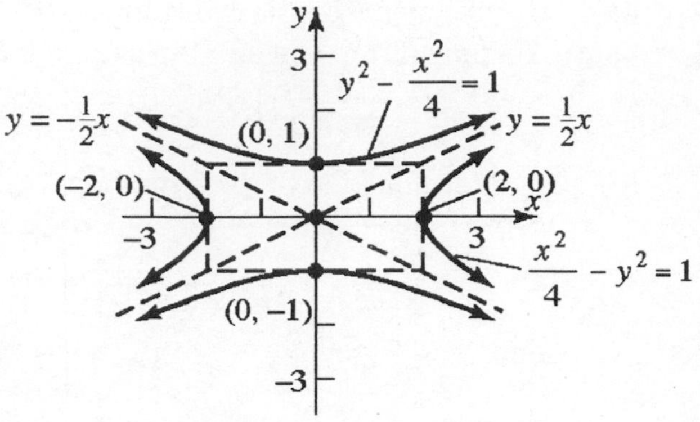

60. $\dfrac{y^2}{a^2} - \dfrac{x^2}{b^2} = 1$
Solve for y:

$$\frac{y^2}{a^2} = 1 + \frac{x^2}{b^2} \rightarrow y^2 = a^2\left(1 + \frac{x^2}{b^2}\right)$$

$$y^2 = \frac{a^2x^2}{b^2}\left(\frac{b^2}{x^2} + 1\right) \rightarrow y = \pm\frac{ax}{b}\sqrt{\frac{b^2}{x^2} + 1}$$

As $x \rightarrow -\infty$ or as $x \rightarrow \infty$, the term $\dfrac{b^2}{x^2}$ gets close to 0, so the expression under the radical gets closer to 1. Thus, the graph of the hyperbola gets closer to the lines $y = -\dfrac{a}{b}x$ and $y = \dfrac{a}{b}x$. These lines are the asymptotes of the hyperbola.

61. Put the equation in standard hyperbola form:

$$Ax^2 + Cy^2 + F = 0 \qquad A \neq 0,\ C \neq 0,\ F \neq 0$$

$$Ax^2 + Cy^2 = -F \rightarrow \frac{Ax^2}{-F} + \frac{Cy^2}{-F} = 1$$

$$\frac{x^2}{-F/A} + \frac{y^2}{-F/C} = 1$$

Since $-F/A$ and $-F/C$ have opposite signs, this is a hyperbola with center at (0, 0).

62. Complete the square on the given equation:

$Ax^2 + Cy^2 + Dx + Ey + F = 0,$ where A and C have opposite signs.

$$A\left(x^2 + \frac{D}{A}x\right) + C\left(y^2 + \frac{E}{C}y\right) = -F$$

$$A\left(x^2 + \frac{D}{A}x + \frac{D^2}{4A^2}\right) + C\left(y^2 + \frac{E}{C}y + \frac{E^2}{4C^2}\right) = \frac{D^2}{4A} + \frac{E^2}{4C} - F$$

$$A\left(x + \frac{D}{2A}\right)^2 + C\left(y + \frac{E}{2C}\right)^2 = \frac{D^2}{4A} + \frac{E^2}{4C} - F$$

(a) If $\frac{D^2}{4A}+\frac{E^2}{4C}-F\neq 0$, this is the equation of a hyperbola whose center is $\left(\frac{-D}{2A},\frac{-E}{2C}\right)$ if $C<0$ or $\left(\frac{-D}{2A},\frac{E}{2C}\right)$ if $A<0$.

(b) If $\frac{D^2}{4A^2}+\frac{E^2}{4C^2}-F=0$, then

$$A\left(x+\frac{D}{2A}\right)^2+C\left(y+\frac{E}{2C}\right)^2=0 \rightarrow \left(y+\frac{E}{2C}\right)^2=\frac{-A}{C}\left(x+\frac{D}{2A}\right)^2$$

$$\rightarrow \quad y+\frac{E}{2C}=\pm\sqrt{\frac{-A}{C}}\left(x+\frac{D}{2A}\right)$$

which is the graph of two intersecting lines.

Chapter 11

Analytic Geometry

11.5 Rotation of Axes; General Form of a Conic

1. $x^2 + 4x + y + 3 = 0$
   $A = 1$ and $C = 0$; $AC = (1)(0) = 0$. Since $AC = 0$, the equation defines a parabola.

2. $2y^2 - 3y + 3x = 0$
   $A = 0$ and $C = 2$; $AC = (0)(2) = 0$. Since $AC = 0$, the equation defines a parabola.

3. $6x^2 + 3y^2 - 12x + 6y = 0$
   $A = 6$ and $C = 3$; $AC = (6)(3) = 18$. Since $AC > 0$ and $A \neq C$, the equation defines an ellipse.

4. $2x^2 + y^2 - 8x + 4y + 2 = 0$
   $A = 2$ and $C = 1$; $AC = (2)(1) = 2$. Since $AC > 0$ and $A \neq C$, the equation defines an ellipse.

5. $3x^2 - 2y^2 + 6x + 4 = 0$
   $A = 3$ and $C = -2$; $AC = (3)(-2) = -6$. Since $AC < 0$, the equation defines a hyperbola.

6. $4x^2 - 3y^2 - 8x + 6y + 1 = 0$
   $A = 4$ and $C = -3$; $AC = (4)(-3) = -12$. Since $AC < 0$, the equation defines a hyperbola.

7. $2y^2 - x^2 - y + x = 0$
   $A = -1$ and $C = 2$; $AC = (-1)(2) = -2$. Since $AC < 0$, the equation defines a hyperbola.

8. $y^2 - 8x^2 - 2x - y = 0$
   $A = -8$ and $C = 1$; $AC = (-8)(1) = -8$. Since $AC < 0$, the equation defines a hyperbola.

9. $x^2 + y^2 - 8x + 4y = 0$
   $A = 1$ and $C = 1$; $AC = (1)(1) = 1$. Since $AC > 0$ and $A = C$, the equation defines a circle.

10. $2x^2 + 2y^2 - 8x + 8y = 0$
    $A = 2$ and $C = 2$; $AC = (2)(2) = 4$. Since $AC > 0$ and $A = C$, the equation defines a circle.

11. $x^2 + 4xy + y^2 - 3 = 0$

$A = 1, B = 4, \text{ and } C = 1;\ \cot(2\theta) = \frac{A - C}{B} = \frac{1-1}{4} = \frac{0}{4} = 0 \ \rightarrow\ 2\theta = \frac{\pi}{2} \ \rightarrow\ \theta = \frac{\pi}{4}$

$x = x'\cos\left(\frac{\pi}{4}\right) - y'\sin\left(\frac{\pi}{4}\right) = \frac{\sqrt{2}}{2}x' - \frac{\sqrt{2}}{2}y' = \frac{\sqrt{2}}{2}(x' - y')$

$y = x'\sin\left(\frac{\pi}{4}\right) + y'\cos\left(\frac{\pi}{4}\right) = \frac{\sqrt{2}}{2}x' + \frac{\sqrt{2}}{2}y' = \frac{\sqrt{2}}{2}(x' + y')$

12. $x^2 - 4xy + y^2 - 3 = 0$

$A = 1, B = -4, \text{ and } C = 1;\ \cot(2\theta) = \frac{A - C}{B} = \frac{1-1}{-4} = \frac{0}{-4} = 0 \rightarrow 2\theta = \frac{\pi}{2} \rightarrow \theta = \frac{\pi}{4}$

$x = x'\cos\left(\frac{\pi}{4}\right) - y'\sin\left(\frac{\pi}{4}\right) = \frac{\sqrt{2}}{2}x' - \frac{\sqrt{2}}{2}y' = \frac{\sqrt{2}}{2}(x' - y')$

$y = x'\sin\left(\frac{\pi}{4}\right) + y'\cos\left(\frac{\pi}{4}\right) = \frac{\sqrt{2}}{2}x' + \frac{\sqrt{2}}{2}y' = \frac{\sqrt{2}}{2}(x' + y')$

13. $5x^2 + 6xy + 5y^2 - 8 = 0$

$A = 5, B = 6, \text{ and } C = 5;\ \cot(2\theta) = \frac{A - C}{B} = \frac{5-5}{6} = \frac{0}{6} = 0 \ \rightarrow\ 2\theta = \frac{\pi}{2} \ \rightarrow\ \theta = \frac{\pi}{4}$

$x = x'\cos\left(\frac{\pi}{4}\right) - y'\sin\left(\frac{\pi}{4}\right) = \frac{\sqrt{2}}{2}x' - \frac{\sqrt{2}}{2}y' = \frac{\sqrt{2}}{2}(x' - y')$

$y = x'\sin\left(\frac{\pi}{4}\right) + y'\cos\left(\frac{\pi}{4}\right) = \frac{\sqrt{2}}{2}x' + \frac{\sqrt{2}}{2}y' = \frac{\sqrt{2}}{2}(x' + y')$

14. $3x^2 - 10xy + 3y^2 - 32 = 0$

$A = 3, B = -10, \text{ and } C = 3;\ \cot(2\theta) = \frac{A - C}{B} = \frac{3-3}{-10} = \frac{0}{-10} = 0 \rightarrow 2\theta = \frac{\pi}{2} \rightarrow \theta = \frac{\pi}{4}$

$x = x'\cos\left(\frac{\pi}{4}\right) - y'\sin\left(\frac{\pi}{4}\right) = \frac{\sqrt{2}}{2}x' - \frac{\sqrt{2}}{2}y' = \frac{\sqrt{2}}{2}(x' - y')$

$y = x'\sin\left(\frac{\pi}{4}\right) + y'\cos\left(\frac{\pi}{4}\right) = \frac{\sqrt{2}}{2}x' + \frac{\sqrt{2}}{2}y' = \frac{\sqrt{2}}{2}(x' + y')$

15. $13x^2 - 6\sqrt{3}xy + 7y^2 - 16 = 0$

$A = 13, B = -6\sqrt{3}, \text{ and } C = 7;\ \cot(2\theta) = \frac{A - C}{B} = \frac{13-7}{-6\sqrt{3}} = \frac{6}{-6\sqrt{3}} = -\frac{\sqrt{3}}{3}$

$2\theta = \frac{2\pi}{3} \ \rightarrow\ \theta = \frac{\pi}{3}$

$$x = x'\cos\left(\frac{\pi}{3}\right) - y'\sin\left(\frac{\pi}{3}\right) = \frac{1}{2}x' - \frac{\sqrt{3}}{2}y' = \frac{1}{2}\left(x' - \sqrt{3}y'\right)$$

$$y = x'\sin\left(\frac{\pi}{3}\right) + y'\cos\left(\frac{\pi}{3}\right) = \frac{\sqrt{3}}{2}x' + \frac{1}{2}y' = \frac{1}{2}\left(\sqrt{3}x' + y'\right)$$

16. $11x^2 + 10\sqrt{3}xy + y^2 - 4 = 0$

$A = 11$, $B = 10\sqrt{3}$, and $C = 1$; $\cot(2\theta) = \dfrac{A-C}{B} = \dfrac{11-1}{10\sqrt{3}} = \dfrac{10}{10\sqrt{3}} = \dfrac{\sqrt{3}}{3}$

$$2\theta = \frac{\pi}{3} \rightarrow \theta = \frac{\pi}{6}$$

$$x = x'\cos\left(\frac{\pi}{6}\right) - y'\sin\left(\frac{\pi}{6}\right) = \frac{\sqrt{3}}{2}x' - \frac{1}{2}y' = \frac{1}{2}\left(\sqrt{3}x' - y'\right)$$

$$y = x'\sin\left(\frac{\pi}{6}\right) + y'\cos\left(\frac{\pi}{6}\right) = \frac{1}{2}x' + \frac{\sqrt{3}}{2}y' = \frac{1}{2}\left(x' + \sqrt{3}y'\right)$$

17. $4x^2 - 4xy + y^2 - 8\sqrt{5}\,x - 16\sqrt{5}\,y = 0$

$A = 4$, $B = -4$, and $C = 1$; $\cot(2\theta) = \dfrac{A-C}{B} = \dfrac{4-1}{-4} = -\dfrac{3}{4}$; $\cos 2\theta = -\dfrac{3}{5}$

$$\sin\theta = \sqrt{\frac{1-\left(-\frac{3}{5}\right)}{2}} = \sqrt{\frac{4}{5}} = \frac{2}{\sqrt{5}} = \frac{2\sqrt{5}}{5}; \quad \cos\theta = \sqrt{\frac{1+\left(-\frac{3}{5}\right)}{2}} = \sqrt{\frac{1}{5}} = \frac{1}{\sqrt{5}} = \frac{\sqrt{5}}{5}$$

$$x = x'\cos\theta - y'\sin\theta = \frac{\sqrt{5}}{5}x' - \frac{2\sqrt{5}}{5}y' = \frac{\sqrt{5}}{5}(x' - 2y')$$

$$y = x'\sin\theta + y'\cos\theta = \frac{2\sqrt{5}}{5}x' + \frac{\sqrt{5}}{5}y' = \frac{\sqrt{5}}{5}(2x' + y')$$

18. $x^2 + 4xy + 4y^2 + 5\sqrt{5}\,y + 5 = 0$

$A = 1$, $B = 4$, and $C = 4$; $\cot(2\theta) = \dfrac{A-C}{B} = \dfrac{1-4}{4} = -\dfrac{3}{4}$; $\cos 2\theta = -\dfrac{3}{5}$

$$\sin\theta = \sqrt{\frac{1-\left(-\frac{3}{5}\right)}{2}} = \sqrt{\frac{4}{5}} = \frac{2}{\sqrt{5}} = \frac{2\sqrt{5}}{5}; \quad \cos\theta = \sqrt{\frac{1+\left(-\frac{3}{5}\right)}{2}} = \sqrt{\frac{1}{5}} = \frac{1}{\sqrt{5}} = \frac{\sqrt{5}}{5}$$

$$x = x'\cos\theta - y'\sin\theta = \frac{\sqrt{5}}{5}x' - \frac{2\sqrt{5}}{5}y' = \frac{\sqrt{5}}{5}(x' - 2y')$$

$$y = x'\sin\theta + y'\cos\theta = \frac{2\sqrt{5}}{5}x' + \frac{\sqrt{5}}{5}y' = \frac{\sqrt{5}}{5}(2x' + y')$$

19. $25x^2 - 36xy + 40y^2 - 12\sqrt{13}\,x - 8\sqrt{13}\,y = 0$

$A = 25,\ B = -36$, and $C = 40$; $\cot(2\theta) = \dfrac{A-C}{B} = \dfrac{25-40}{-36} = \dfrac{5}{12}$; $\cos 2\theta = \dfrac{5}{13}$

$$\sin\theta = \sqrt{\frac{\left(1-\frac{5}{13}\right)}{2}} = \sqrt{\frac{4}{13}} = \frac{2}{\sqrt{13}} = \frac{2\sqrt{13}}{13};\quad \cos\theta = \sqrt{\frac{\left(1+\frac{5}{13}\right)}{2}} = \sqrt{\frac{9}{13}} = \frac{3}{\sqrt{13}} = \frac{3\sqrt{13}}{13}$$

$$x = x'\cos\theta - y'\sin\theta = \frac{3\sqrt{13}}{13}x' - \frac{2\sqrt{13}}{13}y' = \frac{\sqrt{13}}{13}(3x' - 2y')$$

$$y = x'\sin\theta + y'\cos\theta = \frac{2\sqrt{13}}{13}x' + \frac{3\sqrt{13}}{13}y' = \frac{\sqrt{13}}{13}(2x' + 3y')$$

20. $34x^2 - 24xy + 41y^2 - 25 = 0$

$A = 34,\ B = -24$, and $C = 41$; $\cot(2\theta) = \dfrac{A-C}{B} = \dfrac{34-41}{-24} = \dfrac{7}{24}$; $\cos(2\theta) = \dfrac{7}{25}$

$$\sin\theta = \sqrt{\frac{\left(1-\frac{7}{25}\right)}{2}} = \sqrt{\frac{9}{25}} = \frac{3}{5};\quad \cos\theta = \sqrt{\frac{\left(1+\frac{7}{25}\right)}{2}} = \sqrt{\frac{16}{25}} = \frac{4}{5}$$

$$x = x'\cos\theta - y'\sin\theta = \frac{4}{5}x' - \frac{3}{5}y' = \frac{1}{5}(4x' - 3y')$$

$$y = x'\sin\theta + y'\cos\theta = \frac{3}{5}x' + \frac{4}{5}y' = \frac{1}{5}(3x' + 4y')$$

21. $x^2 + 4xy + y^2 - 3 = 0$; $\theta = 45^\circ$ (see Problem 11)

$$\left(\frac{\sqrt{2}}{2}(x'-y')\right)^2 + 4\left(\frac{\sqrt{2}}{2}(x'-y')\right)\left(\frac{\sqrt{2}}{2}(x'+y')\right) + \left(\frac{\sqrt{2}}{2}(x'+y')\right)^2 - 3 = 0$$

$$\frac{1}{2}\left(x'^2 - 2x'y' + y'^2\right) + 2\left(x'^2 - y'^2\right) + \frac{1}{2}\left(x'^2 + 2x'y' + y'^2\right) - 3 = 0$$

$$\frac{1}{2}x'^2 - x'y' + \frac{1}{2}y'^2 + 2x'^2 - 2y'^2 + \frac{1}{2}x'^2 + x'y' + \frac{1}{2}y'^2 = 3$$

$$3x'^2 - y'^2 = 3$$

$$\frac{x'^2}{1} - \frac{y'^2}{3} = 1$$

Hyperbola; center at the origin, transverse axis is the x'-axis, vertices at $(\pm 1, 0)$.

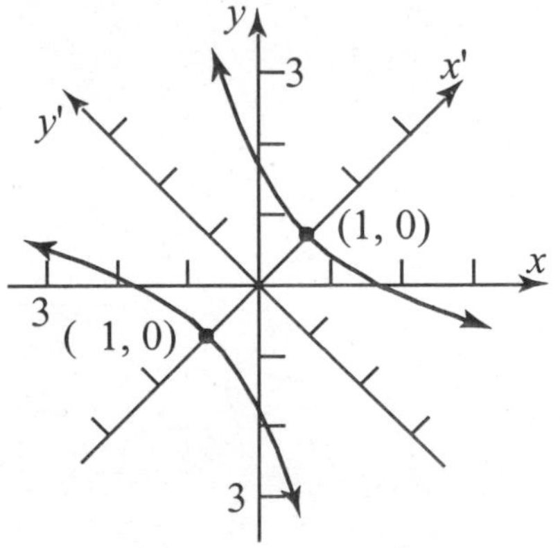

22. $x^2 - 4xy + y^2 - 3 = 0; \quad \theta = 45°$ (see Problem 12)

$$\left(\frac{\sqrt{2}}{2}(x'-y')\right)^2 - 4\left(\frac{\sqrt{2}}{2}(x'-y')\right)\left(\frac{\sqrt{2}}{2}(x'+y')\right) + \left(\frac{\sqrt{2}}{2}(x'+y')\right)^2 - 3 = 0$$

$$\frac{1}{2}\left(x'^2 - 2x'y' + y'^2\right) - 2\left(x'^2 - y'^2\right) + \frac{1}{2}\left(x'^2 + 2x'y' + y'^2\right) - 3 = 0$$

$$\frac{1}{2}x'^2 - x'y' + \frac{1}{2}y'^2 - 2x'^2 + 2y'^2 + \frac{1}{2}x'^2 + x'y' + \frac{1}{2}y'^2 = 3$$

$$-x'^2 + 3y'^2 = 3$$

$$\frac{y'^2}{1} - \frac{x'^2}{3} = 1$$

Hyperbola; center at the origin,
transverse axis is the y'-axis, vertices at (0, ±1).

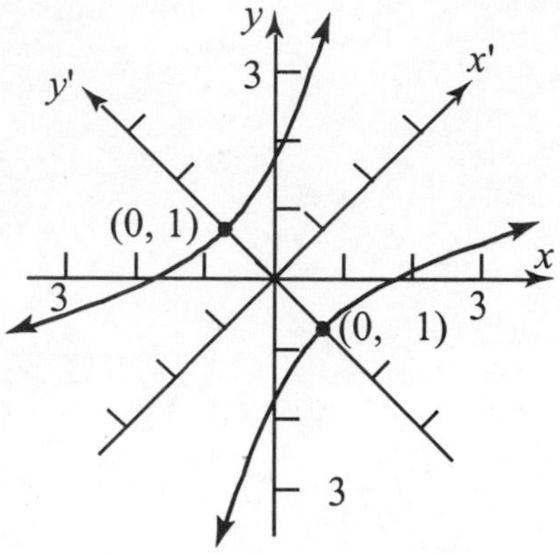

23. $5x^2 + 6xy + 5y^2 - 8 = 0; \quad \theta = 45°$ (see Problem 13)

$$5\left(\frac{\sqrt{2}}{2}(x'-y')\right)^2 + 6\left(\frac{\sqrt{2}}{2}(x'-y')\right)\left(\frac{\sqrt{2}}{2}(x'+y')\right) + 5\left(\frac{\sqrt{2}}{2}(x'+y')\right)^2 - 8 = 0$$

$$\frac{5}{2}\left(x'^2 - 2x'y' + y'^2\right) + 3\left(x'^2 - y'^2\right) + \frac{5}{2}\left(x'^2 + 2x'y' + y'^2\right) - 8 = 0$$

$$\frac{5}{2}x'^2 - 5x'y' + \frac{5}{2}y'^2 + 3x'^2 - 3y'^2 + \frac{5}{2}x'^2 + 5x'y' + \frac{5}{2}y'^2 = 8$$

$$8x'^2 + 2y'^2 = 8$$

$$\frac{x'^2}{1} + \frac{y'^2}{4} = 1$$

Ellipse; center at the origin,
major axis is the y'-axis, vertices at (0, ±2).

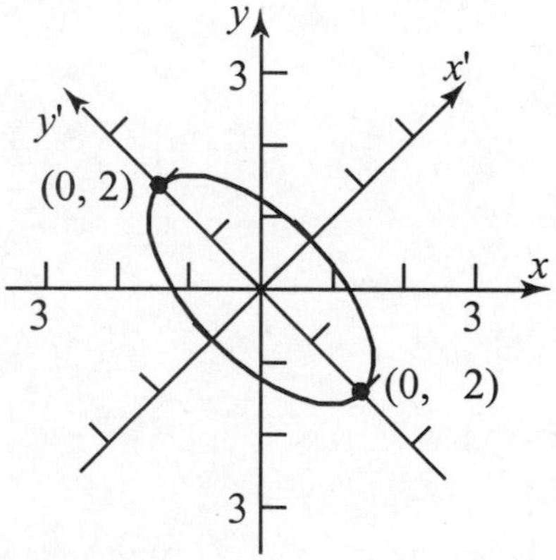

24. $3x^2 - 10xy + 3y^2 - 32 = 0; \quad \theta = 45°$ (see Problem 14)

$$3\left(\frac{\sqrt{2}}{2}(x'-y')\right)^2 - 10\left(\frac{\sqrt{2}}{2}(x'-y')\right)\left(\frac{\sqrt{2}}{2}(x'+y')\right) + 3\left(\frac{\sqrt{2}}{2}(x'+y')\right)^2 - 32 = 0$$

$$\frac{3}{2}\left(x'^2 - 2x'y' + y'^2\right) - 5\left(x'^2 - y'^2\right) + \frac{3}{2}\left(x'^2 + 2x'y' + y'^2\right) - 32 = 0$$

$$\frac{3}{2}x'^2 - 3x'y' + \frac{3}{2}y'^2 - 5x'^2 + 5y'^2 + \frac{3}{2}x'^2 + 3x'y' + \frac{3}{2}y'^2 = 32$$

$$-2x'^2 + 8y'^2 = 32$$

$$\frac{y'^2}{4} - \frac{x'^2}{16} = 1$$

Hyperbola; center at the origin,
transverse axis is the y'-axis, vertices at (0, ±2).

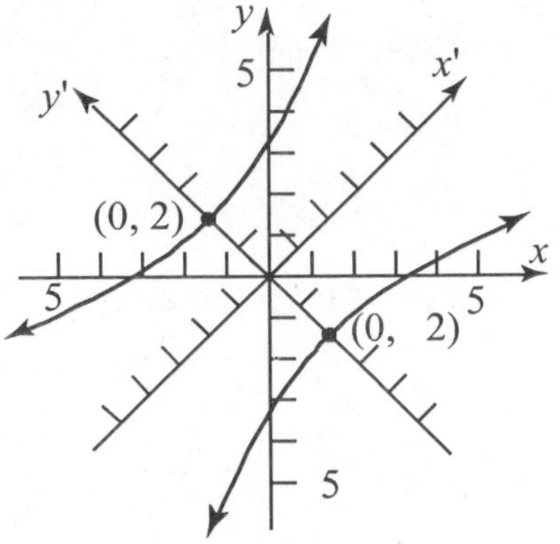

25. $13x^2 - 6\sqrt{3}\,xy + 7y^2 - 16 = 0;\quad \theta = 60^\circ$ (see Problem 15)

$$13\left(\frac{1}{2}(x' - \sqrt{3}y')\right)^2 - 6\sqrt{3}\left(\frac{1}{2}(x' - \sqrt{3}y')\right)\left(\frac{1}{2}(\sqrt{3}x' + y')\right) + 7\left(\frac{1}{2}(\sqrt{3}x' + y')\right)^2 - 16 = 0$$

$$\frac{13}{4}\left(x'^2 - 2\sqrt{3}x'y' + 3y'^2\right) - \frac{3\sqrt{3}}{2}\left(\sqrt{3}x'^2 - 2x'y' - \sqrt{3}y'^2\right) + \frac{7}{4}\left(3x'^2 + 2\sqrt{3}x'y' + y'^2\right) = 16$$

$$\frac{13}{4}x'^2 - \frac{13\sqrt{3}}{2}x'y' + \frac{39}{4}y'^2 - \frac{9}{2}x'^2 + 3\sqrt{3}x'y' + \frac{9}{2}y'^2 + \frac{21}{4}x'^2 + \frac{7\sqrt{3}}{2}x'y' + \frac{7}{4}y'^2 = 16$$

$$4x'^2 + 16y'^2 = 16$$

$$\frac{x'^2}{4} + \frac{y'^2}{1} = 1$$

Ellipse; center at the origin,
major axis is the x'-axis, vertices at (±2, 0).

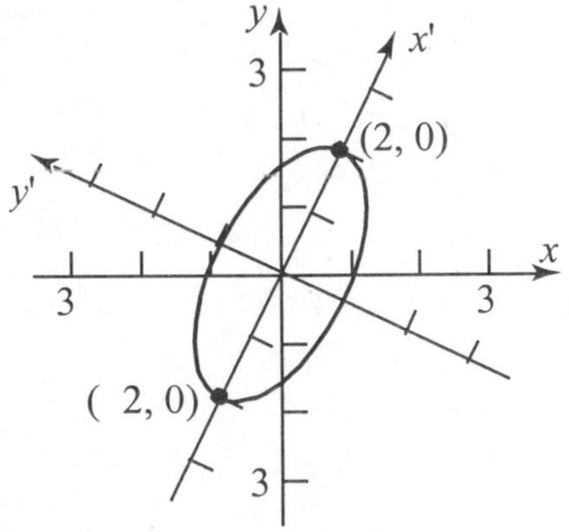

26. $11x^2 + 10\sqrt{3}\,xy + y^2 - 4 = 0;\quad \theta = 30^\circ$ (see Problem 16)

$$11\left(\frac{1}{2}(\sqrt{3}x' - y')\right)^2 + 10\sqrt{3}\left(\frac{1}{2}(\sqrt{3}x' - y')\right)\left(\frac{1}{2}(x' + \sqrt{3}y')\right) + \left(\frac{1}{2}(x' + \sqrt{3}y')\right)^2 - 4 = 0$$

$$\frac{11}{4}\left(3x'^2 - 2\sqrt{3}x'y' + y'^2\right) + \frac{5\sqrt{3}}{2}\left(\sqrt{3}x'^2 + 2x'y' - \sqrt{3}y'^2\right) + \frac{1}{4}\left(x'^2 + 2\sqrt{3}x'y' + 3y'^2\right) = 4$$

$$\frac{33}{4}x'^2 - \frac{11\sqrt{3}}{2}x'y' + \frac{11}{4}y'^2 + \frac{15}{2}x'^2 + 5\sqrt{3}x'y' - \frac{15}{2}y'^2 + \frac{1}{4}x'^2 + \frac{\sqrt{3}}{2}x'y' + \frac{3}{4}y'^2 = 4$$

$$16x'^2 - 4y'^2 = 4$$

$$4x'^2 - y'^2 = 1$$

Hyperbola; center at the origin,
transverse axis is the x'-axis, vertices at (±0.5, 0).

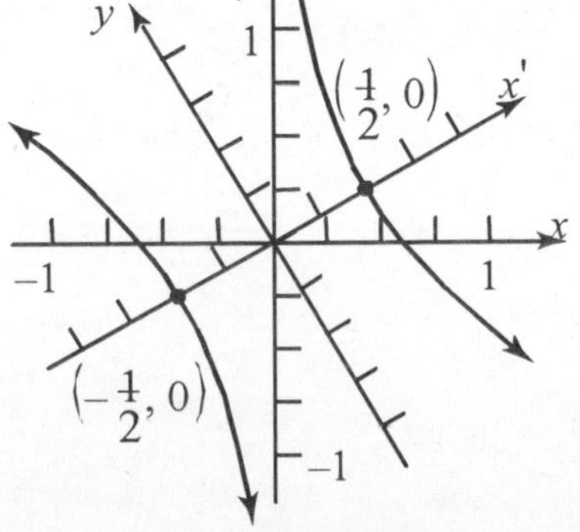

27. $4x^2 - 4xy + y^2 - 8\sqrt{5}\,x - 16\sqrt{5}\,y = 0$; $\theta = 63.4°$ (see Problem 17)

$$4\left(\frac{\sqrt{5}}{5}(x' - 2y')\right)^2 - 4\left(\frac{\sqrt{5}}{5}(x' - 2y')\right)\left(\frac{\sqrt{5}}{5}(2x' + y')\right) + \left(\frac{\sqrt{5}}{5}(2x' + y')\right)^2$$
$$- 8\sqrt{5}\left(\frac{\sqrt{5}}{5}(x' - 2y')\right) - 16\sqrt{5}\left(\frac{\sqrt{5}}{5}(2x' + y')\right) = 0$$

$$\frac{4}{5}\left(x'^2 - 4x'y' + 4y'^2\right) - \frac{4}{5}\left(2x'^2 - 3x'y' - 2y'^2\right) + \frac{1}{5}\left(4x'^2 + 4x'y' + y'^2\right)$$
$$- 8x' + 16y' - 32x' - 16y' = 0$$

$$\frac{4}{5}x'^2 - \frac{16}{5}x'y' + \frac{16}{5}y'^2 - \frac{8}{5}x'^2 + \frac{12}{5}x'y' + \frac{8}{5}y'^2 + \frac{4}{5}x'^2 + \frac{4}{5}x'y' + \frac{1}{5}y'^2 - 40x' = 0$$

$5y'^2 - 40x' = 0$

$y'^2 = 8x'$

Parabola; vertex at the origin, focus at (2, 0).

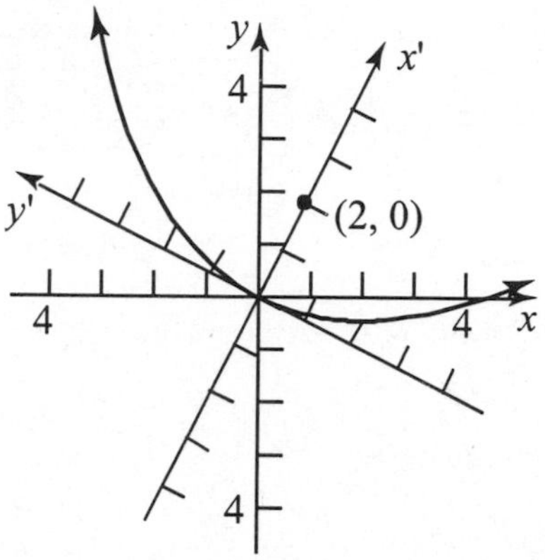

28. $x^2 + 4xy + 4y^2 + 5\sqrt{5}\,y + 5 = 0$; $\theta = 63.4°$ (see Problem 18)

$$\left(\frac{\sqrt{5}}{5}(x' - 2y')\right)^2 + 4\left(\frac{\sqrt{5}}{5}(x' - 2y')\right)\left(\frac{\sqrt{5}}{5}(2x' + y')\right) + 4\left(\frac{\sqrt{5}}{5}(2x' + y')\right)^2$$
$$+ 5\sqrt{5}\left(\frac{\sqrt{5}}{5}(2x' + y')\right) + 5 = 0$$

$$\frac{1}{5}\left(x'^2 - 4x'y' + 4y'^2\right) + \frac{4}{5}\left(2x'^2 - 3x'y' - 2y'^2\right) + \frac{4}{5}\left(4x'^2 + 4x'y' + y'^2\right)$$
$$+ 10x' + 5y' + 5 = 0$$

$$\frac{1}{5}x'^2 - \frac{4}{5}x'y' + \frac{4}{5}y'^2 + \frac{8}{5}x'^2 - \frac{12}{5}x'y' - \frac{8}{5}y'^2 + \frac{16}{5}x'^2 + \frac{16}{5}x'y' + \frac{4}{5}y'^2 + 10x' + 5y' + 5 = 0$$

$5x'^2 + 10x' + 5y' + 5 = 0$

$x'^2 + 2x' + 1 = -y' - 1 + 1$

$y' = -(x' + 1)^2$

Parabola; vertex at (–1, 0),
axis of symmetry parallel to the y'-axis.

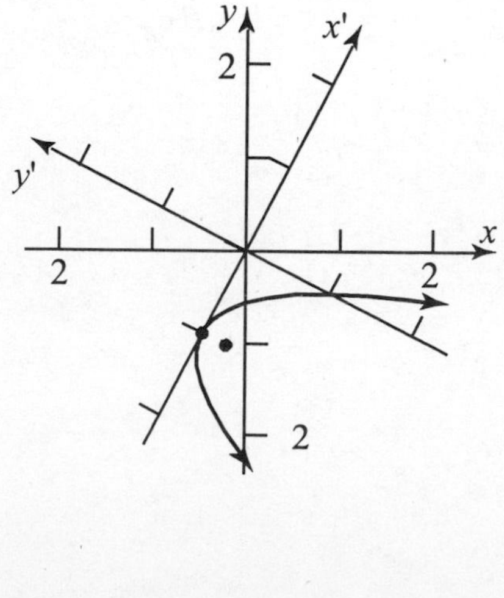

29. $25x^2 - 36xy + 40y^2 - 12\sqrt{13}x - 8\sqrt{13}y = 0$; $\theta \approx 33.7°$ (see Problem 19)

$$25\left(\frac{\sqrt{13}}{13}(3x'-2y')\right)^2 - 36\left(\frac{\sqrt{13}}{13}(3x'-2y')\right)\left(\frac{\sqrt{13}}{13}(2x'+3y')\right) + 40\left(\frac{\sqrt{13}}{13}(2x'+3y')\right)^2$$
$$-12\sqrt{13}\left(\frac{\sqrt{13}}{13}(3x'-2y')\right) - 8\sqrt{13}\left(\frac{\sqrt{13}}{13}(2x'+3y')\right) = 0$$

$$\frac{25}{13}\left(9x'^2 - 12x'y' + 4y'^2\right) - \frac{36}{13}\left(6x'^2 + 5x'y' - 6y'^2\right) + \frac{40}{13}\left(4x'^2 + 12x'y' + 9y'^2\right)$$
$$-36x' + 24y' - 16x' - 24y' = 0$$

$$\frac{225}{13}x'^2 - \frac{300}{13}x'y' + \frac{100}{13}y'^2 - \frac{216}{13}x'^2 - \frac{180}{13}x'y' + \frac{216}{13}y'^2$$
$$+\frac{160}{13}x'^2 + \frac{480}{13}x'y' + \frac{360}{13}y'^2 - 52x' = 0$$

$13x'^2 + 52y'^2 - 52x' = 0$

$x'^2 - 4x' + 4y'^2 = 0$

$(x'-2)^2 + 4y'^2 = 4$

$\frac{(x'-2)^2}{4} + \frac{y'^2}{1} = 1$

Ellipse; center at (2, 0),
major axis is the x'-axis, vertices at (4, 0) and (0, 0).

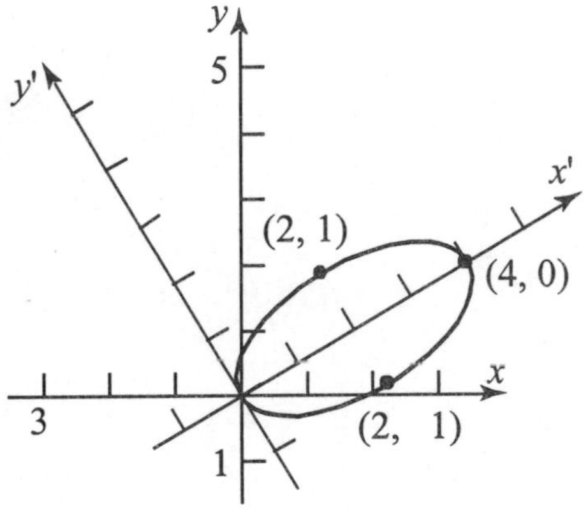

30. $34x^2 - 24xy + 41y^2 - 25 = 0$; $\theta \approx 36.9°$ (see Problem 20)

$$34\left(\frac{1}{5}(4x'-3y')\right)^2 - 24\left(\frac{1}{5}(4x'-3y')\right)\left(\frac{1}{5}(3x'+4y')\right) + 41\left(\frac{1}{5}(3x'+4y')\right)^2 - 25 = 0$$

$$\frac{34}{25}\left(16x'^2 - 24x'y' + 9y'^2\right) - \frac{24}{25}\left(12x'^2 + 7x'y' - 12y'^2\right) + \frac{41}{25}\left(9x'^2 + 24x'y' + 16y'^2\right) = 25$$

$$\frac{544}{25}x'^2 - \frac{816}{25}x'y' + \frac{306}{25}y'^2 - \frac{288}{25}x'^2 - \frac{168}{25}x'y' + \frac{288}{25}y'^2$$
$$+\frac{369}{25}x'^2 + \frac{984}{25}x'y' + \frac{656}{25}y'^2 = 25$$

$25x'^2 + 50y'^2 = 25$

$x'^2 + 2y'^2 = 1$

Ellipse; center at the origin,
major axis is the x'-axis, vertices at (±1, 0).

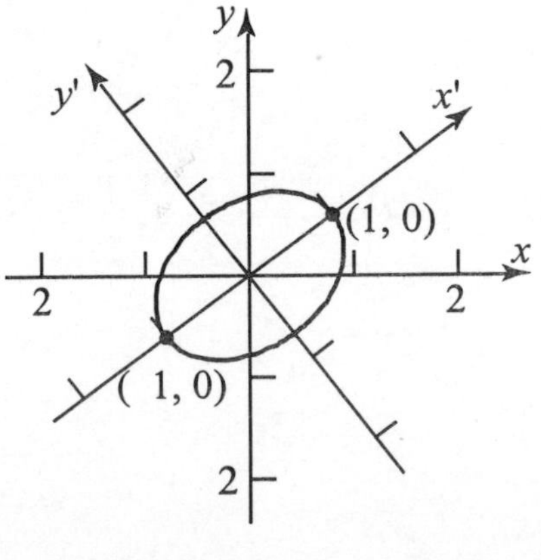

31. $16x^2 + 24xy + 9y^2 - 130x + 90y = 0$

$A = 16, B = 24,$ and $C = 9;$ $\cot(2\theta) = \frac{A-C}{B} = \frac{16-9}{24} = \frac{7}{24} \rightarrow \cos(2\theta) = \frac{7}{25}$

$\sin\theta = \sqrt{\frac{\left(1-\frac{7}{25}\right)}{2}} = \sqrt{\frac{9}{25}} = \frac{3}{5};\quad \cos\theta = \sqrt{\frac{\left(1+\frac{7}{25}\right)}{2}} = \sqrt{\frac{16}{25}} = \frac{4}{5} \rightarrow \theta \approx 36.9°$

$x = x'\cos\theta - y'\sin\theta = \frac{4}{5}x' - \frac{3}{5}y' = \frac{1}{5}(4x' - 3y')$

$y = x'\sin\theta + y'\cos\theta = \frac{3}{5}x' + \frac{4}{5}y' = \frac{1}{5}(3x' + 4y')$

$$16\left(\frac{1}{5}(4x' - 3y')\right)^2 + 24\left(\frac{1}{5}(4x' - 3y')\right)\left(\frac{1}{5}(3x' + 4y')\right) + 9\left(\frac{1}{5}(3x' + 4y')\right)^2$$
$$-130\left(\frac{1}{5}(4x' - 3y')\right) + 90\left(\frac{1}{5}(3x' + 4y')\right) = 0$$

$$\frac{16}{25}(16x'^2 - 24x'y' + 9y'^2) + \frac{24}{25}(12x'^2 + 7x'y' - 12y'^2) + \frac{9}{25}(9x'^2 + 24x'y' + 16y'^2)$$
$$-104x' + 78y' + 54x' + 72y' = 0$$

$$\frac{256}{25}x'^2 - \frac{384}{25}x'y' + \frac{144}{25}y'^2 + \frac{288}{25}x'^2 + \frac{168}{25}x'y' - \frac{288}{25}y'^2$$
$$+\frac{81}{25}x'^2 + \frac{216}{25}x'y' + \frac{144}{25}y'^2 - 50x' + 150y' = 0$$

$25x'^2 - 50x' + 150y' = 0$

$x'^2 - 2x' = -6y'$

$(x' - 1)^2 = -6y' + 1$

$(x' - 1)^2 = -6\left(y' - \frac{1}{6}\right)$

Parabola; vertex at $\left(1, \frac{1}{6}\right)$, focus at $\left(1, -\frac{4}{3}\right)$.

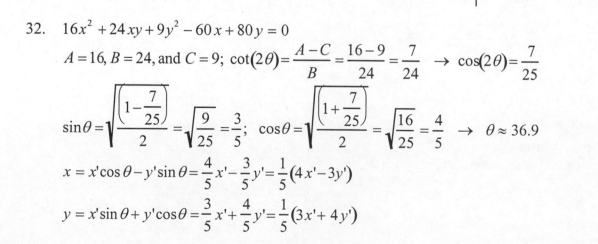

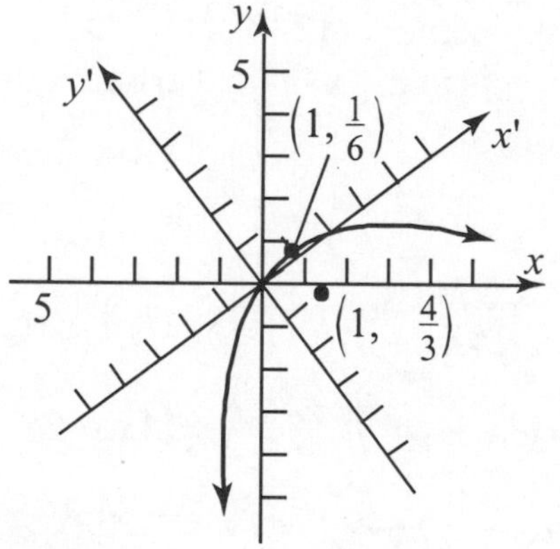

32. $16x^2 + 24xy + 9y^2 - 60x + 80y = 0$

$A = 16, B = 24,$ and $C = 9;$ $\cot(2\theta) = \frac{A-C}{B} = \frac{16-9}{24} = \frac{7}{24} \rightarrow \cos(2\theta) = \frac{7}{25}$

$\sin\theta = \sqrt{\frac{\left(1-\frac{7}{25}\right)}{2}} = \sqrt{\frac{9}{25}} = \frac{3}{5};\quad \cos\theta = \sqrt{\frac{\left(1+\frac{7}{25}\right)}{2}} = \sqrt{\frac{16}{25}} = \frac{4}{5} \rightarrow \theta \approx 36.9$

$x = x'\cos\theta - y'\sin\theta = \frac{4}{5}x' - \frac{3}{5}y' = \frac{1}{5}(4x' - 3y')$

$y = x'\sin\theta + y'\cos\theta = \frac{3}{5}x' + \frac{4}{5}y' = \frac{1}{5}(3x' + 4y')$

$$16\left(\frac{1}{5}(4x'-3y')\right)^2+24\left(\frac{1}{5}(4x'-3y')\right)\left(\frac{1}{5}(3x'+4y')\right)+9\left(\frac{1}{5}(3x'+4y')\right)^2$$
$$-60\left(\frac{1}{5}(4x'-3y')\right)+80\left(\frac{1}{5}(3x'+4y')\right)=0$$

$$\frac{16}{25}\left(16x'^2-24x'y'+9y'^2\right)+\frac{24}{25}\left(12x'^2+7x'y'-12y'^2\right)+\frac{9}{25}\left(9x'^2+24x'y'+16y'^2\right)$$
$$-48x'+36y'+48x'+64y'=0$$

$$\frac{256}{25}x'^2-\frac{384}{25}x'y'+\frac{144}{25}y'^2+\frac{288}{25}x'^2+\frac{168}{25}x'y'-\frac{288}{25}y'^2$$
$$+\frac{81}{25}x'^2+\frac{216}{25}x'y'+\frac{144}{25}y'^2+100y'=0$$

$25x'^2+100y'=0$

$x'^2=-4y'$

Parabola; vertex at (0, 0), focus at (0, –1).

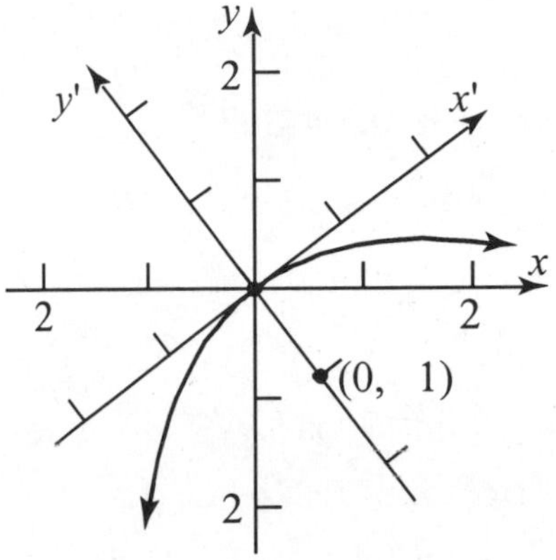

33. $A=1.\ B=3,\ C=-2 \quad B^2-4AC=3^2-4(1)(-2)=17>0$; hyperbola

34. $A=2.\ B=-3,\ C=4 \quad B^2-4AC=(-3)^2-4(2)(4)=-23<0$; ellipse

35. $A=1.\ B=-7,\ C=3 \quad B^2-4AC=(-7)^2-4(1)(3)=37>0$; hyperbola

36. $A=2.\ B=-3,\ C=2 \quad B^2-4AC=(-3)^2-4(2)(2)=-7<0$; ellipse

37. $A=9.\ B=12,\ C=4 \quad B^2-4AC=12^2-4(9)(4)=0$; parabola

38. $A=10.\ B=12,\ C=4 \quad B^2-4AC=12^2-4(10)(4)=-16<0$; ellipse

39. $A=10.\ B=-12,\ C=4 \quad B^2-4AC=(-12)^2-4(10)(4)=-16<0$; ellipse

40. $A=4.\ B=12,\ C=9 \quad B^2-4AC=12^2-4(4)(9)=0$; parabola

41. $A=3.\ B=-2,\ C=1 \quad B^2-4AC=(-2)^2-4(3)(1)=-8<0$; ellipse

42. $A=3.\ B=2,\ C=1 \quad B^2-4AC=2^2-4(3)(1)=-8<0$; ellipse

43. See equation 6 on page 770.

$A' = A\cos^2\theta + B\sin\theta\cos\theta + C\sin^2\theta$

$B' = B(\cos^2\theta - \sin^2\theta) + 2(C - A)(\sin\theta\cos\theta)$

$C' = A\sin^2\theta - B\sin\theta\cos\theta + C\cos^2\theta$

$D' = D\cos\theta + E\sin\theta$

$E' = -D\sin\theta + E\cos\theta$

$F' = F$

44. $A' + C' = \left(A\cos^2\theta + B\sin\theta\cos\theta + C\sin^2\theta\right) + \left(A\sin^2\theta - B\sin\theta\cos\theta + C\cos^2\theta\right)$

$= A\left(\cos^2\theta + \sin^2\theta\right) + C\left(\sin^2\theta + \cos^2\theta\right) = A(1) + C(1) = A + C$

45. $B'^2 - 4A'C'$

$= \left[B(\cos^2\theta - \sin^2\theta) + 2(C - A)\sin\theta\cos\theta\right]^2$

$\quad - 4\left(A\cos^2\theta + B\sin\theta\cos\theta + C\sin^2\theta\right)\left(A\sin^2\theta - B\sin\theta\cos\theta + C\cos^2\theta\right)$

$= B^2\left(\cos^4\theta - 2\cos^2\theta\sin^2\theta + \sin^4\theta\right) + 4B(C - A)\sin\theta\cos\theta(\cos^2\theta - \sin^2\theta)$

$\quad + 4(C - A)^2\sin^2\theta\cos^2\theta - 4\left[A^2\sin^2\theta\cos^2\theta - AB\sin\theta\cos^3\theta + AC\cos^4\theta\right.$

$\quad + AB\sin^3\theta\cos\theta - B^2\sin^2\theta\cos^2\theta + BC\sin\theta\cos^3\theta + AC\sin^4\theta$

$\quad \left. - BC\sin^3\theta\cos\theta + C^2\sin^2\theta\cos^2\theta\right]$

$= B^2\left(\cos^4\theta - 2\cos^2\theta\sin^2\theta + \sin^4\theta + 4\sin^2\theta\cos^2\theta\right)$

$\quad + BC\left(4\sin\theta\cos\theta(\cos^2\theta - \sin^2\theta) - 4\sin\theta\cos^3\theta + 4\sin^3\theta\cos\theta\right)$

$\quad - AB\left(4\sin\theta\cos\theta(\cos^2\theta - \sin^2\theta) - 4\sin\theta\cos^3\theta + 4\sin^3\theta\cos\theta\right)$

$\quad + 4C^2\left(\sin^2\theta\cos^2\theta - \sin^2\theta\cos^2\theta\right) - 4AC\left(2\sin^2\theta\cos^2\theta + \cos^4\theta + \sin^4\theta\right)$

$\quad + 4A^2\left(\sin^2\theta\cos^2\theta - \sin^2\theta\cos^2\theta\right)$

$= B^2\left(\cos^4\theta + 2\sin^2\theta\cos^2\theta + \sin^4\theta\right) - 4AC\left(\cos^4\theta + 2\sin^2\theta\cos^2\theta + \sin^4\theta\right)$

$= B^2\left(\cos^2\theta + \sin^2\theta\right)^2 - 4AC\left(\cos^2\theta + \sin^2\theta\right)^2 = B^2 - 4AC$

46. Since $B^2 - 4AC = B'^2 - 4A'C'$ for any rotation θ (Problem 45), choose θ so that $B' = 0$. Then $B^2 - 4AC = -4A'C'$.

(a) If $B^2 - 4AC = -4A'C' = 0$ then $A'C' = 0$. Using the theorem for identifying conics without completing the square, the equation is a parabola.

(b) If $B^2 - 4AC = -4A'C' < 0$ then $A'C' > 0$. Thus, the equation is an ellipse (or circle).

(c) If $B^2 - 4AC = -4A'C' > 0$ then $A'C' < 0$. Thus, the equation is a hyperbola.

47. $d^2 = (y_2 - y_1)^2 + (x_2 - x_1)^2$

$= (x_2'\sin\theta + y_2'\cos\theta - x_1'\sin\theta - y_1'\cos\theta)^2$

$\quad + (x_2'\cos\theta - y_2'\sin\theta - x_1'\cos\theta + y_1'\sin\theta)^2$

$$= \left((x_2'-x_1')\sin\theta + (y_2'-y_1')\cos\theta\right)^2 + \left((x_2'-x_1')\cos\theta - (y_2'-y_1')\sin\theta\right)^2$$
$$= (x_2'-x_1')^2\sin^2\theta + 2(x_2'-x_1')(y_2'-y_1')\sin\theta\cos\theta + (y_2'-y_1')^2\cos^2\theta$$
$$+ (x_2'-x_1')^2\cos^2\theta - 2(x_2'-x_1')(y_2'-y_1')\sin\theta\cos\theta + (y_2'-y_1')^2\sin^2\theta$$
$$= (x_2'-x_1')^2\sin^2\theta + (x_2'-x_1')^2\cos^2\theta + (y_2'-y_1')^2\cos^2\theta + (y_2'-y_1')^2\sin^2\theta$$
$$= (x_2'-x_1')^2 + (y_2'-y_1')^2$$

48. $x^{1/2} + y^{1/2} = a^{1/2}$

$$y^{1/2} = a^{1/2} - x^{1/2} \rightarrow y = \left(a^{1/2} - x^{1/2}\right)^2 \rightarrow y = a - 2a^{1/2}x^{1/2} + x$$
$$2a^{1/2}x^{1/2} = (a+x) - y \rightarrow 4ax = (a+x)^2 - 2y(a+x) + y^2$$
$$4ax = a^2 + 2ax + x^2 - 2ay - 2xy + y^2 \rightarrow 0 = x^2 - 2xy + y^2 - 2ax - 2ay + a^2$$
$$B^2 - 4AC = (-2)^2 - 4(1)(1) = 4 - 4 = 0$$

The equation is a parabola

Analytic Geometry

11.6 Polar Equations of Conics

1. $e = 1$; $p = 1$; parabola; directrix is perpendicular to the polar axis and 1 unit to the right of the pole.

2. $e = 1$; $p = 3$; parabola; directrix is parallel to the polar axis and 3 units below the pole.

3. $$r = \frac{4}{2 - 3\sin\theta} = \frac{4}{2\left(1 - \frac{3}{2}\sin\theta\right)} = \frac{2}{\left(1 - \frac{3}{2}\sin\theta\right)};\quad ep = 2,\ e = \frac{3}{2};\ p = \frac{4}{3}$$

   Hyperbola; directrix is parallel to the polar axis and $\frac{4}{3}$ units below the pole.

4. $r = \frac{2}{1 + 2\cos\theta}$; $ep = 2$, $e = 2$; $p = 1$

   Hyperbola; directrix is perpendicular to the polar axis and 1 unit to the right of the pole.

5. $$r = \frac{3}{4 - 2\cos\theta} = \frac{3}{4\left(1 - \frac{1}{2}\cos\theta\right)} = \frac{\left(\frac{3}{4}\right)}{\left(1 - \frac{1}{2}\cos\theta\right)};\quad ep = \frac{3}{4},\ e = \frac{1}{2};\ p = \frac{3}{2}$$

   Ellipse; directrix is perpendicular to the polar axis and $\frac{3}{2}$ units to the left of the pole.

6. $$r = \frac{6}{8 + 2\sin\theta} = \frac{6}{8\left(1 + \frac{1}{4}\sin\theta\right)} = \frac{\left(\frac{3}{4}\right)}{\left(1 + \frac{1}{4}\sin\theta\right)};\quad ep = \frac{3}{4},\ e = \frac{1}{4};\ p = 3$$

   Ellipse; directrix is parallel to the polar axis and 3 units above the pole.

7. $r = \dfrac{1}{1+\cos\theta}$

$ep = 1,\ e = 1,\ p = 1$
Parabola; directrix is perpendicular to the polar axis 1 unit to the right of the pole; vertex is $\left(\dfrac{1}{2}, 0\right)$.

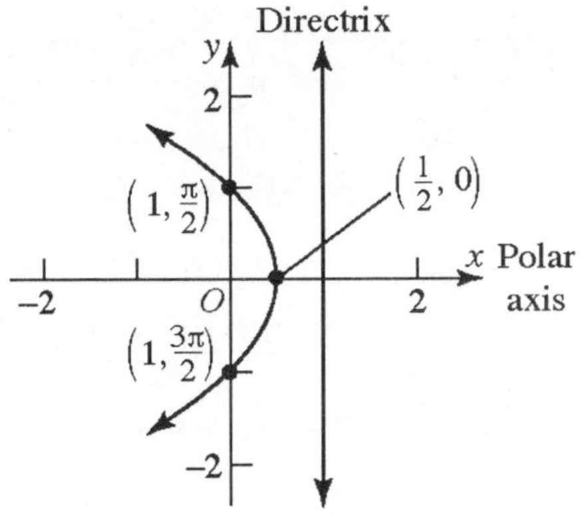

8. $r = \dfrac{3}{1-\sin\theta}$

$ep = 3,\ e = 1,\ p = 3$
Parabola; directrix is parallel to the polar axis 3 units below the pole; vertex is $\left(\dfrac{3}{2}, \dfrac{3\pi}{2}\right)$.

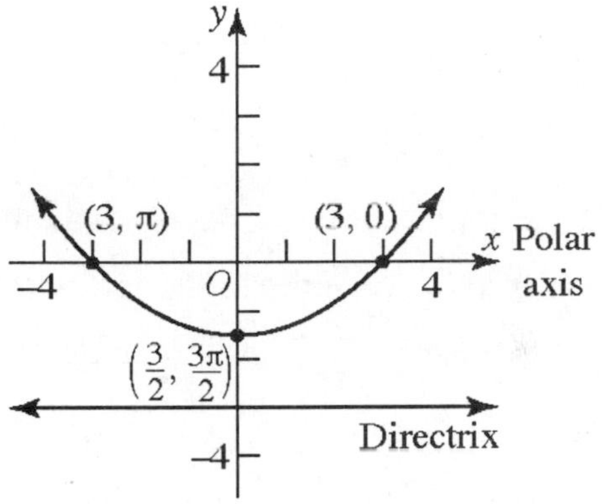

9. $r = \dfrac{8}{4+3\sin\theta}$

$$r = \frac{8}{4\left(1+\frac{3}{4}\sin\theta\right)} = \frac{2}{\left(1+\frac{3}{4}\sin\theta\right)}$$

$ep = 2,\ e = \dfrac{3}{4},\ p = \dfrac{8}{3}$
Ellipse; directrix is parallel to the polar axis $\dfrac{8}{3}$ units above the pole; vertices are $\left(\dfrac{8}{7}, \dfrac{\pi}{2}\right)$ and $\left(8, \dfrac{3\pi}{2}\right)$.

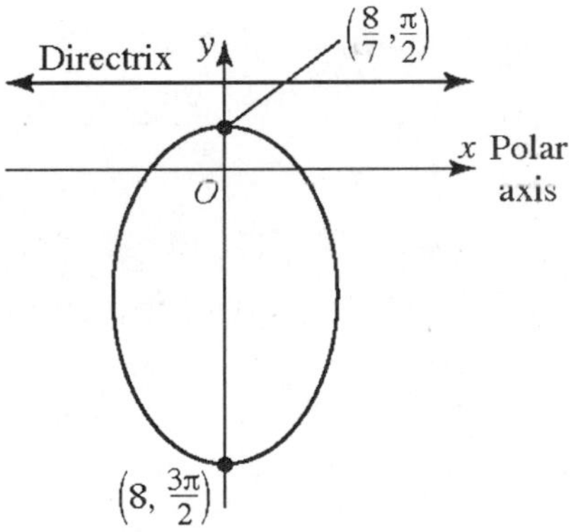

10. $r = \dfrac{10}{5 + 4\cos\theta}$

$r = \dfrac{10}{5\left(1 + \frac{4}{5}\cos\theta\right)} = \dfrac{2}{1 + \frac{4}{5}\cos\theta}$

$ep = 2,\ e = \frac{4}{5},\ p = \frac{5}{2}$

Ellipse; directrix is perpendicular to the polar axis $\frac{5}{2}$ units to the right of the pole; vertices are $\left(\frac{10}{9}, 0\right)$ and $(10, \pi)$.

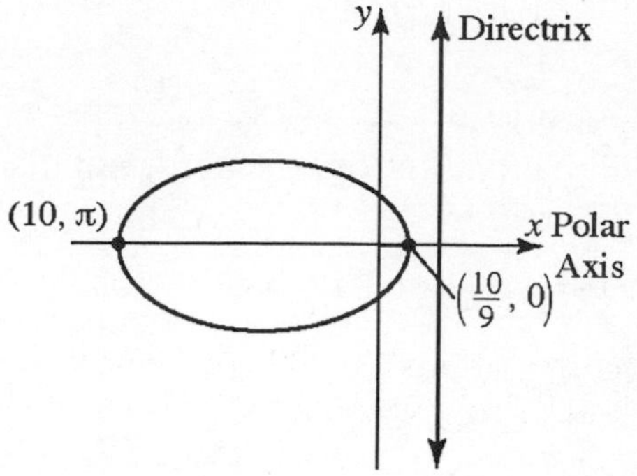

11. $r = \dfrac{9}{3 - 6\cos\theta}$

$r = \dfrac{9}{3(1 - 2\cos\theta)} = \dfrac{3}{1 - 2\cos\theta}$

$ep = 3,\ e = 2,\ p = \frac{3}{2}$

Hyperbola; directrix is perpendicular to the polar axis $\frac{3}{2}$ units to the left of the pole; vertices are $(-3, 0)$ and $(1, \pi)$.

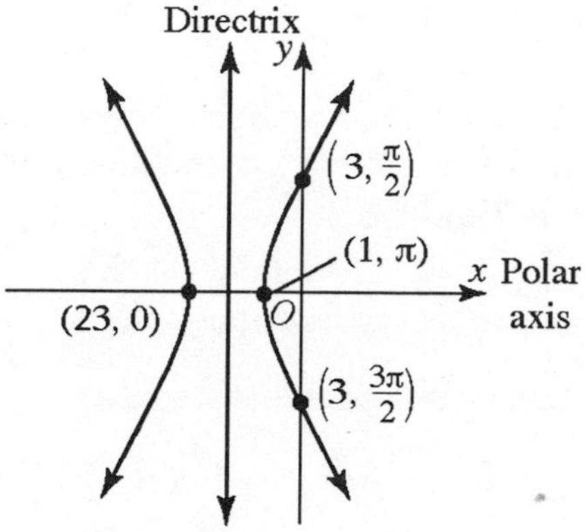

12. $r = \dfrac{12}{4 + 8\sin\theta}$

$r = \dfrac{12}{4(1 + 2\sin\theta)} = \dfrac{3}{1 + 2\sin\theta}$

$ep = 3,\ e = 2,\ p = \frac{3}{2}$

Hyperbola; directrix is parallel to the polar axis $\frac{3}{2}$ units above the pole; vertices are $\left(1, \frac{\pi}{2}\right)$ and $\left(-3, \frac{3\pi}{2}\right)$.

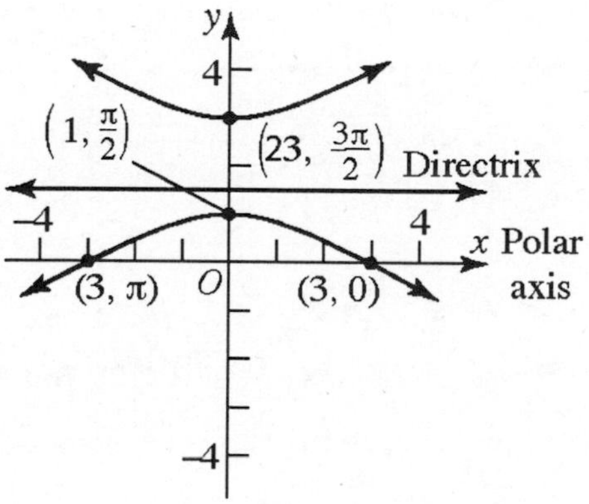

13. $r=\dfrac{8}{2-\sin\theta}$

$$r=\frac{8}{2\left(1-\frac{1}{2}\sin\theta\right)}=\frac{4}{1-\frac{1}{2}\sin\theta}$$

$ep=4,\ e=\frac{1}{2},\ p=8$

Ellipse; directrix is parallel to the polar axis 8 units below the pole; vertices are $\left(8,\frac{\pi}{2}\right)$ and $\left(\frac{8}{3},\frac{3\pi}{2}\right)$.

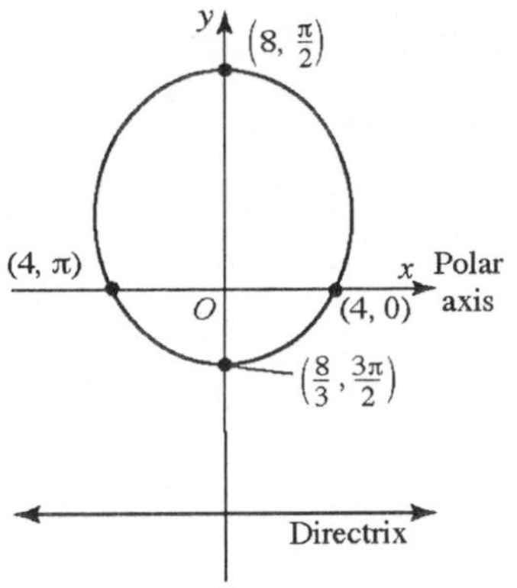

14. $r=\dfrac{8}{2+4\cos\theta}$

$$r=\frac{8}{2(1+2\cos\theta)}=\frac{4}{1+2\cos\theta}$$

$ep=4,\ e=2,\ p=2$

Hyperbola; directrix is perpendicular to the polar axis 2 units to the right of the pole; vertices are $\left(\frac{4}{3},0\right)$ and $(-4,\pi)$.

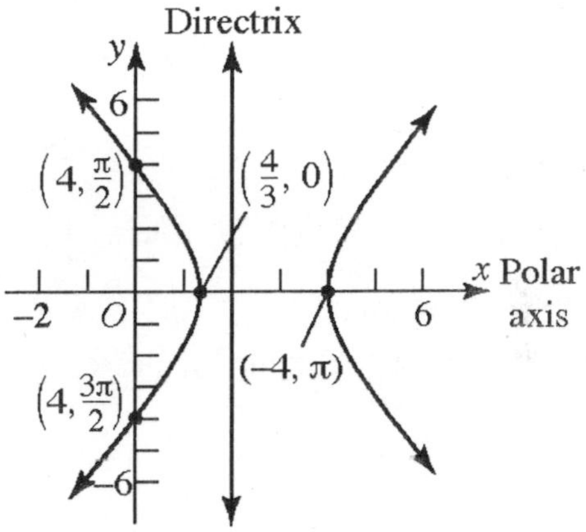

15. $r(3-2\sin\theta)=6 \;\rightarrow\; r=\dfrac{6}{3-2\sin\theta}$

$$r=\frac{6}{3\left(1-\frac{2}{3}\sin\theta\right)}=\frac{2}{1-\frac{2}{3}\sin\theta}$$

$ep=2,\ e=\frac{2}{3},\ p=3$

Ellipse; directrix is parallel to the polar axis 3 units below the pole; vertices are $\left(6,\frac{\pi}{2}\right)$ and $\left(\frac{6}{5},\frac{3\pi}{2}\right)$.

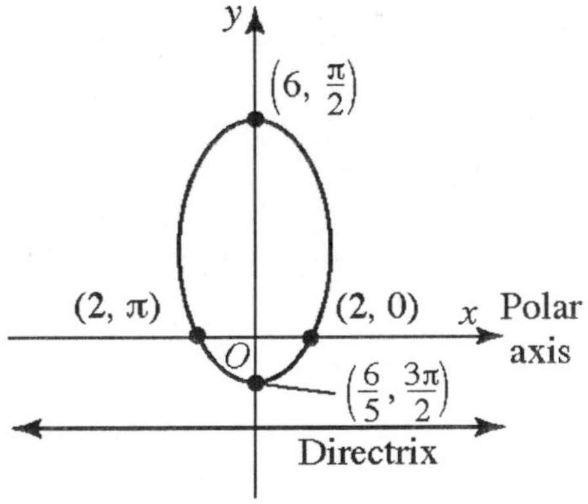

16. $r(2-\cos\theta)=2 \rightarrow r=\dfrac{2}{2-\cos\theta}$

$$r=\frac{2}{2\left(1-\frac{1}{2}\cos\theta\right)}=\frac{1}{\left(1-\frac{1}{2}\cos\theta\right)}$$

$ep=1,\ e=\dfrac{1}{2},\ p=2$

Ellipse; directrix is perpendicular to the polar axis 2 units to the left of the pole; vertices are $(2, 0)$ and $\left(\dfrac{2}{3}, \pi\right)$.

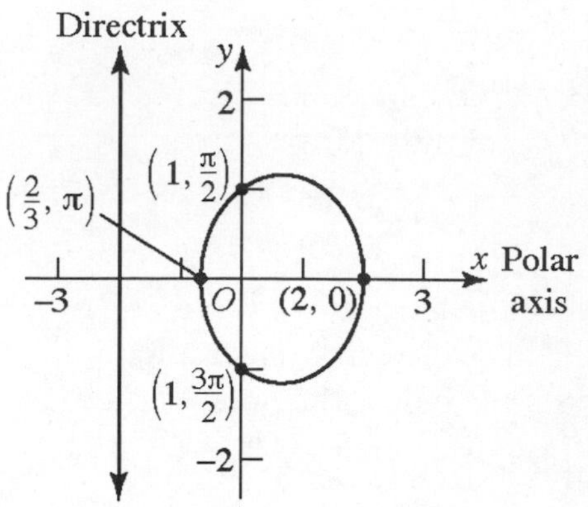

17. $r=\dfrac{6\sec\theta}{2\sec\theta-1}=\dfrac{6}{2-\cos\theta}$

$$r=\frac{6}{2\left(1-\frac{1}{2}\cos\theta\right)}=\frac{3}{1-\frac{1}{2}\cos\theta}$$

$ep=3,\ e=\dfrac{1}{2},\ p=6$

Ellipse; directrix is perpendicular to the polar axis 6 units to the left of the pole; vertices are $(6, 0)$ and $(2, \pi)$.

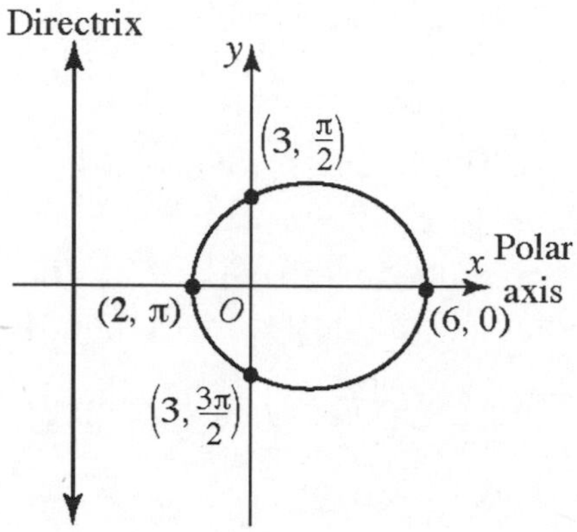

18. $r=\dfrac{3\csc\theta}{\csc\theta-1}=\dfrac{3}{1-\sin\theta}$

$ep=3,\ e=1,\ p=3$

Parabola; directrix is parallel to the polar axis 3 units below the pole; vertex is $\left(\dfrac{3}{2}, \dfrac{3\pi}{2}\right)$.

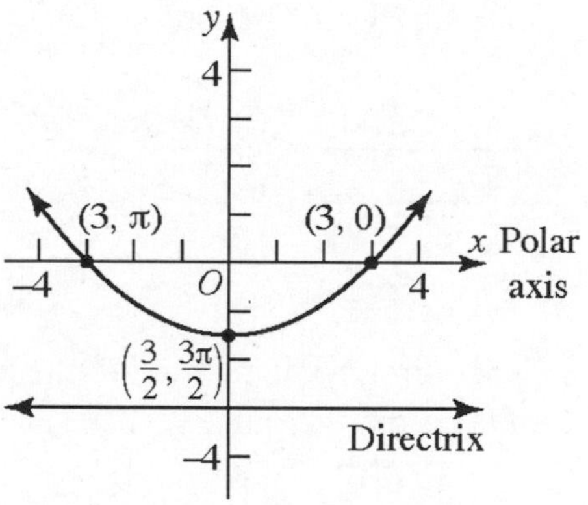

19.
$$\begin{aligned}
r&=\frac{1}{1+\cos\theta}\\
r+r\cos\theta&=1\\
r&=1-r\cos\theta\\
r^2&=(1-r\cos\theta)^2\\
x^2+y^2&=(1-x)^2\\
x^2+y^2&=1-2x+x^2\\
y^2+2x-1&=0
\end{aligned}$$

20.
$$\begin{aligned}
r&=\frac{3}{1-\sin\theta}\\
r-r\sin\theta&=3\\
r&=3+r\sin\theta\\
r^2&=(3+r\sin\theta)^2\\
x^2+y^2&=(3+y)^2\\
x^2+y^2&=9+6y+y^2\\
x^2-6y-9&=0
\end{aligned}$$

21. $r = \dfrac{8}{4 + 3\sin\theta}$

$$\begin{aligned} 4r + 3r\sin\theta &= 8 \\ 4r &= 8 - 3r\sin\theta \\ 16r^2 &= (8 - 3r\sin\theta)^2 \\ 16(x^2 + y^2) &= (8 - 3y)^2 \\ 16x^2 + 16y^2 &= 64 - 48y + 9y^2 \\ 16x^2 + 7y^2 + 48y - 64 &= 0 \end{aligned}$$

22. $r = \dfrac{10}{5 + 4\cos\theta}$

$$\begin{aligned} 5r + 4r\cos\theta &= 10 \\ 5r &= 10 - 4r\cos\theta \\ 25r^2 &= (10 - 4r\cos\theta)^2 \\ 25(x^2 + y^2) &= (10 - 4x)^2 \\ 25x^2 + 25y^2 &= 100 - 80x + 16x^2 \\ 9x^2 + 25y^2 + 80x - 100 &= 0 \end{aligned}$$

23. $r = \dfrac{9}{3 - 6\cos\theta}$

$$\begin{aligned} 3r - 6r\cos\theta &= 9 \\ 3r &= 9 + 6r\cos\theta \\ r &= 3 + 2r\cos\theta \\ r^2 &= (3 + 2r\cos\theta)^2 \\ x^2 + y^2 &= (3 + 2x)^2 \\ x^2 + y^2 &= 9 + 12x + 4x^2 \\ 3x^2 - y^2 + 12x + 9 &= 0 \end{aligned}$$

24. $r = \dfrac{12}{4 + 8\sin\theta}$

$$\begin{aligned} 4r + 8r\sin\theta &= 12 \\ 4r &= 12 - 8r\sin\theta \\ r &= 3 - 2r\sin\theta \\ r^2 &= (3 - 2r\sin\theta)^2 \\ x^2 + y^2 &= (3 - 2y)^2 \\ x^2 + y^2 &= 9 - 12y + 4y^2 \\ x^2 - 3y^2 + 12y - 9 &= 0 \end{aligned}$$

25. $r = \dfrac{8}{2 - \sin\theta}$

$$\begin{aligned} 2r - r\sin\theta &= 8 \\ 2r &= 8 + r\sin\theta \\ 4r^2 &= (8 + r\sin\theta)^2 \\ 4(x^2 + y^2) &= (8 + y)^2 \\ 4x^2 + 4y^2 &= 64 + 16y + y^2 \\ 4x^2 + 3y^2 - 16y - 64 &= 0 \end{aligned}$$

26. $r = \dfrac{8}{2 + 4\cos\theta}$

$$\begin{aligned} 2r + 4r\cos\theta &= 8 \\ 2r &= 8 - 4r\cos\theta \\ r &= 4 - 2r\cos\theta \\ r^2 &= (4 - 2r\cos\theta)^2 \\ x^2 + y^2 &= (4 - 2x)^2 \\ x^2 + y^2 &= 16 - 16x + 4x^2 \\ 3x^2 - y^2 - 16x + 16 &= 0 \end{aligned}$$

27. $r(3 - 2\sin\theta) = 6$

$$\begin{aligned} 3r - 2r\sin\theta &= 6 \\ 3r &= 6 + 2r\sin\theta \\ 9r^2 &= (6 + 2r\sin\theta)^2 \\ 9(x^2 + y^2) &= (6 + 2y)^2 \\ 9x^2 + 9y^2 &= 36 + 24y + 4y^2 \\ 9x^2 + 5y^2 - 24y - 36 &= 0 \end{aligned}$$

28. $r(2 - \cos\theta) = 2$

$$\begin{aligned} 2r - r\cos\theta &= 2 \\ 2r &= 2 + r\cos\theta \\ 4r^2 &= (2 + r\cos\theta)^2 \\ 4(x^2 + y^2) &= (2 + x)^2 \\ 4x^2 + 4y^2 &= 4 + 4x + x^2 \\ 3x^2 + 4y^2 - 4x - 4 &= 0 \end{aligned}$$

29. $r = \dfrac{6\sec\theta}{2\sec\theta - 1}$

$$r = \frac{6}{2-\cos\theta}$$
$$2r - r\cos\theta = 6$$
$$2r = 6 + r\cos\theta$$
$$4r^2 = (6 + r\cos\theta)^2$$
$$4(x^2+y^2) = (6+x)^2$$
$$4x^2 + 4y^2 = 36 + 12x + x^2$$
$$3x^2 + 4y^2 - 12x - 36 = 0$$

30. $r = \dfrac{3\csc\theta}{\csc\theta - 1}$

$$r = \frac{3}{1-\sin\theta}$$
$$r - r\sin\theta = 3$$
$$r = 3 + r\sin\theta$$
$$r^2 = (3 + r\sin\theta)^2$$
$$x^2 + y^2 = (3+y)^2$$
$$x^2 + y^2 = 9 + 6y + y^2$$
$$x^2 - 6y - 9 = 0$$

31. $r = \dfrac{ep}{1+e\sin\theta}$

$e = 1;\quad p = 1$

$$r = \frac{1}{1+\sin\theta}$$

32. $r = \dfrac{ep}{1-e\sin\theta}$

$e = 1;\quad p = 2$

$$r = \frac{2}{1-\sin\theta}$$

33. $r = \dfrac{ep}{1-e\cos\theta}$

$e = \frac{4}{5};\quad p = 3$

$$r = \frac{\left(\frac{12}{5}\right)}{\left(1 - \frac{4}{5}\cos\theta\right)} = \frac{12}{5 - 4\cos\theta}$$

34. $r = \dfrac{ep}{1+e\sin\theta}$

$e = \frac{2}{3};\quad p = 3$

$$r = \frac{2}{\left(1 + \frac{2}{3}\sin\theta\right)} = \frac{6}{3 + 2\sin\theta}$$

35. $r = \dfrac{ep}{1-e\sin\theta}$

$e = 6;\quad p = 2$

$$r = \frac{12}{1-6\sin\theta}$$

36. $r = \dfrac{ep}{1+e\cos\theta}$

$e = 5;\quad p = 5$

$$r = \frac{25}{1+5\cos\theta}$$

37. $d(F, P) = e\cdot d(D, P)$ $\qquad d(D, P) = p - r\cos\theta$

$$r = e(p - r\cos\theta)$$
$$r = ep - er\cos\theta$$

$$r + er\cos\theta = ep \rightarrow r(1 + e\cos\theta) = ep \rightarrow r = \frac{ep}{1+e\cos\theta}$$

38. $d(F, P) = e\cdot d(D, P)$ $\qquad d(D, P) = p - r\sin\theta$

$$r = e(p - r\sin\theta)$$
$$r = ep - er\sin\theta$$

$$r + er\sin\theta = ep \rightarrow r(1 + e\sin\theta) = ep \rightarrow r = \frac{ep}{1+e\sin\theta}$$

39. $d(F, P) = e \cdot d(D, P)$ $\qquad d(D, P) = p + r\sin\theta$

$$r = e(p + r\sin\theta)$$

$$r = ep + er\sin\theta$$

$$r - er\sin\theta = ep \rightarrow r(1 - e\sin\theta) = ep \rightarrow r = \frac{ep}{1 - e\sin\theta}$$

40. $r = \dfrac{3.442 \cdot 10^7}{1 - 0.206\cos\theta}$

At aphelion, the greatest distance from the sun, $\cos\theta = +1$.

$$r = \frac{(3.442)10^7}{1 - 0.206(1)} = \frac{(3.442)10^7}{0.794} \approx 4.335 \times 10^7 \text{ miles}$$

At perihelion, the shortest distance from the sun, $\cos\theta = -1$.

$$r = \frac{(3.442)10^7}{1 - 0.206(-1)} = \frac{(3.442)10^7}{1.206} \approx 2.854 \times 10^7 \text{ miles}$$

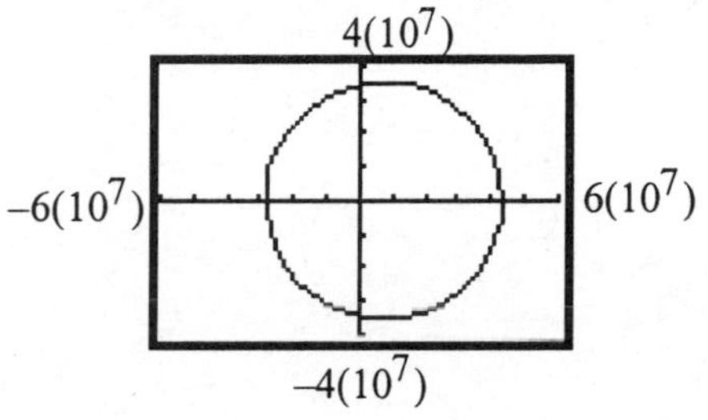

Chapter 11

Analytic Geometry

11.7 Plane Curves and Parametric Equations

1. $x = 3t + 2,\ \ y = t + 1,\ \ 0 \le t \le 4$

$$x = 3(y-1) + 2$$
$$x = 3y - 3 + 2$$
$$x = 3y - 1$$
$$x - 3y + 1 = 0$$

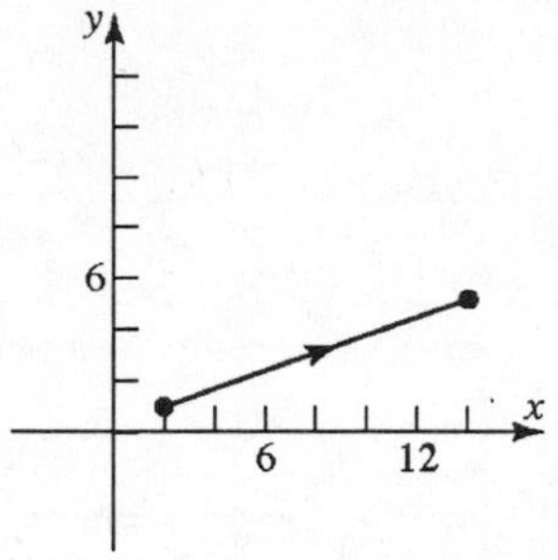

2. $x = t - 3,\ \ y = 2t + 4,\ \ 0 \le t \le 2$

$$y = 2(x+3) + 4$$
$$y = 2x + 6 + 4$$
$$y = 2x + 10$$
$$2x - y + 10 = 0$$

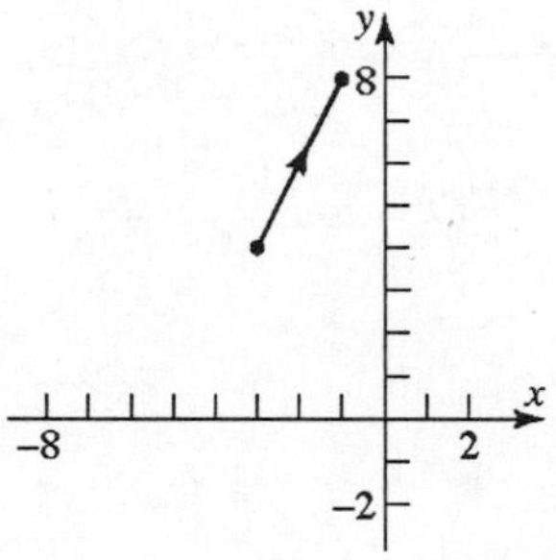

3. $x = t + 2,\ \ y = \sqrt{t},\ \ t \ge 0$

$$y = \sqrt{x-2}$$

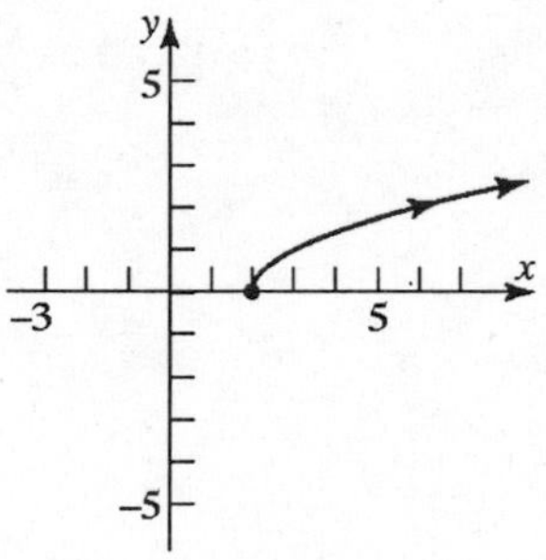

4. $x = \sqrt{2t},\ y = 4t,\ t \geq 0$

$y = 4\left(\frac{x^2}{2}\right) = 2x^2$

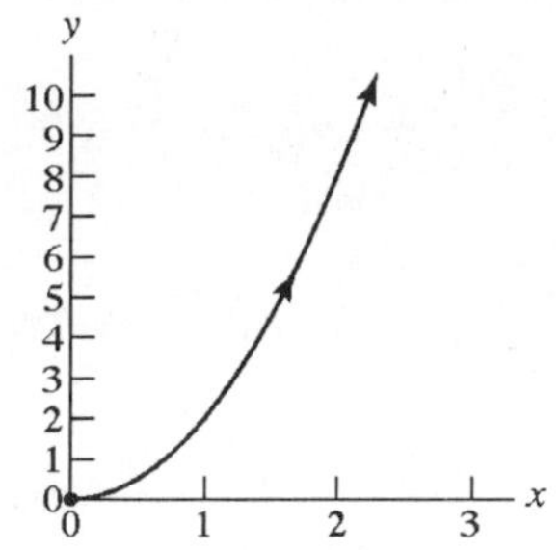

5. $x = t^2 + 4,\ y = t^2 - 4,\ -\infty < t < \infty$

$y = (x - 4) - 4$

$y = x - 8$

For $-\infty < t < 0$ the movement is to the left. For $0 < t < \infty$ the movement is to the right.

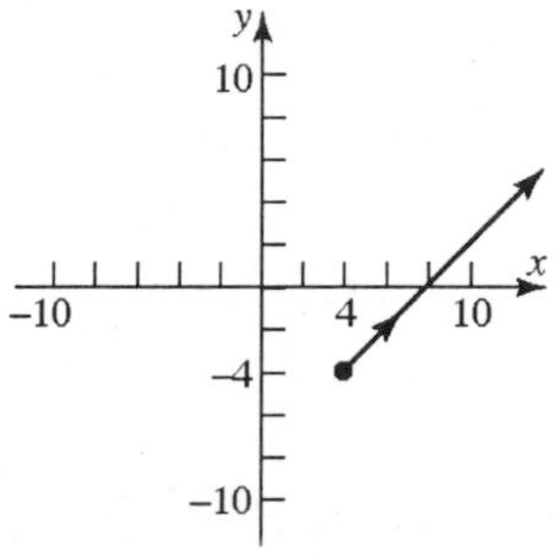

6. $x = \sqrt{t} + 4,\ y = \sqrt{t} - 4,\ t \geq 0$

$y = x - 4 - 4 = x - 8$

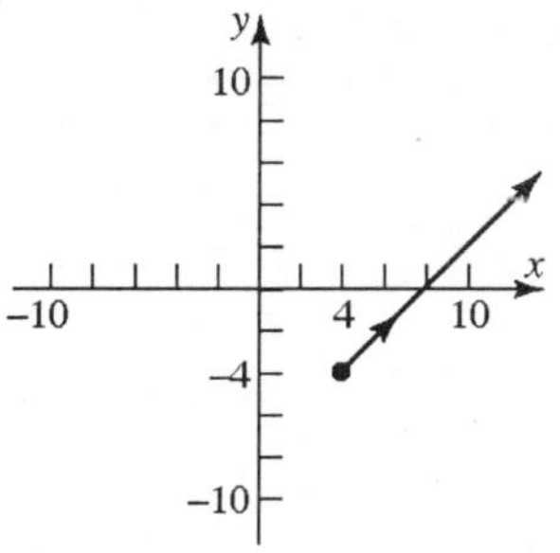

7. $x = 3t^2,\ y = t + 1,\ -\infty < t < \infty$

$x = 3(y - 1)^2$

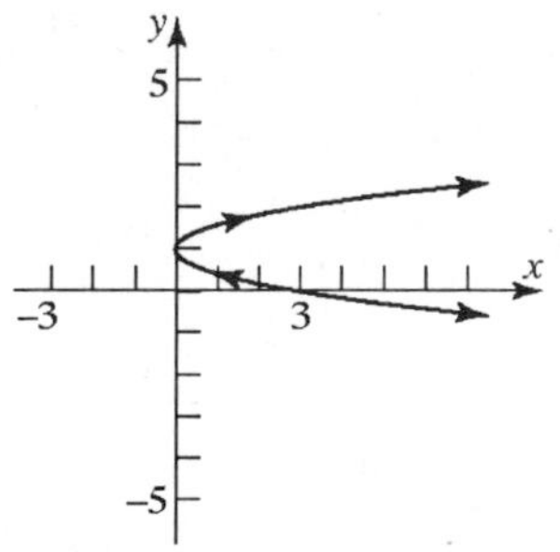

8. $x = 2t - 4,\ y = 4t^2,\ -\infty < t < \infty$

$$y = 4\left(\frac{x+4}{2}\right)^2 = (x+4)^2$$

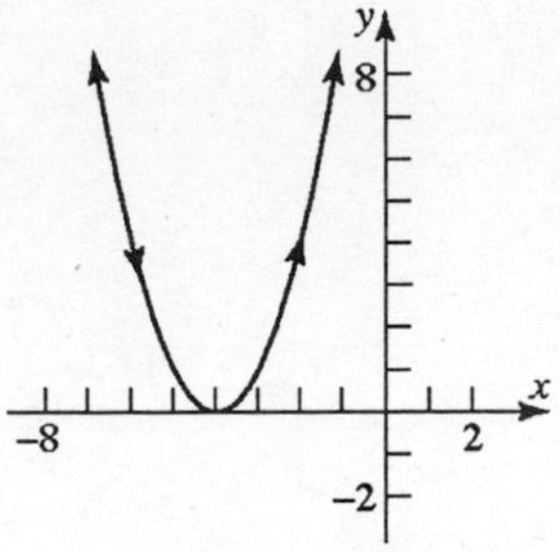

9. $x = 2e^t,\ y = 1 + e^t,\ t \geq 0$

$$y = 1 + \frac{x}{2}$$
$$2y = 2 + x$$

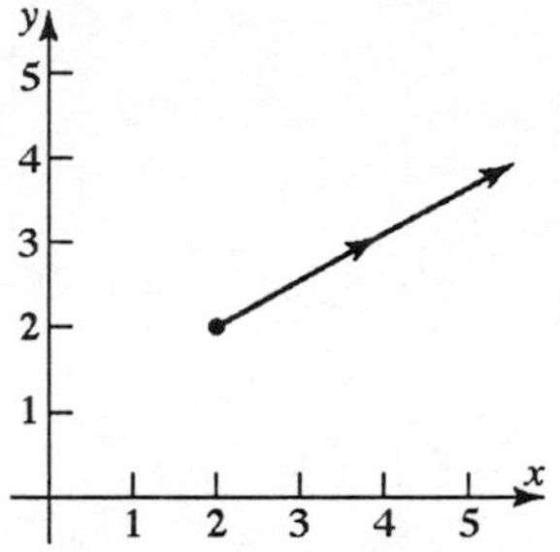

10. $x = e^t,\ y = e^{-t},\ t \geq 0$

$$y = x^{-1} = \frac{1}{x}$$

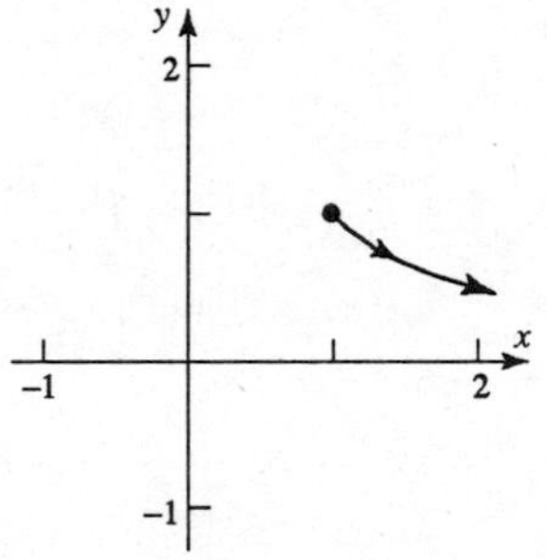

11. $x = \sqrt{t},\ y = t^{3/2},\ t \geq 0$

$$y = \left(x^2\right)^{3/2}$$
$$y = x^3$$

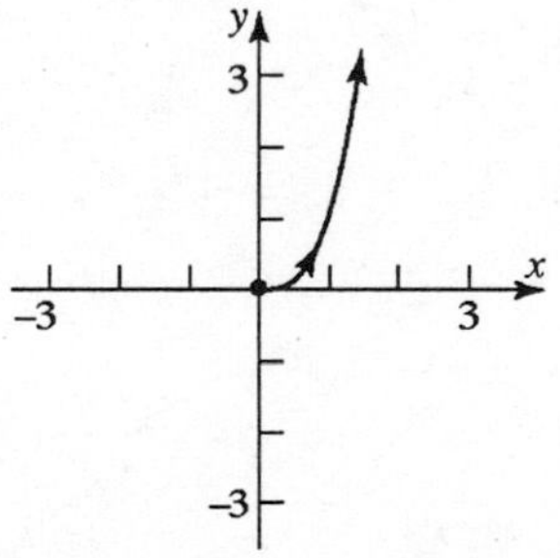

12. $x = t^{3/2} + 1,\ y = \sqrt{t},\ t \geq 0$

$x = (y^2)^{3/2} + 1$

$x = y^3 + 1$

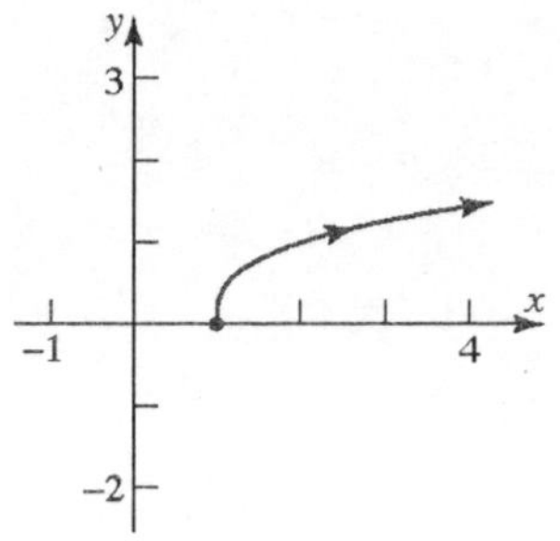

13. $x = 2\cos t,\ y = 3\sin t,\ 0 \leq t \leq 2\pi$

$\frac{x}{2} = \cos t \quad \frac{y}{3} = \sin t$

$\left(\frac{x}{2}\right)^2 + \left(\frac{y}{3}\right)^2 = \cos^2 t + \sin^2 t = 1$

$\frac{x^2}{4} + \frac{y^2}{9} = 1$

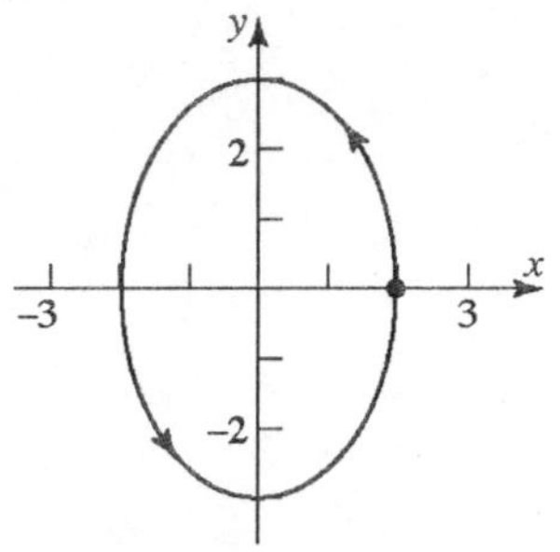

14. $x = 2\cos t,\ y = 3\sin t,\ 0 \leq t \leq \pi$

$\frac{x}{2} = \cos t \quad \frac{y}{3} = \sin t$

$\left(\frac{x}{2}\right)^2 + \left(\frac{y}{3}\right)^2 = \cos^2 t + \sin^2 t = 1$

$\frac{x^2}{4} + \frac{y^2}{9} = 1 \qquad y \geq 0$

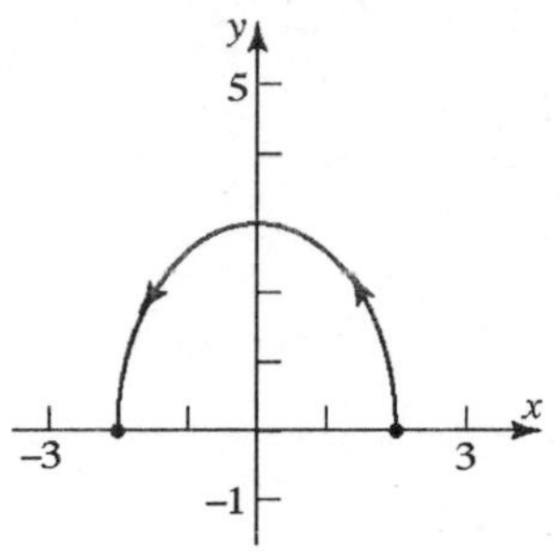

15. $x = 2\cos t,\ y = 3\sin t,\ -\pi \leq t \leq 0$

$\frac{x}{2} = \cos t \quad \frac{y}{3} = \sin t$

$\left(\frac{x}{2}\right)^2 + \left(\frac{y}{3}\right)^2 = \cos^2 t + \sin^2 t = 1$

$\frac{x^2}{4} + \frac{y^2}{9} = 1$

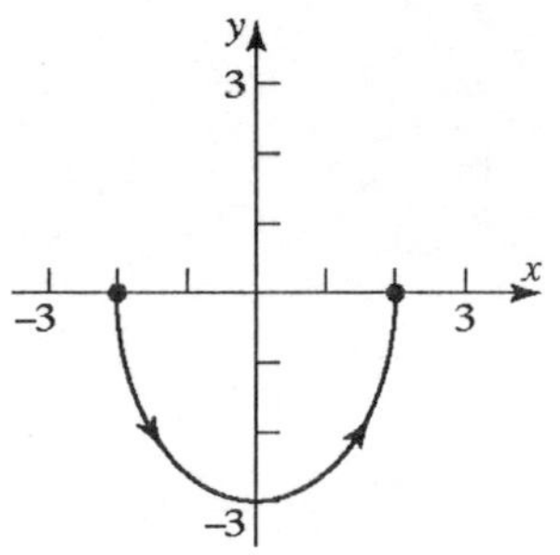

16. $x = 2\cos t,\ y = \sin t,\ 0 \le t \le \frac{\pi}{2}$

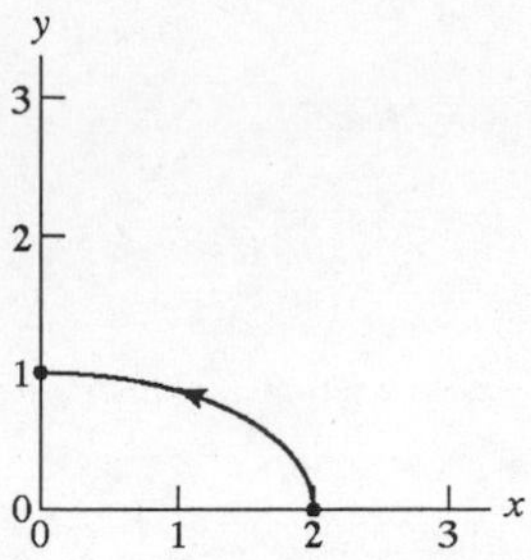

$\frac{x}{2} = \cos t \qquad y = \sin t$

$\left(\frac{x}{2}\right)^2 + (y)^2 = \cos^2 t + \sin^2 t = 1$

$\frac{x^2}{4} + y^2 = 1$

17. $x = \sec t,\ y = \tan t,\ 0 \le t \le \frac{\pi}{4}$

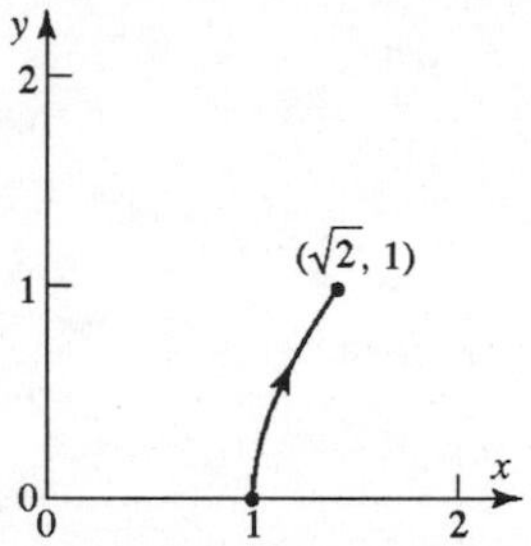

$\sec^2 t = 1 + \tan^2 t$

$x^2 = 1 + y^2$

$x^2 - y^2 = 1$

18. $x = \csc t,\ y = \cot t,\ \frac{\pi}{4} \le t \le \frac{\pi}{2}$

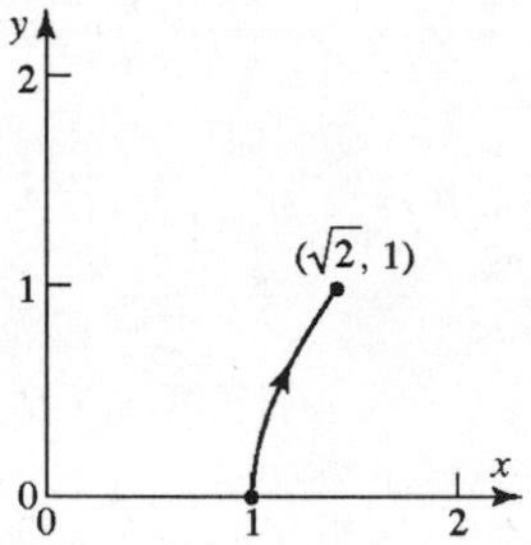

$\csc^2 t = 1 + \cot^2 t$

$x^2 = 1 + y^2$

$x^2 - y^2 = 1$

19. $x = \sin^2 t,\ y = \cos^2 t,\ 0 \le t \le 2\pi$

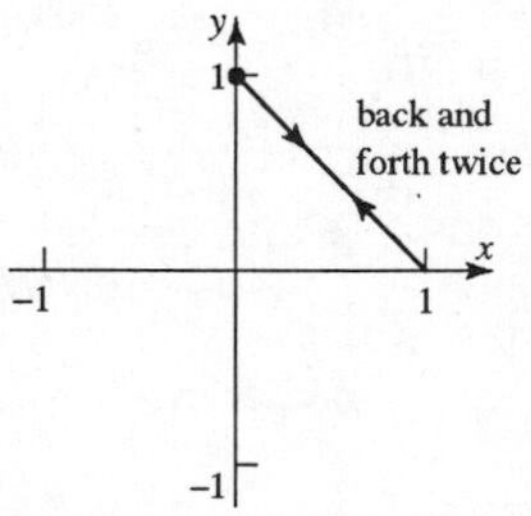

$\sin^2 t + \cos^2 t = 1$

$x + y = 1$

20. $x = t^2,\ y = \ln t,\ t > 0$

$y = \ln\sqrt{x}$

$y = \frac{1}{2}\ln x$

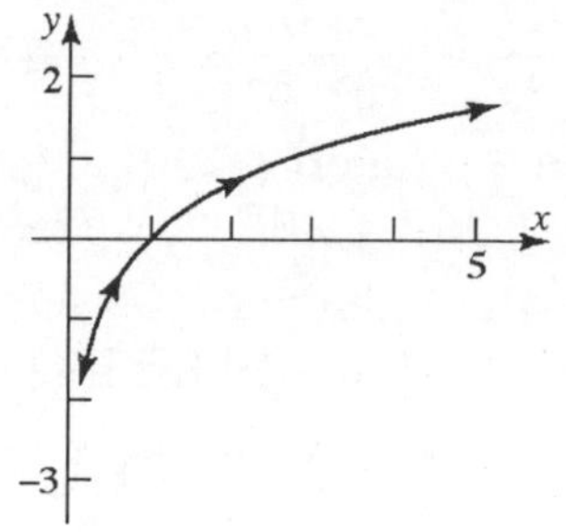

21. (a) Use equation (2):

$x = 50\cos(90°) = 0$

$y = -\frac{1}{2}(32)t^2 + (50\sin(90°))t + 6 = -16t^2 + 50t + 6$

(b) The ball is in the air until $y = 0$. Solve:

$-16t^2 + 50t + 6 = 0$

$t = \frac{-50 \pm \sqrt{50^2 - 4(-16)(6)}}{2(-16)} = \frac{-50 \pm \sqrt{2884}}{-32} \approx -0.12 \text{ or } 3.24$

The ball is in the air for about 3.24 seconds. (The negative solution is extraneous.)

(c) The maximum height occurs at the vertex of the quadratic function.

$t = \frac{-b}{2a} = \frac{-50}{2(-16)} = 1.5625 \text{ seconds}$

Evaluate the function to find the maximum height:

$-16(1.5625)^2 + 50(1.5625) + 6 = 45.0625$

The maximum height is 45.0625 feet.

(d) (We use $x = 3$ so that the line is not on top of the y-axis.)

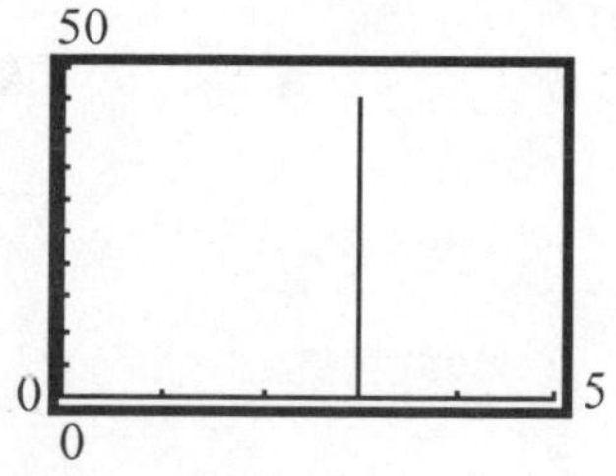

22. (a) Use equation (2):

$x = 40\cos(90°) = 0$

$y = -\frac{1}{2}(32)t^2 + (40\sin(90°))t + 5 = -16t^2 + 40t + 5$

(b) The ball is in the air until $y = 0$. Solve:

$-16t^2 + 40t + 5 = 0$

$t = \frac{-40 \pm \sqrt{40^2 - 4(-16)(5)}}{2(-16)} = \frac{-40 \pm \sqrt{1920}}{-32} \approx -0.12 \text{ or } 2.62$

The ball is in the air for about 2.62 seconds. (The negative solution is extraneous.)

(c) The maximum height occurs at the vertex of the quadratic function.

$$t = \frac{-b}{2a} = \frac{-40}{2(-16)} = 1.25 \text{ seconds}$$

Evaluate the function to find the maximum height:

$$-16(1.25)^2 + 40(1.25) + 5 = 30$$

The maximum height is 30 feet.

(d) (We use $x = 3$ so that the line is not on top of the y-axis.)

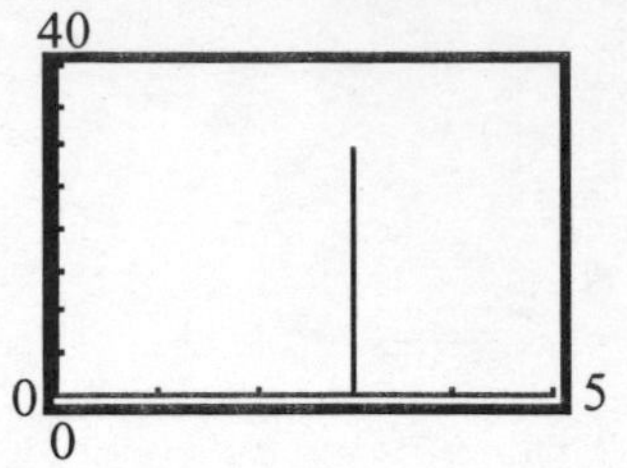

23. (a) Train: Use equation (2) with $g = 2,\ v_0 = 0,\ h = 0$

$$x_1 = \frac{1}{2}(2)t^2 + 0 \cdot t + 0 = t^2$$
$$y_1 = 1$$

Bill:

$$x_2 = 5(t-5)$$
$$y_2 = 3$$

(b) Bill will catch the train if $x_1 = x_2$.

$$t^2 = 5(t-5) \to t^2 = 5t - 25 \to t^2 - 5t + 25 = 0$$

Since $b^2 - 4ac = (-5)^2 - 4(1)(25) = 25 - 100 = -75 < 0$, the equation has no real solution. Thus, Bill will not catch the train.

(c)

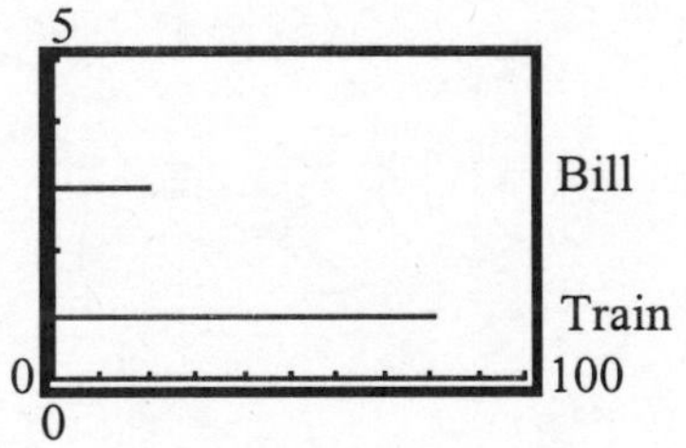

24. (a) Bus: Use equation (2) with $g = 3,\ v_0 = 0,\ h = 0$

$$x_1 = \frac{1}{2}(3)t^2 + 0 \cdot t + 0 = 1.5t^2$$
$$y_1 = 1$$

Jodi:

$$x_2 = 5(t-2)$$
$$y_2 = 3$$

(b) Jodi will catch the bus if $x_1 = x_2$.

$$1.5t^2 = 5(t-2) \to 1.5t^2 = 5t - 10 \to 1.5t^2 - 5t + 10 = 0$$

Since $b^2 - 4ac = (-5)^2 - 4(1.5)(10) = 25 - 60 = -35 < 0$, the equation has no real solution. Thus, Jodi will not catch the bus.

(c)

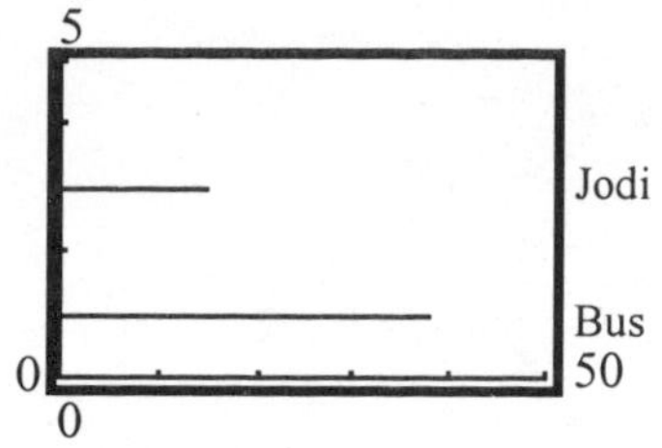

25. (a) Use equation (2):

$$x = (145\cos(20°))\,t$$

$$y = -\frac{1}{2}(32)\,t^2 + (145\sin(20°))\,t + 5$$

(b) The ball is in the air until $y = 0$. Solve:

$$-16t^2 + (145\sin 20°)t + 5 = 0$$

$$t = \frac{-145\sin(20°) \pm \sqrt{(145\sin(20°))^2 - 4(-16)(5)}}{2(-16)}$$

$$\approx \frac{-49.59 \pm \sqrt{2779.46}}{-32} \approx -0.10 \text{ or } 3.20$$

The ball is in the air for about 3.20 seconds. (The negative solution is extraneous.)

(c) The maximum height occurs at the vertex of the quadratic function.

$$t = \frac{-b}{2a} = \frac{-145\sin(20°)}{2(-16)} \approx 1.55 \text{ seconds}$$

Evaluate the function to find the maximum height:

$$-16(1.55)^2 + 145\sin(20°)(1.55) + 5 = 43.43$$

The maximum height is about 43.43 feet.

(d) Find the horizontal displacement:

$$x = (145\cos(20°))(3.20) \approx 436 \text{ feet}$$

(e)

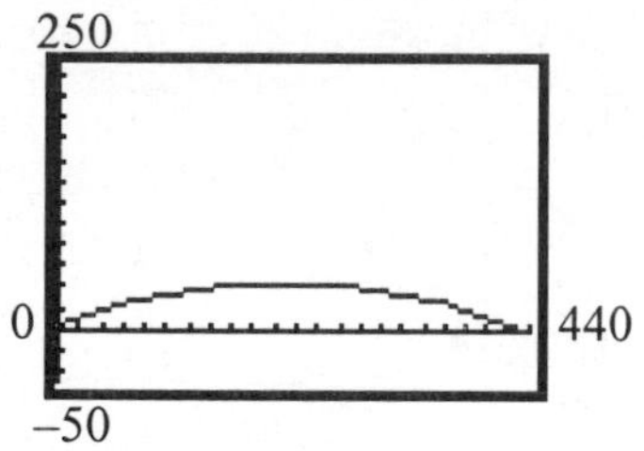

26. (a) Use equation (2):

$$x = (180\cos(40°))\,t$$

$$y = -\frac{1}{2}(32)\,t^2 + (180\sin(40°))\,t + 3$$

(b) The ball is in the air until $y = 0$. Solve:

$$-16t^2 + (180\sin(40°))\,t + 3 = 0$$

$$t = \frac{-180\sin 40° \pm \sqrt{(180\sin(40°))^2 - 4(-16)(3)}}{2(-16)} \approx \frac{-115.7 \pm \sqrt{13578.9}}{-32} \approx -0.03 \text{ or } 7.26$$

The ball is in the air for about 7.26 seconds. (The negative solution is extraneous.)

(c) The maximum height occurs at the vertex of the quadratic function.

$$t = \frac{-b}{2a} = \frac{-180\sin(40°)}{2(-16)} \approx 3.62 \text{ seconds}$$

Evaluate the function to find the maximum height:

$$-16(3.62)^2 + 180\sin(40°)(3.62) + 3 = 212.17$$

The maximum height is about 212.17 feet.

(d) Find the horizontal displacement:

$$x = (180\cos(40°))(7.26) \approx 1001.1 \text{ feet}$$

(e)

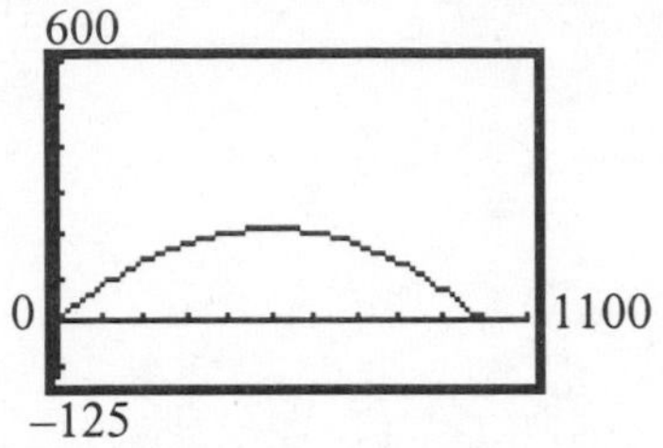

27. (a) Use equation (2):

$$x = (40\cos(45°))\,t$$

$$y = -\frac{1}{2}(9.8)t^2 + (40\sin(45°))t + 300$$

(b) The ball is in the air until $y = 0$. Solve:

$$-4.9t^2 + (40\sin(45°))\,t + 300 = 0$$

$$t = \frac{-20\sqrt{2} \pm \sqrt{(20\sqrt{2})^2 - 4(-4.9)(300)}}{2(-4.9)} = \frac{-20\sqrt{2} \pm \sqrt{6680}}{-9.8} \approx -5.45 \text{ or } 11.23$$

The ball is in the air for about 11.23 seconds. (The negative solution is extraneous.)

(c) The maximum height occurs at the vertex of the quadratic function.

$$t = \frac{-b}{2a} = \frac{-20\sqrt{2}}{2(-4.9)} \approx 2.89 \text{ seconds}$$

Evaluate the function to find the maximum height:

$$-4.9(2.89)^2 + 20\sqrt{2}(2.89) + 300 = 340.8 \text{ meters}$$

(d) Find the horizontal displacement:

$$x = (40\cos(45°))(11.23) \approx 317.6 \text{ meters}$$

(e)

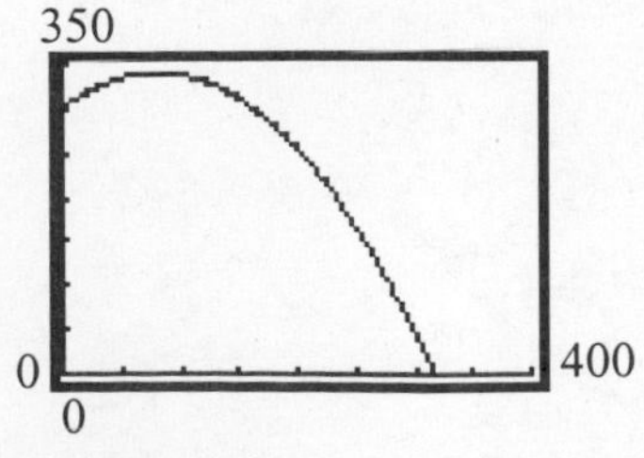

28. (a) Use equation (2):

$$x = (40\cos(45°))\,t$$

$$y = -\frac{1}{2}\cdot\frac{1}{6}(9.8)\,t^2 + (40\sin(45°))\,t + 300 = -\frac{9.8}{12}t^2 + (40\sin(45°))\,t + 300$$

(b) The ball is in the air until $y = 0$. Solve:

$$-\frac{4.9}{6}t^2 + (40\sin(45°))\,t + 300 = 0$$

$$t = \frac{-20\sqrt{2} \pm \sqrt{\left(20\sqrt{2}\right)^2 - 4\left(-\frac{4.9}{6}\right)(300)}}{\left(2\left(\frac{-4.9}{6}\right)\right)} = \frac{-20\sqrt{2} \pm \sqrt{1780}}{\left(\frac{-4.9}{3}\right)} \approx -8.51 \text{ or } 43.15$$

The ball is in the air for about 43.15 seconds. (The negative solution is extraneous.)

(c) The maximum height occurs at the vertex of the quadratic function.

$$t = \frac{-b}{2a} = \frac{-20\sqrt{2}}{2\left(\frac{-4.9}{6}\right)} \approx 17.32 \text{ seconds}$$

Evaluate the function to find the maximum height:

$$-\frac{4.9}{6}(17.32)^2 + 20\sqrt{2}(17.32) + 300 = 544.9 \text{ meters}$$

(d) Find the horizontal displacement:

$$x = (40\cos(45°))(43.15) \approx 1220.5 \text{ meters}$$

(e)

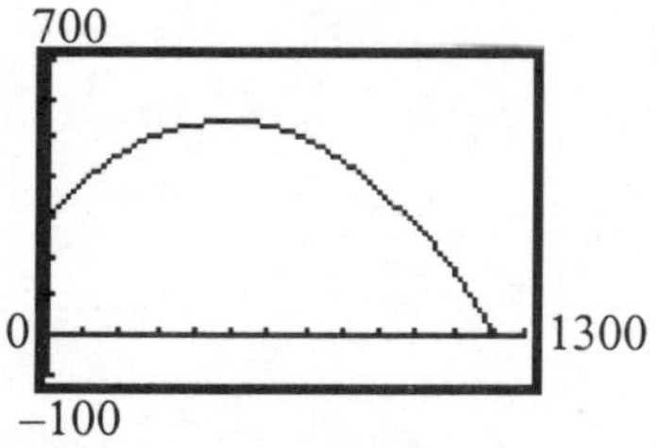

29. (a) At $t = 0$, the Paseo is 5 miles from the intersection (at (0, 0)) traveling east (along the x-axis) at 40 mph. Thus, $x = 40t - 5$ describes the position of the Paseo as a function of time. The Bonneville, at $t = 0$, is 4 miles from the intersection traveling north (along the y-axis) at 30 mph. Thus, $y = 30t - 4$ describes the position of the Bonneville as a function of time.

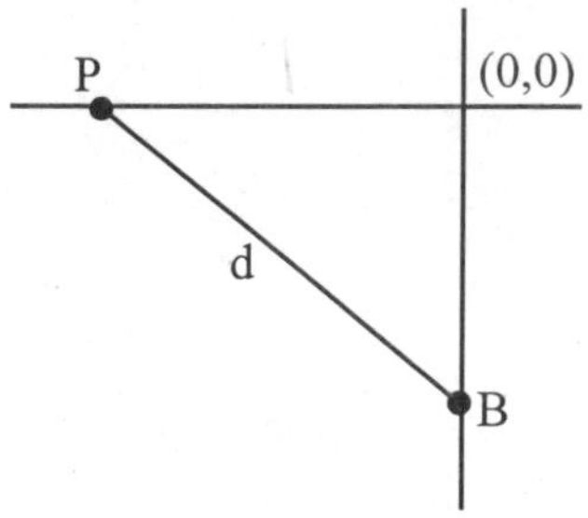

Let d represent the distance between the cars. Use the Pythagorean Theorem to find the distance:

$$d = \sqrt{(40t-5)^2 + (30t-4)^2}$$

(b) From part (a):

Paseo: $x = 40t - 5$, $y = 0$ Bonneville: $x = 0$, $y = 30t - 4$

(c) (Note this is a function graph not a parametric graph.)

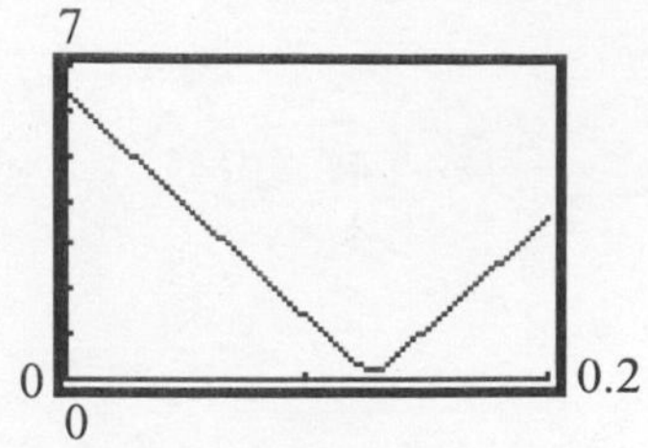

(d) The minimum distance between the cars is 0.2 miles and occurs at 0.128 seconds.

(e)

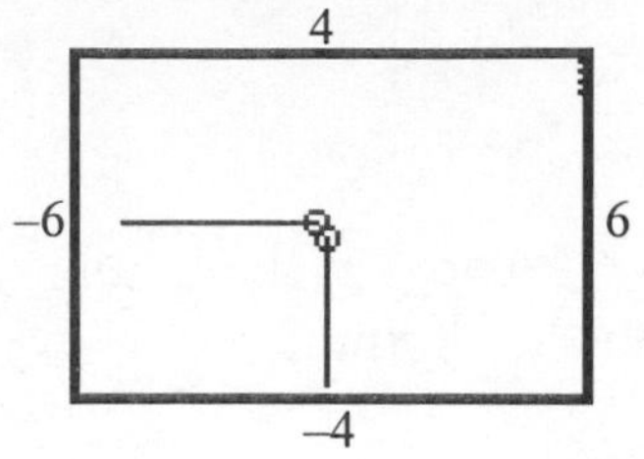

30. (a) At $t = 0$, the Boeing 747 is 550 miles from the intersection (at (0, 0)) traveling west (along the x-axis) at 600 mph. Thus, $x = -600t + 550$ describes the position of the Boeing 747 as a function of time. The Cessna, at $t = 0$, is 100 miles from the intersection traveling south (along the y-axis) at 120 mph. Thus, $y = -120t + 100$ describes the position of the Cessna as a function of time.

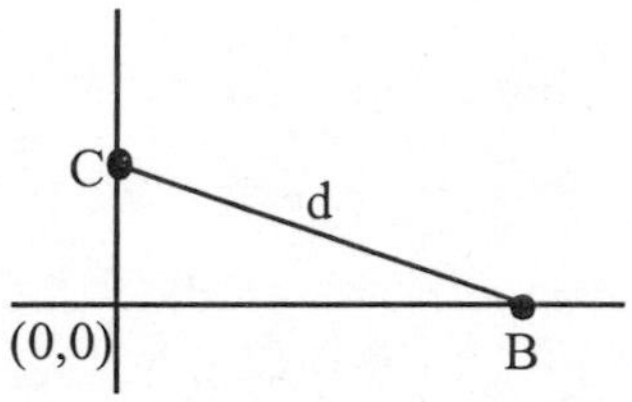

Let d represent the distance between the planes. Use the Pythagorean Theorem to find the distance: $d = \sqrt{(-600t + 550)^2 + (-120t + 100)^2}$

(b) (Note this is a function graph not a parametric graph.)

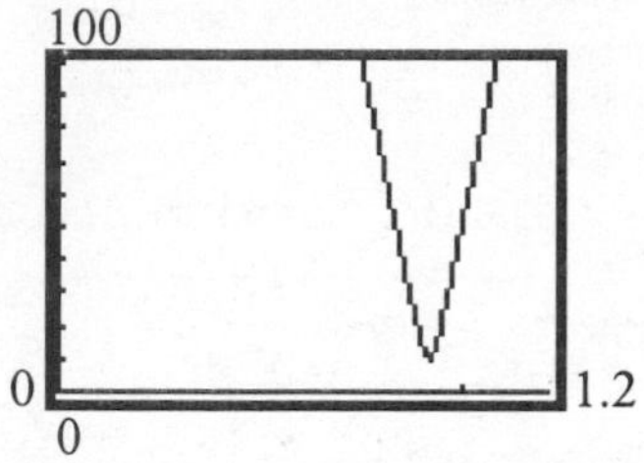

(c) The minimum distance between the planes is 9.8 miles and occurs at 0.91 hours.

(d) From part (a):

Boeing 747: $x = -600t + 550$, $y = 0$ Cessna: $x = 0$, $y = -120t + 100$

(e)

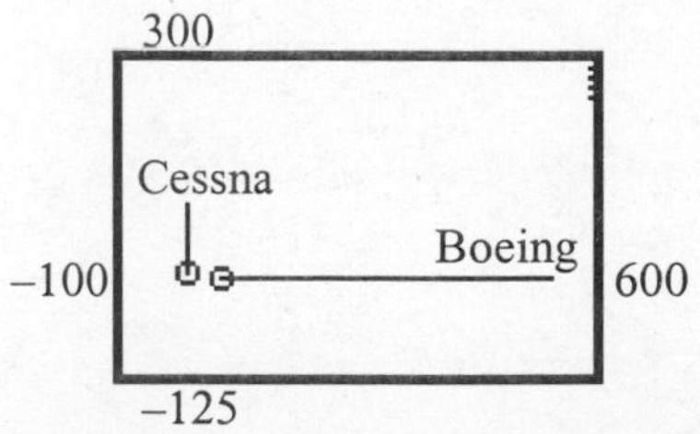

(The axes were turned off to get this graph.)

31. $x = t,\ y = 4t - 1$ $\quad x = t + 1,\ y = 4t + 3$

32. $x = t,\ y = -8t + 3$ $\quad x = t + 1,\ y = -8t - 5$

33. $x = t,\ y = t^2 + 1$ $\quad x = t - 1,\ y = t^2 - 2t + 2$

34. $x = t,\ y = -2t^2 + 1$ $\quad x = t - 1,\ y = -2t^2 + 4t - 1$

35. $x = t,\ y = t^3$ $\quad x = \sqrt[3]{t},\ y = t$

36. $x = t,\ y = t^4 + 1$ $\quad x = \sqrt[4]{t - 1},\ y = t$

37. $x = t^{3/2},\ y = t$ $\quad x = t,\ y = t^{2/3}$

38. $x = \sqrt{t},\ y = t$ $\quad x = t,\ y = t^2$

39. $x = t + 2,\ y = t;\ \ 0 \le t \le 5$

40. $x = t,\ y = -t + 1;\ \ -1 \le t \le 3$

41. $x = 3\cos t,\ y = 2\sin t;\ \ 0 \le t \le 2\pi$

42. $x = \cos t,\ y = 4\sin t;\ \ -\frac{\pi}{2} \le t \le \frac{\pi}{2}$

43. $x = 2\cos(\omega t),\ y = -3\sin(\omega t)$

$\frac{2\pi}{\omega} = 2 \rightarrow \omega = \pi$

$x = 2\cos(\pi t),\ y = -3\sin(\pi t),\ \ 0 \le t \le 2$

44. $x = -2\sin\omega t,\ y = 3\cos\omega t$

$\frac{2\pi}{\omega} = 1 \rightarrow \omega = 2\pi$

$x = -2\sin 2\pi t,\ y = 3\cos 2\pi t,\ \ 0 \le t \le 1$

45. $x = -2\sin(\omega)t,\ y = 3\cos(\omega t)$

$\frac{2\pi}{\omega} = 1 \rightarrow \omega = 2\pi$

$x = -2\sin(2\pi t),\ y = 3\cos(2\pi t),\ \ 0 \le t \le 1$

46. $x = 2\cos\omega t,\ y = 3\sin\omega t$

$\frac{2\pi}{\omega} = 3 \rightarrow \omega = \frac{2\pi}{3}$

$x = 2\cos\left(\frac{2\pi}{3}t\right),\ y = 3\sin\left(\frac{2\pi}{3}t\right),\ \ 0 \le t \le 3$

47. C_1

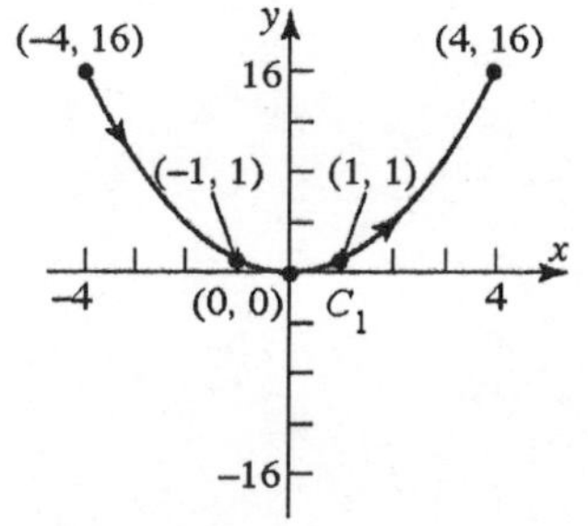

C_2

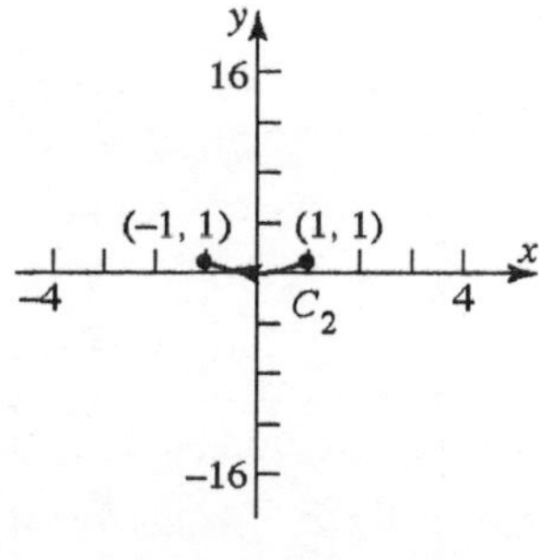

C_3

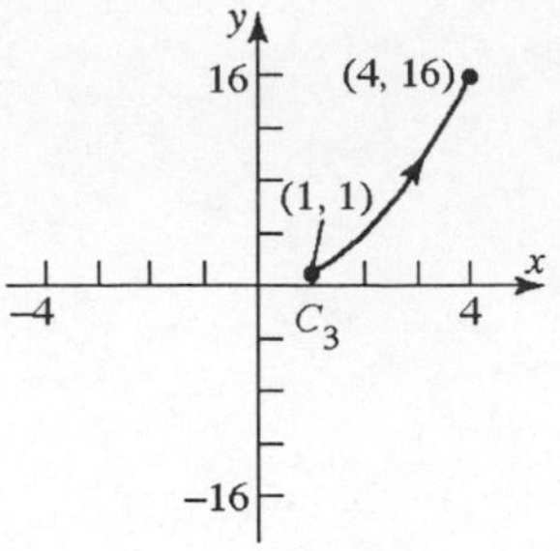

C_4

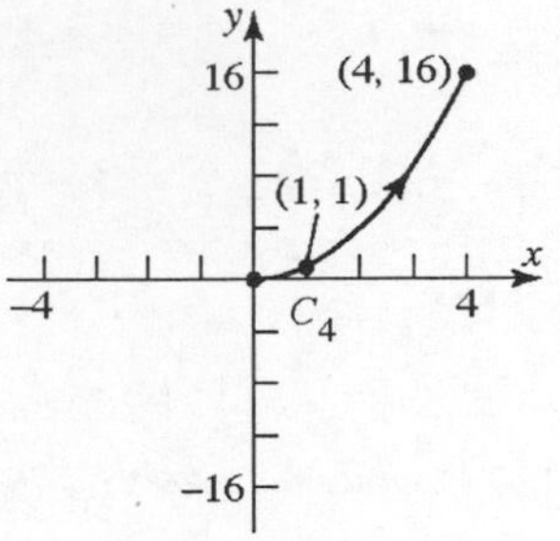

48. C_1

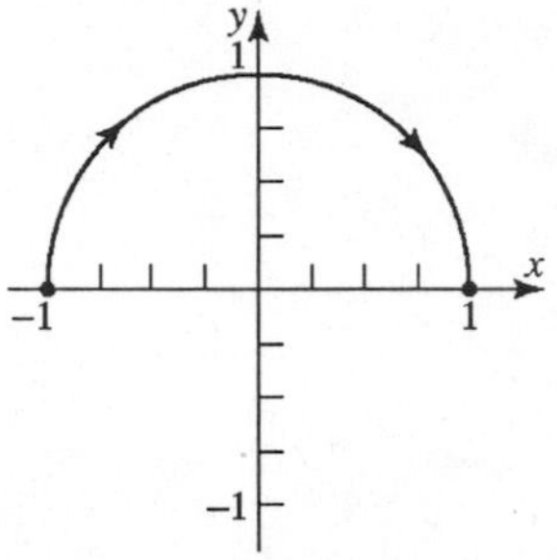

C_2

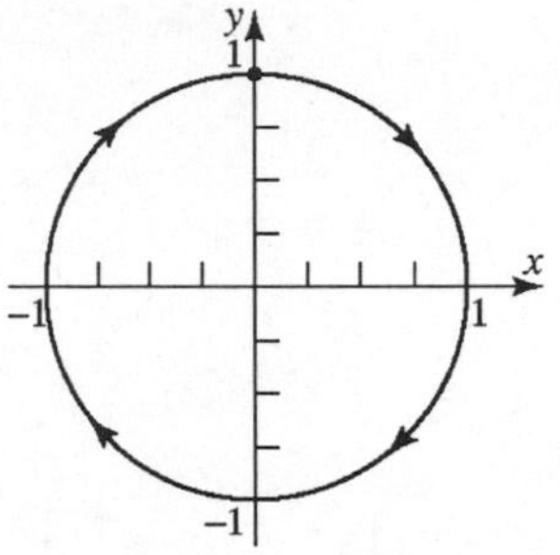

C_3

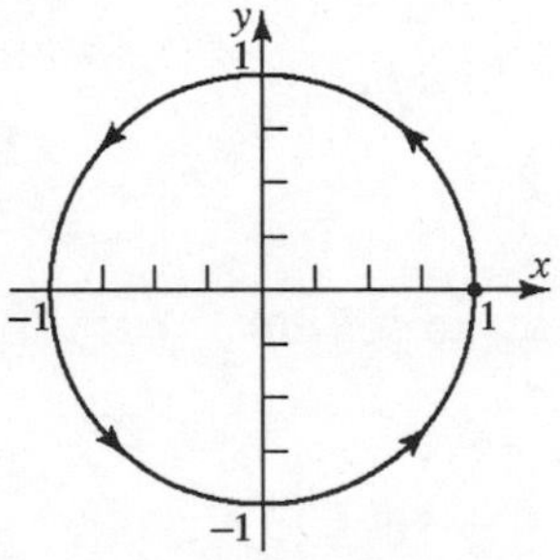

C_4

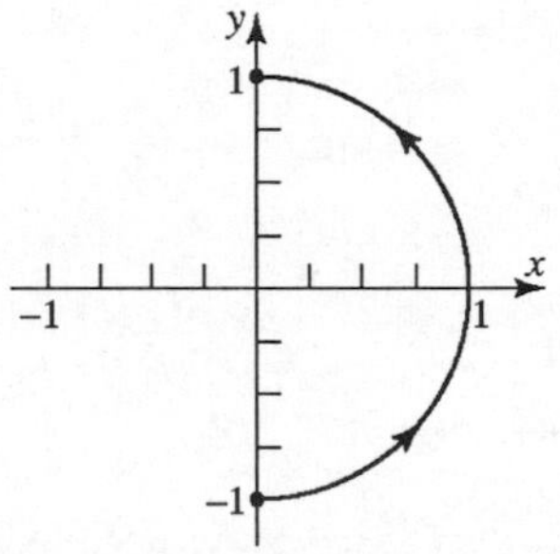

49. $x = (x_2 - x_1)t + x_1, \quad y = (y_2 - y_1)t + y_1, \quad -\infty < t < \infty$

$$\frac{x - x_1}{x_2 - x_1} = t$$

$$y = (y_2 - y_1)\left(\frac{x - x_1}{x_2 - x_1}\right) + y_1 \rightarrow y - y_1 = \left(\frac{y_2 - y_1}{x_2 - x_1}\right)(x - x_1)$$

This is the two point form for the equation of a line. Its orientation is from (x_1, y_1) to (x_2, y_2).

50. (a) $x = (v_0 \cos\theta)t, \quad y = (v_0 \sin\theta)t - 16t^2$

$$t = \frac{x}{v_0 \cos\theta}$$

$$y = v_0 \sin\theta\left(\frac{x}{v_0 \cos\theta}\right) - 16\left(\frac{x}{v_0 \cos\theta}\right)^2 \rightarrow y = (\tan\theta)x - \frac{16}{v_0^2 \cos^2\theta}x^2$$

y is a quadratic function of x; its graph is a parabola.

(b) $y = 0 \rightarrow (v_0 \sin\theta)t - 16t^2 = 0 \rightarrow t(v_0 \sin\theta - 16t) = 0$

$\rightarrow t = 0$ or $v_0 \sin\theta - 16t = 0$

$$t = \frac{v_0 \sin\theta}{16}$$

(c) $x = (v_0 \cos\theta)t = (v_0 \cos\theta)\left(\frac{v_0 \sin\theta}{16}\right) = \frac{v_0^2 \sin 2\theta}{32}$ feet

(d) $x = y$

$(v_0 \cos\theta)t = (v_0 \sin\theta)t - 16t^2$

$16t^2 + (v_0 \cos\theta)t - (v_0 \sin\theta)t = 0 \rightarrow t(16t + (v_0 \cos\theta) - (v_0 \sin\theta)) = 0$

$t = 0$ or $16t + (v_0 \cos\theta) - (v_0 \sin\theta) = 0$

$$t = \frac{v_0 \sin\theta - v_0 \cos\theta}{16} \rightarrow t = \frac{v_0}{16}(\sin\theta - \cos\theta)$$

At $t = \frac{v_0}{16}(\sin\theta - \cos\theta)$:

$$x = v_0 \cos\theta\left(\frac{v_0}{16}(\sin\theta - \cos\theta)\right) = \frac{v_0^2}{16}\cos\theta(\sin\theta - \cos\theta)$$

$$y = v_0 \sin\theta\left(\frac{v_0}{16}(\sin\theta - \cos\theta)\right) - 16\left(\frac{v_0}{16}(\sin\theta - \cos\theta)\right)^2$$

$$= \frac{v_0^2}{16}\sin\theta(\sin\theta - \cos\theta) - \frac{v_0^2}{16}(\sin^2\theta - 2\sin\theta\cos\theta + \cos^2\theta)$$

$$= \frac{v_0^2}{16}\sin\theta(\sin\theta - \cos\theta) - \frac{v_0^2}{16}(1 - 2\sin\theta\cos\theta)$$

$$= \frac{v_o^2}{16}(\sin^2\theta - \sin\theta\cos\theta - 1 + 2\sin\theta\cos\theta)$$

$$= \frac{v_o^2}{16}(-\cos^2\theta + \sin\theta\cos\theta)$$

$$\sqrt{x^2 + y^2} = \sqrt{\left(\frac{v_0^2}{16}\cos\theta(\sin\theta - \cos\theta)\right)^2 + \left(\frac{v_o^2}{16}(-\cos^2\theta + \sin\theta\cos\theta)\right)^2}$$

$$= \sqrt{\left(\frac{v_0^2}{16}\cos\theta(\sin\theta - \cos\theta)\right)^2 + \left(\frac{v_o^2}{16}\cos\theta(\sin\theta - \cos\theta)\right)^2}$$

$$= \sqrt{2\left(\frac{v_o^2}{16}\cos\theta(\sin\theta - \cos\theta)\right)^2}$$

$$= \frac{v_0^2}{16}\sqrt{2}\cos\theta(\sin\theta - \cos\theta)$$

51. $x = t\sin t,\ y = t\cos t$

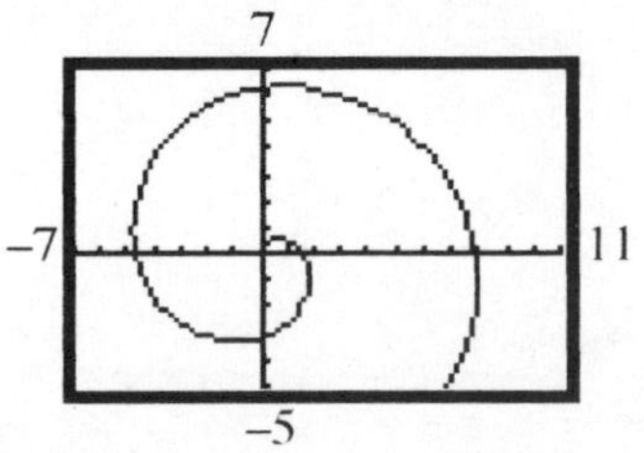

52. $x = \sin t + \cos t,\ y = \sin t - \cos t$

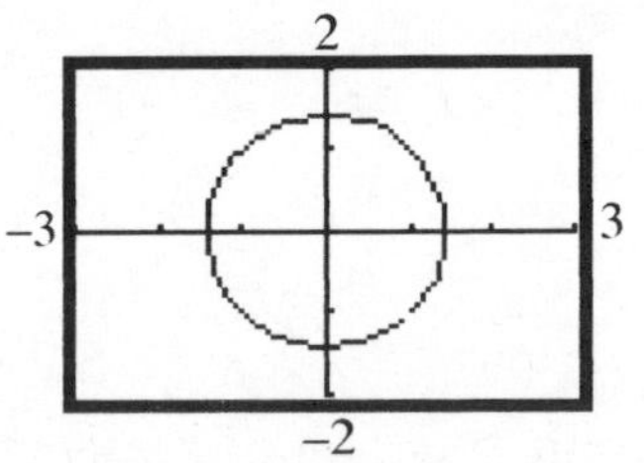

53. $x = 4\sin t - 2\sin(2t)$
$y = 4\cos t - 2\cos(2t)$

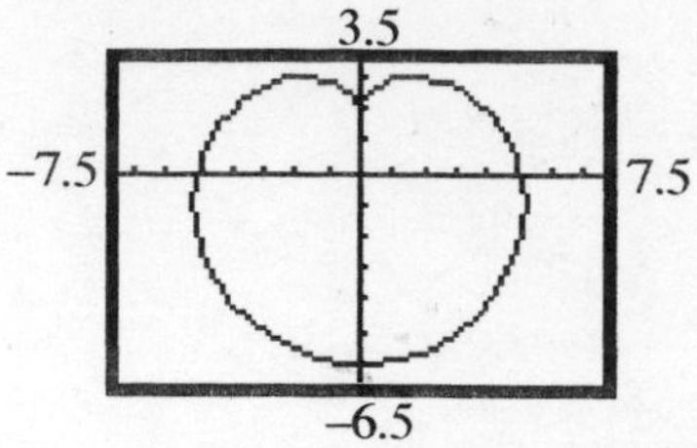

54. $x = 4\sin t + 2\sin(2t)$
$y = 4\cos t + 2\cos(2t)$

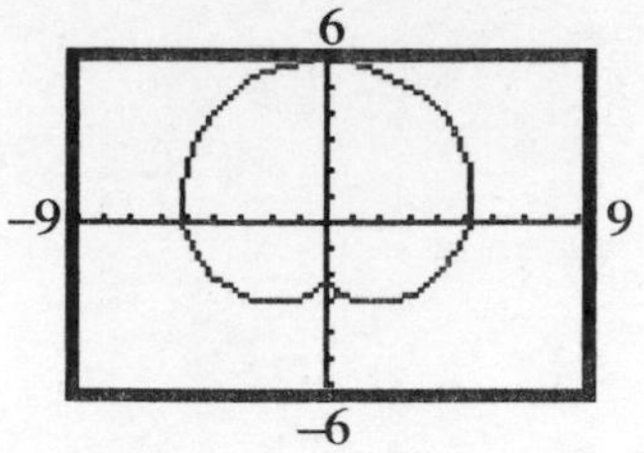

55. (a) $x(t) = \cos^3 t,\ y(t) = \sin^3 t,\quad 0 \le t \le 2\pi$

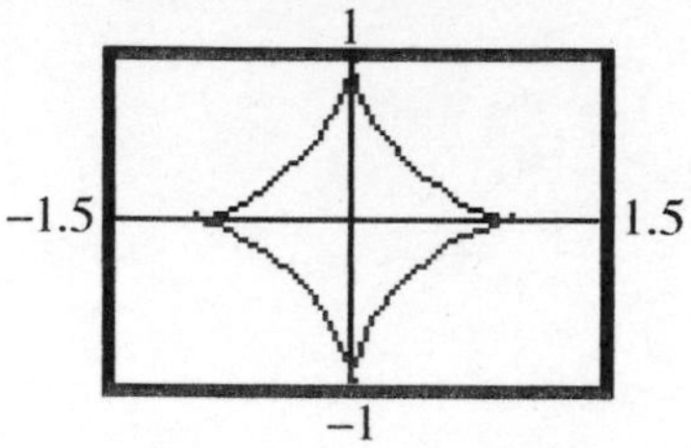

(b) $\cos t = x^{2/3},\ \sin t = y^{2/3}$

$\cos^2 t + \sin^2 t = \left(x^{1/3}\right)^2 + \left(y^{1/3}\right)^2$

$x^{2/3} + y^{2/3} = 1$

Chapter 11

Analytic Geometry

11.R Chapter Review

1. $y^2 = -16x$
This is a parabola.
$a = 4$
Vertex: (0, 0)
Focus: (–4, 0)
Directrix: $x = 4$

2. $16x^2 = y \rightarrow x^2 = \frac{1}{16}y$
This is a parabola.
$a = \frac{1}{64}$
Vertex: (0, 0)
Focus: $\left(0, \frac{1}{64}\right)$
Directrix: $y = -\frac{1}{64}$

3. $\frac{x^2}{25} - y^2 = 1$
This is a hyperbola.
$a = 5,\ b = 1$.

Find the value of c:
$c^2 = a^2 + b^2 = 25 + 1 = 26$
$c = \sqrt{26}$
Center: (0, 0)
Vertices: (5, 0), (–5, 0)
Foci: $\left(\sqrt{26}, 0\right)\ \left(-\sqrt{26}, 0\right)$
Asymptotes: $y = \frac{1}{5}x;\ y = -\frac{1}{5}x$

4. $\frac{y^2}{25} - x^2 = 1$
This is a hyperbola.
$a = 5,\ b = 1$.

Find the value of c:
$c^2 = a^2 + b^2 = 25 + 1 = 26$
$c = \sqrt{26}$
Center: (0, 0)
Vertices: (0, 5), (0, –5)
Foci: $\left(0, \sqrt{26}\right)\ \left(0, -\sqrt{26}\right)$
Asymptotes: $y = 5x;\ y = -5x$

5. $\frac{y^2}{25} + \frac{x^2}{16} = 1$
This is an ellipse.
$a = 5,\ b = 4$.

Find the value of c:
$c^2 = a^2 - b^2 = 25 - 16 = 9$
$c = 3$
Center: (0, 0)
Vertices: (0, 5), (0, –5)
Foci: (0, 3), (0, –3)

6. $\dfrac{x^2}{9}+\dfrac{y^2}{16}=1$

This is an ellipse.

$a=4,\ b=3.$

Find the value of c:

$$c^2=a^2-b^2=16-9=7$$

$$c=\sqrt{7}$$

Center: (0, 0)

Vertices: (0, 4), (0, –4)

Foci: $\left(0,\sqrt{7}\right)\left(0,-\sqrt{7}\right)$

7. $x^2+4y=4$

This is a parabola.

Write in standard form:

$$x^2=-4y+4$$

$$x^2=-4(y-1)$$

$a=1$

Vertex: (0, 1)

Focus: (0, 0)

Directrix: $y=2$

8. $3y^2-x^2=9$

This is a hyperbola.

Write in standard form:

$$\frac{y^2}{3}-\frac{x^2}{9}=1$$

$a=\sqrt{3},\ b=3$

Find the value of c:

$$c^2=a^2+b^2=3+9=12$$

$$c=\sqrt{12}=2\sqrt{3}$$

Center: (0, 0)

Vertices: $\left(0,\sqrt{3}\right)\left(0,-\sqrt{3}\right)$

Foci: $\left(0,2\sqrt{3}\right)\left(0,-2\sqrt{3}\right)$

Asymptotes: $y=\dfrac{\sqrt{3}}{3}x;\ y=-\dfrac{\sqrt{3}}{3}x$

9. $4x^2-y^2=8$

This is a hyperbola.

Write in standard form:

$$\frac{x^2}{2}-\frac{y^2}{8}=1$$

$a=\sqrt{2},\ b=\sqrt{8}=2\sqrt{2}.$

Find the value of c:

$$c^2=a^2+b^2=2+8=10$$

$$c=\sqrt{10}$$

Center: (0, 0)

Vertices: $\left(-\sqrt{2},0\right)\left(\sqrt{2},0\right)$

Foci: $\left(-\sqrt{10},0\right)\left(\sqrt{10},0\right)$

Asymptotes: $y=2x;\ y=-2x$

10. $9x^2+4y^2=36$

This is an ellipse.

Write in standard form:

$$\frac{x^2}{4}+\frac{y^2}{9}=1$$

$a=3,\ b=2.$

Find the value of c:

$$c^2=a^2-b^2=9-4=5$$

$$c=\sqrt{5}$$

Center: (0, 0)

Vertices: (0, 3), (0, –3)

Foci:

$\left(0,\sqrt{5}\right)\left(0,-\sqrt{5}\right)$

11. $x^2 - 4x = 2y$
This is a parabola.
Write in standard form:
$$x^2 - 4x + 4 = 2y + 4$$
$$(x-2)^2 = 2(y+2)$$

$a = \frac{1}{2}$
Vertex: $(2, -2)$
Focus: $\left(2, -\frac{3}{2}\right)$
Directrix: $y = -\frac{5}{2}$

12. $2y^2 - 4y = x - 2$
This is a parabola.
Write in standard form:
$$2(y^2 - 2y + 1) = x - 2 + 2$$
$$(y-1)^2 = \frac{1}{2}x$$

$a = \frac{1}{8}$
Vertex: $(0, 1)$
Focus: $\left(\frac{1}{8}, 1\right)$
Directrix: $x = -\frac{1}{8}$

13. $y^2 - 4y - 4x^2 + 8x = 4$
This is a hyperbola.
Write in standard form:
$$(y^2 - 4y + 4) - 4(x^2 - 2x + 1) = 4 + 4 - 4$$
$$(y-2)^2 - 4(x-1)^2 = 4$$
$$\frac{(y-2)^2}{4} - \frac{(x-1)^2}{1} = 1$$
$a = 2,\ b = 1.$
Find the value of c:

$c^2 = a^2 + b^2 = 4 + 1 = 5$
$c = \sqrt{5}$
Center: $(1, 2)$
Vertices: $(1, 0), (1, 4)$
Foci: $\left(1, 2 - \sqrt{5}\right)\ \left(1, 2 + \sqrt{5}\right)$
Asymptotes:
$y - 2 = 2(x-1);\quad y - 2 = -2(x-1)$

14. $4x^2 + y^2 + 8x - 4y + 4 = 0$
This is an ellipse.
Write in standard form:
$$4(x^2 + 2x + 1) + (y^2 - 4y + 4) = -4 + 4 + 4$$
$$4(x+1)^2 + (y-2)^2 = 4$$
$$\frac{(x+1)^2}{1} + \frac{(y-2)^2}{4} = 1$$
$a = 2,\ b = 1$

Find the value of c:
$$c^2 = a^2 - b^2 = 4 - 1 = 3$$
$$c = \sqrt{3}$$
Center: $(-1, 2)$
Vertices: $(-1, 0), (-1, 4)$
Foci: $\left(-1, 2 - \sqrt{3}\right), \left(-1, 2 + \sqrt{3}\right)$

15. $4x^2 + 9y^2 - 16x - 18y = 11$
This is an ellipse.
Write in standard form:
$$4x^2 + 9y^2 - 16x - 18y = 11$$
$$4(x^2 - 4x + 4) + 9(y^2 - 2y + 1) = 11 + 16 + 9$$
$$4(x-2)^2 + 9(y-1)^2 = 36$$
$$\frac{(x-2)^2}{9} + \frac{(y-1)^2}{4} = 1$$
$a = 3,\ b = 2.$

Find the value of c:
$$c^2 = a^2 - b^2 = 9 - 4 = 5$$
$$c = \sqrt{5}$$
Center: $(2, 1)$
Vertices: $(-1, 1), (5, 1)$
Foci: $\left(2 - \sqrt{5}, 1\right)\ \left(2 + \sqrt{5}, 1\right)$

16. $4x^2+9y^2-16x+18y=11$

This is an ellipse.

Write in standard form:

$$4x^2+9y^2-16x+18y=11$$
$$4(x^2-4x+4)+9(y^2+2y+1)=11+16+9$$
$$4(x-2)^2+9(y+1)^2=36$$
$$\frac{(x-2)^2}{9}+\frac{(y+1)^2}{4}=1$$

$a=3,\ b=2$.

Find the value of c:

$$c^2=a^2-b^2=9-4=5$$
$$c=\sqrt{5}$$

Center: $(2,-1)$

Vertices: $(-1,-1)$, $(5,-1)$

Foci: $\left(2-\sqrt{5},-1\right)$, $\left(2+\sqrt{5},-1\right)$

17. $4x^2-16x+16y+32=0$

This is a parabola.

Write in standard form:

$$4(x^2-4x+4)=-16y-32+16$$
$$4(x-2)^2=-16(y+1)$$
$$(x-2)^2=-4(y+1)$$

$a=-1$

Vertex: $(2,-1)$

Focus: $(2,-2)$

Directrix: $y=0$

18. $4y^2+3x-16y+19=0$

This is a parabola.

Write in standard form:

$$4(y^2-4y+4)=-3x-19+16$$
$$4(y-2)^2=-3(x+1)$$
$$(y-2)^2=-\frac{3}{4}(x+1)$$

$a=-\frac{3}{16}$

Vertex: $(-1,2)$

Focus: $\left(-\frac{19}{16},2\right)$

Directrix: $x=-\frac{13}{16}$

19. $9x^2+4y^2-18x+8y=23$

This is an ellipse.

Write in standard form:

$$9(x^2-2x+1)+4(y^2+2y+1)=23+9+4$$
$$9(x-1)^2+4(y+1)^2=36$$
$$\frac{(x-1)^2}{4}+\frac{(y+1)^2}{9}=1$$

$a=3,\ b=2$.

Find the value of c:

$$c^2=a^2-b^2=9-4=5$$
$$c=\sqrt{5}$$

Center: $(1,-1)$

Vertices: $(1,-4)$, $(1,2)$

Foci: $\left(1,-1-\sqrt{5}\right)$, $\left(1,-1+\sqrt{5}\right)$

20. $x^2-y^2-2x-2y=1$

This is a hyperbola.

Write in standard form:

$$(x^2-2x+1)-(y^2+2y+1)=1+1-1$$
$$(x-1)^2-(y+1)^2=1$$

$a=1,\ b=1$.

Find the value of c:

$$c^2=a^2+b^2=1+1=2$$
$$c=\sqrt{2}$$

Center: $(1,-1)$

Vertices: $(0,-1)$, $(2,-1)$

Foci: $\left(1+\sqrt{2},-1\right)$ $\left(1-\sqrt{2},-1\right)$

Asymptotes:

$y+1=x-1;\quad y+1=-(x-1)$

21. Parabola: The focus is (–2, 0) and the directrix is $x = 2$. The vertex is (0, 0). $a = 2$ and since (–2, 0) is to the left of (0, 0), the parabola opens to the left. The equation of the parabola is:

$$y^2 = -4ax$$
$$y^2 = -4 \cdot 2 \cdot x$$
$$y^2 = -8x$$

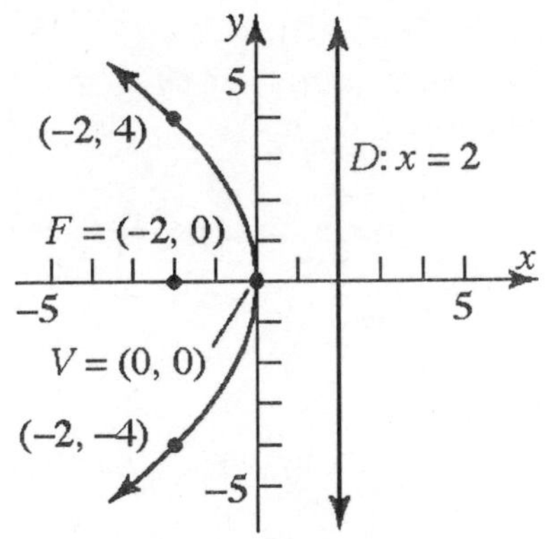

22. Ellipse: The center is (0, 0), a focus is (0, 3), and a vertex is (0, 5). The major axis is $x = 0$. $a = 5,\ c = 3$. Find b: $b^2 = a^2 - c^2 = 25 - 9 = 16$. So, $b = 4$. The equation of the ellipse is:

$$\frac{x^2}{b^2} + \frac{y^2}{a^2} = 1$$
$$\frac{x^2}{4^2} + \frac{y^2}{5^2} = 1$$
$$\frac{x^2}{16} + \frac{y^2}{25} = 1$$

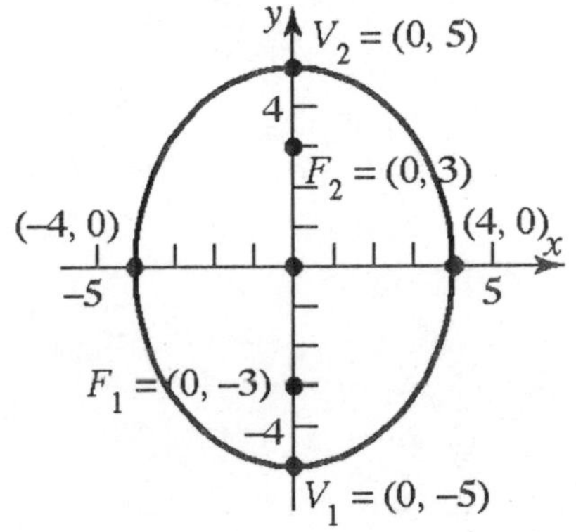

23. Hyperbola: Center: (0, 0);
Focus: (0, 4); Vertex: (0, –2);
Transverse axis is the y-axis;
$a = 2;\ c = 4$.
Find b:

$$b^2 = c^2 - a^2 = 16 - 4 = 12$$
$$b = \sqrt{12} = 2\sqrt{3}$$

Write the equation: $\frac{y^2}{4} - \frac{x^2}{12} = 1$

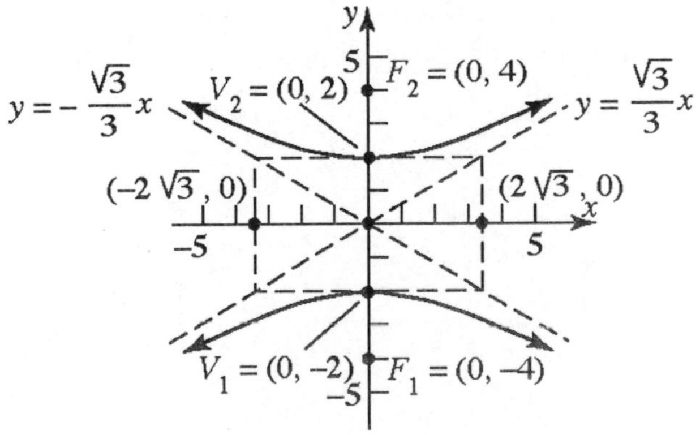

24. Parabola: Vertex: (0, 0); Directrix: $y = -3$; $a = 3$. The graph opens up. The equation of the parabola is:

$$x^2 = 4ay$$
$$x^2 = 4(3)y$$
$$x^2 = 12y$$

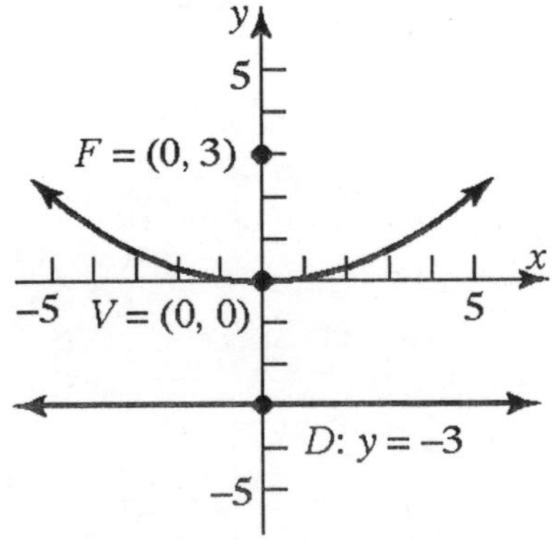

25. Ellipse: Foci: (–3, 0), (3, 0); Vertex: (4, 0); Center: (0, 0); Major axis is the x-axis; $a = 4$; $c = 3$. Find b:

$$b^2 = a^2 - c^2 = 16 - 9 = 7$$
$$b = \sqrt{7}$$

Write the equation: $\frac{x^2}{16} + \frac{y^2}{7} = 1$

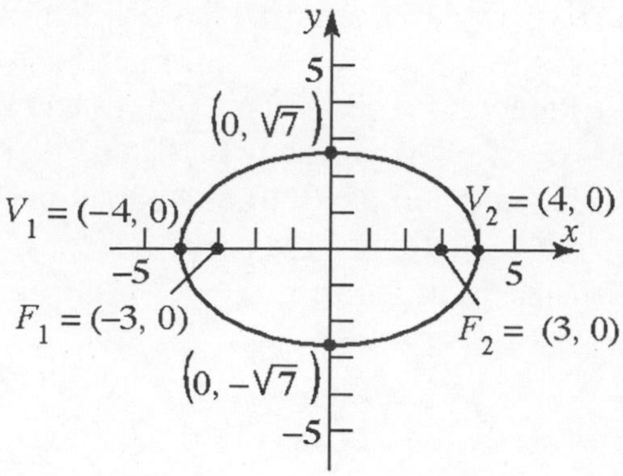

26. Hyperbola: Vertices: (–2, 0), (2, 0); Focus: (4, 0); Center: (0, 0); Transverse axis is the x-axis; $a = 2$; $c = 4$. Find b:

$$b^2 = c^2 - a^2 = 16 - 4 = 12$$
$$b = \sqrt{12} = 2\sqrt{3}$$

Write the equation: $\frac{x^2}{4} - \frac{y^2}{12} = 1$

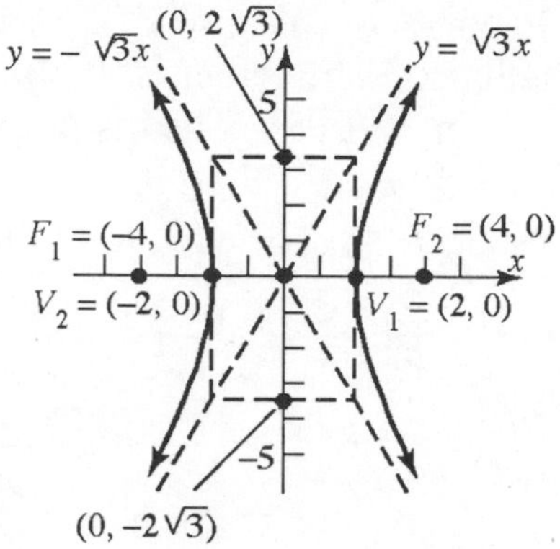

27. Parabola: The focus is (2, –4) and the vertex is (2, –3). Both lie on the vertical line $x = 2$. $a = 1$ and since (2, –4) is below (2, –3), the parabola opens down. The equation of the parabola is:

$$(x-h)^2 = -4a(y-k)$$
$$(x-2)^2 = -4 \cdot 1 \cdot (y-(-3))$$
$$(x-2)^2 = -4(y+3)$$

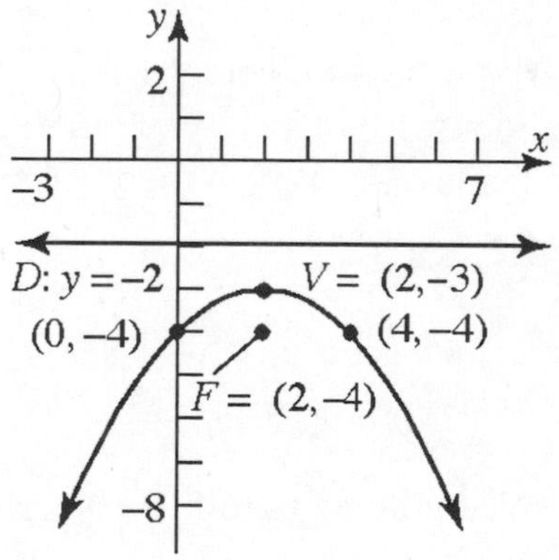

28. Ellipse: Center: (–1, 2); Focus: (0, 2); Vertex: (2, 2). Major axis: $y = 2$. $a = 3$; $c = 1$. Find b:

$$b^2 = a^2 - c^2 = 9 - 1 = 8$$
$$b = \sqrt{8} = 2\sqrt{2}$$

Write the equation: $\frac{(x+1)^2}{9} + \frac{(y-2)^2}{8} = 1$

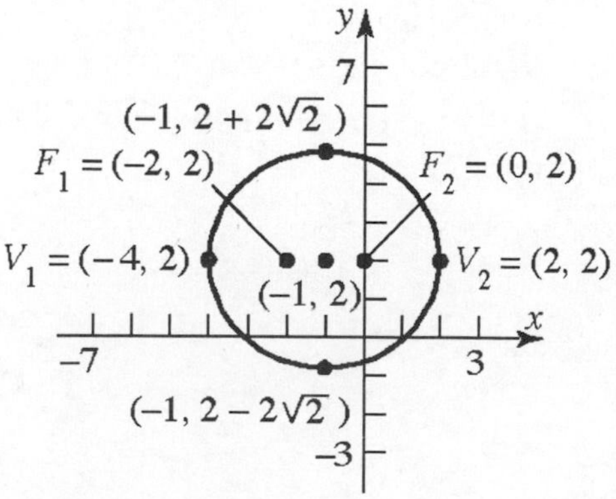

29. Hyperbola: Center: (–2, –3); Focus: (–4, –3); Vertex: (–3, –3); Transverse axis is parallel to the x-axis; $a = 1$; $c = 2$. Find b:

$$b^2 = c^2 - a^2 = 4 - 1 = 3$$
$$b = \sqrt{3}$$

Write the equation: $\dfrac{(x+2)^2}{1} - \dfrac{(y+3)^2}{3} = 1$

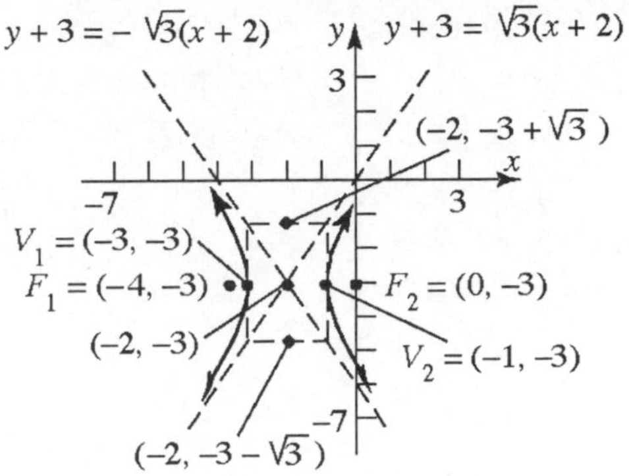

30. Parabola: Focus: (3, 6); Directrix: $y = 8$; Parabola opens down. Vertex: (3, 7) $a = 1$. The equation of the parabola is:

$$(x-h)^2 = -4a(y-k)$$
$$(x-3)^2 = -4(1)(y-7)$$
$$(x-3)^2 = -4(y-7)$$

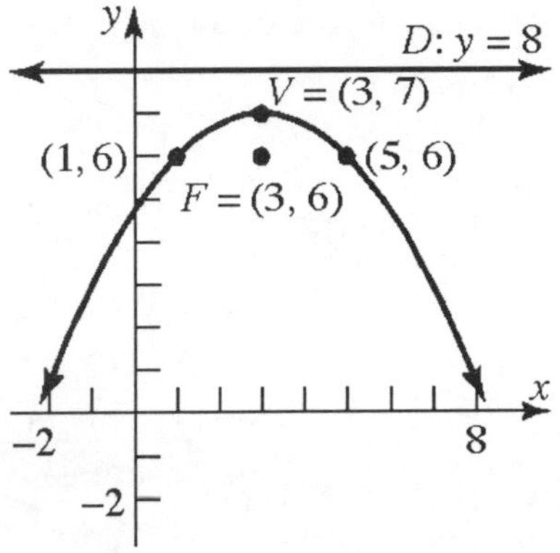

31. Ellipse: Foci: (–4, 2), (–4, 8); Vertex: (–4, 10); Center: (–4, 5); Major axis is parallel to the y-axis; $a = 5$; $c = 3$. Find b:

$$b^2 = a^2 - c^2 = 25 - 9 = 16$$
$$b = 4$$

Write the equation: $\dfrac{(x+4)^2}{16} + \dfrac{(y-5)^2}{25} = 1$

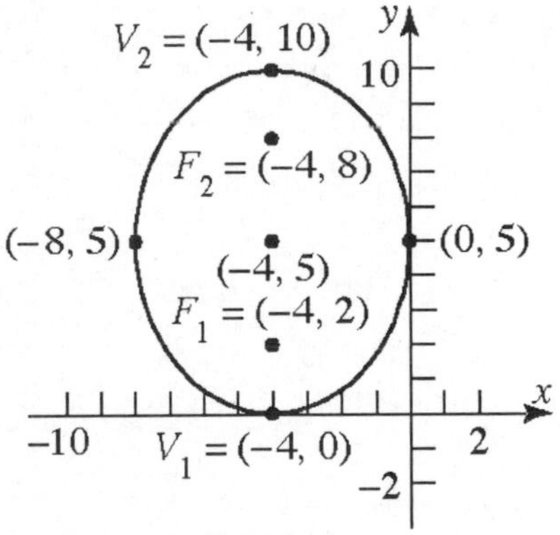

32. Hyperbola: Vertices: (–3, 3), (5, 3); Focus: (7, 3); Center: (1, 3); Major axis is parallel to the x-axis; $a = 4$; $c = 6$. Find b:

$$b^2 = c^2 - a^2 = 36 - 16 = 20$$
$$b = \sqrt{20} = 2\sqrt{5}$$

Write the equation:

$$\frac{(x-1)^2}{16} - \frac{(y-3)^2}{20} = 1$$

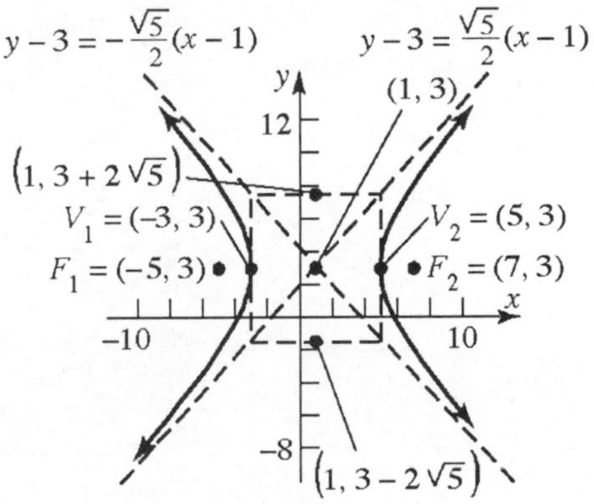

33. Hyperbola: Center: $(-1, 2)$; $a = 3$; $c = 4$; Transverse axis parallel to the x-axis;

Find b:

$$b^2 = c^2 - a^2 = 16 - 9 = 7$$

$$b = \sqrt{7}$$

Write the equation:

$$\frac{(x+1)^2}{9} - \frac{(y-2)^2}{7} = 1$$

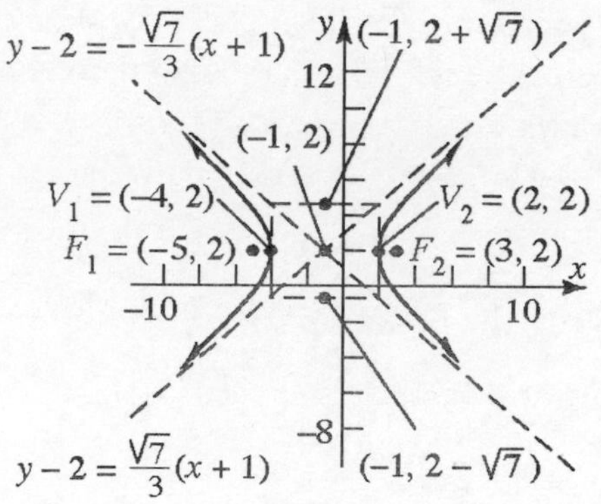

34. Hyperbola: Center: $(4, -2)$; $a = 1$; $c = 4$; Transverse axis parallel to the y-axis;

Find b:

$$b^2 = c^2 - a^2 = 16 - 1 = 15 \rightarrow b = \sqrt{15}$$

Write the equation: $\frac{(y+2)^2}{1} - \frac{(x-4)^2}{15} = 1$

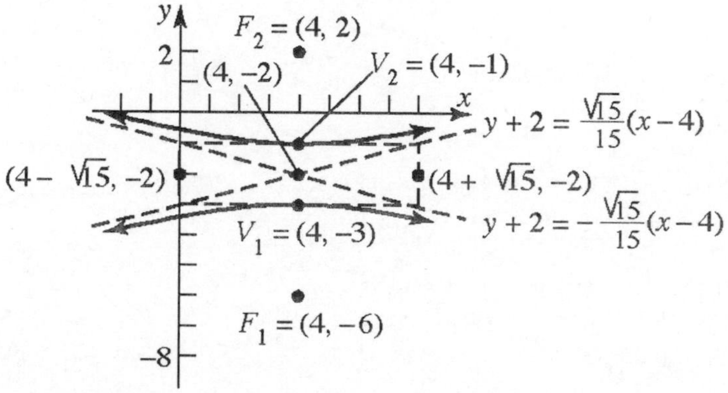

35. Hyperbola: Vertices: $(0, 1)$, $(6, 1)$; Asymptote: $3y + 2x - 9 = 0$; Center: $(3, 1)$;

Transverse axis is parallel to the x-axis; $a = 3$; The slope of the asymptote is $-\frac{2}{3}$;

Find b:

$$\frac{-b}{a} = \frac{-b}{3} = \frac{-2}{3} \rightarrow -3b = -6 \rightarrow b = 2$$

Write the equation: $\frac{(x-3)^2}{9} - \frac{(y-1)^2}{4} = 1$

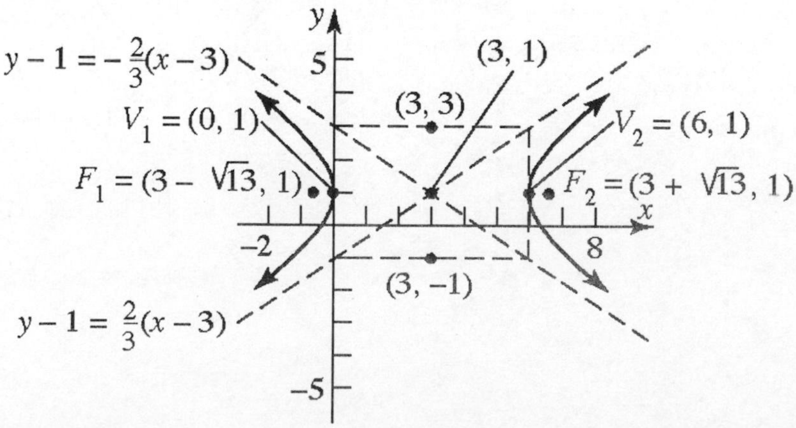

36. Hyperbola: Vertices: (4, 0), (4, 4);
Asymptote: $y + 2x - 10 = 0$; Center: (4, 2);
Transverse axis is parallel to the y-axis; $a = 2$;
The slope of the asymptote is -2; Find b:
$$\frac{-a}{b} = \frac{-2}{b} = -2 \rightarrow -2b = -2 \rightarrow b = 1$$
Write the equation: $\frac{(y-2)^2}{4} - \frac{(x-4)^2}{1} = 1$

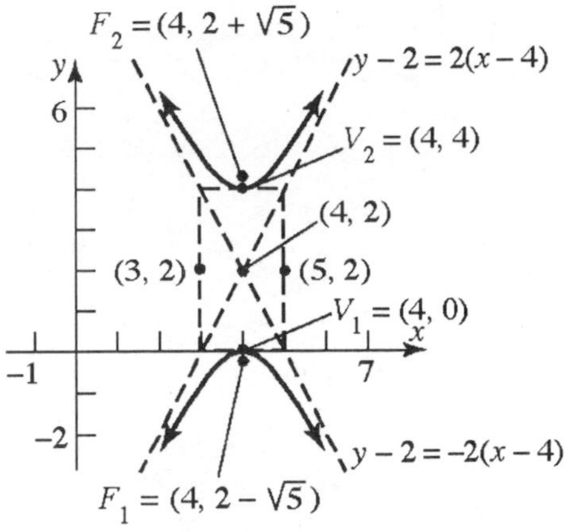

37. $y^2 + 4x + 3y - 8 = 0$
$A = 0$ and $C = 1$; $AC = (0)(1) = 0$. Since $AC = 0$, the equation defines a parabola.

38. $2x^2 - y + 8x = 0$
$A = 2$ and $C = 0$; $AC = (2)(0) = 0$. Since $AC = 0$, the equation defines a parabola.

39. $x^2 + 2y^2 + 4x - 8y + 2 = 0$
$A = 1$ and $C = 2$; $AC = (1)(2) = 2$. Since $AC > 0$ and $A \neq C$, the equation defines an ellipse.

40. $x^2 - 8y^2 - x - 2y = 0$
$A = 1$ and $C = -8$; $AC = (1)(-8) = -8$. Since $AC < 0$, the equation defines a hyperbola.

41. $9x^2 - 12xy + 4y^2 + 8x + 12y = 0$
$A = 9,\ B = -12,\ C = 4$ $\quad B^2 - 4AC = (-12)^2 - 4(9)(4) = 0$; parabola

42. $4x^2 + 4xy + y^2 - 8\sqrt{5}\,x + 16\sqrt{5}\,y = 0$
$A = 4,\ B = 4,\ C = 1$ $\quad B^2 - 4AC = 4^2 - 4(4)(1) = 0$; parabola

43. $4x^2 + 10xy + 4y^2 - 9 = 0$
$A = 4,\ B = 10,\ C = 4$ $\quad B^2 - 4AC = 10^2 - 4(4)(4) = 36 > 0$; hyperbola

44. $4x^2 - 10xy + 4y^2 - 9 = 0$
$A = 4,\ B = -10,\ C = 4$ $\quad B^2 - 4AC = (-10)^2 - 4(4)(4) = 36 > 0$; hyperbola

45. $x^2 - 2xy + 3y^2 + 2x + 4y - 1 = 0$
$A = 1,\ B = -2,\ C = 3$ $\quad B^2 - 4AC = (-2)^2 - 4(1)(3) = -8 < 0$; ellipse

46. $4x^2 + 12xy - 10y^2 + x + y - 10 = 0$
$A = 4,\ B = 12,\ C = -10$ $\quad B^2 - 4AC = 12^2 - 4(4)(-10) = 304 > 0$; hyperbola

47. $2x^2+5xy+2y^2-\frac{9}{2}=0$

$A=2, B=5, \text{ and } C=2;\ \cot(2\theta)=\frac{A-C}{B}=\frac{2-2}{5}=0 \rightarrow 2\theta=\frac{\pi}{2} \rightarrow \theta=\frac{\pi}{4}$

$x=x'\cos\theta-y'\sin\theta=\frac{\sqrt{2}}{2}x'-\frac{\sqrt{2}}{2}y'=\frac{\sqrt{2}}{2}(x'-y')$

$y=x'\sin\theta+y'\cos\theta=\frac{\sqrt{2}}{2}x'+\frac{\sqrt{2}}{2}y'=\frac{\sqrt{2}}{2}(x'+y')$

$2\left(\frac{\sqrt{2}}{2}(x'-y')\right)^2+5\left(\frac{\sqrt{2}}{2}(x'-y')\right)\left(\frac{\sqrt{2}}{2}(x'+y')\right)+2\left(\frac{\sqrt{2}}{2}(x'+y')\right)^2-\frac{9}{2}=0$

$\left(x'^2-2x'y'+y'^2\right)+\frac{5}{2}\left(x'^2-y'^2\right)+\left(x'^2+2x'y'+y'^2\right)-\frac{9}{2}=0$

$\frac{9}{2}x'^2-\frac{1}{2}y'^2=\frac{9}{2} \rightarrow 9x'^2-y'^2=9 \rightarrow \frac{x'^2}{1}-\frac{y'^2}{9}=1$

Hyperbola; center at (0, 0), transverse axis is the x'-axis, vertices at (±1, 0).

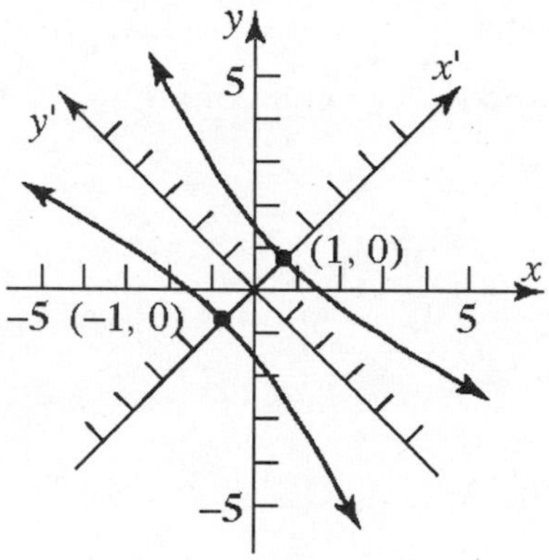

48. $2x^2-5xy+2y^2-\frac{9}{2}=0$

$A=2, B=-5, \text{ and } C=2;\ \cot(2\theta)=\frac{A-C}{B}=\frac{2-2}{-5}=0 \rightarrow 2\theta=\frac{\pi}{2} \rightarrow \theta=\frac{\pi}{4}$

$x=x'\cos\theta-y'\sin\theta=\frac{\sqrt{2}}{2}x'-\frac{\sqrt{2}}{2}y'=\frac{\sqrt{2}}{2}(x'-y')$

$y=x'\sin\theta+y'\cos\theta=\frac{\sqrt{2}}{2}x'+\frac{\sqrt{2}}{2}y'=\frac{\sqrt{2}}{2}(x'+y')$

$2\left(\frac{\sqrt{2}}{2}(x'-y')\right)^2-5\left(\frac{\sqrt{2}}{2}(x'-y')\right)\left(\frac{\sqrt{2}}{2}(x'+y')\right)+2\left(\frac{\sqrt{2}}{2}(x'+y')\right)^2-\frac{9}{2}=0$

$\left(x'^2-2x'y'+y'^2\right)-\frac{5}{2}\left(x'^2-y'^2\right)+\left(x'^2+2x'y'+y'^2\right)-\frac{9}{2}=0$

$-\frac{1}{2}x'^2+\frac{9}{2}y'^2=\frac{9}{2} \rightarrow -x'^2+9y'^2=9 \rightarrow \frac{y'^2}{1}-\frac{x'^2}{9}=1$

Hyperbola; center at (0, 0), transverse axis is the y'-axis, vertices at (0, ±1).

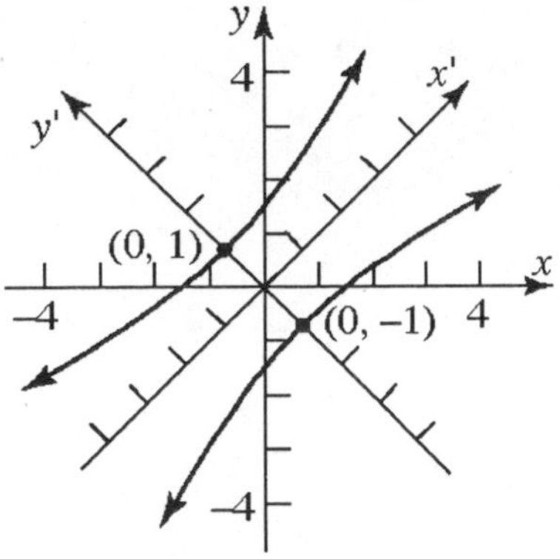

49. $6x^2 + 4xy + 9y^2 - 20 = 0$

$A = 6$, $B = 4$, and $C = 9$; $\cot(2\theta) = \dfrac{A-C}{B} = \dfrac{6-9}{4} = -\dfrac{3}{4} \rightarrow \cos(2\theta) = -\dfrac{3}{5}$

$$\sin\theta = \sqrt{\frac{\left(1-\left(-\frac{3}{5}\right)\right)}{2}} = \sqrt{\frac{4}{5}} = \frac{2\sqrt{5}}{5};\quad \cos\theta = \sqrt{\frac{\left(1+\left(-\frac{3}{5}\right)\right)}{2}} = \sqrt{\frac{1}{5}} = \frac{\sqrt{5}}{5} \rightarrow \theta \approx 63.4°$$

$$x = x'\cos\theta - y'\sin\theta = \frac{\sqrt{5}}{5}x' - \frac{2\sqrt{5}}{5}y' = \frac{\sqrt{5}}{5}(x' - 2y')$$

$$y = x'\sin\theta + y'\cos\theta = \frac{2\sqrt{5}}{5}x' + \frac{\sqrt{5}}{5}y' = \frac{\sqrt{5}}{5}(2x' + y')$$

$$6\left(\frac{\sqrt{5}}{5}(x'-2y')\right)^2 + 4\left(\frac{\sqrt{5}}{5}(x'-2y')\right)\left(\frac{\sqrt{5}}{5}(2x'+y')\right) + 9\left(\frac{\sqrt{5}}{5}(2x'+y')\right)^2 - 20 = 0$$

$$\frac{6}{5}\left(x'^2 - 4x'y' + 4y'^2\right) + \frac{4}{5}\left(2x'^2 - 3x'y' - 2y'^2\right) + \frac{9}{5}\left(4x'^2 + 4x'y' + y'^2\right) - 20 = 0$$

$$\frac{6}{5}x'^2 - \frac{24}{5}x'y' + \frac{24}{5}y'^2 + \frac{8}{5}x'^2 - \frac{12}{5}x'y' - \frac{8}{5}y'^2 + \frac{36}{5}x'^2 + \frac{36}{5}x'y' + \frac{9}{5}y'^2 = 20$$

$$10x'^2 + 5y'^2 = 20 \rightarrow \frac{x'^2}{2} + \frac{y'^2}{4} = 1$$

Ellipse; center at the origin, major axis is the y'-axis, vertices at (0, ±2).

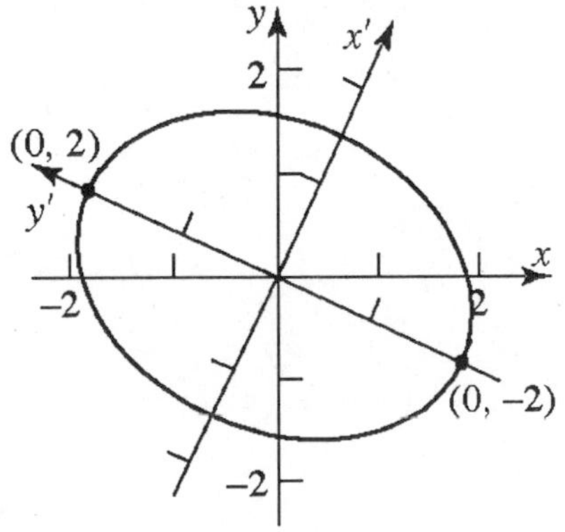

50. $x^2+4xy+4y^2+16\sqrt{5}x-8\sqrt{5}y=0$

$A=1,\ B=4,$ and $C=4;\ \cot(2\theta)=\dfrac{A-C}{B}=\dfrac{1-4}{4}=-\dfrac{3}{4};\ \cos(2\theta)=-\dfrac{3}{5}$

$$\sin\theta=\sqrt{\frac{1-\left(-\frac{3}{5}\right)}{2}}=\sqrt{\frac{4}{5}}=\frac{2\sqrt{5}}{5};\ \cos\theta=\sqrt{\frac{1+\left(-\frac{3}{5}\right)}{2}}=\sqrt{\frac{1}{5}}=\frac{\sqrt{5}}{5}\ \rightarrow\ \theta=63.4^\circ$$

$$x=x'\cos\theta-y'\sin\theta=\frac{\sqrt{5}}{5}x'-\frac{2\sqrt{5}}{5}y'=\frac{\sqrt{5}}{5}(x'-2y')$$

$$y=x'\sin\theta+y'\cos\theta=\frac{2\sqrt{5}}{5}x'+\frac{\sqrt{5}}{5}y'=\frac{\sqrt{5}}{5}(2x'+y')$$

$$\left(\frac{\sqrt{5}}{5}(x'-2y')\right)^2+4\left(\frac{\sqrt{5}}{5}(x'-2y')\right)\left(\frac{\sqrt{5}}{5}(2x'+y')\right)+4\left(\frac{\sqrt{5}}{5}(2x'+y')\right)^2$$
$$+16\sqrt{5}\left(\frac{\sqrt{5}}{5}(x'-2y')\right)-8\sqrt{5}\left(\frac{\sqrt{5}}{5}(2x'+y')\right)=0$$

$$\frac{1}{5}\left(x'^2-4x'y'+4y'^2\right)+\frac{4}{5}\left(2x'^2-3x'y'-2y'^2\right)+\frac{4}{5}\left(4x'^2+4x'y'+y'^2\right)$$
$$+16x'-32y'-16x'-8y'=0$$

$$\frac{1}{5}x'^2-\frac{4}{5}x'y'+\frac{4}{5}y'^2+\frac{8}{5}x'^2-\frac{12}{5}x'y'-\frac{8}{5}y'^2+\frac{16}{5}x'^2+\frac{16}{5}x'y'+\frac{4}{5}y'^2-40y'=0$$

$5x'^2-40y'=0\rightarrow x'^2=8y'$

Parabola; vertex at the origin, focus at (0, 2).

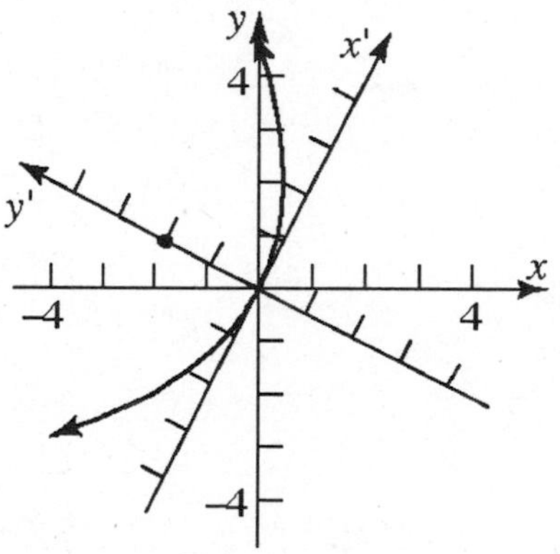

51. $4x^2-12xy+9y^2+12x+8y=0$

$A=4,\ B=-12,$ and $C=9;\ \cot(2\theta)=\dfrac{A-C}{B}=\dfrac{4-9}{-12}=\dfrac{5}{12}\ \rightarrow\ \cos(2\theta)=\dfrac{5}{13}$

$$\sin\theta=\sqrt{\frac{\left(1-\frac{5}{13}\right)}{2}}=\sqrt{\frac{4}{13}}=\frac{2\sqrt{13}}{13};\ \cos\theta=\sqrt{\frac{\left(1+\frac{5}{13}\right)}{2}}=\sqrt{\frac{9}{13}}=\frac{3\sqrt{13}}{13}\ \rightarrow\ \theta\approx 33.7^\circ$$

$$x=x'\cos\theta-y'\sin\theta=\frac{3\sqrt{13}}{13}x'-\frac{2\sqrt{13}}{13}y'=\frac{\sqrt{13}}{13}(3x'-2y')$$

$$y=x'\sin\theta+y'\cos\theta=\frac{2\sqrt{13}}{13}x'+\frac{3\sqrt{13}}{13}y'=\frac{\sqrt{13}}{13}(2x'+3y')$$

$$4\left(\frac{\sqrt{13}}{13}(3x'-2y')\right)^2-12\left(\frac{\sqrt{13}}{13}(3x'-2y')\right)\left(\frac{\sqrt{13}}{13}(2x'+3y')\right)+9\left(\frac{\sqrt{13}}{13}(2x'+3y')\right)^2$$
$$+12\left(\frac{\sqrt{13}}{13}(3x'-2y')\right)+8\left(\frac{\sqrt{13}}{13}(2x'+3y')\right)=0$$

$$\frac{4}{13}\left(9x'^2-12x'y'+4y'^2\right)-\frac{12}{13}\left(6x'^2+5x'y'-6y'^2\right)+\frac{9}{13}\left(4x'^2+12x'y'+9y'^2\right)$$
$$+\frac{36\sqrt{13}}{13}x'-\frac{24\sqrt{13}}{13}y'+\frac{16\sqrt{13}}{13}x'+\frac{24\sqrt{13}}{13}y'=0$$

$$\frac{36}{13}x'^2-\frac{48}{13}x'y'+\frac{16}{13}y'^2-\frac{72}{13}x'^2-\frac{60}{13}x'y'+\frac{72}{13}y'^2$$
$$+\frac{36}{13}x'^2+\frac{108}{13}x'y'+\frac{81}{13}y'^2+4\sqrt{13}x'=0$$

$$13y'^2+4\sqrt{13}x'=0$$
$$y'^2=-\frac{4\sqrt{13}}{13}x'$$

Parabola; vertex at the origin, focus at $\left(-\frac{\sqrt{13}}{13},0\right)$.

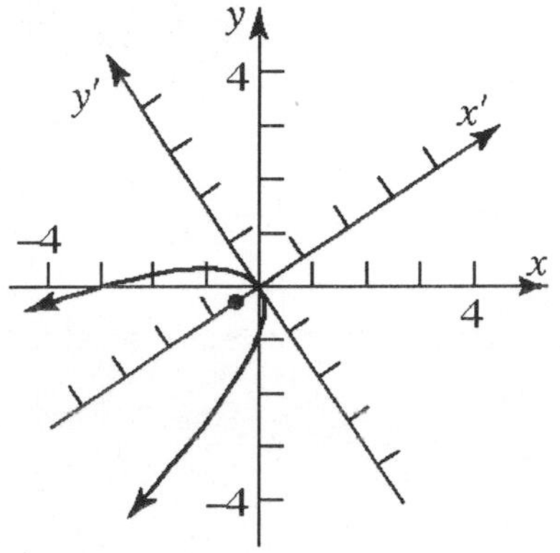

52. $9x^2-24xy+16y^2+80x+60y=0$

$A=9,\ B=-24,$ and $C=16;\ \cot(2\theta)=\frac{A-C}{B}=\frac{9-16}{-24}=\frac{7}{24}\ \rightarrow\ \cos(2\theta)=\frac{7}{25}$

$$\sin\theta=\sqrt{\frac{\left(1-\frac{7}{25}\right)}{2}}=\sqrt{\frac{9}{25}}=\frac{3}{5};\quad \cos\theta=\sqrt{\frac{\left(1+\frac{7}{25}\right)}{2}}=\sqrt{\frac{16}{25}}=\frac{4}{5}\ \rightarrow\ \theta\approx 36.9$$

$$x=x'\cos\theta-y'\sin\theta=\frac{4}{5}x'-\frac{3}{5}y'=\frac{1}{5}(4x'-3y')$$

$$y=x'\sin\theta+y'\cos\theta=\frac{3}{5}x'+\frac{4}{5}y'=\frac{1}{5}(3x'+4y')$$

$$9\left(\frac{1}{5}(4x'-3y')\right)^2-24\left(\frac{1}{5}(4x'-3y')\right)\left(\frac{1}{5}(3x'+4y')\right)+16\left(\frac{1}{5}(3x'+4y')\right)^2$$
$$+80\left(\frac{1}{5}(4x'-3y')\right)+60\left(\frac{1}{5}(3x'+4y')\right)=0$$

$$\frac{9}{25}\left(16x'^2-24x'y'+9y'^2\right)-\frac{24}{25}\left(12x'^2+7x'y'-12y'^2\right)+\frac{16}{25}\left(9x'^2+24x'y'+16y'^2\right)$$
$$+64x'-48y'+36x'+48y'=0$$

$$\frac{144}{25}x'^2-\frac{216}{25}x'y'+\frac{81}{25}y'^2-\frac{288}{25}x'^2-\frac{168}{25}x'y'+\frac{288}{25}y'^2$$
$$+\frac{144}{25}x'^2+\frac{384}{25}x'y'+\frac{256}{25}y'^2+100x'=0$$

$25y'^2+100x'=0 \rightarrow y'^2=-4x'$

Parabola; vertex at (0, 0), focus at (–1, 0).

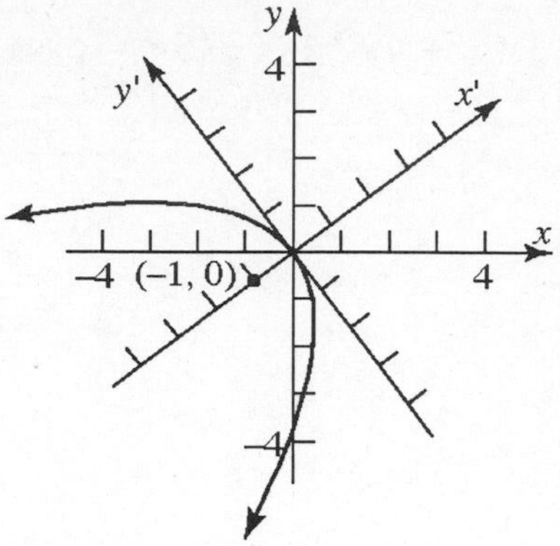

53. $r=\dfrac{4}{1-\cos\theta}$

$ep=4,\ e=1,\ p=4$

Parabola; directrix is perpendicular to the polar axis 4 units to the left of the pole; vertex is $(2, \pi)$.

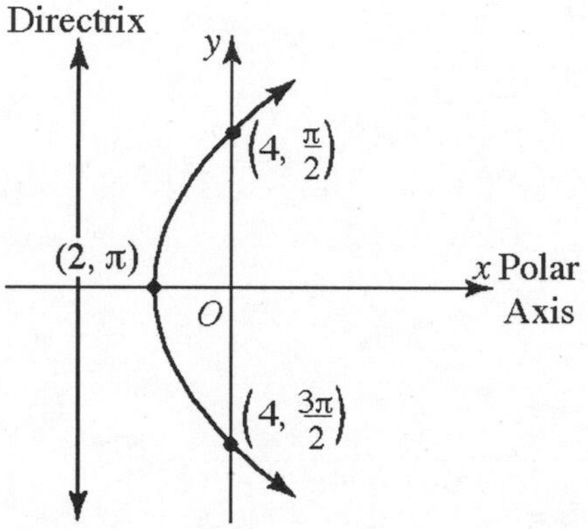

54. $r=\dfrac{6}{1+\sin\theta}$

$ep=6,\ e=1,\ p=6$

Parabola; directrix is parallel to the polar axis 6 units above the pole; vertex is $\left(3, \frac{\pi}{2}\right)$.

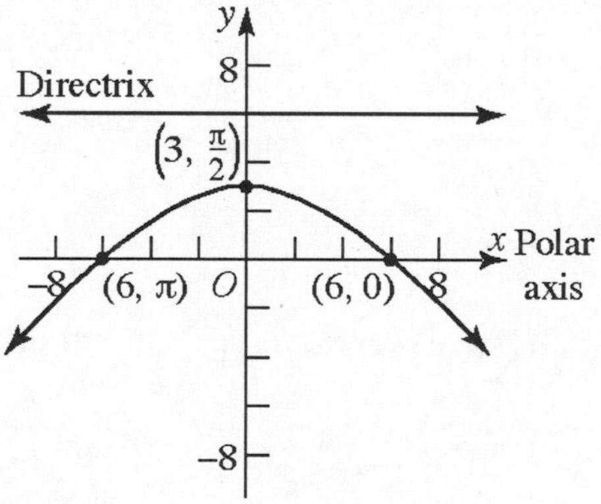

55. $r = \dfrac{6}{2-\sin\theta} = \dfrac{3}{\left(1-\dfrac{1}{2}\sin\theta\right)}$

$ep = 3,\ e = \dfrac{1}{2},\ p = 6$

Ellipse; directrix is parallel to the polar axis 6 units below the pole; vertices are $\left(6, \dfrac{\pi}{2}\right)$ and $\left(2, \dfrac{3\pi}{2}\right)$.

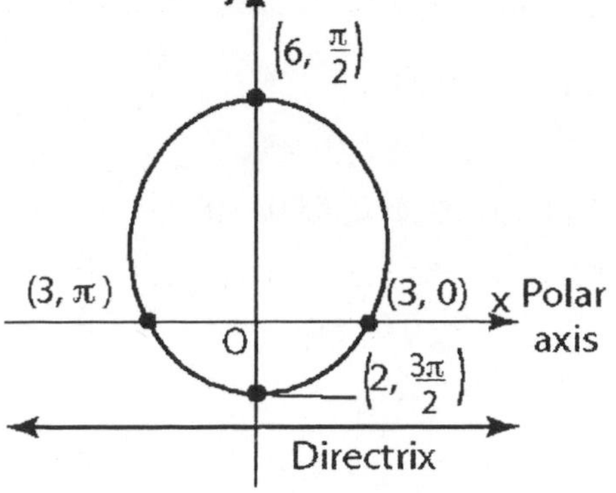

56. $r = \dfrac{2}{3+2\cos\theta} = \dfrac{\left(\dfrac{2}{3}\right)}{\left(1+\dfrac{2}{3}\cos\theta\right)}$

$ep = \dfrac{2}{3},\ e = \dfrac{2}{3},\ p = 1$

Ellipse; directrix is perpendicular to the polar axis 1 unit to the right of the pole; vertices are $\left(\dfrac{2}{5}, 0\right)$ and $(2, \pi)$.

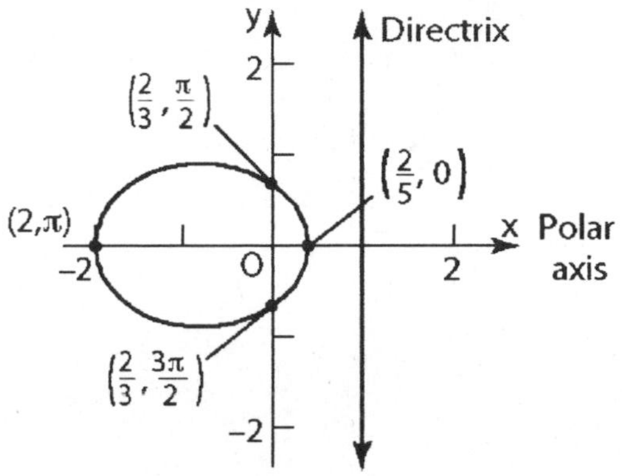

57. $r = \dfrac{8}{4+8\cos\theta} = \dfrac{2}{1+2\cos\theta}$

$ep = 2,\ e = 2,\ p = 1$

Hyperbola; directrix is perpendicular to the polar axis 1 unit to the right of the pole; vertices are $\left(\dfrac{2}{3}, 0\right)$ and $(-2, \pi)$.

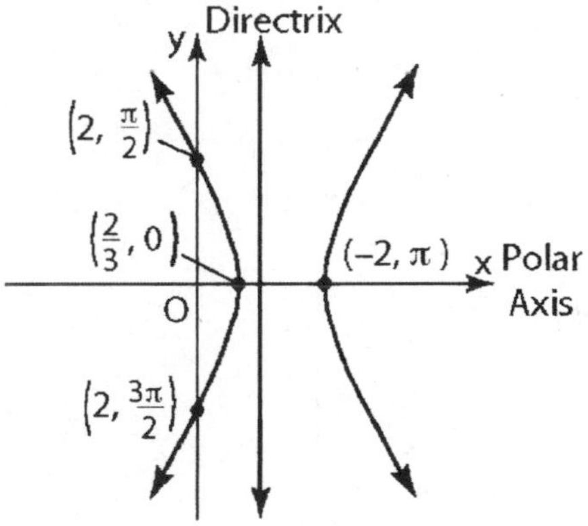

58. $r = \dfrac{10}{5+20\sin\theta} = \dfrac{2}{1+4\sin\theta}$

$ep = 2,\ e = 4,\ p = \dfrac{1}{2}$

Hyperbola; directrix is parallel to the polar axis $\dfrac{1}{2}$ unit above the pole; vertices are $\left(\dfrac{2}{5}, \dfrac{\pi}{2}\right)$ and $\left(-\dfrac{2}{3}, \dfrac{3\pi}{2}\right)$.

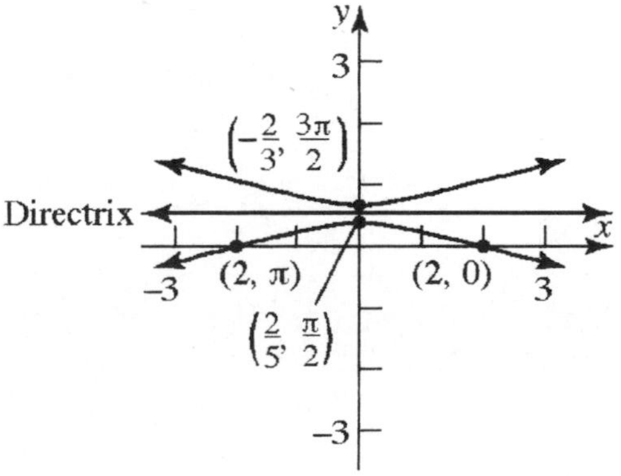

59. $r = \dfrac{4}{1-\cos\theta}$

$r - r\cos\theta = 4$

$r = 4 + r\cos\theta$

$r^2 = (4 + r\cos\theta)^2$

$x^2 + y^2 = (4+x)^2$

$x^2 + y^2 = 16 + 8x + x^2$

$y^2 - 8x - 16 = 0$

60. $r = \dfrac{6}{2-\sin\theta}$

$2r - r\sin\theta = 6$

$2r = 6 + r\sin\theta$

$4r^2 = (6 + r\sin\theta)^2$

$4(x^2 + y^2) = (6+y)^2$

$4x^2 + 4y^2 = 36 + 12y + y^2$

$4x^2 + 3y^2 - 12y - 36 = 0$

61. $r = \dfrac{8}{4+8\cos\theta}$

$4r + 8r\cos\theta = 8$

$4r = 8 - 8r\cos\theta$

$r = 2 - 2r\cos\theta$

$r^2 = (2 - 2r\cos\theta)^2$

$x^2 + y^2 = (2-2x)^2$

$x^2 + y^2 = 4 - 8x + 4x^2$

$3x^2 - y^2 - 8x + 4 = 0$

62. $r = \dfrac{2}{3+2\cos\theta}$

$3r + 2r\cos\theta = 2$

$3r = 2 - 2r\cos\theta$

$9r^2 = (2 - 2r\cos\theta)^2$

$9(x^2 + y^2) = (2-2x)^2$

$9x^2 + 9y^2 = 4 - 8x + 4x^2$

$5x^2 + 9y^2 + 8x - 4 = 0$

63. $x = 4t - 2, \ y = 1 - t, \ -\infty < t < \infty$

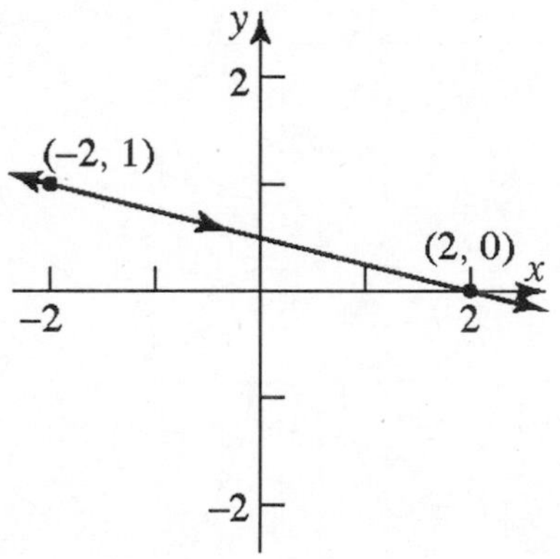

$x = 4(1-y) - 2$

$x = 4 - 4y - 2$

$x + 4y = 2$

64. $x = 2t^2 + 6, \ y = 5 - t, \ -\infty < t < \infty$

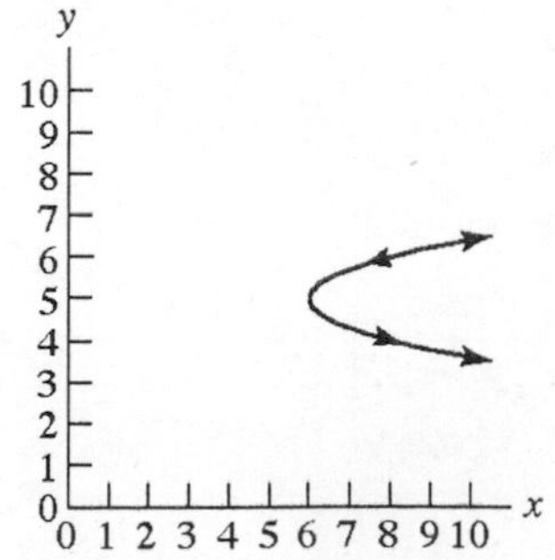

$x = 2(5-y)^2 + 6$

$x = 2(25 - 10y + y^2) + 6$

$x = 50 - 20y + 2y^2 + 6$

$x = 2y^2 - 20y + 56$

65. $x = 3\sin t,\ y = 4\cos t + 2,\ 0 \le t \le 2\pi$

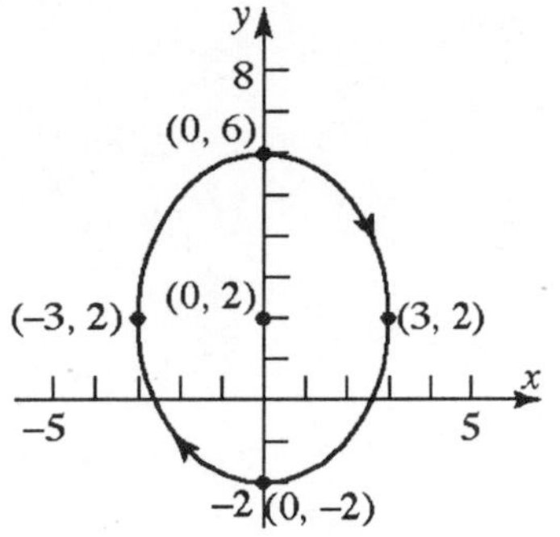

$$\frac{x}{3} = \sin t,\quad \frac{y-2}{4} = \cos t$$
$$\sin^2 t + \cos^2 t = 1$$
$$\left(\frac{x}{3}\right)^2 + \left(\frac{y-2}{4}\right)^2 = 1$$
$$\frac{x^2}{9} + \frac{(y-2)^2}{16} = 1$$

66. $x = \ln t,\ y = t^3,\ t > 0$

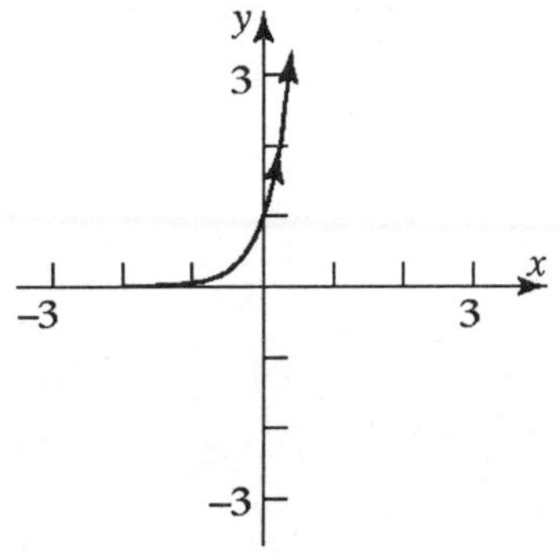

$$x = \ln y^{1/3} \rightarrow x = \frac{1}{3}\ln y$$

67. $x = \sec^2 t,\ y = \tan^2 t,\ 0 \le t \le \frac{\pi}{4}$

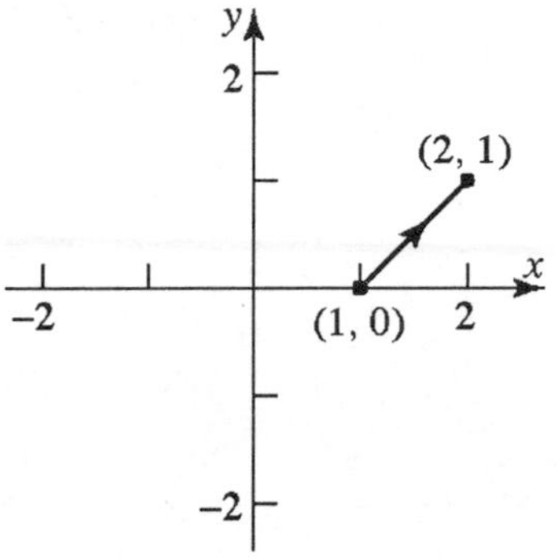

$$\tan^2 t + 1 = \sec^2 t \rightarrow y + 1 = x$$

68. $x = t^{3/2},\ y = 2t + 4,\ t \ge 0$

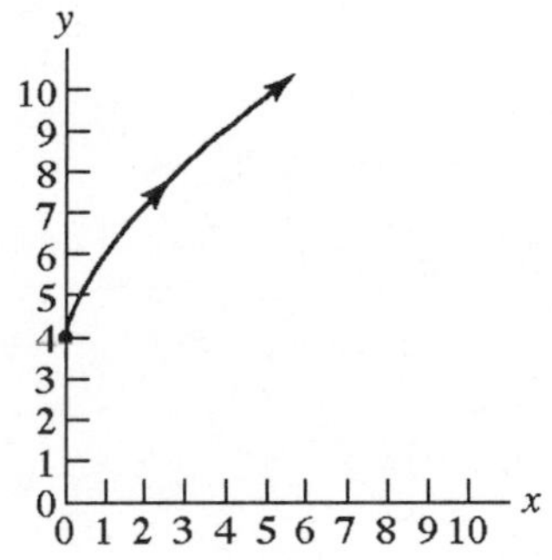

$$y = 2x^{2/3} + 4$$

69. Write the equation in standard form:

$$4x^2 + 9y^2 = 36 \rightarrow \frac{x^2}{9} + \frac{y^2}{4} = 1$$

The center of the ellipse is (0, 0). The major axis is the x-axis.
$a = 3;\ b = 2;\ c^2 = a^2 - b^2 = 9 - 4 = 5 \rightarrow c = \sqrt{5}$.
For the ellipse:
Vertices: (–3, 0), (3, 0)
Foci: $\left(-\sqrt{5}, 0\right)\left(\sqrt{5}, 0\right)$

For the hyperbola:

Foci: (–3, 0), (3, 0)

Vertices: $\left(-\sqrt{5}, 0\right)\left(\sqrt{5}, 0\right)$

Center: (0, 0)

$a=\sqrt{5};\ c=3;\ b^2=c^2-a^2=9-5=4 \rightarrow b=2$

The equation of the hyperbola is: $\dfrac{x^2}{5}-\dfrac{y^2}{4}=1$

70. Write the equation in standard form:

$$x^2-4y^2=16 \rightarrow \frac{x^2}{16}-\frac{y^2}{4}=1$$

The center of the hyperbola is (0, 0). The transverse axis is the x-axis.

$a=4;\ b=2;\ c^2=a^2+b^2=16+4=20 \rightarrow c=\sqrt{20}=2\sqrt{5}.$

For the hyperbola:

Vertices: (–4, 0), (4, 0)

Foci: $\left(-2\sqrt{5}, 0\right)\left(2\sqrt{5}, 0\right)$

For the ellipse:

Foci: (–4, 0), (4, 0)

Vertices: $\left(-2\sqrt{5}, 0\right)\left(2\sqrt{5}, 0\right)$

Center: (0, 0)

$a=2\sqrt{5};\ c=4;\ b^2=a^2-c^2=20-16=4 \rightarrow b=2$

The equation of the ellipse is: $\dfrac{x^2}{20}+\dfrac{y^2}{4}=1$

71. Let (x, y) be any point in the collection of points.

The distance from (x, y) to $(3, 0)=\sqrt{(x-3)^2+y^2}$.

The distance from (x, y) to the line $x=\dfrac{16}{3}$ is $\left|x-\dfrac{16}{3}\right|$.

Relating the distances, we have:

$$\sqrt{(x-3)^2+y^2}=\frac{3}{4}\left|x-\frac{16}{3}\right| \rightarrow (x-3)^2+y^2=\frac{9}{16}\left(x-\frac{16}{3}\right)^2$$

$$x^2-6x+9+y^2=\frac{9}{16}\left(x^2-\frac{32}{3}x+\frac{256}{9}\right)$$

$$16x^2-96x+144+16y^2=9x^2-96x+256$$

$$7x^2+16y^2=112 \rightarrow \frac{7x^2}{112}+\frac{16y^2}{112}=1 \rightarrow \frac{x^2}{16}+\frac{y^2}{7}=1$$

The set of points is an ellipse.

72. Let (x, y) be any point in the collection of points.

The distance from (x, y) to $(5, 0)=\sqrt{(x-5)^2+y^2}$.

The distance from (x, y) to the line $x=\dfrac{16}{5}$ is $\left|x-\dfrac{16}{5}\right|$.

Relating the distances, we have:

$$\sqrt{(x-5)^2+y^2}=\frac{5}{4}\left|x-\frac{16}{5}\right| \rightarrow (x-5)^2+y^2=\frac{25}{16}\left(x-\frac{16}{5}\right)^2$$

$$x^2-10x+25+y^2=\frac{25}{16}\left(x^2-\frac{32}{5}x+\frac{256}{25}\right)$$

$$16x^2-160x+400+16y^2=25x^2-160x+256$$

$$9x^2-16y^2=144 \rightarrow \frac{9x^2}{144}-\frac{16y^2}{144}=1 \rightarrow \frac{x^2}{16}-\frac{y^2}{9}=1$$

The set of points is a hyperbola.

73. Locate the parabola so that the vertex is at (0, 0) and opens up. It then has the equation: $x^2 = 4ay$. Since the light source is located at the focus and is 1 foot from the base, $a = 1$. The diameter is 2, so the point (1, y) is located on the parabola. Solve for y:

$$1^2 = 4(1)y \rightarrow 1 = 4y \rightarrow y = 0.25 \text{ feet}$$

The mirror should be 0.25 feet deep or 3 inches deep.

74. Set up the problem so that the vertex of the parabola is at (0, 0) and it opens down. Then the equation of the parabola has the form: $x^2 = cy$.
The point (30, –20) is a point on the parabola.
Solve for c and find the equation:

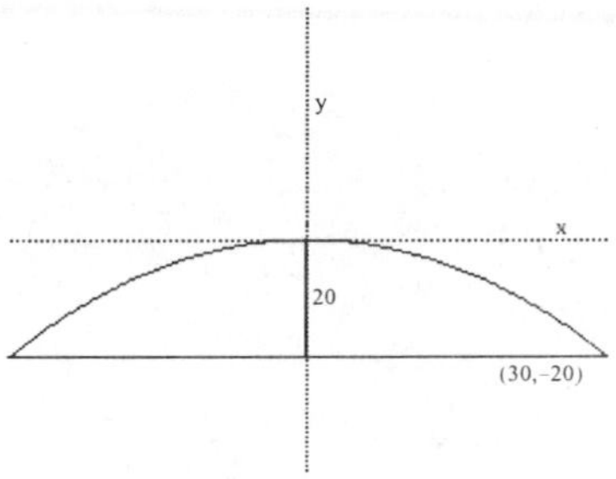

$$30^2 = c(-20) \rightarrow c = -45$$

$$x^2 = -45y$$

To find the height of the bridge, 5 feet from the center, the point (5, y) is a point on the parabola. Solve for y:

$$5^2 = -45y \rightarrow 25 = -45y \rightarrow y \approx -0.56$$

The height of the bridge, 5 feet from the center, is 20 – 0.56 = 19.44 feet.
To find the height of the bridge, 10 feet from the center, the point (10, y) is a point on the parabola. Solve for y:

$$10^2 = -45y \rightarrow 100 = -45y \rightarrow y \approx -2.22$$

The height of the bridge, 10 feet from the center, is 20 – 2.22 = 17.78 feet.
To find the height of the bridge, 20 feet from the center, the point (20, y) is a point on the parabola. Solve for y:

$$20^2 = -45y \rightarrow 400 = -45y \rightarrow y \approx -8.89$$

The height of the bridge, 20 feet from the center, is 20 – 8.89 = 11.11 feet.

75. Place the semielliptical arch so that the x-axis coincides with the water and the y-axis passes through the center of the arch. Since the bridge has a span of 60 feet, the length of the major axis is 60, or $2a = 60$ or $a = 30$. The maximum height of the bridge is 20 feet, so $b = 20$. The equation is: $\frac{x^2}{900}+\frac{y^2}{400}=1$.

The height 5 feet from the center:

$$\frac{5^2}{900}+\frac{y^2}{400}=1 \rightarrow \frac{y^2}{400}=1-\frac{25}{900} \rightarrow y^2 = 400\cdot\frac{875}{900} \rightarrow y \approx 19.72 \text{ feet}$$

The height 10 feet from the center:

$$\frac{10^2}{900}+\frac{y^2}{400}=1\to\frac{y^2}{400}=1-\frac{100}{900}\to y^2=400\cdot\frac{800}{900}\to y\approx 18.86\text{ feet}$$

The height 20 feet from the center:

$$\frac{20^2}{900}+\frac{y^2}{400}=1\to\frac{y^2}{400}=1-\frac{400}{900}\to y^2=400\cdot\frac{500}{900}\to y\approx 14.91\text{ feet}$$

76. The major axis is 80 feet; therefore, $2a=80$ or $a=40$. The maximum height is 25 feet, so $b=25$. To locate the foci, find c:

$$c^2=a^2-b^2=1600-625=975 \quad\to\quad c\approx 31.2$$

The foci are 31.2 feet from the center of the room or 8.8 feet from each wall.

77. (a) Set up a coordinate system so that the two stations lie on the x-axis and the origin is midway between them. The ship lies on a hyperbola whose foci are the locations of the two stations. Since the time difference is 0.00032 seconds and the speed of the signal is 186,000 miles per second, the difference in the distances of the ships from each station is:

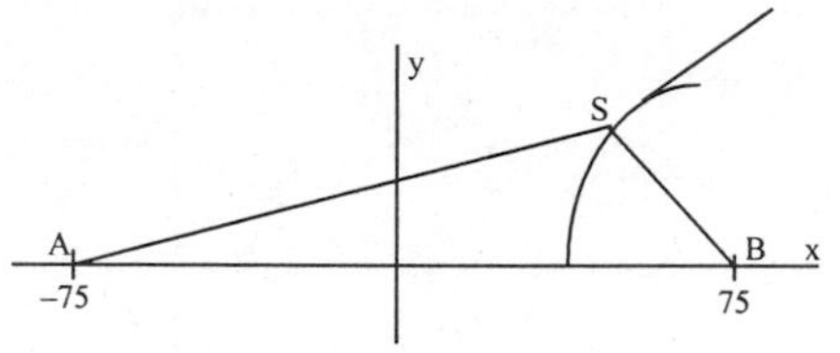

distance = (186,000)(0.00032) = 59.52 miles

The difference of the distances from the ship to each station, 59.52, equals $2a$, so $a=29.76$ and the vertex of the corresponding hyperbola is at (29.76, 0). Since the focus is at (75, 0), following this hyperbola, the ship would reach shore 45.24 miles from the master station.

(b) The ship should follow a hyperbola with a vertex at (60, 0). For this hyperbola, $a=60$, so the constant difference of the distances from the ship to each station is 120. The time difference the ship should look for is:

$$\text{time}=\frac{120}{186{,}000}=0.000645\text{ seconds}$$

(c) Find the equation of the hyperbola with vertex at (60, 0) and a focus at (75, 0). The form of the equation of the hyperbola is:

$$\frac{x^2}{a^2}-\frac{y^2}{b^2}=1 \quad\text{where } a=60.$$

Since $c=75$ and $b^2=c^2-a^2\ \to\ b^2=75^2-60^2=2025$.

The equation of the hyperbola is: $\dfrac{x^2}{3600}-\dfrac{y^2}{2025}=1$.

Since the ship is 20 miles off shore, we have $y=20$.

Solve the equation for x:

$$\frac{x^2}{3600}-\frac{20^2}{2025}=1\ \to\ \frac{x^2}{3600}=1+\frac{400}{2025}=\frac{97}{81}\ \to\ x^2=3600\cdot\frac{97}{81}$$

$$x\approx 66\text{ miles}$$

The ship's location is (66, 20).

78. (a) Train: Use equation (2) with $g = 3,\ v_0 = 0,\ h = 0$

$$x_1 = \frac{1}{2}(3)t^2 + 0 \cdot t + 0 = \frac{3}{2}t^2; \qquad y_1 = 1$$

Mary:

$$x_2 = 6(t-2); \qquad y_2 = 3$$

(b) Mary will catch the train if $x_1 = x_2$.

$$\frac{3}{2}t^2 = 6(t-2) \rightarrow \frac{3}{2}t^2 = 6t - 12 \rightarrow t^2 - 4t + 8 = 0$$

Since $b^2 - 4ac = (-4)^2 - 4(1)(8) = 16 - 32 = -16 < 0$, the equation has no real solution. Thus, Mary will not catch the train.

(c)

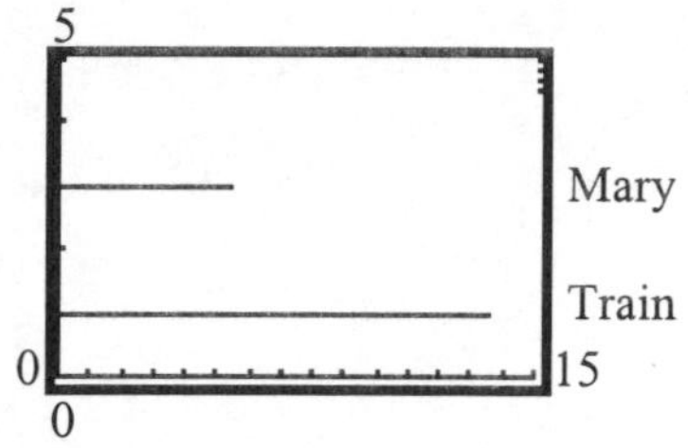

79. (a) Use equation (2):

$$x = (100\cos(35°))t; \qquad y = -\frac{1}{2}(32)t^2 + (100\sin(35°))t + 6$$

(b) The ball is in the air until $y = 0$. Solve:

$$-16t^2 + (100\sin(35°))t + 6 = 0$$

$$t = \frac{-100\sin(35°) \pm \sqrt{(100\sin(35°))^2 - 4(-16)(6)}}{2(-16)} \approx \frac{-57.36 \pm \sqrt{3673.9}}{-32} \approx -0.10 \text{ or } 3.69$$

The ball is in the air for about 3.69 seconds. (The negative solution is extraneous.)

(c) The maximum height occurs at the vertex of the quadratic function.

$$t = \frac{-b}{2a} = \frac{-100\sin(35°)}{2(-16)} \approx 1.79 \text{ seconds}$$

Evaluate the function to find the maximum height:

$$-16(1.79)^2 + 100\sin(35°)(1.79) + 6 \approx 57.4 \text{ feet}$$

(d) Find the horizontal displacement:

$$x = (100\cos(35°))(3.69) \approx 302 \text{ feet}$$

(e)

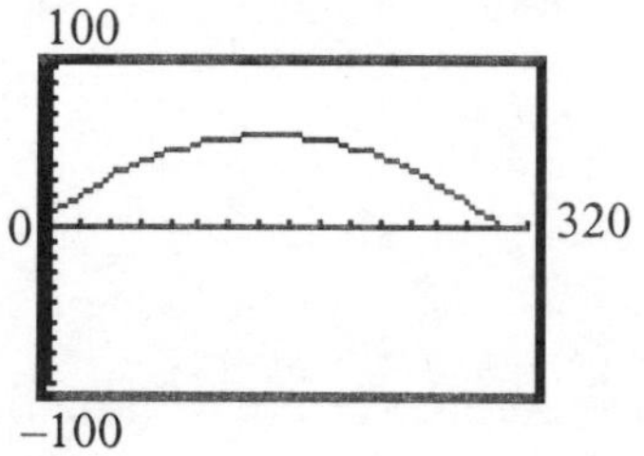

Chapter 12

Systems of Equations and Inequalities

12.1 Systems of Linear Equations: Two Equations Containing Two Variables

1. Substituting the values of the variables:

$$\begin{cases} 2x - y = 5 & \rightarrow \quad 2(2) - (-1) = 4 + 1 = 5 \\ 5x + 2y = 8 & \rightarrow \quad 5(2) + 2(-1) = 10 - 2 = 8 \end{cases}$$

Each equation is satisfied, so $x = 2,\ y = -1$ is a solution to the system of equations.

2. Substituting the values of the variables:

$$\begin{cases} 3x + 2y = \ \ 2 & \rightarrow \quad 3(-2) + 2(4) = -6 + 8 = 2 \\ x - 7y = -30 & \rightarrow \quad (-2) - 7(4) = -2 - 28 = -30 \end{cases}$$

Each equation is satisfied, so $x = -2,\ y = 4$ is a solution to the system of equations.

3. Substituting the values of the variables:

$$\begin{cases} 3x - 4y = 4 & \rightarrow \quad 3(2) - 4\left(\frac{1}{2}\right) = 6 - 2 = 4 \\ \frac{1}{2}x - 3y = -\frac{1}{2} & \rightarrow \quad \frac{1}{2}(2) - 3\left(\frac{1}{2}\right) = 1 - \frac{3}{2} = -\frac{1}{2} \end{cases}$$

Each equation is satisfied, so $x = 2,\ y = \frac{1}{2}$ is a solution to the system of equations.

4. Substituting the values of the variables:

$$\begin{cases} 2x + \frac{1}{2}y = \ \ 0 & \rightarrow \quad 2\left(-\frac{1}{2}\right) + \frac{1}{2}(2) = -1 + 1 = 0 \\ 3x - 4y = -\frac{19}{2} & \rightarrow \quad 3\left(-\frac{1}{2}\right) - 4(2) = -\frac{3}{2} - 8 = -\frac{19}{2} \end{cases}$$

Each equation is satisfied, so $x = -\frac{1}{2},\ y = 2$ is a solution to the system of equations.

5. Substituting the values of the variables:

$$\begin{cases} x^2 - y^2 = 3 & \rightarrow \quad 2^2 - 1^2 = 4 - 1 = 3 \\ xy = 2 & \rightarrow \quad (2)(1) = 2 \end{cases}$$

Each equation is satisfied, so $x = 2, y = 1$ is a solution to the system of equations.

6. Substituting the values of the variables:

$$\begin{cases} x^2 - y^2 = 3 & \rightarrow \quad (-2)^2 - (-1)^2 = 4 - 1 = 3 \\ xy = 2 & \rightarrow \quad (-2)(-1) = 2 \end{cases}$$

Each equation is satisfied, so $x = -2, y = -1$ is a solution to the system of equations.

7. Substituting the values of the variables:

$$\begin{cases} \dfrac{x}{1+x} + 3y = 6 & \rightarrow \quad \dfrac{0}{1+0} + 3(2) = 0 + 6 = 6 \\ x + 9y^2 = 36 & \rightarrow \quad 0 + 9(2)^2 = 0 + 9 \cdot 4 = 36 \end{cases}$$

Each equation is satisfied, so $x = 0, y = 2$ is a solution to the system.

8. Substituting the values of the variables:

$$\begin{cases} \dfrac{x}{x-1} + y = 5 & \rightarrow \quad \dfrac{2}{2-1} + 3 = 2 + 3 = 5 \\ 3x - y = 3 & \rightarrow \quad 3(2) - 3 = 6 - 3 = 3 \end{cases}$$

Each equation is satisfied, so $x = 2, y = 3$ is a solution to the system.

9. Solve the first equation for y, substitute into the second equation and solve:

$$\begin{cases} x + y = 8 & \rightarrow \quad y = 8 - x \\ x - y = 4 \end{cases}$$

$$x - (8 - x) = 4 \rightarrow x - 8 + x = 4$$

$$2x = 12 \rightarrow x = 6$$

Since $x = 6, \; y = 8 - 6 = 2$

The solution of the system is $x = 6, \; y = 2$.

10. Solve the first equation for x, substitute into the second equation and solve:

$$\begin{cases} x + 2y = 5 & \rightarrow \quad x = 5 - 2y \\ x + \; y = 3 \end{cases}$$

$$(5 - 2y) + y = 3 \rightarrow 5 - y = 3$$

$$-y = -2 \rightarrow y = 2$$

Since $y = 2, \; x = 5 - 2(2) = 1$ The solution of the system is $x = 1, \; y = 2$.

11. Multiply each side of the first equation by 3 and add the equations:

$$\begin{cases} 5x - \; y = 13 & \xrightarrow{3} \quad 15x - 3y = 39 \\ 2x + 3y = 12 & \longrightarrow \quad \underline{2x + 3y = 12} \end{cases}$$

$$17x \qquad = 51$$

$$x \qquad = 3$$

Substitute and solve for y:

$$5(3) - y = 13 \rightarrow 15 - y = 13 \rightarrow -y = -2 \rightarrow y = 2$$

The solution of the system is $x = 3, \; y = 2$.

12. Add the equations:

$$\begin{cases} x+3y = 5 \\ 2x-3y=-8 \end{cases}$$

$$3x = -3$$

$$x = -1$$

Substitute and solve for y:

$$-1+3y=5 \rightarrow 3y=6 \rightarrow y=2$$

The solution of the system is $x=-1,\ y=2$.

13. Solve the first equation for x and substitute into the second equation:

$$\begin{cases} 3x = 24 \rightarrow x=8 \\ x+2y = 0 \end{cases}$$

$$8+2y=0 \rightarrow 2y=-8 \rightarrow y=-4$$

The solution of the system is $x=8,\ y=-4$.

14. Solve the second equation for y and substitute into the first equation:

$$\begin{cases} 4x+5y=-3 \\ -2y=-4 \rightarrow y=2 \end{cases}$$

$$4x+5(2)=-3 \rightarrow 4x+10=-3 \rightarrow 4x=-13$$

$$x=-\frac{13}{4}$$

The solution of the system is $x=-\frac{13}{4},\ y=2$.

15. Multiply each side of the first equation by 2 and each side of the second equation by 3 to eliminate y:

$$\begin{cases} 3x-6y=2 \xrightarrow{2} 6x-12y=4 \\ 5x+4y=1 \xrightarrow{3} 15x+12y=3 \end{cases}$$

$$21x = 7$$

$$x = \frac{1}{3}$$

Substitute and solve for y:

$$3\left(\frac{1}{3}\right)-6y=2 \rightarrow 1-6y=2 \rightarrow -6y=1 \rightarrow y=-\frac{1}{6}$$

The solution of the system is $x=\frac{1}{3},\ y=-\frac{1}{6}$.

16. Multiply each side of the first equation by 5 and each side of the second equation by 4 to eliminate y:

$$\begin{cases} 2x+4y=\dfrac{2}{3} & \xrightarrow{5} & 10x+20y=\dfrac{10}{3} \\ 3x-5y=-10 & \xrightarrow{4} & 12x-20y=-40 \end{cases}$$

$$22x = -\frac{110}{3}$$

$$x = -\frac{5}{3}$$

Substitute and solve for y:

$$3\left(-\frac{5}{3}\right)-5y=-10 \rightarrow -5-5y=-10 \rightarrow -5y=-5 \rightarrow y=1$$

The solution of the system is $x=-\frac{5}{3},\ y=1$.

17. Solve the first equation for y, substitute into the second equation and solve:

$$\begin{cases} 2x+\ y=1 & \rightarrow & y=1-2x \\ 4x+2y=3 \end{cases}$$

$$4x+2(1-2x)=3 \rightarrow 4x+2-4x=3 \rightarrow 0x=1$$

This has no solution, so the system is inconsistent.

18. Solve the first equation for x, substitute into the second equation and solve:

$$\begin{cases} x-\ y=5 & \rightarrow & x=y+5 \\ -3x+3y=2 \end{cases}$$

$$-3(y+5)+3y=2 \rightarrow -3y-15+3y=2 \rightarrow 0y=17$$

This has no solution, so the system is inconsistent.

19. Solve the first equation for y, substitute into the second equation and solve:

$$\begin{cases} 2x-\ y=0 & \rightarrow & 2x=y \\ 3x+2y=7 \end{cases}$$

$$3x+2(2x)=7 \rightarrow 3x+4x=7 \rightarrow 7x=7 \rightarrow x=1$$

Since $x=1,\ y=2(1)=2$ The solution of the system is $x=1,\ y=2$.

20. Solve the second equation for y, substitute into the first equation and solve:

$$\begin{cases} 3x+3y=-1 \\ 4x+\ y=\dfrac{8}{3} & \rightarrow & y=\dfrac{8}{3}-4x \end{cases}$$

$$3x+3\left(\frac{8}{3}-4x\right)=-1 \rightarrow 3x+8-12x=-1 \rightarrow -9x=-9 \rightarrow x=1$$

Since $x=1,\ y=\frac{8}{3}-4(1)=\frac{8}{3}-4=-\frac{4}{3}$

The solution of the system is $x=1,\ y=-\frac{4}{3}$.

21. Solve the first equation for x, substitute into the second equation and solve:

$$\begin{cases} x+2y=4 \rightarrow x=4-2y \\ 2x+4y=8 \end{cases}$$

$$2(4-2y)+4y=8 \rightarrow 8-4y+4y=8 \rightarrow 0y=0$$

These equations are dependent. Any real number is a solution for y.
The solution of the system is $x=4-2y$, where y is any real number.

22. Solve the first equation for y, substitute into the second equation and solve:

$$\begin{cases} 3x-y=7 \rightarrow y=3x-7 \\ 9x-3y=21 \end{cases}$$

$$9x-3(3x-7)=21 \rightarrow 9x-9x+21=21 \rightarrow 0x=0$$

These equations are dependent. Any real number is a solution for x.
The solution of the system is $y=3x-7$, where x is any real number.

23. Multiply each side of the first equation by –5, and add the equations to eliminate x:

$$\begin{cases} 2x-3y=-1 \xrightarrow{-5} -10x+15y=5 \\ 10x+y=11 \longrightarrow \underline{10x+y=11} \end{cases}$$

$$16y=16$$

$$y=1$$

Substitute and solve for x:

$$2x-3(1)=-1 \rightarrow 2x-3=-1 \rightarrow 2x=2 \rightarrow x=1$$

The solution of the system is $x=1,\ y=1$.

24. Multiply each side of the first equation by 5, and add the equations to eliminate y:

$$\begin{cases} 3x-2y=0 \xrightarrow{5} 15x-10y=0 \\ 5x+10y=4 \longrightarrow \underline{5x+10y=4} \end{cases}$$

$$20x=4$$

$$x=\frac{1}{5}$$

Substitute and solve for y:

$$5\left(\frac{1}{5}\right)+10y=4 \rightarrow 1+10y=4 \rightarrow 10y=3 \rightarrow y=\frac{3}{10}$$

The solution of the system is $x=\frac{1}{5},\ y=\frac{3}{10}$.

25. Solve the second equation for x, substitute into the first equation and solve:

$$\begin{cases} 2x+3y=6 \\ x-\ y=\dfrac{1}{2} \quad \rightarrow \quad x=y+\dfrac{1}{2} \end{cases}$$

$$2\left(y+\frac{1}{2}\right)+3y=6 \rightarrow 2y+1+3y=6 \rightarrow 5y=5 \rightarrow y=1$$

Since $y=1,\ x=1+\frac{1}{2}=\frac{3}{2}$ The solution of the system is $x=\frac{3}{2},\ y=1$.

26. Solve the second equation for x, substitute into the first equation and solve:

$$\begin{cases} \dfrac{1}{2}x+y=-2 \\ x-2y=\ 8 \quad \rightarrow \quad x=2y+8 \end{cases}$$

$$\frac{1}{2}(2y+8)+y=-2 \rightarrow y+4+y=-2 \rightarrow 2y=-6 \rightarrow y=-3$$

Since $y=-3,\ x=2(-3)+8=-6+8=2$ The solution of the system is $x=2,\ y=-3$.

27. Multiply each side of the first equation by –6 and each side of the second equation by 12 to eliminate x:

$$\begin{cases} \dfrac{1}{2}x+\dfrac{1}{3}y=\ 3 \xrightarrow{-6} -3x-2y=-18 \\ \dfrac{1}{4}x-\dfrac{2}{3}y=-1 \xrightarrow{12} \underline{3x-8y=-12} \end{cases}$$

$$-10y=-30$$

$$y=3$$

Substitute and solve for x:

$$\frac{1}{2}x+\frac{1}{3}(3)=3 \rightarrow \frac{1}{2}x+1=3 \rightarrow \frac{1}{2}x=2 \rightarrow x=4$$

The solution of the system is $x=4,\ y=3$.

28. Multiply each side of the first equation by 6 and each side of the second equation by 12 to eliminate the fractions:

$$\begin{cases} \dfrac{1}{3}x-\dfrac{3}{2}y=-5 \xrightarrow{6} 2x-9y=-30 \xrightarrow{-9} -18x+81y=270 \\ \dfrac{3}{4}x+\dfrac{1}{3}y=11 \xrightarrow{12} 9x+4y=132 \xrightarrow{2} \underline{18x+\ 8y=264} \end{cases}$$

$$89y=534$$

$$y=6$$

Substitute and solve for x:

$$\frac{3}{4}x+\frac{1}{3}(6)=11 \rightarrow \frac{3}{4}x+2=11 \rightarrow \frac{3}{4}x=9 \rightarrow x=12$$

The solution of the system is $x=12,\ y=6$.

29. Add the equations to eliminate y and solve for x:

$$\begin{cases} 3x - 5y = 3 \\ 15x + 5y = 21 \end{cases}$$
$$18x = 24$$
$$x = \frac{4}{3}$$

Substitute and solve for y:

$$3\left(\frac{4}{3}\right) - 5y = 3 \rightarrow 4 - 5y = 3 \rightarrow -5y = -1 \rightarrow y = \frac{1}{5}$$

The solution of the system is $x = \frac{4}{3},\ y = \frac{1}{5}$.

30. Multiply each side of the second equation by 2, add the equations to eliminate y and solve for x:

$$\begin{cases} 2x - y = -1 & \longrightarrow & 2x - y = -1 \\ x + \frac{1}{2}y = \frac{3}{2} & \xrightarrow{2} & 2x + y = 3 \end{cases}$$
$$4x = 2$$
$$x = \frac{1}{2}$$

Substitute and solve for y:

$$2\left(\frac{1}{2}\right) - y = -1 \rightarrow 1 - y = -1 \rightarrow -y = -2 \rightarrow y = 2$$

The solution of the system is $x = \frac{1}{2},\ y = 2$.

31. Rewrite letting $a = \frac{1}{x},\ b = \frac{1}{y}$:

$$\begin{cases} \frac{1}{x} + \frac{1}{y} = 8 & \longrightarrow & a + b = 8 \\ \frac{3}{x} - \frac{5}{y} = 0 & \longrightarrow & 3a - 5b = 0 \end{cases}$$

Solve the first equation for a, substitute into the second equation and solve:

$$\begin{cases} a + b = 8 \rightarrow a = 8 - b \\ 3a - 5b = 0 \end{cases}$$

$$3(8 - b) - 5b = 0 \rightarrow 24 - 3b - 5b = 0 \rightarrow -8b = -24 \rightarrow b = 3$$

Since $b = 3,\ a = 8 - 3 = 5$

Thus, $x = \frac{1}{a} = \frac{1}{5},\ y = \frac{1}{b} = \frac{1}{3}$

The solution of the system is $x = \frac{1}{5},\ y = \frac{1}{3}$.

32. Rewrite letting $a = \frac{1}{x}, \; b = \frac{1}{y}$:

$$\begin{cases} \frac{4}{x} - \frac{3}{y} = 0 & \longrightarrow & 4a - 3b = 0 & \longrightarrow & 4a - 3b = 0 \\ \frac{6}{x} + \frac{3}{2y} = 2 & \longrightarrow & 6a + \frac{3}{2}b = 2 & \xrightarrow{2} & \underline{12a + 3b = 4} \end{cases}$$

$$16a = 4$$

$$a = \frac{1}{4}$$

Substitute and solve for b:

$$4\left(\frac{1}{4}\right) - 3b = 0 \rightarrow 1 - 3b = 0 \rightarrow -3b = -1 \rightarrow b = \frac{1}{3}$$

Thus, $x = \frac{1}{a} = 4, \; y = \frac{1}{b} = 3$ The solution of the system is $x = 4, \; y = 3$.

33. Graph the two equations as y_1 and y_2, and use INTERSECT to solve:

$$\begin{cases} y_1 = \sqrt{2}x - 20\sqrt{7} \\ y_2 = -0.1x + 20 \end{cases}$$

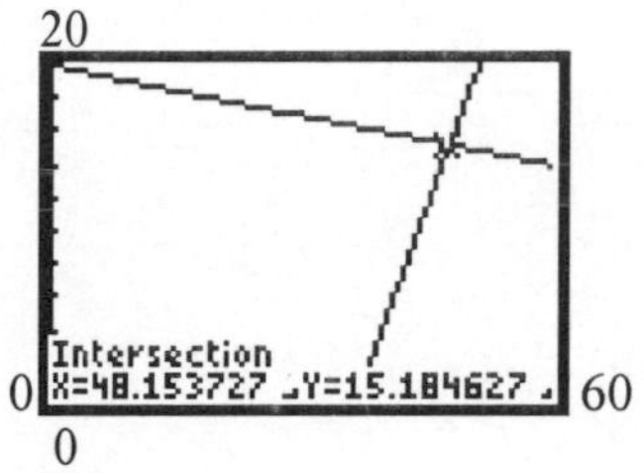

The solution of the system is $x = 48.15, \; y = 15.18$.

34. Graph the two equations as y_1 and y_2, and use INTERSECT to solve:

$$\begin{cases} y_1 = -\sqrt{2}x + 100 \\ y_2 = 0.2x + \sqrt{19} \end{cases}$$

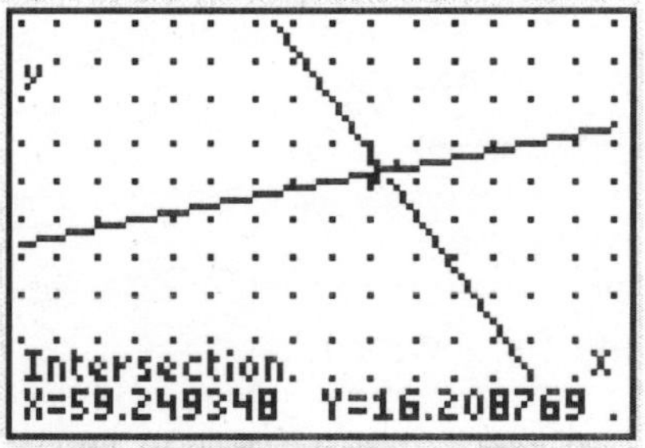

The solution of the system is $x = 59.25, \; y = 16.21$.

35. Solve for y in each equation, graph the two equations as y_1 and y_2, and use INTERSECT to solve:

$$\begin{cases} \sqrt{2}x + \sqrt{3}y + \sqrt{6} = 0 \\ \sqrt{3}x - \sqrt{2}y + 60 = 0 \end{cases}$$

$$\begin{cases} y_1 = \dfrac{-\sqrt{2}x - \sqrt{6}}{\sqrt{3}} \\ y_2 = \dfrac{\sqrt{3}x + 60}{\sqrt{2}} \end{cases}$$

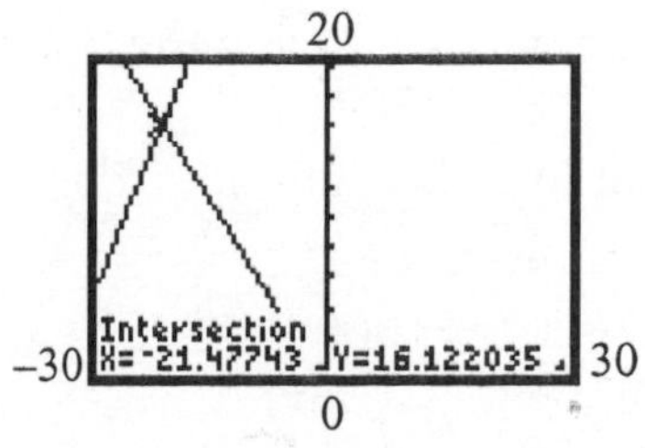

The solution of the system is $x = -21.48, \; y = 16.12$.

36. Solve for y in each equation, graph the two equations as y_1 and y_2, and use INTERSECT to solve:

$$\begin{cases} \sqrt{5}x - \sqrt{6}y + 60 = 0 \\ 0.2x + 0.3y + \sqrt{5} = 0 \end{cases}$$

$$\begin{cases} y_1 = \dfrac{\sqrt{5}x + 60}{\sqrt{6}} \\ y_2 = \dfrac{-0.2x - \sqrt{5}}{0.3} \end{cases}$$

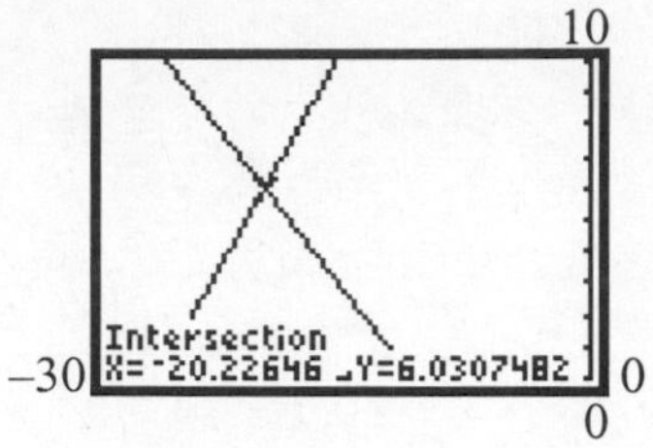

The solution of the system is $x = -20.23,\ y = 6.03$.

37. Solve for y in each equation, graph the two equations as y_1 and y_2, and use INTERSECT to solve:

$$\begin{cases} \sqrt{3}x + \sqrt{2}y = \sqrt{0.3} \\ 100x - 95y = 20 \end{cases}$$

$$\begin{cases} y_1 = \dfrac{-\sqrt{3}x + \sqrt{0.3}}{\sqrt{2}} \\ y_2 = \dfrac{100x - 20}{95} \end{cases}$$

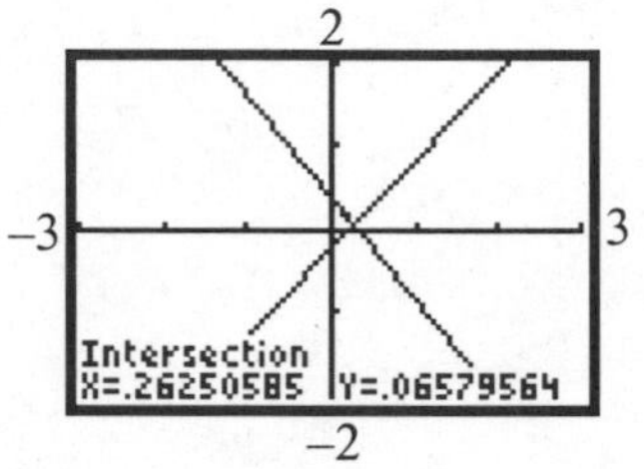

The solution of the system is $x = 0.26,\ y = 0.07$.

38. Solve for y in each equation, graph the two equations as y_1 and y_2, and use INTERSECT to solve:

$$\begin{cases} \sqrt{6}x - \sqrt{5}y + \sqrt{1.1} = 0 \\ y = -0.2x + 0.1 \end{cases}$$

$$\begin{cases} y_1 = \dfrac{\sqrt{6}x + \sqrt{1.1}}{\sqrt{5}} \\ y_2 = -0.2x + 0.1 \end{cases}$$

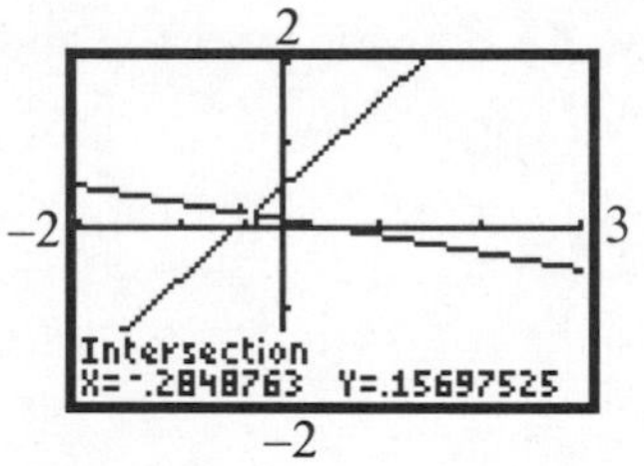

The solution of the system is $x = -0.28,\ y = 0.16$.

39. Solve the system by substitution:

$$Q_s = Q_d$$

$$-200 + 50p = 1000 - 25p \rightarrow 75p = 1200 \rightarrow p = 16$$

Therefore, $Q_s = -200 + 50(16) = -200 + 800 = 600$

The equilibrium price is \$16 and the equilibrium quantity is 600 T-shirts.

40. Solve the system by substitution:

$$Q_s = Q_d$$

$$-2000 + 3000p = 10000 - 1000p \rightarrow 4000p = 12000 \rightarrow p = 3$$

Therefore, $Q_s = -2000 + 3000(3) = -2000 + 9000 = 7000$

The equilibrium price is \$3 and the equilibrium quantity is 7000 hot dogs.

41. Let l be the length of the rectangle and w be the width of the rectangle. Then:

$$2l + 2w = 90$$
$$l = 2w$$

Solve by substitution:

$$2(2w) + 2w = 90$$
$$4w + 2w = 90 \to 6w = 90 \to w = 15 \text{ feet}$$
$$l = 2(15) = 30 \text{ feet}$$

The dimensions of the floor are 15 feet by 30 feet.

42. Let l be the length of the rectangle and w be the width of the rectangle. Then:

$$2l + 2w = 3000$$
$$l = w + 50$$

Solve by substitution:

$$2(w+50) + 2w = 3000 \to 2w + 100 + 2w = 3000 \to 4w = 2900 \to w = 725 \text{ meters}$$
$$l = 725 + 50 = 775 \text{ meters}$$

The dimensions of the field are 725 meters by 775 meters.

43. Let x = the cost of one cheeseburger and y = the cost of one shake. Then:

$$4x + 2y = 790$$
$$2y = x + 15$$

Solve by substitution:

$$4x + x + 15 = 790 \to 5x = 775 \to x = 155$$
$$2y = 155 + 15 \to 2y = 170 \to y = 85$$

A cheeseburger cost \$1.55 and a shake costs \$0.85.

44. Let x = the number of adult tickets sold and y = the number of senior tickets sold. Then:

$$x + y = 325 \quad \to \quad y = 325 - x$$
$$9x + 7y = 2495$$

Solve by substitution:

$$9x + 7(325 - x) = 2495$$
$$9x + 2275 - 7x = 2495$$
$$2x = 220 \to x = 110 \to y = 325 - 110 = 215$$

There were 110 adult tickets sold and 215 senior citizen tickets sold.

45. Let x = the number of pounds of cashews.
Then $x + 30$ is the number of pounds in the mixture.
The value of the cashews is $5x$.
The value of the peanuts is $1.50(30) = 45$.
The value of the mixture is $3(x+30)$.
Setting up a value equation:

$$5x + 45 = 3(x+30)$$
$$5x + 45 = 3x + 90$$
$$2x = 45$$
$$x = 22.5$$

22.5 pounds of cashews should be used in the mixture.

46. Let x = the amount invested in AA bonds.
Let y = the amount invested in the Bank Certificate.
(a) Then $x + y = 150{,}000$ represents the total investment.
$0.10x + 0.05y = 12{,}000$ represents the earnings on the investment.
Solve by substitution:

$$\begin{aligned} 0.10(150{,}000 - y) + 0.05y &= 12{,}000 \\ 15{,}000 - 0.10y + 0.05y &= 12{,}000 \\ -0.05y &= -3000 \\ y &= 60{,}000 \\ x &= 150{,}000 - 60{,}000 = 90{,}000 \end{aligned}$$

$90,000 should be invested in AA Bonds and $60,000 in a Bank Certificate.

(b) Then $x + y = 150{,}000$ represents the total investment.
$0.10x + 0.05y = 14{,}000$ represents the earnings on the investment.
Solve by substitution:

$$\begin{aligned} 0.10(150{,}000 - y) + 0.05y &= 14{,}000 \\ 15{,}000 - 0.10y + 0.05y &= 14{,}000 \\ -0.05y &= -1000 \\ y &= 20{,}000 \\ x &= 150{,}000 - 20{,}000 = 130{,}000 \end{aligned}$$

$130,000 should be invested in AA Bonds and $20,000 in a Bank Certificate.

47. Let x = the plane's air speed and y = the wind speed.

	Rate	Time	Distance
With Wind	$x+y$	3	600
Against	$x-y$	4	600

$$(x+y)(3) = 600 \rightarrow x+y = 200$$
$$(x-y)(4) = 600 \rightarrow x-y = 150$$

Solving by elimination:

$$\begin{aligned} 2x &= 350 \\ x &= 175 \\ y &= 200 - x = 200 - 175 = 25 \end{aligned}$$

The airspeed of the plane is 175 mph, and the wind speed is 25 mph.

48. Let y = the wind speed.

	Rate	Time	Distance
With Wind	$150+y$	2	$300+2y$
Against	$150-y$	3	$450-3y$

The distances are equal, so equate and solve:

$$\begin{aligned} 300 + 2y &= 450 - 3y \\ 5y &= 150 \\ y &= 30 \end{aligned}$$

The wind speed is 30 mph.

49. Let x = the number of one design.
Let y = the number of the second design.
Then $x+y$ = the total number of sets of dishes.
$25x+45y$ = the cost of the dishes.
Setting up the equations and solving by substitution:

$$\begin{cases} x + y = 200 \rightarrow y = 200 - x \\ 25x+45y = 7400 \end{cases}$$

$$25x+45(200-x) = 7400$$
$$25x+9000-45x = 7400$$
$$-20x = -1600$$
$$x = 80$$
$$y = 200-80 = 120$$

80 sets of the \$25 dishes and 120 sets of the \$45 dishes should be ordered.

50. Let x = the cost of a hot dog.
Let y = the cost of a soft drink.
Setting up the equations and solving by substitution:

$$\begin{cases} 10x+5y = 12.50 \xrightarrow{1/5} 2x+y = 2.50 \rightarrow y = 2.50-2x \\ 7x+4y = 9.00 \end{cases}$$

$$7x+4(2.50-2x) = 9.00$$
$$7x+10.00-8x = 9.00$$
$$-x = -1$$
$$x = 1.00$$
$$y = 2.50-2(1) = 0.50$$

A hot dog costs \$1.00 and a soft drink costs \$0.50.

51. Let x = the cost per package of bacon.
Let y = the cost of a carton of eggs.
Set up a system of equations for the problem:

$$\begin{cases} 3x+2y = 7.45 \\ 2x+3y = 6.45 \end{cases}$$

Multiply each side of the first equation by 3 and each side of the second equation by –2 and solve by elimination:

$$\begin{cases} 3x+2y = 7.45 \xrightarrow{3} 9x+6y = 22.35 \\ 2x+3y = 6.45 \xrightarrow{-2} -4x-6y = -12.90 \end{cases}$$

$$5x = 9.45$$
$$x = 1.89$$

Substitute and solve for y:

$$3(1.89)+2y = 7.45$$
$$5.67+2y = 7.45 \rightarrow 2y = 1.78 \rightarrow y = 0.89$$

A package of bacon costs \$1.89 and a carton of eggs cost \$0.89.
The refund for 2 packages of bacon and 2 cartons of eggs will be \$5.56.

52. Let x = Pamela's speed in still water.
Let y = the speed of the current.

	Rate	Time	Distance
Downstream	$x+y$	3	15
Upstream	$x-y$	5	15

Set up a system of equations for the problem:

$$\begin{cases} 3(x+y)=15 \xrightarrow{1/3} x+y=5 \rightarrow y=5-x \\ 5(x-y)=15 \xrightarrow{1/5} x-y=3 \end{cases}$$

Solve by substitution:

$$x-(5-x)=3 \rightarrow x-5+x=3 \rightarrow 2x=8 \rightarrow x=4$$
$$y=5-4=1$$

Pamela's speed is 4 miles per hour and the speed of the current is 1 mile per hour.

53. Let x = the # of mg of liquid 1.
Let y = the # of mg of liquid 2.
Setting up the equations and solving by substitution:

$$\begin{cases} 0.2x+0.4y=40 \text{ vitamin C} \\ 0.3x+0.2y=30 \text{ vitamin D} \end{cases}$$

multiplying each equation by 10 yields

$$\begin{cases} 2x+4y=400 \longrightarrow 2x+4y=400 \\ 3x+2y=300 \xrightarrow{2} 6x+4y=600 \end{cases}$$

subtracting the bottom equation from the top equation yields

$$2x+4y-(6x+4y)=-200$$
$$2x-6x=-200 \rightarrow -4x=-200 \rightarrow x=50$$
$$\rightarrow 2(50)+4y=400 \rightarrow 100+4y=400$$
$$\rightarrow 4y=300 \rightarrow y=\frac{300}{4}=75$$

So 50 mg of liquid 1 should be mixed with 75 mg of liquid 2.

54. Let x = the # of units of powder 1.
Let y = the # of units of powder 2.
Setting up the equations and solving by substitution

$$\begin{cases} 0.2x+0.4y=12 \text{ vitamin } B_{12} \\ 0.3x+0.2y=12 \text{ vitamin E} \end{cases}$$

multiplying each equation by 10 yields

$$\begin{cases} 2x+4y=120 \longrightarrow 2x+4y=120 \\ 3x+2y=120 \xrightarrow{2} 6x+4y=240 \end{cases}$$

subtracting the bottom equation from the top equation yields

$2x+4y-(6x+4y)=-120 \rightarrow 2x-6x=-120 \rightarrow -4x=-120 \rightarrow x=30$

$\rightarrow 2(30)+4y=120 \rightarrow 60+4y=120$

$\rightarrow 4y=60$

$y=\dfrac{60}{4}=15$

So 30 units of powder 1 should be mixed with 15 units of powder 2.

55. Solve the system by substitution:

$R=C$

$8x=4.5x+17500 \rightarrow 3.5x=17500 \rightarrow x=5000$

5000 units must be produced and sold for the firm to break-even.

56. Solve the system by substitution:

$R=C$

$12x=10x+15000 \rightarrow 2x=15000 \rightarrow x=7500$

7500 units must be produced and sold for the firm to break-even.

57. $\begin{cases} y=m_1x+b_1 \\ y=m_2x+b_2 \end{cases}$ subtracting the 2 equations yields

$0=m_1x+b_1-m_2x+b_2$

$-b_2=x(m_1-m_2)$

$\dfrac{-b_2}{m_1-m_2}=x,$ provided $m_1 \neq m_2$

so $y=m_1\left(\dfrac{-b_2}{m_1-m_2}\right)+b_1=\left(\dfrac{-b_2m_1}{m_1-m_2}\right)+b_1=\dfrac{-b_2m_1+b_1(m_1-m_2)}{m_1-m_2}$

Therefore the solution set is $\left\{x=\dfrac{-b_2}{m_1-m_2}, y=\dfrac{-b_2m_1+b_1(m_1-m_2)}{m_1-m_2}\right\}$, provided $m_1 \neq m_2$.

58. $\begin{cases} y=m_1x+b_1 \\ y=m_2x+b_2 \end{cases}$ where $m_1=m_2=m$ and $b_1 \neq b_2$

$\begin{cases} y=mx+b_1 \\ y=mx+b_2 \end{cases}$ subtracting the 2 equations yields

$0=0+b_1-b_2$

$0=b_1-b_2$

$b_2=b_1$

But this contradicts the assumption that $b_1 \neq b_2$, so there is no solution to the system. That is, the system is inconsistent.

59. $\begin{cases} y = m_1 x + b_1 \\ y = m_2 x + b_2 \end{cases}$ where $m_1 = m_2 = m$ and $b_1 = b_2$

$\begin{cases} y = mx + b_1 \\ y = mx + b_1 \end{cases}$ subtracting the 2 equations yields

$0 = 0$

Since this statement is always true, there are infinitely many solutions to the system. That is, the system is dependent.

60. Answers will vary. 61. Answers will vary. 62. Answers will vary.

Chapter 12

Systems of Equations and Inequalities

12.2 Systems of Linear Equations: Three Equations Containing Three Variables

1. Substituting the values of the variables:

$$\begin{cases} 3x+3y+2z=4 & \longrightarrow & 3(1)+3(-1)+2(2)=3-3+4=4 \\ x-y-z=0 & \longrightarrow & 1-(-1)-2=1+1-2=0 \\ 2y-3z=-8 & \longrightarrow & 2(-1)-3(2)=-2-6=-8 \end{cases}$$

Each equation is satisfied, so $x=1, y=-1, z=2$ is a solution to the system of equations.

2. Substituting the values of the variables:

$$\begin{cases} 4x-z=7 & \longrightarrow & 4(2)-(1)=8-1=7 \\ 8x+5y-z=0 & \longrightarrow & 8(2)+5(-3)-1=16-15-1=0 \\ -x-y+5z=6 & \longrightarrow & -2-(-3)+5(1)=-2+3+5=6 \end{cases}$$

Each equation is satisfied, so $x=2, y=-3, z=1$ is a solution to the system of equations.

3. Multiply each side of the first equation by –2 and add to the second equation to eliminate x:

$$\begin{cases} x-y=6 & \xrightarrow{-2} & -2x+2y=-12 \\ 2x-3z=16 & \longrightarrow & \underline{2x-3z=16} \\ 2y+z=4 & & 2y-3z=4 \end{cases}$$

Multiply each side of the result by –1 and add to the original third equation to eliminate y:

$$\begin{aligned} 2y-3z=4 &\xrightarrow{-1} -2y+3z=-4 \\ 2y+z=4 &\longrightarrow \underline{2y+z=4} \\ &\qquad 4z=0 \\ &\qquad z=0 \end{aligned}$$

Substituting and solving for the other variables:

$$\begin{aligned} 2y+0&=4 & 2x-3(0)&=16 \\ 2y&=4 & 2x&=16 \\ y&=2 & x&=8 \end{aligned}$$

The solution is $x=8,\ y=2,\ z=0$.

4. Multiply each side of the first equation by 2 and add to the second equation to eliminate y:

$$\begin{cases} 2x + y = -4 \\ -2y + 4z = 0 \\ 3x - 2z = -11 \end{cases} \qquad \begin{array}{rl} \xrightarrow{2} & 4x + 2y \qquad = -8 \\ \longrightarrow & \underline{\quad -2y + 4z = 0} \\ & 4x \qquad + 4z = -8 \end{array}$$

Multiply each side of the result by $\frac{1}{2}$ and add to the original third equation to eliminate z:

$$\begin{array}{rcl} 4x + 4z = -8 & \xrightarrow{1/2} & 2x + 2z = -4 \\ 3x - 2z = -11 & \longrightarrow & \underline{3x - 2z = -11} \\ & & 5x \qquad = -15 \\ & & x = -3 \end{array}$$

Substituting and solving for the other variables:

$$\begin{array}{rr} 2(-3) + y = -4 & 3(-3) - 2z = -11 \\ -6 + y = -4 & -9 - 2z = -11 \\ y = 2 & -2z = -2 \\ & z = 1 \end{array}$$

The solution is $x = -3,\ y = 2,\ z = 1$.

5. Multiply each side of the first equation by –2 and add to the second equation to eliminate x; and multiply each side of the first equation by 3 and add to the third equation to eliminate x:

$$\begin{cases} x - 2y + 3z = 7 \\ 2x + y + z = 4 \\ -3x + 2y - 2z = -10 \end{cases} \qquad \begin{array}{rl} \xrightarrow{-2} & -2x + 4y - 6z = -14 \\ \longrightarrow & \underline{2x + y + z = 4} \\ & 5y - 5z = -10 \xrightarrow{1/5} y - z = -2 \\ \xrightarrow{3} & 3x - 6y + 9z = 21 \\ \longrightarrow & \underline{-3x + 2y - 2z = -10} \\ & -4y + 7z = 11 \end{array}$$

Multiply each side of the first result by 4 and add to the second result to eliminate y:

$$\begin{array}{rcl} y - z = -2 & \xrightarrow{4} & 4y - 4z = -8 \\ -4y + 7z = 11 & \longrightarrow & \underline{-4y + 7z = 11} \\ & & 3z = 3 \rightarrow z = 1 \end{array}$$

Substituting and solving for the other variables:

$$\begin{array}{ll} y - 1 = -2 & \\ y = -1 & x - 2(-1) + 3(1) = 7 \\ & x + 2 + 3 = 7 \rightarrow x = 2 \end{array}$$

The solution is $x = 2,\ y = -1,\ z = 1$.

6. Multiply each side of the first equation by –2 and add to the second equation to eliminate y; and multiply each side of the first equation by 4 and add to the third equation to eliminate y:

$$\begin{cases} 2x + y - 3z = 0 \\ -2x + 2y + z = -7 \\ 3x - 4y - 3z = 7 \end{cases} \qquad \begin{array}{rl} \xrightarrow{-2} & -4x - 2y + 6z = 0 \\ \longrightarrow & \underline{-2x + 2y + z = -7} \\ & -6x \qquad + 7z = -7 \end{array}$$

$$\xrightarrow{4} \quad 8x+4y-12z=0$$
$$\longrightarrow \quad \underline{3x-4y-\ \ 3z=7}$$
$$11x \qquad -15z=7$$

Multiply each side of the first result by 11 and multiply each side of the second result by 6 to eliminate x:

$$\begin{aligned} -6x+\ 7z&=-7 \xrightarrow{11} & -66x+77z&=-77 \\ 11x-15z&=\ 7 \xrightarrow{6} & \underline{66x-90z}&\underline{=\ 42} \\ & & -13z&=-35 \\ & & z&=\frac{35}{13} \end{aligned}$$

Substituting and solving for the other variables:

$$-6x+7\left(\frac{35}{13}\right)=-7$$

$$-6x+\frac{245}{13}=-7 \qquad\qquad 2\left(\frac{56}{13}\right)+y-3\left(\frac{35}{13}\right)=0$$

$$-6x=-\frac{336}{13} \qquad\qquad \frac{112}{13}+y-\frac{105}{13}=0$$

$$x=\frac{56}{12} \qquad\qquad y=-\frac{7}{13}$$

The solution is $x=\frac{56}{13},\ y=-\frac{7}{13},\ z=\frac{35}{13}$.

7. Add the first and second equations to eliminate z:

$$\begin{cases} x-\ y-z=1 \\ 2x+3y+z=2 \\ 3x+2y\qquad=0 \end{cases} \quad \begin{aligned} &\longrightarrow & x-\ y-z&=1 \\ &\longrightarrow & \underline{2x+3y+z}&\underline{=2} \\ & & 3x+2y\qquad&=3 \end{aligned}$$

Multiply each side of the result by –1 and add to the original third equation to eliminate y:

$$\begin{aligned} 3x+2y=3 &\xrightarrow{-1} & -3x-2y&=-3 \\ 3x+2y=0 &\longrightarrow & \underline{3x+2y}&\underline{=\ 0} \\ & & 0&=-3 \end{aligned}$$

This result has no solution, so the system is inconsistent.

8. Add the first and second equations to eliminate z; then add the second and third equations to eliminate z:

$$\begin{cases} 2x-3y-z=0 \\ -x+2y+z=5 \\ 3x-4y-z=1 \end{cases} \quad \begin{aligned} &\longrightarrow & 2x-3y-z&=0 \\ &\longrightarrow & \underline{-x+2y+z}&\underline{=5} \\ & & x-\ y\qquad&=5 \end{aligned}$$

$$\begin{aligned} &\longrightarrow & -x+2y+z&=5 \\ &\longrightarrow & \underline{3x-4y-z}&\underline{=1} \\ & & 2x-2y\qquad&=6 \xrightarrow{1/2} x-y=3 \end{aligned}$$

Multiply each side of the first result by –1 and add to the second result to eliminate y:

$$\begin{array}{lcr} x-y=5 & \xrightarrow{-1} & -x+y=-5 \\ x-y=3 & \longrightarrow & \underline{x-y=\ \ 3} \\ & & 0=-2 \end{array}$$

This result has no solution, so the system is inconsistent.

9. Add the first and second equations to eliminate x; and multiply the first equation by –3 and add to the third equation to eliminate x:

$$\begin{cases} x-y-z=1 \\ -x+2y-3z=-4 \\ 3x-2y-7z=0 \end{cases} \begin{array}{lr} \longrightarrow & x-y-z=1 \\ \longrightarrow & \underline{-x+2y-3z=-4} \\ & y-4z=-3 \end{array}$$

$$\begin{array}{lr} \xrightarrow{-3} & -3x+3y+3z=-3 \\ \longrightarrow & \underline{3x-2y-7z=\ \ 0} \\ & y-4z=-3 \end{array}$$

Multiply each side of the first result by –1 and add to the second result to eliminate y:

$$\begin{array}{lcr} y-4z=-3 & \xrightarrow{-1} & -y+4z=\ \ 3 \\ y-4z=-3 & \longrightarrow & \underline{y-4z=-3} \\ & & 0=\ \ 0 \end{array}$$

The system is dependent. If z is any real number, then $y=4z-3$.
Solving for x in terms of z in the first equation:

$$x-(4z-3)-z=1$$
$$x-4z+3-z=1$$
$$x-5z+3=1$$
$$x=5z-2$$

The solution is $x=5z-2$, $y=4z-3$, z is any real number.

10. Multiply the first equation by 2 and add to the second equation to eliminate z; and multiply the first equation by 3 and add to the third equation to eliminate z:

$$\begin{cases} 2x-3y-z=0 \\ 3x+2y+2z=2 \\ x+5y+3z=2 \end{cases} \begin{array}{lr} \xrightarrow{2} & 4x-6y-2z=0 \\ \longrightarrow & \underline{3x+2y+2z=2} \\ & 7x-4y\qquad=2 \end{array}$$

$$\begin{array}{lr} \xrightarrow{3} & 6x-9y-3z=0 \\ \longrightarrow & \underline{x+5y+3z=2} \\ & 7x-4y\qquad=2 \end{array}$$

Multiply each side of the first result by –1 and add to the second result to eliminate y:

$$\begin{array}{lcr} 7x-4y=2 & \xrightarrow{-1} & -7x+4y=-2 \\ 7x-4y=2 & \longrightarrow & \underline{7x-4y=\ \ 2} \\ & & 0=\ \ 0 \end{array}$$

The system is dependent. If x is any real number, then $y=\dfrac{7x-2}{4}$.

Solving for z in terms of x in the first equation:

$$z = 2x - 3y = 2x - 3\left(\frac{7x-2}{4}\right) = \frac{8x - 21x + 6}{4} = \frac{6-13x}{4}$$

The solution is $y = \dfrac{7x-2}{4}$, $z = \dfrac{6-13x}{4}$, x is any real number.

11. Multiply the first equation by –2 and add to the second equation to eliminate x; and add the first and third equations to eliminate x:

$$\begin{cases} 2x - 2y + 3z = 6 \\ 4x - 3y + 2z = 0 \\ -2x + 3y - 7z = 1 \end{cases}$$

$$\begin{array}{r} -4x + 4y - 6z = -12 \\ 4x - 3y + 2z = 0 \\ \hline y - 4z = -12 \end{array}$$

$$\begin{array}{r} 2x - 2y + 3z = 6 \\ -2x + 3y - 7z = 1 \\ \hline y - 4z = 7 \end{array}$$

Multiply each side of the first result by –1 and add to the second result to eliminate y:

$$\begin{array}{r} -y + 4z = 12 \\ y - 4z = 7 \\ \hline 0 = 19 \end{array}$$

This result has no solution, so the system is inconsistent.

12. Multiply the first equation by –1 and add to the second equation to eliminate z; and multiply the first equation by –2 and add to the third equation to eliminate z:

$$\begin{cases} 3x - 2y + 2z = 6 \\ 7x - 3y + 2z = -1 \\ 2x - 3y + 4z = 0 \end{cases}$$

$$\begin{array}{r} -3x + 2y - 2z = -6 \\ 7x - 3y + 2z = -1 \\ \hline 4x - y \quad = -7 \end{array}$$

$$\begin{array}{r} -6x + 4y - 4z = -12 \\ 2x - 3y + 4z = 0 \\ \hline -4x + y \quad = -12 \end{array}$$

Add the first result to the second result to eliminate y:

$$\begin{array}{r} 4x - y = -7 \\ -4x + y = -12 \\ \hline 0 = -19 \end{array}$$

This result has no solution, so the system is inconsistent.

13. Add the first and second equations to eliminate z; and multiply the second equation by 2 and add to the third equation to eliminate z:

$$\begin{cases} x + y - z = 6 \\ 3x - 2y + z = -5 \\ x + 3y - 2z = 14 \end{cases}$$

$$\begin{array}{r} x + y - z = 6 \\ 3x - 2y + z = -5 \\ \hline 4x - y \quad = 1 \end{array}$$

$$\begin{array}{r} 6x - 4y + 2z = -10 \\ x + 3y - 2z = 14 \\ \hline 7x - y \quad = 4 \end{array}$$

Multiply each side of the first result by –1 and add to the second result to eliminate y:

$$\begin{array}{lcr} 4x - y = 1 & \xrightarrow{-1} & -4x + y = -1 \\ 7x - y = 4 & \longrightarrow & 7x - y = 4 \\ \hline & & 3x \quad = 3 \\ & & x \quad = 1 \end{array}$$

Substituting and solving for the other variables:

$$\begin{aligned} 4(1) - y &= 1 \\ -y &= -3 \\ y &= 3 \end{aligned} \qquad \begin{aligned} 3(1) - 2(3) + z &= -5 \\ 3 - 6 + z &= -5 \\ z &= -2 \end{aligned}$$

The solution is $x = 1,\ y = 3,\ z = -2$.

14. Multiply the first equation by –3 and add to the second equation to eliminate y; and add the first and third equations to eliminate y:

$$\begin{cases} x - y + z = -4 \\ 2x - 3y + 4z = -15 \\ 5x + y - 2z = 12 \end{cases} \qquad \begin{array}{lr} \xrightarrow{-3} & -3x + 3y - 3z = 12 \\ \longrightarrow & 2x - 3y + 4z = -15 \\ \hline & -x \quad + z = -3 \quad \rightarrow \quad z = x - 3 \\ \longrightarrow & x - y + z = -4 \\ \longrightarrow & 5x + y - 2z = 12 \\ \hline & 6x \quad - z = 8 \end{array}$$

Substitute and solve:

$$\begin{aligned} 6x - (x - 3) &= 8 \\ 6x - x + 3 &= 8 \\ 5x &= 5 \quad z = 1 - 3 = -2 \\ x &= 1 \quad y = 12 - 5x + 2z = 12 - 5(1) + 2(-2) = 12 - 5 - 4 = 3 \end{aligned}$$

The solution is $x = 1,\ y = 3,\ z = -2$.

15. Add the first and second equations to eliminate z; and multiply the second equation by 3 and add to the third equation to eliminate z:

$$\begin{cases} x + 2y - z = -3 \\ 2x - 4y + z = -7 \\ -2x + 2y - 3z = 4 \end{cases} \qquad \begin{array}{lr} \longrightarrow & x + 2y - z = -3 \\ \longrightarrow & 2x - 4y + z = -7 \\ \hline & 3x - 2y \quad = -10 \\ \xrightarrow{3} & 6x - 12y + 3z = -21 \\ \longrightarrow & -2x + 2y - 3z = 4 \\ \hline & 4x - 10y \quad = -17 \end{array}$$

Multiply each side of the first result by –5 and add to the second result to eliminate y:

$$\begin{array}{lcr} 3x - 2y = -10 & \xrightarrow{-5} & -15x + 10y = 50 \\ 4x - 10y = -17 & \longrightarrow & 4x - 10y = -17 \\ \hline & & -11x \quad = 33 \\ & & x \quad = -3 \end{array}$$

Substituting and solving for the other variables:

$$\begin{aligned} 3(-3)-2y&=-10 \\ -9-2y&=-10 \\ -2y&=-1 \\ y&=\frac{1}{2} \end{aligned} \qquad \begin{aligned} -3+2\left(\frac{1}{2}\right)-z&=-3 \\ -3+1-z&=-3 \\ -z&=-1 \\ z&=1 \end{aligned}$$

The solution is $x=-3,\ y=\frac{1}{2},\ z=1$.

16. Add the first and second equations to eliminate z; and multiply the first equation by 2 and add to the third equation to eliminate z:

$$\begin{cases} x+4y-3z=-8 \\ 3x-y+3z=12 \\ x+y+6z=1 \end{cases} \begin{aligned} &\longrightarrow & x+4y-3z&=-8 \\ &\longrightarrow & 3x-y+3z&=12 \\ & & \overline{4x+3y\qquad}&=4 \end{aligned}$$

$$\begin{aligned} &\xrightarrow{2} & 2x+8y-6z&=-16 \\ &\longrightarrow & x+y+6z&=1 \\ & & \overline{3x+9y\qquad}&=-15 \xrightarrow{1/3} x+3y=-5 \end{aligned}$$

Multiply each side of the second result by –1 and add to the first result to eliminate y:

$$\begin{aligned} 4x+3y&=4 &\longrightarrow\quad 4x+3y&=4 \\ x+3y&=-5 &\xrightarrow{-1}\quad -x-3y&=5 \\ & & \overline{3x\qquad}&=9 \\ & & x&=3 \end{aligned}$$

Substituting and solving for the other variables:

$$\begin{aligned} 3+3y&=-5 \\ 3y&=-8 \\ y&=-\frac{8}{3} \end{aligned} \qquad \begin{aligned} 3+\left(-\frac{8}{3}\right)+6z&=1 \\ 6z&=\frac{2}{3} \\ z&=\frac{1}{9} \end{aligned}$$

The solution is $x=3,\ y=-\frac{8}{3},\ z=\frac{1}{9}$.

17. $y=ax^2+bx+c$

At (–1, 4) the equation becomes:

$$\begin{aligned} 4&=a(-1)^2+b(-1)+c \\ 4&=a-b+c \end{aligned}$$

$$a-b+c=4$$

At (2, 3) the equation becomes:

$$\begin{aligned} 3&=a(2)^2+b(2)+c \\ 3&=4a+2b+c \end{aligned}$$

$$4a+2b+c=3$$

At (0, 1) the equation becomes:

$$1 = a(0)^2 + b(0) + c$$
$$c = 1$$

The system of equations is:

$$\begin{cases} a - b + c = 4 \\ 4a + 2b + c = 3 \\ c = 1 \end{cases}$$

Substitute $c = 1$ into the first and second equations and simplify:

$$\begin{cases} a - b + 1 = 4 \rightarrow a - b = 3 \rightarrow a = b + 3 \\ 4a + 2b + 1 = 3 \rightarrow 4a + 2b = 2 \end{cases}$$

Solve the first equation for a, substitute into the second equation and solve:

$$4(b+3) + 2b = 2$$
$$4b + 12 + 2b = 2$$
$$6b = -10 \rightarrow b = -\frac{5}{3}$$
$$a = -\frac{5}{3} + 3 = \frac{4}{3}$$

The solution is $a = \frac{4}{3}$, $b = -\frac{5}{3}$, $c = 1$. So the equation is $y = \frac{4}{3}x^2 - \frac{5}{3}x + 1$.

18. $y = ax^2 + bx + c$

At (–1, –2) the equation becomes:

$$-2 = a(-1)^2 + b(-1) + c$$
$$-2 = a - b + c$$
$$a - b + c = -2$$

At (1, –4) the equation becomes:

$$-4 = a(1)^2 + b(1) + c$$
$$a + b + c = -4$$

At (2, 4) the equation becomes:

$$4 = a(2)^2 + b(2) + c$$
$$4a + 2b + c = 4$$

The system of equations is:

$$\begin{cases} a - b + c = -2 \\ a + b + c = -4 \\ 4a + 2b + c = 4 \end{cases}$$

Multiply the first equation by –1 and add to the second equation; and multiply the first equation by –1 and add to the third equation to eliminate c:

$$\begin{cases} a - b + c = -2 \xrightarrow{-1} -a + b - c = 2 \\ a + b + c = -4 \longrightarrow \underline{a + b + c = -4} \\ 4a + 2b + c = 4 \quad\quad 2b = -2 \xrightarrow{1/2} b = -1 \end{cases}$$

$$\xrightarrow{-1} -a + b - c = 2$$
$$\longrightarrow \underline{4a + 2b + c = 4}$$
$$3a + 3b = 6 \xrightarrow{1/3} a + b = 2$$

Substitute and solve:

$a + (-1) = 2 \rightarrow a = 3$

$c = -a - b - 4 = -3 - (-1) - 4 = -6$

The solution is $a = 3,\ b = -1,\ c = -6$. The equation is $y = 3x^2 - x - 6$

19. Substitute the expression for I_2 into the second and third equations and simplify:

$$\begin{cases} I_2 = I_1 + I_3 \\ 5 - 3I_1 - 5I_2 = 0 \rightarrow 5 - 3I_1 - 5(I_1 + I_3) = 0 \rightarrow -8I_1 - 5I_3 = -5 \\ 10 - 5I_2 - 7I_3 = 0 \rightarrow 10 - 5(I_1 + I_3) - 7I_3 = 0 \rightarrow -5I_1 - 12I_3 = -10 \end{cases}$$

Multiply both sides of the second equation by 5 and multiply both sides of the third equation by –8 to eliminate I_1:

$$\begin{array}{lcr} -8I_1 - 5I_3 = -5 & \xrightarrow{5} & -40I_1 - 25I_3 = -25 \\ -5I_1 - 12I_3 = -10 & \xrightarrow{-8} & 40I_1 + 96I_3 = 80 \\ \hline & & 71I_3 = 55 \\ & & I_3 = \frac{55}{71} \end{array}$$

Substituting and solving for the other variables:

$$-8I_1 - 5\left(\frac{55}{71}\right) = -5 \qquad I_2 = \frac{10}{71} + \frac{55}{71}$$

$$-8I_1 - \frac{275}{71} = -5 \qquad I_2 = \frac{65}{71}$$

$$-8I_1 = -\frac{80}{71}$$

$$I_1 = \frac{10}{71}$$

The solution is $I_1 = \frac{10}{71},\ I_2 = \frac{65}{71},\ I_3 = \frac{55}{71}$.

20. Substitute the expression for I_3 into the second equation and simplify:

$$\begin{cases} I_3 = I_1 + I_2 \\ 8 = 4I_3 + 6I_2 \rightarrow 8 = 4(I_1 + I_2) + 6I_2 \rightarrow 8 = 4I_1 + 10I_2 \\ 8I_1 = 4 + 6I_2 \rightarrow 8I_1 - 6I_2 = 4 \end{cases}$$

Multiply both sides of the second equation by –2 and add to the third equation to eliminate I_1:

$$\begin{array}{lcr} 4I_1 + 10I_2 = 8 & \xrightarrow{-2} & -8I_1 - 20I_2 = -16 \\ 8I_1 - 6I_2 = 4 & \longrightarrow & 8I_1 - 6I_2 = 4 \\ \hline & & -26I_2 = -12 \\ & & I_2 = \frac{6}{13} \end{array}$$

Substituting and solving for the other variables:

$$4I_1 + 10\left(\frac{6}{13}\right) = 8 \rightarrow 4I_1 + \frac{60}{13} = 8 \rightarrow 4I_1 = \frac{44}{13} \rightarrow I_1 = \frac{11}{13}$$

$$I_3 = I_1 + I_2 = \frac{11}{13} + \frac{6}{13} = \frac{17}{13}$$

The solution is $I_1 = \frac{11}{13},\ I_2 = \frac{6}{13},\ I_3 = \frac{17}{13}$.

21. Let x = the number of orchestra seats.
Let y = the number of main seats.
Let z = the number of balcony seats.
Since the total number of seats is 500, $x+y+z=500$.
Since the total revenue is \$17,100 if all seats are sold, $50x+35y+25z=17{,}100$.
If only half of the orchestra seats are sold, the revenue is \$14,600. So,
$50(\frac{1}{2}x)+35y+25z=14{,}600$.
Multiply each side of the first equation by –25 and add to the second equation to eliminate z; and multiply each side of the third equation by –1 and add to the second equation to eliminate z:

$$\begin{cases} x+y+z=500 \\ 50x+35y+25z=17100 \\ 25x+35y+25z=14600 \end{cases} \quad \begin{array}{l} \xrightarrow{-25} -25x-25y-25z=-12500 \\ \longrightarrow \underline{\quad 50x+35y+25z=\quad 17100} \\ \qquad 25x+10y \qquad = \quad 4600 \end{array}$$

$$\begin{array}{l} \longrightarrow \quad 50x+35y+25z= \quad 17100 \\ \xrightarrow{-1} \underline{-25x-35y-25z=-14600} \\ \qquad 25x \qquad\qquad = \quad 2500 \\ \qquad\qquad\qquad x= \quad 100 \end{array}$$

Substituting and solving for the other variables:

$$\begin{aligned} 25(100)+10y&=4600 \\ 2500+10y&=4600 \\ 10y&=2100 \\ y&=210 \end{aligned} \qquad \begin{aligned} 100+210+z&=500 \\ 310+z&=500 \\ z&=190 \end{aligned}$$

There are 100 orchestra seats, 210 main seats, and 190 balcony seats.

22. Let x = the number of adult tickets.
Let y = the number of child tickets.
Let z = the number of senior citizen tickets.
Since the total number of tickets is 405, $x+y+z=405$.
Since the total revenue is \$2320, $8x+4.50y+6z=2320$.
Twice as many children's tickets as adult tickets are sold. So, $y=2x$.
Substitute for y in the first two equations and simplify:

$$\begin{cases} x+y+z=405 \rightarrow \quad x+2x+z=405 \rightarrow 3x+z=405 \\ 8x+4.50y+6z=2320 \rightarrow 8x+4.50(2x)+6z=2320 \rightarrow 17x+6z=2320 \\ y=2x \end{cases}$$

Multiply the first equation by –6 and add to the second equation to eliminate z:

$$\begin{cases} 3x+z=405 \\ 17x+6z=2320 \end{cases} \quad \begin{array}{l} \xrightarrow{-6} -18x-6z=-2430 \\ \longrightarrow \underline{\quad 17x+6z=\quad 2320} \\ \qquad -x \qquad = -110 \rightarrow x=110 \end{array}$$

$y=2x=2(110)=220$
$3x+z=405 \rightarrow z=405-3(110)=405-330=75$

There were 110 adults, 220 children, and 75 senior citizens that bought tickets.

23. Let x = the number of servings of chicken.
Let y = the number of servings of corn.
Let z = the number of servings of 2% milk.
Protein equation: $30x + 3y + 9z = 66$
Carbohydrate equation: $35x + 16y + 13z = 94.5$
Calcium equation: $200x + 10y + 300z = 910$
Multiply each side of the first equation by –16 and multiply each side of the second equation by 3 and add them to eliminate y; and multiply each side of the second equation by –5 and multiply each side of the third equation by 8 and add to eliminate y:

$$\begin{cases} 30x + 3y + 9z = 66 & \xrightarrow{-16} & -480x - 48y - 144z = -1056 \\ 35x + 16y + 13z = 94.5 & \xrightarrow{3} & 105x + 48y + 39z = 283.5 \\ 200x + 10y + 300z = 910 & & -375x \quad - 105z = -772.5 \end{cases}$$

$$\begin{aligned} &\xrightarrow{-5} & -175x - 80y - 65z &= -472.5 \\ &\xrightarrow{8} & 1600x + 80y + 2400z &= 7280 \\ & & 1425x \quad + 2335z &= 6807.5 \end{aligned}$$

Multiply each side of the first result by 19 and multiply each side of the second result by 5 to eliminate x:

$$\begin{aligned} -375x - 105z = -772.5 &\xrightarrow{19} & -7125x - 1995z &= -14677.5 \\ 1425x + 2335z = 6807.5 &\xrightarrow{5} & 7125x + 11675z &= 34037.5 \\ & & 9680z &= 19360 \\ & & z &= 2 \end{aligned}$$

Substituting and solving for the other variables:

$$\begin{aligned} -375x - 105(2) &= -772.5 & \qquad 30(1.5) + 3y + 9(2) &= 66 \\ -375x - 210 &= -772.5 & 45 + 3y + 18 &= 66 \\ -375x &= -562.5 & 3y &= 3 \\ x &= 1.5 & y &= 1 \end{aligned}$$

The dietitian should serve 1.5 servings of chicken, 1 serving of corn, and 2 servings of 2% milk.

24. Let x = the amount in Treasury bills.
Let y = the amount in Treasury bonds.
Let z = the amount in corporate bonds.
Since the total investment is \$20,000, $x + y + z = 20{,}000$
Since the total income is to be \$1390, $0.05x + 0.07y + 0.10z = 1390$
The investment in Treasury bills is to be \$3000 more than the investment in corporate bonds. So, $x = 3000 + z$
Substitute for x in the first two equations and simplify:

$$\begin{cases} x + y + z = 20000 \rightarrow 3000 + z + y + z = 20000 & \rightarrow \quad y + 2z = 17000 \\ 0.05x + 0.07y + 0.10z = 1390 \rightarrow 5(3000 + z) + 7y + 10z = 139000 & \\ x = 3000 + z & \rightarrow \quad 7y + 15z = 124000 \end{cases}$$

Multiply each side of the first result by –7 and to the second result to eliminate y:

$$\begin{cases} y+2z = 17000 & \xrightarrow{-7} & -7y-14z = -119000 \\ 7y+15z = 124000 & \longrightarrow & \underline{7y+15z = 124000} \\ & & z = 5000 \end{cases}$$

$x = 3000 + z = 3000 + 5000 = 8000$

$y+2z = 17000 \rightarrow y = 17000 - 2(5000) = 7000$

Kelly should invest \$8000 in Treasury bills, \$7000 in Treasury bonds, and \$5000 in corporate bonds.

25. Let x = the price of 1 hamburger.
Let y = the price of 1 order of fries.
Let z = the price of 1 drink.

We can construct the system

$$\begin{cases} 8x+6y+6z = 26.10 \\ 10x+6y+8z = 31.60 \end{cases}$$

A system involving only 2 equations that contain 3 or more unknowns cannot be solved uniquely. In other words, we can create as many solutions as we want by choosing a specific value for one of the variables and then solving the resulting
2 x 2 system.
For example, suppose we know that

$$\$1.75 < \text{hamburger price} < \$2.25$$
$$\$0.75 < \text{fries price} < \$1.00$$
$$\$0.60 < \text{fries price} < \$0.90$$

Pick a specific value for x, y or z	2x2 system	Solution
$x = \$2.00$	$\begin{cases} 8(2)+6y+6z = 26.10 \\ 10(2)+6y+8z = 31.60 \end{cases}$ $\Downarrow$ $\begin{cases} 16+6y+6z = 26.10 \\ 20+6y+8z = 31.60 \end{cases}$ $\Downarrow$ $\begin{cases} 6y+6z = 10.10 \\ 6y+8z = 11.60 \end{cases}$	$x = \$2.00$ $y = \$0.93$ $z = \$0.75$

$y = \$0.90$

$$\begin{cases} 8x + 6(0.9) + 6z = 26.10 \\ 10x + 6(0.9) + 8z = 31.60 \end{cases}$$
$$\Downarrow$$
$$\begin{cases} 8x + 5.4 + 6z = 26.10 \\ 10x + 5.4 + 8z = 31.60 \end{cases}$$
$$\Downarrow$$
$$\begin{cases} 8x + 6z = 20.7 \\ 10x + 8z = 26.2 \end{cases}$$

$x = \$2.00$

$y = \$0.90$

$z = \$0.65$

$z = \$0.80$

$$\begin{cases} 8x + 6y + 6(.8) = 26.10 \\ 10x + 6y + 8(.8) = 31.60 \end{cases}$$
$$\Downarrow$$
$$\begin{cases} 8x + 6y + 4.8 = 26.10 \\ 10x + 6y + 6.4 = 31.60 \end{cases}$$
$$\Downarrow$$
$$\begin{cases} 8x + 6y = 21.3 \\ 10x + 6y = 25.2 \end{cases}$$

$x = \$1.95$

$y = \$0.95$

$z = \$0.80$

26. Let x = the price of 1 hamburger.
Let y = the price of 1 order of fries.
Let z = the price of 1 drink

We can construct the system

$$\begin{cases} 8x + 6y + 6z = 26.10 \\ 10x + 6y + 8z = 31.60 \\ 3x + 2y + 4z = 10.95 \end{cases}$$

subtracting the second equation from the first equation yields

$$\begin{array}{r} 8x + 6y + 6z = 26.10 \\ 10x + 6y + 8z = 31.60 \\ \hline -2x - 2z = -5.5 \end{array}$$

Now consider the second and third equations

$$\begin{cases} 10x + 6y + 8z = 31.60 \longrightarrow 10x + 6y + 8z = 31.60 \\ 3x + 2y + 4z = 10.95 \xrightarrow{-3} -9x - 6y - 12z = -32.85 \end{cases}$$

adding these 2 equations yields

$$\begin{array}{r} 10x + 6y + 8z = 31.60 \\ -9x - 6y - 12z = -32.85 \\ \hline x - 4z = -1.25 \end{array}$$

Now consider the system

$$\begin{cases} -2x - 2z = -5.5 \longrightarrow -2x - 2z = -5.5 \\ x - 4z = -1.25 \xrightarrow{2} 2x - 8z = -2.5 \end{cases}$$

adding these 2 equations yields

$$\begin{array}{r} -2x-2z=-5.5 \\ \underline{2x-8z=-2.5} \\ -10z=-8 \end{array}$$

$$\rightarrow z=0.8 \longrightarrow 2x-8(.8)=-2.5 \rightarrow x=1.95$$

plugging into the first equation in the original system

$$8(1.95)+6y+6(.8)=26.10$$

$$15.6+6y+4.8=26.10 \rightarrow 6y=5.7 \rightarrow y=0.95$$

Therefore, one hamburger costs \$1.95, one order of fries costs \$0.95 and one drink costs \$0.80.

27. Let x = Beth's time working alone.
Let y = Bill's time working alone.
Let z = Edie's time working alone.

We can use the following tables to organize our work:

	Beth	Bill	Edie	Together
Hours to do job	x	y	z	10
Part of job done in 1 hour	$\frac{1}{x}$	$\frac{1}{y}$	$\frac{1}{z}$	$\frac{1}{10}$

Equation $\frac{1}{x}+\frac{1}{y}+\frac{1}{z}=\frac{1}{10}$

	Bill	Edie	Together
Hours to do job	y	z	15
Part of job done in 1 hour	$\frac{1}{y}$	$\frac{1}{z}$	$\frac{1}{15}$

Equation $\frac{1}{y}+\frac{1}{z}=\frac{1}{15}$

	Beth	Bill	Edie	All three	Beth and Bill
Hours to do job	x	y	z	4	8
Part of job done in 1 hour	$\frac{1}{x}$	$\frac{1}{y}$	$\frac{1}{z}$	$\frac{1}{4}$	$\frac{1}{8}$

Equation

$$4\left(\frac{1}{x}+\frac{1}{y}+\frac{1}{z}\right)+8\left(\frac{1}{x}+\frac{1}{y}\right)=1 \rightarrow \frac{12}{x}+\frac{12}{y}+\frac{4}{z}=1$$

We can construct the system

$$\begin{cases} \frac{1}{x}+\frac{1}{y}+\frac{1}{z}=\frac{1}{10} \\ \frac{1}{y}+\frac{1}{z}=\frac{1}{15} \\ \frac{12}{x}+\frac{12}{y}+\frac{4}{z}=1 \end{cases}$$

subtracting the second equation from the first equation yields

$$\longrightarrow \begin{array}{r} \frac{1}{x}+\frac{1}{y}+\frac{1}{z}=\frac{1}{10} \\ \frac{1}{y}+\frac{1}{z}=\frac{1}{15} \\ \hline \frac{1}{x}=\frac{1}{10}-\frac{1}{15} \end{array} \rightarrow \frac{1}{x}=\frac{1}{30} \rightarrow x=30$$

Plugging $x = 30$ into the original system yields

$$\begin{cases} \frac{1}{30}+\frac{1}{y}+\frac{1}{z}=\frac{1}{10} \longrightarrow \frac{1}{y}+\frac{1}{z}=\frac{1}{10}-\frac{1}{30} \longrightarrow \frac{1}{y}+\frac{1}{z}=\frac{1}{15} \\ \frac{1}{y}+\frac{1}{z}=\frac{1}{15} \\ \frac{12}{30}+\frac{12}{y}+\frac{4}{z}=1 \longrightarrow \frac{12}{y}+\frac{4}{z}=1-\frac{12}{30} \longrightarrow \frac{12}{y}+\frac{4}{z}=\frac{3}{5} \end{cases}$$

Now consider the system

$$\begin{cases} \frac{1}{y}+\frac{1}{z}=\frac{1}{15} \xrightarrow{-12} \frac{-12}{y}+\frac{-12}{z}=\frac{-12}{15} \\ \frac{12}{y}+\frac{4}{z}=\frac{3}{5} \longrightarrow \frac{12}{y}+\frac{4}{z}=\frac{3}{5} \end{cases}$$

adding these 2 equations yields

$$\begin{array}{r} \frac{-12}{y}+\frac{-12}{z}=\frac{-12}{15} \\ \frac{12}{y}+\frac{4}{z}=\frac{3}{5} \\ \hline \frac{-12}{z}+\frac{4}{z}=\frac{-12}{15}+\frac{3}{5} \end{array} \rightarrow \frac{-8}{z}=\frac{-3}{15} \rightarrow \frac{8}{z}=\frac{1}{5} \rightarrow z=40$$

plugging $z = 40$ into the equation

$$\frac{12}{y}+\frac{4}{z}=\frac{3}{5} \rightarrow \frac{12}{y}+\frac{4}{40}=\frac{3}{5}$$

$$\frac{12}{y}+\frac{1}{10}=\frac{3}{5} \rightarrow \frac{12}{y}=\frac{3}{5}-\frac{1}{10} \rightarrow \frac{12}{y}=\frac{1}{2} \rightarrow y=24$$

So, working alone, it would take Beth 30 hours, Bill 24 hours and Edie 40 hours to finish the job.

Chapter 12

Systems of Equations and Inequalities

12.3 Systems of Linear Equations: Matrices

1. Writing the augmented matrix for the system of equations:
$$\begin{cases} x-5y=5 \\ 4x+3y=6 \end{cases} \rightarrow \left[\begin{array}{rr|r} 1 & -5 & 5 \\ 4 & 3 & 6 \end{array}\right]$$

2. Writing the augmented matrix for the system of equations:
$$\begin{cases} 3x+4y=7 \\ 4x-2y=5 \end{cases} \rightarrow \left[\begin{array}{rr|r} 3 & 4 & 7 \\ 4 & -2 & 5 \end{array}\right]$$

3. Writing the augmented matrix for the system of equations:
$$\begin{cases} 2x+3y-6=0 \\ 4x-6y+2=0 \end{cases} \rightarrow \begin{cases} 2x+3y=6 \\ 4x-6y=-2 \end{cases} \rightarrow \left[\begin{array}{rr|r} 2 & 3 & 6 \\ 4 & -6 & -2 \end{array}\right]$$

4. Writing the augmented matrix for the system of equations:
$$\begin{cases} 9x-y=0 \\ 3x-y-4=0 \end{cases} \rightarrow \begin{cases} 9x-y=0 \\ 3x-y=4 \end{cases} \rightarrow \left[\begin{array}{rr|r} 9 & -1 & 0 \\ 3 & -1 & 4 \end{array}\right]$$

5. Writing the augmented matrix for the system of equations:
$$\begin{cases} 0.01x-0.03y=0.06 \\ 0.13x+0.10y=0.20 \end{cases} \rightarrow \left[\begin{array}{rr|r} 0.01 & -0.03 & 0.06 \\ 0.13 & 0.10 & 0.20 \end{array}\right]$$

6. Writing the augmented matrix for the system of equations:
$$\begin{cases} \frac{4}{3}x-\frac{3}{2}y=\frac{3}{4} \\ -\frac{1}{4}x+\frac{1}{3}y=\frac{2}{3} \end{cases} \rightarrow \left[\begin{array}{rr|r} \frac{4}{3} & -\frac{3}{2} & \frac{3}{4} \\ -\frac{1}{4} & \frac{1}{3} & \frac{2}{3} \end{array}\right]$$

7. Writing the augmented matrix for the system of equations:
$$\begin{cases} x-y+z=10 \\ 3x+3y=5 \\ x+y+2z=2 \end{cases} \rightarrow \left[\begin{array}{rrr|r} 1 & -1 & 1 & 10 \\ 3 & 3 & 0 & 5 \\ 1 & 1 & 2 & 2 \end{array}\right]$$

8. Writing the augmented matrix for the system of equations:

$$\begin{cases} 5x - y - z = 0 \\ x + y = 5 \\ 2x - 3z = 2 \end{cases} \rightarrow \left[\begin{array}{ccc|c} 5 & -1 & -1 & 0 \\ 1 & 1 & 0 & 5 \\ 2 & 0 & -3 & 2 \end{array}\right]$$

9. Writing the augmented matrix for the system of equations:

$$\begin{cases} x + y - z = 2 \\ 3x - 2y = 2 \\ 5x + 3y - z = 1 \end{cases} \rightarrow \left[\begin{array}{ccc|c} 1 & 1 & -1 & 2 \\ 3 & -2 & 0 & 2 \\ 5 & 3 & -1 & 1 \end{array}\right]$$

10. Writing the augmented matrix for the system of equations:

$$\begin{cases} 2x + 3y - 4z = 0 \\ x - 5z + 2 = 0 \\ x + 2y - 3z = -2 \end{cases} \rightarrow \left[\begin{array}{ccc|c} 2 & 3 & -4 & 0 \\ 1 & 0 & -5 & -2 \\ 1 & 2 & -3 & -2 \end{array}\right]$$

11. Writing the augmented matrix for the system of equations:

$$\begin{cases} x - y - z = 10 \\ 2x + y + 2z = -1 \\ -3x + 4y = 5 \\ 4x - 5y + z = 0 \end{cases} \rightarrow \left[\begin{array}{ccc|c} 1 & -1 & -1 & 10 \\ 2 & 1 & 2 & -1 \\ -3 & 4 & 0 & 5 \\ 4 & -5 & 1 & 0 \end{array}\right]$$

12. Writing the augmented matrix for the system of equations:

$$\begin{cases} x - y + 2z - w = 5 \\ x + 3y - 4z + 2w = 2 \\ 3x - y - 5z - w = -1 \end{cases} \rightarrow \left[\begin{array}{cccc|c} 1 & -1 & 2 & -1 & 5 \\ 1 & 3 & -4 & 2 & 2 \\ 3 & -1 & -5 & -1 & -1 \end{array}\right]$$

13. $$\left[\begin{array}{cc|c} 1 & -3 & -2 \\ 2 & -5 & 5 \end{array}\right] \rightarrow \left[\begin{array}{cc|c} 1 & -3 & -2 \\ 0 & 1 & 9 \end{array}\right]$$

$R_2 = -2r_1 + r_2$

14. $$\left[\begin{array}{cc|c} 1 & -3 & -3 \\ 2 & -5 & -4 \end{array}\right] \rightarrow \left[\begin{array}{cc|c} 1 & -3 & -3 \\ 0 & 1 & 2 \end{array}\right]$$

$R_2 = -2r_1 + r_2$

15. $$\left[\begin{array}{ccc|c} 1 & -3 & 4 & 3 \\ 2 & -5 & 6 & 6 \\ -3 & 3 & 4 & 6 \end{array}\right] \rightarrow \left[\begin{array}{ccc|c} 1 & -3 & 4 & 3 \\ 0 & 1 & -2 & 0 \\ -3 & 3 & 4 & 6 \end{array}\right] \rightarrow \left[\begin{array}{ccc|c} 1 & -3 & 4 & 3 \\ 0 & 1 & -2 & 0 \\ 0 & -6 & 16 & 15 \end{array}\right]$$

(a) $R_2 = -2r_1 + r_2$ (b) $R_3 = 3r_1 + r_3$

16. $\left[\begin{array}{rrr|r} 1 & -3 & 3 & -5 \\ 2 & -5 & -3 & -5 \\ -3 & -2 & 4 & 6 \end{array}\right] \to \left[\begin{array}{rrr|r} 1 & -3 & 3 & -5 \\ 0 & 1 & -9 & 5 \\ -3 & -2 & 4 & 6 \end{array}\right] \to \left[\begin{array}{rrr|r} 1 & -3 & 3 & -5 \\ 0 & 1 & -9 & 5 \\ 0 & -11 & 13 & -9 \end{array}\right]$

(a) $R_2 = -2r_1 + r_2$ (b) $R_3 = 3r_1 + r_3$

17. $\left[\begin{array}{rrr|r} 1 & -3 & 2 & -6 \\ 2 & -5 & 3 & -4 \\ -3 & -6 & 4 & 6 \end{array}\right] \to \left[\begin{array}{rrr|r} 1 & -3 & 2 & -6 \\ 0 & 1 & -1 & 8 \\ -3 & -6 & 4 & 6 \end{array}\right] \to \left[\begin{array}{rrr|r} 1 & -3 & 2 & -6 \\ 0 & 1 & -1 & 8 \\ 0 & -15 & 10 & -12 \end{array}\right]$

(a) $R_2 = -2r_1 + r_2$ (b) $R_3 = 3r_1 + r_3$

18. $\left[\begin{array}{rrr|r} 1 & -3 & -4 & -6 \\ 2 & -5 & 6 & -6 \\ -3 & 1 & 4 & 6 \end{array}\right] \to \left[\begin{array}{rrr|r} 1 & -3 & -4 & -6 \\ 0 & 1 & 14 & 6 \\ -3 & 1 & 4 & 6 \end{array}\right] \to \left[\begin{array}{rrr|r} 1 & -3 & -4 & -6 \\ 0 & 1 & 14 & 6 \\ 0 & -8 & -8 & -12 \end{array}\right]$

(a) $R_2 = -2r_1 + r_2$ (b) $R_3 = 3r_1 + r_3$

19. $\left[\begin{array}{rrr|r} 1 & -3 & 1 & -2 \\ 2 & -5 & 6 & -2 \\ -3 & 1 & 4 & 6 \end{array}\right] \to \left[\begin{array}{rrr|r} 1 & -3 & 1 & -2 \\ 0 & 1 & 4 & 2 \\ -3 & 1 & 4 & 6 \end{array}\right] \to \left[\begin{array}{rrr|r} 1 & -3 & 1 & -2 \\ 0 & 1 & 4 & 2 \\ 0 & -8 & 7 & 0 \end{array}\right]$

(a) $R_2 = -2r_1 + r_2$ (b) $R_3 = 3r_1 + r_3$

20. $\left[\begin{array}{rrr|r} 1 & -3 & -1 & 2 \\ 2 & -5 & 2 & 6 \\ -3 & -6 & 4 & 6 \end{array}\right] \to \left[\begin{array}{rrr|r} 1 & -3 & -1 & 2 \\ 0 & 1 & 4 & 2 \\ -3 & -6 & 4 & 6 \end{array}\right] \to \left[\begin{array}{rrr|r} 1 & -3 & -1 & 2 \\ 0 & 1 & 4 & 2 \\ 0 & -15 & 1 & 12 \end{array}\right]$

(a) $R_2 = -2r_1 + r_2$ (b) $R_3 = 3r_1 + r_3$

21. $\begin{cases} x = 5 \\ y = -1 \end{cases}$ consistent $x = 5$, $y = -1$

22. $\begin{cases} x = -4 \\ y = 0 \end{cases}$ consistent $x = -4$, $y = 0$

23. $\begin{cases} x = 1 \\ y = 2 \\ 0 = 3 \end{cases}$ inconsistent

24. $\begin{cases} x = 0 \\ y = 0 \\ 0 = 2 \end{cases}$ inconsistent

25. $\begin{cases} x+2z=-1 \\ y-4z=-2 \\ 0=0 \end{cases}$ consistent $x=-1-2z, y=-2+4z$, z is any real number

26. $\begin{cases} x+4z=4 \\ y+3z=2 \\ 0=0 \end{cases}$ consistent $x=4-4z$, $y=2-3z$, z is any real number

27. $\begin{cases} x_1=1 \\ x_2+x_4=2 \\ x_3+2x_4=3 \end{cases}$ consistent $x_1=1, x_2=2-x_4, x_3=3-2x_4, x_4$ is any real number

28. $\begin{cases} x_1=1 \\ x_2+2x_4=2 \\ x_3+3x_4=0 \end{cases}$ consistent $x_1=1, x_2=2-2x_4, x_3=-3x_4$, x_4 is any real number

29. $\begin{cases} x_1+4x_4=2 \\ x_2++x_3+3x_4=3 \\ 0=0 \end{cases}$ consistent $x_1=2-4x_4, x_2=3-x_3-3x_4$, x_3, x_4 are any real numbers

30. $\begin{cases} x_1=1 \\ x_2=2 \\ x_3+2x_4=3 \end{cases}$ consistent $x_1=1, x_2=2, x_3=3-2x_4$, x_4 is any real number

31. $\begin{cases} x_1+x_4=-2 \\ x_2+2x_4=2 \\ x_3-x_4=0 \\ 0=0 \end{cases}$ consistent $x_1=-2-x_4, x_2=2-2x_4, x_3=x_4$, x_4 is any real number

32. $\begin{cases} x_1=1 \\ x_2=2 \\ x_3=3 \\ x_4=0 \end{cases}$ consistent $x_1=1_4, x_2=2, x_3=3, x_4=0$

33. $\begin{cases} x+y=8 \\ x-y=4 \end{cases}$ can be written as: $\left[\begin{array}{cc|c} 1 & 1 & 8 \\ 1 & -1 & 4 \end{array}\right]$

$$\rightarrow \left[\begin{array}{cc|c} 1 & 1 & 8 \\ 0 & -2 & -4 \end{array}\right] \rightarrow \left[\begin{array}{cc|c} 1 & 1 & 8 \\ 0 & 1 & 2 \end{array}\right] \rightarrow \left[\begin{array}{cc|c} 1 & 0 & 6 \\ 0 & 1 & 2 \end{array}\right]$$

$R_2 = -r_1 + r_2 \quad R_2 = -\tfrac{1}{2} r_2 \quad R_1 = -r_2 + r_1$

The solution is $x = 6,\ y = 2$.

34. $\begin{cases} x+2y=5 \\ x+\ \ y=3 \end{cases}$ can be written as: $\left[\begin{array}{cc|c} 1 & 2 & 5 \\ 1 & 1 & 3 \end{array}\right]$

$$\rightarrow \left[\begin{array}{cc|c} 1 & 2 & 5 \\ 0 & -1 & -2 \end{array}\right] \rightarrow \left[\begin{array}{cc|c} 1 & 2 & 5 \\ 0 & 1 & 2 \end{array}\right] \rightarrow \left[\begin{array}{cc|c} 1 & 0 & 1 \\ 0 & 1 & 2 \end{array}\right]$$

$R_2 = -r_1 + r_2 \quad R_2 = -r_2 \quad R_1 = -2r_2 + r_1$

The solution is $x = 1,\ y = 2$.

35. $\begin{cases} 2x-4y=-2 \\ 3x+2y=\ \ 3 \end{cases}$ can be written as: $\left[\begin{array}{cc|c} 2 & -4 & -2 \\ 3 & 2 & 3 \end{array}\right]$

$$\rightarrow \left[\begin{array}{cc|c} 1 & -2 & -1 \\ 3 & 2 & 3 \end{array}\right] \rightarrow \left[\begin{array}{cc|c} 1 & -2 & -1 \\ 0 & 8 & 6 \end{array}\right] \rightarrow \left[\begin{array}{cc|c} 1 & -2 & -1 \\ 0 & 1 & \frac{3}{4} \end{array}\right] \rightarrow \left[\begin{array}{cc|c} 1 & 0 & \frac{1}{2} \\ 0 & 1 & \frac{3}{4} \end{array}\right]$$

$R_1 = \tfrac{1}{2} r_1 \quad R_2 = -3r_1 + r_2 \quad R_2 = \tfrac{1}{8} r_2 \quad R_1 = 2r_2 + r_1$

The solution is $x = \dfrac{1}{2},\ y = \dfrac{3}{4}$.

36. $\begin{cases} 3x+3y=3 \\ 4x+2y=\frac{8}{3} \end{cases}$ can be written as: $\left[\begin{array}{cc|c} 3 & 3 & 3 \\ 4 & 2 & \frac{8}{3} \end{array}\right]$

$$\rightarrow \left[\begin{array}{cc|c} 1 & 1 & 1 \\ 4 & 2 & \frac{8}{3} \end{array}\right] \rightarrow \left[\begin{array}{cc|c} 1 & 1 & 1 \\ 0 & -2 & -\frac{4}{3} \end{array}\right] \rightarrow \left[\begin{array}{cc|c} 1 & 1 & 1 \\ 0 & 1 & \frac{2}{3} \end{array}\right] \rightarrow \left[\begin{array}{cc|c} 1 & 0 & \frac{1}{3} \\ 0 & 1 & \frac{2}{3} \end{array}\right]$$

$R_1 = \tfrac{1}{3} r_1 \quad R_2 = -4r_1 + r_2 \quad R_2 = -\tfrac{1}{2} r_2 \quad R_1 = -r_2 + r_1$

The solution is $x = \dfrac{1}{3},\ y = \dfrac{2}{3}$.

37. $\begin{cases} x+2y=4 \\ 2x+4y=8 \end{cases}$ can be written as: $\left[\begin{array}{cc|c} 1 & 2 & 4 \\ 2 & 4 & 8 \end{array}\right]$

$$\rightarrow \left[\begin{array}{cc|c} 1 & 2 & 4 \\ 0 & 0 & 0 \end{array}\right]$$

$R_2 = -2r_1 + r_2$

This is a dependent system and the solution is $x = -2y + 4$, y is any real number.

38. $\begin{cases} 3x - y = 7 \\ 9x - 3y = 21 \end{cases}$ can be written as: $\left[\begin{array}{cc|c} 3 & -1 & 7 \\ 9 & -3 & 21 \end{array}\right]$

$$\rightarrow \left[\begin{array}{cc|c} 1 & -\frac{1}{3} & \frac{7}{3} \\ 9 & -3 & 21 \end{array}\right] \rightarrow \left[\begin{array}{cc|c} 1 & -\frac{1}{3} & \frac{7}{3} \\ 0 & 0 & 0 \end{array}\right]$$

$R_1 = \frac{1}{3} r_1 \qquad R_2 = -9r_1 + r_2$

This is a dependent system and the solution is $x = \frac{1}{3}y + \frac{7}{3}$, y is any real number.

39. $\begin{cases} 2x + 3y = 6 \\ x - y = \dfrac{1}{2} \end{cases}$ can be written as: $\left[\begin{array}{cc|c} 2 & 3 & 6 \\ 1 & -1 & \frac{1}{2} \end{array}\right]$

$$\rightarrow \left[\begin{array}{cc|c} 1 & \frac{3}{2} & 3 \\ 1 & -1 & \frac{1}{2} \end{array}\right] \rightarrow \left[\begin{array}{cc|c} 1 & \frac{3}{2} & 3 \\ 0 & -\frac{5}{2} & -\frac{5}{2} \end{array}\right] \rightarrow \left[\begin{array}{cc|c} 1 & \frac{3}{2} & 3 \\ 0 & 1 & 1 \end{array}\right] \rightarrow \left[\begin{array}{cc|c} 1 & 0 & \frac{3}{2} \\ 0 & 1 & 1 \end{array}\right]$$

$R_1 = \frac{1}{2} r_1 \qquad R_2 = -r_1 + r_2 \qquad R_2 = -\frac{2}{5} r_2 \qquad R_1 = -\frac{3}{2} r_2 + r_1$

The solution is $x = \dfrac{3}{2}, y = 1$.

40. $\begin{cases} \dfrac{1}{2}x + y = -2 \\ x - 2y = 8 \end{cases}$ can be written as: $\left[\begin{array}{cc|c} \frac{1}{2} & 1 & -2 \\ 1 & -2 & 8 \end{array}\right]$

$$\rightarrow \left[\begin{array}{cc|c} 1 & 2 & -4 \\ 1 & -2 & 8 \end{array}\right] \rightarrow \left[\begin{array}{cc|c} 1 & 2 & -4 \\ 0 & -4 & 12 \end{array}\right] \rightarrow \left[\begin{array}{cc|c} 1 & 2 & -4 \\ 0 & 1 & -3 \end{array}\right] \rightarrow \left[\begin{array}{cc|c} 1 & 0 & 2 \\ 0 & 1 & -3 \end{array}\right]$$

$R_1 = 2r_1 \qquad R_2 = -r_1 + r_2 \qquad R_2 = -\frac{1}{4} r_2 \qquad R_1 = -2r_2 + r_1$

The solution is $x = 2, y = -3$.

41. $\begin{cases} 3x - 5y = 3 \\ 15x + 5y = 21 \end{cases}$ can be written as: $\left[\begin{array}{cc|c} 3 & -5 & 3 \\ 15 & 5 & 21 \end{array}\right]$

$$\rightarrow \left[\begin{array}{cc|c} 1 & -\frac{5}{3} & 1 \\ 15 & 5 & 21 \end{array}\right] \rightarrow \left[\begin{array}{cc|c} 1 & -\frac{5}{3} & 1 \\ 0 & 30 & 6 \end{array}\right] \rightarrow \left[\begin{array}{cc|c} 1 & -\frac{5}{3} & 1 \\ 0 & 1 & \frac{1}{5} \end{array}\right] \rightarrow \left[\begin{array}{cc|c} 1 & 0 & \frac{4}{3} \\ 0 & 1 & \frac{1}{5} \end{array}\right]$$

$R_1 = \frac{1}{3} r_1 \qquad R_2 = -15r_1 + r_2 \qquad R_2 = \frac{1}{30} r_2 \qquad R_1 = \frac{5}{3} r_2 + r_1$

The solution is $x = \dfrac{4}{3}, y = \dfrac{1}{5}$.

42. $\begin{cases} 2x - y = -1 \\ x + \dfrac{1}{2}y = \dfrac{3}{2} \end{cases}$ can be written as: $\left[\begin{array}{cc|c} 2 & -1 & -1 \\ 1 & \frac{1}{2} & \frac{3}{2} \end{array}\right]$

$$\rightarrow \left[\begin{array}{cc|c} 1 & -\frac{1}{2} & -\frac{1}{2} \\ 1 & \frac{1}{2} & \frac{3}{2} \end{array}\right] \rightarrow \left[\begin{array}{cc|c} 1 & -\frac{1}{2} & -\frac{1}{2} \\ 0 & 1 & 2 \end{array}\right] \rightarrow \left[\begin{array}{cc|c} 1 & 0 & \frac{1}{2} \\ 0 & 1 & 2 \end{array}\right]$$

$R_1 = \frac{1}{2} r_1 \qquad R_2 = -1r_1 + r_2 \qquad R_1 = \frac{1}{2} r_2 + r_1$

The solution is $x = \dfrac{1}{2}, y = 2$.

43. $\begin{cases} x - y = 6 \\ 2x - 3z = 16 \\ 2y + z = 4 \end{cases}$ can be written as: $\left[\begin{array}{ccc|c} 1 & -1 & 0 & 6 \\ 2 & 0 & -3 & 16 \\ 0 & 2 & 1 & 4 \end{array}\right]$

$$\rightarrow \left[\begin{array}{ccc|c} 1 & -1 & 0 & 6 \\ 0 & 2 & -3 & 4 \\ 0 & 2 & 1 & 4 \end{array}\right] \rightarrow \left[\begin{array}{ccc|c} 1 & -1 & 0 & 6 \\ 0 & 1 & -\frac{3}{2} & 2 \\ 0 & 2 & 1 & 4 \end{array}\right] \rightarrow \left[\begin{array}{ccc|c} 1 & 0 & -\frac{3}{2} & 8 \\ 0 & 1 & -\frac{3}{2} & 2 \\ 0 & 0 & 4 & 0 \end{array}\right] \rightarrow \left[\begin{array}{ccc|c} 1 & 0 & -\frac{3}{2} & 8 \\ 0 & 1 & -\frac{3}{2} & 2 \\ 0 & 0 & 1 & 0 \end{array}\right]$$

$R_2 = -2r_1 + r_2$ $R_2 = \frac{1}{2}r_2$ $R_1 = r_2 + r_1$, $R_3 = -2r_2 + r_3$ $R_3 = \frac{1}{4}r_3$

$$\rightarrow \left[\begin{array}{ccc|c} 1 & 0 & 0 & 8 \\ 0 & 1 & 0 & 2 \\ 0 & 0 & 1 & 0 \end{array}\right]$$

$R_1 = \frac{3}{2}r_3 + r_1$
$R_2 = \frac{3}{2}r_3 + r_2$

The solution is $x = 8, y = 2, z = 0$.

44. $\begin{cases} 2x + y = -4 \\ -2y + 4z = 0 \\ 3x - 2z = -11 \end{cases}$ can be written as: $\left[\begin{array}{ccc|c} 2 & 1 & 0 & -4 \\ 0 & -2 & 4 & 0 \\ 3 & 0 & -2 & -11 \end{array}\right]$

$$\rightarrow \left[\begin{array}{ccc|c} 1 & \frac{1}{2} & 0 & -2 \\ 0 & -2 & 4 & 0 \\ 3 & 0 & -2 & -11 \end{array}\right] \rightarrow \left[\begin{array}{ccc|c} 1 & \frac{1}{2} & 0 & -2 \\ 0 & -2 & 4 & 0 \\ 0 & -\frac{3}{2} & -2 & -5 \end{array}\right] \rightarrow \left[\begin{array}{ccc|c} 1 & \frac{1}{2} & 0 & -2 \\ 0 & 1 & -2 & 0 \\ 0 & -\frac{3}{2} & -2 & -5 \end{array}\right]$$

$R_1 = \frac{1}{2}r_1$ $R_3 = -3r_1 + r_3$ $R_2 = -\frac{1}{2}r_2$

$$\rightarrow \left[\begin{array}{ccc|c} 1 & 0 & 1 & -2 \\ 0 & 1 & -2 & 0 \\ 0 & 0 & -5 & -5 \end{array}\right] \rightarrow \left[\begin{array}{ccc|c} 1 & 0 & 1 & -2 \\ 0 & 1 & -2 & 0 \\ 0 & 0 & 1 & 1 \end{array}\right] \rightarrow \left[\begin{array}{ccc|c} 1 & 0 & 0 & -3 \\ 0 & 1 & 0 & 2 \\ 0 & 0 & 1 & 1 \end{array}\right]$$

$R_1 = -\frac{1}{2}r_2 + r_1$, $R_3 = \frac{3}{2}r_2 + r_3$ $R_3 = -\frac{1}{5}r_3$ $R_1 = -r_3 + r_1$, $R_2 = 2r_3 + r_2$

The solution is $x = -3, y = 2, z = 1$.

45. $\begin{cases} x-2y+3z=7 \\ 2x+y+z=4 \\ -3x+2y-2z=-10 \end{cases}$ can be written as: $\left[\begin{array}{rrr|r} 1 & -2 & 3 & 7 \\ 2 & 1 & 1 & 4 \\ -3 & 2 & -2 & -10 \end{array}\right]$

$$\rightarrow \left[\begin{array}{rrr|r} 1 & -2 & 3 & 7 \\ 0 & 5 & -5 & -10 \\ 0 & -4 & 7 & 11 \end{array}\right] \rightarrow \left[\begin{array}{rrr|r} 1 & -2 & 3 & 7 \\ 0 & 1 & -1 & -2 \\ 0 & -4 & 7 & 11 \end{array}\right] \rightarrow \left[\begin{array}{rrr|r} 1 & 0 & 1 & 3 \\ 0 & 1 & -1 & -2 \\ 0 & 0 & 3 & 3 \end{array}\right]$$

$R_2 = -2r_1 + r_2$ $\quad R_2 = \frac{1}{5}r_2$ $\quad R_1 = 2r_2 + r_1$

$R_3 = 3r_1 + r_3$ $\quad R_3 = 4r_2 + r_3$

$$\rightarrow \left[\begin{array}{rrr|r} 1 & 0 & 1 & 3 \\ 0 & 1 & -1 & -2 \\ 0 & 0 & 1 & 1 \end{array}\right] \rightarrow \left[\begin{array}{rrr|r} 1 & 0 & 0 & 2 \\ 0 & 1 & 0 & -1 \\ 0 & 0 & 1 & 1 \end{array}\right]$$

$R_3 = \frac{1}{3}r_3$ $\quad R_1 = -r_3 + r_1$

$R_2 = r_3 + r_2$

The solution is $x = 2, y = -1, z = 1$.

46. $\begin{cases} 2x+y-3z=0 \\ -2x+2y+z=-7 \\ 3x-4y-3z=7 \end{cases}$ can be written as: $\left[\begin{array}{rrr|r} 2 & 1 & -3 & 0 \\ -2 & 2 & 1 & -7 \\ 3 & -4 & -3 & 7 \end{array}\right]$

$$\rightarrow \left[\begin{array}{rrr|r} 1 & \frac{1}{2} & -\frac{3}{2} & 0 \\ -2 & 2 & 1 & -7 \\ 3 & -4 & -3 & 7 \end{array}\right] \rightarrow \left[\begin{array}{rrr|r} 1 & \frac{1}{2} & -\frac{3}{2} & 0 \\ 0 & 3 & -2 & -7 \\ 0 & -\frac{11}{2} & \frac{3}{2} & 7 \end{array}\right] \rightarrow \left[\begin{array}{rrr|r} 1 & \frac{1}{2} & -\frac{3}{2} & 0 \\ 0 & 1 & -\frac{2}{3} & -\frac{7}{3} \\ 0 & -\frac{11}{2} & \frac{3}{2} & 7 \end{array}\right]$$

$R_1 = \frac{1}{2}r_1$ $\quad R_2 = 2r_1 + r_2$ $\quad R_2 = \frac{1}{3}r_2$

$R_3 = -3r_1 + r_3$

$$\rightarrow \left[\begin{array}{rrr|r} 1 & 0 & -\frac{7}{6} & \frac{7}{6} \\ 0 & 1 & -\frac{2}{3} & -\frac{7}{3} \\ 0 & 0 & -\frac{13}{6} & -\frac{35}{6} \end{array}\right] \rightarrow \left[\begin{array}{rrr|r} 1 & 0 & -\frac{7}{6} & \frac{7}{6} \\ 0 & 1 & -\frac{2}{3} & -\frac{7}{3} \\ 0 & 0 & 1 & \frac{35}{13} \end{array}\right] \rightarrow \left[\begin{array}{rrr|r} 1 & 0 & 0 & \frac{56}{13} \\ 0 & 1 & 0 & -\frac{7}{13} \\ 0 & 0 & 1 & \frac{35}{13} \end{array}\right]$$

$R_1 = -\frac{1}{2}r_2 + r_1$ $\quad R_3 = -\frac{6}{13}r_3$ $\quad R_1 = \frac{7}{6}r_3 + r_1$

$R_3 = \frac{11}{2}r_2 + r_3$ $\quad R_2 = \frac{2}{3}r_3 + r_2$

The solution is $x = \frac{56}{13}, y = -\frac{7}{13}, z = \frac{35}{13}$.

47. $\begin{cases} 2x-2y-2z=2 \\ 2x+3y+z=2 \\ 3x+2y=0 \end{cases}$ can be written as: $\left[\begin{array}{ccc|c} 2 & -2 & -2 & 2 \\ 2 & 3 & 1 & 2 \\ 3 & 2 & 0 & 0 \end{array}\right]$

$$\rightarrow \left[\begin{array}{ccc|c} 1 & -1 & -1 & 1 \\ 2 & 3 & 1 & 2 \\ 3 & 2 & 0 & 0 \end{array}\right] \rightarrow \left[\begin{array}{ccc|c} 1 & -1 & -1 & 1 \\ 0 & 5 & 3 & 0 \\ 0 & 5 & 3 & -3 \end{array}\right] \rightarrow \left[\begin{array}{ccc|c} 1 & -1 & -1 & 1 \\ 0 & 5 & 3 & 0 \\ 0 & 0 & 0 & -3 \end{array}\right]$$

$R_1 = \frac{1}{2}r_1$ $\quad R_2 = -2r_1 + r_2$, $R_3 = -3r_1 + r_3$ $\quad R_3 = -r_2 + r_3$

There is no solution. The system is inconsistent.

48. $\begin{cases} 2x-3y-z=0 \\ -x+2y+z=5 \\ 3x-4y-z=1 \end{cases}$ can be written as: $\left[\begin{array}{ccc|c} 2 & -3 & -1 & 0 \\ -1 & 2 & 1 & 5 \\ 3 & -4 & -1 & 1 \end{array}\right]$

$$\rightarrow \left[\begin{array}{ccc|c} 1 & -2 & -1 & -5 \\ 2 & -3 & -1 & 0 \\ 3 & -4 & -1 & 1 \end{array}\right] \rightarrow \left[\begin{array}{ccc|c} 1 & -2 & -1 & -5 \\ 0 & 1 & 1 & 10 \\ 0 & 2 & 2 & 16 \end{array}\right] \rightarrow \left[\begin{array}{ccc|c} 1 & -2 & -1 & -5 \\ 0 & 1 & 1 & 10 \\ 0 & 0 & 0 & -4 \end{array}\right]$$

Interchange r_1 and $-r_2$ $\quad R_2 = -2r_1 + r_2$, $R_3 = -3r_1 + r_3$ $\quad R_3 = -2r_2 + r_3$

There is no solution. The system is inconsistent.

49. $\begin{cases} -x+y+z=-1 \\ -x+2y-3z=-4 \\ 3x-2y-7z=0 \end{cases}$ can be written as: $\left[\begin{array}{ccc|c} -1 & 1 & 1 & -1 \\ -1 & 2 & -3 & -4 \\ 3 & -2 & -7 & 0 \end{array}\right]$

$$\rightarrow \left[\begin{array}{ccc|c} 1 & -1 & -1 & 1 \\ -1 & 2 & -3 & -4 \\ 3 & -2 & -7 & 0 \end{array}\right] \rightarrow \left[\begin{array}{ccc|c} 1 & -1 & -1 & 1 \\ 0 & 1 & -4 & -3 \\ 0 & 1 & -4 & -3 \end{array}\right] \rightarrow \left[\begin{array}{ccc|c} 1 & 0 & -5 & -2 \\ 0 & 1 & -4 & -3 \\ 0 & 0 & 0 & 0 \end{array}\right] \rightarrow \begin{array}{l} x-5z=-2 \\ y-4z=-3 \end{array}$$

$R_1 = -r_1$ $\quad R_2 = r_1 + r_2$, $R_3 = -3r_1 + r_3$ $\quad R_1 = r_2 + r_1$, $R_3 = -r_2 + r_3$

The solution is $x = 5z-2, y = 4z-3, z$ is any real number.

50. $\begin{cases} 2x-3y-z=0 \\ 3x+2y+2z=2 \\ x+5y+3z=2 \end{cases}$ can be written as: $\left[\begin{array}{ccc|c} 2 & -3 & -1 & 0 \\ 3 & 2 & 2 & 2 \\ 1 & 5 & 3 & 2 \end{array}\right]$

$$\rightarrow \left[\begin{array}{ccc|c} 1 & 5 & 3 & 2 \\ 3 & 2 & 2 & 2 \\ 2 & -3 & -1 & 0 \end{array}\right] \rightarrow \left[\begin{array}{ccc|c} 1 & 5 & 3 & 2 \\ 0 & -13 & -7 & -4 \\ 0 & -13 & -7 & -4 \end{array}\right] \rightarrow \left[\begin{array}{ccc|c} 1 & 5 & 3 & 2 \\ 0 & 1 & \frac{7}{13} & \frac{4}{13} \\ 0 & 0 & 0 & 0 \end{array}\right]$$

Interchange r_1 and r_3 $\quad R_2 = -3r_1 + r_2$, $R_3 = -2r_1 + r_3$ $\quad R_3 = -r_2 + r_3$, $R_2 = -\frac{1}{13}r_2$

$$\rightarrow\left[\begin{array}{ccc|c} 1 & 0 & \frac{4}{13} & \frac{6}{13} \\ 0 & 1 & \frac{7}{13} & \frac{4}{13} \\ 0 & 0 & 0 & 0 \end{array}\right] \rightarrow \begin{array}{l} x+\frac{4}{13}z=\frac{6}{13} \\ y+\frac{7}{13}z=\frac{4}{13} \end{array}$$

$R_1=-5r_2+r_1$

The solution is $x=\dfrac{6}{13}-\dfrac{4}{13}z,\ y=\dfrac{4}{13}-\dfrac{7}{13}z,\ z$ is any real number.

51. $\begin{cases} 2x-2y+3z=6 \\ 4x-3y+2z=0 \\ -2x+3y-7z=1 \end{cases}$ can be written as: $\left[\begin{array}{ccc|c} 2 & -2 & 3 & 6 \\ 4 & -3 & 2 & 0 \\ -2 & 3 & -7 & 1 \end{array}\right]$

$$\rightarrow\left[\begin{array}{ccc|c} 1 & -1 & \frac{3}{2} & 3 \\ 4 & -3 & 2 & 0 \\ -2 & 3 & -7 & 1 \end{array}\right] \rightarrow \left[\begin{array}{ccc|c} 1 & -1 & \frac{3}{2} & 3 \\ 0 & 1 & -4 & -12 \\ 0 & 1 & -4 & 7 \end{array}\right] \rightarrow \left[\begin{array}{ccc|c} 1 & 0 & -\frac{5}{2} & -9 \\ 0 & 1 & -4 & -12 \\ 0 & 0 & 0 & 19 \end{array}\right]$$

$R_1=\frac{1}{2}r_1$ $\qquad R_2=-4r_1+r_2$, $R_3=2r_1+r_3$ $\qquad R_1=r_2+r_1$, $R_3=-r_2+r_3$

There is no solution. The system is inconsistent.

52. $\begin{cases} 3x-2y+2z=6 \\ 7x-3y+2z=-1 \\ 2x-3y+4z=0 \end{cases}$ can be written as: $\left[\begin{array}{ccc|c} 3 & -2 & 2 & 6 \\ 7 & -3 & 2 & -1 \\ 2 & -3 & 4 & 0 \end{array}\right]$

$$\rightarrow\left[\begin{array}{ccc|c} 1 & -\frac{2}{3} & \frac{2}{3} & 2 \\ 7 & -3 & 2 & -1 \\ 2 & -3 & 4 & 0 \end{array}\right] \rightarrow \left[\begin{array}{ccc|c} 1 & -\frac{2}{3} & \frac{2}{3} & 2 \\ 0 & \frac{5}{3} & -\frac{8}{3} & -15 \\ 0 & -\frac{5}{3} & \frac{8}{3} & -4 \end{array}\right] \rightarrow \left[\begin{array}{ccc|c} 1 & -\frac{2}{3} & \frac{2}{3} & 2 \\ 0 & \frac{5}{3} & -\frac{8}{3} & -15 \\ 0 & 0 & 0 & -19 \end{array}\right]$$

$R_1=\frac{1}{3}r_1$ $\qquad R_2=-7r_1+r_2$, $R_3=-2r_1+r_3$ $\qquad R_3=r_2+r_3$

There is no solution. The system is inconsistent.

53. $\begin{cases} x+y-z=6 \\ 3x-2y+z=-5 \\ x+3y-2z=14 \end{cases}$ can be written as: $\left[\begin{array}{ccc|c} 1 & 1 & -1 & 6 \\ 3 & -2 & 1 & -5 \\ 1 & 3 & -2 & 14 \end{array}\right]$

$$\rightarrow\left[\begin{array}{ccc|c} 1 & 1 & -1 & 6 \\ 0 & -5 & 4 & -23 \\ 0 & 2 & -1 & 8 \end{array}\right] \rightarrow \left[\begin{array}{ccc|c} 1 & 1 & -1 & 6 \\ 0 & 1 & -\frac{4}{5} & \frac{23}{5} \\ 0 & 2 & -1 & 8 \end{array}\right] \rightarrow \left[\begin{array}{ccc|c} 1 & 0 & -\frac{1}{5} & \frac{7}{5} \\ 0 & 1 & -\frac{4}{5} & \frac{23}{5} \\ 0 & 0 & \frac{3}{5} & -\frac{6}{5} \end{array}\right]$$

$R_2=-3r_1+r_2$, $R_3=-r_1+r_3$ $\qquad R_2=-\frac{1}{5}r_2$ $\qquad R_1=-r_2+r_1$, $R_3=-2r_2+r_3$

$$\rightarrow\left[\begin{array}{ccc|c} 1 & 0 & -\frac{1}{5} & \frac{7}{5} \\ 0 & 1 & -\frac{4}{5} & \frac{23}{5} \\ 0 & 0 & 1 & -2 \end{array}\right] \rightarrow \left[\begin{array}{ccc|c} 1 & 0 & 0 & 1 \\ 0 & 1 & 0 & 3 \\ 0 & 0 & 1 & -2 \end{array}\right]$$

$R_3 = \frac{5}{3}r_3$ $\quad R_1 = \frac{1}{5}r_3 + r_1$

$R_2 = \frac{4}{5}r_3 + r_2$

The solution is $x = 1,\ y = 3,\ z = -2$.

54. $\begin{cases} x - y + z = -4 \\ 2x - 3y + 4z = -15 \\ 5x + y - 2z = 12 \end{cases}$ can be written as: $\left[\begin{array}{ccc|c} 1 & -1 & 1 & -4 \\ 2 & -3 & 4 & -15 \\ 5 & 1 & -2 & 12 \end{array}\right]$

$$\rightarrow\left[\begin{array}{ccc|c} 1 & -1 & 1 & -4 \\ 0 & -1 & 2 & -7 \\ 0 & 6 & -7 & 32 \end{array}\right] \rightarrow \left[\begin{array}{ccc|c} 1 & -1 & 1 & -4 \\ 0 & 1 & -2 & 7 \\ 0 & 6 & -7 & 32 \end{array}\right] \rightarrow \left[\begin{array}{ccc|c} 1 & 0 & -1 & 3 \\ 0 & 1 & -2 & 7 \\ 0 & 0 & 5 & -10 \end{array}\right]$$

$R_2 = -2r_1 + r_2$ $\quad R_2 = -r_2$ $\quad R_1 = r_2 + r_1$

$R_3 = -5r_1 + r_3$ $\quad R_3 = -6r_2 + r_3$

$$\rightarrow\left[\begin{array}{ccc|c} 1 & 0 & -1 & 3 \\ 0 & 1 & -2 & 7 \\ 0 & 0 & 1 & -2 \end{array}\right] \rightarrow \left[\begin{array}{ccc|c} 1 & 0 & 0 & 1 \\ 0 & 1 & 0 & 3 \\ 0 & 0 & 1 & -2 \end{array}\right]$$

$R_3 = \frac{1}{5}r_3$ $\quad R_1 = r_3 + r_1$

$R_2 = 2r_3 + r_2$

The solution is $x = 1,\ y = 3,\ z = -2$.

55. $\begin{cases} x + 2y - z = -3 \\ 2x - 4y + z = -7 \\ -2x + 2y - 3z = 4 \end{cases}$ can be written as: $\left[\begin{array}{ccc|c} 1 & 2 & -1 & -3 \\ 2 & -4 & 1 & -7 \\ -2 & 2 & -3 & 4 \end{array}\right]$

$$\rightarrow\left[\begin{array}{ccc|c} 1 & 2 & -1 & -3 \\ 0 & -8 & 3 & -1 \\ 0 & 6 & -5 & -2 \end{array}\right] \rightarrow \left[\begin{array}{ccc|c} 1 & 2 & -1 & -3 \\ 0 & 1 & -\frac{3}{8} & \frac{1}{8} \\ 0 & 6 & -5 & -2 \end{array}\right] \rightarrow \left[\begin{array}{ccc|c} 1 & 0 & -\frac{1}{4} & -\frac{13}{4} \\ 0 & 1 & -\frac{3}{8} & \frac{1}{8} \\ 0 & 0 & -\frac{11}{4} & -\frac{11}{4} \end{array}\right]$$

$R_2 = -2r_1 + r_2$ $\quad R_2 = -\frac{1}{8}r_2$ $\quad R_1 = -2r_2 + r_1$

$R_3 = 2r_1 + r_3$ $\quad R_3 = -6r_2 + r_3$

$$\rightarrow\left[\begin{array}{ccc|c} 1 & 0 & -\frac{1}{4} & -\frac{13}{4} \\ 0 & 1 & -\frac{3}{8} & \frac{1}{8} \\ 0 & 0 & 1 & 1 \end{array}\right] \rightarrow \left[\begin{array}{ccc|c} 1 & 0 & 0 & -3 \\ 0 & 1 & 0 & \frac{1}{2} \\ 0 & 0 & 1 & 1 \end{array}\right]$$

$R_3 = -\frac{4}{11}r_3$ $\quad R_1 = \frac{1}{4}r_3 + r_1$

$R_2 = \frac{3}{8}r_3 + r_2$

The solution is $x = -3,\ y = \frac{1}{2},\ z = 1$.

56. $\begin{cases} x+4y-3z=-8 \\ 3x-y+3z=12 \\ x+y+6z=1 \end{cases}$ can be written as: $\left[\begin{array}{ccc|c} 1 & 4 & -3 & -8 \\ 3 & -1 & 3 & 12 \\ 1 & 1 & 6 & 1 \end{array}\right]$

$$\rightarrow \left[\begin{array}{ccc|c} 1 & 4 & -3 & -8 \\ 0 & -13 & 12 & 36 \\ 0 & -3 & 9 & 9 \end{array}\right] \rightarrow \left[\begin{array}{ccc|c} 1 & 4 & -3 & -8 \\ 0 & 1 & -\frac{12}{13} & -\frac{36}{13} \\ 0 & -3 & 9 & 9 \end{array}\right] \rightarrow \left[\begin{array}{ccc|c} 1 & 0 & \frac{9}{13} & \frac{40}{13} \\ 0 & 1 & -\frac{12}{13} & -\frac{36}{13} \\ 0 & 0 & \frac{81}{13} & \frac{9}{13} \end{array}\right]$$

$R_2 = -3r_1 + r_2$, $R_3 = -r_1 + r_3$ $\quad$ $R_2 = -\frac{1}{13}r_2$ $\quad$ $R_1 = -4r_2 + r_1$, $R_3 = 3r_2 + r_3$

$$\rightarrow \left[\begin{array}{ccc|c} 1 & 0 & \frac{9}{13} & \frac{40}{13} \\ 0 & 1 & -\frac{12}{13} & -\frac{36}{13} \\ 0 & 0 & 1 & \frac{1}{9} \end{array}\right] \rightarrow \left[\begin{array}{ccc|c} 1 & 0 & 0 & 3 \\ 0 & 1 & 0 & -\frac{8}{3} \\ 0 & 0 & 1 & \frac{1}{9} \end{array}\right]$$

$R_3 = \frac{13}{81}r_3$ $\quad$ $R_1 = -\frac{9}{13}r_3 + r_1$, $R_2 = \frac{12}{13}r_3 + r_2$

The solution is $x = 3, y = -\frac{8}{3}, z = \frac{1}{9}$.

57. $\begin{cases} 3x+y-z=\frac{2}{3} \\ 2x-y+z=1 \\ 4x+2y=\frac{8}{3} \end{cases}$ can be written as: $\left[\begin{array}{ccc|c} 3 & 1 & -1 & \frac{2}{3} \\ 2 & -1 & 1 & 1 \\ 4 & 2 & 0 & \frac{8}{3} \end{array}\right]$

$$\rightarrow \left[\begin{array}{ccc|c} 1 & \frac{1}{3} & -\frac{1}{3} & \frac{2}{9} \\ 2 & -1 & 1 & 1 \\ 4 & 2 & 0 & \frac{8}{3} \end{array}\right] \rightarrow \left[\begin{array}{ccc|c} 1 & \frac{1}{3} & -\frac{1}{3} & \frac{2}{9} \\ 0 & -\frac{5}{3} & \frac{5}{3} & \frac{5}{9} \\ 0 & \frac{2}{3} & \frac{4}{3} & \frac{16}{9} \end{array}\right] \rightarrow \left[\begin{array}{ccc|c} 1 & \frac{1}{3} & -\frac{1}{3} & \frac{2}{9} \\ 0 & 1 & -1 & -\frac{1}{3} \\ 0 & \frac{2}{3} & \frac{4}{3} & \frac{16}{9} \end{array}\right] \rightarrow \left[\begin{array}{ccc|c} 1 & 0 & 0 & \frac{1}{3} \\ 0 & 1 & -1 & -\frac{1}{3} \\ 0 & 0 & 2 & 2 \end{array}\right]$$

$R_1 = \frac{1}{3}r_1$ $\quad$ $R_2 = -2r_1 + r_2$, $R_3 = -4r_1 + r_3$ $\quad$ $R_2 = -\frac{3}{5}r_2$ $\quad$ $R_1 = -\frac{1}{3}r_2 + r_1$, $R_3 = -\frac{2}{3}r_2 + r_3$

$$\rightarrow \left[\begin{array}{ccc|c} 1 & 0 & 0 & \frac{1}{3} \\ 0 & 1 & -1 & -\frac{1}{3} \\ 0 & 0 & 1 & 1 \end{array}\right] \rightarrow \left[\begin{array}{ccc|c} 1 & 0 & 0 & \frac{1}{3} \\ 0 & 1 & 0 & \frac{2}{3} \\ 0 & 0 & 1 & 1 \end{array}\right]$$

$R_3 = \frac{1}{2}r_3$ $\quad$ $R_2 = r_3 + r_2$

The solution is $x = \frac{1}{3}, y = \frac{2}{3}, z = 1$.

58. $\begin{cases} x+y=1 \\ 2x-y+z=1 \\ x+2y+z=\frac{8}{3} \end{cases}$ can be written as: $\left[\begin{array}{ccc|c} 1 & 1 & 0 & 1 \\ 2 & -1 & 1 & 1 \\ 1 & 2 & 1 & \frac{8}{3} \end{array}\right]$

$$\rightarrow \left[\begin{array}{ccc|c} 1 & 1 & 0 & 1 \\ 0 & -3 & 1 & -1 \\ 0 & 1 & 1 & \frac{5}{3} \end{array}\right] \rightarrow \left[\begin{array}{ccc|c} 1 & 1 & 0 & 1 \\ 0 & 1 & 1 & \frac{5}{3} \\ 0 & -3 & 1 & -1 \end{array}\right] \rightarrow \left[\begin{array}{ccc|c} 1 & 0 & -1 & -\frac{2}{3} \\ 0 & 1 & 1 & \frac{5}{3} \\ 0 & 0 & 4 & 4 \end{array}\right]$$

$R_2=-2r_1+r_2$, $R_3=-r_1+r_3$ Interchange r_2 and r_3 $R_1=-r_2+r_1$, $R_3=3r_2+r_3$

$$\rightarrow \left[\begin{array}{ccc|c} 1 & 0 & -1 & -\frac{2}{3} \\ 0 & 1 & 1 & \frac{5}{3} \\ 0 & 0 & 1 & 1 \end{array}\right] \rightarrow \left[\begin{array}{ccc|c} 1 & 0 & 0 & \frac{1}{3} \\ 0 & 1 & 0 & \frac{2}{3} \\ 0 & 0 & 1 & 1 \end{array}\right]$$

$R_3=\frac{1}{4}r_3$ $R_1=r_3+r_1$, $R_2=-r_3+r_2$

The solution is $x=\dfrac{1}{3}, y=\dfrac{2}{3}, z=1$.

59. $\begin{cases} x+y+z+w=4 \\ 2x-y+z=0 \\ 3x+2y+z-w=6 \\ x-2y-2z+2w=-1 \end{cases}$ can be written as: $\left[\begin{array}{cccc|c} 1 & 1 & 1 & 1 & 4 \\ 2 & -1 & 1 & 0 & 0 \\ 3 & 2 & 1 & -1 & 6 \\ 1 & -2 & -2 & 2 & -1 \end{array}\right]$

$$\rightarrow \left[\begin{array}{cccc|c} 1 & 1 & 1 & 1 & 4 \\ 0 & -3 & -1 & -2 & -8 \\ 0 & -1 & -2 & -4 & -6 \\ 0 & -3 & -3 & 1 & -5 \end{array}\right] \rightarrow \left[\begin{array}{cccc|c} 1 & 1 & 1 & 1 & 4 \\ 0 & -1 & -2 & -4 & -6 \\ 0 & -3 & -1 & -2 & -8 \\ 0 & -3 & -3 & 1 & -5 \end{array}\right] \rightarrow \left[\begin{array}{cccc|c} 1 & 1 & 1 & 1 & 4 \\ 0 & 1 & 2 & 4 & 6 \\ 0 & -3 & -1 & -2 & -8 \\ 0 & -3 & -3 & 1 & -5 \end{array}\right]$$

$R_2=-2r_1+r_2$, $R_3=-3r_1+r_3$, $R_4=-r_1+r_4$ Interchange r_2 and r_3 $R_2=-r_2$

$$\rightarrow \left[\begin{array}{cccc|c} 1 & 0 & -1 & -3 & -2 \\ 0 & 1 & 2 & 4 & 6 \\ 0 & 0 & 5 & 10 & 10 \\ 0 & 0 & 3 & 13 & 13 \end{array}\right] \rightarrow \left[\begin{array}{cccc|c} 1 & 0 & -1 & -3 & -2 \\ 0 & 1 & 2 & 4 & 6 \\ 0 & 0 & 1 & 2 & 2 \\ 0 & 0 & 3 & 13 & 13 \end{array}\right] \rightarrow \left[\begin{array}{cccc|c} 1 & 0 & 0 & -1 & 0 \\ 0 & 1 & 0 & 0 & 2 \\ 0 & 0 & 1 & 2 & 2 \\ 0 & 0 & 0 & 7 & 7 \end{array}\right]$$

$R_1=-r_2+r_1$, $R_3=3r_2+r_3$, $R_4=3r_2+r_4$ $R_3=\frac{1}{5}r_3$ $R_1=r_3+r_1$, $R_2=-2r_3+r_2$, $R_4=-3r_3+r_4$

$$\rightarrow\begin{bmatrix} 1 & 0 & 0 & -1 & 0 \\ 0 & 1 & 0 & 0 & 2 \\ 0 & 0 & 1 & 2 & 2 \\ 0 & 0 & 0 & 1 & 1 \end{bmatrix} \rightarrow \begin{bmatrix} 1 & 0 & 0 & 0 & 1 \\ 0 & 1 & 0 & 0 & 2 \\ 0 & 0 & 1 & 0 & 0 \\ 0 & 0 & 0 & 1 & 1 \end{bmatrix}$$

$R_4 = \frac{1}{7}r_4$ $\quad$ $R_1 = r_4 + r_1$, $R_3 = -2r_4 + r_3$

The solution is $x = 1$, $y = 2$, $z = 0$, $w = 1$.

60. $\begin{cases} x + y + z + w = 4 \\ -x + 2y + z = 0 \\ 2x + 3y + z - w = 6 \\ -2x + y - 2z + 2w = -1 \end{cases}$ can be written as: $\begin{bmatrix} 1 & 1 & 1 & 1 & 4 \\ -1 & 2 & 1 & 0 & 0 \\ 2 & 3 & 1 & -1 & 6 \\ -2 & 1 & -2 & 2 & -1 \end{bmatrix}$

$$\rightarrow\begin{bmatrix} 1 & 1 & 1 & 1 & 4 \\ 0 & 3 & 2 & 1 & 4 \\ 0 & 1 & -1 & -3 & -2 \\ 0 & 3 & 0 & 4 & 7 \end{bmatrix} \rightarrow \begin{bmatrix} 1 & 1 & 1 & 1 & 4 \\ 0 & 1 & -1 & -3 & -2 \\ 0 & 3 & 2 & 1 & 4 \\ 0 & 3 & 0 & 4 & 7 \end{bmatrix} \rightarrow \begin{bmatrix} 1 & 0 & 2 & 4 & 6 \\ 0 & 1 & -1 & -3 & -2 \\ 0 & 0 & 5 & 10 & 10 \\ 0 & 0 & 3 & 13 & 13 \end{bmatrix}$$

$R_2 = r_1 + r_2$, $R_3 = -2r_1 + r_3$, $R_4 = 2r_1 + r_4$ $\quad$ Interchange r_2 and r_3 $\quad$ $R_1 = -r_2 + r_1$, $R_3 = -3r_2 + r_3$, $R_4 = -3r_2 + r_4$

$$\rightarrow\begin{bmatrix} 1 & 0 & 2 & 4 & 6 \\ 0 & 1 & -1 & -3 & -2 \\ 0 & 0 & 5 & 10 & 10 \\ 0 & 0 & 0 & -35 & -35 \end{bmatrix} \rightarrow \begin{bmatrix} 1 & 0 & 2 & 4 & 6 \\ 0 & 1 & -1 & -3 & -2 \\ 0 & 0 & 1 & 2 & 2 \\ 0 & 0 & 0 & 1 & 1 \end{bmatrix}$$

$R_4 = 3r_3 - 5r_4$ $\quad$ $R_3 = \frac{1}{5}r_3$, $R_4 = -\frac{1}{35}r_4$

So $w = 1$. Now substitute and solve.

$$w = 1$$
$$z + 2\cdot(1) = 2 \rightarrow z = 0$$
$$y - (0) - 3\cdot(1) = -2 \rightarrow y = 1$$
$$x + 0\cdot(1) + 2\cdot(0) + 4\cdot(1) = 6 \rightarrow x = 2$$

$\therefore$ the solution is $x = 2, y = 1, z = 0, w = 1$.

61. $\begin{cases} x + 2y + z = 1 \\ 2x - y + 2z = 2 \\ 3x + y + 3z = 3 \end{cases}$ can be written as: $\begin{bmatrix} 1 & 2 & 1 & 1 \\ 2 & -1 & 2 & 2 \\ 3 & 1 & 3 & 3 \end{bmatrix}$

$$\rightarrow\begin{bmatrix} 1 & 2 & 1 & 1 \\ 0 & -5 & 0 & 0 \\ 0 & -5 & 0 & 0 \end{bmatrix} \rightarrow \begin{bmatrix} 1 & 2 & 1 & 1 \\ 0 & -5 & 0 & 0 \\ 0 & 0 & 0 & 0 \end{bmatrix} \rightarrow \begin{matrix} x + 2y + z = 1 \\ -5y = 0 \end{matrix}$$

$R_2 = -2r_1 + r_2$, $R_3 = -3r_1 + r_3$ $\quad$ $R_3 = -r_2 + r_3$

Substitute and solve:

$$\begin{aligned} y &= 0 \\ x + 2(0) + z &= 1 \\ x + z &= 1 \\ x &= 1 - z \end{aligned}$$

The solution is $y = 0,\ x = 1 - z,\ z$ is any real number .

62. $\begin{cases} x + 2y - z = 3 \\ 2x - y + 2z = 6 \\ x - 3y + 3z = 4 \end{cases}$ can be written as: $\left[\begin{array}{ccc|c} 1 & 2 & -1 & 3 \\ 2 & -1 & 2 & 6 \\ 1 & -3 & 3 & 4 \end{array}\right]$

$$\rightarrow \left[\begin{array}{ccc|c} 1 & 2 & -1 & 3 \\ 0 & -5 & 4 & 0 \\ 0 & -5 & 4 & 1 \end{array}\right] \rightarrow \left[\begin{array}{ccc|c} 1 & 2 & -1 & 3 \\ 0 & -5 & 4 & 0 \\ 0 & 0 & 0 & 1 \end{array}\right]$$

$R_2 = -2r_1 + r_2 \quad R_3 = -r_2 + r_3$

$R_3 = -r_1 + r_3$

There is no solution. The system is inconsistent.

63. $\begin{cases} x - y + z = 5 \\ 3x + 2y - 2z = 0 \end{cases}$ can be written as: $\left[\begin{array}{ccc|c} 1 & -1 & 1 & 5 \\ 3 & 2 & -2 & 0 \end{array}\right]$

$$\rightarrow \left[\begin{array}{ccc|c} 1 & -1 & 1 & 5 \\ 0 & 5 & -5 & -15 \end{array}\right] \rightarrow \left[\begin{array}{ccc|c} 1 & -1 & 1 & 5 \\ 0 & 1 & -1 & -3 \end{array}\right] \rightarrow \left[\begin{array}{ccc|c} 1 & 0 & 0 & 2 \\ 0 & 1 & -1 & -3 \end{array}\right]$$

$R_2 = -3r_1 + r_2 \qquad R_2 = \frac{1}{5} r_2 \qquad R_1 = r_2 + r_1$

The matrix in the third step represents the system $\begin{cases} x = 2 \\ y - z = -3 \end{cases}$

Therefore the solution is $x = 2; y = -3 + z;\ z$ is any real number

or

$x = 2; z = y + 3;\ y$ is any real number

64. $\begin{cases} 2x + y - z = 4 \\ -x + y + 3z = 1 \end{cases}$ can be written as: $\left[\begin{array}{ccc|c} 2 & 1 & -1 & 4 \\ -1 & 1 & 3 & 1 \end{array}\right]$

$$\rightarrow \left[\begin{array}{ccc|c} 1 & -1 & -3 & -1 \\ 2 & 1 & -1 & 4 \end{array}\right] \longrightarrow \left[\begin{array}{ccc|c} 1 & -1 & -3 & -1 \\ 0 & 3 & 5 & 6 \end{array}\right] \rightarrow \left[\begin{array}{ccc|c} 1 & -1 & 3 & -1 \\ 0 & 1 & \frac{5}{3} & 2 \end{array}\right]$$

interchange r_1 and $-r_2$ $\qquad R_2 = -2r_1 + r_2 \qquad R_2 = \frac{1}{3} r_2$

$$\left[\begin{array}{ccc|c} 1 & -1 & 3 & -1 \\ 0 & 1 & \frac{5}{3} & 2 \end{array}\right] \rightarrow \left[\begin{array}{ccc|c} 1 & 0 & \frac{4}{3} & 1 \\ 0 & 1 & \frac{5}{3} & 2 \end{array}\right]$$

$R_1 = r_2 + r_1$

The matrix in the last step represents the system $\begin{cases} x + \frac{4}{3}z = 1 \\ y - \frac{5}{3}z = 2 \end{cases}$

Therefore the solution is:

$$x = 1 - \frac{4}{3}z;\; y = 2 - \frac{5}{3}z;\; z \text{ is any real number}$$

65.

$\begin{cases} 2x + 3y - z = 3 \\ x - y - z = 0 \\ -x + y + z = 0 \\ x + y + 3z = 5 \end{cases}$ can be written as: $\left[\begin{array}{ccc|c} 2 & 3 & -1 & 3 \\ 1 & -1 & -1 & 0 \\ -1 & 1 & 1 & 0 \\ 1 & 1 & 3 & 5 \end{array}\right]$

$$\rightarrow \left[\begin{array}{ccc|c} 1 & -1 & -1 & 0 \\ 2 & 3 & -1 & 3 \\ -1 & 1 & 1 & 0 \\ 1 & 1 & 3 & 5 \end{array}\right] \longrightarrow \left[\begin{array}{ccc|c} 1 & -1 & -1 & 0 \\ 0 & 5 & 1 & 3 \\ 0 & 0 & 0 & 0 \\ 0 & 2 & 4 & 5 \end{array}\right] \rightarrow \left[\begin{array}{ccc|c} 1 & -1 & -1 & 0 \\ 0 & 5 & 1 & 3 \\ 0 & 2 & 4 & 5 \\ 0 & 0 & 0 & 0 \end{array}\right]$$

interchange r_1 and r_2 — $R_2 = -2r_1 + r_2$, $R_3 = r_1 + r_3$, $R_4 = -r_1 + r_4$ — interchange r_3 and r_4

$$\rightarrow \left[\begin{array}{ccc|c} 1 & -1 & -1 & 0 \\ 0 & 1 & -7 & -7 \\ 0 & 2 & 4 & 5 \\ 0 & 0 & 0 & 0 \end{array}\right] \longrightarrow \left[\begin{array}{ccc|c} 1 & 0 & -8 & -7 \\ 0 & 1 & -7 & -7 \\ 0 & 1 & 18 & 19 \\ 0 & 0 & 0 & 0 \end{array}\right] \rightarrow \left[\begin{array}{ccc|c} 1 & 0 & -8 & -7 \\ 0 & 1 & -7 & -7 \\ 0 & 0 & 1 & \frac{19}{18} \\ 0 & 0 & 0 & 0 \end{array}\right]$$

$R_2 = -2r_3 + r_2$ — $R_1 = r_2 + r_1$, $R_3 = -2r_2 + r_3$ — $R_3 = \frac{1}{18}r_3$

The matrix in the last step represents the system $\begin{cases} x - 8z = -7 \\ y - 7z = -7 \\ z = \frac{19}{18} \end{cases}$

Therefore the solution is

$z = \frac{19}{18}$

$x = -7 + 8z = -7 + 8\left(\frac{19}{18}\right) = \frac{13}{9};\quad y = -7 + 7z = -7 + 7\left(\frac{19}{18}\right) = \frac{7}{18}$

66.

$$\begin{cases} x-3y+z=1 \\ 2x-y-4z=0 \\ x-3y+2z=1 \\ x-2y=5 \end{cases} \text{ can be written as : } \left[\begin{array}{ccc|c} 1 & 3 & 1 & 1 \\ 1 & -1 & -4 & 0 \\ 1 & -3 & 2 & 1 \\ 1 & -2 & 0 & 5 \end{array}\right]$$

$$\rightarrow \left[\begin{array}{ccc|c} 1 & 3 & 1 & 1 \\ 0 & 4 & 5 & 1 \\ 0 & 6 & -1 & 0 \\ 0 & 5 & -4 & -5 \end{array}\right] \longrightarrow \left[\begin{array}{ccc|c} 1 & 3 & 1 & 1 \\ 0 & 4 & 5 & 1 \\ 0 & 0 & -34 & -6 \\ 0 & 0 & 41 & 25 \end{array}\right] \longrightarrow \left[\begin{array}{ccc|c} 1 & 3 & 1 & 1 \\ 0 & 4 & 5 & 1 \\ 0 & 0 & 1 & \frac{2}{17} \\ 0 & 0 & 1 & \frac{25}{41} \end{array}\right]$$

$R_2 = r_1 - r_2$ $\quad R_3 = 4r_3 - 6r_2$ $\quad R_3 = -\frac{1}{34} r_3$

$R_3 = r_1 - r_3$ $\quad R_4 = 5r_2 - 4r_4$ $\quad R_4 = \frac{1}{41} r_4$

$R_4 = r_1 - r_4$

The matrix in the last step represents an inconsistent system since $R_3 \Rightarrow z = \dfrac{2}{17}$ and $R_4 \Rightarrow z = \dfrac{25}{41}$.

67. $\begin{cases} 4x+y+z-w=4 \\ x-y+2z+3w=3 \end{cases}$ can be written as: $\left[\begin{array}{cccc|c} 4 & 1 & 1 & -1 & 4 \\ 1 & -1 & 2 & 3 & 3 \end{array}\right]$

$$\rightarrow \left[\begin{array}{cccc|c} 1 & -1 & 2 & 3 & 3 \\ 4 & 1 & 1 & -1 & 4 \end{array}\right] \longrightarrow \left[\begin{array}{cccc|c} 1 & -1 & 2 & 3 & 3 \\ 0 & 5 & -7 & -13 & -8 \end{array}\right]$$

interchange r_1 and r_2 $\quad R_2 = -4r_1 + r_2$

The matrix in the last step represents the system $\begin{cases} x-y+2z+3w=3 \\ 5y-7z-13w=-8 \end{cases}$

The second equation yields

$$5y-7z-13w=-8 \rightarrow 5y=-8+7z+13w \rightarrow y=-\frac{8}{5}+\frac{7}{5}z+\frac{13}{5}w$$

The first equation yields

$$x-y+2z+3w=3 \rightarrow x=3+y-2z-3w$$

substituting for y

$$x=3+\left(-\frac{8}{5}+\frac{7}{5}z+\frac{13}{5}w\right)-2z-3w$$

$$x=-\frac{3}{5}z-\frac{2}{5}w+\frac{7}{5}$$

Therefore the solution is

$$x=-\frac{3}{5}z-\frac{2}{5}w+\frac{7}{5};\; y=-\frac{8}{5}+\frac{7}{5}z+\frac{13}{5}w$$

z and w are any real numbers

68. $\begin{cases} -4x+y=5 \\ 2x-y+z-w=5 \\ z+w=4 \end{cases}$ can be written as : $\left[\begin{array}{cccc|c} -4 & 1 & 0 & 0 & 5 \\ 2 & -1 & 1 & -1 & 5 \\ 0 & 0 & 1 & 1 & 4 \end{array}\right]$

$$\rightarrow\left[\begin{array}{cccc|c} 1 & -\frac{1}{4} & 0 & 0 & -\frac{5}{4} \\ 2 & -1 & 1 & -1 & 5 \\ 0 & 0 & 1 & 1 & 4 \end{array}\right]\rightarrow\left[\begin{array}{cccc|c} 1 & -\frac{1}{4} & 0 & 0 & -\frac{5}{4} \\ 0 & -\frac{1}{2} & 1 & -1 & \frac{15}{2} \\ 0 & 0 & 1 & 1 & 4 \end{array}\right]\rightarrow\left[\begin{array}{cccc|c} 1 & -\frac{1}{4} & 0 & 0 & -\frac{5}{4} \\ 0 & 1 & -2 & 2 & -15 \\ 0 & 0 & 1 & 1 & 4 \end{array}\right]$$

$R_1=-\frac{1}{4}r_1$ $\qquad R_2=-2r_1+r_2$ $\qquad R_2=-2r_2$

$$\rightarrow\left[\begin{array}{cccc|c} 1 & 0 & -\frac{1}{2} & \frac{1}{2} & -5 \\ 0 & 1 & -2 & 2 & -15 \\ 0 & 0 & 1 & 1 & 4 \end{array}\right]\rightarrow\left[\begin{array}{cccc|c} 1 & 0 & 0 & 1 & -3 \\ 0 & 1 & 0 & 4 & -7 \\ 0 & 0 & 1 & 1 & 4 \end{array}\right]$$

$R_1=\frac{1}{4}r_2+r_1$ $\qquad R_1=\frac{1}{2}r_3+r_1$, $R_2=2r_3+r_2$

The matrix in the last step represents the system $\begin{cases} x+w=-3 \\ y+4w=-7 \\ z+w=4 \end{cases}$

Therefore the solution is

$x=-3-w$

$y=-7-4w$

$z=4-w$

w is any real number

69. Each of the points must satisfy the equation $y = ax^2 + bx + c$.

(1,2): $2 = a + b + c$

(−2,−7): $-7 = 4a - 2b + c$

(2,−3): $-3 = 4a + 2b + c$

Set up a matrix and solve:

$$\left[\begin{array}{ccc|c} 1 & 1 & 1 & 2 \\ 4 & -2 & 1 & -7 \\ 4 & 2 & 1 & -3 \end{array}\right] \to \left[\begin{array}{ccc|c} 1 & 1 & 1 & 2 \\ 0 & -6 & -3 & -15 \\ 0 & -2 & -3 & -11 \end{array}\right] \to \left[\begin{array}{ccc|c} 1 & 1 & 1 & 2 \\ 0 & 1 & \frac{1}{2} & \frac{5}{2} \\ 0 & -2 & -3 & -11 \end{array}\right] \to \left[\begin{array}{ccc|c} 1 & 0 & \frac{1}{2} & -\frac{1}{2} \\ 0 & 1 & \frac{1}{2} & \frac{5}{2} \\ 0 & 0 & -2 & -6 \end{array}\right]$$

$R_2 = -4r_1 + r_2$ $\quad R_2 = -\frac{1}{6}r_2$ $\quad R_1 = -r_2 + r_1$

$R_3 = -4r_1 + r_3$ $\quad R_3 = 2r_2 + r_3$

$$\to \left[\begin{array}{ccc|c} 1 & 0 & \frac{1}{2} & -\frac{1}{2} \\ 0 & 1 & \frac{1}{2} & \frac{5}{2} \\ 0 & 0 & 1 & 3 \end{array}\right] \to \left[\begin{array}{ccc|c} 1 & 0 & 0 & -2 \\ 0 & 1 & 0 & 1 \\ 0 & 0 & 1 & 3 \end{array}\right]$$

$R_3 = -\frac{1}{2}r_3$ $\quad R_1 = -\frac{1}{2}r_3 + r_1$

$R_2 = -\frac{1}{2}r_3 + r_2$

The solution is $a = -2$, $b = 1$, $c = 3$; so the equation is $y = -2x^2 + x + 3$.

70. Each of the points must satisfy the equation $y = ax^2 + bx + c$.

(1, − 1): $-1 = a + b + c$

(3, − 1): $-1 = 9a + 3b + c$

(−2,14): $14 = 4a - 2b + c$

Set up a matrix and solve:

$$\left[\begin{array}{ccc|c} 1 & 1 & 1 & -1 \\ 9 & 3 & 1 & -1 \\ 4 & -2 & 1 & 14 \end{array}\right] \to \left[\begin{array}{ccc|c} 1 & 1 & 1 & -1 \\ 0 & -6 & -8 & 8 \\ 0 & -6 & -3 & 18 \end{array}\right] \to \left[\begin{array}{ccc|c} 1 & 1 & 1 & -1 \\ 0 & 1 & \frac{4}{3} & -\frac{4}{3} \\ 0 & 0 & 5 & 10 \end{array}\right] \to \left[\begin{array}{ccc|c} 1 & 0 & -\frac{1}{3} & \frac{1}{3} \\ 0 & 1 & \frac{4}{3} & -\frac{4}{3} \\ 0 & 0 & 1 & 2 \end{array}\right]$$

$R_2 = -9r_1 + r_2$ $\quad R_2 = -\frac{1}{6}r_2$ $\quad R_1 = -r_2 + r_1$

$R_3 = -4r_1 + r_3$ $\quad R_3 = -r_2 + r_3$ $\quad R_3 = \frac{1}{5}r_3$

$$\to \left[\begin{array}{ccc|c} 1 & 0 & 0 & 1 \\ 0 & 1 & 0 & -4 \\ 0 & 0 & 1 & 2 \end{array}\right]$$

$R_1 = \frac{1}{3}r_3 + r_1$

$R_2 = -\frac{4}{3}r_3 + r_2$

The solution is $a = 1$, $b = -4$, $c = 2$; so the equation is $y = x^2 - 4x + 2$.

71. Each of the points must satisfy the equation $f(x) = ax^3 + bx^2 + cx + d$.

$f(-3) = -112$: $\quad -27a + 9b - 3c + d = -112$

$f(-1) = -2$: $\quad -a + b - c + d = -2$

$f(1) = 4$: $\quad a + b + c + d = 4$

$f(2) = 13$: $\quad 8a + 4b + 2c + d = 13$

Set up a matrix and solve:

$$\left[\begin{array}{cccc|c} -27 & 9 & -3 & 1 & -112 \\ -1 & 1 & -1 & 1 & -2 \\ 1 & 1 & 1 & 1 & 4 \\ 8 & 4 & 2 & 1 & 13 \end{array}\right] \rightarrow \left[\begin{array}{cccc|c} 1 & 1 & 1 & 1 & 4 \\ -1 & 1 & -1 & 1 & -2 \\ -27 & 9 & -3 & 1 & -112 \\ 8 & 4 & 2 & 1 & 13 \end{array}\right] \rightarrow \left[\begin{array}{cccc|c} 1 & 1 & 1 & 1 & 4 \\ 0 & 2 & 0 & 2 & 2 \\ 0 & 36 & 24 & 28 & -4 \\ 0 & -4 & -6 & -7 & -19 \end{array}\right]$$

Interchange r_3 and r_1 $\quad R_2 = r_1 + r_2$, $R_3 = 27r_1 + r_3$, $R_4 = -8r_1 + r_4$

$$\rightarrow \left[\begin{array}{cccc|c} 1 & 1 & 1 & 1 & 4 \\ 0 & 1 & 0 & 1 & 1 \\ 0 & 36 & 24 & 28 & -4 \\ 0 & -4 & -6 & -7 & -19 \end{array}\right] \rightarrow \left[\begin{array}{cccc|c} 1 & 0 & 1 & 0 & 3 \\ 0 & 1 & 0 & 1 & 1 \\ 0 & 0 & 24 & -8 & -40 \\ 0 & 0 & -6 & -3 & -15 \end{array}\right] \rightarrow \left[\begin{array}{cccc|c} 1 & 0 & 1 & 0 & 3 \\ 0 & 1 & 0 & 1 & 1 \\ 0 & 0 & 1 & -\frac{1}{3} & -\frac{5}{3} \\ 0 & 0 & -6 & -3 & -15 \end{array}\right]$$

$R_2 = \frac{1}{2}r_2$ $\quad R_1 = -r_2 + r_1$, $R_3 = -36r_2 + r_3$, $R_4 = 4r_2 + r_4$ $\quad R_3 = \frac{1}{24}r_3$

$$\rightarrow \left[\begin{array}{cccc|c} 1 & 0 & 0 & \frac{1}{3} & \frac{14}{3} \\ 0 & 1 & 0 & 1 & 1 \\ 0 & 0 & 1 & -\frac{1}{3} & -\frac{5}{3} \\ 0 & 0 & 0 & -5 & -25 \end{array}\right] \rightarrow \left[\begin{array}{cccc|c} 1 & 0 & 0 & \frac{1}{3} & \frac{14}{3} \\ 0 & 1 & 0 & 1 & 1 \\ 0 & 0 & 1 & -\frac{1}{3} & -\frac{5}{3} \\ 0 & 0 & 0 & 1 & 5 \end{array}\right] \rightarrow \left[\begin{array}{cccc|c} 1 & 0 & 0 & 0 & 3 \\ 0 & 1 & 0 & 0 & -4 \\ 0 & 0 & 1 & 0 & 0 \\ 0 & 0 & 0 & 1 & 5 \end{array}\right]$$

$R_1 = -r_3 + r_1$, $R_4 = 6r_3 + r_4$ $\quad R_4 = -\frac{1}{5}r_4$ $\quad R_1 = -\frac{1}{3}r_4 + r_1$, $R_2 = -r_4 + r_2$, $R_3 = \frac{1}{3}r_4 + r_3$

The solution is $a = 3, b = -4, c = 0, d = 5$; so the equation is $f(x) = 3x^3 - 4x^2 + 5$.

72. Each of the points must satisfy the equation $f(x) = ax^3 + bx^2 + cx + d$.

$f(-2) = -10$: $\quad -8a + 4b - 2c + d = -10$

$f(-1) = 3$: $\quad -a + b - c + d = 3$

$f(1) = 5$: $\quad a + b + c + d = 5$

$f(3) = 15$: $\quad 27a + 9b + 3c + d = 15$

Set up a matrix and solve:

$$\left[\begin{array}{cccc|c} -8 & 4 & -2 & 1 & -10 \\ -1 & 1 & -1 & 1 & 3 \\ 1 & 1 & 1 & 1 & 5 \\ 27 & 9 & 3 & 1 & 15 \end{array}\right] \rightarrow \left[\begin{array}{cccc|c} 1 & 1 & 1 & 1 & 5 \\ -1 & 1 & -1 & 1 & 3 \\ -8 & 4 & -2 & 1 & -10 \\ 27 & 9 & 3 & 1 & 15 \end{array}\right] \rightarrow \left[\begin{array}{cccc|c} 1 & 1 & 1 & 1 & 5 \\ 0 & 2 & 0 & 2 & 8 \\ 0 & 12 & 6 & 9 & 30 \\ 0 & -18 & -24 & -26 & -120 \end{array}\right]$$

Interchange r_3 and r_1 $\quad R_2 = r_1 + r_2$, $R_3 = 8r_1 + r_3$, $R_4 = -27r_1 + r_4$

$$\rightarrow\left[\begin{array}{cccc|c}1 & 1 & 1 & 1 & 5\\ 0 & 1 & 0 & 1 & 4\\ 0 & 12 & 6 & 9 & 30\\ 0 & -18 & -24 & -26 & -120\end{array}\right]\rightarrow\left[\begin{array}{cccc|c}1 & 0 & 1 & 0 & 1\\ 0 & 1 & 0 & 1 & 4\\ 0 & 0 & 6 & -3 & -18\\ 0 & 0 & -24 & -8 & -48\end{array}\right]\rightarrow\left[\begin{array}{cccc|c}1 & 0 & 1 & 0 & 1\\ 0 & 1 & 0 & 1 & 4\\ 0 & 0 & 1 & -\frac{1}{2} & -3\\ 0 & 0 & -24 & -8 & -48\end{array}\right]$$

$R_2 = \frac{1}{2}r_2$ $\quad$ $R_1 = -r_2 + r_1$, $R_3 = -12r_2 + r_3$, $R_4 = 18r_2 + r_4$ $\quad$ $R_3 = \frac{1}{6}r_3$

$$\rightarrow\left[\begin{array}{cccc|c}1 & 0 & 0 & \frac{1}{2} & 4\\ 0 & 1 & 0 & 1 & 4\\ 0 & 0 & 1 & -\frac{1}{2} & -3\\ 0 & 0 & 0 & -20 & -120\end{array}\right]\rightarrow\left[\begin{array}{cccc|c}1 & 0 & 0 & \frac{1}{2} & 4\\ 0 & 1 & 0 & 1 & 4\\ 0 & 0 & 1 & -\frac{1}{2} & -3\\ 0 & 0 & 0 & 1 & 6\end{array}\right]\rightarrow\left[\begin{array}{cccc|c}1 & 0 & 0 & 0 & 1\\ 0 & 1 & 0 & 0 & -2\\ 0 & 0 & 1 & 0 & 0\\ 0 & 0 & 0 & 1 & 6\end{array}\right]$$

$R_1 = -r_3 + r_1$, $R_4 = 24r_3 + r_4$ $\quad$ $R_4 = -\frac{1}{20}r_4$ $\quad$ $R_1 = -\frac{1}{2}r_4 + r_1$, $R_2 = -r_4 + r_2$, $R_3 = \frac{1}{2}r_4 + r_3$

The solution is $a = 1, b = -2, c = 0, d = 6$; so the equation is $f(x) = x^3 - 2x^2 + 6$.

73. Let x = the number of servings of salmon steak.
Let y = the number of servings of baked eggs.
Let z = the number of servings of acorn squash.
Protein equation: $30x + 15y + 3z = 78$
Carbohydrate equation: $20x + 2y + 25z = 59$
Vitamin A equation: $2x + 20y + 32z = 75$
Set up a matrix and solve:

$$\left[\begin{array}{ccc|c}30 & 15 & 3 & 78\\ 20 & 2 & 25 & 59\\ 2 & 20 & 32 & 75\end{array}\right]\rightarrow\left[\begin{array}{ccc|c}2 & 20 & 32 & 75\\ 20 & 2 & 25 & 59\\ 30 & 15 & 3 & 78\end{array}\right]\rightarrow\left[\begin{array}{ccc|c}1 & 10 & 16 & 37.5\\ 20 & 2 & 25 & 59\\ 30 & 15 & 3 & 78\end{array}\right]$$

Interchange r_3 and r_1 $\quad$ $R_1 = \frac{1}{2}r_1$

$$\rightarrow\left[\begin{array}{ccc|c}1 & 10 & 16 & 37.5\\ 0 & -198 & -295 & -691\\ 0 & -285 & -477 & -1047\end{array}\right]\rightarrow\left[\begin{array}{ccc|c}1 & 10 & 16 & 37.5\\ 0 & -198 & -295 & -691\\ 0 & 0 & -\frac{3457}{66} & -\frac{3457}{66}\end{array}\right]$$

$R_2 = -20r_1 + r_2$, $R_3 = -30r_1 + r_3$ $\quad$ $R_3 = -\frac{95}{66}r_2 + r_3$

$$\rightarrow\left[\begin{array}{ccc|c}1 & 10 & 16 & 37.5\\ 0 & -198 & -295 & -691\\ 0 & 0 & 1 & 1\end{array}\right]$$

$R_3 = -\frac{66}{3457}r_3$

Substitute $z = 1$ and solve:

$$-198y - 295(1) = -691 \qquad x + 10(2) + 16(1) = 37.5$$
$$-198y = -396 \qquad x + 36 = 37.5$$
$$y = 2 \qquad x = 1.5$$

The dietitian should serve 1.5 servings of salmon steak, 2 servings of baked eggs, and 1 serving of acorn squash.

74. Let x = the number of servings of pork chops.
Let y = the number of servings of corn on the cob.
Let z = the number of servings of 2% milk.
Protein equation: $23x + 3y + 9z = 47$
Carbohydrate equation: $16y + 13z = 58$
Calcium equation: $10x + 10y + 300z = 630$

Set up a matrix and solve:

$$\left[\begin{array}{ccc|c} 23 & 3 & 9 & 47 \\ 0 & 16 & 13 & 58 \\ 10 & 10 & 300 & 630 \end{array}\right] \rightarrow \left[\begin{array}{ccc|c} 1 & 1 & 30 & 63 \\ 0 & 16 & 13 & 58 \\ 23 & 3 & 9 & 47 \end{array}\right] \rightarrow \left[\begin{array}{ccc|c} 1 & 1 & 30 & 63 \\ 0 & 1 & \frac{13}{16} & \frac{29}{8} \\ 0 & -20 & -681 & -1402 \end{array}\right]$$

Interchange $\frac{1}{10}r_3$ and r_1 $\quad R_3 = -23r_1 + r_3$, $R_2 = \frac{1}{16}r_2$

$$\rightarrow \left[\begin{array}{ccc|c} 1 & 0 & \frac{467}{16} & \frac{475}{8} \\ 0 & 1 & \frac{13}{16} & \frac{29}{8} \\ 0 & 0 & -\frac{2659}{4} & -\frac{2659}{2} \end{array}\right] \rightarrow \left[\begin{array}{ccc|c} 1 & 0 & \frac{467}{16} & \frac{475}{8} \\ 0 & 1 & \frac{13}{16} & \frac{29}{8} \\ 0 & 0 & 1 & 2 \end{array}\right] \rightarrow \left[\begin{array}{ccc|c} 1 & 0 & 0 & 1 \\ 0 & 1 & 0 & 2 \\ 0 & 0 & 1 & 2 \end{array}\right]$$

$R_1 = -r_2 + r_1$, $R_3 = 20r_2 + r_3$ $\quad R_3 = -\frac{4}{2659}r_3$ $\quad R_1 = -\frac{467}{16}r_3 + r_1$, $R_2 = -\frac{13}{16}r_3 + r_2$

The dietitian should provide 1 serving of pork chops, 2 servings of corn on the cob, and 2 servings of 2% milk.

75. Let x = the amount invested in Treasury bills.
Let y = the amount invested in Treasury bonds.
Let z = the amount invested in corporate bonds.
Total investment equation: $x + y + z = 10000$
Annual income equation: $0.06x + 0.07y + 0.08z = 680$
Condition on investment equation: $z = \frac{1}{2}x$
Set up a matrix and solve:

$$\left[\begin{array}{ccc|c} 1 & 1 & 1 & 10000 \\ 0.06 & 0.07 & 0.08 & 680 \\ 1 & 0 & -2 & 0 \end{array}\right] \rightarrow \left[\begin{array}{ccc|c} 1 & 1 & 1 & 10000 \\ 0 & 0.01 & 0.02 & 80 \\ 0 & -1 & -3 & -10000 \end{array}\right] \rightarrow \left[\begin{array}{ccc|c} 1 & 1 & 1 & 10000 \\ 0 & 1 & 2 & 8000 \\ 0 & -1 & -3 & -10000 \end{array}\right]$$

$R_2 = -0.06r_1 + r_2$, $R_3 = -r_1 + r_3$ $\quad R_2 = 100r_2$

$$\rightarrow \left[\begin{array}{ccc|c} 1 & 0 & -1 & 2000 \\ 0 & 1 & 2 & 8000 \\ 0 & 0 & -1 & -2000 \end{array}\right] \rightarrow \left[\begin{array}{ccc|c} 1 & 0 & -1 & 2000 \\ 0 & 1 & 2 & 8000 \\ 0 & 0 & 1 & 2000 \end{array}\right] \rightarrow \left[\begin{array}{ccc|c} 1 & 0 & 0 & 4000 \\ 0 & 1 & 0 & 4000 \\ 0 & 0 & 1 & 2000 \end{array}\right]$$

$R_1 = -r_2 + r_1$, $R_3 = r_2 + r_3$ $\quad R_3 = -r_3$ $\quad R_1 = r_3 + r_1$, $R_2 = -2r_3 + r_2$

Carletta should invest \$4000 in Treasury bills, \$4000 in Treasury bonds, and \$2000 in corporate bonds.

76. Let x = the amount invested in Treasury bills.
Let y = the amount invested in Treasury bonds.
Let z = the amount invested in corporate bonds.
Total investment equation: $x+y+z=20000$
Annual income equation: $0.05x+0.07y+0.09z=1280$
Condition on investment equation: $x=2z$

Set up a matrix and solve:

$$\left[\begin{array}{ccc|c} 1 & 1 & 1 & 20000 \\ 0.05 & 0.07 & 0.09 & 1280 \\ 1 & 0 & -2 & 0 \end{array}\right] \to \left[\begin{array}{ccc|c} 1 & 1 & 1 & 20000 \\ 0 & 0.02 & 0.04 & 280 \\ 0 & -1 & -3 & -20000 \end{array}\right] \to \left[\begin{array}{ccc|c} 1 & 1 & 1 & 20000 \\ 0 & 1 & 2 & 14000 \\ 0 & -1 & -3 & -20000 \end{array}\right]$$

$R_2 = -0.05r_1 + r_2$ $\quad$ $R_2 = 50r_2$
$R_3 = -r_1 + r_3$

$$\to \left[\begin{array}{ccc|c} 1 & 0 & -1 & 6000 \\ 0 & 1 & 2 & 14000 \\ 0 & 0 & -1 & -6000 \end{array}\right] \to \left[\begin{array}{ccc|c} 1 & 0 & -1 & 6000 \\ 0 & 1 & 2 & 14000 \\ 0 & 0 & 1 & 6000 \end{array}\right] \to \left[\begin{array}{ccc|c} 1 & 0 & 0 & 12000 \\ 0 & 1 & 0 & 2000 \\ 0 & 0 & 1 & 6000 \end{array}\right]$$

$R_1 = -r_2 + r_1$ $\quad$ $R_3 = -r_3$ $\quad$ $R_1 = r_3 + r_1$
$R_3 = r_2 + r_3$ $\quad$ $R_2 = -2r_3 + r_2$

John should invest \$12,000 in Treasury bills, \$2,000 in Treasury bonds, and \$6,000 in corporate bonds.

77. Let x = the number of Deltas produced.
Let y = the number of Betas produced.
Let z = the number of Sigmas produced.
Painting equation: $10x+16y+8z=240$
Drying equation: $3x+5y+2z=69$
Polishing equation: $2x+3y+z=41$
Set up a matrix and solve:

$$\left[\begin{array}{ccc|c} 10 & 16 & 8 & 240 \\ 3 & 5 & 2 & 69 \\ 2 & 3 & 1 & 41 \end{array}\right] \to \left[\begin{array}{ccc|c} 1 & 1 & 2 & 33 \\ 3 & 5 & 2 & 69 \\ 2 & 3 & 1 & 41 \end{array}\right] \to \left[\begin{array}{ccc|c} 1 & 1 & 2 & 33 \\ 0 & 2 & -4 & -30 \\ 0 & 1 & -3 & -25 \end{array}\right] \to \left[\begin{array}{ccc|c} 1 & 1 & 2 & 33 \\ 0 & 1 & -2 & -15 \\ 0 & 1 & -3 & -25 \end{array}\right]$$

$R_1 = -3r_2 + r_1$ $\quad$ $R_2 = -3r_1 + r_2$ $\quad$ $R_2 = \frac{1}{2}r_2$
$R_3 = -2r_1 + r_3$

$$\to \left[\begin{array}{ccc|c} 1 & 0 & 4 & 48 \\ 0 & 1 & -2 & -15 \\ 0 & 0 & -1 & -10 \end{array}\right] \to \left[\begin{array}{ccc|c} 1 & 0 & 4 & 48 \\ 0 & 1 & -2 & -15 \\ 0 & 0 & 1 & 10 \end{array}\right] \to \left[\begin{array}{ccc|c} 1 & 0 & 0 & 8 \\ 0 & 1 & 0 & 5 \\ 0 & 0 & 1 & 10 \end{array}\right]$$

$R_1 = -r_2 + r_1$ $\quad$ $R_3 = -r_3$ $\quad$ $R_1 = -4r_3 + r_1$
$R_3 = -r_2 + r_3$ $\quad$ $R_2 = 2r_3 + r_2$

The company should produce 8 Deltas, 5 Betas, and 10 Sigmas.

78. Let $x =$ the number of cases of orange juice produced.
Let $y =$ the number of cases of grapefruit juice produced.
Let $z =$ the number of cases of tomato juice produced.
Sterilizing equation: $9x+10y+12z=398$
Filling equation: $6x+4y+4z=164$
Labeling equation: $x+2y+z=58$

Set up a matrix and solve:

$$\left[\begin{array}{ccc|c} 9 & 10 & 12 & 398 \\ 6 & 4 & 4 & 164 \\ 1 & 2 & 1 & 58 \end{array}\right] \to \left[\begin{array}{ccc|c} 1 & 2 & 1 & 58 \\ 6 & 4 & 4 & 164 \\ 9 & 10 & 12 & 398 \end{array}\right] \to \left[\begin{array}{ccc|c} 1 & 2 & 1 & 58 \\ 0 & -8 & -2 & -184 \\ 0 & -8 & 3 & -124 \end{array}\right] \to \left[\begin{array}{ccc|c} 1 & 2 & 1 & 58 \\ 0 & 1 & \frac{1}{4} & 23 \\ 0 & -8 & 3 & -124 \end{array}\right]$$

Interchange r_1 and r_3 $\quad R_2=-6r_1+r_2$, $R_3=-9r_1+r_3$ $\quad R_2=-\frac{1}{8}r_2$

$$\to \left[\begin{array}{ccc|c} 1 & 0 & \frac{1}{2} & 12 \\ 0 & 1 & \frac{1}{4} & 23 \\ 0 & 0 & 5 & 60 \end{array}\right] \to \left[\begin{array}{ccc|c} 1 & 0 & \frac{1}{2} & 12 \\ 0 & 1 & \frac{1}{4} & 23 \\ 0 & 0 & 1 & 12 \end{array}\right] \to \left[\begin{array}{ccc|c} 1 & 0 & 0 & 6 \\ 0 & 1 & 0 & 20 \\ 0 & 0 & 1 & 12 \end{array}\right]$$

$R_1=-2r_2+r_1$, $R_3=8r_2+r_3$ $\quad R_3=\frac{1}{5}r_3$ $\quad R_1=-\frac{1}{2}r_3+r_1$, $R_2=-\frac{1}{4}r_3+r_2$

The company should prepare 6 cases of orange juice, 20 cases of grapefruit juice, and 12 cases of tomato juice.

79. Rewrite the system as set up and solve the matrix:

$$\begin{cases} -4+8-2I_2=0 \\ 8=5I_4+I_1 \\ 4=3I_3+I_1 \\ I_3+I_4=I_1 \end{cases} \to \begin{cases} 2I_2=4 \\ I_1+5I_4=8 \\ I_1+3I_3=4 \\ I_1-I_3-I_4=0 \end{cases}$$

$$\left[\begin{array}{cccc|c} 0 & 2 & 0 & 0 & 4 \\ 1 & 0 & 0 & 5 & 8 \\ 1 & 0 & 3 & 0 & 4 \\ 1 & 0 & -1 & -1 & 0 \end{array}\right] \to \left[\begin{array}{cccc|c} 1 & 0 & 0 & 5 & 8 \\ 0 & 2 & 0 & 0 & 4 \\ 1 & 0 & 3 & 0 & 4 \\ 1 & 0 & -1 & -1 & 0 \end{array}\right] \to \left[\begin{array}{cccc|c} 1 & 0 & 0 & 5 & 8 \\ 0 & 1 & 0 & 0 & 2 \\ 0 & 0 & 3 & -5 & -4 \\ 0 & 0 & -1 & -6 & -8 \end{array}\right]$$

Interchange r_2 and r_1 $\quad R_2=\frac{1}{2}r_2$, $R_3=-r_1+r_3$, $R_4=-r_1+r_4$

$$\rightarrow\left[\begin{array}{cccc|c} 1 & 0 & 0 & 5 & 8 \\ 0 & 1 & 0 & 0 & 2 \\ 0 & 0 & -1 & -6 & -8 \\ 0 & 0 & 3 & -5 & -4 \end{array}\right]\rightarrow\left[\begin{array}{cccc|c} 1 & 0 & 0 & 5 & 8 \\ 0 & 1 & 0 & 0 & 2 \\ 0 & 0 & 1 & 6 & 8 \\ 0 & 0 & 0 & -23 & -28 \end{array}\right]\rightarrow\left[\begin{array}{cccc|c} 1 & 0 & 0 & 5 & 8 \\ 0 & 1 & 0 & 0 & 2 \\ 0 & 0 & 1 & 6 & 8 \\ 0 & 0 & 0 & 1 & \frac{28}{23} \end{array}\right]$$

Interchange r_3 and r_4 $\quad R_3 = -r_3$, $R_4 = -3r_3 + r_4$ $\quad R_4 = -\frac{1}{23}r_4$

$$\rightarrow\left[\begin{array}{cccc|c} 1 & 0 & 0 & 0 & \frac{44}{23} \\ 0 & 1 & 0 & 0 & 2 \\ 0 & 0 & 1 & 0 & \frac{16}{23} \\ 0 & 0 & 0 & 1 & \frac{28}{23} \end{array}\right]$$

$R_1 = -5r_4 + r_1$

$R_3 = -6r_4 + r_3$

The solution is $I_1 = \dfrac{44}{23},\ I_2 = 2,\ I_3 = \dfrac{16}{23},\ I_4 = \dfrac{28}{23}$.

80. Rewrite the system as set up and solve the matrix:

$$\begin{cases} I_1 = I_3 + I_2 \\ 24 - 6I_1 - 3I_3 = 0 \\ 12 + 24 - 6I_1 - 6I_2 = 0 \end{cases} \rightarrow \begin{cases} I_1 - I_2 - I_3 = 0 \\ -6I_1 - 3I_3 = -24 \\ -6I_1 - 6I_2 = -36 \end{cases}$$

$$\left[\begin{array}{ccc|c} 1 & -1 & -1 & 0 \\ -6 & 0 & -3 & -24 \\ -6 & -6 & 0 & -36 \end{array}\right]\rightarrow\left[\begin{array}{ccc|c} 1 & -1 & -1 & 0 \\ 0 & -6 & -9 & -24 \\ 0 & -12 & -6 & -36 \end{array}\right]\rightarrow\left[\begin{array}{ccc|c} 1 & -1 & -1 & 0 \\ 0 & 1 & \frac{3}{2} & 4 \\ 0 & -12 & -6 & -36 \end{array}\right]$$

$R_2 = 6r_1 + r_2$, $R_3 = 6r_1 + r_3$ $\quad R_2 = -\frac{1}{6}r_2$

$$\rightarrow\left[\begin{array}{ccc|c} 1 & 0 & \frac{1}{2} & 4 \\ 0 & 1 & \frac{3}{2} & 4 \\ 0 & 0 & 12 & 12 \end{array}\right]\rightarrow\left[\begin{array}{ccc|c} 1 & 0 & \frac{1}{2} & 4 \\ 0 & 1 & \frac{3}{2} & 4 \\ 0 & 0 & 1 & 1 \end{array}\right]\rightarrow\left[\begin{array}{ccc|c} 1 & 0 & 0 & 3.5 \\ 0 & 1 & 0 & 2.5 \\ 0 & 0 & 1 & 1 \end{array}\right]$$

$R_1 = r_2 + r_1$, $R_3 = 12r_2 + r_3$ $\quad R_3 = \frac{1}{12}r_3$ $\quad R_1 = -\frac{1}{2}r_3 + r_1$, $R_2 = -\frac{3}{2}r_3 + r_2$

The solution is $I_1 = 3.5,\ I_2 = 2.5,\ I_3 = 1$.

81. Let x = the amount invested in Treasury bills.
Let y = the amount invested in Treasury bonds.
Let z = the amount invested in corporate bonds.

(a) Total investment equation: $x + y + z = 20000$
Annual income equation: $0.07x + 0.09y + 0.11z = 2000$

Set up a matrix and solve:

$$\left[\begin{array}{ccc|c} 1 & 1 & 1 & 20000 \\ .07 & .09 & .11 & 2000 \end{array}\right] \rightarrow \left[\begin{array}{ccc|c} 1 & 1 & 1 & 20000 \\ 7 & 9 & 11 & 200000 \end{array}\right] \rightarrow \left[\begin{array}{ccc|c} 1 & 1 & 1 & 20000 \\ 0 & 2 & 4 & 60000 \end{array}\right]$$

$R_2 = 100r_2 \qquad R_2 = r_2 - 7r_1$

$$\rightarrow \left[\begin{array}{ccc|c} 1 & 1 & 1 & 20000 \\ 0 & 1 & 2 & 30000 \end{array}\right] \rightarrow \left[\begin{array}{ccc|c} 1 & 0 & -1 & -10000 \\ 0 & 1 & 2 & 30000 \end{array}\right]$$

$R_2 = \frac{1}{2}r_2 \qquad R_1 = r_1 - r_2$

The matrix in the last step represents the system $\begin{cases} x - z = -10000 \\ y + 2z = 30000 \end{cases}$

Therefore the solution is

$x = -10000 + z;\ y = 30000 - 2z;\ z$ is any real number

Possible investment strategies:

Amount invested at

7%	9%	11%
0	10000	10000
1000	8000	11000
2000	6000	12000
3000	4000	13000
4000	2000	14000
5000	0	15000

(b) Total investment equation: $x + y + z = 25000$
Annual income equation: $0.07x + 0.09y + 0.11z = 2000$

Set up a matrix and solve:

$$\left[\begin{array}{ccc|c} 1 & 1 & 1 & 25000 \\ .07 & .09 & .11 & 2000 \end{array}\right] \rightarrow \left[\begin{array}{ccc|c} 1 & 1 & 1 & 25000 \\ 7 & 9 & 11 & 200000 \end{array}\right] \rightarrow \left[\begin{array}{ccc|c} 1 & 1 & 1 & 25000 \\ 0 & 2 & 4 & 25000 \end{array}\right]$$

$R_2 = 100r_2 \qquad R_2 = r_2 - 7r_1$

$$\rightarrow \left[\begin{array}{ccc|c} 1 & 1 & 1 & 25000 \\ 0 & 1 & 2 & 12500 \end{array}\right] \rightarrow \left[\begin{array}{ccc|c} 1 & 0 & -1 & 12500 \\ 0 & 1 & 2 & 12500 \end{array}\right]$$

$R_2 = \frac{1}{2}r_2 \qquad R_1 = r_1 - r_2$

The matrix in the last step represents the system $\begin{cases} x - z = 12500 \\ y + 2z = 12500 \end{cases}$

Therefore the solution is

$$x = 12500 + z;\ \ y = 12500 - 2z;\ \ z \text{ is any real number}$$

Possible investment strategies:

Amount invested at

7%	9%	11%
12500	12500	0
14500	8500	2000
16500	4500	4000
18750	0	6250

(c) Total investment equation: $x + y + z = 30000$
Annual income equation: $0.07x + 0.09y + 0.11z = 2000$
Set up a matrix and solve:

$$\left[\begin{array}{ccc|c} 1 & 1 & 1 & 30000 \\ .07 & .09 & .11 & 2000 \end{array}\right] \rightarrow \left[\begin{array}{ccc|c} 1 & 1 & 1 & 30000 \\ 7 & 9 & 11 & 200000 \end{array}\right] \rightarrow \left[\begin{array}{ccc|c} 1 & 1 & 1 & 30000 \\ 0 & 2 & 4 & -10000 \end{array}\right]$$

$$R_2 = 100r_2 \qquad\qquad R_1 = r_2 - 7r_1$$

$$\rightarrow \left[\begin{array}{ccc|c} 1 & 1 & 1 & 30000 \\ 0 & 1 & 2 & -5000 \end{array}\right] \rightarrow \left[\begin{array}{ccc|c} 1 & 0 & -1 & 35000 \\ 0 & 1 & 2 & -5000 \end{array}\right]$$

$$R_2 = \tfrac{1}{2}r_2 \qquad\qquad R_1 = r_1 - r_2$$

The matrix in the last step represents the system $\begin{cases} x - z = 35000 \\ y + 2z = -5000 \end{cases}$

Therefore the solution is

$$x = 35000 + z;\ \ y = -5000 - 2z;\ \ z \text{ is any real number}$$

One possible investment strategy

Amount invested at

7%	9%	11%
30000	0	0

This will yield (\$30000)(.07) = \$2100, which is more than the required income.

82. Let x = the amount invested in Treasury bills.
Let y = the amount invested in Treasury bonds.
Let z = the amount invested in corporate bonds.
Let I = income

Total investment equation: $x + y + z = 20000$
Annual income equation: $0.07x + 0.09y + 0.11z = I$

Set up a matrix and solve:

$$\left[\begin{array}{ccc|c} 1 & 1 & 1 & 25000 \\ .07 & .09 & .11 & I \end{array}\right] \to \left[\begin{array}{ccc|c} 1 & 1 & 1 & 25000 \\ 7 & 9 & 11 & 100I \end{array}\right] \to \left[\begin{array}{ccc|c} 1 & 1 & 1 & 20000 \\ 0 & 2 & 4 & 100I - 175000 \end{array}\right]$$

$$R_2 = 100r_2 \qquad\qquad R_1 = r_2 - 7r_1$$

$$\to \left[\begin{array}{ccc|c} 1 & 1 & 1 & 25000 \\ 0 & 1 & 2 & 50I - 87500 \end{array}\right] \to \left[\begin{array}{ccc|c} 1 & 0 & -1 & 112500 - 50I \\ 0 & 1 & 2 & 50I - 87500 \end{array}\right]$$

$$R_2 = \tfrac{1}{2}r_2 \qquad\qquad R_1 = r_1 - r_2$$

The matrix in the last step represents the system $\begin{cases} x - z = 112500 - 50I \\ y + 2z = 50I - 87500 \end{cases}$

Therefore the solution is

$$x = 112500 - 50I + z$$
$$y = 50I - 87500 - 2z$$
z is any real number

(a) $I = 1500$

$x = 112500 - 50(1500) + z = 37500 + z$

$y = 50I - 87500 - 2z = 50(1500) - 87500 - 2z = -12500 - 2z$

z is any real number

Investing all of the money at 7% yields more than \$1500.

(b) $I = 2000$

$x = 112500 - 50(2000) + z = 12500 + z$

$y = 50I - 87500 - 2z = 50(2000) - 87500 - 2z = 12500 - 2z$

z is any real number

Possible investment strategies:

Amount invested at

7%	9%	11%
12500	12500	0
15500	6500	3000
18750	0	6250

(c) $I = 2500$

$x = 112500 - 50(2500) + z = -12500 + z$

$y = 50I - 87500 - 2z = 50(2500) - 87500 - 2z = 37500 - 2z$

z is any real number

Possible investment strategies:

Amount invested at

7%	9%	11%
0	12500	12500
1000	10500	13500
6250	0	18750

83. Let x = the amount of liquid 1.
Let y = the amount of liquid 2.
Let z = the amount of liquid 3.

$$.20x + .40y + .30z = 40 \text{ Vitamin C}$$
$$.30x + .20y + .50z = 30 \text{ Vitamin D}$$

multiplying each equation by 10 yields

$$2x + 4y + 3z = 400$$
$$3x + 2y + 5z = 300$$

Set up a matrix and solve: $\left[\begin{array}{ccc|c} 2 & 4 & 3 & 400 \\ 3 & 2 & 5 & 300 \end{array}\right] \to \left[\begin{array}{ccc|c} 1 & 2 & \frac{3}{2} & 200 \\ 3 & 2 & 5 & 300 \end{array}\right] \to \left[\begin{array}{ccc|c} 1 & 2 & \frac{3}{2} & 200 \\ 0 & -4 & \frac{1}{2} & -300 \end{array}\right]$

$R_1 = \frac{1}{2}r_1$ $\qquad R_2 = r_2 - 3r_1$

$$\to \left[\begin{array}{ccc|c} 1 & 2 & \frac{3}{2} & 200 \\ 0 & 1 & -\frac{1}{8} & 75 \end{array}\right] \to \left[\begin{array}{ccc|c} 1 & 0 & \frac{7}{4} & 50 \\ 0 & 1 & -\frac{1}{8} & 75 \end{array}\right]$$

$R_2 = -\frac{1}{4}r_2$ $\qquad R_1 = r_1 - 2r_2$

The matrix in the last step represents the system $\begin{cases} x + \frac{7}{4}z = 50 \\ y - \frac{1}{8}z = 75 \end{cases}$

Therefore the solution is

$$x = 50 - \frac{7}{4}z; \; y = 75 + \frac{1}{8}z; \; z \text{ is any real number}$$

Possible combinations:

Liquid 1	Liquid 2	Liquid 3
50mg	75mg	0mg
36mg	76mg	8mg
22mg	77mg	16mg
8mg	78mg	24mg

84. Let x = the amount of powder 1.
Let y = the amount of powder 2.
Let z = the amount of powder 3.

$$.20x + .40y + .30z = 12 \text{ Vitamin } B_{12}$$
$$.30x + .20y + .40z = 12 \text{ Vitamin E}$$

multiplying each equation by 10 yields

$$2x + 4y + 3z = 120$$
$$3x + 2y + 4z = 120$$

Set up a matrix and solve:

$$\left[\begin{array}{ccc|c} 2 & 4 & 3 & 120 \\ 3 & 2 & 4 & 120 \end{array}\right] \to \left[\begin{array}{ccc|c} 2 & 4 & 3 & 120 \\ 0 & -4 & -.5 & -60 \end{array}\right] \to \left[\begin{array}{ccc|c} 2 & 0 & 2.5 & 60 \\ 0 & -4 & -.5 & -60 \end{array}\right]$$

$R_2 = r_2 - \frac{3}{2}r_1$ $\qquad R_1 = r_1 + r_2$

The matrix in the last step represents the system $\begin{cases} 2x + 2.5z = 60 \\ -4y - .5z = -60 \end{cases}$

Therefore the solution is

$x = 30 - 1.25z$

$y = 15 - .125z$

z is any real number

Possible combinations:

Powder 1	Powder 2	Powder 3
30mg	15mg	0mg
20mg	14mg	8mg
10mg	13mg	16mg
0mg	12mg	24mg

85 – 87. Answers will vary.

Chapter 12

Systems of Equations and Inequalities

12.4 Systems of Linear Equations: Determinants

1. Evaluating the determinant:
$$\begin{vmatrix} 3 & 1 \\ 4 & 2 \end{vmatrix} = 3(2) - 4(1) = 6 - 4 = 2$$

2. Evaluating the determinant:
$$\begin{vmatrix} 6 & 1 \\ 5 & 2 \end{vmatrix} = 6(2) - 5(1) = 12 - 5 = 7$$

3. Evaluating the determinant:
$$\begin{vmatrix} 6 & 4 \\ -1 & 3 \end{vmatrix} = 6(3) - (-1)(4) = 18 + 4 = 22$$

4. Evaluating the determinant:
$$\begin{vmatrix} 8 & -3 \\ 4 & 2 \end{vmatrix} = 8(2) - 4(-3) = 16 + 12 = 28$$

5. Evaluating the determinant:
$$\begin{vmatrix} -3 & -1 \\ 4 & 2 \end{vmatrix} = -3(2) - 4(-1) = -6 + 4 = -2$$

6. Evaluating the determinant:
$$\begin{vmatrix} -4 & 2 \\ -5 & 3 \end{vmatrix} = -4(3) - (-5)(2) = -12 + 10 = -2$$

7. Evaluating the determinant:
$$\begin{vmatrix} 3 & 4 & 2 \\ 1 & -1 & 5 \\ 1 & 2 & -2 \end{vmatrix} = 3\begin{vmatrix} -1 & 5 \\ 2 & -2 \end{vmatrix} - 4\begin{vmatrix} 1 & 5 \\ 1 & -2 \end{vmatrix} + 2\begin{vmatrix} 1 & -1 \\ 1 & 2 \end{vmatrix}$$
$$= 3[(-1)(-2) - 2(5)] - 4[1(-2) - 1(5)] + 2[1(2) - 1(-1)]$$
$$= 3(2 - 10) - 4(-2 - 5) + 2(2 + 1)$$
$$= 3(-8) - 4(-7) + 2(3)$$
$$= -24 + 28 + 6$$
$$= 10$$

8. Evaluating the determinant:

$$\begin{vmatrix} 1 & 3 & -2 \\ 6 & 1 & -5 \\ 8 & 2 & 3 \end{vmatrix} = 1\begin{vmatrix} 1 & -5 \\ 2 & 3 \end{vmatrix} - 3\begin{vmatrix} 6 & -5 \\ 8 & 3 \end{vmatrix} + (-2)\begin{vmatrix} 6 & 1 \\ 8 & 2 \end{vmatrix}$$

$$\begin{aligned} &= 1[1(3)-2(-5)]-3[6(3)-8(-5)]-2[6(2)-8(1)] \\ &= 1(3+10)-3(18+40)-2(12-8) \\ &= 1(13)-3(58)-2(4) \\ &= 13-174-8 \\ &= -169 \end{aligned}$$

9. Evaluating the determinant:

$$\begin{vmatrix} 4 & -1 & 2 \\ 6 & -1 & 0 \\ 1 & -3 & 4 \end{vmatrix} = 4\begin{vmatrix} -1 & 0 \\ -3 & 4 \end{vmatrix} - (-1)\begin{vmatrix} 6 & 0 \\ 1 & 4 \end{vmatrix} + 2\begin{vmatrix} 6 & -1 \\ 1 & -3 \end{vmatrix}$$

$$\begin{aligned} &= 4[-1(4)-0(-3)]+1[6(4)-1(0)]+2[6(-3)-1(-1)] \\ &= 4(-4)+1(24)+2(-17) \\ &= -16+24-34 \\ &= -26 \end{aligned}$$

10. Evaluating the determinant:

$$\begin{vmatrix} 3 & -9 & 4 \\ 1 & 4 & 0 \\ 8 & -3 & 1 \end{vmatrix} = 3\begin{vmatrix} 4 & 0 \\ -3 & 1 \end{vmatrix} - (-9)\begin{vmatrix} 1 & 0 \\ 8 & 1 \end{vmatrix} + 4\begin{vmatrix} 1 & 4 \\ 8 & -3 \end{vmatrix}$$

$$\begin{aligned} &= 3[4(1)-(-3)(0)]+9[1(1)-8(0)]+4[1(-3)-8(4)] \\ &= 3(4)+9(1)+4(-35) \\ &= 12+9-140 \\ &= -119 \end{aligned}$$

11. Set up and evaluate the determinants to use Cramer's Rule:

$$\begin{cases} x+y=8 \\ x-y=4 \end{cases}$$

$$D = \begin{vmatrix} 1 & 1 \\ 1 & -1 \end{vmatrix} = 1(-1)-1(1) = -1-1 = -2$$

$$D_x = \begin{vmatrix} 8 & 1 \\ 4 & -1 \end{vmatrix} = 8(-1)-4(1) = -8-4 = -12$$

$$D_y = \begin{vmatrix} 1 & 8 \\ 1 & 4 \end{vmatrix} = 1(4)-1(8) = 4-8 = -4$$

Find the solutions by Cramer's Rule:

$$x = \frac{D_x}{D} = \frac{-12}{-2} = 6 \qquad y = \frac{D_y}{D} = \frac{-4}{-2} = 2$$

12. Set up and evaluate the determinants to use Cramer's Rule:

$$\begin{cases} x+2y=5 \\ x-\ \ y=3 \end{cases}$$

$$D=\begin{vmatrix} 1 & 2 \\ 1 & -1 \end{vmatrix}=1(-1)-1(2)=-1-2=-3$$

$$D_x=\begin{vmatrix} 5 & 2 \\ 3 & -1 \end{vmatrix}=5(-1)-3(2)=-5-6=-11$$

$$D_y=\begin{vmatrix} 1 & 5 \\ 1 & 3 \end{vmatrix}=1(3)-1(5)=3-5=-2$$

Find the solutions by Cramer's Rule:

$$x=\frac{D_x}{D}=\frac{-11}{-3}=\frac{11}{3} \qquad y=\frac{D_y}{D}=\frac{-2}{-3}=\frac{2}{3}$$

13. Set up and evaluate the determinants to use Cramer's Rule:

$$\begin{cases} 5x-\ \ y=13 \\ 2x+3y=12 \end{cases}$$

$$D=\begin{vmatrix} 5 & -1 \\ 2 & 3 \end{vmatrix}=5(3)-2(-1)=15+2=17$$

$$D_x=\begin{vmatrix} 13 & -1 \\ 12 & 3 \end{vmatrix}=13(3)-12(-1)=39+12=51$$

$$D_y=\begin{vmatrix} 5 & 13 \\ 2 & 12 \end{vmatrix}=5(12)-2(13)=60-26=34$$

Find the solutions by Cramer's Rule:

$$x=\frac{D_x}{D}=\frac{51}{17}=3 \qquad y=\frac{D_y}{D}=\frac{34}{17}=2$$

14. Set up and evaluate the determinants to use Cramer's Rule:

$$\begin{cases} x+3y=\ \ 5 \\ 2x-3y=-8 \end{cases}$$

$$D=\begin{vmatrix} 1 & 3 \\ 2 & -3 \end{vmatrix}=1(-3)-2(3)=-3-6=-9$$

$$D_x=\begin{vmatrix} 5 & 3 \\ -8 & -3 \end{vmatrix}=5(-3)-(-8)(3)=-15+24=9$$

$$D_y=\begin{vmatrix} 1 & 5 \\ 2 & -8 \end{vmatrix}=1(-8)-2(5)=-8-10=-18$$

Find the solutions by Cramer's Rule:

$$x=\frac{D_x}{D}=\frac{9}{-9}=-1 \qquad y=\frac{D_y}{D}=\frac{-18}{-9}=2$$

15. Set up and evaluate the determinants to use Cramer's Rule:

$$\begin{cases} 3x = 24 \\ x + 2y = 0 \end{cases}$$

$$D = \begin{vmatrix} 3 & 0 \\ 1 & 2 \end{vmatrix} = 6 - 0 = 6$$

$$D_x = \begin{vmatrix} 24 & 0 \\ 0 & 2 \end{vmatrix} = 48 - 0 = 48$$

$$D_y = \begin{vmatrix} 3 & 24 \\ 1 & 0 \end{vmatrix} = 0 - 24 = -24$$

Find the solutions by Cramer's Rule:

$$x = \frac{D_x}{D} = \frac{48}{6} = 8 \qquad y = \frac{D_y}{D} = \frac{-24}{6} = -4$$

16. Set up and evaluate the determinants to use Cramer's Rule:

$$\begin{cases} 4x + 5y = -3 \\ -2y = -4 \end{cases}$$

$$D = \begin{vmatrix} 4 & 5 \\ 0 & -2 \end{vmatrix} = -8 - 0 = -8$$

$$D_x = \begin{vmatrix} -3 & 5 \\ -4 & -2 \end{vmatrix} = 6 + 20 = 26$$

$$D_y = \begin{vmatrix} 4 & -3 \\ 0 & -4 \end{vmatrix} = -16 - 0 = -16$$

Find the solutions by Cramer's Rule:

$$x = \frac{D_x}{D} = \frac{26}{-8} = -\frac{13}{4} \qquad y = \frac{D_y}{D} = \frac{-16}{-8} = 2$$

17. Set up and evaluate the determinants to use Cramer's Rule:

$$\begin{cases} 3x - 6y = 24 \\ 5x + 4y = 12 \end{cases}$$

$$D = \begin{vmatrix} 3 & -6 \\ 5 & 4 \end{vmatrix} = 12 - (-30) = 42$$

$$D_x = \begin{vmatrix} 24 & -6 \\ 12 & 4 \end{vmatrix} = 96 - (-72) = 168$$

$$D_y = \begin{vmatrix} 3 & 24 \\ 5 & 12 \end{vmatrix} = 36 - 120 = -84$$

Find the solutions by Cramer's Rule:

$$x = \frac{D_x}{D} = \frac{168}{42} = 4 \qquad y = \frac{D_y}{D} = \frac{-84}{42} = -2$$

18. Set up and evaluate the determinants to use Cramer's Rule:

$$\begin{cases} 2x+4y = 16 \\ 3x-5y = -9 \end{cases}$$

$$D = \begin{vmatrix} 2 & 4 \\ 3 & -5 \end{vmatrix} = -10-12 = -22$$

$$D_x = \begin{vmatrix} 16 & 4 \\ -9 & -5 \end{vmatrix} = -80+36 = -44$$

$$D_y = \begin{vmatrix} 2 & 16 \\ 3 & -9 \end{vmatrix} = -18-48 = -66$$

Find the solutions by Cramer's Rule:

$$x = \frac{D_x}{D} = \frac{-44}{-22} = 2 \qquad y = \frac{D_y}{D} = \frac{-66}{-22} = 3$$

19. Set up and evaluate the determinants to use Cramer's Rule:

$$\begin{cases} 3x-2y = 4 \\ 6x-4y = 0 \end{cases}$$

$$D = \begin{vmatrix} 3 & -2 \\ 6 & -4 \end{vmatrix} = -12-(-12) = 0$$

Since $D = 0$, Cramer's Rule does not apply.

20. Set up and evaluate the determinants to use Cramer's Rule:

$$\begin{cases} -x+2y = 5 \\ 4x-8y = 6 \end{cases}$$

$$D = \begin{vmatrix} -1 & 2 \\ 4 & -8 \end{vmatrix} = 8-8 = 0$$

Since $D = 0$, Cramer's Rule does not apply.

21. Set up and evaluate the determinants to use Cramer's Rule:

$$\begin{cases} 2x-4y = -2 \\ 3x+2y = 3 \end{cases}$$

$$D = \begin{vmatrix} 2 & -4 \\ 3 & 2 \end{vmatrix} = 4-(-12) = 16$$

$$D_x = \begin{vmatrix} -2 & -4 \\ 3 & 2 \end{vmatrix} = -4-(-12) = 8$$

$$D_y = \begin{vmatrix} 2 & -2 \\ 3 & 3 \end{vmatrix} = 6-(-6) = 12$$

Find the solutions by Cramer's Rule:

$$x = \frac{D_x}{D} = \frac{8}{16} = \frac{1}{2} \qquad y = \frac{D_y}{D} = \frac{12}{16} = \frac{3}{4}$$

22. (a) Set up and evaluate the determinants to use Cramer's Rule:

$$\begin{cases} 3x + 3y = 3 \\ 4x + 2y = \dfrac{8}{3} \end{cases}$$

$$D = \begin{vmatrix} 3 & 3 \\ 4 & 2 \end{vmatrix} = 6 - 12 = -6$$

$$D_x = \begin{vmatrix} 3 & 3 \\ \frac{8}{3} & 2 \end{vmatrix} = 6 - 8 = -2$$

$$D_y = \begin{vmatrix} 3 & 3 \\ 4 & \frac{8}{3} \end{vmatrix} = 8 - 12 = -4$$

Find the solutions by Cramer's Rule:

$$x = \frac{D_x}{D} = \frac{-2}{-6} = \frac{1}{3} \qquad y = \frac{D_y}{D} = \frac{-4}{-6} = \frac{2}{3}$$

23. Set up and evaluate the determinants to use Cramer's Rule:

$$\begin{cases} 2x - 3y = -1 \\ 10x + 10y = 5 \end{cases}$$

$$D = \begin{vmatrix} 2 & -3 \\ 10 & 10 \end{vmatrix} = 20 - (-30) = 50$$

$$D_x = \begin{vmatrix} -1 & -3 \\ 5 & 10 \end{vmatrix} = -10 - (-15) = 5$$

$$D_y = \begin{vmatrix} 2 & -1 \\ 10 & 5 \end{vmatrix} = 10 - (-10) = 20$$

Find the solutions by Cramer's Rule:

$$x = \frac{D_x}{D} = \frac{5}{50} = \frac{1}{10} \qquad y = \frac{D_y}{D} = \frac{20}{50} = \frac{2}{5}$$

24. Set up and evaluate the determinants to use Cramer's Rule:

$$\begin{cases} 3x - 2y = 0 \\ 5x + 10y = 4 \end{cases}$$

$$D = \begin{vmatrix} 3 & -2 \\ 5 & 10 \end{vmatrix} = 30 - (-10) = 40$$

$$D_x = \begin{vmatrix} 0 & -2 \\ 4 & 10 \end{vmatrix} = 0 - (-8) = 8$$

$$D_y = \begin{vmatrix} 3 & 0 \\ 5 & 4 \end{vmatrix} = 12 - 0 = 12$$

Find the solutions by Cramer's Rule:

$$x = \frac{D_x}{D} = \frac{8}{40} = \frac{1}{5} \qquad y = \frac{D_y}{D} = \frac{12}{40} = \frac{3}{10}$$

25. Set up and evaluate the determinants to use Cramer's Rule:

$$\begin{cases} 2x+3y=6 \\ x-\ y=\dfrac{1}{2} \end{cases}$$

$$D=\begin{vmatrix} 2 & 3 \\ 1 & -1 \end{vmatrix}=-2-3=-5$$

$$D_x=\begin{vmatrix} 6 & 3 \\ \frac{1}{2} & -1 \end{vmatrix}=-6-\frac{3}{2}=-\frac{15}{2}$$

$$D_y=\begin{vmatrix} 2 & 6 \\ 1 & \frac{1}{2} \end{vmatrix}=1-6=-5$$

Find the solutions by Cramer's Rule:

$$x=\frac{D_x}{D}=\frac{\left(-\frac{15}{2}\right)}{-5}=\frac{3}{2} \qquad y=\frac{D_y}{D}=\frac{-5}{-5}=1$$

26. Set up and evaluate the determinants to use Cramer's Rule:

$$\begin{cases} \dfrac{1}{2}x+\ y=-2 \\ x-2y=\ 8 \end{cases}$$

$$D=\begin{vmatrix} \frac{1}{2} & 1 \\ 1 & -2 \end{vmatrix}=-1-1=-2$$

$$D_x=\begin{vmatrix} -2 & 1 \\ 8 & -2 \end{vmatrix}=4-8=-4$$

$$D_y=\begin{vmatrix} \frac{1}{2} & -2 \\ 1 & 8 \end{vmatrix}=4-(-2)=6$$

Find the solutions by Cramer's Rule:

$$x=\frac{D_x}{D}=\frac{-4}{-2}=2 \qquad y=\frac{D_y}{D}=\frac{6}{-2}=-3$$

27. Set up and evaluate the determinants to use Cramer's Rule:

$$\begin{cases} 3x-5y=3 \\ 15x+5y=21 \end{cases}$$

$$D=\begin{vmatrix} 3 & -5 \\ 15 & 5 \end{vmatrix}=15-(-75)=90$$

$$D_x=\begin{vmatrix} 3 & -5 \\ 21 & 5 \end{vmatrix}=15-(-105)=120$$

$$D_y=\begin{vmatrix} 3 & 3 \\ 15 & 21 \end{vmatrix}=63-45=18$$

Find the solutions by Cramer's Rule:

$$x=\frac{D_x}{D}=\frac{120}{90}=\frac{4}{3} \qquad y=\frac{D_y}{D}=\frac{18}{90}=\frac{1}{5}$$

28. Set up and evaluate the determinants to use Cramer's Rule:

$$\begin{cases} 2x - y = -1 \\ x + \frac{1}{2}y = \frac{3}{2} \end{cases}$$

$$D = \begin{vmatrix} 2 & -1 \\ 1 & \frac{1}{2} \end{vmatrix} = 1 - (-1) = 2$$

$$D_x = \begin{vmatrix} -1 & -1 \\ \frac{3}{2} & \frac{1}{2} \end{vmatrix} = -\frac{1}{2} - \left(-\frac{3}{2}\right) = 1$$

$$D_y = \begin{vmatrix} 2 & -1 \\ 1 & \frac{3}{2} \end{vmatrix} = 3 - (-1) = 4$$

Find the solutions by Cramer's Rule:

$$x = \frac{D_x}{D} = \frac{1}{2} \qquad y = \frac{D_y}{D} = \frac{4}{2} = 2$$

29. Set up and evaluate the determinants to use Cramer's Rule:

$$\begin{cases} x + y - z = 6 \\ 3x - 2y + z = -5 \\ x + 3y - 2z = 14 \end{cases}$$

$$D = \begin{vmatrix} 1 & 1 & -1 \\ 3 & -2 & 1 \\ 1 & 3 & -2 \end{vmatrix} = 1\begin{vmatrix} -2 & 1 \\ 3 & -2 \end{vmatrix} - 1\begin{vmatrix} 3 & 1 \\ 1 & -2 \end{vmatrix} + (-1)\begin{vmatrix} 3 & -2 \\ 1 & 3 \end{vmatrix}$$

$$= 1(4-3) - 1(-6-1) - 1(9+2) = 1 + 7 - 11 = -3$$

$$D_x = \begin{vmatrix} 6 & 1 & -1 \\ -5 & -2 & 1 \\ 14 & 3 & -2 \end{vmatrix} = 6\begin{vmatrix} -2 & 1 \\ 3 & -2 \end{vmatrix} - 1\begin{vmatrix} -5 & 1 \\ 14 & -2 \end{vmatrix} + (-1)\begin{vmatrix} -5 & -2 \\ 14 & 3 \end{vmatrix}$$

$$= 6(4-3) - 1(10-14) - 1(-15+28) = 6 + 4 - 13 = -3$$

$$D_y = \begin{vmatrix} 1 & 6 & -1 \\ 3 & -5 & 1 \\ 1 & 14 & -2 \end{vmatrix} = 1\begin{vmatrix} -5 & 1 \\ 14 & -2 \end{vmatrix} - 6\begin{vmatrix} 3 & 1 \\ 1 & -2 \end{vmatrix} + (-1)\begin{vmatrix} 3 & -5 \\ 1 & 14 \end{vmatrix}$$

$$= 1(10-14) - 6(-6-1) - 1(42+5) = -4 + 42 - 47 = -9$$

$$D_z = \begin{vmatrix} 1 & 1 & 6 \\ 3 & -2 & -5 \\ 1 & 3 & 14 \end{vmatrix} = 1\begin{vmatrix} -2 & -5 \\ 3 & 14 \end{vmatrix} - 1\begin{vmatrix} 3 & -5 \\ 1 & 14 \end{vmatrix} + 6\begin{vmatrix} 3 & -2 \\ 1 & 3 \end{vmatrix}$$

$$= 1(-28+15) - 1(42+5) + 6(9+2) = -13 - 47 + 66 = 6$$

Find the solutions by Cramer's Rule:

$$x = \frac{D_x}{D} = \frac{-3}{-3} = 1 \qquad y = \frac{D_y}{D} = \frac{-9}{-3} = 3 \qquad z = \frac{D_z}{D} = \frac{6}{-3} = -2$$

30. Set up and evaluate the determinants to use Cramer's Rule:

$$\begin{cases} x - y + z = -4 \\ 2x - 3y + 4z = -15 \\ 5x + y - 2z = 12 \end{cases}$$

$$D = \begin{vmatrix} 1 & -1 & 1 \\ 2 & -3 & 4 \\ 5 & 1 & -2 \end{vmatrix} = 1\begin{vmatrix} -3 & 4 \\ 1 & -2 \end{vmatrix} - (-1)\begin{vmatrix} 2 & 4 \\ 5 & -2 \end{vmatrix} + 1\begin{vmatrix} 2 & -3 \\ 5 & 1 \end{vmatrix}$$

$$= 1(6-4) + 1(-4-20) + 1(2+15) = 2 - 24 + 17 = -5$$

$$D_x = \begin{vmatrix} -4 & -1 & 1 \\ -15 & -3 & 4 \\ 12 & 1 & -2 \end{vmatrix} = -4\begin{vmatrix} -3 & 4 \\ 1 & -2 \end{vmatrix} - (-1)\begin{vmatrix} -15 & 4 \\ 12 & -2 \end{vmatrix} + 1\begin{vmatrix} -15 & -3 \\ 12 & 1 \end{vmatrix}$$

$$= -4(6-4) + 1(30-48) + 1(-15+36) = -8 - 18 + 21 = -5$$

$$D_y = \begin{vmatrix} 1 & -4 & 1 \\ 2 & -15 & 4 \\ 5 & 12 & -2 \end{vmatrix} = 1\begin{vmatrix} -15 & 4 \\ 12 & -2 \end{vmatrix} - (-4)\begin{vmatrix} 2 & 4 \\ 5 & -2 \end{vmatrix} + 1\begin{vmatrix} 2 & -15 \\ 5 & 12 \end{vmatrix}$$

$$= 1(30-48) + 4(-4-20) + 1(24+75) = -18 - 96 + 99 = -15$$

$$D_z = \begin{vmatrix} 1 & -1 & -4 \\ 2 & -3 & -15 \\ 5 & 1 & 12 \end{vmatrix} = 1\begin{vmatrix} -3 & -15 \\ 1 & 12 \end{vmatrix} - (-1)\begin{vmatrix} 2 & -15 \\ 5 & 12 \end{vmatrix} + (-4)\begin{vmatrix} 2 & -3 \\ 5 & 1 \end{vmatrix}$$

$$= 1(-36+15) + 1(24+75) - 4(2+15) = -21 + 99 - 68 = 10$$

Find the solutions by Cramer's Rule:

$$x = \frac{D_x}{D} = \frac{-5}{-5} = 1 \qquad y = \frac{D_y}{D} = \frac{-15}{-5} = 3 \qquad z = \frac{D_z}{D} = \frac{10}{-5} = -2$$

31. Set up and evaluate the determinants to use Cramer's Rule:

$$\begin{cases} x + 2y - z = -3 \\ 2x - 4y + z = -7 \\ -2x + 2y - 3z = 4 \end{cases}$$

$$D = \begin{vmatrix} 1 & 2 & -1 \\ 2 & -4 & 1 \\ -2 & 2 & -3 \end{vmatrix} = 1\begin{vmatrix} -4 & 1 \\ 2 & -3 \end{vmatrix} - 2\begin{vmatrix} 2 & 1 \\ -2 & -3 \end{vmatrix} + (-1)\begin{vmatrix} 2 & -4 \\ -2 & 2 \end{vmatrix}$$

$$= 1(12-2) - 2(-6+2) - 1(4-8) = 10 + 8 + 4 = 22$$

$$D_x = \begin{vmatrix} -3 & 2 & -1 \\ -7 & -4 & 1 \\ 4 & 2 & -3 \end{vmatrix} = -3\begin{vmatrix} -4 & 1 \\ 2 & -3 \end{vmatrix} - 2\begin{vmatrix} -7 & 1 \\ 4 & -3 \end{vmatrix} + (-1)\begin{vmatrix} -7 & -4 \\ 4 & 2 \end{vmatrix}$$

$$= -3(12-2) - 2(21-4) - 1(-14+16) = -30 - 34 - 2 = -66$$

$$D_y = \begin{vmatrix} 1 & -3 & -1 \\ 2 & -7 & 1 \\ -2 & 4 & -3 \end{vmatrix} = 1\begin{vmatrix} -7 & 1 \\ 4 & -3 \end{vmatrix} - (-3)\begin{vmatrix} 2 & 1 \\ -2 & -3 \end{vmatrix} + (-1)\begin{vmatrix} 2 & -7 \\ -2 & 4 \end{vmatrix}$$

$$= 1(21-4) + 3(-6+2) - 1(8-14) = 17 - 12 + 6 = 11$$

$$D_z = \begin{vmatrix} 1 & 2 & -3 \\ 2 & -4 & -7 \\ -2 & 2 & 4 \end{vmatrix} = 1\begin{vmatrix} -4 & -7 \\ 2 & 4 \end{vmatrix} - 2\begin{vmatrix} 2 & -7 \\ -2 & 4 \end{vmatrix} + (-3)\begin{vmatrix} 2 & -4 \\ -2 & 2 \end{vmatrix}$$

$$= 1(-16+14) - 2(8-14) - 3(4-8) = -2 + 12 + 12 = 22$$

Find the solutions by Cramer's Rule:

$$x = \frac{D_x}{D} = \frac{-66}{22} = -3 \qquad y = \frac{D_y}{D} = \frac{11}{22} = \frac{1}{2} \qquad z = \frac{D_z}{D} = \frac{22}{22} = 1$$

32. Set up and evaluate the determinants to use Cramer's Rule:

$$\begin{cases} x + 4y - 3z = -8 \\ 3x - y + 3z = 12 \\ x + y + 6z = 1 \end{cases}$$

$$D = \begin{vmatrix} 1 & 4 & -3 \\ 3 & -1 & 3 \\ 1 & 1 & 6 \end{vmatrix} = 1\begin{vmatrix} -1 & 3 \\ 1 & 6 \end{vmatrix} - 4\begin{vmatrix} 3 & 3 \\ 1 & 6 \end{vmatrix} + (-3)\begin{vmatrix} 3 & -1 \\ 1 & 1 \end{vmatrix}$$

$$= 1(-6-3) - 4(18-3) - 3(3+1) = -9 - 60 - 12 = -81$$

$$D_x = \begin{vmatrix} -8 & 4 & -3 \\ 12 & -1 & 3 \\ 1 & 1 & 6 \end{vmatrix} = -8\begin{vmatrix} -1 & 3 \\ 1 & 6 \end{vmatrix} - 4\begin{vmatrix} 12 & 3 \\ 1 & 6 \end{vmatrix} + (-3)\begin{vmatrix} 12 & -1 \\ 1 & 1 \end{vmatrix}$$

$$= -8(-6-3) - 4(72-3) - 3(12+1) = 72 - 276 - 39 = -243$$

$$D_y = \begin{vmatrix} 1 & -8 & -3 \\ 3 & 12 & 3 \\ 1 & 1 & 6 \end{vmatrix} = 1\begin{vmatrix} 12 & 3 \\ 1 & 6 \end{vmatrix} - (-8)\begin{vmatrix} 3 & 3 \\ 1 & 6 \end{vmatrix} + (-3)\begin{vmatrix} 3 & 12 \\ 1 & 1 \end{vmatrix}$$

$$= 1(72-3) + 8(18-3) - 3(3-12) = 69 + 120 + 27 = 216$$

$$D_z = \begin{vmatrix} 1 & 4 & -8 \\ 3 & -1 & 12 \\ 1 & 1 & 1 \end{vmatrix} = 1\begin{vmatrix} -1 & 12 \\ 1 & 1 \end{vmatrix} - 4\begin{vmatrix} 3 & 12 \\ 1 & 1 \end{vmatrix} + (-8)\begin{vmatrix} 3 & -1 \\ 1 & 1 \end{vmatrix}$$

$$= 1(-1-12) - 4(3-12) - 8(3+1) = -13 + 36 - 32 = -9$$

Find the solutions by Cramer's Rule:

$$x = \frac{D_x}{D} = \frac{-243}{-81} = 3 \qquad y = \frac{D_y}{D} = \frac{216}{-81} = -\frac{8}{3} \qquad z = \frac{D_z}{D} = \frac{-9}{-81} = \frac{1}{9}$$

33. Set up and evaluate the determinants to use Cramer's Rule:

$$\begin{cases} x - 2y + 3z = 1 \\ 3x + y - 2z = 0 \\ 2x - 4y + 6z = 2 \end{cases}$$

$$D = \begin{vmatrix} 1 & -2 & 3 \\ 3 & 1 & -2 \\ 2 & -4 & 6 \end{vmatrix} = 1\begin{vmatrix} 1 & -2 \\ -4 & 6 \end{vmatrix} - (-2)\begin{vmatrix} 3 & -2 \\ 2 & 6 \end{vmatrix} + 3\begin{vmatrix} 3 & 1 \\ 2 & -4 \end{vmatrix}$$

$$= 1(6-8) + 2(18+4) + 3(-12-2) = -2 + 44 - 42 = 0$$

Since $D = 0$, Cramer's Rule does not apply.

34. Set up and evaluate the determinants to use Cramer's Rule:

$$\begin{cases} x - y + 2z = 5 \\ 3x + 2y = 4 \\ -2x + 2y - 4z = -10 \end{cases}$$

$$D = \begin{vmatrix} 1 & -1 & 2 \\ 3 & 2 & 0 \\ -2 & 2 & -4 \end{vmatrix} = 1\begin{vmatrix} 2 & 0 \\ 2 & -4 \end{vmatrix} - (-1)\begin{vmatrix} 3 & 0 \\ -2 & -4 \end{vmatrix} + 2\begin{vmatrix} 3 & 2 \\ -2 & 2 \end{vmatrix}$$

$$= 1(-8-0) + 1(-12-0) + 2(6+4) = -8 - 12 + 20 = 0$$

Since $D = 0$, Cramer's Rule does not apply.

35. Set up and evaluate the determinants to use Cramer's Rule:

$$\begin{cases} x + 2y - z = 0 \\ 2x - 4y + z = 0 \\ -2x + 2y - 3z = 0 \end{cases}$$

$$D = \begin{vmatrix} 1 & 2 & -1 \\ 2 & -4 & 1 \\ -2 & 2 & -3 \end{vmatrix} = 1\begin{vmatrix} -4 & 1 \\ 2 & -3 \end{vmatrix} - 2\begin{vmatrix} 2 & 1 \\ -2 & -3 \end{vmatrix} + (-1)\begin{vmatrix} 2 & -4 \\ -2 & 2 \end{vmatrix}$$

$$= 1(12-2) - 2(-6+2) - 1(4-8) = 10 + 8 + 4 = 22$$

$$D_x = \begin{vmatrix} 0 & 2 & -1 \\ 0 & -4 & 1 \\ 0 & 2 & -3 \end{vmatrix} = 0 \quad \text{(By Theorem 12)}$$

$$D_y = \begin{vmatrix} 1 & 0 & -1 \\ 2 & 0 & 1 \\ -2 & 0 & -3 \end{vmatrix} = 0 \quad \text{(By Theorem 12)}$$

$$D_z = \begin{vmatrix} 1 & 2 & 0 \\ 2 & -4 & 0 \\ -2 & 2 & 0 \end{vmatrix} = 0 \quad \text{(By Theorem 12)}$$

Find the solutions by Cramer's Rule:

$$x = \frac{D_x}{D} = \frac{0}{22} = 0 \qquad y = \frac{D_y}{D} = \frac{0}{22} = 0 \qquad z = \frac{D_z}{D} = \frac{0}{22} = 0$$

36. Set up and evaluate the determinants to use Cramer's Rule:

$$\begin{cases} x + 4y - 3z = 0 \\ 3x - y + 3z = 0 \\ x + y + 6z = 0 \end{cases}$$

$$D = \begin{vmatrix} 1 & 4 & -3 \\ 3 & -1 & 3 \\ 1 & 1 & 6 \end{vmatrix} = 1\begin{vmatrix} -1 & 3 \\ 1 & 6 \end{vmatrix} - 4\begin{vmatrix} 3 & 3 \\ 1 & 6 \end{vmatrix} + (-3)\begin{vmatrix} 3 & -1 \\ 1 & 1 \end{vmatrix}$$

$$= 1(-6-3) - 4(18-3) - 3(3+1) = -9 - 60 - 12 = -81$$

$$D_x = \begin{vmatrix} 0 & 4 & -3 \\ 0 & -1 & 3 \\ 0 & 1 & 6 \end{vmatrix} = 0 \quad \text{(By Theorem 12)}$$

$$D_y = \begin{vmatrix} 1 & 0 & -3 \\ 3 & 0 & 3 \\ 1 & 0 & 6 \end{vmatrix} = 0 \quad \text{(By Theorem 12)}$$

$$D_z = \begin{vmatrix} 1 & 4 & 0 \\ 3 & -1 & 0 \\ 1 & 1 & 0 \end{vmatrix} = 0 \quad \text{(By Theorem 12)}$$

Find the solutions by Cramer's Rule:

$$x = \frac{D_x}{D} = \frac{0}{-81} = 0 \qquad y = \frac{D_y}{D} = \frac{0}{-81} = 0 \qquad z = \frac{D_z}{D} = \frac{0}{-81} = 0$$

37. Set up and evaluate the determinants to use Cramer's Rule:

$$\begin{cases} x - 2y + 3z = 0 \\ 3x + \ \ y - 2z = 0 \\ 2x - 4y + 6z = 0 \end{cases}$$

$$D = \begin{vmatrix} 1 & -2 & 3 \\ 3 & 1 & -2 \\ 2 & -4 & 6 \end{vmatrix} = 1\begin{vmatrix} 1 & -2 \\ -4 & 6 \end{vmatrix} - (-2)\begin{vmatrix} 3 & -2 \\ 2 & 6 \end{vmatrix} + 3\begin{vmatrix} 3 & 1 \\ 2 & -4 \end{vmatrix}$$

$$= 1(6-8) + 2(18+4) + 3(-12-2) = -2 + 44 - 42 = 0$$

Since $D = 0$, Cramer's Rule does not apply.

38. Set up and evaluate the determinants to use Cramer's Rule:

$$\begin{cases} x - \ y + 2z = 0 \\ 3x + 2y \qquad = 0 \\ -2x + 2y - 4z = 0 \end{cases}$$

$$D = \begin{vmatrix} 1 & -1 & 2 \\ 3 & 2 & 0 \\ -2 & 2 & -4 \end{vmatrix} = 1\begin{vmatrix} 2 & 0 \\ 2 & -4 \end{vmatrix} - (-1)\begin{vmatrix} 3 & 0 \\ -2 & -4 \end{vmatrix} + 2\begin{vmatrix} 3 & 2 \\ -2 & 2 \end{vmatrix}$$

$$= 1(-8-0) + 1(-12-0) + 2(6+4) = -8 - 12 + 20 = 0$$

Since $D = 0$, Cramer's Rule does not apply.

39. Rewrite the system letting $u = \frac{1}{x}$ and $v = \frac{1}{y}$:

$$\begin{cases} \frac{1}{x} + \frac{1}{y} = 8 \\ \frac{3}{x} - \frac{5}{y} = 0 \end{cases} \quad \rightarrow \quad \begin{cases} u + \ v = 8 \\ 3u - 5v = 0 \end{cases}$$

Set up and evaluate the determinants to use Cramer's Rule:

$$D = \begin{vmatrix} 1 & 1 \\ 3 & -5 \end{vmatrix} = -5 - 3 = -8$$

$$D_u = \begin{vmatrix} 8 & 1 \\ 0 & -5 \end{vmatrix} = -40 - 0 = -40$$

$$D_v = \begin{vmatrix} 1 & 8 \\ 3 & 0 \end{vmatrix} = 0 - 24 = -24$$

Find the solutions by Cramer's Rule:

$$u = \frac{D_u}{D} = \frac{-40}{-8} = 5 \qquad v = \frac{D_v}{D} = \frac{-24}{-8} = 3$$

The solutions are $x = \frac{1}{5},\ y = \frac{1}{3}$

40. Rewrite the system letting $u = \frac{1}{x}$ and $v = \frac{1}{y}$:

$$\begin{cases} \frac{4}{x} - \frac{3}{y} = 0 \\ \frac{6}{x} + \frac{3}{2y} = 2 \end{cases} \rightarrow \begin{cases} 4u - 3v = 0 \\ 6u + \frac{3}{2}v = 2 \end{cases}$$

Set up and evaluate the determinants to use Cramer's Rule:

$$D = \begin{vmatrix} 4 & -3 \\ 6 & \frac{3}{2} \end{vmatrix} = 6 + 18 = 24$$

$$D_u = \begin{vmatrix} 0 & -3 \\ 2 & \frac{3}{2} \end{vmatrix} = 0 + 6 = 6$$

$$D_v = \begin{vmatrix} 4 & 0 \\ 6 & 2 \end{vmatrix} = 8 - 0 = 8$$

Find the solutions by Cramer's Rule:

$$u = \frac{D_u}{D} = \frac{6}{24} = \frac{1}{4} \qquad v = \frac{D_v}{D} = \frac{8}{24} = \frac{1}{3}$$

The solutions are $x = 4,\ y = 3$

41. Solve for x:

$$\begin{vmatrix} x & x \\ 4 & 3 \end{vmatrix} = 3x - 4x = -x$$

$$-x = 5 \rightarrow x = -5$$

42. Solve for x:

$$\begin{vmatrix} x & 1 \\ 3 & x \end{vmatrix} = x^2 - 3 = -2 \rightarrow x^2 = 1 \rightarrow x = \pm 1$$

43. Solve for x:

$$\begin{vmatrix} x & 1 & 1 \\ 4 & 3 & 2 \\ -1 & 2 & 5 \end{vmatrix} = x\begin{vmatrix} 3 & 2 \\ 2 & 5 \end{vmatrix} - 1\begin{vmatrix} 4 & 2 \\ -1 & 5 \end{vmatrix} + 1\begin{vmatrix} 4 & 3 \\ -1 & 2 \end{vmatrix}$$

$$= x(15-4) - (20+2) + (8+3) = 11x - 22 + 11 = 11x - 11$$

So, $11x - 11 = 2 \rightarrow 11x = 13 \rightarrow x = \frac{13}{11}$

44. Solve for x:

$$\begin{vmatrix} 3 & 2 & 4 \\ 1 & x & 5 \\ 0 & 1 & -2 \end{vmatrix} = 3\begin{vmatrix} x & 5 \\ 1 & -2 \end{vmatrix} - 2\begin{vmatrix} 1 & 5 \\ 0 & -2 \end{vmatrix} + 4\begin{vmatrix} 1 & x \\ 0 & 1 \end{vmatrix}$$

$$= 3(-2x-5)-2(-2-0)+4(1-0) = -6x-15+4+4 = -6x-7$$

$$-6x-7=0 \rightarrow -6x=7 \rightarrow x=-\frac{7}{6}$$

45. Solve for x:

$$\begin{vmatrix} x & 2 & 3 \\ 1 & x & 0 \\ 6 & 1 & -2 \end{vmatrix} = x\begin{vmatrix} x & 0 \\ 1 & -2 \end{vmatrix} - 2\begin{vmatrix} 1 & 0 \\ 6 & -2 \end{vmatrix} + 3\begin{vmatrix} 1 & x \\ 6 & 1 \end{vmatrix}$$

$$= x(-2x-0)-2(-2-0)+3(1-6x)$$

$$= -2x^2+4+3-18x = -2x^2-18x+7$$

So, $-2x^2-18x+7=7$

$$-2x^2-18x=0 \rightarrow -2x(x+9)=0 \rightarrow x=0 \text{ or } x=-9$$

46. Solve for x:

$$\begin{vmatrix} x & 1 & 2 \\ 1 & x & 3 \\ 0 & 1 & 2 \end{vmatrix} = x\begin{vmatrix} x & 3 \\ 1 & 2 \end{vmatrix} - 1\begin{vmatrix} 1 & 3 \\ 0 & 2 \end{vmatrix} + 2\begin{vmatrix} 1 & x \\ 0 & 1 \end{vmatrix}$$

$$= x(2x-3)-1(2-0)+2(1-0) = 2x^2-3x-2+2 = 2x^2-3x$$

So, $2x^2-3x=-4x \rightarrow 2x^2+x=0 \rightarrow x(2x+1)=0$

$$x=0 \text{ or } x=-\frac{1}{2}$$

47. Let $\begin{vmatrix} x & y & z \\ u & v & w \\ 1 & 2 & 3 \end{vmatrix} = 4$

Then $\begin{vmatrix} 1 & 2 & 3 \\ u & v & w \\ x & y & z \end{vmatrix} = -4$ by Theorem 11

The value of the determinant changes sign when two rows are interchanged.

48. Let $\begin{vmatrix} x & y & z \\ u & v & w \\ 1 & 2 & 3 \end{vmatrix} = 4$

Then $\begin{vmatrix} x & y & z \\ u & v & w \\ 2 & 4 & 6 \end{vmatrix} = 2\begin{vmatrix} x & y & z \\ u & v & w \\ 1 & 2 & 3 \end{vmatrix} = 2(4) = 8$ by Theorem 14

The value of the determinant is multiplied by k when the elements of a row are multiplied by k.

Problems 49 – 54 use the Laws for Determinants in reverse order.

49. Let $\begin{vmatrix} x & y & z \\ u & v & w \\ 1 & 2 & 3 \end{vmatrix} = 4$

$$\begin{vmatrix} x & y & z \\ -3 & -6 & -9 \\ u & v & w \end{vmatrix} = -3\begin{vmatrix} x & y & z \\ 1 & 2 & 3 \\ u & v & w \end{vmatrix} = -3(-1)\begin{vmatrix} x & y & z \\ u & v & w \\ 1 & 2 & 3 \end{vmatrix} = 3(4) = 12$$

Theorem 14 Theorem 11

50. Let $\begin{vmatrix} x & y & z \\ u & v & w \\ 1 & 2 & 3 \end{vmatrix} = 4$

$$\begin{vmatrix} 1 & 2 & 3 \\ x-u & y-v & z-w \\ u & v & w \end{vmatrix} = \begin{vmatrix} 1 & 2 & 3 \\ x & y & z \\ u & v & w \end{vmatrix} = (-1)\begin{vmatrix} x & y & z \\ 1 & 2 & 3 \\ u & v & w \end{vmatrix} = (-1)(-1)\begin{vmatrix} x & y & z \\ u & v & w \\ 1 & 2 & 3 \end{vmatrix}$$

Theorem 15 Theorem 11 Theorem 11

$$= \begin{vmatrix} x & y & z \\ u & v & w \\ 1 & 2 & 3 \end{vmatrix} = 4$$

51. Let $\begin{vmatrix} x & y & z \\ u & v & w \\ 1 & 2 & 3 \end{vmatrix} = 4$

$$\begin{vmatrix} 1 & 2 & 3 \\ x-3 & y-6 & z-9 \\ 2u & 2v & 2w \end{vmatrix} = 2\begin{vmatrix} 1 & 2 & 3 \\ x-3 & y-6 & z-9 \\ u & v & w \end{vmatrix} = 2(-1)\begin{vmatrix} x-3 & y-6 & z-9 \\ 1 & 2 & 3 \\ u & v & w \end{vmatrix}$$

Theorem 14 Theorem 11

$$= 2(-1)(-1)\begin{vmatrix} x-3 & y-6 & z-9 \\ u & v & w \\ 1 & 2 & 3 \end{vmatrix} = 2(-1)(-1)\begin{vmatrix} x & y & z \\ u & v & w \\ 1 & 2 & 3 \end{vmatrix} = 2(-1)(-1)(4) = 8$$

Theorem 11 Theorem 15 $(R_1 = -3r_3 + r_1)$

52. Let $\begin{vmatrix} x & y & z \\ u & v & w \\ 1 & 2 & 3 \end{vmatrix} = 4$

$$= \begin{vmatrix} x & y & z-x \\ u & v & w-u \\ 1 & 2 & 2 \end{vmatrix} = \begin{vmatrix} x & y & z \\ u & v & w \\ 1 & 2 & 3 \end{vmatrix} = 4$$

Theorem 15 $(C_3 = -c_1 + c_3)$

53. Let $\begin{vmatrix} x & y & z \\ u & v & w \\ 1 & 2 & 3 \end{vmatrix} = 4$

$$\begin{vmatrix} 1 & 2 & 3 \\ 2x & 2y & 2z \\ u-1 & v-2 & w-3 \end{vmatrix} \underset{\text{Theorem 14}}{=} 2\begin{vmatrix} 1 & 2 & 3 \\ x & y & z \\ u-1 & v-2 & w-3 \end{vmatrix} \underset{\text{Theorem 11}}{=} 2(-1)\begin{vmatrix} x & y & z \\ 1 & 2 & 3 \\ u-1 & v-2 & w-3 \end{vmatrix}$$

$$\underset{\text{Theorem 11}}{=} 2(-1)(-1)\begin{vmatrix} x & y & z \\ u-1 & v-2 & w-3 \\ 1 & 2 & 3 \end{vmatrix} \underset{\text{Theorem 15 } (R_2=-r_3+r_2)}{=} 2(-1)(-1)\begin{vmatrix} x & y & z \\ u & v & w \\ 1 & 2 & 3 \end{vmatrix} = 2(-1)(-1)(4) = 8$$

54. Let $\begin{vmatrix} x & y & z \\ u & v & w \\ 1 & 2 & 3 \end{vmatrix} = 4$

$$\begin{vmatrix} x+3 & y+6 & z+9 \\ 3u-1 & 3v-2 & 3w-3 \\ 1 & 2 & 3 \end{vmatrix} \underset{\text{Theorem 15 } (R_1=3r_3+r_1)}{=} \begin{vmatrix} x & y & z \\ 3u-1 & 3v-2 & 3w-3 \\ 1 & 2 & 3 \end{vmatrix} \underset{\text{Theorem 15 } (R_2=-r_3+r_2)}{=} \begin{vmatrix} x & y & z \\ 3u & 3v & 3w \\ 1 & 2 & 3 \end{vmatrix}$$

$$\underset{\text{Theorem 14}}{=} 3\begin{vmatrix} x & y & z \\ u & v & w \\ 1 & 2 & 3 \end{vmatrix} = 3(4) = 12$$

55. Expanding the determinant:

$$\begin{vmatrix} x & y & 1 \\ x_1 & y_1 & 1 \\ x_2 & y_2 & 1 \end{vmatrix} = x\begin{vmatrix} y_1 & 1 \\ y_2 & 1 \end{vmatrix} - y\begin{vmatrix} x_1 & 1 \\ x_2 & 1 \end{vmatrix} + 1\begin{vmatrix} x_1 & y_1 \\ x_2 & y_2 \end{vmatrix}$$

$$= x(y_1 - y_2) - y(x_1 - x_2) + (x_1y_2 - x_2y_1) = 0$$

$$x(y_1 - y_2) + y(x_2 - x_1) = x_2y_1 - x_1y_2$$

$$y(x_2 - x_1) = x_2y_1 - x_1y_2 + x(y_2 - y_1)$$

$$y(x_2 - x_1) - y_1(x_2 - x_1) = x_2y_1 - x_1y_2 + x(y_2 - y_1) - y_1(x_2 - x_1)$$

$$(x_2 - x_1)(y - y_1) = x(y_2 - y_1) + x_2y_1 - x_1y_2 - y_1x_2 + y_1x_1$$

$$(x_2 - x_1)(y - y_1) = (y_2 - y_1)x - (y_2 - y_1)x_1$$

$$(x_2 - x_1)(y - y_1) = (y_2 - y_1)(x - x_1)$$

$$(y - y_1) = \frac{(y_2 - y_1)}{(x_2 - x_1)}(x - x_1)$$

56. Any point (x, y) on the line containing (x_2, y_2) and (x_3, y_3) satisfies:

$$\begin{vmatrix} x & y & 1 \\ x_2 & y_2 & 1 \\ x_3 & y_3 & 1 \end{vmatrix} = 0$$

If the point (x_1, y_1) is on the line containing (x_2, y_2) and (x_3, y_3) (the points are collinear), then:

$$\begin{vmatrix} x_1 & y_1 & 1 \\ x_2 & y_2 & 1 \\ x_3 & y_3 & 1 \end{vmatrix} = 0$$

Conversely, if $\begin{vmatrix} x_1 & y_1 & 1 \\ x_2 & y_2 & 1 \\ x_3 & y_3 & 1 \end{vmatrix} = 0$, then (x_1, y_1) is on the line containing (x_2, y_2) and (x_3, y_3) and the points are collinear.

57. Expanding the determinant:

$$\begin{aligned}
\begin{vmatrix} x^2 & x & 1 \\ y^2 & y & 1 \\ z^2 & z & 1 \end{vmatrix} &= x^2\begin{vmatrix} y & 1 \\ z & 1 \end{vmatrix} - x\begin{vmatrix} y^2 & 1 \\ z^2 & 1 \end{vmatrix} + 1\begin{vmatrix} y^2 & y \\ z^2 & z \end{vmatrix} \\
&= x^2(y-z) - x(y^2 - z^2) + 1(y^2 z - z^2 y) \\
&= x^2(y-z) - x(y-z)(y+z) + yz(y-z) \\
&= (y-z)\left[x^2 - xy - xz + yz\right] \\
&= (y-z)\left[x(x-y) - z(x-y)\right] \\
&= (y-z)(x-y)(x-z)
\end{aligned}$$

58. Cramer's Rule for two equations containing two variables asserts that the solution to the system of equations

$$\begin{aligned} ax + by &= s \\ cs + dy &= t \end{aligned}$$

is given by $x = \dfrac{\begin{vmatrix} s & b \\ t & d \end{vmatrix}}{\begin{vmatrix} a & b \\ c & d \end{vmatrix}}$ $y = \dfrac{\begin{vmatrix} a & s \\ c & t \end{vmatrix}}{\begin{vmatrix} a & b \\ c & d \end{vmatrix}}$ provided that $D = \begin{vmatrix} a & b \\ c & d \end{vmatrix} = ad - bc \neq 0$.

Case 1:If $a = 0$, then $b \neq 0$ and $c \neq 0$, so $D = -bc \neq 0$.

Then, $x = \dfrac{sd - bt}{-bc}$, $y = \dfrac{-sc}{-bc}$ is a solution.

Case 2:If $b = 0$, then $a \neq 0$ and $d \neq 0$, so $D = ad \neq 0$.

Then, $x = \dfrac{sd}{ad}$, $y = \dfrac{at - sc}{ad}$ is a solution.

Case 3:If $c = 0$, then $a \neq 0$ and $d \neq 0$, so $D = ad \neq 0$.

Then, $x = \dfrac{sd - bt}{ad}$, $y = \dfrac{at}{ad}$ is a solution.

Case 4:If $d = 0$, then $b \neq 0$ and $c \neq 0$, so $D = -bc \neq 0$.

Then, $x = \dfrac{-bt}{-bc}$, $y = \dfrac{at - sc}{-bc}$ is a solution.

59. Evaluating the determinant to show the relationship:

$$\begin{vmatrix} a_{13} & a_{12} & a_{11} \\ a_{23} & a_{22} & a_{21} \\ a_{33} & a_{32} & a_{31} \end{vmatrix} = a_{13}\begin{vmatrix} a_{22} & a_{21} \\ a_{32} & a_{31} \end{vmatrix} - a_{12}\begin{vmatrix} a_{23} & a_{21} \\ a_{33} & a_{31} \end{vmatrix} + a_{11}\begin{vmatrix} a_{23} & a_{22} \\ a_{33} & a_{32} \end{vmatrix}$$

$$= a_{13}(a_{22}a_{31} - a_{21}a_{32}) - a_{12}(a_{23}a_{31} - a_{21}a_{33}) + a_{11}(a_{23}a_{32} - a_{22}a_{33})$$

$$= a_{13}a_{22}a_{31} - a_{13}a_{21}a_{32} - a_{12}a_{23}a_{31} + a_{12}a_{21}a_{33} + a_{11}a_{23}a_{32} - a_{11}a_{22}a_{33}$$

$$= -a_{11}a_{22}a_{33} + a_{11}a_{23}a_{32} + a_{12}a_{21}a_{33} - a_{12}a_{23}a_{31} - a_{13}a_{21}a_{32} + a_{13}a_{22}a_{31}$$

$$= -a_{11}(a_{22}a_{33} - a_{23}a_{32}) + a_{12}(a_{21}a_{33} - a_{23}a_{31}) - a_{13}(a_{21}a_{32} - a_{22}a_{31})$$

$$= -a_{11}\begin{vmatrix} a_{22} & a_{23} \\ a_{32} & a_{33} \end{vmatrix} + a_{12}\begin{vmatrix} a_{21} & a_{23} \\ a_{31} & a_{33} \end{vmatrix} - a_{13}\begin{vmatrix} a_{21} & a_{22} \\ a_{31} & a_{32} \end{vmatrix}$$

$$= -\left[a_{11}\begin{vmatrix} a_{22} & a_{23} \\ a_{32} & a_{33} \end{vmatrix} - a_{12}\begin{vmatrix} a_{21} & a_{23} \\ a_{31} & a_{33} \end{vmatrix} + a_{13}\begin{vmatrix} a_{21} & a_{22} \\ a_{31} & a_{32} \end{vmatrix}\right]$$

$$= -\begin{vmatrix} a_{11} & a_{12} & a_{13} \\ a_{21} & a_{22} & a_{23} \\ a_{31} & a_{32} & a_{33} \end{vmatrix}$$

60. Evaluating the determinant to show the relationship:

$$\begin{vmatrix} a_{11} & a_{12} & a_{13} \\ ka_{21} & ka_{22} & ka_{23} \\ a_{31} & a_{32} & a_{33} \end{vmatrix} = a_{11}\begin{vmatrix} ka_{22} & ka_{23} \\ a_{32} & a_{33} \end{vmatrix} - a_{12}\begin{vmatrix} ka_{21} & ka_{23} \\ a_{31} & a_{33} \end{vmatrix} + a_{13}\begin{vmatrix} ka_{21} & ka_{22} \\ a_{31} & a_{32} \end{vmatrix}$$

$$= a_{11}(ka_{22}a_{33} - ka_{23}a_{32}) - a_{12}(ka_{21}a_{33} - ka_{23}a_{31}) + a_{13}(ka_{21}a_{32} - ka_{22}a_{31})$$

$$= ka_{11}(a_{22}a_{33} - a_{23}a_{32}) - ka_{12}(a_{21}a_{33} - a_{23}a_{31}) + ka_{13}(a_{21}a_{32} - a_{22}a_{31})$$

$$= k\big(a_{11}(a_{22}a_{33} - a_{23}a_{32}) - a_{12}(a_{21}a_{33} - a_{23}a_{31}) + a_{13}(a_{21}a_{32} - a_{22}a_{31})\big)$$

$$= k\left(a_{11}\begin{vmatrix} a_{22} & a_{23} \\ a_{32} & a_{33} \end{vmatrix} - a_{12}\begin{vmatrix} a_{21} & a_{23} \\ a_{31} & a_{33} \end{vmatrix} + a_{13}\begin{vmatrix} a_{21} & a_{22} \\ a_{31} & a_{32} \end{vmatrix}\right)$$

$$= k\begin{vmatrix} a_{11} & a_{12} & a_{13} \\ a_{21} & a_{22} & a_{23} \\ a_{31} & a_{32} & a_{33} \end{vmatrix}$$

61. Set up a 3 by 3 determinant in which the first column and third column are the same and evaluate:

$$\begin{vmatrix} a & b & a \\ c & d & c \\ e & f & e \end{vmatrix} = -b\begin{vmatrix} c & c \\ e & e \end{vmatrix} + d\begin{vmatrix} a & a \\ e & e \end{vmatrix} - f\begin{vmatrix} a & a \\ c & c \end{vmatrix}$$

$$= -b(ce - ce) + d(ae - ae) - f(ac - ac) = -b(0) + d(0) - f(0) = 0$$

62. Evaluating the determinant to show the relationship:

$$\begin{vmatrix} a_{11}+ka_{21} & a_{12}+ka_{22} & a_{13}+ka_{23} \\ a_{21} & a_{22} & a_{23} \\ a_{31} & a_{32} & a_{33} \end{vmatrix}$$

$$= (a_{11}+ka_{21})\begin{vmatrix} a_{22} & a_{23} \\ a_{32} & a_{33} \end{vmatrix} - (a_{12}+ka_{22})\begin{vmatrix} a_{21} & a_{23} \\ a_{31} & a_{33} \end{vmatrix} + (a_{13}+ka_{23})\begin{vmatrix} a_{21} & a_{22} \\ a_{31} & a_{32} \end{vmatrix}$$

$$= (a_{11}+ka_{21})(a_{22}a_{33}-a_{23}a_{32}) - (a_{12}+ka_{22})(a_{21}a_{33}-a_{23}a_{31})$$
$$+ (a_{13}+ka_{23})(a_{21}a_{32}-a_{22}a_{31})$$

$$= a_{11}(a_{22}a_{33}-a_{23}a_{32}) + ka_{21}(a_{22}a_{33}-a_{23}a_{32}) - a_{12}(a_{21}a_{33}-a_{23}a_{31})$$
$$- ka_{22}(a_{21}a_{33}-a_{23}a_{31}) + a_{13}(a_{21}a_{32}-a_{22}a_{31}) + ka_{23}(a_{21}a_{32}-a_{22}a_{31})$$

$$= a_{11}(a_{22}a_{33}-a_{23}a_{32}) + ka_{21}a_{22}a_{33} - ka_{21}a_{23}a_{32} - a_{12}(a_{21}a_{33}-a_{23}a_{31})$$
$$- ka_{22}a_{21}a_{33} + ka_{22}a_{23}a_{31} + a_{13}(a_{21}a_{32}-a_{22}a_{31}) + ka_{23}a_{21}a_{32} - ka_{23}a_{22}a_{31}$$

$$= a_{11}(a_{22}a_{33}-a_{23}a_{32}) - a_{12}(a_{21}a_{33}-a_{23}a_{31}) + a_{13}(a_{21}a_{32}-a_{22}a_{31})$$

$$= a_{11}\begin{vmatrix} a_{22} & a_{23} \\ a_{32} & a_{33} \end{vmatrix} - a_{12}\begin{vmatrix} a_{21} & a_{23} \\ a_{31} & a_{33} \end{vmatrix} + a_{13}\begin{vmatrix} a_{21} & a_{22} \\ a_{31} & a_{32} \end{vmatrix}$$

$$= \begin{vmatrix} a_{11} & a_{12} & a_{13} \\ a_{21} & a_{22} & a_{23} \\ a_{31} & a_{32} & a_{33} \end{vmatrix}$$

Chapter 12

Systems of Equations and Inequalities

12.5 Matrix Algebra

1. $A+B=\begin{bmatrix}0 & 3 & -5\\ 1 & 2 & 6\end{bmatrix}+\begin{bmatrix}4 & 1 & 0\\ -2 & 3 & -2\end{bmatrix}=\begin{bmatrix}0+4 & 3+1 & -5+0\\ 1+(-2) & 2+3 & 6+(-2)\end{bmatrix}=\begin{bmatrix}4 & 4 & -5\\ -1 & 5 & 4\end{bmatrix}$

2. $A-B=\begin{bmatrix}0 & 3 & -5\\ 1 & 2 & 6\end{bmatrix}-\begin{bmatrix}4 & 1 & 0\\ -2 & 3 & -2\end{bmatrix}=\begin{bmatrix}0-4 & 3-1 & -5-0\\ 1-(-2) & 2-3 & 6-(-2)\end{bmatrix}=\begin{bmatrix}-4 & 2 & -5\\ 3 & -1 & 8\end{bmatrix}$

3. $4A=4\begin{bmatrix}0 & 3 & -5\\ 1 & 2 & 6\end{bmatrix}=\begin{bmatrix}4\cdot 0 & 4\cdot 3 & 4(-5)\\ 4\cdot 1 & 4\cdot 2 & 4\cdot 6\end{bmatrix}=\begin{bmatrix}0 & 12 & -20\\ 4 & 8 & 24\end{bmatrix}$

4. $-3B=-3\begin{bmatrix}4 & 1 & 0\\ -2 & 3 & -2\end{bmatrix}=\begin{bmatrix}-3\cdot 4 & -3\cdot 1 & -3\cdot 0\\ -3\cdot -2 & -3\cdot 3 & -3\cdot -2\end{bmatrix}=\begin{bmatrix}-12 & -3 & 0\\ 6 & -9 & 6\end{bmatrix}$

5. $3A-2B=3\begin{bmatrix}0 & 3 & -5\\ 1 & 2 & 6\end{bmatrix}-2\begin{bmatrix}4 & 1 & 0\\ -2 & 3 & -2\end{bmatrix}$

$=\begin{bmatrix}0 & 9 & -15\\ 3 & 6 & 18\end{bmatrix}-\begin{bmatrix}8 & 2 & 0\\ -4 & 6 & -4\end{bmatrix}=\begin{bmatrix}-8 & 7 & -15\\ 7 & 0 & 22\end{bmatrix}$

6. $2A+4B=2\begin{bmatrix}0 & 3 & -5\\ 1 & 2 & 6\end{bmatrix}+4\begin{bmatrix}4 & 1 & 0\\ -2 & 3 & -2\end{bmatrix}$

$=\begin{bmatrix}0 & 6 & -10\\ 2 & 4 & 12\end{bmatrix}+\begin{bmatrix}16 & 4 & 0\\ -8 & 12 & -8\end{bmatrix}=\begin{bmatrix}16 & 10 & -10\\ -6 & 16 & 4\end{bmatrix}$

7. $AC=\begin{bmatrix}0 & 3 & -5\\ 1 & 2 & 6\end{bmatrix}\cdot\begin{bmatrix}4 & 1\\ 6 & 2\\ -2 & 3\end{bmatrix}$

$=\begin{bmatrix}0(4)+3(6)+(-5)(-2) & 0(1)+3(2)+(-5)(3)\\ 1(4)+2(6)+6(-2) & 1(1)+2(2)+6(3)\end{bmatrix}=\begin{bmatrix}28 & -9\\ 4 & 23\end{bmatrix}$

8. $BC=\begin{bmatrix}4 & 1 & 0\\ -2 & 3 & -2\end{bmatrix}\cdot\begin{bmatrix}4 & 1\\ 6 & 2\\ -2 & 3\end{bmatrix}$

$=\begin{bmatrix}4(4)+1(6)+0(-2) & 4(1)+1(2)+0(3)\\ -2(4)+3(6)+(-2)(-2) & -2(1)+3(2)+(-2)(3)\end{bmatrix}=\begin{bmatrix}22 & 6\\ 14 & -2\end{bmatrix}$

9. $CA = \begin{bmatrix} 4 & 1 \\ 6 & 2 \\ -2 & 3 \end{bmatrix} \cdot \begin{bmatrix} 0 & 3 & -5 \\ 1 & 2 & 6 \end{bmatrix}$

$= \begin{bmatrix} 4(0)+1(1) & 4(3)+1(2) & 4(-5)+1(6) \\ 6(0)+2(1) & 6(3)+2(2) & 6(-5)+2(6) \\ -2(0)+3(1) & -2(3)+3(2) & -2(-5)+3(6) \end{bmatrix} = \begin{bmatrix} 1 & 14 & -14 \\ 2 & 22 & -18 \\ 3 & 0 & 28 \end{bmatrix}$

10. $CB = \begin{bmatrix} 4 & 1 \\ 6 & 2 \\ -2 & 3 \end{bmatrix} \cdot \begin{bmatrix} 4 & 1 & 0 \\ -2 & 3 & -2 \end{bmatrix}$

$= \begin{bmatrix} 4(4)+1(-2) & 4(1)+1(3) & 4(0)+1(-2) \\ 6(4)+2(-2) & 6(1)+2(3) & 6(0)+2(-2) \\ -2(4)+3(-2) & -2(1)+3(3) & -2(0)+3(-2) \end{bmatrix} = \begin{bmatrix} 14 & 7 & -2 \\ 20 & 12 & -4 \\ -14 & 7 & -6 \end{bmatrix}$

11. $C(A+B) = \begin{bmatrix} 4 & 1 \\ 6 & 2 \\ -2 & 3 \end{bmatrix} \left(\begin{bmatrix} 0 & 3 & -5 \\ 1 & 2 & 6 \end{bmatrix} + \begin{bmatrix} 4 & 1 & 0 \\ -2 & 3 & -2 \end{bmatrix} \right)$

$= \begin{bmatrix} 4 & 1 \\ 6 & 2 \\ -2 & 3 \end{bmatrix} \cdot \begin{bmatrix} 4 & 4 & -5 \\ -1 & 5 & 4 \end{bmatrix} = \begin{bmatrix} 15 & 21 & -16 \\ 22 & 34 & -22 \\ -11 & 7 & 22 \end{bmatrix}$

12. $(A+B)C = \left(\begin{bmatrix} 0 & 3 & -5 \\ 1 & 2 & 6 \end{bmatrix} + \begin{bmatrix} 4 & 1 & 0 \\ -2 & 3 & -2 \end{bmatrix} \right) \begin{bmatrix} 4 & 1 \\ 6 & 2 \\ -2 & 3 \end{bmatrix}$

$= \begin{bmatrix} 4 & 4 & -5 \\ -1 & 5 & 4 \end{bmatrix} \cdot \begin{bmatrix} 4 & 1 \\ 6 & 2 \\ -2 & 3 \end{bmatrix} = \begin{bmatrix} 50 & -3 \\ 18 & 21 \end{bmatrix}$

13. $AC - 3I_2 = \begin{bmatrix} 0 & 3 & -5 \\ 1 & 2 & 6 \end{bmatrix} \cdot \begin{bmatrix} 4 & 1 \\ 6 & 2 \\ -2 & 3 \end{bmatrix} - 3\begin{bmatrix} 1 & 0 \\ 0 & 1 \end{bmatrix} = \begin{bmatrix} 28 & -9 \\ 4 & 23 \end{bmatrix} - \begin{bmatrix} 3 & 0 \\ 0 & 3 \end{bmatrix} = \begin{bmatrix} 25 & -9 \\ 4 & 20 \end{bmatrix}$

14. $CA + 5I_3 = \begin{bmatrix} 4 & 1 \\ 6 & 2 \\ -2 & 3 \end{bmatrix} \cdot \begin{bmatrix} 0 & 3 & -5 \\ 1 & 2 & 6 \end{bmatrix} + 5\begin{bmatrix} 1 & 0 & 0 \\ 0 & 1 & 0 \\ 0 & 0 & 1 \end{bmatrix}$

$= \begin{bmatrix} 1 & 14 & -14 \\ 2 & 22 & -18 \\ 3 & 0 & 28 \end{bmatrix} + \begin{bmatrix} 5 & 0 & 0 \\ 0 & 5 & 0 \\ 0 & 0 & 5 \end{bmatrix} = \begin{bmatrix} 6 & 14 & -14 \\ 2 & 27 & -18 \\ 3 & 0 & 33 \end{bmatrix}$

15. $CA - CB = \begin{bmatrix} 4 & 1 \\ 6 & 2 \\ -2 & 3 \end{bmatrix} \cdot \begin{bmatrix} 0 & 3 & -5 \\ 1 & 2 & 6 \end{bmatrix} - \begin{bmatrix} 4 & 1 \\ 6 & 2 \\ -2 & 3 \end{bmatrix} \cdot \begin{bmatrix} 4 & 1 & 0 \\ -2 & 3 & -2 \end{bmatrix}$

$= \begin{bmatrix} 1 & 14 & -14 \\ 2 & 22 & -18 \\ 3 & 0 & 28 \end{bmatrix} - \begin{bmatrix} 14 & 7 & -2 \\ 20 & 12 & -4 \\ -14 & 7 & -6 \end{bmatrix} = \begin{bmatrix} -13 & 7 & -12 \\ -18 & 10 & -14 \\ 17 & -7 & 34 \end{bmatrix}$

16. $AC+BC=\begin{bmatrix}0&3&-5\\1&2&6\end{bmatrix}\cdot\begin{bmatrix}4&1\\6&2\\-2&3\end{bmatrix}+\begin{bmatrix}4&1&0\\-2&3&-2\end{bmatrix}\cdot\begin{bmatrix}4&1\\6&2\\-2&3\end{bmatrix}$

$=\begin{bmatrix}28&-9\\4&23\end{bmatrix}+\begin{bmatrix}22&6\\14&-2\end{bmatrix}=\begin{bmatrix}50&-3\\18&21\end{bmatrix}$

17. $\begin{bmatrix}2&-2\\1&0\end{bmatrix}\begin{bmatrix}2&1&4&6\\3&-1&3&2\end{bmatrix}$

$=\begin{bmatrix}2(2)+(-2)(3)&2(1)+(-2)(-1)&2(4)+(-2)(3)&2(6)+(-2)(2)\\1(2)+0(3)&1(1)+0(-1)&1(4)+0(3)&1(6)+0(2)\end{bmatrix}$

$=\begin{bmatrix}-2&4&2&8\\2&1&4&6\end{bmatrix}$

18. $\begin{bmatrix}4&1\\2&1\end{bmatrix}\begin{bmatrix}-6&6&1&0\\2&5&4&-1\end{bmatrix}$

$=\begin{bmatrix}4(-6)+1(2)&4(6)+1(5)&4(1)+1(4)&4(0)+1(-1)\\2(-6)+1(2)&2(6)+1(5)&2(1)+1(4)&2(0)+1(-1)\end{bmatrix}$

$=\begin{bmatrix}-22&29&8&-1\\-10&17&6&-1\end{bmatrix}$

19. $\begin{bmatrix}1&0&1\\2&4&1\\3&6&1\end{bmatrix}\begin{bmatrix}1&3\\6&2\\8&-1\end{bmatrix}=\begin{bmatrix}1(1)+0(6)+1(8)&1(3)+0(2)+1(-1)\\2(1)+4(6)+1(8)&2(3)+4(2)+1(-1)\\3(1)+6(6)+1(8)&3(3)+6(2)+1(-1)\end{bmatrix}=\begin{bmatrix}9&2\\34&13\\47&20\end{bmatrix}$

20. $\begin{bmatrix}4&-2&3\\0&1&2\\-1&0&1\end{bmatrix}\begin{bmatrix}2&6\\1&-1\\0&2\end{bmatrix}=\begin{bmatrix}4(2)+(-2)(1)+3(0)&4(6)+(-2)(-1)+3(2)\\0(2)+1(1)+2(0)&0(6)+1(-1)+2(2)\\-1(2)+0(1)+1(0)&-1(6)+0(-1)+1(2)\end{bmatrix}$

$=\begin{bmatrix}6&32\\1&3\\-2&-4\end{bmatrix}$

21. Augment the matrix with the identity and use row operations to find the inverse:

$A=\begin{bmatrix}2&1\\1&1\end{bmatrix}\to\left[\begin{array}{cc|cc}2&1&1&0\\1&1&0&1\end{array}\right]$

$\to\left[\begin{array}{cc|cc}1&1&0&1\\2&1&1&0\end{array}\right]\to\left[\begin{array}{cc|cc}1&1&0&1\\0&-1&1&-2\end{array}\right]\to\left[\begin{array}{cc|cc}1&1&0&1\\0&1&-1&2\end{array}\right]\to\left[\begin{array}{cc|cc}1&0&1&-1\\0&1&-1&2\end{array}\right]$

Interchange r_1 and r_2 $\quad R_2=-2r_1+r_2 \quad R_2=-r_2 \quad R_1=-r_2+r_1$

$A^{-1}=\begin{bmatrix}1&-1\\-1&2\end{bmatrix}$

22. Augment the matrix with the identity and use row operations to find the inverse:

$A=\begin{bmatrix}3&-1\\-2&1\end{bmatrix}\to\left[\begin{array}{cc|cc}3&-1&1&0\\-2&1&0&1\end{array}\right]$

$$\rightarrow\left[\begin{array}{rr|rr}1&0&1&1\\-2&1&0&1\end{array}\right]\rightarrow\left[\begin{array}{rr|rr}1&0&1&1\\0&1&2&3\end{array}\right]$$

$R_1 = r_2 + r_1 \qquad R_2 = 2r_1 + r_2$

$$A^{-1}=\begin{bmatrix}1&1\\2&3\end{bmatrix}$$

23. Augment the matrix with the identity and use row operations to find the inverse:

$$A=\begin{bmatrix}6&5\\2&2\end{bmatrix}\rightarrow\left[\begin{array}{rr|rr}6&5&1&0\\2&2&0&1\end{array}\right]$$

$$\rightarrow\left[\begin{array}{rr|rr}2&2&0&1\\6&5&1&0\end{array}\right]\rightarrow\left[\begin{array}{rr|rr}2&2&0&1\\0&-1&1&-3\end{array}\right]\rightarrow\left[\begin{array}{rr|rr}1&1&0&\frac{1}{2}\\0&1&-1&3\end{array}\right]\rightarrow\left[\begin{array}{rr|rr}1&0&1&-\frac{5}{2}\\0&1&-1&3\end{array}\right]$$

Interchange r_1 and r_2 $\qquad R_2 = -3r_1 + r_2 \qquad R_1 = \frac{1}{2}r_1,\ R_2 = -r_2 \qquad R_1 = -r_2 + r_1$

$$A^{-1}=\begin{bmatrix}1&-\frac{5}{2}\\-1&3\end{bmatrix}$$

24. Augment the matrix with the identity and use row operations to find the inverse:

$$A=\begin{bmatrix}-4&1\\6&-2\end{bmatrix}\rightarrow\left[\begin{array}{rr|rr}-4&1&1&0\\6&-2&0&1\end{array}\right]$$

$$\rightarrow\left[\begin{array}{rr|rr}1&-\frac{1}{4}&-\frac{1}{4}&0\\6&-2&0&1\end{array}\right]\rightarrow\left[\begin{array}{rr|rr}1&-\frac{1}{4}&-\frac{1}{4}&0\\0&-\frac{1}{2}&\frac{3}{2}&1\end{array}\right]\rightarrow\left[\begin{array}{rr|rr}1&-\frac{1}{4}&-\frac{1}{4}&0\\0&1&-3&-2\end{array}\right]\rightarrow\left[\begin{array}{rr|rr}1&0&-1&-\frac{1}{2}\\0&1&-3&-2\end{array}\right]$$

$R_1 = -\frac{1}{4}r_1 \qquad R_2 = -6r_1 + r_2 \qquad R_2 = -2r_2 \qquad R_1 = \frac{1}{4}r_2 + r_1$

$$A^{-1}=\begin{bmatrix}-1&-\frac{1}{2}\\-3&-2\end{bmatrix}$$

25. Augment the matrix with the identity and use row operations to find the inverse:

$$A=\begin{bmatrix}2&1\\a&a\end{bmatrix}\rightarrow\left[\begin{array}{rr|rr}2&1&1&0\\a&a&0&1\end{array}\right]\text{ where } a\neq 0.$$

$$\rightarrow\left[\begin{array}{rr|rr}1&\frac{1}{2}&\frac{1}{2}&0\\a&a&0&1\end{array}\right]\rightarrow\left[\begin{array}{rr|rr}1&\frac{1}{2}&\frac{1}{2}&0\\0&\frac{1}{2}a&-\frac{1}{2}a&1\end{array}\right]\rightarrow\left[\begin{array}{rr|rr}1&\frac{1}{2}&\frac{1}{2}&0\\0&1&-1&\frac{2}{a}\end{array}\right]\rightarrow\left[\begin{array}{rr|rr}1&0&1&-\frac{1}{a}\\0&1&-1&\frac{2}{a}\end{array}\right]$$

$R_1 = \frac{1}{2}r_1 \qquad R_2 = -a r_1 + r_2 \qquad R_2 = \left(\frac{2}{a}\right)r_2 \qquad R_1 = -\frac{1}{2}r_2 + r_1$

$$A^{-1}=\begin{bmatrix}1&-\frac{1}{a}\\-1&\frac{2}{a}\end{bmatrix}$$

26. Augment the matrix with the identity and use row operations to find the inverse:

$$A=\begin{bmatrix}b&3\\b&2\end{bmatrix}\rightarrow\left[\begin{array}{rr|rr}b&3&1&0\\b&2&0&1\end{array}\right]\text{ where } b\neq 0.$$

$$\rightarrow\left[\begin{array}{rr|rr}b&3&1&0\\0&-1&-1&1\end{array}\right]\rightarrow\left[\begin{array}{rr|rr}1&\frac{3}{b}&\frac{1}{b}&0\\0&-1&-1&1\end{array}\right]\rightarrow\left[\begin{array}{rr|rr}1&\frac{3}{b}&\frac{1}{b}&0\\0&1&1&-1\end{array}\right]\rightarrow\left[\begin{array}{rr|rr}1&0&-\frac{2}{b}&\frac{3}{b}\\0&1&1&-1\end{array}\right]$$

$R_2 = -r_1 + r_2 \qquad R_1 = \frac{1}{b}r_1 \qquad R_2 = -r_2 \qquad R_1 = -\frac{3}{b}r_2 + r_1$

$$A^{-1}=\begin{bmatrix}-\frac{2}{b}&\frac{3}{b}\\1&-1\end{bmatrix}$$

27. Augment the matrix with the identity and use row operations to find the inverse:

$$A=\begin{bmatrix}1&-1&1\\0&-2&1\\-2&-3&0\end{bmatrix}\to\left[\begin{array}{ccc|ccc}1&-1&1&1&0&0\\0&-2&1&0&1&0\\-2&-3&0&0&0&1\end{array}\right]$$

$$\to\left[\begin{array}{ccc|ccc}1&-1&1&1&0&0\\0&-2&1&0&1&0\\0&-5&2&2&0&1\end{array}\right]\to\left[\begin{array}{ccc|ccc}1&-1&1&1&0&0\\0&1&-\frac{1}{2}&0&-\frac{1}{2}&0\\0&-5&2&2&0&1\end{array}\right]\to\left[\begin{array}{ccc|ccc}1&0&\frac{1}{2}&1&-\frac{1}{2}&0\\0&1&-\frac{1}{2}&0&-\frac{1}{2}&0\\0&0&-\frac{1}{2}&2&-\frac{5}{2}&1\end{array}\right]$$

$R_3=2r_1+r_3$ $\quad R_2=-\frac{1}{2}r_2$ $\quad R_1=r_2+r_1$, $R_3=5r_2+r_3$

$$\to\left[\begin{array}{ccc|ccc}1&0&\frac{1}{2}&1&-\frac{1}{2}&0\\0&1&-\frac{1}{2}&0&-\frac{1}{2}&0\\0&0&1&-4&5&-2\end{array}\right]\to\left[\begin{array}{ccc|ccc}1&0&0&3&-3&1\\0&1&0&-2&2&-1\\0&0&1&-4&5&-2\end{array}\right]$$

$R_3=-2r_3$ $\quad R_1=-\frac{1}{2}r_3+r_1$, $R_2=\frac{1}{2}r_3+r_2$

$$A^{-1}=\begin{bmatrix}3&-3&1\\-2&2&-1\\-4&5&-2\end{bmatrix}$$

28. Augment the matrix with the identity and use row operations to find the inverse:

$$A=\begin{bmatrix}1&0&2\\-1&2&3\\1&-1&0\end{bmatrix}\to\left[\begin{array}{ccc|ccc}1&0&2&1&0&0\\-1&2&3&0&1&0\\1&-1&0&0&0&1\end{array}\right]$$

$$\to\left[\begin{array}{ccc|ccc}1&0&2&1&0&0\\0&2&5&1&1&0\\0&-1&-2&-1&0&1\end{array}\right]\to\left[\begin{array}{ccc|ccc}1&0&2&1&0&0\\0&1&\frac{5}{2}&\frac{1}{2}&\frac{1}{2}&0\\0&-1&-2&-1&0&1\end{array}\right]\to\left[\begin{array}{ccc|ccc}1&0&2&1&0&0\\0&1&\frac{5}{2}&\frac{1}{2}&\frac{1}{2}&0\\0&0&\frac{1}{2}&-\frac{1}{2}&\frac{1}{2}&1\end{array}\right]$$

$R_2=r_1+r_2$, $R_3=-r_1+r_3$ $\quad R_2=\frac{1}{2}r_2$ $\quad R_3=r_2+r_3$

$$\to\left[\begin{array}{ccc|ccc}1&0&2&1&0&0\\0&1&\frac{5}{2}&\frac{1}{2}&\frac{1}{2}&0\\0&0&1&-1&1&2\end{array}\right]\to\left[\begin{array}{ccc|ccc}1&0&0&3&-2&-4\\0&1&0&3&-2&-5\\0&0&1&-1&1&2\end{array}\right]$$

$R_3=2r_3$ $\quad R_1=-2r_3+r_1$, $R_2=-\frac{5}{2}r_3+r_2$

$$A^{-1}=\begin{bmatrix}3&-2&-4\\3&-2&-5\\-1&1&2\end{bmatrix}$$

29. Augment the matrix with the identity and use row operations to find the inverse:

$$A=\begin{bmatrix}1&1&1\\3&2&-1\\3&1&2\end{bmatrix}\to\left[\begin{array}{ccc|ccc}1&1&1&1&0&0\\3&2&-1&0&1&0\\3&1&2&0&0&1\end{array}\right]$$

$$\to\left[\begin{array}{ccc|ccc}1&1&1&1&0&0\\0&-1&-4&-3&1&0\\0&-2&-1&-3&0&1\end{array}\right]\to\left[\begin{array}{ccc|ccc}1&1&1&1&0&0\\0&1&4&3&-1&0\\0&-2&-1&-3&0&1\end{array}\right]\to\left[\begin{array}{ccc|ccc}1&0&-3&-2&1&0\\0&1&4&3&-1&0\\0&0&7&3&-2&1\end{array}\right]$$

$R_2=-3r_1+r_2$, $R_3=-3r_1+r_3$ $\quad R_2=-r_2$ $\quad R_1=-r_2+r_1$, $R_3=2r_2+r_3$

$$\rightarrow\left[\begin{array}{ccc|ccc} 1 & 0 & -3 & -2 & 1 & 0 \\ 0 & 1 & 4 & 3 & -1 & 0 \\ 0 & 0 & 1 & \frac{3}{7} & -\frac{2}{7} & \frac{1}{7}\end{array}\right] \rightarrow \left[\begin{array}{ccc|ccc} 1 & 0 & 0 & -\frac{5}{7} & \frac{1}{7} & \frac{3}{7} \\ 0 & 1 & 0 & \frac{9}{7} & \frac{1}{7} & -\frac{4}{7} \\ 0 & 0 & 1 & \frac{3}{7} & -\frac{2}{7} & \frac{1}{7}\end{array}\right]$$

$R_3 = \frac{1}{7} r_3$ $R_1 = 3r_3 + r_1$, $R_2 = -4r_3 + r_2$

$$A^{-1} = \begin{bmatrix} -\frac{5}{7} & \frac{1}{7} & \frac{3}{7} \\ \frac{9}{7} & \frac{1}{7} & -\frac{4}{7} \\ \frac{3}{7} & -\frac{2}{7} & \frac{1}{7}\end{bmatrix}$$

30. Augment the matrix with the identity and use row operations to find the inverse:

$$A = \begin{bmatrix} 3 & 3 & 1 \\ 1 & 2 & 1 \\ 2 & -1 & 1\end{bmatrix} \rightarrow \left[\begin{array}{ccc|ccc} 3 & 3 & 1 & 1 & 0 & 0 \\ 1 & 2 & 1 & 0 & 1 & 0 \\ 2 & -1 & 1 & 0 & 0 & 1\end{array}\right]$$

$$\rightarrow\left[\begin{array}{ccc|ccc} 1 & 2 & 1 & 0 & 1 & 0 \\ 3 & 3 & 1 & 1 & 0 & 0 \\ 2 & -1 & 1 & 0 & 0 & 1\end{array}\right] \rightarrow \left[\begin{array}{ccc|ccc} 1 & 2 & 1 & 0 & 1 & 0 \\ 0 & -3 & -2 & 1 & -3 & 0 \\ 0 & -5 & -1 & 0 & -2 & 1\end{array}\right] \rightarrow \left[\begin{array}{ccc|ccc} 1 & 2 & 1 & 0 & 1 & 0 \\ 0 & 1 & \frac{2}{3} & -\frac{1}{3} & 1 & 0 \\ 0 & -5 & -1 & 0 & -2 & 1\end{array}\right]$$

Interchange r_1 and r_2 $R_2 = -3r_1 + r_2$, $R_3 = -2r_1 + r_3$ $R_2 = -\frac{1}{3} r_2$

$$\rightarrow\left[\begin{array}{ccc|ccc} 1 & 0 & -\frac{1}{3} & \frac{2}{3} & -1 & 0 \\ 0 & 1 & \frac{2}{3} & -\frac{1}{3} & 1 & 0 \\ 0 & 0 & \frac{7}{3} & -\frac{5}{3} & 3 & 1\end{array}\right] \rightarrow \left[\begin{array}{ccc|ccc} 1 & 0 & -\frac{1}{3} & \frac{2}{3} & -1 & 0 \\ 0 & 1 & \frac{2}{3} & -\frac{1}{3} & 1 & 0 \\ 0 & 0 & 1 & -\frac{5}{7} & \frac{9}{7} & \frac{3}{7}\end{array}\right] \rightarrow \left[\begin{array}{ccc|ccc} 1 & 0 & 0 & \frac{3}{7} & -\frac{4}{7} & \frac{1}{7} \\ 0 & 1 & 0 & \frac{1}{7} & \frac{1}{7} & -\frac{2}{7} \\ 0 & 0 & 1 & -\frac{5}{7} & \frac{9}{7} & \frac{3}{7}\end{array}\right]$$

$R_1 = -2r_2 + r_1$, $R_3 = 5r_2 + r_3$ $R_3 = \frac{3}{7} r_3$ $R_1 = \frac{1}{3} r_3 + r_1$, $R_2 = -\frac{2}{3} r_3 + r_2$

$$A^{-1} = \begin{bmatrix} \frac{3}{7} & -\frac{4}{7} & \frac{1}{7} \\ \frac{1}{7} & \frac{1}{7} & -\frac{2}{7} \\ -\frac{5}{7} & \frac{9}{7} & \frac{3}{7}\end{bmatrix}$$

31. Rewrite the system of equations in matrix form:

$$\begin{cases} 2x + y = 8 \\ x + y = 5 \end{cases} \quad A = \begin{bmatrix} 2 & 1 \\ 1 & 1\end{bmatrix}, \quad X = \begin{bmatrix} x \\ y\end{bmatrix}, \quad B = \begin{bmatrix} 8 \\ 5\end{bmatrix}$$

Find the inverse of A and solve $X = A^{-1}B$:

From Problem 21, $A^{-1} = \begin{bmatrix} 1 & -1 \\ -1 & 2\end{bmatrix}$ and $X = A^{-1}B = \begin{bmatrix} 1 & -1 \\ -1 & 2\end{bmatrix}\begin{bmatrix} 8 \\ 5\end{bmatrix} = \begin{bmatrix} 3 \\ 2\end{bmatrix}$.

The solution is $x = 3$, $y = 2$.

32. Rewrite the system of equations in matrix form:

$$\begin{cases} 3x - y = 8 \\ -2x + y = 4 \end{cases} \quad A = \begin{bmatrix} 3 & -1 \\ -2 & 1\end{bmatrix}, \quad X = \begin{bmatrix} x \\ y\end{bmatrix}, \quad B = \begin{bmatrix} 8 \\ 4\end{bmatrix}$$

Find the inverse of A and solve $X = A^{-1}B$:

From Problem 22, $A^{-1} = \begin{bmatrix} 1 & 1 \\ 2 & 3\end{bmatrix}$ and $X = A^{-1}B = \begin{bmatrix} 1 & 1 \\ 2 & 3\end{bmatrix}\begin{bmatrix} 8 \\ 4\end{bmatrix} = \begin{bmatrix} 12 \\ 28\end{bmatrix}$.

The solution is $x = 12$, $y = 28$.

33. Rewrite the system of equations in matrix form:

$$\begin{cases} 2x + y = 0 \\ x + y = 5 \end{cases} \qquad A = \begin{bmatrix} 2 & 1 \\ 1 & 1 \end{bmatrix}, \quad X = \begin{bmatrix} x \\ y \end{bmatrix}, \quad B = \begin{bmatrix} 0 \\ 5 \end{bmatrix}$$

Find the inverse of A and solve $X = A^{-1}B$:

From Problem 21, $A^{-1} = \begin{bmatrix} 1 & -1 \\ -1 & 2 \end{bmatrix}$ and $X = A^{-1}B = \begin{bmatrix} 1 & -1 \\ -1 & 2 \end{bmatrix}\begin{bmatrix} 0 \\ 5 \end{bmatrix} = \begin{bmatrix} -5 \\ 10 \end{bmatrix}$.

The solution is $x = -5,\ y = 10$.

34. Rewrite the system of equations in matrix form:

$$\begin{cases} 3x - y = 4 \\ -2x + y = 5 \end{cases} \qquad A = \begin{bmatrix} 3 & -1 \\ -2 & 1 \end{bmatrix}, \quad X = \begin{bmatrix} x \\ y \end{bmatrix}, \quad B = \begin{bmatrix} 4 \\ 5 \end{bmatrix}$$

Find the inverse of A and solve $X = A^{-1}B$:

From Problem 22, $A^{-1} = \begin{bmatrix} 1 & 1 \\ 2 & 3 \end{bmatrix}$ and $X = A^{-1}B = \begin{bmatrix} 1 & 1 \\ 2 & 3 \end{bmatrix}\begin{bmatrix} 4 \\ 5 \end{bmatrix} = \begin{bmatrix} 9 \\ 23 \end{bmatrix}$.

The solution is $x = 9,\ y = 23$.

35. Rewrite the system of equations in matrix form:

$$\begin{cases} 6x + 5y = 7 \\ 2x + 2y = 2 \end{cases} \qquad A = \begin{bmatrix} 6 & 5 \\ 2 & 2 \end{bmatrix}, \quad X = \begin{bmatrix} x \\ y \end{bmatrix}, \quad B = \begin{bmatrix} 7 \\ 2 \end{bmatrix}$$

Find the inverse of A and solve $X = A^{-1}B$:

From Problem 23, $A^{-1} = \begin{bmatrix} 1 & -\frac{5}{2} \\ -1 & 3 \end{bmatrix}$ and $X = A^{-1}B = \begin{bmatrix} 1 & -\frac{5}{2} \\ -1 & 3 \end{bmatrix}\begin{bmatrix} 7 \\ 2 \end{bmatrix} = \begin{bmatrix} 2 \\ -1 \end{bmatrix}$.

The solution is $x = 2,\ y = -1$.

36. Rewrite the system of equations in matrix form:

$$\begin{cases} -4x + y = 0 \\ 6x - 2y = 14 \end{cases} \qquad A = \begin{bmatrix} -4 & 1 \\ 6 & -2 \end{bmatrix}, \quad X = \begin{bmatrix} x \\ y \end{bmatrix}, \quad B = \begin{bmatrix} 0 \\ 14 \end{bmatrix}$$

Find the inverse of A and solve $X = A^{-1}B$:

From Problem 24, $A^{-1} = \begin{bmatrix} -1 & -\frac{1}{2} \\ -3 & -2 \end{bmatrix}$ and $X = A^{-1}B = \begin{bmatrix} -1 & -\frac{1}{2} \\ -3 & -2 \end{bmatrix}\begin{bmatrix} 0 \\ 14 \end{bmatrix} = \begin{bmatrix} -7 \\ -28 \end{bmatrix}$.

The solution is $x = -7,\ y = -28$.

37. Rewrite the system of equations in matrix form:

$$\begin{cases} 6x + 5y = 13 \\ 2x + 2y = 5 \end{cases} \qquad A = \begin{bmatrix} 6 & 5 \\ 2 & 2 \end{bmatrix}, \quad X = \begin{bmatrix} x \\ y \end{bmatrix}, \quad B = \begin{bmatrix} 13 \\ 5 \end{bmatrix}$$

Find the inverse of A and solve $X = A^{-1}B$:

From Problem 23, $A^{-1} = \begin{bmatrix} 1 & -\frac{5}{2} \\ -1 & 3 \end{bmatrix}$ and $X = A^{-1}B = \begin{bmatrix} 1 & -\frac{5}{2} \\ -1 & 3 \end{bmatrix}\begin{bmatrix} 13 \\ 5 \end{bmatrix} = \begin{bmatrix} \frac{1}{2} \\ 2 \end{bmatrix}$.

The solution is $x = \frac{1}{2},\ y = 2$.

38. Rewrite the system of equations in matrix form:

$$\begin{cases} -4x + y = 5 \\ 6x - 2y = -9 \end{cases} \qquad A = \begin{bmatrix} -4 & 1 \\ 6 & -2 \end{bmatrix}, \quad X = \begin{bmatrix} x \\ y \end{bmatrix}, \quad B = \begin{bmatrix} 5 \\ -9 \end{bmatrix}$$

Find the inverse of A and solve $X = A^{-1}B$:

From Problem 24, $A^{-1}=\begin{bmatrix}-1 & -\frac{1}{2}\\ -3 & -2\end{bmatrix}$ and $X=A^{-1}B=\begin{bmatrix}-1 & -\frac{1}{2}\\ -3 & -2\end{bmatrix}\begin{bmatrix}5\\ -9\end{bmatrix}=\begin{bmatrix}-\frac{1}{2}\\ 3\end{bmatrix}$.

The solution is $x=-\dfrac{1}{2}, y=3$.

39. Rewrite the system of equations in matrix form:

$$\begin{cases}2x+\ \ y=-3\\ ax+ay=-a\end{cases}\quad a\neq 0\qquad A=\begin{bmatrix}2 & 1\\ a & a\end{bmatrix},\ X=\begin{bmatrix}x\\ y\end{bmatrix},\ B=\begin{bmatrix}-3\\ -a\end{bmatrix}$$

Find the inverse of A and solve $X=A^{-1}B$:

From Problem 25, $A^{-1}=\begin{bmatrix}1 & -\frac{1}{a}\\ -1 & \frac{2}{a}\end{bmatrix}$ and $X=A^{-1}B=\begin{bmatrix}1 & -\frac{1}{a}\\ -1 & \frac{2}{a}\end{bmatrix}\begin{bmatrix}-3\\ -a\end{bmatrix}=\begin{bmatrix}-2\\ 1\end{bmatrix}$.

The solution is $x=-2, y=1$.

40. Rewrite the system of equations in matrix form:

$$\begin{cases}bx+3y=2b+3\\ bx+2y=2b+2\end{cases}\quad b\neq 0\qquad A=\begin{bmatrix}b & 3\\ b & 2\end{bmatrix},\ X=\begin{bmatrix}x\\ y\end{bmatrix},\ B=\begin{bmatrix}2b+3\\ 2b+2\end{bmatrix}$$

Find the inverse of A and solve $X=A^{-1}B$:

From Problem 26, $A^{-1}=\begin{bmatrix}-\frac{2}{b} & \frac{3}{b}\\ 1 & -1\end{bmatrix}$ and $X=A^{-1}B=\begin{bmatrix}-\frac{2}{b} & \frac{3}{b}\\ 1 & -1\end{bmatrix}\begin{bmatrix}2b+3\\ 2b+2\end{bmatrix}=\begin{bmatrix}2\\ 1\end{bmatrix}$.

The solution is $x=2, y=1$.

41. Rewrite the system of equations in matrix form:

$$\begin{cases}2x+\ \ y=\dfrac{7}{a}\\ ax+ay=5\end{cases}\quad a\neq 0\qquad A=\begin{bmatrix}2 & 1\\ a & a\end{bmatrix},\ X=\begin{bmatrix}x\\ y\end{bmatrix},\ B=\begin{bmatrix}\frac{7}{a}\\ 5\end{bmatrix}$$

Find the inverse of A and solve $X=A^{-1}B$:

From Problem 25, $A^{-1}=\begin{bmatrix}1 & -\frac{1}{a}\\ -1 & \frac{2}{a}\end{bmatrix}$ and $X=A^{-1}B=\begin{bmatrix}1 & -\frac{1}{a}\\ -1 & \frac{2}{a}\end{bmatrix}\begin{bmatrix}\frac{7}{a}\\ 5\end{bmatrix}=\begin{bmatrix}\frac{2}{a}\\ \frac{3}{a}\end{bmatrix}$.

The solution is $x=\dfrac{2}{a}, y=\dfrac{3}{a}$.

42. Rewrite the system of equations in matrix form:

$$\begin{cases}bx+3y=14\\ bx+2y=10\end{cases}\quad b\neq 0\qquad A=\begin{bmatrix}b & 3\\ b & 2\end{bmatrix},\ X=\begin{bmatrix}x\\ y\end{bmatrix},\ B=\begin{bmatrix}14\\ 10\end{bmatrix}$$

Find the inverse of A and solve $X=A^{-1}B$:

From Problem 26, $A^{-1}=\begin{bmatrix}-\frac{2}{b} & \frac{3}{b}\\ 1 & -1\end{bmatrix}$ and $X=A^{-1}B=\begin{bmatrix}-\frac{2}{b} & \frac{3}{b}\\ 1 & -1\end{bmatrix}\begin{bmatrix}14\\ 10\end{bmatrix}=\begin{bmatrix}\frac{2}{b}\\ 4\end{bmatrix}$.

The solution is $x=\dfrac{2}{b}, y=4$.

43. Rewrite the system of equations in matrix form:

$$\begin{cases}x-\ \ y+z=\ 0\\ \quad -2y+z=-1\\ -2x-3y\quad\ =-5\end{cases}\qquad A=\begin{bmatrix}1 & -1 & 1\\ 0 & -2 & 1\\ -2 & -3 & 0\end{bmatrix},\ X=\begin{bmatrix}x\\ y\\ z\end{bmatrix},\ B=\begin{bmatrix}0\\ -1\\ -5\end{bmatrix}$$

Find the inverse of A and solve $X=A^{-1}B$:

From Problem 27,

$$A^{-1}=\begin{bmatrix}3 & -3 & 1\\ -2 & 2 & -1\\ -4 & 5 & -2\end{bmatrix} \text{ and } X=A^{-1}B=\begin{bmatrix}3 & -3 & 1\\ -2 & 2 & -1\\ -4 & 5 & -2\end{bmatrix}\begin{bmatrix}0\\ -1\\ -5\end{bmatrix}=\begin{bmatrix}-2\\ 3\\ 5\end{bmatrix}.$$

The solution is $x=-2,\ y=3,\ z=5$.

44. Rewrite the system of equations in matrix form:

$$\begin{cases}x \quad +2z=6\\ -x+2y+3z=-5\\ x-y \quad =6\end{cases} \qquad A=\begin{bmatrix}1 & 0 & 2\\ -1 & 2 & 3\\ 1 & -1 & 0\end{bmatrix},\quad X=\begin{bmatrix}x\\ y\\ z\end{bmatrix},\quad B=\begin{bmatrix}6\\ -5\\ 6\end{bmatrix}$$

Find the inverse of A and solve $X=A^{-1}B$:

From Problem 28,

$$A^{-1}=\begin{bmatrix}3 & -2 & -4\\ 3 & -2 & -5\\ -1 & 1 & 2\end{bmatrix} \text{ and } X=A^{-1}B=\begin{bmatrix}3 & -2 & -4\\ 3 & -2 & -5\\ -1 & 1 & 2\end{bmatrix}\begin{bmatrix}6\\ -5\\ 6\end{bmatrix}=\begin{bmatrix}4\\ -2\\ 1\end{bmatrix}.$$

The solution is $x=4,\ y=-2,\ z=1$.

45. Rewrite the system of equations in matrix form:

$$\begin{cases}x-y+z=2\\ -2y+z=2\\ -2x-3y \quad =\dfrac{1}{2}\end{cases} \qquad A=\begin{bmatrix}1 & -1 & 1\\ 0 & -2 & 1\\ -2 & -3 & 0\end{bmatrix},\quad X=\begin{bmatrix}x\\ y\\ z\end{bmatrix},\quad B=\begin{bmatrix}2\\ 2\\ \frac{1}{2}\end{bmatrix}$$

Find the inverse of A and solve $X=A^{-1}B$:

From Problem 27,

$$A^{-1}=\begin{bmatrix}3 & -3 & 1\\ -2 & 2 & -1\\ -4 & 5 & -2\end{bmatrix} \text{ and } X=A^{-1}B=\begin{bmatrix}3 & -3 & 1\\ -2 & 2 & -1\\ -4 & 5 & -2\end{bmatrix}\begin{bmatrix}2\\ 2\\ \frac{1}{2}\end{bmatrix}=\begin{bmatrix}\frac{1}{2}\\ -\frac{1}{2}\\ 1\end{bmatrix}.$$

The solution is $x=\dfrac{1}{2},\ y=-\dfrac{1}{2},\ z=1$.

46. Rewrite the system of equations in matrix form:

$$\begin{cases}x \quad +2z=2\\ -x+2y+3z=-\dfrac{3}{2}\\ x-y \quad =2\end{cases} \qquad A=\begin{bmatrix}1 & 0 & 2\\ -1 & 2 & 3\\ 1 & -1 & 0\end{bmatrix},\quad X=\begin{bmatrix}x\\ y\\ z\end{bmatrix},\quad B=\begin{bmatrix}2\\ -\frac{3}{2}\\ 2\end{bmatrix}$$

Find the inverse of A and solve $X=A^{-1}B$:

From Problem 28,

$$A^{-1}=\begin{bmatrix}3 & -2 & -4\\ 3 & -2 & -5\\ -1 & 1 & 2\end{bmatrix} \text{ and } X=A^{-1}B=\begin{bmatrix}3 & -2 & -4\\ 3 & -2 & -5\\ -1 & 1 & 2\end{bmatrix}\begin{bmatrix}2\\ -\frac{3}{2}\\ 2\end{bmatrix}=\begin{bmatrix}1\\ -1\\ \frac{1}{2}\end{bmatrix}.$$

The solution is $x=1,\ y=-1,\ z=\dfrac{1}{2}$.

47. Rewrite the system of equations in matrix form:

$$\begin{cases} x+\ y+\ z=9 \\ 3x+2y-\ z=8 \\ 3x+\ y+2z=1 \end{cases} \qquad A=\begin{bmatrix} 1 & 1 & 1 \\ 3 & 2 & -1 \\ 3 & 1 & 2 \end{bmatrix},\quad X=\begin{bmatrix} x \\ y \\ z \end{bmatrix},\quad B=\begin{bmatrix} 9 \\ 8 \\ 1 \end{bmatrix}$$

Find the inverse of A and solve $X=A^{-1}B$:
From Problem 29,

$$A^{-1}=\begin{bmatrix} -\frac{5}{7} & \frac{1}{7} & \frac{3}{7} \\ \frac{9}{7} & \frac{1}{7} & -\frac{4}{7} \\ \frac{3}{7} & -\frac{2}{7} & \frac{1}{7} \end{bmatrix} \text{ and } X=A^{-1}B=\begin{bmatrix} -\frac{5}{7} & \frac{1}{7} & \frac{3}{7} \\ \frac{9}{7} & \frac{1}{7} & -\frac{4}{7} \\ \frac{3}{7} & -\frac{2}{7} & \frac{1}{7} \end{bmatrix}\begin{bmatrix} 9 \\ 8 \\ 1 \end{bmatrix}=\begin{bmatrix} -\frac{34}{7} \\ \frac{85}{7} \\ \frac{12}{7} \end{bmatrix}.$$

The solution is $x=-\dfrac{34}{7}, y=\dfrac{85}{7}, z=\dfrac{12}{7}$.

48. Rewrite the system of equations in matrix form:

$$\begin{cases} 3x+3y+z=8 \\ x+2y+z=5 \\ 2x-\ y+z=4 \end{cases} \qquad A=\begin{bmatrix} 3 & 3 & 1 \\ 1 & 2 & 1 \\ 2 & -1 & 1 \end{bmatrix},\quad X=\begin{bmatrix} x \\ y \\ z \end{bmatrix},\quad B=\begin{bmatrix} 8 \\ 5 \\ 4 \end{bmatrix}$$

Find the inverse of A and solve $X=A^{-1}B$:
From Problem 30,

$$A^{-1}=\begin{bmatrix} \frac{3}{7} & -\frac{4}{7} & \frac{1}{7} \\ \frac{1}{7} & \frac{1}{7} & -\frac{2}{7} \\ -\frac{5}{7} & \frac{9}{7} & \frac{3}{7} \end{bmatrix} \text{ and } X=A^{-1}B=\begin{bmatrix} \frac{3}{7} & -\frac{4}{7} & \frac{1}{7} \\ \frac{1}{7} & \frac{1}{7} & -\frac{2}{7} \\ -\frac{5}{7} & \frac{9}{7} & \frac{3}{7} \end{bmatrix}\begin{bmatrix} 8 \\ 5 \\ 4 \end{bmatrix}=\begin{bmatrix} \frac{8}{7} \\ \frac{5}{7} \\ \frac{17}{7} \end{bmatrix}.$$

The solution is $x=\dfrac{8}{7}, y=\dfrac{5}{7}, z=\dfrac{17}{7}$.

49. Rewrite the system of equations in matrix form:

$$\begin{cases} x+\ y+\ z=2 \\ 3x+2y-\ z=\dfrac{7}{3} \\ 3x+\ y+2z=\dfrac{10}{3} \end{cases} \qquad A=\begin{bmatrix} 1 & 1 & 1 \\ 3 & 2 & -1 \\ 3 & 1 & 2 \end{bmatrix},\quad X=\begin{bmatrix} x \\ y \\ z \end{bmatrix},\quad B=\begin{bmatrix} 2 \\ \frac{7}{3} \\ \frac{10}{3} \end{bmatrix}$$

Find the inverse of A and solve $X=A^{-1}B$:
From Problem 29,

$$A^{-1}=\begin{bmatrix} -\frac{5}{7} & \frac{1}{7} & \frac{3}{7} \\ \frac{9}{7} & \frac{1}{7} & -\frac{4}{7} \\ \frac{3}{7} & -\frac{2}{7} & \frac{1}{7} \end{bmatrix} \text{ and } X=A^{-1}B=\begin{bmatrix} -\frac{5}{7} & \frac{1}{7} & \frac{3}{7} \\ \frac{9}{7} & \frac{1}{7} & -\frac{4}{7} \\ \frac{3}{7} & -\frac{2}{7} & \frac{1}{7} \end{bmatrix}\begin{bmatrix} 2 \\ \frac{7}{3} \\ \frac{10}{3} \end{bmatrix}=\begin{bmatrix} \frac{1}{3} \\ 1 \\ \frac{2}{3} \end{bmatrix}.$$

The solution is $x=\dfrac{1}{3}, y=1, z=\dfrac{2}{3}$.

50. Rewrite the system of equations in matrix form:

$$\begin{cases} 3x+3y+z=1 \\ x+2y+z=0 \\ 2x-\ y+z=4 \end{cases} \qquad A=\begin{bmatrix} 3 & 3 & 1 \\ 1 & 2 & 1 \\ 2 & -1 & 1 \end{bmatrix},\quad X=\begin{bmatrix} x \\ y \\ z \end{bmatrix},\quad B=\begin{bmatrix} 1 \\ 0 \\ 4 \end{bmatrix}$$

Find the inverse of A and solve $X=A^{-1}B$:

From Problem 30,

$$A^{-1}=\begin{bmatrix}\frac{3}{7} & -\frac{4}{7} & \frac{1}{7}\\ \frac{1}{7} & \frac{1}{7} & -\frac{2}{7}\\ -\frac{5}{7} & \frac{9}{7} & \frac{3}{7}\end{bmatrix} \text{ and } X=A^{-1}B=\begin{bmatrix}\frac{3}{7} & -\frac{4}{7} & \frac{1}{7}\\ \frac{1}{7} & \frac{1}{7} & -\frac{2}{7}\\ -\frac{5}{7} & \frac{9}{7} & \frac{3}{7}\end{bmatrix}\begin{bmatrix}1\\0\\4\end{bmatrix}=\begin{bmatrix}1\\-1\\1\end{bmatrix}.$$

The solution is $x=1,\ y=-1,\ z=1$.

51. Augment the matrix with the identity and use row operations to find the inverse:

$$A=\begin{bmatrix}4 & 2\\ 2 & 1\end{bmatrix} \rightarrow \left[\begin{array}{cc|cc}4 & 2 & 1 & 0\\ 2 & 1 & 0 & 1\end{array}\right]$$

$$\rightarrow \left[\begin{array}{cc|cc}4 & 2 & 1 & 0\\ 0 & 0 & -\frac{1}{2} & 1\end{array}\right] \rightarrow \left[\begin{array}{cc|cc}1 & \frac{1}{2} & \frac{1}{4} & 0\\ 0 & 0 & -\frac{1}{2} & 1\end{array}\right]$$

$$R_2=-\tfrac{1}{2}r_1+r_2 \qquad R_1=\tfrac{1}{4}r_1$$

There is no way to obtain the identity matrix on the left; thus, there is no inverse.

52. Augment the matrix with the identity and use row operations to find the inverse:

$$A=\begin{bmatrix}-3 & \frac{1}{2}\\ 6 & -1\end{bmatrix} \rightarrow \left[\begin{array}{cc|cc}-3 & \frac{1}{2} & 1 & 0\\ 6 & -1 & 0 & 1\end{array}\right]$$

$$\rightarrow \left[\begin{array}{cc|cc}-3 & \frac{1}{2} & 1 & 0\\ 0 & 0 & 2 & 1\end{array}\right] \rightarrow \left[\begin{array}{cc|cc}1 & -\frac{1}{6} & -\frac{1}{3} & 0\\ 0 & 0 & 2 & 1\end{array}\right]$$

$$R_2=2r_1+r_2 \qquad R_1=-\tfrac{1}{3}r_1$$

There is no way to obtain the identity matrix on the left; thus, there is no inverse.

53. Augment the matrix with the identity and use row operations to find the inverse:

$$A=\begin{bmatrix}15 & 3\\ 10 & 2\end{bmatrix} \rightarrow \left[\begin{array}{cc|cc}15 & 3 & 1 & 0\\ 10 & 2 & 0 & 1\end{array}\right]$$

$$\rightarrow \left[\begin{array}{cc|cc}15 & 3 & 1 & 0\\ 0 & 0 & -\frac{2}{3} & 1\end{array}\right] \rightarrow \left[\begin{array}{cc|cc}1 & \frac{1}{5} & \frac{1}{15} & 0\\ 0 & 0 & -\frac{2}{3} & 1\end{array}\right]$$

$$R_2=-\tfrac{2}{3}r_1+r_2 \qquad R_1=\tfrac{1}{15}r_1$$

There is no way to obtain the identity matrix on the left; thus, there is no inverse.

54. Augment the matrix with the identity and use row operations to find the inverse:

$$A=\begin{bmatrix}-3 & 0\\ 4 & 0\end{bmatrix} \rightarrow \left[\begin{array}{cc|cc}-3 & 0 & 1 & 0\\ 4 & 0 & 0 & 1\end{array}\right]$$

$$\rightarrow \left[\begin{array}{cc|cc}-3 & 0 & 1 & 0\\ 0 & 0 & \frac{4}{3} & 1\end{array}\right] \rightarrow \left[\begin{array}{cc|cc}1 & 0 & -\frac{1}{3} & 0\\ 0 & 0 & \frac{4}{3} & 1\end{array}\right]$$

$$R_2=\tfrac{4}{3}r_1+r_2 \qquad R_1=-\tfrac{1}{3}r_1$$

There is no way to obtain the identity matrix on the left; thus, there is no inverse.

55. Augment the matrix with the identity and use row operations to find the inverse:

$$A=\begin{bmatrix}-3 & 1 & -1\\ 1 & -4 & -7\\ 1 & 2 & 5\end{bmatrix} \rightarrow \left[\begin{array}{ccc|ccc}-3 & 1 & -1 & 1 & 0 & 0\\ 1 & -4 & -7 & 0 & 1 & 0\\ 1 & 2 & 5 & 0 & 0 & 1\end{array}\right]$$

$$\rightarrow \left[\begin{array}{rrr|rrr} 1 & 2 & 5 & 0 & 0 & 1 \\ 1 & -4 & -7 & 0 & 1 & 0 \\ -3 & 1 & -1 & 1 & 0 & 0 \end{array}\right] \rightarrow \left[\begin{array}{rrr|rrr} 1 & 2 & 5 & 0 & 0 & 1 \\ 0 & -6 & -12 & 0 & 1 & -1 \\ 0 & 7 & 14 & 1 & 0 & 3 \end{array}\right] \rightarrow \left[\begin{array}{rrr|rrr} 1 & 2 & 5 & 0 & 0 & 1 \\ 0 & 1 & 2 & 0 & -\frac{1}{6} & \frac{1}{6} \\ 0 & 7 & 14 & 1 & 0 & 3 \end{array}\right]$$

Interchange r_1 and r_3 $\quad R_2 = -r_1 + r_2$, $R_3 = 3r_1 + r_3$ $\quad R_2 = -\frac{1}{6}r_2$

$$\rightarrow \left[\begin{array}{rrr|rrr} 1 & 0 & 1 & 0 & \frac{1}{3} & \frac{2}{3} \\ 0 & 1 & 2 & 0 & -\frac{1}{6} & \frac{1}{6} \\ 0 & 0 & 0 & 1 & \frac{7}{6} & \frac{11}{6} \end{array}\right]$$

$R_1 = -2r_2 + r_1$
$R_3 = -7r_2 + r_3$

There is no way to obtain the identity matrix on the left; thus, there is no inverse.

56. Augment the matrix with the identity and use row operations to find the inverse:

$$A = \begin{bmatrix} 1 & 1 & -3 \\ 2 & -4 & 1 \\ -5 & 7 & 1 \end{bmatrix} \rightarrow \left[\begin{array}{rrr|rrr} 1 & 1 & -3 & 1 & 0 & 0 \\ 2 & -4 & 1 & 0 & 1 & 0 \\ -5 & 7 & 1 & 0 & 0 & 1 \end{array}\right]$$

$$\rightarrow \left[\begin{array}{rrr|rrr} 1 & 1 & -3 & 1 & 0 & 0 \\ 0 & -6 & 7 & -2 & 1 & 0 \\ 0 & 12 & -14 & 5 & 0 & 1 \end{array}\right] \rightarrow \left[\begin{array}{rrr|rrr} 1 & 1 & -3 & 1 & 0 & 0 \\ 0 & 1 & -\frac{7}{6} & \frac{1}{3} & -\frac{1}{6} & 0 \\ 0 & 12 & -14 & 5 & 0 & 1 \end{array}\right] \rightarrow \left[\begin{array}{rrr|rrr} 1 & 0 & -\frac{11}{6} & \frac{2}{3} & \frac{1}{6} & 0 \\ 0 & 1 & -\frac{7}{6} & \frac{1}{3} & -\frac{1}{6} & 0 \\ 0 & 0 & 0 & 1 & 2 & 1 \end{array}\right]$$

$R_2 = -2r_1 + r_2$, $R_3 = 5r_1 + r_3$ $\quad R_2 = -\frac{1}{6}r_2$ $\quad R_1 = -r_2 + r_1$, $R_3 = -12r_2 + r_3$

There is no way to obtain the identity matrix on the left; thus, there is no inverse.

57. $\begin{bmatrix} 0.01 & 0.05 & -0.01 \\ 0.01 & -0.02 & 0.01 \\ -0.02 & 0.01 & 0.03 \end{bmatrix}$

58. $\begin{bmatrix} 0.26 & -0.29 & -0.20 \\ -1.21 & 1.63 & 1.20 \\ -1.84 & 2.53 & 1.80 \end{bmatrix}$

59. $\begin{bmatrix} 0.02 & -0.04 & -0.01 & 0.01 \\ -0.02 & 0.05 & 0.03 & -0.03 \\ 0.02 & 0.01 & -0.04 & 0.00 \\ -0.02 & 0.06 & 0.07 & 0.06 \end{bmatrix}$

60. $\begin{bmatrix} 0.01 & 0.04 & -0.00 & 0.03 \\ 0.02 & -0.02 & 0.01 & 0.01 \\ -0.04 & 0.02 & 0.04 & 0.06 \\ 0.05 & -0.02 & -0.00 & -0.09 \end{bmatrix}$

61. $x = 4.57,\ y = -6.44,\ z = -24.07$

62. $x = 4.56,\ y = -6.06,\ z = -22.55$

63. $x = -1.19,\ y = 2.46,\ z = 8.27$

64. $x = -2.05,\ y = 3.88,\ z = 13.36$

65. (a) The rows of the 2 by 3 matrix represent stainless steel and aluminum. The columns represent 10-gallon, 5-gallon, and 1-gallon.

The 2 by 3 matrix is: $\begin{bmatrix} 500 & 350 & 400 \\ 700 & 500 & 850 \end{bmatrix}$ $\quad$ The 3 by 2 matrix is: $\begin{bmatrix} 500 & 700 \\ 350 & 500 \\ 400 & 850 \end{bmatrix}$

(b) The 3 by 1 matrix representing the amount of material is: $\begin{bmatrix} 15 \\ 8 \\ 3 \end{bmatrix}$

(c) The days usage of materials is:

$$\begin{bmatrix} 500 & 350 & 400 \\ 700 & 500 & 850 \end{bmatrix} \cdot \begin{bmatrix} 15 \\ 8 \\ 3 \end{bmatrix} = \begin{bmatrix} 11{,}500 \\ 17{,}050 \end{bmatrix}$$

11,500 pounds of stainless steel and 17,050 pounds of aluminum are used each day.

(d) The 1 by 2 matrix representing cost is:

$$\begin{bmatrix} 0.10 & 0.05 \end{bmatrix}$$

(e) The total cost of the days production was:

$$\begin{bmatrix} 0.10 & 0.05 \end{bmatrix} \cdot \begin{bmatrix} 11{,}500 \\ 17{,}050 \end{bmatrix} = \begin{bmatrix} 2002.50 \end{bmatrix}$$

The total cost of the days production was $2,002.50.

66. (a) The rows of the 2 by 3 matrix represent the location. The columns represent the type of car sold.

The 2 by 3 matrix for January is:

$$\begin{bmatrix} 400 & 250 & 50 \\ 450 & 200 & 140 \end{bmatrix}$$

The 2 by 3 matrix for February is:

$$\begin{bmatrix} 350 & 100 & 30 \\ 350 & 300 & 100 \end{bmatrix}$$

(b) Adding the matrices:

$$\begin{bmatrix} 400 & 250 & 50 \\ 450 & 200 & 140 \end{bmatrix} + \begin{bmatrix} 350 & 100 & 30 \\ 350 & 300 & 100 \end{bmatrix} = \begin{bmatrix} 750 & 350 & 80 \\ 800 & 500 & 240 \end{bmatrix}$$

(c) The 3 by 1 matrix representing profit:

$$\begin{bmatrix} 100 \\ 150 \\ 200 \end{bmatrix}$$

(d) Multiplying to find the profit at each location:

$$\begin{bmatrix} 750 & 350 & 80 \\ 800 & 500 & 240 \end{bmatrix} \cdot \begin{bmatrix} 100 \\ 150 \\ 200 \end{bmatrix} = \begin{bmatrix} 143{,}500 \\ 203{,}000 \end{bmatrix}$$

The city location has a two month profit of $143,500. The suburban location has a two month profit of $203,000.

67. We need to consider 2 different cases.

Case 1: $a \neq 0,\ D = ad - bc \neq 0$.

$$A = \left[\begin{array}{cc|cc} a & b & 1 & 0 \\ c & d & 0 & 1 \end{array}\right] \longrightarrow \left[\begin{array}{cc|cc} 1 & \frac{b}{a} & \frac{1}{a} & 0 \\ c & d & 0 & 1 \end{array}\right] \longrightarrow \left[\begin{array}{cc|cc} 1 & \frac{b}{a} & \frac{1}{a} & 0 \\ c & d - \frac{cb}{a} & -\frac{c}{a} & 1 \end{array}\right] = \left[\begin{array}{cc|cc} 1 & \frac{b}{b} & \frac{1}{a} & 0 \\ c & \frac{ad - cb}{a} & -\frac{c}{a} & 1 \end{array}\right]$$

$$R_1 = \tfrac{1}{a} \cdot r_1 \qquad R_2 = -c \cdot r_1 + r_2$$

$$\longrightarrow \left[\begin{array}{cc|cc} 1 & \frac{b}{a} & \frac{1}{a} & 0 \\ 0 & 1 & -\frac{c}{ad - bc} & \frac{a}{ad - bc} \end{array}\right] \longrightarrow \left[\begin{array}{cc|cc} 1 & 0 & \frac{1}{a} + \frac{bc}{a(ad - bc)} & \frac{-b}{ad - bc} \\ 0 & 1 & -\frac{c}{ad - bc} & \frac{a}{ad - bc} \end{array}\right]$$

$$R_2 = \left(\frac{a}{ad - bc}\right) \cdot r_2 \qquad R_1 = \left(-\frac{b}{a}\right) r_2 + r_1$$

Note that $\dfrac{1}{a}+\dfrac{bc}{a(ad-bc)}=\dfrac{1\cdot(ad-bc)+bc}{a(ad-bc)}=\dfrac{ad-bc+bc}{a(ad-bc)}=\dfrac{ad}{a(ad-bc)}=\dfrac{d}{ad-bc}$

So, we have $\left[\begin{array}{cc|cc} 1 & 0 & \dfrac{1}{a}+\dfrac{bc}{a(ad-bc)} & \dfrac{-b}{ad-bc} \\ 0 & 1 & -\dfrac{c}{ad-bc} & \dfrac{a}{ad-bc} \end{array}\right]=\left[\begin{array}{cc|cc} 1 & 0 & \dfrac{d}{ad-bc} & \dfrac{-b}{ad-bc} \\ 0 & 1 & -\dfrac{c}{ad-bc} & \dfrac{a}{ad-bc} \end{array}\right].$

Therefore $A^{-1}=\begin{bmatrix} \dfrac{d}{ad-bc} & \dfrac{-b}{ad-bc} \\ -\dfrac{c}{ad-bc} & \dfrac{a}{ad-bc} \end{bmatrix}=\left(\dfrac{1}{ad-bc}\right)\begin{bmatrix} d & -b \\ -c & a \end{bmatrix}=\left(\dfrac{1}{D}\right)\begin{bmatrix} d & -b \\ -c & a \end{bmatrix},$
where $D=ad-bc$.

Case 2: $a=0,\ D=ad-bc\neq 0$.

First note that $D=ad-bc=0\cdot d-bc=-bc\neq 0\Rightarrow b\neq 0$ and $c\neq 0$.

$$A=\left[\begin{array}{cc|cc} 0 & b & 1 & 0 \\ c & d & 0 & 1 \end{array}\right]\longrightarrow\left[\begin{array}{cc|cc} c & d & 0 & 1 \\ 0 & b & 1 & 0 \end{array}\right]\longrightarrow\left[\begin{array}{cc|cc} 1 & \dfrac{d}{c} & 0 & \dfrac{1}{c} \\ 0 & b & 1 & 0 \end{array}\right]\longrightarrow\left[\begin{array}{cc|cc} 1 & \dfrac{d}{c} & 0 & \dfrac{1}{c} \\ 0 & 1 & \dfrac{1}{b} & 0 \end{array}\right]$$

interchange r_1 and r_2 $\qquad R_1=\dfrac{1}{c}\cdot r_1$ $\qquad R_2=\dfrac{1}{b}\cdot r_2$

$$\longrightarrow\left[\begin{array}{cc|cc} 1 & 0 & \dfrac{-d}{bc} & \dfrac{1}{c} \\ 0 & 1 & \dfrac{1}{b} & 0 \end{array}\right]$$

$R_1=\left(\dfrac{-d}{c}\right)\cdot r_2+r_1$

Therefore $A^{-1}=\begin{bmatrix} \dfrac{-d}{bc} & \dfrac{1}{c} \\ \dfrac{1}{b} & 0 \end{bmatrix}=\left(\dfrac{1}{-bc}\right)\begin{bmatrix} d & -b \\ -c & 0 \end{bmatrix}=\left(\dfrac{1}{D}\right)\begin{bmatrix} d & -b \\ -c & 0 \end{bmatrix},$
where $D=ad-bc=0\cdot d-bc=-bc$.

Chapter 12

Systems of Equations and Inequalities

12.6 Partial Fraction Decomposition

1. The rational expression $\frac{x}{x^2-1}$ is proper, since the degree of the numerator is less than the degree of the denominator.

2. The rational expression $\frac{5x+2}{x^3-1}$ is proper, since the degree of the numerator is less than the degree of the denominator.

3. The rational expression $\frac{x^2+5}{x^2-4}$ is improper, so perform the division:

$$\begin{array}{r} 1 \\ x^2-4\overline{\smash{)}x^2+5} \\ \underline{x^2-4} \\ 9 \end{array}$$

The proper rational expression is:

$$\frac{x^2+5}{x^2-4}=1+\frac{9}{x^2-4}$$

4. The rational expression $\frac{3x^2-2}{x^2-1}$ is improper, so perform the division:

$$\begin{array}{r} 3 \\ x^2-1\overline{\smash{)}3x^2-2} \\ \underline{3x^2-3} \\ 1 \end{array}$$

The proper rational expression is:

$$\frac{3x^2-2}{x^2-1}=3+\frac{1}{x^2-1}$$

5. The rational expression $\frac{5x^3+2x-1}{x^2-4}$ is improper, so perform the division:

$$\begin{array}{r} 5x \\ x^2-4\overline{\smash{)}5x^3+0x^2+2x-1} \\ \underline{5x^3\qquad -20x} \\ 22x-1 \end{array}$$

The proper rational expression is:

$$\frac{5x^3+2x-1}{x^2-4}=5x+\frac{22x-1}{x^2-4}$$

6. The rational expression $\frac{3x^4+x^2-2}{x^3+8}$ is improper, so perform the division:

$$\begin{array}{r} 3x \\ x^3+8\overline{\smash{)}3x^4+x^2+0x-2} \\ \underline{3x^4\qquad +24x} \\ x^2-24x-2 \end{array}$$

The proper rational expression is:

$$\frac{3x^4+x^2-2}{x^3+8}=3x+\frac{x^2-24x-2}{x^3+8}$$

7. The rational expression $\frac{x(x-1)}{(x+4)(x-3)}=\frac{x^2-x}{x^2+x-12}$ is improper, so perform the division:

$$\begin{array}{r} 1 \\ x^2+x-12\overline{)\,x^2-x+0} \\ \underline{x^2+x-12} \\ -2x+12 \end{array}$$

The proper rational expression is: $\frac{x(x-1)}{(x+4)(x-3)}=1+\frac{-2x+12}{x^2+x-12}$

8. The rational expression $\frac{2x(x^2+4)}{x^2+1}=\frac{2x^3+8x}{x^2+1}$ is improper, so perform the division:

$$\begin{array}{r} 2x \\ x^2+1\overline{)\,2x^3+8x} \\ \underline{2x^3+2x} \\ 6x \end{array}$$

The proper rational expression is: $\frac{2x(x^2+4)}{x^2+1}=2x+\frac{6x}{x^2+1}$

9. Find the partial fraction decomposition:

$$\frac{4}{x(x-1)}=\frac{A}{x}+\frac{B}{x-1}$$

$4=A(x-1)+Bx$ (Multiply both sides by $x(x-1)$.)

Let $x=1$: then $4=A(0)+B\rightarrow B=4$

Let $x=0$: then $4=A(-1)+B(0)\rightarrow A=-4$

$$\frac{4}{x(x-1)}=\frac{-4}{x}+\frac{4}{x-1}$$

10. Find the partial fraction decomposition:

$$\frac{3x}{(x+2)(x-1)}=\frac{A}{x+2}+\frac{B}{x-1}$$

$3x=A(x-1)+B(x+2)$ (Multiply both sides by $(x+2)(x-1)$.)

Let $x=1$: then $3(1)=A(0)+B(3)\rightarrow 3B=3 \rightarrow B=1$

Let $x=-2$: then $3(-2)=A(-3)+B(0)\rightarrow -3A=-6 \rightarrow A=2$

$$\frac{3x}{(x+2)(x-1)}=\frac{2}{x+2}+\frac{1}{x-1}$$

11. Find the partial fraction decomposition:

$$\frac{1}{x(x^2+1)}=\frac{A}{x}+\frac{Bx+C}{x^2+1}$$

$1=A(x^2+1)+(Bx+C)x$ (Multiply both sides by $x(x^2+1)$.)

Let $x=0$: then $1=A(1)+(B(0)+C)(0)\rightarrow A=1$

Let $x=1$: then $1=A(1+1)+(B(1)+C)(1)\rightarrow 1=2A+B+C$

so $1=2(1)+B+C\rightarrow -1=B+C$

Let $x=-1$: then $1=A(1+1)+(B(-1)+C)(-1) \rightarrow 1=2A+B-C$

so $1=2(1)+B-C \rightarrow -1=B-C$

Solve the system of equations:

$$\begin{aligned} B+C &= -1 \\ B-C &= -1 \\ \hline 2B &= -2 \\ B &= -1 \end{aligned} \qquad \begin{aligned} -1+C &= -1 \\ C &= 0 \end{aligned}$$

$$\frac{1}{x(x^2+1)}=\frac{1}{x}+\frac{-x}{x^2+1}$$

12. Find the partial fraction decomposition:

$$\frac{1}{(x+1)(x^2+4)}=\frac{A}{x+1}+\frac{Bx+C}{x^2+4}$$

$$1 = A(x^2+4)+(Bx+C)(x+1)$$

(Multiply both sides by $(x+1)(x^2+4)$.)

Let $x=-1$: then $1=A(5)+(B(-1)+C)(0) \rightarrow 5A=1 \rightarrow A=\frac{1}{5}$

Let $x=1$: then $1=A(1+4)+(B(1)+C)(1+1) \rightarrow 1=5A+2B+2C$

$\rightarrow 1=5\left(\frac{1}{5}\right)+2B+2C \rightarrow 0=2B+2C$

$\rightarrow 0=B+C$

Let $x=0$: then $1=A(0+4)+(B(0)+C)(0+1) \rightarrow 1=4A+C$

$\rightarrow 1=4\left(\frac{1}{5}\right)+C \rightarrow \frac{1}{5}=C$

$$B+\frac{1}{5}=0 \rightarrow B=-\frac{1}{5}$$

$$\frac{1}{(x+1)(x^2+4)}=\frac{\left(\frac{1}{5}\right)}{x+1}+\frac{\left(-\frac{1}{5}x+\frac{1}{5}\right)}{x^2+4}$$

13. Find the partial fraction decomposition:

$$\frac{x}{(x-1)(x-2)}=\frac{A}{x-1}+\frac{B}{x-2}$$

$x = A(x-2)+B(x-1)$ (Multiply both sides by $(x-1)(x-2)$.)

Let $x = 1$: then $1 = A(1-2)+B(1-1) \rightarrow 1=-A \rightarrow A=-1$

Let $x = 2$: then $2 = A(2-2)+B(2-1) \rightarrow 2=B \rightarrow B=2$

$$\frac{x}{(x-1)(x-2)}=\frac{-1}{x-1}+\frac{2}{x-2}$$

14. Find the partial fraction decomposition:

$$\frac{3x}{(x+2)(x-4)} = \frac{A}{x+2} + \frac{B}{x-4}$$

$$3x = A(x-4) + B(x+2) \quad \text{(Multiply both sides by } (x+2)(x-4).)$$

Let $x = -2$: then $3(-2) = A(-2-4) + B(-2+2) \rightarrow -6 = -6A \rightarrow A = 1$

Let $x = 4$: then $3(4) = A(4-4) + B(4+2) \rightarrow 12 = 6B \rightarrow B = 2$

$$\frac{3x}{(x+2)(x-4)} = \frac{1}{x+2} + \frac{2}{x-4}$$

15. Find the partial fraction decomposition:

$$\frac{x^2}{(x-1)^2(x+1)} = \frac{A}{x-1} + \frac{B}{(x-1)^2} + \frac{C}{x+1}$$

(Multiply both sides by $(x-1)^2(x+1)$.)

$$x^2 = A(x-1)(x+1) + B(x+1) + C(x-1)^2$$

Let $x = 1$: then $1^2 = A(1-1)(1+1) + B(1+1) + C(1-1)^2$

$$\rightarrow 1 = 2B \rightarrow B = \frac{1}{2}$$

Let $x = -1$: then $(-1)^2 = A(-1-1)(-1+1) + B(-1+1) + C(-1-1)^2$

$$\rightarrow 1 = 4C \rightarrow C = \frac{1}{4}$$

Let $x = 0$: then $0^2 = A(0-1)(0+1) + B(0+1) + C(0-1)^2$

$$\rightarrow 0 = -A + B + C \rightarrow A = \frac{1}{2} + \frac{1}{4} = \frac{3}{4}$$

$$\frac{x^2}{(x-1)^2(x+1)} = \frac{\left(\frac{3}{4}\right)}{x-1} + \frac{\left(\frac{1}{2}\right)}{(x-1)^2} + \frac{\left(\frac{1}{4}\right)}{x+1}$$

16. Find the partial fraction decomposition:

$$\frac{x+1}{x^2(x-2)} = \frac{A}{x} + \frac{B}{x^2} + \frac{C}{x-2} \quad \text{(Multiply both sides by } x^2(x-2).)$$

$$x + 1 = Ax(x-2) + B(x-2) + Cx^2$$

Let $x = 0$: then $0 + 1 = A(0)(0-2) + B(0-2) + C(0)^2$

$$\rightarrow 1 = -2B \rightarrow B = -\frac{1}{2}$$

Let $x = 2$: then $2 + 1 = A(2)(2-2) + B(2-2) + C(2)^2$

$$\rightarrow 3 = 4C \rightarrow C = \frac{3}{4}$$

Let $x = 1$: then $1 + 1 = A(1)(1-2) + B(1-2) + C(1)^2$

$$\rightarrow 2 = -A - B + C \rightarrow A = -B + C - 2 = -\left(-\frac{1}{2}\right) + \frac{3}{4} - 2 = -\frac{3}{4}$$

$$\frac{x+1}{x^2(x-2)}=\frac{-\left(\frac{3}{4}\right)}{x}+\frac{-\left(\frac{1}{2}\right)}{x^2}+\frac{\left(\frac{3}{4}\right)}{x-2}$$

17. Find the partial fraction decomposition:

$$\frac{1}{x^3-8}=\frac{1}{(x-2)(x^2+2x+4)}=\frac{A}{x-2}+\frac{Bx+C}{x^2+2x+4}$$

(Multiply both sides by $(x-2)(x^2+2x+4)$.)

$$1=A(x^2+2x+4)+(Bx+C)(x-2)$$

Let $x=2$: then $1=A\left(2^2+2(2)+4\right)+(B(2)+C)(2-2)$

$$\rightarrow 1=12A \rightarrow A=\frac{1}{12}$$

Let $x=0$: then $1=A\left(0^2+2(0)+4\right)+(B(0)+C)(0-2)$

$$\rightarrow 1=4A-2C \rightarrow 1=4\left(\frac{1}{12}\right)-2C$$

$$\rightarrow -2C=\frac{2}{3} \rightarrow C=-\frac{1}{3}$$

Let $x=1$: then $1=A\left(1^2+2(1)+4\right)+(B(1)+C)(1-2)$

$$\rightarrow 1=7A-B-C \rightarrow 1=7\left(\frac{1}{12}\right)-B+\frac{1}{3} \rightarrow B=-\frac{1}{12}$$

$$\frac{1}{x^3-8}=\frac{\left(\frac{1}{12}\right)}{x-2}+\frac{-\left(\frac{1}{12}\right)x-\frac{1}{3}}{x^2+2x+4}$$

18. Find the partial fraction decomposition:

$$\frac{2x+4}{x^3-1}=\frac{2x+4}{(x-1)(x^2+x+1)}=\frac{A}{x-1}+\frac{Bx+C}{x^2+x+1}$$

(Multiply both sides by $(x-1)(x^2+x+1)$.)

$$2x+4=A(x^2+x+1)+(Bx+C)(x-1)$$

Let $x=1$: then $2(1)+4=A\left(1^2+1+1\right)+(B(1)+C)(1-1)$

$$\rightarrow 6=3A \rightarrow A=2$$

Let $x=0$: then $2(0)+4=A\left(0^2+0+1\right)+(B(0)+C)(0-1)$

$$\rightarrow 4=A-C \rightarrow 4=2-C \rightarrow C=-2$$

Let $x=-1$: then $2(-1)+4=A\left((-1)^2+(-1)+1\right)+(B(-1)+C)(-1-1)$

$$\rightarrow 2=A+2B-2C \rightarrow 2=2+2B-2(-2)$$

$$\rightarrow 2B=-4 \rightarrow B=-2$$

$$\frac{2x+4}{x^3-1}=\frac{2}{x-1}+\frac{-2x-2}{x^2+x+1}$$

19. Find the partial fraction decomposition:

$$\frac{x^2}{(x-1)^2(x+1)^2}=\frac{A}{x-1}+\frac{B}{(x-1)^2}+\frac{C}{x+1}+\frac{D}{(x+1)^2}$$

(Multiply both sides by $(x-1)^2(x+1)^2$.)

$$x^2 = A(x-1)(x+1)^2+B(x+1)^2+C(x-1)^2(x+1)+D(x-1)^2$$

Let $x=1$: then $1^2 = A(1-1)(1+1)^2+B(1+1)^2+C(1-1)^2(1+1)+D(1-1)^2$

$$\rightarrow 1=4B \rightarrow B=\frac{1}{4}$$

Let $x=-1$: then

$$(-1)^2 = A(-1-1)(-1+1)^2+B(-1+1)^2+C(-1-1)^2(-1+1)+D(-1-1)^2$$

$$\rightarrow 1=4D \rightarrow D=\frac{1}{4}$$

Let $x=0$: then

$$0^2 = A(0-1)(0+1)^2+B(0+1)^2+C(0-1)^2(0+1)+D(0-1)^2$$

$$\rightarrow 0=-A+B+C+D \rightarrow A-C=\frac{1}{4}+\frac{1}{4}=\frac{1}{2}$$

Let $x=2$: then

$$2^2 = A(2-1)(2+1)^2+B(2+1)^2+C(2-1)^2(2+1)+D(2-1)^2$$

$$\rightarrow 4=9A+9B+3C+D \rightarrow 9A+3C=4-\frac{9}{4}-\frac{1}{4}=\frac{3}{2}$$

$$\rightarrow 3A+C=\frac{1}{2}$$

Solve the system of equations:

$$A-C=\frac{1}{2}$$

$$\underline{3A+C=\frac{1}{2}}$$

$$4A \quad =1$$

$$A \quad =\frac{1}{4} \rightarrow \frac{3}{4}+C=\frac{1}{2} \rightarrow C=-\frac{1}{4}$$

$$\frac{x^2}{(x-1)^2(x+1)^2}=\frac{\left(\frac{1}{4}\right)}{x-1}+\frac{\left(\frac{1}{4}\right)}{(x-1)^2}+\frac{\left(-\frac{1}{4}\right)}{x+1}+\frac{\left(\frac{1}{4}\right)}{(x+1)^2}$$

20. Find the partial fraction decomposition:

$$\frac{x+1}{x^2(x-2)^2}=\frac{A}{x}+\frac{B}{x^2}+\frac{C}{x-2}+\frac{D}{(x-2)^2}$$

(Multiply both sides by $x^2(x-2)^2$.)

$$x+1 = Ax(x-2)^2+B(x-2)^2+Cx^2(x-2)+Dx^2$$

Let $x=0$: then $0+1=A(0)(0-2)^2+B(0-2)^2+C(0)^2(0-2)+D(0)^2$

$\rightarrow 1=4B \rightarrow B=\frac{1}{4}$

Let $x=2$: then $2+1=A(2)(2-2)^2+B(2-2)^2+C(2)^2(2-2)+D(2)^2$

$\rightarrow 3=4D \rightarrow D=\frac{3}{4}$

Let $x=1$: then $1+1=A(1)(1-2)^2+B(1-2)^2+C(1)^2(1-2)+D(1)^2$

$\rightarrow 2=A+B-C+D \rightarrow A-C=2-\frac{1}{4}-\frac{3}{4}=1$

Let $x=3$: then $3+1=A(3)(3-2)^2+B(3-2)^2+C(3)^2(3-2)+D(3)^2$

$\rightarrow 4=3A+B+9C+9D \rightarrow 3A+9C=4-\frac{1}{4}-\frac{27}{4}=-3$

$\rightarrow A+3C=-1$

Solve the system of equations:

$A-C=1 \rightarrow A=C+1$

$A+3C=-1$

$C+1+3C=-1 \rightarrow 4C=-2 \rightarrow C=-\frac{1}{2}$

$A=-\frac{1}{2}+1=\frac{1}{2}$

$$\frac{x+1}{x^2(x-2)^2}=\frac{\left(\frac{1}{2}\right)}{x}+\frac{\left(\frac{1}{4}\right)}{x^2}+\frac{\left(-\frac{1}{2}\right)}{x-2}+\frac{\left(\frac{3}{4}\right)}{(x-2)^2}$$

21. Find the partial fraction decomposition:

$$\frac{x-3}{(x+2)(x+1)^2}=\frac{A}{x+2}+\frac{B}{x+1}+\frac{C}{(x+1)^2}$$

(Multiply both sides by $(x+2)(x+1)^2$.)

$x-3=A(x+1)^2+B(x+2)(x+1)+C(x+2)$

Let $x=-2$: then $-2-3=A(-2+1)^2+B(-2+2)(-2+1)+C(-2+2)$

$\rightarrow -5=A \rightarrow A=-5$

Let $x=-1$: then $-1-3=A(-1+1)^2+B(-1+2)(-1+1)+C(-1+2)$

$\rightarrow -4=C \rightarrow C=-4$

Let $x=0$: then

$0-3=A(0+1)^2+B(0+2)(0+1)+C(0+2) \rightarrow -3=A+2B+2C$

$\rightarrow -3=-5+2B+2(-4) \rightarrow 2B=10 \rightarrow B=5$

$$\frac{x-3}{(x+2)(x+1)^2}=\frac{-5}{x+2}+\frac{5}{x+1}+\frac{-4}{(x+1)^2}$$

22. Find the partial fraction decomposition:

$$\frac{x^2+x}{(x+2)(x-1)^2}=\frac{A}{x+2}+\frac{B}{x-1}+\frac{C}{(x-1)^2}$$

(Multiply both sides by $(x+2)(x-1)^2$.)

$$x^2+x=A(x-1)^2+B(x+2)(x-1)+C(x+2)$$

Let $x=-2$: then $(-2)^2+(-2)=A(-2-1)^2+B(-2+2)(-2-1)+C(-2+2)$

$$\rightarrow 2=9A \rightarrow A=\frac{2}{9}$$

Let $x=1$: then $1^2+1=A(1-1)^2+B(1+2)(1-1)+C(1+2)$

$$\rightarrow 2=3C \rightarrow C=\frac{2}{3}$$

Let $x=0$: then $0^2+0=A(0-1)^2+B(0+2)(0-1)+C(0+2)$

$$\rightarrow 0=A-2B+2C \rightarrow 2B=\frac{2}{9}+2\left(\frac{2}{3}\right)=\frac{14}{9} \rightarrow B=\frac{7}{9}$$

$$\frac{x^2+x}{(x+2)(x-1)^2}=\frac{\left(\frac{2}{9}\right)}{x+2}+\frac{\left(\frac{7}{9}\right)}{x-1}+\frac{\left(\frac{2}{3}\right)}{(x-1)^2}$$

23. Find the partial fraction decomposition:

$$\frac{x+4}{x^2(x^2+4)}=\frac{A}{x}+\frac{B}{x^2}+\frac{Cx+D}{x^2+4}$$ (Multiply both sides by $x^2(x^2+4)$.)

$$x+4=Ax(x^2+4)+B(x^2+4)+(Cx+D)x^2$$

Let $x=0$: then $0+4=A(0)(0^2+4)+B(0^2+4)+(C0+D)(0)^2$

$\rightarrow 4=4B \rightarrow B=1$

Let $x=1$: then $1+4=A(1)(1^2+4)+B(1^2+4)+(C(1)+D)(1)^2$

$\rightarrow 5=5A+5B+C+D \rightarrow 5=5A+5+C+D$

$\rightarrow 5A+C+D=0$

Let $x=-1$: then

$-1+4=A(-1)((-1)^2+4)+B((-1)^2+4)+(C(-1)+D)(-1)^2$

$\rightarrow 3=-5A+5B-C+D \rightarrow 3=-5A+5-C+D$

$\rightarrow -5A-C+D=-2$

Let $x=2$: then $2+4=A(2)(2^2+4)+B(2^2+4)+(C(2)+D)(2)^2$

$\rightarrow 6=16A+8B+8C+4D \rightarrow 6=16A+8+8C+4D$

$\rightarrow 16A+8C+4D=-2$

Solve the system of equations:

$$\begin{array}{r} 5A+C+D=\ \ 0 \\ -5A-C+D=-2 \\ \hline 2D=-2 \\ D=-1 \end{array} \qquad \begin{array}{r} 5A+C-1=0 \\ C=1-5A \end{array}$$

$$16A + 8(1-5A) + 4(-1) = -2$$
$$16A + 8 - 40A - 4 = -2$$
$$-24A = -6$$
$$A = \frac{1}{4}$$

$$C = 1 - 5\left(\frac{1}{4}\right)$$
$$C = 1 - \frac{5}{4} = -\frac{1}{4}$$

$$\frac{x+4}{x^2(x^2+4)} = \frac{\left(\frac{1}{4}\right)}{x} + \frac{1}{x^2} + \frac{\left(-\frac{1}{4}x - 1\right)}{x^2+4}$$

24. Find the partial fraction decomposition:

$$\frac{10x^2 + 2x}{(x-1)^2(x^2+2)} = \frac{A}{x-1} + \frac{B}{(x-1)^2} + \frac{Cx+D}{x^2+2}$$

(Multiply both sides by $(x-1)^2(x^2+2)$.)

$$10x^2 + 2x = A(x-1)(x^2+2) + B(x^2+2) + (Cx+D)(x-1)^2$$

Let $x = 1$: then $10(1)^2 + 2(1) = A(1-1)(1^2+2) + B(1^2+2) + (C(1)+D)(1-1)^2$

$\rightarrow 12 = 3B \rightarrow B = 4$

Let $x = 0$: then $10(0)^2 + 2 \cdot 0 = A(0-1)(0^2+2) + B(0^2+2) + (C(0)+D)(0-1)^2$

$\rightarrow 0 = -2A + 2B + D \rightarrow 0 = -2A + 8 + D$

$\rightarrow 2A - D = 8$

Let $x = -1$: then

$$10(-1)^2 + 2(-1) = A(-1-1)((-1)^2+2) + B((-1)^2+2) + (C(-1)+D)(-1-1)^2$$

$\rightarrow 8 = -6A + 3B - 4C + 4D \rightarrow 8 = -6A + 12 - 4C + 4D$

$\rightarrow -6A - 4C + 4D = -4$

Let $x = 2$: then $10(2)^2 + 2(2) = A(2-1)(2^2+2) + B(2^2+2) + (C(2)+D)(2-1)^2$

$\rightarrow 44 = 6A + 6B + 2C + D \rightarrow 44 = 6A + 24 + 2C + D$

$\rightarrow 6A + 2C + D = 20$

Solve the system of equations (Substitute for D):

$D = 2A - 8$

$-6A - 4C + 4D = -4 \rightarrow -6A - 4C + 4(2A - 8) = -4$

$\rightarrow 2A - 4C = 28 \rightarrow A - 2C = 14$

$6A + 2C + D = 20 \rightarrow 6A + 2C + 2A - 8 = 20 \rightarrow 8A + 2C = 28$

Add the equations and solve:

$A - 2C = 14$

$\underline{8A + 2C = 28}$

$9A \quad = 42 \rightarrow A = \frac{14}{3}$

$2C = A - 14$

$2C = \frac{14}{3} - 14 = -\frac{28}{3} = -\frac{14}{3}$

$D = 2A - 8$

$D = 2\left(\frac{14}{3}\right) - 8 = \frac{4}{3}$

$$\frac{10x^2 + 2x}{(x-1)^2(x^2+2)} = \frac{\left(\frac{14}{3}\right)}{x-1} + \frac{4}{(x-1)^2} + \frac{\left(-\frac{14}{3}x + \frac{4}{3}\right)}{x^2+2}$$

25. Find the partial fraction decomposition:

$$\frac{x^2+2x+3}{(x+1)(x^2+2x+4)}=\frac{A}{x+1}+\frac{Bx+C}{x^2+2x+4}$$

(Multiply both sides by $(x+1)(x^2+2x+4)$.)

$$x^2+2x+3=A(x^2+2x+4)+(Bx+C)(x+1)$$

Let $x=-1$: then

$$(-1)^2+2(-1)+3=A((-1)^2+2(-1)+4)+(B(-1)+C)(-1+1)$$

$$\rightarrow 2=3A \rightarrow A=\frac{2}{3}$$

Let $x=0$: then $0^2+2(0)+3=A(0^2+2(0)+4)+(B(0)+C)(0+1)$

$$\rightarrow 3=4A+C \rightarrow 3=4\left(\frac{2}{3}\right)+C \rightarrow C=\frac{1}{3}$$

Let $x=1$: then

$$1^2+2(1)+3=A(1^2+2(1)+4)+(B(1)+C)(1+1)$$

$$\rightarrow 6=7A+2B+2C \rightarrow 6=7\left(\frac{2}{3}\right)+2B+2\left(\frac{1}{3}\right)$$

$$\rightarrow 2B=6-\frac{14}{3}-\frac{2}{3} \rightarrow 2B=\frac{2}{3} \rightarrow B=\frac{1}{3}$$

$$\frac{x^2+2x+3}{(x+1)(x^2+2x+4)}=\frac{\left(\frac{2}{3}\right)}{x+1}+\frac{\left(\frac{1}{3}x+\frac{1}{3}\right)}{x^2+2x+4}$$

26. Find the partial fraction decomposition:

$$\frac{x^2-11x-18}{x(x^2+3x+3)}=\frac{A}{x}+\frac{Bx+C}{x^2+3x+3}$$ (Multiply both sides by $x(x^2+3x+3)$.)

$$x^2-11x-18=A(x^2+3x+3)+(Bx+C)(x)$$

Let $x=0$: then $0^2-11(0)-18=A(0^2+3(0)+3)+(B(0)+C)(0)$

$$\rightarrow -18=3A \rightarrow A=-6$$

Let $x=1$: then $1^2-11(1)-18=A(1^2+3(1)+3)+(B(1)+C)(1)$

$$\rightarrow -28=7A+B+C \rightarrow -28=7(-6)+B+C \rightarrow B+C=14$$

Let $x=-1$: then $(-1)^2-11(-1)-18=A((-1)^2+3(-1)+3)+(B(-1)+C)(-1)$

$$\rightarrow -6=A+B-C \rightarrow -6=-6+B-C \rightarrow B-C=0$$

Add the last two equations and solve:

$$2B=14 \rightarrow B=7$$

$$C=14-B=14-7=7$$

$$\frac{x^2-11x-18}{x(x^2+3x+3)}=\frac{-6}{x}+\frac{7x+7}{x^2+3x+3}$$

27. Find the partial fraction decomposition:

$$\frac{x}{(3x-2)(2x+1)}=\frac{A}{3x-2}+\frac{B}{2x+1}$$ (Multiply both sides by $(3x-2)(2x+1)$.)

$$x=A(2x+1)+B(3x-2)$$

Let $x = -\frac{1}{2}$: then $-\frac{1}{2} = A\left(2\left(-\frac{1}{2}\right)+1\right) + B\left(3\left(-\frac{1}{2}\right)-2\right)$

$\rightarrow -\frac{1}{2} = -\frac{7}{2}B \rightarrow B = \frac{1}{7}$

Let $x = \frac{2}{3}$: then $\frac{2}{3} = A\left(2\left(\frac{2}{3}\right)+1\right) + B\left(3\left(\frac{2}{3}\right)-2\right) \rightarrow \frac{2}{3} = \frac{7}{3}A \rightarrow A = \frac{2}{7}$

$$\frac{x}{(3x-2)(2x+1)} = \frac{\left(\frac{2}{7}\right)}{3x-2} + \frac{\left(\frac{1}{7}\right)}{2x+1}$$

28. Find the partial fraction decomposition:

$$\frac{1}{(2x+3)(4x-1)} = \frac{A}{2x+3} + \frac{B}{4x-1}$$

(Multiply both sides by $(2x+3)(4x-1)$.)

$$1 = A(4x-1) + B(2x+3)$$

Let $x = -\frac{3}{2}$: then $1 = A\left(4\left(-\frac{3}{2}\right)-1\right) + B\left(2\left(-\frac{3}{2}\right)+3\right)$

$\rightarrow 1 = -7A \rightarrow A = -\frac{1}{7}$

Let $x = \frac{1}{4}$: then $1 = A\left(4\left(\frac{1}{4}\right)-1\right) + B\left(2\left(\frac{1}{4}\right)+3\right) \rightarrow 1 = \frac{7}{2}B \rightarrow B = \frac{2}{7}$

$$\frac{1}{(2x+3)(4x-1)} = \frac{\left(-\frac{1}{7}\right)}{2x+3} + \frac{\left(\frac{2}{7}\right)}{4x-1}$$

29. Find the partial fraction decomposition:

$$\frac{x}{x^2+2x-3} = \frac{x}{(x+3)(x-1)} = \frac{A}{x+3} + \frac{B}{x-1}$$

(Multiply both sides by $(x+3)(x-1)$.)

$$x = A(x-1) + B(x+3)$$

Let $x = 1$: then $1 = A(1-1) + B(1+3) \rightarrow 1 = 4B \rightarrow B = \frac{1}{4}$

Let $x = -3$: then $-3 = A(-3-1) + B(-3+3) \rightarrow -3 = -4A \rightarrow A = \frac{3}{4}$

$$\frac{x}{x^2+2x-3} = \frac{\left(\frac{3}{4}\right)}{x+3} + \frac{\left(\frac{1}{4}\right)}{x-1}$$

30. Find the partial fraction decomposition:

$$\frac{x^2-x-8}{(x+1)(x^2+5x+6)} = \frac{x^2-x-8}{(x+1)(x+2)(x+3)} = \frac{A}{x+1} + \frac{B}{x+2} + \frac{C}{x+3}$$

(Multiply both sides by $(x+1)(x+2)(x+3)$.)

$$x^2 - x - 8 = A(x+2)(x+3) + B(x+1)(x+3) + C(x+1)(x+2)$$

Let $x=-1$: then

$$(-1)^2-(-1)-8=A(-1+2)(-1+3)+B(-1+1)(-1+3)+C(-1+1)(-1+2)$$
$$\to -6=2A \to A=-3$$

Let $x=-2$: then

$$(-2)^2-(-2)-8=A(-2+2)(-2+3)+B(-2+1)(-2+3)+C(-2+1)(-2+2)$$
$$\to -2=-B \to B=2$$

Let $x=-3$: then

$$(-3)^2-(-3)-8=A(-3+2)(-3+3)+B(-3+1)(-3+3)+C(-3+1)(-3+2)$$
$$\to 4=2C \to C=2$$

$$\frac{x^2-x-8}{(x+1)(x^2+5x+6)}=\frac{-3}{x+1}+\frac{2}{x+2}+\frac{2}{x+3}$$

31. Find the partial fraction decomposition:

$$\frac{x^2+2x+3}{(x^2+4)^2}=\frac{Ax+B}{x^2+4}+\frac{Cx+D}{(x^2+4)^2}$$

(Multiply both sides by $(x^2+4)^2$.)

$$x^2+2x+3=(Ax+B)(x^2+4)+Cx+D$$
$$x^2+2x+3=Ax^3+Bx^2+4Ax+4B+Cx+D$$
$$x^2+2x+3=Ax^3+Bx^2+(4A+C)x+4B+D$$
$$A=0$$
$$B=1$$
$$4A+C=2 \to 4(0)+C=2 \to C=2$$
$$4B+D=3 \to 4(1)+D=3 \to D=-1$$
$$\frac{x^2+2x+3}{(x^2+4)^2}=\frac{1}{x^2+4}+\frac{2x-1}{(x^2+4)^2}$$

32. Find the partial fraction decomposition:

$$\frac{x^3+1}{(x^2+16)^2}=\frac{Ax+B}{x^2+16}+\frac{Cx+D}{(x^2+16)^2}$$ (Multiply both sides by $(x^2+16)^2$.)

$$x^3+1=(Ax+B)(x^2+16)+Cx+D$$
$$x^3+1=Ax^3+Bx^2+16Ax+16B+Cx+D$$
$$x^3+1=Ax^3+Bx^2+(16A+C)x+16B+D$$
$$A=1$$
$$B=0$$
$$16A+C=0 \to 16(1)+C=0 \to C=-16$$
$$16B+D=1 \to 16(0)+D=1 \to D=1$$
$$\frac{x^3+1}{(x^2+16)^2}=\frac{x}{x^2+16}+\frac{-16x+1}{(x^2+16)^2}$$

33. Find the partial fraction decomposition:

$$\frac{7x+3}{x^3-2x^2-3x}=\frac{7x+3}{x(x-3)(x+1)}=\frac{A}{x}+\frac{B}{x-3}+\frac{C}{x+1}$$

(Multiply both sides by $x(x-3)(x+1)$.)

$$7x+3=A(x-3)(x+1)+Bx(x+1)+Cx(x-3)$$

Let $x=0$: then $7(0)+3=A(0-3)(0+1)+B(0)(0+1)+C(0)(0-3)$

$\rightarrow 3=-3A \rightarrow A=-1$

Let $x=3$: then $7(3)+3=A(3-3)(3+1)+B(3)(3+1)+C(3)(3-3)$

$\rightarrow 24=12B \rightarrow B=2$

Let $x=-1$: then

$7(-1)+3=A(-1-3)(-1+1)+B(-1)(-1+1)+C(-1)(-1-3)$

$\rightarrow -4=4C \rightarrow C=-1$

$$\frac{7x+3}{x^3-2x^2-3x}=\frac{-1}{x}+\frac{2}{x-3}+\frac{-1}{x+1}$$

34. Find the partial fraction decomposition:

$$\frac{x^5+1}{x^6-x^4}=\frac{(x+1)(x^4-x^3+x^2-x+1)}{x^4(x-1)(x+1)}=\frac{x^4-x^3+x^2-x+1}{x^4(x-1)}$$

$$=\frac{A}{x}+\frac{B}{x^2}+\frac{C}{x^3}+\frac{D}{x^4}+\frac{E}{x-1}$$ (Multiply both sides by $x^4(x-1)$.)

$$x^4-x^3+x^2-x+1=Ax^3(x-1)+Bx^2(x-1)+Cx(x-1)+D(x-1)+Ex^4$$

Let $x=0$: then

$0^4-0^3+0^2-0+1=A\cdot 0^3(0-1)+B\cdot 0^2(0-1)+C\cdot 0(0-1)+D(0-1)+E\cdot 0^4$

$\rightarrow 1=-D \rightarrow D=-1$

Let $x=1$: then

$1^4-1^3+1^2-1+1=A\cdot 1^3(1-1)+B\cdot 1^2(1-1)+C\cdot 1(1-1)+D(1-1)+E\cdot 1^4$

$\rightarrow 1=E \rightarrow E=1$

Let $x=-1$: then

$(-1)^4-(-1)^3+(-1)^2-(-1)+1$

$=A(-1)^3(-1-1)+B(-1)^2(-1-1)+C(-1)(-1-1)+D(-1-1)+E(-1)^4$

$\rightarrow 5=2A-2B+2C-2D+E \rightarrow 5=2A-2B+2C+2+1$

$\rightarrow 2A-2B+2C=2 \rightarrow A-B+C=1$

Let $x=2$: then

$2^4-2^3+2^2-2+1=A\cdot 2^3(2-1)+B\cdot 2^2(2-1)+C\cdot 2(2-1)+D(2-1)+E\cdot 2^4$

$\rightarrow 11=8A+4B+2C+D+16E \rightarrow 11=8A+4B+2C-1+16$

$\rightarrow 8A+4B+2C=-4 \rightarrow 4A+2B+C=-2$

Let $x = -2$: then

$$(-2)^4 - (-2)^3 + (-2)^2 - (-2) + 1$$
$$= A(-2)^3(-2-1) + B(-2)^2(-2-1) + C(-2)(-2-1) + D(-2-1) + E(-2)^4$$
$$\rightarrow 31 = 24A - 12B + 6C - 3D + 16E$$
$$\rightarrow 31 = 24A - 12B + 6C + 3 + 16$$
$$\rightarrow 24A - 12B + 6C = 12 \rightarrow 4A - 2B + C = 2$$

$$(4A + 2B + C) - (4A - 2B + C) = -2 - 2 \rightarrow 4B = -4 \rightarrow B = -1$$
$$A + 1 + C = 1 \rightarrow A + C = 0 \rightarrow A = -C$$
$$4(-C) - 2(-1) + C = 2 \rightarrow -3C = 0 \rightarrow C = 0$$
$$A = -0 = 0$$
$$\frac{x^5 + 1}{x^6 - x^4} = \frac{x^4 - x^3 + x^2 - x + 1}{x^4(x-1)} = \frac{-1}{x^2} + \frac{-1}{x^4} + \frac{1}{x-1}$$

35. Perform synthetic division to find a factor:

$$\begin{array}{r|rrrr} 2 & 1 & -4 & 5 & -2 \\ & & 2 & -4 & 2 \\ \hline & 1 & -2 & 1 & 0 \end{array}$$

$$x^3 - 4x^2 + 5x - 2 = (x-2)(x^2 - 2x + 1) = (x-2)(x-1)^2$$

Find the partial fraction decomposition:

$$\frac{x^2}{x^3 - 4x^2 + 5x - 2} = \frac{x^2}{(x-2)(x-1)^2} = \frac{A}{x-2} + \frac{B}{x-1} + \frac{C}{(x-1)^2}$$

(Multiply both sides by $(x-2)(x-1)^2$.)

$$x^2 = A(x-1)^2 + B(x-2)(x-1) + C(x-2)$$

Let $x = 2$: then $2^2 = A(2-1)^2 + B(2-2)(2-1) + C(2-2)$
$$\rightarrow 4 = A \rightarrow A = 4$$

Let $x = 1$: then $1^2 = A(1-1)^2 + B(1-2)(1-1) + C(1-2)$
$$\rightarrow 1 = -C \rightarrow C = -1$$

Let $x = 0$: then $0^2 = A(0-1)^2 + B(0-2)(0-1) + C(0-2)$
$$\rightarrow 0 = A + 2B - 2C \rightarrow 0 = 4 + 2B - 2(-1)$$
$$\rightarrow 2B = -6 \rightarrow B = -3$$

$$\frac{x^2}{x^3 - 4x^2 + 5x - 2} = \frac{4}{x-2} + \frac{-3}{x-1} + \frac{-1}{(x-1)^2}$$

36. Perform synthetic division to find a factor:

$$\begin{array}{r|rrrr} 1 & 1 & 1 & -5 & 3 \\ & & 1 & 2 & -3 \\ \hline & 1 & 2 & -3 & 0 \end{array}$$

$$x^3 + x^2 - 5x + 3 = (x-1)(x^2 + 2x - 3) = (x+3)(x-1)^2$$

Find the partial fraction decomposition:

$$\frac{x^2 + 1}{x^3 + x^2 - 5x + 3} = \frac{x^2 + 1}{(x+3)(x-1)^2} = \frac{A}{x+3} + \frac{B}{x-1} + \frac{C}{(x-1)^2}$$

(Multiply both sides by $(x+3)(x-1)^2$.)

$$x^2 + 1 = A(x-1)^2 + B(x+3)(x-1) + C(x+3)$$

Let $x=-3$: then $(-3)^2+1=A(-3-1)^2+B(-3+3)(-3-1)+C(-3+3)$

$$\rightarrow 10=16A \rightarrow A=\frac{5}{8}$$

Let $x=1$: then $1^2+1=A(1-1)^2+B(1+3)(1-1)+C(1+3)$

$$\rightarrow 2=4C \rightarrow C=\frac{1}{2}$$

Let $x=0$: then $0^2+1=A(0-1)^2+B(0+3)(0-1)+C(0+3)$

$$\rightarrow 1=A-3B+3C \rightarrow 1=\frac{5}{8}-3B+3\left(\frac{1}{2}\right)$$

$$\rightarrow 3B=\frac{9}{8} \rightarrow B=\frac{3}{8}$$

$$\frac{x^2+1}{x^3+x^2-5x+3}=\frac{\left(\frac{5}{8}\right)}{x+3}+\frac{\left(\frac{3}{8}\right)}{x-1}+\frac{\left(\frac{1}{2}\right)}{(x-1)^2}$$

37. Find the partial fraction decomposition:

$$\frac{x^3}{(x^2+16)^3}=\frac{Ax+B}{x^2+16}+\frac{Cx+D}{(x^2+16)^2}+\frac{Ex+F}{(x^2+16)^3}$$

(Multiply both sides by $(x^2+16)^3$.)

$$x^3=(Ax+B)(x^2+16)^2+(Cx+D)(x^2+16)+Ex+F$$
$$x^3=(Ax+B)(x^4+32x^2+256)+Cx^3+Dx^2+16Cx+16D+Ex+F$$
$$x^3=Ax^5+Bx^4+32Ax^3+32Bx^2+256Ax+256B+Cx^3+Dx^2$$
$$+16Cx+16D+Ex+F$$
$$x^3=Ax^5+Bx^4+(32A+C)x^3+(32B+D)x^2+(256A+16C+E)x$$
$$+(256B+16D+F)$$

$$A=0$$
$$B=0$$
$$32A+C=1 \rightarrow 32(0)+C=1 \rightarrow C=1$$
$$32B+D=0 \rightarrow 32(0)+D=0 \rightarrow D=0$$
$$256A+16C+E=0 \rightarrow 256(0)+16(1)+E=0 \rightarrow E=-16$$
$$256B+16D+F=0 \rightarrow 256(0)+16(0)+F=0 \rightarrow F=0$$

$$\frac{x^3}{(x^2+16)^3}=\frac{x}{(x^2+16)^2}+\frac{-16x}{(x^2+16)^3}$$

38. Find the partial fraction decomposition:

$$\frac{x^2}{(x^2+4)^3}=\frac{Ax+B}{x^2+4}+\frac{Cx+D}{(x^2+4)^2}+\frac{Ex+F}{(x^2+4)^3}$$

(Multiply both sides by $(x^2+4)^3$.)

$$x^2=(Ax+B)(x^2+4)^2+(Cx+D)(x^2+4)+Ex+F$$
$$x^2=(Ax+B)(x^4+8x^2+16)+Cx^3+Dx^2+4Cx+4D+Ex+F$$

$$x^2 = Ax^5 + Bx^4 + 8Ax^3 + 8Bx^2 + 16Ax + 16B + Cx^3 + Dx^2$$
$$+ 4Cx + 4D + Ex + F$$
$$x^2 = Ax^5 + Bx^4 + (8A + C)x^3 + (8B + D)x^2 + (16A + 4C + E)x$$
$$+ (16B + 4D + F)$$
$$A = 0$$
$$B = 0$$
$$8A + C = 0 \rightarrow 8(0) + C = 0 \rightarrow C = 0$$
$$8B + D = 1 \rightarrow 8(0) + D = 1 \rightarrow D = 1$$
$$16A + 4C + E = 0 \rightarrow 16(0) + 4(0) + E = 0 \rightarrow E = 0$$
$$16B + 4D + F = 0 \rightarrow 16(0) + 4(1) + F = 0 \rightarrow F = -4$$
$$\frac{x^2}{(x^2+4)^3} = \frac{1}{(x^2+4)^2} + \frac{-4}{(x^2+4)^3}$$

39. Find the partial fraction decomposition:
$$\frac{4}{2x^2 - 5x - 3} = \frac{4}{(x-3)(2x+1)} = \frac{A}{x-3} + \frac{B}{2x+1}$$
(Multiply both sides by $(x-3)(2x+1)$.)
$$4 = A(2x+1) + B(x-3)$$
Let $x = -\frac{1}{2}$: then $4 = A\left(2\left(-\frac{1}{2}\right)+1\right) + B\left(-\frac{1}{2} - 3\right)$
$$\rightarrow 4 = -\frac{7}{2}B \rightarrow B = -\frac{8}{7}$$
Let $x = 3$: then $4 = A(2(3)+1) + B(3-3) \rightarrow 4 = 7A \rightarrow A = \frac{4}{7}$
$$\frac{4}{2x^2 - 5x - 3} = \frac{4}{(x-3)(2x+1)} = \frac{\left(\frac{4}{7}\right)}{x-3} + \frac{\left(-\frac{8}{7}\right)}{2x+1}$$

40. Find the partial fraction decomposition:
$$\frac{4x}{2x^2 + 3x - 2} = \frac{4x}{(x+2)(2x-1)} = \frac{A}{x+2} + \frac{B}{2x-1}$$
(Multiply both sides by $(x+2)(2x-1)$.)
$$4x = A(2x-1) + B(x+2)$$
Let $x = \frac{1}{2}$: then $4\left(\frac{1}{2}\right) = A\left(2\left(\frac{1}{2}\right)-1\right) + B\left(\frac{1}{2}+2\right) \rightarrow 2 = \frac{5}{3}B \rightarrow B = \frac{4}{5}$

Let $x = -2$: then $4(-2) = A(2(-2)-1) + B(-2+2)$
$$\rightarrow -8 = -5A \rightarrow A = \frac{8}{5}$$
$$\frac{4x}{2x^2 + 3x - 2} = \frac{4x}{(x+2)(2x-1)} = \frac{\left(\frac{8}{5}\right)}{x+2} + \frac{\left(\frac{4}{5}\right)}{2x-1}$$

41. Find the partial fraction decomposition:

$$\frac{2x+3}{x^4-9x^2}=\frac{2x+3}{x^2(x-3)(x+3)}=\frac{A}{x}+\frac{B}{x^2}+\frac{C}{x-3}+\frac{D}{x+3}$$

(Multiply both sides by $x^2(x-3)(x+3)$.)

$$2x+3=Ax(x-3)(x+3)+B(x-3)(x+3)+Cx^2(x+3)+Dx^2(x-3)$$

Let $x=0$: then

$$2\cdot 0+3=A\cdot 0(0-3)(0+3)+B(0-3)(0+3)+C\cdot 0^2(0+3)+D\cdot 0^2(0-3)$$

$$\rightarrow 3=-9B \rightarrow B=-\frac{1}{3}$$

Let $x=3$: then

$$2\cdot 3+3=A\cdot 3(3-3)(3+3)+B(3-3)(3+3)+C\cdot 3^2(3+3)+D\cdot 3^2(3-3)$$

$$\rightarrow 9=54C \rightarrow C=\frac{1}{6}$$

Let $x=-3$: then

$$2(-3)+3=A(-3)(-3-3)(-3+3)+B(-3-3)(-3+3)+C(-3)^2(-3+3)$$
$$+D(-3)^2(-3-3)$$

$$\rightarrow -3=-54D \rightarrow D=\frac{1}{18}$$

Let $x=1$: then

$$2\cdot 1+3=A\cdot 1(1-3)(1+3)+B(1-3)(1+3)+C\cdot 1^2(1+3)+D\cdot 1^2(1-3)$$

$$\rightarrow 5=-8A-8B+4C-2D$$

$$\rightarrow 5=-8A-8\left(-\frac{1}{3}\right)+4\left(\frac{1}{6}\right)-2\left(\frac{1}{18}\right)$$

$$\rightarrow 5=-8A+\frac{8}{3}+\frac{2}{3}-\frac{1}{9} \rightarrow -8A=\frac{16}{9} \rightarrow A=-\frac{2}{9}$$

$$\frac{2x+3}{x^4-9x^2}=\frac{2x+3}{x^2(x-3)(x+3)}=\frac{\left(-\frac{2}{9}\right)}{x}+\frac{\left(-\frac{1}{3}\right)}{x^2}+\frac{\left(\frac{1}{6}\right)}{x-3}+\frac{\left(\frac{1}{18}\right)}{x+3}$$

42. Find the partial fraction decomposition:

$$\frac{x^2+9}{x^4-2x^2-8}=\frac{x^2+9}{(x^2+2)(x-2)(x+2)}=\frac{A}{x-2}+\frac{B}{x+2}+\frac{Cx+D}{x^2+2}$$

(Multiply both sides by $(x^2+2)(x-2)(x+2)$.)

$$x^2+9=A(x^2+2)(x+2)+B(x-2)(x^2+2)+(Cx+D)(x-2)(x+2)$$

Let $x=2$: then

$$2^2+9=A(2^2+2)(2+2)+B(2-2)(2^2+2)+(C(2)+D)(2-2)(2+2)$$

$$\rightarrow 13=24A \rightarrow A=\frac{13}{24}$$

Let $x = -2$: then

$$(-2)^2 + 9 = A((-2)^2 + 2)(-2+2) + B(-2-2)((-2)^2 + 2)$$
$$+ (C(-2) + D)(-2-2)(-2+2)$$
$$\rightarrow 13 = -24B \rightarrow B = -\frac{13}{24}$$

Let $x = 0$: then

$$0^2 + 9 = A(0^2 + 2)(0+2) + B(0-2)(0^2 + 2) + (C(0) + D)(0-2)(0+2)$$
$$\rightarrow 9 = 4A - 4B - 4D \rightarrow 9 = \frac{13}{16} + \frac{13}{6} - 4D$$
$$\rightarrow 4D = -\frac{14}{3} \rightarrow D = -\frac{7}{6}$$

Let $x = 1$: then

$$1^2 + 9 = A(1^2 + 2)(1+2) + B(1-2)(1^2 + 2) + (C(1) + D)(1-2)(1+2)$$
$$\rightarrow 10 = 9A - 3B - 3C - 3D$$
$$\rightarrow 10 = \frac{39}{8} + \frac{13}{8} - 3C + \frac{7}{2}$$
$$\rightarrow 3C = 0 \rightarrow C = 0$$

$$\frac{x^2+9}{x^4 - 2x^2 - 8} = \frac{x^2+9}{(x^2+2)(x-2)(x+2)} = \frac{\left(\frac{13}{24}\right)}{x-2} + \frac{\left(-\frac{13}{24}\right)}{x+2} + \frac{\left(-\frac{7}{6}\right)}{x^2+2}$$

Systems of Equations and Inequalities

12.7 Systems of Nonlinear Equations

1. $\begin{cases} y = x^2 + 1 \\ y = x + 1 \end{cases}$

Graph: $y_1 = x^2 + 1; \quad y_2 = x + 1$

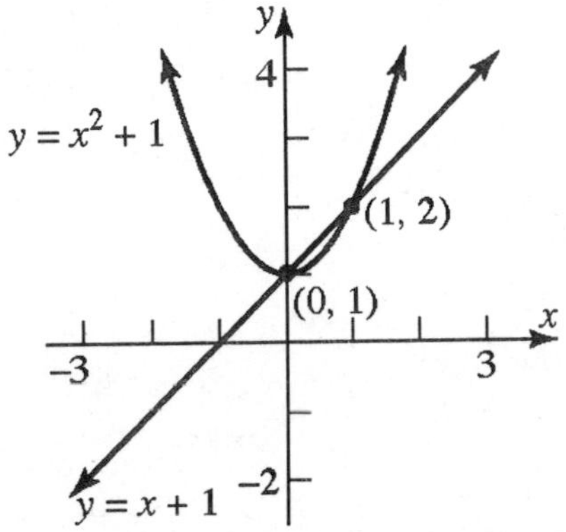

(0, 1) and (1, 2) are the intersection points.

Solve by substitution:

$$\begin{aligned} x^2 + 1 &= x + 1 \\ x^2 - x &= 0 \\ x(x-1) &= 0 \\ x = 0 \quad &\text{or} \quad x = 1 \\ y = 1 \quad &\quad\;\; y = 2 \end{aligned}$$

Solutions: (0, 1) and (1, 2)

2. $\begin{cases} y = x^2 + 1 \\ y = 4x + 1 \end{cases}$

Graph: $y_1 = x^2 + 1; \quad y_2 = 4x + 1$

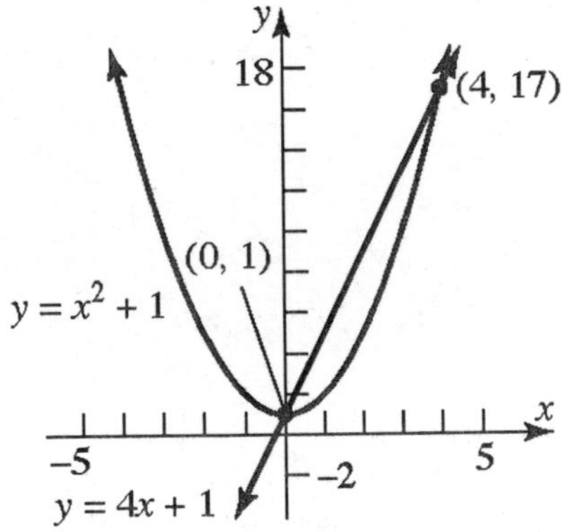

(0, 1) and (4, 17) are the intersection points.

Solve by substitution:

$$\begin{aligned} x^2 + 1 &= 4x + 1 \\ x^2 - 4x &= 0 \\ x(x-4) &= 0 \\ x = 0 \quad &\text{or} \quad x = 4 \\ y = 1 \quad &\quad\;\; y = 17 \end{aligned}$$

Solutions: (0, 1) and (4, 17)

3. $\begin{cases} y = \sqrt{36 - x^2} \\ y = 8 - x \end{cases}$

Graph: $y_1 = \sqrt{36 - x^2}$; $y_2 = 8 - x$

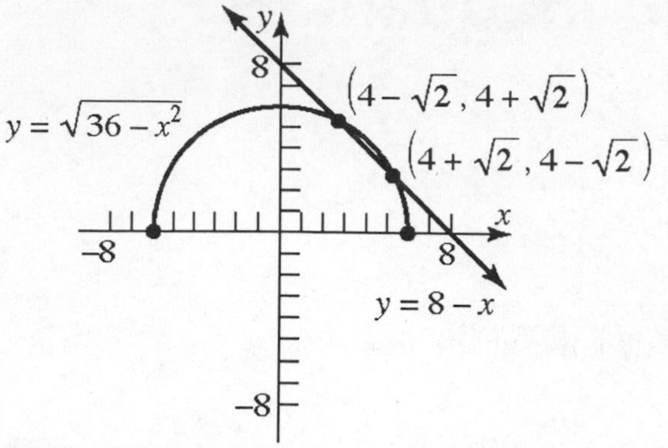

(2.59, 5.41) and (5.41, 2.59) are the intersection points.

Solve by substitution:

$$\sqrt{36 - x^2} = 8 - x$$
$$36 - x^2 = 64 - 16x + x^2$$
$$2x^2 - 16x + 28 = 0$$
$$x^2 - 8x + 14 = 0$$
$$x = \frac{8 \pm \sqrt{64 - 56}}{2}$$
$$x = \frac{8 \pm 2\sqrt{2}}{2}$$
$$x = 4 \pm \sqrt{2}$$

If $x = 4 + \sqrt{2}$, $y = 8 - \left(4 + \sqrt{2}\right) = 4 - \sqrt{2}$

If $x = 4 - \sqrt{2}$, $y = 8 - \left(4 - \sqrt{2}\right) = 4 + \sqrt{2}$

Solutions:

$\left(4 + \sqrt{2}, 4 - \sqrt{2}\right)$ and $\left(4 - \sqrt{2}, 4 + \sqrt{2}\right)$

4. $\begin{cases} y = \sqrt{4 - x^2} \\ y = 2x + 4 \end{cases}$

Graph: $y_1 = \sqrt{4 - x^2}$; $y_2 = 2x + 4$

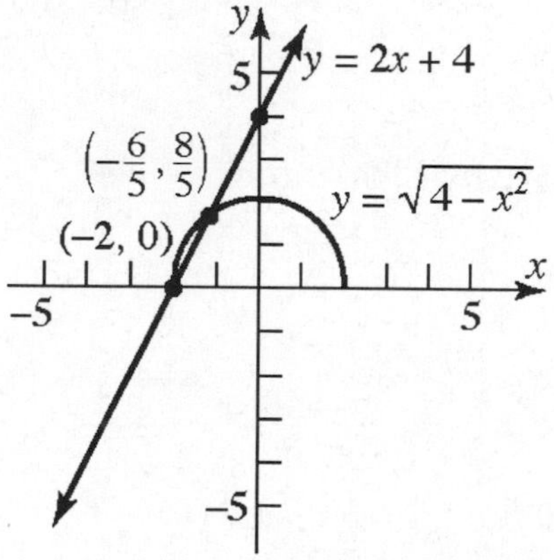

(−2, 0) and (−1.2, 1.6) are the intersection points.
Note: (−2, 0) is difficult to find using INTERSECT because it is at the end of the domain of the function.

Solve by substitution:

$$\sqrt{4 - x^2} = 2x + 4$$
$$4 - x^2 = 4x^2 + 16x + 16$$
$$5x^2 + 16x + 12 = 0$$
$$(x + 2)(5x + 6) = 0$$
$$x = -2 \text{ or } x = -\frac{6}{5}$$
$$y = 0 \quad \text{or } y = \frac{8}{5}$$

Solutions: $(-2, 0)$ and $\left(-\frac{6}{5}, \frac{8}{5}\right)$

5. $\begin{cases} y = \sqrt{x} \\ y = 2 - x \end{cases}$

Graph: $y_1 = \sqrt{x}; \quad y_2 = 2 - x$

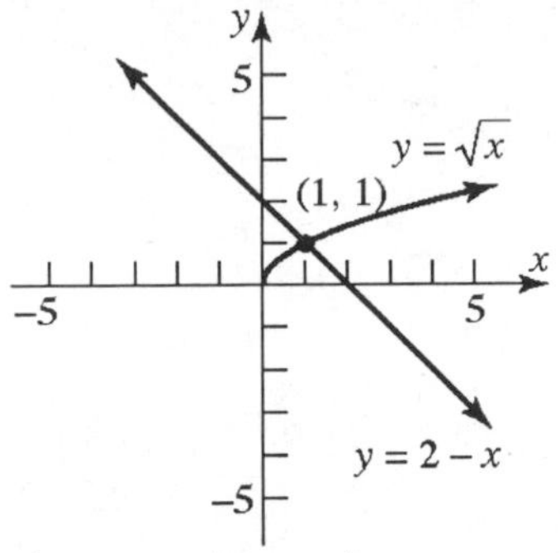

(1, 1) is the intersection point.

Solve by substitution:

$$\sqrt{x} = 2 - x$$
$$x = 4 - 4x + x^2$$
$$x^2 - 5x + 4 = 0$$
$$(x-4)(x-1) = 0$$
$$x = 4 \quad \text{or } x = 1$$
$$y = -2 \quad \text{or } y = 1$$

Eliminate (4, –2); it does not check.
Solution: (1, 1)

6. $\begin{cases} y = \sqrt{x} \\ y = 6 - x \end{cases}$

Graph: $y_1 = \sqrt{x}; \quad y_2 = 6 - x$

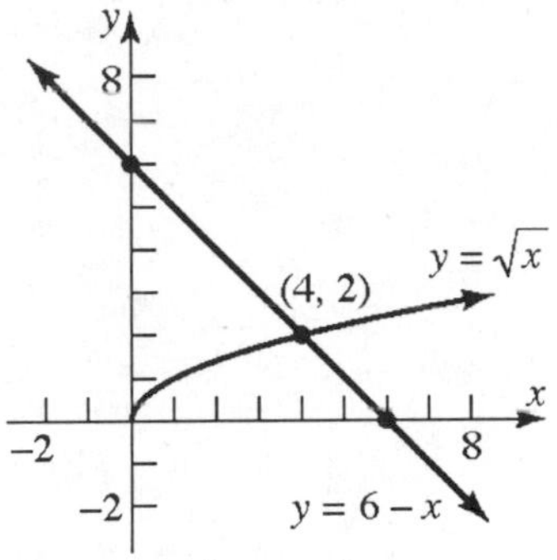

(4, 2) is the intersection point.

Solve by substitution:

$$\sqrt{x} = 6 - x$$
$$x = 36 - 12x + x^2$$
$$x^2 - 13x + 36 = 0$$
$$(x-4)(x-9) = 0$$
$$x = 4 \quad \text{or } x = 9$$
$$y = 2 \quad \text{or } y = -3$$

Eliminate (9, –3); it does not check.
Solution: (4, 2)

7. $\begin{cases} x = 2y \\ x = y^2 - 2y \end{cases}$

Solve each equation for y in order to enter it into the graphing utility:

$$y^2 - 2y + 1 = x + 1 \rightarrow (y-1)^2 = x + 1 \rightarrow y - 1 = \pm\sqrt{x+1} \rightarrow y = 1 \pm \sqrt{x+1}$$

Graph: $y_1 = \frac{x}{2}; \; y_2 = 1 + \sqrt{x+1}; \; y_3 = 1 - \sqrt{x+1}$

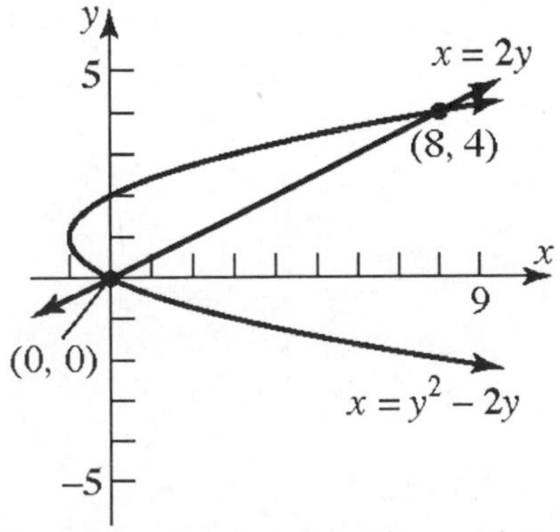

(0, 0) and (8, 4) are the intersection points.

Solve by substitution:

$$2y = y^2 - 2y$$
$$y^2 - 4y = 0$$
$$y(y-4) = 0$$
$$y = 0 \text{ or } y = 4$$
$$x = 0 \text{ or } x = 8$$

Solutions: (0, 0) and (8, 4)

8. $\begin{cases} y = x - 1 \\ y = x^2 - 6x + 9 \end{cases}$

Graph: $y_1 = x - 1$; $y_2 = x^2 - 6x + 9$;

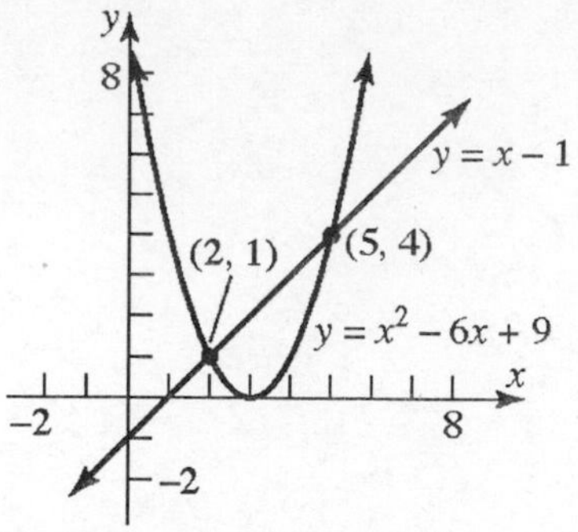

(2, 1) and (5, 4) are the intersection points.

Solve by substitution:

$$x^2 - 6x + 9 = x - 1$$
$$x^2 - 7x + 10 = 0$$
$$(x - 2)(x - 5) = 0$$
$$x = 2 \text{ or } x = 5$$
$$y = 1 \text{ or } y = 4$$

Solutions: (2, 1) and (5, 4)

9. $\begin{cases} x^2 + y^2 = 4 \\ x^2 + 2x + y^2 = 0 \end{cases}$

Graph: $y_1 = \sqrt{4 - x^2}$; $y_2 = -\sqrt{4 - x^2}$; $y_3 = \sqrt{-x^2 - 2x}$; $y_4 = -\sqrt{-x^2 - 2x}$

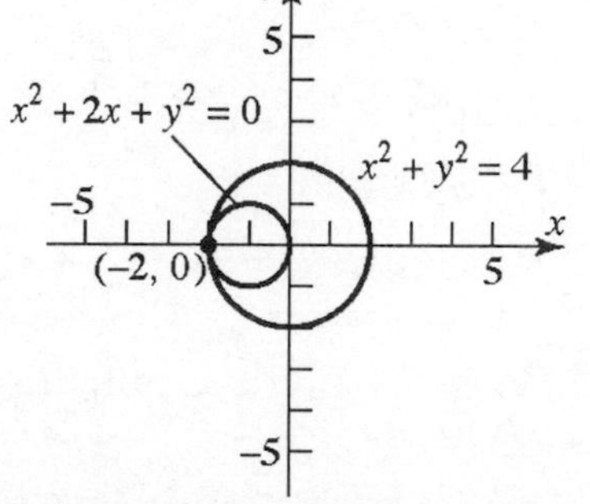

(–2, 0) is the intersection point. Note: This intersection point is impossible to find on your graphing utility unless you have just the right window and make an excellent guess.

Substitute 4 for $x^2 + y^2$ in the second equation:

$$2x + 4 = 0$$
$$2x = -4$$
$$x = -2$$
$$y = \sqrt{4 - (-2)^2} = 0$$

Solution: (–2, 0)

10. $\begin{cases} x^2 + y^2 = 8 \\ x^2 + y^2 + 4y = 0 \end{cases}$

Graph: $y_1 = \sqrt{8 - x^2}$; $y_2 = -\sqrt{8 - x^2}$; $y_3 = -2 + \sqrt{4 - x^2}$; $y_4 = -2 - \sqrt{4 - x^2}$

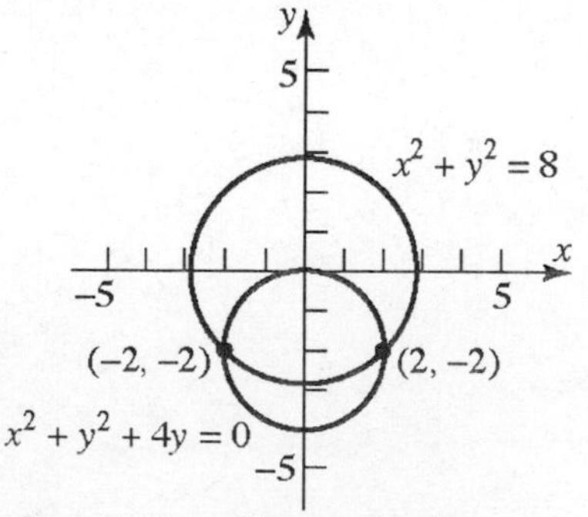

(–2, –2) and (2, –2) are the intersection points.

Substitute 8 for $x^2 + y^2$ in the second equation:

$$8 + 4y = 0$$
$$4y = -8$$
$$y = -2$$
$$x = \pm\sqrt{8 - (-2)^2} = \pm 2$$

Solution: (–2, –2) and (2, –2)

11. $\begin{cases} y = 3x - 5 \\ x^2 + y^2 = 5 \end{cases}$

Graph: $y_1 = 3x - 5$; $y_2 = \sqrt{5 - x^2}$;
$y_3 = -\sqrt{5 - x^2}$

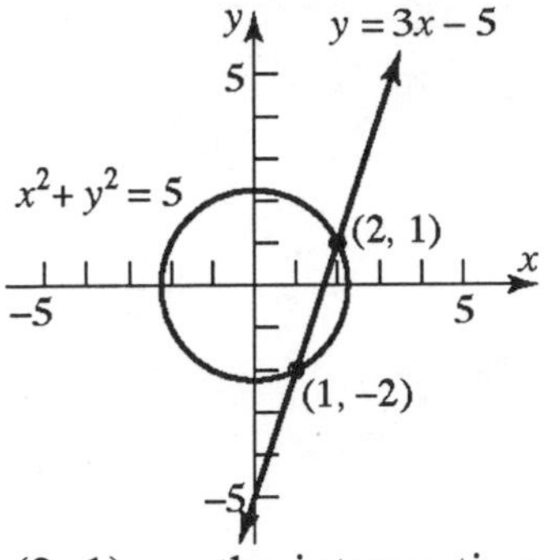

(1, –2) and (2, 1) are the intersection points.

Solve by substitution:

$$x^2 + (3x - 5)^2 = 5$$
$$x^2 + 9x^2 - 30x + 25 = 5$$
$$10x^2 - 30x + 20 = 0$$
$$x^2 - 3x + 2 = 0$$
$$(x - 1)(x - 2) = 0$$
$$x = 1 \quad \text{or} \quad x = 2$$
$$y = 3(1) - 5 \qquad y = 3(2) - 5$$
$$y = -2 \qquad y = 1$$

Solutions: (1, –2) and (2, 1)

12. $\begin{cases} x^2 + y^2 = 10 \\ y = x + 2 \end{cases}$

Graph: $y_1 = x + 2$; $y_2 = \sqrt{10 - x^2}$;
$y_3 = -\sqrt{10 - x^2}$

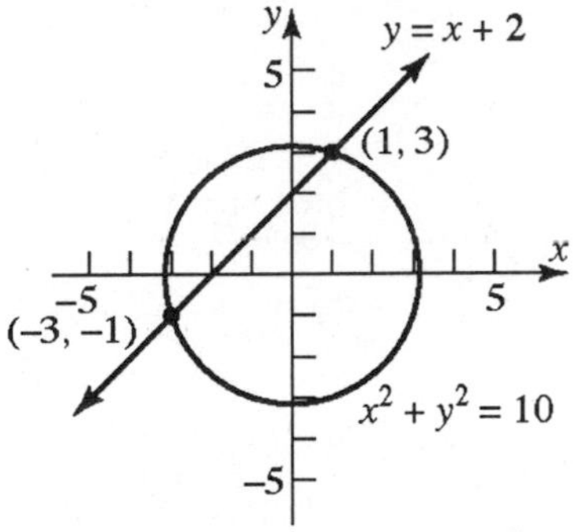

(1, 3) and (–3, –1) are the intersection points.

Solve by substitution:

$$x^2 + (x + 2)^2 = 10$$
$$x^2 + x^2 + 4x + 4 = 10$$
$$2x^2 + 4x - 6 = 0$$
$$x^2 + 2x - 3 = 0$$
$$(x + 3)(x - 1) = 0$$
$$x = -3 \quad \text{or} \quad x = 1$$
$$y = -1 \qquad y = 3$$

Solutions: (–3, –1) and (1, 3)

13. $\begin{cases} x^2 + y^2 = 4 \\ y^2 - x = 4 \end{cases}$

Graph: $y_1 = \sqrt{4 - x^2}$; $y_2 = -\sqrt{4 - x^2}$; $y_3 = \sqrt{x + 4}$; $y_4 = -\sqrt{x + 4}$

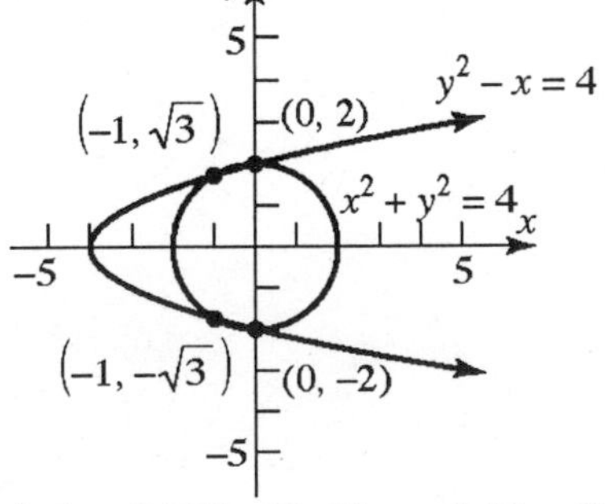

(–1, 1.73), (–1, –1.73), (0, 2), and (0, –2) are the intersection points.

Substitute $x + 4$ for y^2 in the first equation:

$$x^2 + x + 4 = 4$$
$$x^2 + x = 0$$
$$x(x + 1) = 0$$
$$x = 0 \quad \text{or} \quad x = -1$$
$$y^2 = 4 \qquad y^2 = 3$$
$$y = \pm 2 \qquad y^2 = \pm\sqrt{3}$$

Solutions:

$(0, -2), (0, 2), \left(-1, \sqrt{3}\right), \left(-1, -\sqrt{3}\right)$

14. $\begin{cases} x^2 + y^2 = 16 \\ x^2 - 2y = 8 \end{cases}$

Graph: $y_1 = \sqrt{16 - x^2}$; $y_2 = -\sqrt{16 - x^2}$; $y_3 = (x^2 - 8)/2$

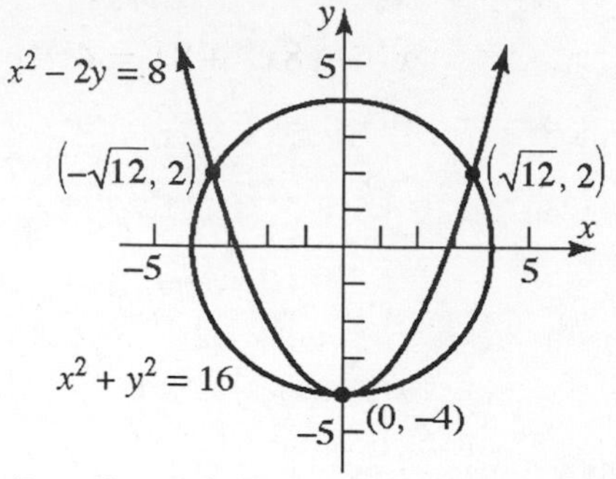

(−3.46, 2), (0, −4), and (3.46, 2) are the intersection points.

Substitute $2y + 8$ for x^2 in the first equation:

$$2y + 8 + y^2 = 16$$
$$y^2 + 2y - 8 = 0$$
$$(y + 4)(y - 2) = 0$$
$$y = -4 \text{ or } y = 2$$
$$x^2 = 0 \text{ or } x^2 = 12$$
$$x = 0 \qquad x = \pm 2\sqrt{3}$$

Solutions: $(0, -4), \left(2\sqrt{3}, 2\right) \left(-2\sqrt{3}, 2\right)$

15. $\begin{cases} xy = 4 \\ x^2 + y^2 = 8 \end{cases}$

Graph: $y_1 = \dfrac{4}{x}$; $y_2 = \sqrt{8 - x^2}$;

$y_3 = -\sqrt{8 - x^2}$

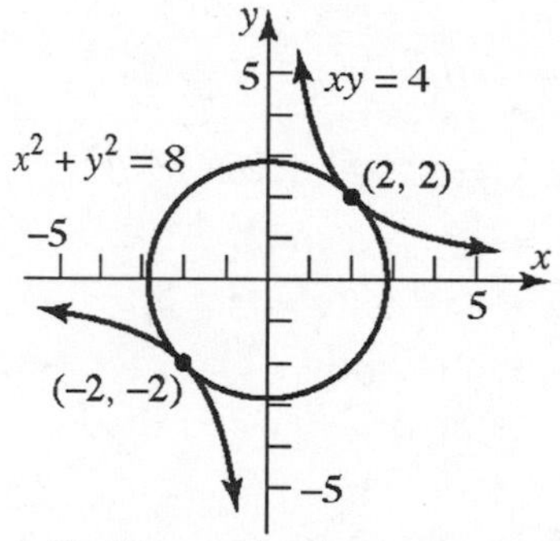

(−2, −2) and (2, 2) are the intersection points.

Solve by substitution:

$$x^2 + \left(\frac{4}{x}\right)^2 = 8$$
$$x^2 + \frac{16}{x^2} = 8$$
$$x^4 + 16 = 8x^2$$
$$x^4 - 8x^2 + 16 = 0$$
$$\left(x^2 - 4\right)^2 = 0$$
$$x^2 - 4 = 0$$
$$x^2 = 4$$
$$x = 2 \text{ or } x = -2$$
$$y = 2 \qquad y = -2$$

Solutions: (−2, −2) and (2, 2)

16. $\begin{cases} x^2 = y \\ xy = 1 \end{cases}$

Graph: $y_1 = x^2$; $y_2 = \dfrac{1}{x}$

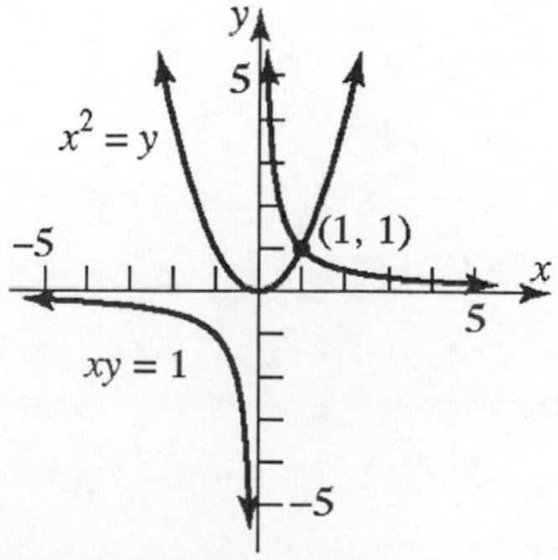

(1, 1) is the intersection point.

Solve by substitution:

$$x^2 = \frac{1}{x}$$
$$x^3 = 1$$
$$x = 1$$
$$y = 1$$

Solutions: (1, 1)

17. $\begin{cases} x^2 + y^2 = 4 \\ y = x^2 - 9 \end{cases}$

Graph: $y_1 = x^2 - 9$; $y_2 = \sqrt{4 - x^2}$; $y_3 = -\sqrt{4 - x^2}$

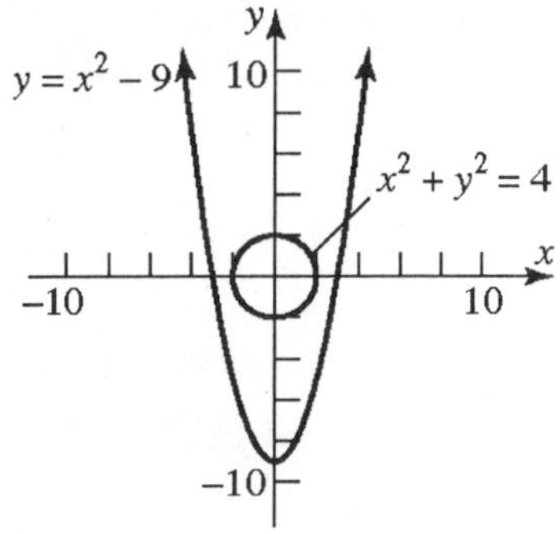

No solution; Inconsistent.

Solve by substitution:

$$x^2 + (x^2 - 9)^2 = 4$$
$$x^2 + x^4 - 18x^2 + 81 = 4$$
$$x^4 - 17x^2 + 77 = 0$$
$$x^2 = \frac{17 \pm \sqrt{289 - 4(77)}}{2}$$
$$x^2 = \frac{17 \pm \sqrt{-19}}{2}$$

There are no real solutions to this expression; Inconsistent.

18. $\begin{cases} xy = 1 \\ y = 2x + 1 \end{cases}$

Graph: $y_1 = \frac{1}{x}$; $y_2 = 2x + 1$

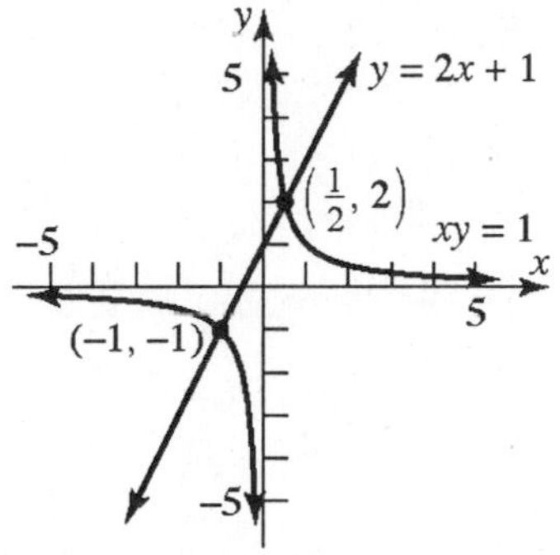

(–1, –1) and (0.5, 2) are the intersection points.

Solve by substitution:

$$x(2x + 1) = 1$$
$$2x^2 + x - 1 = 0$$
$$(x + 1)(2x - 1) = 0$$
$$x = -1 \quad \text{or} \quad x = \frac{1}{2}$$
$$y = -1 \qquad y = 2$$

Solutions: $(-1, -1)$ and $\left(\frac{1}{2}, 2\right)$

19. $\begin{cases} y = x^2 - 4 \\ y = 6x - 13 \end{cases}$

Graph: $y_1 = x^2 - 4$; $y_2 = 6x - 13$

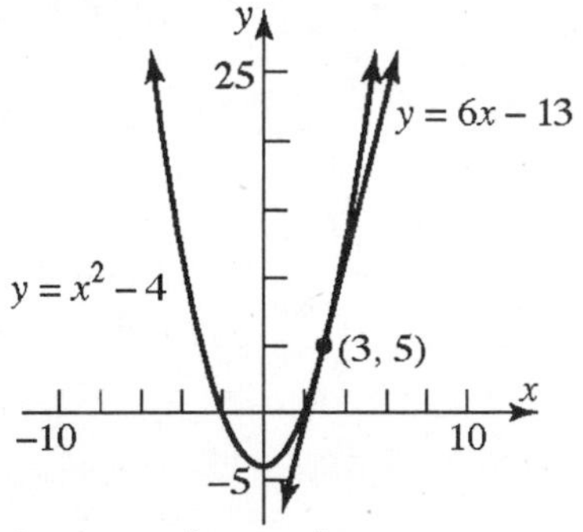

(3,5) is the intersection point.

Solve by substitution:

$$x^2 - 4 = 6x - 13$$
$$x^2 - 6x + 9 = 0$$
$$(x - 3)^2 = 0$$
$$x - 3 = 0$$
$$x = 3$$
$$y = 6(3) - 13 = 5$$

Solutions: (3,5)

20. $\begin{cases} x^2 + y^2 = 10 \\ xy = 3 \end{cases}$

Graph: $y_1 = \frac{3}{x}$; $y_2 = \sqrt{10 - x^2}$;

$y_3 = -\sqrt{10 - x^2}$

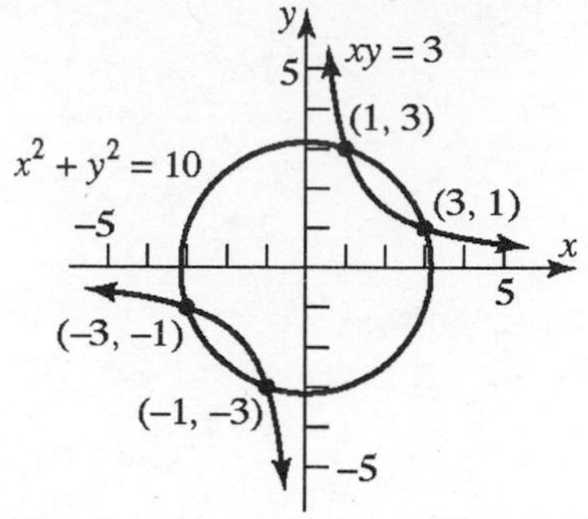

(1, 3), (3, 1), (−3, −1), and (−1, −3) are the intersection points.

Solve by substitution:

$$x^2 + \left(\frac{3}{x}\right)^2 = 10$$
$$x^2 + \frac{9}{x^2} = 10$$
$$x^4 + 9 = 10x^2$$
$$x^4 - 10x^2 + 9 = 0$$
$$(x^2 - 9)(x^2 - 1) = 0$$
$$(x-3)(x+3)(x-1)(x+1) = 0$$
$$x = 3 \text{ or } x = -3 \text{ or } x = 1 \text{ or } x = -1$$
$$y = 1 \quad y = -1 \quad y = 3 \quad y = -3$$

Solutions: (3, 1), (−3, −1), (1, 3), (−1, −3)

21. Solve the second equation for y, substitute into the first equation and solve:

$$\begin{cases} 2x^2 + y^2 = 18 \\ xy = 4 \rightarrow y = \frac{4}{x} \end{cases}$$

$$2x^2 + \left(\frac{4}{x}\right)^2 = 18 \rightarrow 2x^2 + \frac{16}{x^2} = 18$$

$$2x^4 + 16 = 18x^2 \rightarrow 2x^4 - 18x^2 + 16 = 0 \rightarrow x^4 - 9x^2 + 8 = 0 \rightarrow (x^2 - 8)(x^2 - 1) = 0$$

$$x^2 = 8 \rightarrow x = \pm\sqrt{8} = \pm 2\sqrt{2}$$

or $x^2 = 1 \rightarrow x = \pm 1$

If $x = 2\sqrt{2}$: $\quad y = \frac{4}{2\sqrt{2}} = \sqrt{2}$

If $x = -2\sqrt{2}$: $\quad y = \frac{4}{-2\sqrt{2}} = -\sqrt{2}$

If $x = 1$: $\quad y = \frac{4}{1} = 4$

If $x = -1$: $\quad y = \frac{4}{-1} = -4$

Solutions: $\left(2\sqrt{2}, \sqrt{2}\right)$, $\left(-2\sqrt{2}, -\sqrt{2}\right)$, (1, 4), (−1, −4)

22. Solve the second equation for y, substitute into the first equation and solve:

$$\begin{cases} x^2 - y^2 = 21 \\ x + y = 7 \rightarrow y = 7 - x \end{cases}$$

$$x^2 - (7-x)^2 = 21 \rightarrow x^2 - \left(49 - 14x + x^2\right) = 21 \rightarrow 14x = 70 \rightarrow x = 5 \rightarrow y = 7 - 5 = 2$$

Solution: (5, 2)

23. Substitute the first equation into the second equation and solve:

$$\begin{cases} y = 2x+1 \\ 2x^2 + y^2 = 1 \end{cases}$$

$$2x^2 + (2x+1)^2 = 1 \rightarrow 2x^2 + 4x^2 + 4x + 1 = 1 \rightarrow 6x^2 + 4x = 0 \rightarrow 2x(3x+2) = 0$$

$$2x = 0 \rightarrow x = 0$$

$$\text{or} \quad 3x + 2 = 0 \rightarrow x = -\frac{2}{3}$$

If $x = 0$: $\quad y = 2(0) + 1 = 1$

If $x = -\frac{2}{3}$: $\quad y = 2\left(-\frac{2}{3}\right) + 1 = -\frac{4}{3} + 1 = -\frac{1}{3}$

Solutions: $(0, 1), \left(-\frac{2}{3}, -\frac{1}{3}\right)$

24. Solve the second equation for x and substitute into the first equation and solve:

$$\begin{cases} x^2 - 4y^2 = 16 \\ 2y - x = 2 \rightarrow x = 2y - 2 \end{cases}$$

$$(2y-2)^2 - 4y^2 = 16 \rightarrow 4y^2 - 8y + 4 - 4y^2 = 16$$

$$-8y = 12 \rightarrow y = -\frac{3}{2} \rightarrow x = 2\left(-\frac{3}{2}\right) - 2 = -5$$

Solutions: $\left(-5, -\frac{3}{2}\right)$

25. Solve the first equation for y, substitute into the second equation and solve:

$$\begin{cases} x + y + 1 = 0 \rightarrow y = -x - 1 \\ x^2 + y^2 + 6y - x = -5 \end{cases}$$

$$x^2 + (-x-1)^2 + 6(-x-1) - x = -5 \rightarrow x^2 + x^2 + 2x + 1 - 6x - 6 - x = -5$$

$$2x^2 - 5x = 0 \rightarrow x(2x-5) = 0 \rightarrow x = 0 \quad \text{or} \quad x = \frac{5}{2}$$

If $x = 0$: $\quad y = -(0) - 1 = -1$

If $x = \frac{5}{2}$: $\quad y = -\frac{5}{2} - 1 = -\frac{7}{2}$

Solutions: $(0, -1), \left(\frac{5}{2}, -\frac{7}{2}\right)$

26. Solve the second equation for y, substitute into the first equation and solve:

$$\begin{cases} 2x^2 - xy + y^2 = 8 \\ xy = 4 \rightarrow y = \frac{4}{x} \end{cases}$$

$$2x^2 - x\left(\frac{4}{x}\right) + \left(\frac{4}{x}\right)^2 = 8 \rightarrow 2x^2 - 4 + \frac{16}{x^2} = 8 \rightarrow 2x^4 + 16 = 12x^2 \rightarrow x^4 - 6x^2 + 8 = 0$$

$$(x^2 - 4)(x^2 - 2) = 0 \rightarrow (x-2)(x+2)\left(x - \sqrt{2}\right)\left(x + \sqrt{2}\right) = 0$$

$x = 2$ or $x = -2$ or $x = \sqrt{2}$ or $x = -\sqrt{2}$

$y = 2$ $\quad y = -2$ $\quad y = 2\sqrt{2}$ $\quad y = -2\sqrt{2}$

Solutions: $(2, 2), (-2, -2), \left(\sqrt{2}, 2\sqrt{2}\right), \left(-\sqrt{2}, -2\sqrt{2}\right)$

27. Solve the second equation for y, substitute into the first equation and solve:

$$\begin{cases} 4x^2 - 3xy + 9y^2 = 15 \\ 2x + 3y = 5 \rightarrow y = -\frac{2}{3}x + \frac{5}{3} \end{cases}$$

$$4x^2 - 3x\left(-\frac{2}{3}x + \frac{5}{3}\right) + 9\left(-\frac{2}{3}x + \frac{5}{3}\right)^2 = 15 \rightarrow 4x^2 + 2x^2 - 5x + 4x^2 - 20x + 25 = 15$$

$$10x^2 - 25x + 10 = 0 \rightarrow 2x^2 - 5x + 2 = 0$$

$$(2x-1)(x-2) = 0 \rightarrow x = \frac{1}{2} \text{ or } x = 2$$

If $x = \frac{1}{2}$: $\quad y = -\frac{2}{3}\left(\frac{1}{2}\right) + \frac{5}{3} = \frac{4}{3}$

If $x = 2$: $\quad y = -\frac{2}{3}(2) + \frac{5}{3} = \frac{1}{3}$

Solutions: $\left(\frac{1}{2}, \frac{4}{3}\right), \left(2, \frac{1}{3}\right)$

28. Solve the second equation for x, substitute into the first equation and solve:

$$\begin{cases} 2y^2 - 3xy + 6y + 2x + 4 = 0 \\ 2x - 3y + 4 = 0 \rightarrow 2x = 3y - 4 \rightarrow x = \frac{3y-4}{2} \end{cases}$$

$$2y^2 - 3\left(\frac{3y-4}{2}\right)y + 6y + 2\left(\frac{3y-4}{2}\right) = -4$$

$$2y^2 - \frac{9}{2}y^2 + 6y + 6y + 3y - 4 = -4 \rightarrow -\frac{5}{2}y^2 + 15y = 0$$

$$-5y^2 + 30y = 0 \rightarrow -5y(y-6) = 0 \rightarrow y = 0 \text{ or } y = 6 \rightarrow x = -2 \quad x = 7$$

Solutions: $(-2, 0), (7, 6)$

29. Multiply each side of the second equation by 4 and add the equations to eliminate y:

$$\begin{cases} x^2 - 4y^2 = -7 \longrightarrow x^2 - 4y^2 = -7 \\ 3x^2 + y^2 = 31 \xrightarrow{4} \underline{12x^2 + 4y^2 = 124} \end{cases}$$

$$13x^2 \qquad = 117 \rightarrow x^2 = 9 \rightarrow x = \pm 3$$

If $x = 3$: $\quad 3(3)^2 + y^2 = 31 \rightarrow y^2 = 4 \rightarrow y = \pm 2$

If $x = -3$: $\quad 3(-3)^2 + y^2 = 31 \rightarrow y^2 = 4 \rightarrow y = \pm 2$

Solutions: $(3, 2), (3, -2), (-3, 2), (-3, -2)$

30. Multiply each side of the second equation by –2 and add the equations to eliminate y:

$$\begin{cases} 3x^2 - 2y^2 = -5 \longrightarrow & 3x^2 - 2y^2 = -5 \\ 2x^2 - y^2 = -2 \xrightarrow{-2} & \underline{-4x^2 + 2y^2 = 4} \end{cases}$$

$$-x^2 \quad = -1 \rightarrow x^2 = 1 \rightarrow x = \pm 1$$

If $x = 1$: $2(1)^2 - y^2 = -2 \rightarrow y^2 = 4 \rightarrow y = \pm 2$

If $x = -1$: $2(-1)^2 - y^2 = -2 \rightarrow y^2 = 4 \rightarrow y = \pm 2$

Solutions: (1, 2), (1, –2), (–1, 2), (–1, –2)

31. Multiply each side of the first equation by 5 and each side of the second equation by 3 to eliminate y:

$$\begin{cases} 7x^2 - 3y^2 = -5 \xrightarrow{5} & 35x^2 - 15y^2 = -25 \\ 3x^2 + 5y^2 = 12 \xrightarrow{3} & \underline{9x^2 + 15y^2 = 36} \end{cases}$$

$$44x^2 \quad = 11 \rightarrow x^2 = \frac{1}{4} \rightarrow x = \pm\frac{1}{2}$$

If $x = \frac{1}{2}$: $3\left(\frac{1}{2}\right)^2 + 5y^2 = 12 \rightarrow 5y^2 = \frac{45}{4} \rightarrow y^2 = \frac{9}{4} \rightarrow y = \pm\frac{3}{2}$

If $x = -\frac{1}{2}$: $3\left(-\frac{1}{2}\right)^2 + 5y^2 = 12 \rightarrow 5y^2 = \frac{45}{4} \rightarrow y^2 = \frac{9}{4} \rightarrow y = \pm\frac{3}{2}$

Solutions: $\left(\frac{1}{2}, \frac{3}{2}\right), \left(\frac{1}{2}, -\frac{3}{2}\right), \left(-\frac{1}{2}, \frac{3}{2}\right), \left(-\frac{1}{2}, -\frac{3}{2}\right)$

32. Multiply each side of the first equation by –2 and add the equations to eliminate x:

$$\begin{cases} x^2 - 3y^2 = -1 \xrightarrow{-2} & -2x^2 + 6y^2 = 2 \\ 2x^2 - 7y^2 = -5 \longrightarrow & \underline{2x^2 - 7y^2 = -5} \end{cases}$$

$$-y^2 = -3 \rightarrow y^2 = 3 \rightarrow y = \pm\sqrt{3}$$

If $y = \sqrt{3}$: $x^2 - 3\left(\sqrt{3}\right)^2 = -1 \rightarrow x^2 = 8 \rightarrow x = \pm 2\sqrt{2}$

If $y = -\sqrt{3}$: $x^2 - 3\left(-\sqrt{3}\right)^2 = -1 \rightarrow x^2 = 8 \rightarrow x = \pm 2\sqrt{2}$

Solutions: $\left(2\sqrt{2}, \sqrt{3}\right)\left(2\sqrt{2}, -\sqrt{3}\right)\left(-2\sqrt{2}, \sqrt{3}\right)\left(-2\sqrt{2}, -\sqrt{3}\right)$

33. Multiply each side of the second equation by 2 and add to eliminate xy:

$$\begin{cases} x^2 + 2xy = 10 \longrightarrow & x^2 + 2xy = 10 \\ 3x^2 - xy = 2 \xrightarrow{2} & \underline{6x^2 - 2xy = 4} \end{cases}$$

$$7x^2 \quad = 14 \rightarrow x^2 = 2 \rightarrow x = \pm\sqrt{2}$$

If $x = \sqrt{2}$: $3\left(\sqrt{2}\right)^2 - \sqrt{2} \cdot y = 2 \rightarrow -\sqrt{2} \cdot y = -4 \rightarrow y = \frac{4}{\sqrt{2}} \rightarrow y = 2\sqrt{2}$

If $x = -\sqrt{2}$: $3\left(-\sqrt{2}\right)^2 - \left(-\sqrt{2}\right)y = 2 \rightarrow \sqrt{2} \cdot y = -4 \rightarrow y = \frac{-4}{\sqrt{2}} \rightarrow y = -2\sqrt{2}$

Solutions: $\left(\sqrt{2}, 2\sqrt{2}\right)\left(-\sqrt{2}, -2\sqrt{2}\right)$

34. Multiply each side of the second equation by –5 and add to eliminate xy:

$$\begin{cases} 5xy+13y^2=-36 \longrightarrow & 5xy+13y^2=-36 \\ xy+7y^2=6 \xrightarrow{-5} & \underline{-5xy-35y^2=-30} \end{cases}$$

$$-22y^2=-66 \rightarrow y^2=3 \rightarrow y=\pm\sqrt{3}$$

If $y=\sqrt{3}$: $x(\sqrt{3})+7(\sqrt{3})^2=6 \rightarrow \sqrt{3}\cdot x=-15 \rightarrow x=\dfrac{-15}{\sqrt{3}} \rightarrow x=-5\sqrt{3}$

If $y=-\sqrt{3}$: $x(-\sqrt{3})+7(-\sqrt{3})^2=6 \rightarrow -\sqrt{3}\cdot x=-15 \rightarrow x=\dfrac{15}{\sqrt{3}} \rightarrow x=5\sqrt{3}$

Solutions: $(-5\sqrt{3},\sqrt{3}),(5\sqrt{3},-\sqrt{3})$

35. Multiply each side of the first equation by 2 and add the equations to eliminate y:

$$\begin{cases} 2x^2+y^2=2 \xrightarrow{2} & 4x^2+2y^2=4 \\ x^2-2y^2=-8 \longrightarrow & \underline{x^2-2y^2=-8} \end{cases}$$

$$5x^2 \quad =-4 \rightarrow x^2=-\frac{4}{5}$$

No solution. The system is inconsistent.

36. Multiply each side of the first equation by 2 and add the equations to eliminate x:

$$\begin{cases} -x^2+y^2=-4 \xrightarrow{2} & -2x^2+2y^2=-8 \\ 2x^2+3y^2=6 \longrightarrow & \underline{2x^2+3y^2=6} \end{cases}$$

$$5y^2=-2 \rightarrow y^2=-\frac{2}{5}$$

No solution. The system is inconsistent.

37. Multiply each side of the second equation by 2 and add the equations to eliminate y:

$$\begin{cases} x^2+2y^2=16 \longrightarrow & x^2+2y^2=16 \\ 4x^2-y^2=24 \xrightarrow{2} & \underline{8x^2-2y^2=48} \end{cases}$$

$$9x^2 \quad =64 \rightarrow x^2=\frac{64}{9} \rightarrow x=\pm\frac{8}{3}$$

If $x=\frac{8}{3}$: $\left(\frac{8}{3}\right)^2+2y^2=16 \rightarrow 2y^2=\frac{80}{9} \rightarrow y^2=\frac{40}{9} \rightarrow y=\pm\frac{2\sqrt{10}}{3}$

If $x=-\frac{8}{3}$: $\left(-\frac{8}{3}\right)^2+2y^2=16 \rightarrow 2y^2=\frac{80}{9} \rightarrow y^2=\frac{40}{9} \rightarrow y=\pm\frac{2\sqrt{10}}{3}$

Solutions: $\left(\frac{8}{3},\frac{2\sqrt{10}}{3}\right),\left(\frac{8}{3},\frac{-2\sqrt{10}}{3}\right),\left(-\frac{8}{3},\frac{2\sqrt{10}}{3}\right),\left(-\frac{8}{3},\frac{-2\sqrt{10}}{3}\right)$

38. Multiply each side of the first equation by 2 and add the equations to eliminate y:

$$\begin{cases} 4x^2+3y^2=4 \xrightarrow{2} & 8x^2+6y^2=8 \\ 2x^2-6y^2=-3 \longrightarrow & \underline{2x^2-6y^2=-3} \end{cases}$$

$$10x^2 \quad =5 \rightarrow x^2=\frac{1}{2} \rightarrow x=\pm\frac{\sqrt{2}}{2}$$

If $x = \frac{\sqrt{2}}{2}$: $\quad 4\left(\frac{\sqrt{2}}{2}\right)^2 + 3y^2 = 4 \rightarrow 3y^2 = 2 \rightarrow y^2 = \frac{2}{3} \rightarrow y = \pm\frac{\sqrt{6}}{3}$

If $x = -\frac{\sqrt{2}}{2}$: $\quad 4\left(-\frac{\sqrt{2}}{2}\right)^2 + 3y^2 = 4 \rightarrow 3y^2 = 2 \rightarrow y^2 = \frac{2}{3} \rightarrow y = \pm\frac{\sqrt{6}}{3}$

Solutions: $\left(\frac{\sqrt{2}}{2}, \frac{\sqrt{6}}{3}\right), \left(\frac{\sqrt{2}}{2}, -\frac{\sqrt{6}}{3}\right), \left(-\frac{\sqrt{2}}{2}, \frac{\sqrt{6}}{3}\right), \left(-\frac{\sqrt{2}}{2}, -\frac{\sqrt{6}}{3}\right)$

39. Multiply each side of the second equation by 2 and add the equations to eliminate y:

$$\begin{cases} \frac{5}{x^2} - \frac{2}{y^2} = -3 \longrightarrow \frac{5}{x^2} - \frac{2}{y^2} = -3 \\ \frac{3}{x^2} + \frac{1}{y^2} = 7 \xrightarrow{2} \frac{6}{x^2} + \frac{2}{y^2} = 14 \end{cases}$$

$$\frac{11}{x^2} = 11 \rightarrow 11 = 11x^2 \rightarrow x^2 = 1 \rightarrow x = \pm 1$$

If $x = 1$: $\quad \frac{3}{(1)^2} + \frac{1}{y^2} = 7 \rightarrow \frac{1}{y^2} = 4 \rightarrow y^2 = \frac{1}{4} \rightarrow y = \pm\frac{1}{2}$

If $x = -1$: $\quad \frac{3}{(-1)^2} + \frac{1}{y^2} = 7 \rightarrow \frac{1}{y^2} = 4 \rightarrow y^2 = \frac{1}{4} \rightarrow y = \pm\frac{1}{2}$

Solutions: $\left(1, \frac{1}{2}\right), \left(1, -\frac{1}{2}\right), \left(-1, \frac{1}{2}\right), \left(-1, -\frac{1}{2}\right)$

40. Multiply each side of the first equation by –3 and add the equations to eliminate x:

$$\begin{cases} \frac{2}{x^2} - \frac{3}{y^2} = -1 \xrightarrow{-3} \frac{-6}{x^2} + \frac{9}{y^2} = 3 \\ \frac{6}{x^2} - \frac{7}{y^2} = -2 \longrightarrow \frac{6}{x^2} - \frac{7}{y^2} = -2 \end{cases}$$

$$\frac{2}{y^2} = 1 \rightarrow 2 = y^2 \rightarrow y = \pm\sqrt{2}$$

If $y = \sqrt{2}$: $\quad \frac{2}{x^2} - \frac{3}{(\sqrt{2})^2} = -1 \rightarrow \frac{2}{x^2} = \frac{1}{2} \rightarrow x^2 = 4 \rightarrow x = \pm 2$

If $y = -\sqrt{2}$: $\quad \frac{2}{x^2} - \frac{3}{(-\sqrt{2})^2} = -1 \rightarrow \frac{2}{x^2} = \frac{1}{2} \rightarrow x^2 = 4 \rightarrow x = \pm 2$

Solutions: $(2, \sqrt{2})\ (2, -\sqrt{2}), (-2, \sqrt{2}), (-2, -\sqrt{2})$

41. Multiply each side of the first equation by –2 and add the equations to eliminate x:

$$\begin{cases} \dfrac{1}{x^4}+\dfrac{6}{y^4}=6 \xrightarrow{-2} \dfrac{-2}{x^4}-\dfrac{12}{y^4}=-12 \\ \dfrac{2}{x^4}-\dfrac{2}{y^4}=19 \longrightarrow \dfrac{2}{x^4}-\dfrac{2}{y^4}=19 \end{cases}$$

$$\frac{-14}{y^4}=7 \rightarrow -14=7y^4 \rightarrow y^4=-2$$

There are no real solutions. The system is inconsistent.

42. Add the equations to eliminate y:

$$\begin{cases} \dfrac{1}{x^4}-\dfrac{1}{y^4}=1 \\ \dfrac{1}{x^4}+\dfrac{1}{y^4}=4 \end{cases}$$

$$\frac{2}{x^4}=5 \rightarrow 2=5x^4 \rightarrow x^4=\frac{2}{5} \rightarrow x=\pm\sqrt[4]{\frac{2}{5}}$$

If $x=\sqrt[4]{\frac{2}{5}}$: $\dfrac{1}{\left(\sqrt[4]{\frac{2}{5}}\right)^4}+\dfrac{1}{y^4}=4 \rightarrow \dfrac{1}{y^4}=\dfrac{3}{2} \rightarrow y^4=\dfrac{2}{3} \rightarrow y=\pm\sqrt[4]{\dfrac{2}{3}}$

If $x=-\sqrt[4]{\frac{2}{5}}$: $\dfrac{1}{\left(-\sqrt[4]{\frac{2}{5}}\right)^4}+\dfrac{1}{y^4}=4 \rightarrow \dfrac{1}{y^4}=\dfrac{3}{2} \rightarrow y^4=\dfrac{2}{3} \rightarrow y=\pm\sqrt[4]{\dfrac{2}{3}}$

Solutions: $\left(\sqrt[4]{\frac{2}{5}},\sqrt[4]{\frac{2}{3}}\right),\left(\sqrt[4]{\frac{2}{5}},-\sqrt[4]{\frac{2}{3}}\right),\left(-\sqrt[4]{\frac{2}{5}},\sqrt[4]{\frac{2}{3}}\right),\left(-\sqrt[4]{\frac{2}{5}},-\sqrt[4]{\frac{2}{3}}\right)$

43. Factor the first equation, solve for x, substitute into the second equation and solve:

$$\begin{cases} x^2-3xy+2y^2=0 \rightarrow (x-2y)(x-y)=0 \rightarrow x=2y \text{ or } x=y \\ x^2+xy=6 \end{cases}$$

Substitute $x=2y$ and solve:

$$x^2+xy=6$$
$$(2y)^2+(2y)y=6$$
$$4y^2+2y^2=6 \rightarrow 6y^2=6$$
$$y^2=1 \rightarrow y=\pm 1$$

If $y=1$: $x=2\cdot 1=2$

If $y=-1$: $x=2(-1)=-2$

Substitute $x=y$ and solve:

$$x^2+xy=6$$
$$y^2+y\cdot y=6$$
$$y^2+y^2=6 \rightarrow 2y^2=6$$
$$y^2=3 \rightarrow y=\pm\sqrt{3}$$

If $y=\sqrt{3}$: $x=\sqrt{3}$

If $y=-\sqrt{3}$: $x=-\sqrt{3}$

Solutions: $(2,1)$, $(-2,-1)$, $\left(\sqrt{3},\sqrt{3}\right)$, $\left(-\sqrt{3},-\sqrt{3}\right)$

44. Factor the first equation, solve for x, substitute into the second equation and solve:

$$\begin{cases} x^2 - xy - 2y^2 = 0 \rightarrow (x-2y)(x+y) = 0 \rightarrow x = 2y \text{ or } x = -y \\ xy + x = -6 \end{cases}$$

Substitute $x = 2y$ and solve:

$$\begin{aligned} xy + x &= -6 \\ (2y)y + 2y &= -6 \\ 2y^2 + 2y + 6 &= 0 \\ 2(y^2 + y + 6) &= 0 \\ y &= \frac{-1 \pm \sqrt{1^2 - 4(1)(6)}}{2(1)} \end{aligned}$$

No real solution

Substitute $x = -y$ and solve:

$$\begin{aligned} xy + x &= -6 \\ -y \cdot y + (-y) &= -6 \\ -y^2 - y + 6 &= 0 \\ (-y-3)(y-2) &= 0 \\ y = -3 &\text{ or } y = 2 \end{aligned}$$

If $y = -3$: $x = 3$

If $y = 2$: $x = -2$

Solutions: $(3, -3)$, $(-2, 2)$

45. Multiply each side of the second equation by $-y$ and add the equations to eliminate y:

$$\begin{cases} y^2 + y + x^2 - x - 2 = 0 \longrightarrow y^2 + y + x^2 - x - 2 = 0 \\ y + 1 + \dfrac{x-2}{y} = 0 \xrightarrow{-y} -y^2 - y \quad - x + 2 = 0 \end{cases}$$

$$x^2 - 2x = 0 \rightarrow x(x-2) = 0$$

$$x = 0 \text{ or } x = 2$$

If $x = 0$: $y^2 + y + 0^2 - 0 - 2 = 0 \rightarrow y^2 + y - 2 = 0 \rightarrow (y+2)(y-1) = 0$
$\rightarrow y = -2 \text{ or } y = 1$

If $x = 2$: $y^2 + y + 2^2 - 2 - 2 = 0 \rightarrow y^2 + y = 0 \rightarrow y(y+1) = 0$
$\rightarrow y = 0 \text{ or } y = -1$

Solutions: $(0, -2)$, $(0, 1)$, $(2, 0)$, $(2, -1)$

46. Multiply each side of the second equation by $-x^2$ and add the equations to eliminate x:

$$\begin{cases} x^3 - 2x^2 + y^2 + 3y - 4 = 0 \longrightarrow x^3 - 2x^2 + y^2 + 3y = 4 \\ x - 2 + \dfrac{y^2 - y}{x^2} = 0 \xrightarrow{-x^2} -x^3 + 2x^2 - y^2 + y = 0 \end{cases}$$

$$4y = 4 \rightarrow y = 1$$

If $y = 1$: $x^3 - 2x^2 + 1^2 + 3 \cdot 1 - 4 = 0 \rightarrow x^3 - 2x^2 = 0 \rightarrow x^2(x-2) = 0$
$\rightarrow x = 0 \text{ or } x = 2$ (Note: $x \neq 0$ - division by zero)

Solutions: $(2, 1)$

47. Rewrite each equation in exponential form:

$$\begin{cases} \log_x y = 3 \rightarrow y = x^3 \\ \log_x (4y) = 5 \rightarrow 4y = x^5 \end{cases}$$

Substitute the first equation into the second and solve:

$$4x^3 = x^5$$

$$x^5 - 4x^3 = 0 \rightarrow x^3(x^2 - 4) = 0 \rightarrow x^3 = 0 \text{ or } x^2 = 4 \rightarrow x = 0 \text{ or } x = \pm 2$$

The base of a logarithm must be positive, thus $x \neq 0$ and $x \neq -2$.

If $x = 2$: $y = 2^3 = 8$

Solution: $(2, 8)$

48. Rewrite each equation in exponential form:

$$\begin{cases} \log_x(2y) = 3 \rightarrow & 2y = x^3 \\ \log_x(4y) = 2 \rightarrow & 4y = x^2 \end{cases}$$

Substitute the first equation into the second and solve:

$$2x^3 = x^2 \rightarrow 2x^3 - x^2 = 0 \rightarrow x^2(2x-1) = 0 \rightarrow x^2 = 0 \text{ or } x = \frac{1}{2} \rightarrow x = \frac{1}{2} \text{ or } x = 0$$

The base of a logarithm must be positive, thus $x \neq 0$.

If $x = \frac{1}{2}$: $4y = \left(\frac{1}{2}\right)^2 = \frac{1}{4} \rightarrow y = \frac{1}{16}$ Solution: $\left(\frac{1}{2}, \frac{1}{16}\right)$

49. Rewrite each equation in exponential form:

$$\begin{cases} \ln x = 4\ln y \rightarrow & x = e^{4\ln y} = e^{\ln y^4} = y^4 \\ \log_3 x = 2 + 2\log_3 y \rightarrow & x = 3^{2+2\log_3 y} = 3^2 \cdot 3^{2\log_3 y} = 3^2 \cdot 3^{\log_3 y^2} = 9y^2 \end{cases}$$

So we have the system

$$\begin{cases} x = y^4 \\ x = 9y^2 \end{cases}$$

Therefore we have

$$9y^2 = y^4 \rightarrow 9y^2 - y^4 = 0 \rightarrow y^2(9 - y^2) = 0$$

$$y^2(3+y)(3-y) = 0 \rightarrow y = 0 \text{ or } y = -3 \text{ or } y = 3$$

Since $\ln y$ is undefined when $y \leq 0$, the only solution is $y = 3$.

If $y = 3$: $x = y^4 \rightarrow x = 3^4 = 81$

Solution: $(81, 3)$

50. Rewrite each equation in exponential form:

$$\begin{cases} \ln x = 5\ln y \rightarrow & x = e^{5\ln y} = e^{\ln y^5} = y^5 \\ \log_2 x = 3 + 2\log_2 y \rightarrow & x = 2^{3+2\log_2 y} = 2^3 \cdot 2^{2\log_2 y} = 2^3 \cdot 2^{\log_2 y^2} = 8y^2 \end{cases}$$

So we have the system $\begin{cases} x = y^5 \\ x = 8y^2 \end{cases}$

Therefore we have

$$8y^2 = y^5 \rightarrow 8y^2 - y^5 = 0$$

$$y^2(8 - y^3) = 0 \rightarrow y = 0 \text{ or } 8 - y^3 = 0 \rightarrow 8 = y^3 \rightarrow 2 = y$$

Since $\ln y$ is undefined when $y \leq 0$, the only solution is $y = 2$.

If $y = 2$: $x = y^5 \rightarrow x = 2^5 = 32$

Solution: $(32, 2)$

51. Solve the first equation for x, substitute into the second equation and solve:

$$\begin{cases} x+2y=0 \rightarrow x=-2y \\ (x-1)^2+(y-1)^2=5 \end{cases}$$

$$(-2y-1)^2+(y-1)^2=5$$

$$4y^2+4y+1+y^2-2y+1=5 \rightarrow 5y^2+2y-3=0$$

$$(5y-3)(y+1)=0$$

$$y=\frac{3}{5}=0.6 \quad \text{or} \quad y=-1$$

$$x=-\frac{6}{5}=-1.2 \quad \text{or} \; x=2$$

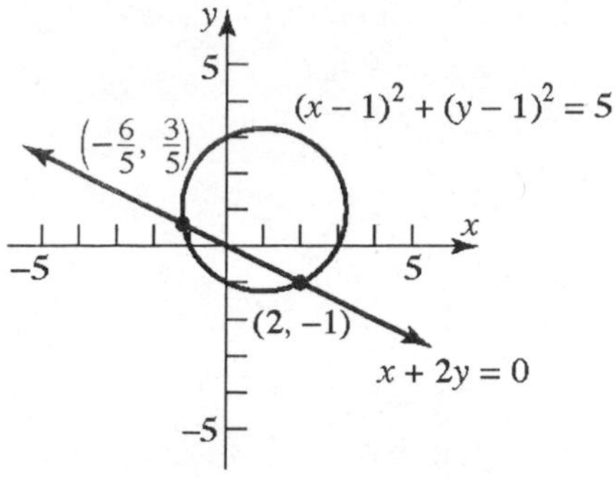

The points of intersection are $(-1.2, 0.6), (2,-1)$.

52. Solve the first equation for x, substitute into the second equation and solve:

$$\begin{cases} x+2y=-6 \rightarrow x=-2y-6 \\ (x+1)^2+(y+1)^2=5 \end{cases}$$

$$(-2y-6+1)^2+(y+1)^2=5$$

$$4y^2+20y+25+y^2+2y+1=5$$

$$5y^2+22y+21=0 \rightarrow (5y+7)(y+3)=0$$

$$y=-\frac{7}{5} \quad \text{or} \quad y=-3$$

$$x=-\frac{16}{5} \quad \text{or} \quad x=0$$

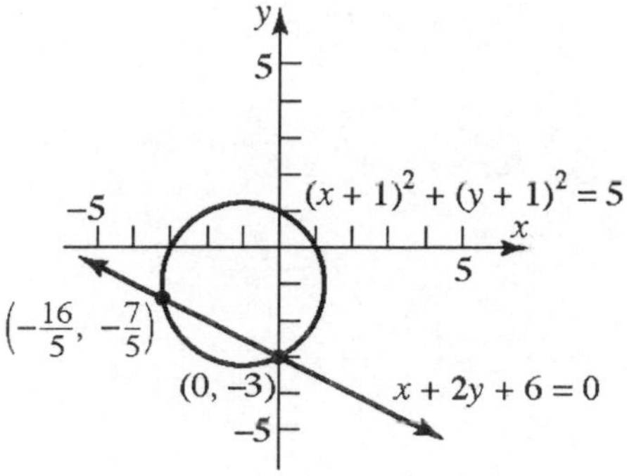

The points of intersection are $\left(-\frac{16}{5}, -\frac{7}{5}\right), (0,-3)$.

53. Complete the square on the second equation, substitute into the first equation and solve:

$$\begin{cases} (x-1)^2+(y+2)^2=4 \\ y^2+4y-x+1=0 \rightarrow y^2+4y+4=x-1+4 \rightarrow (y+2)^2=x+3 \end{cases}$$

$$(x-1)^2+x+3=4$$

$$x^2-2x+1+x+3=4$$

$$x^2-x=0$$

$$x(x-1)=0$$

$$x=0 \quad \text{or} \quad x=1$$

If $x=0$: $(y+2)^2=0+3$

$$y+2=\pm\sqrt{3} \rightarrow y=-2\pm\sqrt{3}$$

If $x=1$: $(y+2)^2=1+3$

$$y+2=\pm 2 \rightarrow y=-2\pm 2$$

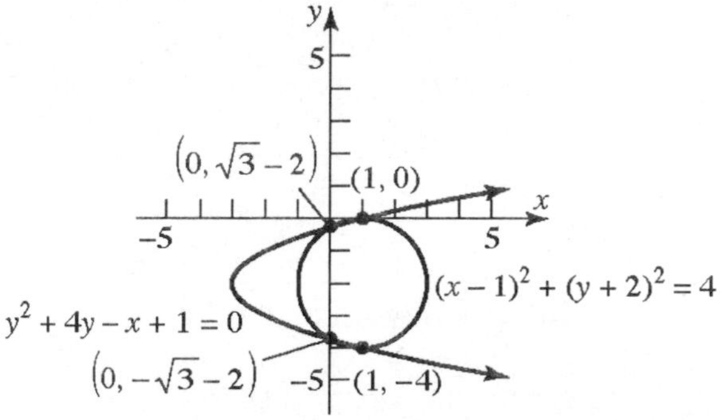

The points of intersection are:

$(0,-2-\sqrt{3}), (0,-2+\sqrt{3}), (1,-4), (1,0)$.

54. Complete the square on the second equation, substitute into the first equation and solve:

$$\begin{cases}(x+2)^2+(y-1)^2=4\\ y^2-2y-x-5=0 \rightarrow y^2-2y+1=x+5+1 \rightarrow (y-1)^2=x+6\end{cases}$$

$$(x+2)^2+x+6=4$$
$$x^2+4x+4+x+6=4$$
$$x^2+5x+6=0$$
$$(x+2)(x+3)=0$$
$$x=-2 \quad \text{or} \quad x=-3$$

If $x=-2$: $(y-1)^2=-2+6 \rightarrow y-1=\pm 2$
$\rightarrow y=-1$ or $y=3$

If $x=-3$: $(y-1)^2=-3+6 \rightarrow y-1=\pm\sqrt{3}$
$\rightarrow y=1\pm\sqrt{3}$

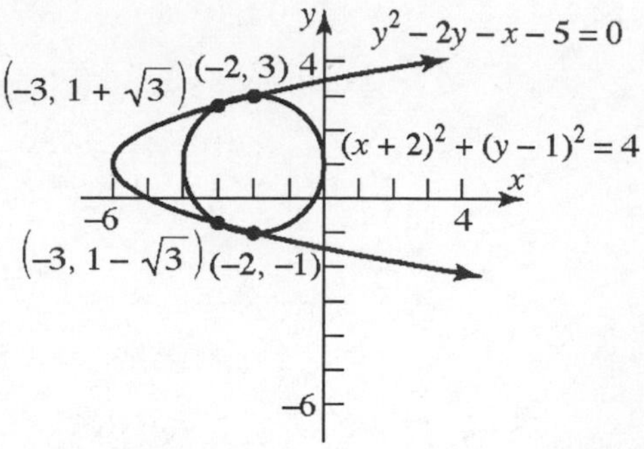

The points of intersection are
$(-3, 1-\sqrt{3})$, $(-3, 1+\sqrt{3})$, $(-2, -1)$, $(-2, 3)$.

55. Solve the first equation for x, substitute into the second equation and solve:

$$\begin{cases} y=\dfrac{4}{x-3} \rightarrow x-3=\dfrac{4}{y} \rightarrow x=\dfrac{4}{y}+3\\ x^2-6x+y^2+1=0\end{cases}$$

$$\left(\frac{4}{y}+3\right)^2-6\left(\frac{4}{y}+3\right)+y^2+1=0$$
$$\frac{16}{y^2}+\frac{24}{y}+9-\frac{24}{y}-18+y^2+1=0$$
$$\frac{16}{y^2}+y^2-8=0$$
$$16+y^4-8y^2=0$$
$$y^4-8y^2+16=0$$
$$(y^2-4)^2=0$$
$$y^2-4=0$$
$$y^2=4$$
$$y=\pm 2$$

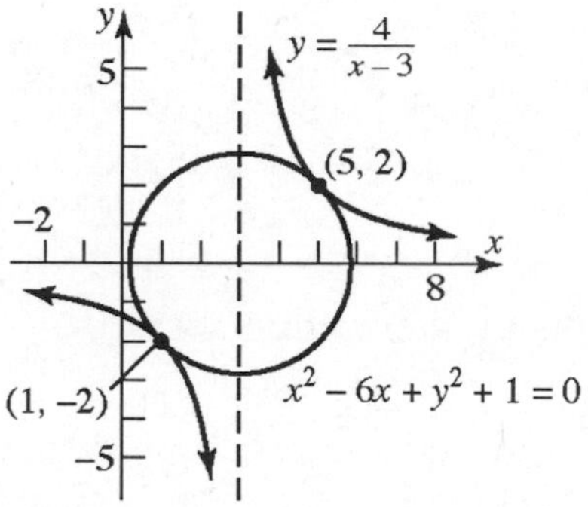

If $y=2$: $\quad x=\dfrac{4}{2}+3=5$

If $y=-2$: $\quad x=\dfrac{4}{-2}+3=1$

The points of intersection are: $(1, -2)$, $(5, 2)$.

56. Substitute the first equation into the second equation and solve:

$$\begin{cases} y = \dfrac{4}{x+2} \\ x^2 + 4x + y^2 - 4 = 0 \end{cases}$$

$$x^2 + 4x + \left(\frac{4}{x+2}\right)^2 - 4 = 0$$

$$x^2 + 4x - 4 = -\left(\frac{4}{x+2}\right)^2$$

$$(x+2)^2\left(x^2 + 4x - 4\right) = -16$$

$$\left(x^2 + 4x + 4\right)\left(x^2 + 4x - 4\right) = -16$$

$$x^4 + 8x^3 + 16x^2 - 16 = -16$$

$$x^4 + 8x^3 + 16x^2 = 0$$

$$x^2\left(x^2 + 8x + 16\right) = 0$$

$$x^2(x+4)^2 = 0$$

$$x = 0 \text{ or } x = -4$$

$$y = 2 \qquad y = -2$$

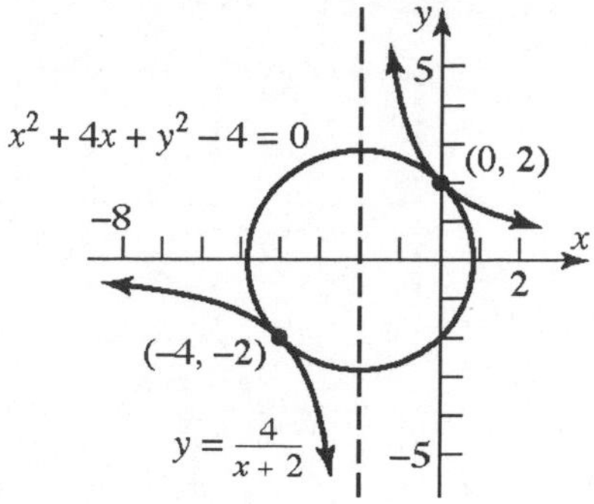

The points of intersection are: (0, 2), (–4, –2).

57. Graph: $y_1 = x \wedge (2/3)$; $y_2 = e \wedge (-x)$
Use INTERSECT to solve:

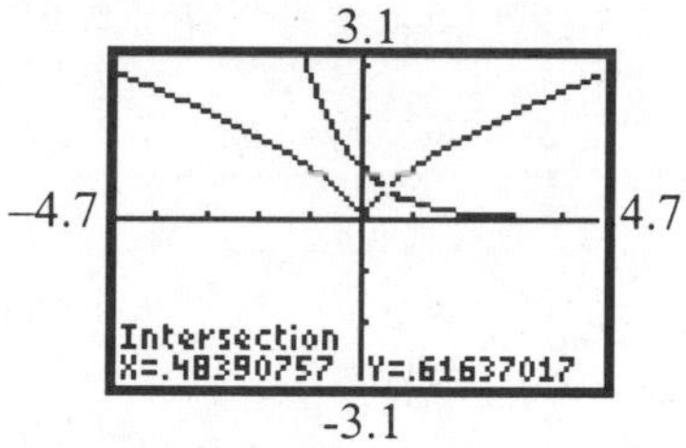

Solution: (0.48, 0.62)

58. Graph: $y_1 = x \wedge (3/2)$; $y_2 = e \wedge (-x)$
Use INTERSECT to solve:

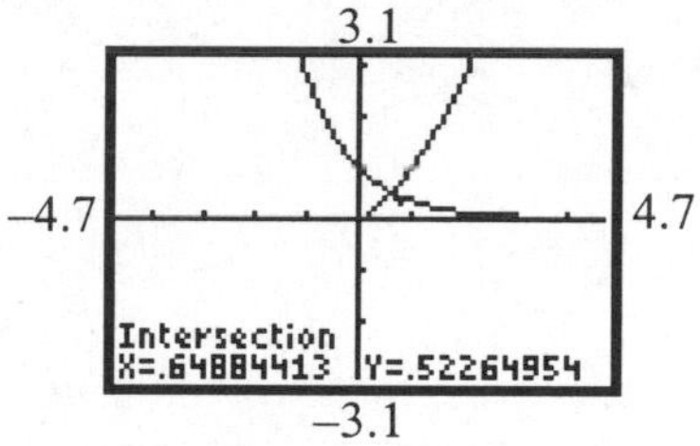

Solution: (0.65, 0.52)

59. Graph: $y_1 = \sqrt[3]{(2 - x^2)}$; $y_2 = 4/x^3$
Use INTERSECT to solve:

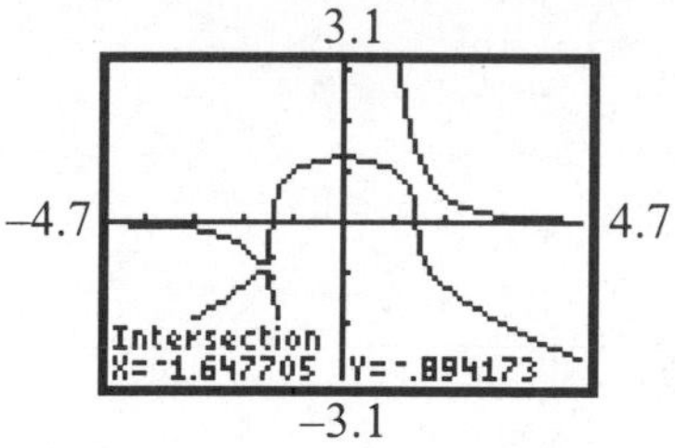

Solution: (–1.65, –0.89)

60. Graph:
$y_1 = \sqrt{2 - x^3}$; $y_2 = -\sqrt{2 - x^3}$;
$y_3 = 4/x^2$
Use INTERSECT to solve:

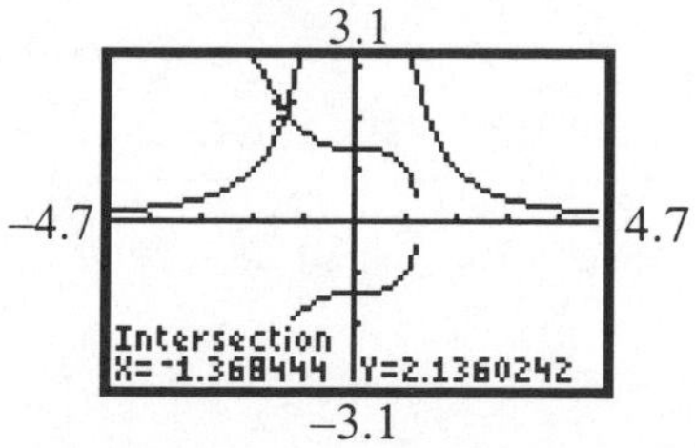

Solution: (–1.37, 2.14)

61. Graph:

$y_1 = \sqrt[4]{(12 - x^4)}$; $y_2 = -\sqrt[4]{(12 - x^4)}$;

$y_3 = \sqrt{2/x}$; $y_4 = -\sqrt{2/x}$

Use INTERSECT to solve:

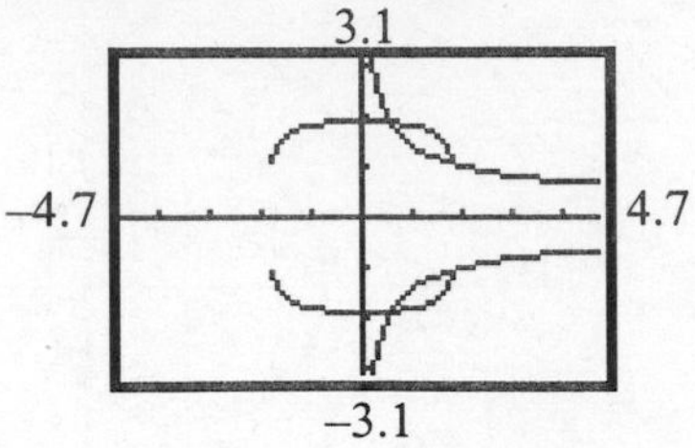

Solutions: (0.58, 1.86), (1.81, 1.05),
(1.81, –1.05), (0.58, –1.86)

62. Graph:

$y_1 = \sqrt[4]{(6 - x^4)}$; $y_2 = -\sqrt[4]{(6 - x^4)}$;

$y_3 = 1/x$

Use INTERSECT to solve:

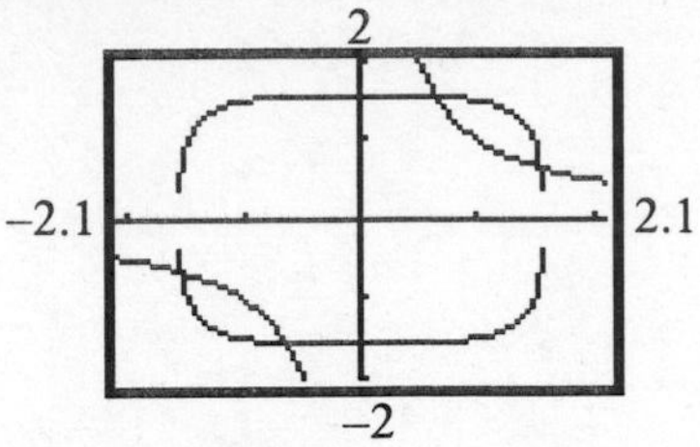

Solutions: (0.64, 1.55), (1.55, 0.64),
(–0.64, –1.55), (–1.55, –0.64)

63. Graph: $y_1 = 2/x$; $y_2 = \ln x$

Use INTERSECT to solve:

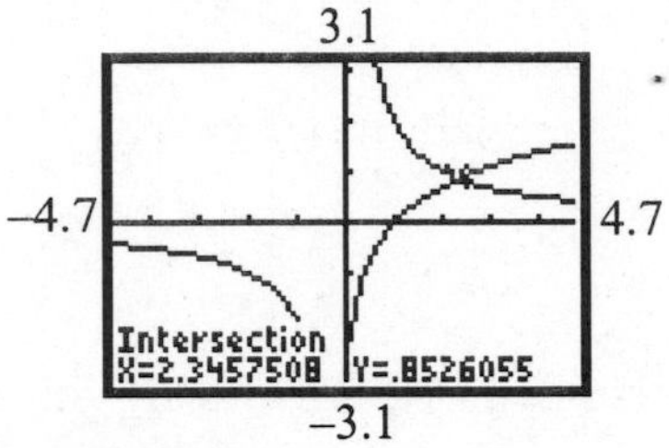

Solution: (2.35, 0.85)

64. Graph:

$y_1 = \sqrt{4 - x^2}$; $y_2 = -\sqrt{4 - x^2}$;

$y_3 = \ln x$

Use INTERSECT to solve:

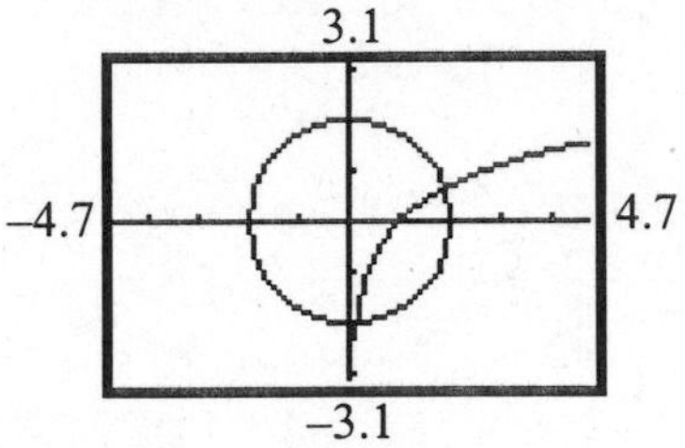

Solution: (1.90, 0.64), (0.14, –2.00)

65. Let x and y be the two numbers. The system of equations is:

$$\begin{cases} x - y = 2 \\ x^2 + y^2 = 10 \end{cases}$$

Solve the first equation for x, substitute into the second equation and solve:

$$(y+2)^2 + y^2 = 10 \rightarrow y^2 + 4y + 4 + y^2 = 10$$

$$2y^2 + 4y - 6 = 0 \rightarrow y^2 + 2y - 3 = 0 \rightarrow (y+3)(y-1) = 0 \rightarrow y = -3 \text{ or } y = 1$$

If $y = -3$: $x = -3 + 2 = -1$

If $y = 1$: $x = 1 + 2 = 3$

The two numbers are 1 and 3 or –1 and –3.

66. Let x and y be the two numbers. The system of equations is:

$$\begin{cases} x + y = 7 \\ x^2 - y^2 = 21 \end{cases}$$

Solve the first equation for x, substitute into the second equation and solve:

$$(7 - y)^2 - y^2 = 21 \rightarrow 49 - 14y + y^2 - y^2 = 21$$

$$-14y = -28 \rightarrow y = 2 \rightarrow x = 7 - 2 = 5$$

The two numbers are 2 and 5.

67. Let x and y be the two numbers. The system of equations is:

$$\begin{cases} xy = 4 \\ x^2 + y^2 = 8 \end{cases}$$

Solve the first equation for x, substitute into the second equation and solve:

$$\left(\frac{4}{y}\right)^2 + y^2 = 8 \rightarrow \frac{16}{y^2} + y^2 = 8 \rightarrow 16 + y^4 = 8y^2$$

$$y^4 - 8y^2 + 16 = 0 \rightarrow (y^2 - 4)^2 = 0 \rightarrow y^2 - 4 = 0 \rightarrow y^2 = 4 \rightarrow y = \pm 2$$

If $y = 2$: $\quad x = \frac{4}{2} = 2$

If $y = -2$: $\quad x = \frac{4}{-2} = -2$

The two numbers are 2 and 2 or –2 and –2.

68. Let x and y be the two numbers. The system of equations is:

$$\begin{cases} xy = 10 \\ x^2 - y^2 = 21 \end{cases}$$

Solve the first equation for x, substitute into the second equation and solve:

$$\left(\frac{10}{y}\right)^2 - y^2 = 21 \rightarrow \frac{100}{y^2} - y^2 = 21$$

$$100 - y^4 = 21y^2 \rightarrow y^4 + 21y^2 - 100 = 0 \rightarrow (y^2 - 4)(y^2 + 25) = 0$$

$$y^2 = 4 \rightarrow y = \pm 2$$

or $y^2 = -25$ which is impossible

If $y = 2$: $\quad x = \frac{10}{2} = 5$

If $y = -2$: $\quad x = \frac{10}{-2} = -5$

The two numbers are 2 and 5 or –2 and –5.

69. Let x and y be the two numbers. The system of equations is:

$$\begin{cases} x - y = xy \\ \frac{1}{x} + \frac{1}{y} = 5 \end{cases}$$

Solve the first equation for x, substitute into the second equation and solve:

$$x - xy = y \rightarrow x(1-y) = y \rightarrow x = \frac{y}{1-y}$$

$$\frac{1}{\left(\frac{y}{1-y}\right)} + \frac{1}{y} = 5 \rightarrow \frac{1-y}{y} + \frac{1}{y} = 5 \rightarrow \frac{2-y}{y} = 5 \rightarrow 2 - y = 5y \rightarrow 6y = 2 \rightarrow y = \frac{1}{3}$$

If $y = \frac{1}{3}$: $\quad x = \frac{\left(\frac{1}{3}\right)}{\left(1 - \frac{1}{3}\right)} = \frac{\left(\frac{1}{3}\right)}{\left(\frac{2}{3}\right)} = \frac{1}{2}$ $\quad \therefore$ The two numbers are $\frac{1}{2}$ and $\frac{1}{3}$.

70. Let x and y be the two numbers. The system of equations is:

$$\begin{cases} x+y=xy \\ \dfrac{1}{x}-\dfrac{1}{y}=3 \end{cases}$$

Solve the first equation for x, substitute into the second equation and solve:

$$xy-x=y \rightarrow x(y-1)=y \rightarrow x=\frac{y}{y-1} \rightarrow \frac{1}{\left(\frac{y}{y-1}\right)}-\frac{1}{y}=3$$

$$\frac{y-1}{y}-\frac{1}{y}=3 \rightarrow \frac{y-2}{y}=3 \rightarrow y-2=3y \rightarrow 2y=-2 \rightarrow y=-1$$

If $y=-1$: $x=\dfrac{-1}{-1-1}=\dfrac{-1}{-2}=\dfrac{1}{2}$ $\therefore$ The two numbers are $\dfrac{1}{2}$ and -1.

71. $$\begin{cases} \dfrac{a}{b}=\dfrac{2}{3} \\ a+b=10 \end{cases}$$

Solve the second equation for a, substitute into the first equation and solve:

$$\frac{10-b}{b}=\frac{2}{3} \rightarrow 3(10-b)=2b \rightarrow 30-3b=2b \rightarrow 30=5b$$

$$b=6 \rightarrow a=4$$

$a+b=10$; $b-a=2$ $\therefore$ The ratio of $a+b$ to $b-a$ is $\dfrac{10}{2}=5$.

72. $$\begin{cases} \dfrac{a}{b}=\dfrac{4}{3} \\ a+b=14 \end{cases}$$

Solve the second equation for a, substitute into the first equation and solve:

$$\frac{14-b}{b}=\frac{4}{3} \rightarrow 3(14-b)=4b \rightarrow 42-3b=4b \rightarrow 42=7b$$

$$b=6 \rightarrow a=8$$

$a-b=2$; $a+b=14$

The ratio of $a-b$ to $a+\text{b}$ is $\dfrac{2}{14}=\dfrac{1}{7}$.

73. Let x = the width of the rectangle.
Let y = the length of the rectangle.

$$\begin{cases} 2x+2y=16 \\ xy=15 \end{cases}$$

Solve the first equation for y, substitute into the second equation and solve:

$$2x+2y=16 \rightarrow 2y=16-2x \rightarrow y=8-x$$

$$x(8-x)=15 \rightarrow 8x-x^2=15 \rightarrow x^2-8x+15=0 \rightarrow (x-5)(x-3)=0$$

$$x=5 \text{ or } x=3$$

$$y=3 \qquad y=5$$

The dimensions of the rectangle are 3 inches by 5 inches.

74. Let $2x$ = the side of the first square.
Let $3x$ = the side of the second square.

$$(2x)^2 + (3x)^2 = 52 \rightarrow 4x^2 + 9x^2 = 52 \rightarrow 13x^2 = 52 \rightarrow x^2 = 4 \rightarrow x = 2$$

The sides of the first square are 4 feet and the sides of the second square are 6 feet.

75. Let x = the radius of the first circle.
Let y = the radius of the second circle.

$$\begin{cases} 2\pi x + 2\pi y = 12\pi \\ \pi x^2 + \pi y^2 = 20\pi \end{cases}$$

Solve the first equation for y, substitute into the second equation and solve:

$$\begin{aligned} 2\pi x + 2\pi y &= 12\pi \\ x + y &= 6 \\ y &= 6 - x \end{aligned}$$

$$\begin{aligned} \pi x^2 + \pi y^2 &= 20\pi \\ x^2 + y^2 &= 20 \\ x^2 + (6-x)^2 &= 20 \\ x^2 + 36 - 12x + x^2 &= 20 \\ 2x^2 - 12x + 16 &= 0 \\ x^2 - 6x + 8 &= 0 \\ (x-4)(x-2) &= 0 \\ x = 4 \quad &\text{or} \quad x = 2 \\ y = 2 \quad &\quad\;\;\; y = 4 \end{aligned}$$

The radii of the circles are 2 centimeters and 4 centimeters.

76. Let x = the length of each of the two equal sides in the isosceles triangle.
Let y = the length of the base.
The perimeter of the triangle: $x + x + y = 18$
Since the altitude to the base y is 3, the Pythagorean theorem will produce another equation: $\left(\frac{y}{2}\right)^2 + 3^2 = x^2$

Solve the system of equations:

$$\begin{cases} 2x + y = 18 \rightarrow y = 18 - 2x \\ \frac{y^2}{4} + 9 = x^2 \end{cases}$$

Solve the first equation for y, substitute into the second equation and solve:

$$\frac{(18-2x)^2}{4} + 9 = x^2 \rightarrow \frac{324 - 72x + 4x^2}{4} + 9 = x^2$$

$$81 - 18x + x^2 + 9 = x^2 \rightarrow -18x = -90 \rightarrow x = 5 \rightarrow y = 18 - 2(5) = 8$$

The base of the triangle is 8 centimeters.

77. The tortoise takes $9 + 3 = 12$ minutes or 0.2 hour longer to complete the race than the hare.
Let r = the rate of the hare.
Let t = the time for the hare to complete the race.
Then $t + 0.2$ = the time for the tortoise and $r - 0.5$ = the rate for the tortoise.
Since the length of the race is 21 meters, the distance equations are:

$$\begin{cases} rt = 21 \\ (r - 0.5)(t + 0.2) = 21 \end{cases}$$

Solve the first equation for r, substitute into the second equation and solve:

$$\left(\frac{21}{t}-0.5\right)(t+0.2)=21 \rightarrow 21+\frac{4.2}{t}-0.5t-0.1=21$$

$$10t\cdot\left(21+\frac{4.2}{t}-0.5t-0.1\right)=10t\cdot(21)$$

$$210t+42-5t^2-t=210t \rightarrow 5t^2+t-42=0 \rightarrow (5t-14)(t+3)=0$$

$$t=\frac{14}{5}=2.8 \text{ or } t=-3$$

$t=-3$ makes no sense, since time cannot be negative.

Solve for r:

$$r=\frac{21}{2.8}=7.5$$

The average speed of the hare is 7.5 meters per hour, and the average speed for the tortoise is 7 meters per hour.

78. Let $v_1, v_2, v_3 =$ the speeds of runners 1, 2, 3.
Let $t_1, t_2, t_3 =$ the times of runners 1, 2, 3.
Then by the conditions of the problem, we have the following system:

$$\begin{cases} 5280 = v_1 t_1 \\ 5270 = v_2 t_1 \\ 5260 = v_3 t_1 \\ 5280 = v_2 t_2 \end{cases}$$

Distance between the second runner and the third runner after t_2 seconds is:

$$5280 - v_3 t_2 = 5280 - v_3 t_1\left(\frac{v_2 t_2}{v_2 t_1}\right) = 5280 - 5260\left(\frac{5280}{5270}\right) = 10.02$$

The second place runner beats the third place runner by 10.02 feet.

79. Let x = the width of the cardboard.
Let y = the length of the cardboard.
The width of the box will be $x-4$, the length of the box will be $y-4$, and the height is 2.
The volume is $V=(x-4)(y-4)(2)$.
Solve the system of equations:

$$\begin{cases} xy = 216 \\ 2(x-4)(y-4) = 224 \end{cases}$$

Solve the first equation for y, substitute into the second equation and solve:

$$(2x-8)\left(\frac{216}{x}-4\right)=224 \rightarrow 432-8x-\frac{1728}{x}+32=224$$

$$432x-8x^2-1728+32x=224x \rightarrow -8x^2+240x-1728=0$$

$$x^2-30x+216=0 \rightarrow (x-12)(x-18)=0$$

$$x=12 \text{ or } x=18$$

$$y=18 \qquad y=12$$

The cardboard should be 12 centimeters by 18 centimeters.

80. Let x = the width of the cardboard.
Let y = the length of the cardboard.
The area of the cardboard is: $xy = 216$

The volume of the tube is: $V = \pi r^2 h = 224$ where $h = y$ and $2\pi r = x$ or $r = \dfrac{x}{2\pi}$.

Solve the system of equations:

$$\begin{cases} xy = 216 \quad \rightarrow \quad y = \dfrac{216}{x} \\ \pi\left(\dfrac{x}{2\pi}\right)^2 y = 224 \quad \rightarrow \quad \dfrac{x^2 y}{4\pi} = 224 \end{cases}$$

Solve the first equation for y, substitute into the second equation and solve:

$$\frac{x^2\left(\dfrac{216}{x}\right)}{4\pi} = 224 \rightarrow 216x = 896\pi \rightarrow x = \frac{896\pi}{216} \approx 13.03 \rightarrow y = \frac{216}{13.03} \approx 16.58$$

The cardboard should be 13.03 centimeters by 16.58 centimeters.

81. Find equations relating area and perimeter:

$$\begin{cases} x^2 + y^2 = 4500 \\ 3x + 3y + (x - y) = 300 \end{cases}$$

Solve the second equation for y, substitute into the first equation and solve:

$$\begin{aligned} 4x + 2y &= 300 \\ 2y &= 300 - 4x \\ y &= 150 - 2x \end{aligned}$$

$$\begin{aligned} x^2 + (150 - 2x)^2 &= 4500 \\ x^2 + 22500 - 600x + 4x^2 &= 4500 \\ 5x^2 - 600x + 18000 &= 0 \\ x^2 - 120x + 3600 &= 0 \\ (x - 60)^2 &= 0 \\ x - 60 &= 0 \\ x &= 60 \\ y &= 150 - 2(60) = 30 \end{aligned}$$

The sides of the squares are 30 feet and 60 feet.

82. Let x = the length of a side of the square.
Let r = the radius of the circle.
The area of the square is x^2 and the area of the circle is πr^2.
The perimeter of the square is $4x$ and the circumference of the circle is $2\pi r$.
Find equations relating area and perimeter:

$$\begin{cases} x^2 + \pi r^2 = 100 \\ 4x + 2\pi r = 60 \end{cases}$$

Solve the second equation for x, substitute into the first equation and solve:

$$\begin{aligned} 4x + 2\pi r &= 60 \\ 4x &= 60 - 2\pi r \\ x &= 15 - \frac{1}{2}\pi r \end{aligned}$$

$$\begin{aligned} \left(15 - \frac{1}{2}\pi r\right)^2 + \pi r^2 &= 100 \\ 225 - 15\pi r + \frac{1}{4}\pi^2 r^2 + \pi r^2 &= 100 \\ \left(\frac{1}{4}\pi^2 + \pi\right) r^2 - 15\pi r + 125 &= 0 \end{aligned}$$

$$b^2-4ac=(-15\pi)^2-4\left(\frac{1}{4}\pi^2+\pi\right)(125)=225\pi^2-500\left(\frac{1}{4}\pi^2+\pi\right)$$
$$=100\pi^2-500\pi<0$$

Since the discriminant is less than zero, it is impossible to cut the wire into two pieces which have a total are of 100 square feet.

83. Solve the system for l and w:

$$\begin{cases} 2l+2w=P \\ lw=A \end{cases}$$

Solve the first equation for l, substitute into the second equation and solve:

$$2l=P-2w \rightarrow l=\frac{P}{2}-w$$

$$\left(\frac{P}{2}-w\right)w=A \rightarrow \frac{P}{2}w-w^2=A \rightarrow w^2-\frac{P}{2}w+A=0$$

$$w=\frac{\left(\frac{P}{2}\pm\sqrt{\frac{P^2}{4}-4A}\right)}{2}=\frac{\left(\frac{P}{2}\pm\sqrt{\frac{P^2-16A}{4}}\right)}{2}=\frac{\left(\frac{P}{2}\pm\frac{\sqrt{P^2-16A}}{2}\right)}{2}$$

$$w=\frac{P\pm\sqrt{P^2-16A}}{4}$$

If $w=\frac{P+\sqrt{P^2-16A}}{4}$ then $l=\frac{P}{2}-\frac{P+\sqrt{P^2-16A}}{4}=\frac{P-\sqrt{P^2-16A}}{4}$

If $w=\frac{P-\sqrt{P^2-16A}}{4}$ then $l=\frac{P}{2}-\frac{P-\sqrt{P^2-16A}}{4}=\frac{P+\sqrt{P^2-16A}}{4}$

If it is required that length be greater than width, then the solution is:

$$w=\frac{P-\sqrt{P^2-16A}}{4} \text{ and } l=\frac{P+\sqrt{P^2-16A}}{4}$$

84. Solve the system for l and b:

$$\begin{cases} P=b+2l \rightarrow b=P-2l \\ h^2+\frac{b^2}{4}=l^2 \end{cases}$$

Solve the first equation for b, substitute into the second equation and solve:

$$4h^2+b^2=4l^2 \rightarrow 4h^2+(P-2l)^2=4l^2$$

$$4h^2+P^2-4Pl+4l^2=4l^2 \rightarrow 4h^2+P^2=4Pl$$

$$l=\frac{4h^2+P^2}{4P} \rightarrow b=P-\frac{4h^2+P^2}{2P}$$

85. Solve the equation:

$$m^2-4(2m-4)=0 \rightarrow m^2-8m+16=0 \rightarrow (m-4)^2=0 \rightarrow m-4=0 \rightarrow m=4$$

Use the point-slope equation with slope 4 and the point (2, 4) to obtain the equation of the tangent line:

$$y-4=4(x-2) \rightarrow y-4=4x-8 \rightarrow y=4x-4$$

86. Solve the system:
$$\begin{cases} x^2 + y^2 = 10 \\ y = mx + b \end{cases}$$
Solve the system by substitution:
$$x^2 + (mx+b)^2 = 10 \rightarrow x^2 + m^2x^2 + 2bmx + b^2 - 10 = 0$$
$$(1+m^2)x^2 + 2bmx + b^2 - 10 = 0$$
Note that the tangent line passes through (1, 3). Find the relation between m and b:
$$3 = m(1) + b \rightarrow b = 3 - m$$
There is one solution to the quadratic if the discriminant is zero.
$$(2bm)^2 - 4(m^2+1)(b^2-10) = 0$$
$$4b^2m^2 - 4b^2m^2 + 40m^2 - 4b^2 + 40 = 0 \rightarrow 40m^2 - 4b^2 + 40 = 0$$
Substitute for b and solve:
$$40m^2 - 4(3-m)^2 + 40 = 0$$
$$40m^2 - 4m^2 + 24m - 36 + 40 = 0 \rightarrow 36m^2 + 24m + 4 = 0$$
$$9m^2 + 6m + 1 = 0 \rightarrow (3m+1)^2 = 0 \rightarrow m = -\frac{1}{3}$$
$$b = 3 - \left(-\frac{1}{3}\right) = \frac{10}{3}$$
The equation of the tangent line is $y = -\frac{1}{3}x + \frac{10}{3}$.

87. Solve the system:
$$\begin{cases} y = x^2 + 2 \\ y = mx + b \end{cases}$$
Solve the system by substitution:
$$x^2 + 2 = mx + b \rightarrow x^2 - mx + 2 - b = 0$$
Note that the tangent line passes through (1, 3). Find the relation between m and b:
$$3 = m(1) + b \rightarrow b = 3 - m$$
Substitute into the quadratic to eliminate b:
$$x^2 - mx + 2 - (3-m) = 0 \rightarrow x^2 - mx + (m-1) = 0$$
Find when the discriminant is 0:
$$(-m)^2 - 4(1)(m-1) = 0 \rightarrow m^2 - 4m + 4 = 0 \rightarrow (m-2)^2 = 0$$
$$m - 2 = 0 \rightarrow m = 2 \rightarrow b = 3 - 2 = 1$$
The equation of the tangent line is $y = 2x + 1$.

88. Solve the system:
$$\begin{cases} x^2 + y = 5 \\ y = mx + b \end{cases}$$
Solve the system by substitution:
$$x^2 + mx + b = 5 \rightarrow x^2 + mx + b - 5 = 0$$
Note that the tangent line passes through (–2, 1). Find the relation between m and b:
$$1 = m(-2) + b \rightarrow b = 2m + 1$$

Substitute into the quadratic to eliminate b:

$$x^2 + mx + 2m + 1 - 5 = 0 \to x^2 + mx + (2m - 4) = 0$$

Find when the discriminant is 0:

$$(m)^2 - 4(1)(2m - 4) = 0 \to m^2 - 8m + 16 = 0 \to (m - 4)^2 = 0$$

$$m - 4 = 0 \to m = 4 \to b = 2(4) + 1 = 9$$

The equation of the tangent line is $y = 4x + 9$.

89. Solve the system:

$$\begin{cases} 2x^2 + 3y^2 = 14 \\ y = mx + b \end{cases}$$

Solve the system by substitution:

$$2x^2 + 3(mx + b)^2 = 14 \to 2x^2 + 3m^2x^2 + 6mbx + 3b^2 = 14$$

$$(3m^2 + 2)x^2 + 6mbx + 3b^2 - 14 = 0$$

Note that the tangent line passes through (1, 2). Find the relation between m and b:

$$2 = m(1) + b \to b = 2 - m$$

Substitute into the quadratic to eliminate b:

$$(3m^2 + 2)x^2 + 6m(2 - m)x + 3(2 - m)^2 - 14 = 0$$

$$(3m^2 + 2)x^2 + (12m - 6m^2)x + 12 - 12m + 3m^2 - 14 = 0$$

$$(3m^2 + 2)x^2 + (12m - 6m^2)x + (3m^2 - 12m - 2) = 0$$

Find when the discriminant is 0:

$$(12m - 6m^2)^2 - 4(3m^2 + 2)(3m^2 - 12m - 2) = 0$$

$$144m^2 - 144m^3 + 36m^4 - 4(9m^4 - 36m^3 - 24m - 4) = 0$$

$$144m^2 - 144m^3 + 36m^4 - 36m^4 + 144m^3 + 96m + 16 = 0$$

$$144m^2 + 96m + 16 = 0$$

$$9m^2 + 6m + 1 = 0$$

$$(3m + 1)^2 = 0$$

$$3m + 1 = 0$$

$$m = -\frac{1}{3} \qquad b = 2 - \left(-\frac{1}{3}\right) = \frac{7}{3}$$

The equation of the tangent line is $y = -\frac{1}{3}x + \frac{7}{3}$.

90. Solve the system:

$$\begin{cases} 3x^2 + y^2 = 7 \\ y = mx + b \end{cases}$$

Solve the system by substitution:

$$3x^2 + (mx + b)^2 = 7 \to 3x^2 + m^2x^2 + 2mbx + b^2 = 7$$

$$(m^2 + 3)x^2 + 2mbx + b^2 - 7 = 0$$

Note that the tangent line passes through (–1, 2).
Find the relation between m and b:

$$2 = m(-1) + b \to b = m + 2$$

There is one solution to the quadratic if the discriminant is zero.

$$(2bm)^2 - 4(m^2 + 3)(b^2 - 7) = 0 \to 4b^2m^2 - 4b^2m^2 + 28m^2 - 12b^2 + 84 = 0$$

$$28m^2 - 12b^2 + 84 = 0 \to 7m^2 - 3b^2 + 21 = 0$$

Substitute for b and solve:

$$7m^2-3(m+2)^2+21=0 \rightarrow 7m^2-3m^2-12m-12+21=0$$

$$4m^2-12m+9=0 \rightarrow (2m-3)^2=0 \rightarrow m=\frac{3}{2}$$

$$b=\frac{3}{2}+2=\frac{7}{2}$$

The equation of the tangent line is $y=\frac{3}{2}x+\frac{7}{2}$.

91. Solve the system:

$$\begin{cases} x^2-y^2=3 \\ y=mx+b \end{cases}$$

Solve the system by substitution:

$$x^2-(mx+b)^2=3 \rightarrow x^2-m^2x^2-2mbx-b^2=3 \rightarrow (1-m^2)x^2-2mbx-b^2-3=0$$

Note that the tangent line passes through (2, 1). Find the relation between m and b:

$$1=m(2)+b \rightarrow b=1-2m$$

Substitute into the quadratic to eliminate b:

$$(1-m^2)x^2-2m(1-2m)x-(1-2m)^2-3=0$$

$$(1-m^2)x^2+(-2m+4m^2)x-1+4m-4m^2-3=0$$

$$(1-m^2)x^2+(-2m+4m^2)x+(-4m^2+4m-4)=0$$

Find when the discriminant is 0:

$$(-2m+4m^2)^2-4(1-m^2)(-4m^2+4m-4)=0$$

$$4m^2-16m^3+16m^4-4(4m^4-4m^3+4m-4)=0$$

$$4m^2-16m^3+16m^4-16m^4+16m^3-16m+16=0$$

$$4m^2-16m+16=0 \rightarrow m^2-4m+4=0$$

$$(m-2)^2=0 \rightarrow m-2=0 \rightarrow m=2 \rightarrow b=1-2(2)=-3$$

The equation of the tangent line is $y=2x-3$.

92. Solve the system:

$$\begin{cases} 2y^2-x^2=14 \\ y=mx+b \end{cases}$$

Solve the system by substitution:

$$2(mx+b)^2-x^2=14 \rightarrow 2m^2x^2+4mbx+2b^2-x^2=14$$

$$(2m^2-1)x^2+4mbx+2b^2-14=0$$

Note that the tangent line passes through (2, 3). Find the relation between m and b:

$$3=m(2)+b \rightarrow b=3-2m$$

There is one solution to the quadratic if the discriminant is zero.

$$(4bm)^2-4(2m^2-1)(2b^2-14)=0$$

$$16b^2m^2-16b^2m^2+112m^2+8b^2-56=0 \rightarrow 112m^2+8b^2-56=0 \rightarrow 14m^2+b^2-7=0$$

Substitute for b and solve:

$$14m^2+(3-2m)^2-7=0$$

$$14m^2+4m^2-12m+9-7=0 \to 18m^2-12m+2=0 \to 9m^2-6m+1=0$$

$$(3m-1)^2=0 \to m=\frac{1}{3} \to b=3-2\left(\frac{1}{3}\right)=\frac{7}{3}$$

The equation of the tangent line is $y=\frac{1}{3}x+\frac{7}{3}$.

93. Solve for r_1 and r_2:

$$\begin{cases} r_1+r_2=-\frac{b}{a} \\ r_1 r_2=\frac{c}{a} \end{cases}$$

Substitute and solve:

$$r_1=-r_2-\frac{b}{a} \to \left(-r_2-\frac{b}{a}\right)r_2=\frac{c}{a} \to -r_2^2-\frac{b}{a}r_2-\frac{c}{a}=0 \to a r_2^2+br_2+c=0$$

$$r_2=\frac{-b\pm\sqrt{b^2-4ac}}{2a}$$

$$r_1=-r_2-\frac{b}{a}=-\left(\frac{-b\pm\sqrt{b^2-4ac}}{2a}\right)-\frac{2b}{2a}=\frac{-b\mp\sqrt{b^2-4ac}}{2a}$$

The solutions are: $\frac{-b+\sqrt{b^2-4ac}}{2a}$ and $\frac{-b-\sqrt{b^2-4ac}}{2a}$.

94. Consider the circle with equation $(x-h)^2+(y-k)^2=r^2$ and the third degree polynomial with equation $y=ax^3+bx^2+cx+d$.

Substituting the first equation into the first equation yields

$$(x-h)^2+(ax^3+bx^2+cx+d-k)^2=r^2.$$

In order to find the roots for this equation we can expand the terms on the left hand side of the equation.

Notice that $(x-h)^2$ yields a 2nd degree polynomial, and $(ax^3+bx^2+cx+d-k)^2$ yields a 6th degree polynomial.

Therefore, we need to find the roots of a 6th degree equation, and the Fundamental Theorem of Algebra states that there will be at most six real roots. Thus, the circle and the 3rd degree polynomial will intersect at most six times.

Now consider the circle with equation $(x-h)^2+(y-k)^2=r^2$ and the polynomial of degree n with equation $y=a_0+a_1x+a_2x^2+a_3x^3+...+a_nx^n$.

Substituting the first equation into the first equation yields

$$(x-h)^2+(a_0+a_1x+a_2x^2+a_3x^3+...+a_nx^n)^2=r^2.$$

In order to find the roots for this equation we can expand the terms on the left hand side of the equation.

Notice that $(x-h)^2$ yields a 2nd degree polynomial, and $\left(a_0 + a_1x + a_2x^2 + a_3x^3 + \ldots + a_nx^n\right)^2$ yields a polynomial of degree *2n*.
Therefore, we need to find the roots of an equation of degree *2n*, and the Fundamental Theorem of Algebra states that there will be at most *2n* real roots. Thus, the circle and the nth degree polynomial will intersect at most *2n* times.

95. Since the area of the square piece of sheet metal is 100 square feet, the sheet's dimensions are 10 feet by 10 feet. Let x = the length of the cut.

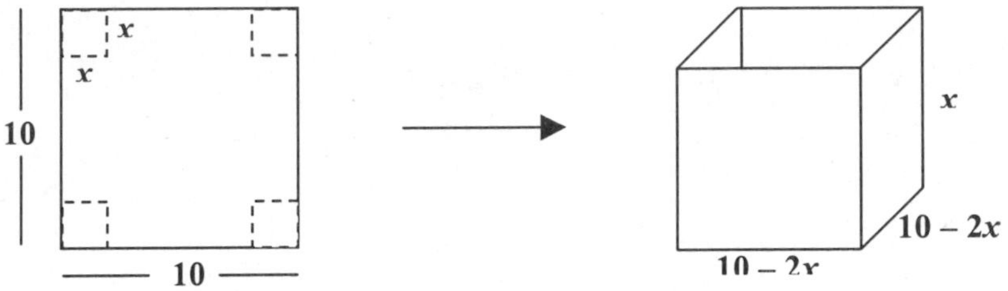

The dimensions of the box are length $=10-2x$; width $=10-2x$; height $=x$
Note that each of these expressions must be positive. So we must have

$$x>0 \text{ and } 10-2x>0 \rightarrow x<5, \text{ that is, } 0<x<5.$$

So the volume of the box is given by

$$V=(length)\cdot(width)\cdot(height)=(10-2x)(10-2x)(x)=(10-2x)^2(x)$$

(a) In order to get a volume equal to 9 cubic feet, we solve $(10-2x)^2(x)=9$.

$$(10-2x)^2(x)=9 \rightarrow (100-40x+4x^2)x=9 \rightarrow 100x-40x^2+4x^3=9$$

So we need to solve the equation $4x^3-40x^2+100x-9=0$.
Graphing the function $y_1=4x^3-40x^2+100x-9$ on a calculator yields the graph

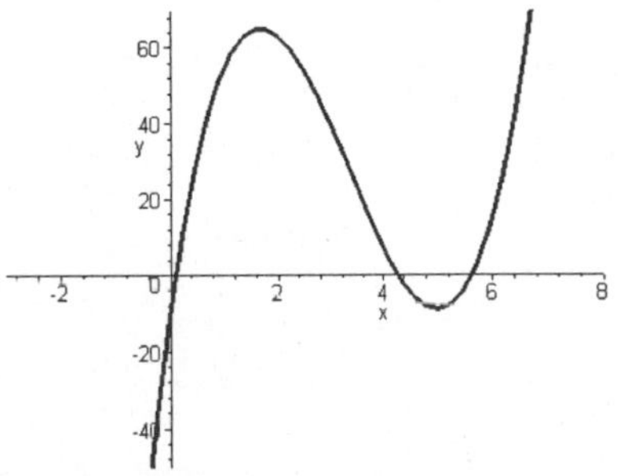

The graph indicates that there three real zeros on the interval [0,6].
Using the ZERO feature of a graphing calculator, we find that the three roots shown occur at $x \approx 0.09$, $x \approx 4.27$ and $x \approx 5.63$.
But we've already noted that we must have $0<x<5$, so the only practical values for the cut are $x \approx 0.09$ feet and $x \approx 4.27$ feet.

(b) If the sheet metal has dimensions *k* feet by *k* feet, then the volume equation becomes

$$V=(k-2x)(k-2x)(x)=(k-2x)^2(x)=9$$

Solving for *k* we get the quadratic equation

$$xk^2-4x^2k+4x^3-9=0$$

Using the quadratic formula we get:

$$k=\frac{-(-4x^2)\pm\sqrt{(-4x^2)^2-4(x)(4x^3-9)}}{2x}=\frac{4x^2\pm\sqrt{16x^4-16x^4+36x}}{2x}$$

$$=\frac{4x^2\pm\sqrt{36x}}{2x}=\frac{4x^2\pm 6\sqrt{x}}{2x}$$

Therefore, we get a real solution for k provided $x>0$ and $4x^2\pm 6\sqrt{x}\ge 0$.

$$4x^2\pm 6\sqrt{x}\ge 0\rightarrow 4x^2\ge 6\sqrt{x}\rightarrow 16x^4\ge 36x$$

$$16x^4-36x\ge 0\rightarrow 4x(4x^3-9)\ge 0$$

This last inequality holds provided $x\ge\sqrt[3]{\frac{9}{4}}$.

Chapter 12

Systems of Equations and Inequalities

12.8 Systems of Inequalities

1. $x \geq 0$
Graph the line $x = 0$. Use a solid line since the inequality uses $\geq$.
Choose a test point not on the line, such as (2, 0). Since $2 \geq 0$ is true, shade the side of the line containing (2, 0).

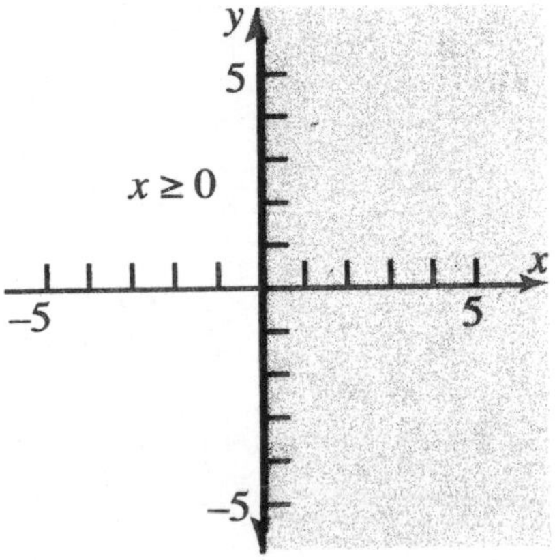

2. $y \geq 0$
Graph the line $y = 0$. Use a solid line since the inequality uses $\geq$.
Choose a test point not on the line, such as (0, 2). Since $2 \geq 0$ is true, shade the side of the line containing (0, 2).

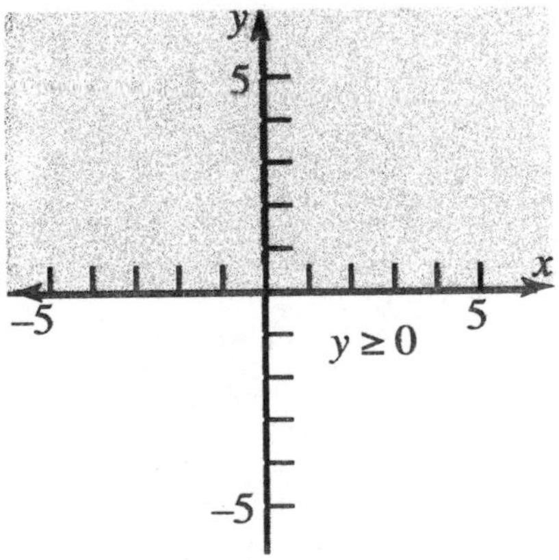

3. $x \geq 4$
Graph the line $x = 4$. Use a solid line since the inequality uses $\geq$.
Choose a test point not on the line, such as (5, 0).
Since $5 \geq 0$ is true, shade the side of the line containing (5, 0).

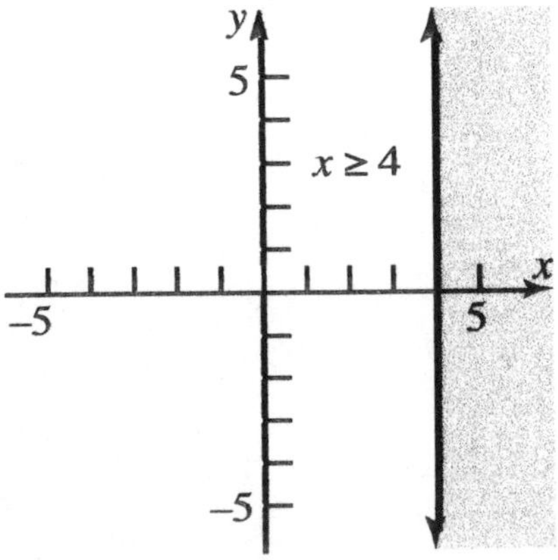

4. $y \le 2$

Graph the line $y = 2$. Use a solid line since the inequality uses $\le$.

Choose a test point not on the line, such as (5, 0).

Since $0 \le 2$ is true, shade the side of the line containing (5, 0).

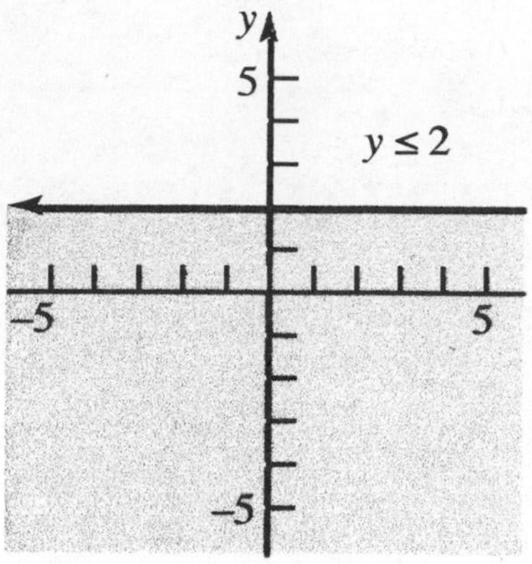

5. $2x + y \ge 6$

Graph the line $2x + y = 6$. Use a solid line since the inequality uses $\ge$.

Choose a test point not on the line, such as (0, 0).

Since $2(0) + 0 \ge 6$ is false, shade the opposite side of the Line from (0, 0).

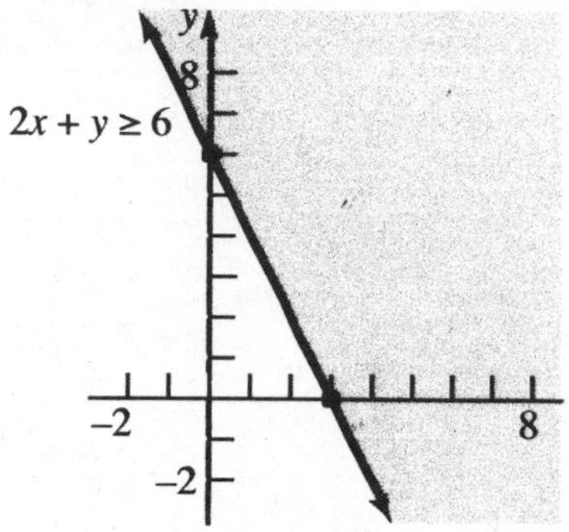

6. $3x + 2y \le 6$

Graph the line $3x + 2y = 6$. Use a solid line since the inequality uses $\le$.

Choose a test point not on the line, such as (0, 0).

Since $3(0) + 2(0) \le 6$ is true, shade the side of the line containing (0, 0).

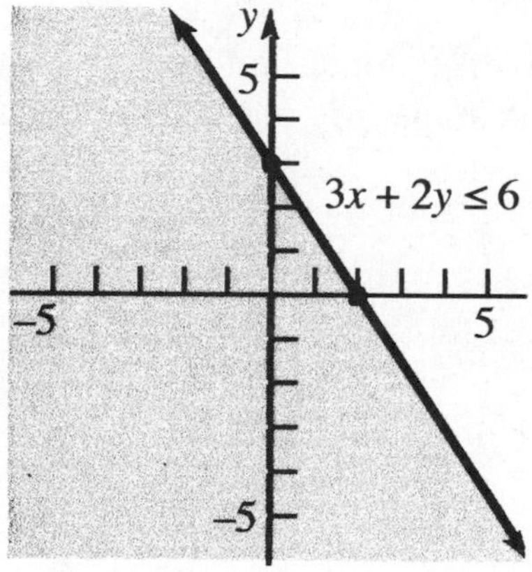

7. $x^2 + y^2 > 1$

Graph the circle $x^2 + y^2 > 1$. Use a dashed line since the inequality uses >.
Choose a test point not on the circle, such as (0, 0).
Since $0^2 + 0^2 > 1$ is false, shade the opposite side of the circle from (0, 0).

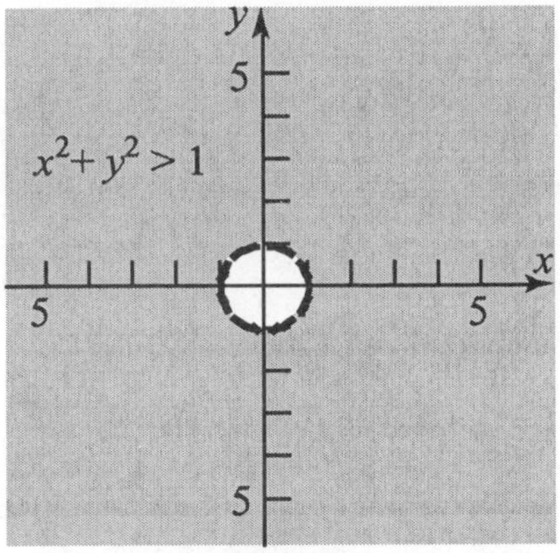

8. $x^2 + y^2 \le 9$

Graph the circle $x^2 + y^2 = 9$. Use a solid line since the inequality uses ≤ .
Choose a test point not on the circle, such as (0, 0).
Since $0^2 + 0^2 \le 9$ is true, shade the same side of the circle as (0, 0).

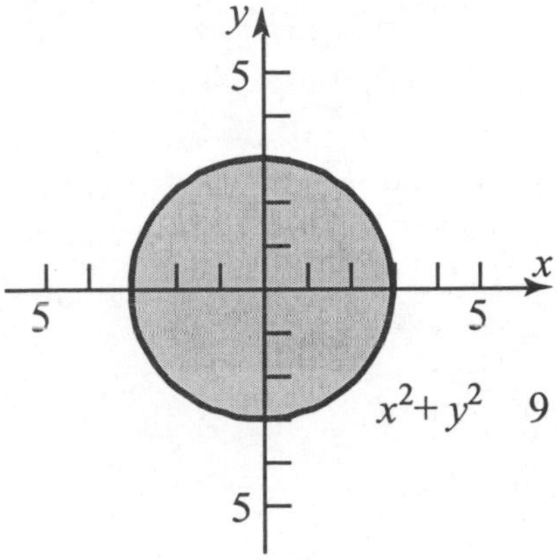

9. $y \le x^2 - 1$

Graph the parabola $y = x^2 - 1$. Use a solid line since the inequality uses ≤.
Choose a test point not on the parabola, such as (0, 0).
Since $0 \le 0^2 - 1$ is false, shade the opposite side of the parabola from (0, 0).

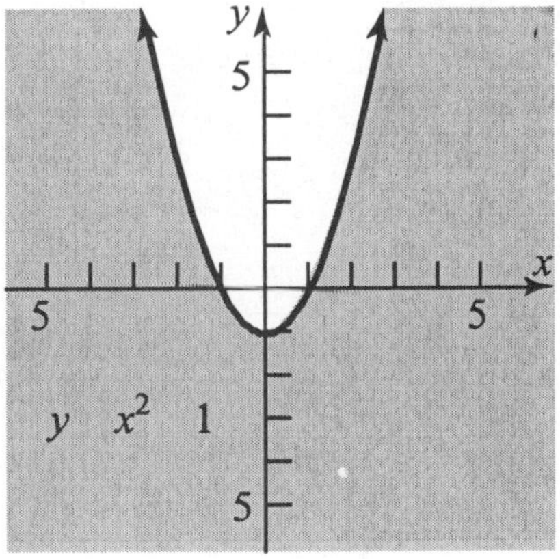

10. $y > x^2 + 2$

Graph the line $y = x^2 + 2$. Use a dashed line since the inequality uses >.
Choose a test point not on the line, such as (0, 0). Since $0 > 0^2 + 2$ is false, shade the opposite side of the parabola from (0, 0).

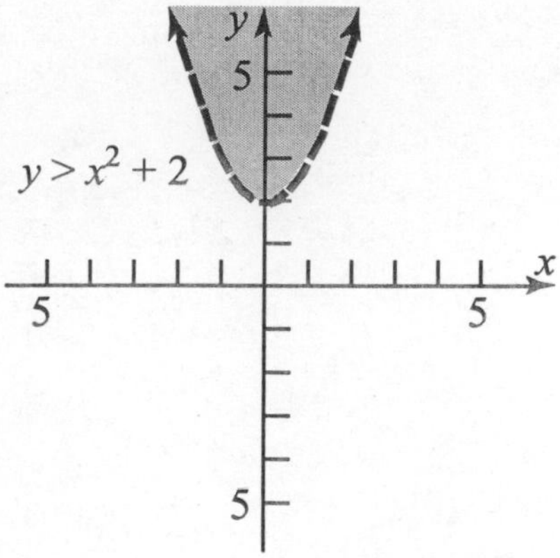

11. $xy \geq 4$

Graph the hyperbola $xy = 4$. Use a solid line since the inequality uses ≥.
Choose a test point not on the hyperbola, such as (0, 0). Since $0 \cdot 0 \geq 4$ is false, shade the opposite side of the hyperbola from (0, 0).

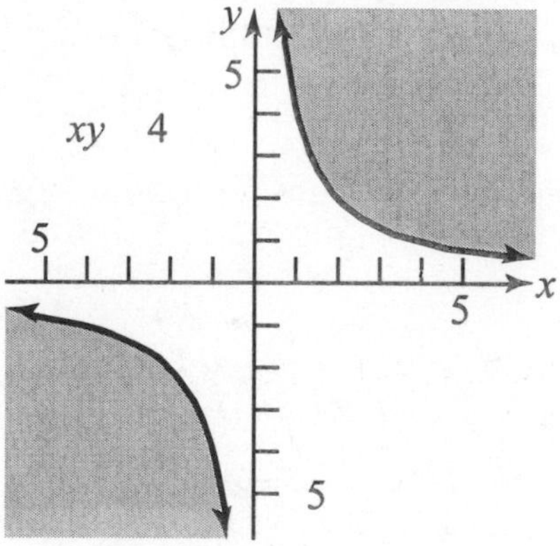

12. $xy \leq 1$

Graph the hyperbola $xy = 1$. Use a solid line since the inequality uses ≥.
Choose a test point not on the hyperbola, such as (0, 0). Since $0 \cdot 0 \leq 1$ is true, shade the same side of the hyperbola as (0, 0).

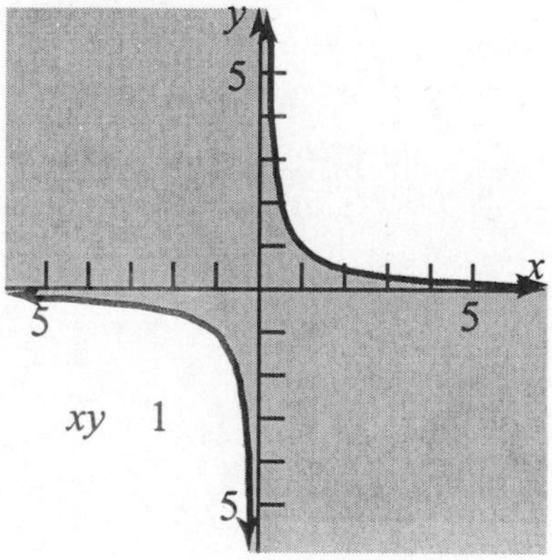

13. $\begin{cases} x + y \leq 2 \\ 2x + y \geq 4 \end{cases}$

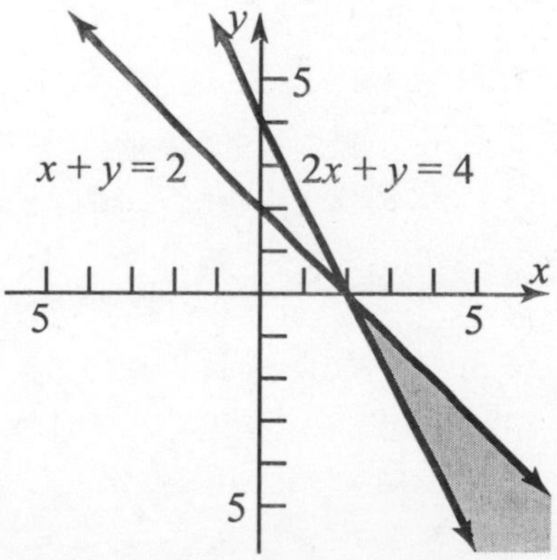

(a) Graph the line $x + y = 2$. Use a solid line since the inequality uses $\le$.
Choose a test point not on the line, such as (0, 0). Since $0 + 0 \le 2$ is true, shade the side of the line containing (0, 0).

(b) Graph the line $2x + y = 4$. Use a solid line since the inequality uses $\ge$.
Choose a test point not on the line, such as (0, 0). Since $2(0) + 0 \ge 4$ is false, shade the opposite side of the line from (0, 0).

(c) The overlapping region is the solution.

14. $\begin{cases} 3x - y \ge 6 \\ x + 2y \le 2 \end{cases}$

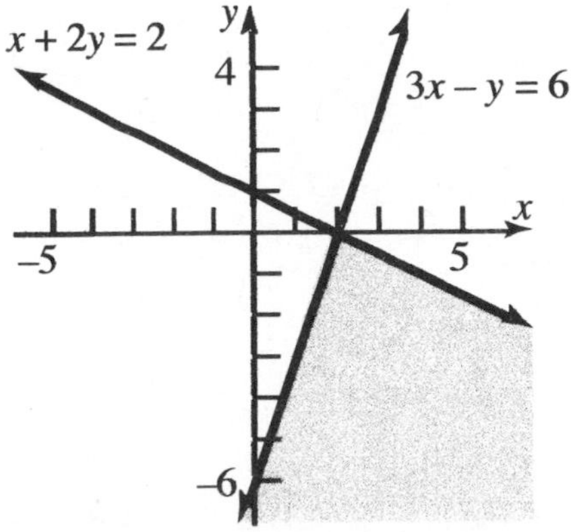

(a) Graph the line $3x - y = 6$. Use a solid line since the inequality uses $\ge$.
Choose a test point not on the line, such as (0, 0). Since $3(0) - 0 \ge 6$ is false, shade the opposite side of the line from (0, 0).

(b) Graph the line $x + 2y = 2$. Use a solid line since the inequality uses $\le$.
Choose a test point not on the line, such as (0, 0). Since $0 + 2(0) \le 2$ is true, shade the side of the line containing (0, 0).

(c) The overlapping region is the solution.

15. $\begin{cases} 2x - y \le 4 \\ 3x + 2y \ge -6 \end{cases}$

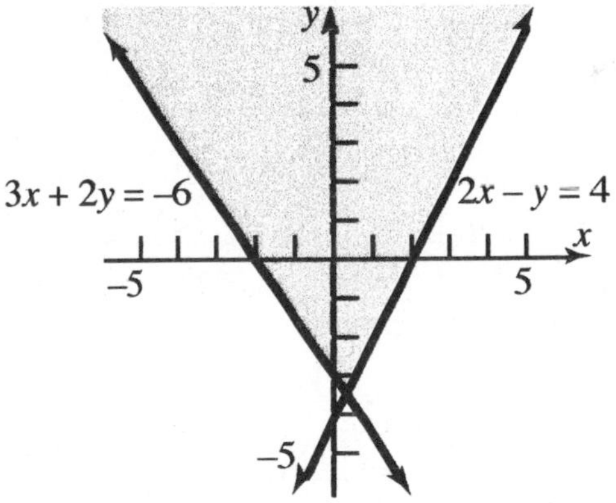

(a) Graph the line $2x - y = 4$. Use a solid line since the inequality uses $\le$.
Choose a test point not on the line, such as (0, 0). Since $2(0) - 0 \le 4$ is true, shade the side of the line containing (0, 0).

(b) Graph the line $3x + 2y = -6$. Use a solid line since the inequality uses $\ge$.
Choose a test point not on the line, such as (0, 0). Since $3(0) + 2(0) \ge -6$ is true, shade the side of the line containing (0, 0).

(c) The overlapping region is the solution.

16. $\begin{cases} 4x - 5y \le 0 \\ 2x - y \ge 2 \end{cases}$

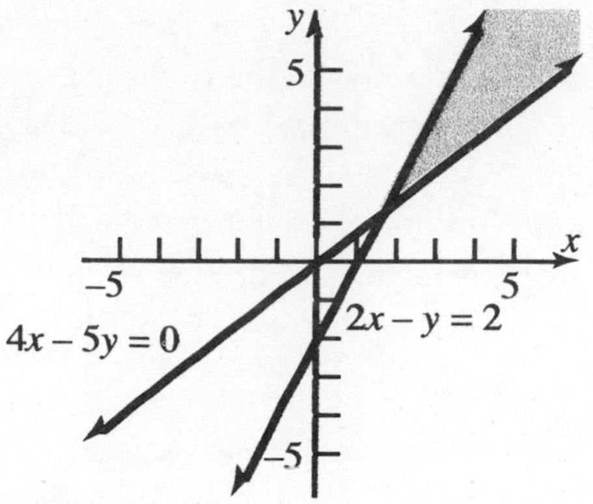

(a) Graph the line $4x - 5y = 0$. Use a solid line since the inequality uses $\le$. Choose a test point not on the line, such as (2, 0). Since $4(2) - 5(0) \le 0$ is false, shade the opposite side of the line from (2, 0).

(b) Graph the line $2x - y = 2$. Use a solid line since the inequality uses $\ge$. Choose a test point not on the line, such as (0, 0). Since $2(0) - 0 \ge 2$ is false, shade the opposite side of the line from (0, 0).

(c) The overlapping region is the solution.

17. $\begin{cases} 2x - 3y \le 0 \\ 3x + 2y \le 6 \end{cases}$

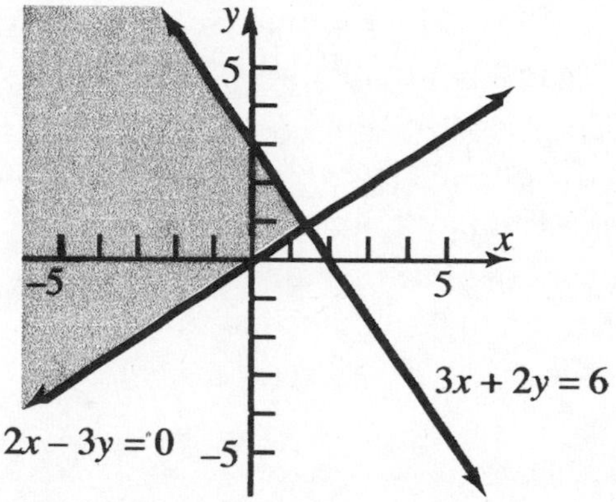

(a) Graph the line $2x - 3y = 0$. Use a solid line since the inequality uses $\le$. Choose a test point not on the line, such as (0, 3). Since $2(0) - 3(3) \le 0$ is true, shade the side of the line containing (0, 3).

(b) Graph the line $3x + 2y = 6$. Use a solid line since the inequality uses $\le$. Choose a test point not on the line, such as (0, 0). Since $3(0) + 2(0) \le 6$ is true, shade the side of the line containing (0, 0).

(c) The overlapping region is the solution.

18. $\begin{cases} 4x - y \geq 2 \\ x + 2y \geq 2 \end{cases}$

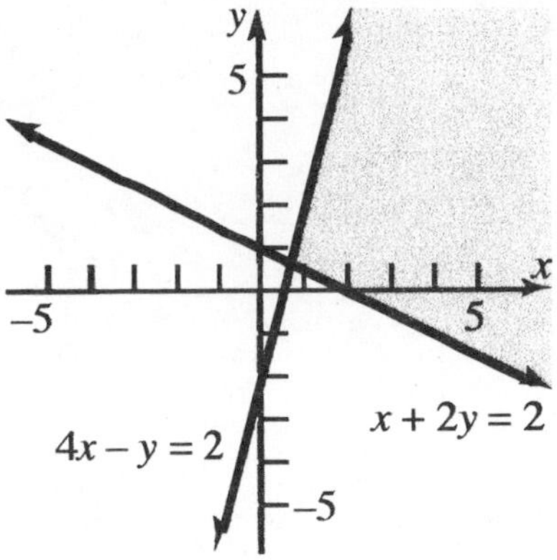

(a) Graph the line $4x - y = 2$. Use a solid line since the inequality uses $\geq$. Choose a test point not on the line, such as (0, 0). Since $4(0) - 0 \geq 2$ is false, shade the opposite side of the line from (0, 0).

(b) Graph the line $x + 2y = 2$. Use a solid line since the inequality uses $\geq$. Choose a test point not on the line, such as (0, 0). Since $0 + 2(0) \geq 2$ is false, shade the opposite side of the line from (0, 0).

(c) The overlapping region is the solution.

19. $\begin{cases} x^2 + y^2 \leq 9 \\ x + y \geq 3 \end{cases}$

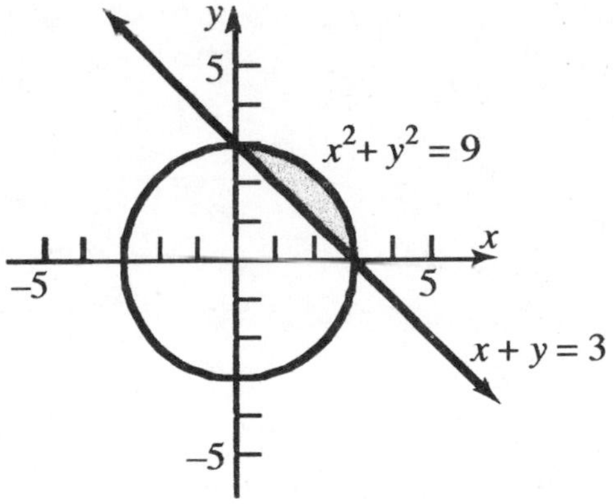

(a) Graph the circle $x^2 + y^2 = 9$. Use a solid line since the inequality uses $\geq$. Choose a test point not on the circle, such as (0, 0). Since $0^2 + 0^2 \leq 9$ is true, shade the same side of the circle as (0, 0).

(b) Graph the line $x + y = 3$. Use a solid line since the inequality uses $\geq$. Choose a test point not on the line, such as (0, 0). Since $0 + 0 \geq 3$ is false, shade the opposite side of the line from (0, 0).

(c) The overlapping region is the solution.

20. $\begin{cases} x^2 + y^2 \geq 9 \\ x + y \leq 3 \end{cases}$

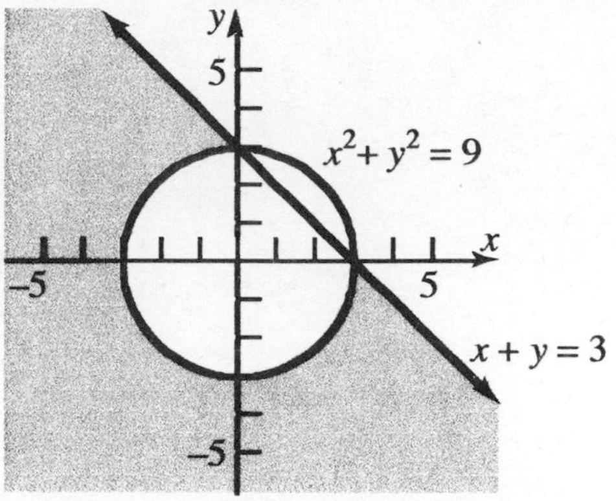

(a) Graph the circle $x^2 + y^2 = 9$.
Use a solid line since the inequality uses $\geq$. Choose a test point not on the circle, such as (0, 0). Since $0^2 + 0^2 \geq 9$ is false, shade the opposite side of the circle as (0, 0).

(b) Graph the line $x + y = 3$. Use a solid line since the inequality uses $\leq$. Choose a test point not on the line, such as (0, 0). Since $0 + 0 \leq 3$ is true, shade the same side of the line as (0, 0).

(c) The overlapping region is the solution.

21. $\begin{cases} y \geq x^2 - 4 \\ y \leq x - 2 \end{cases}$

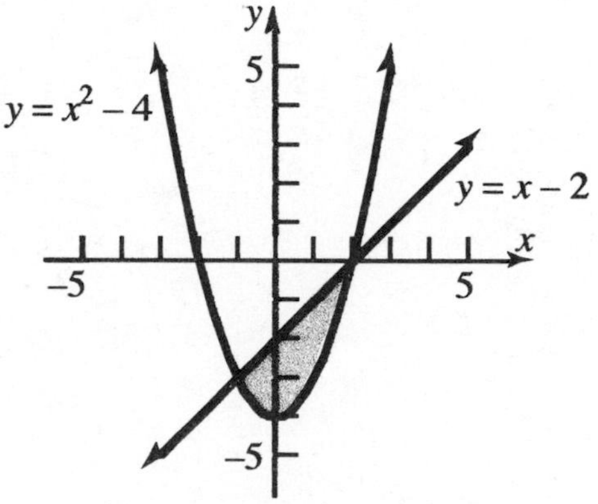

(a) Graph the parabola $y = x^2 - 4$.
Use a solid line since the inequality uses $\geq$. Choose a test point not on the parabola, such as (0, 0). Since $0 \geq 0^2 - 4$ is true, shade the same side of the parabola as (0, 0).

(b) Graph the line $y = x - 2$. Use a solid line since the inequality uses $\leq$. Choose a test point not on the line, such as (0, 0). Since $0 \leq 0 - 2$ is false, shade the opposite side of the line from (0, 0).

(c) The overlapping region is the solution.

22. $\begin{cases} y^2 \le x \\ y \ge x \end{cases}$

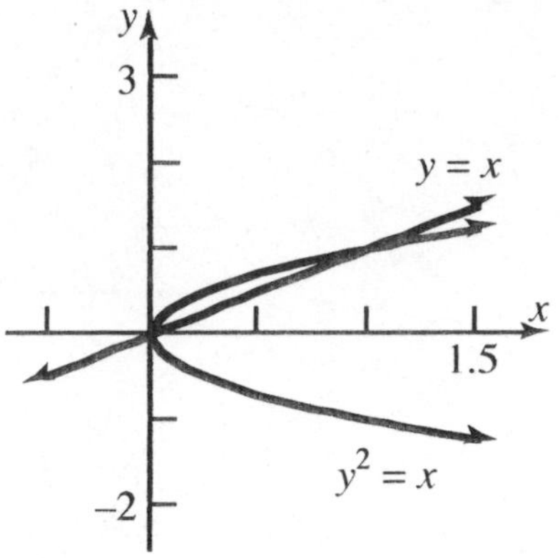

(a) Graph the parabola $y^2 = x$.
Use a solid line since the inequality uses $\le$. Choose a test point not on the parabola, such as (1, 2). Since $2^2 \le 1$ is false, shade the opposite side of the parabola from (1, 2).

(b) Graph the line $y = x$. Use a solid line since the inequality uses $\ge$. Choose a test point not on the line, such as (1, 2). Since $2 \ge 1$ is true, shade the same side of the line as (1, 2).

(c) The overlapping region is the solution.

23. $\begin{cases} xy \ge 4 \\ y \ge x^2 + 1 \end{cases}$

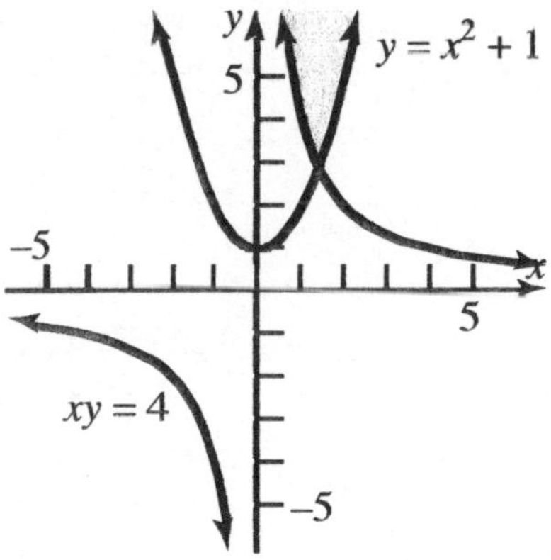

(a) Graph the hyperbola $xy = 4$.
Use a solid line since the inequality uses $\ge$. Choose a test point not on the parabola, such as (0, 0). Since $0 \cdot 0 \ge 4$ is false, shade the opposite side of the hyperbola from (0, 0).

(b) Graph the parabola $y = x^2 + 1$. Use a solid line since the inequality uses $\ge$. Choose a test point not on the parabola, such as (0, 0). Since $0 \ge 0^2 + 1$ is false, shade the opposite side of the parabola from (0, 0).

(c) The overlapping region is the solution.

24. $\begin{cases} y + x^2 \le 1 \\ y \ge x^2 - 1 \end{cases}$

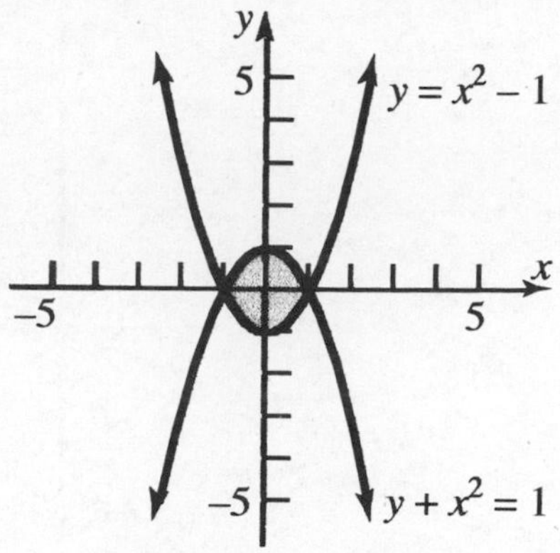

(a) Graph the parabola $y + x^2 = 1$.
Use a solid line since the inequality uses $\le$. Choose a test point not on the parabola, such as (0, 0). Since $0 + 0^2 \le 1$ is true, shade the same side of the parabola as (0, 0).

(b) Graph the parabola $y = x^2 - 1$. Use a solid line since the inequality uses $\ge$. Choose a test point not on the parabola, such as (0, 0). Since $0 \ge 0^2 - 1$ is false, shade the opposite side of the parabola from (0, 0).

(c) The overlapping region is the solution.

25. $\begin{cases} x - 2y \le 6 \\ 2x - 4y \ge 0 \end{cases}$

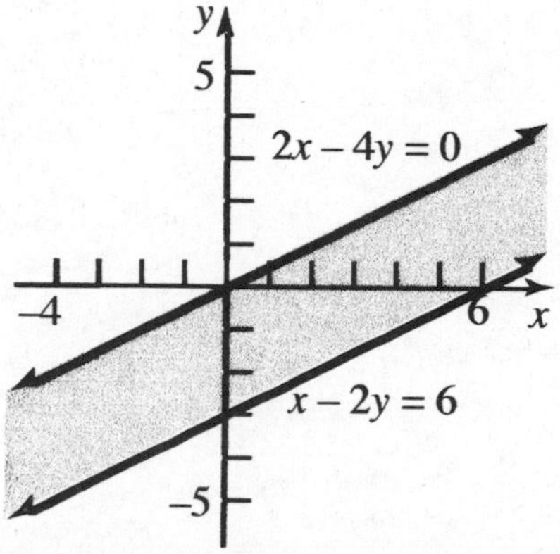

(a) Graph the line $x - 2y = 6$. Use a solid line since the inequality uses $\le$.
Choose a test point not on the line, such as (0, 0). Since $0 - 2(0) \le 6$ is true, shade the side of the line containing (0, 0).

(b) Graph the line $2x - 4y = 0$. Use a solid line since the inequality uses $\ge$.
Choose a test point not on the line, such as (0, 2). Since $2(0) - 4(2) \ge 0$ is false, shade the opposite side of the line from (0, 2).

(c) The overlapping region is the solution.

26. $\begin{cases} x + 4y \le 8 \\ x + 4y \ge 4 \end{cases}$

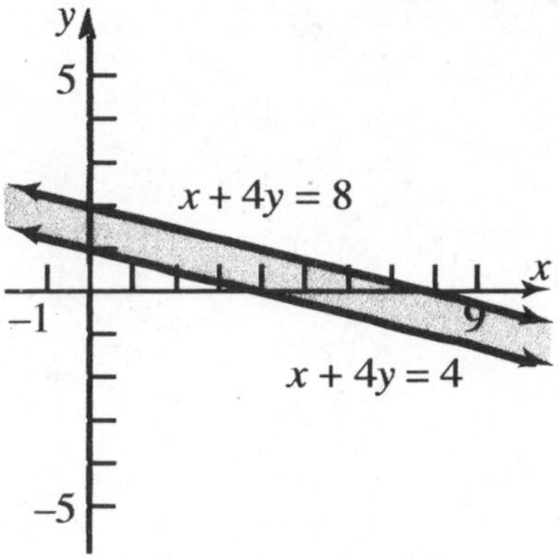

(a) Graph the line $x + 4y = 8$. Use a solid line since the inequality uses $\le$.
Choose a test point not on the line, such as (0, 0). Since $0 + 4(0) \le 8$ is true, shade the side of the line containing (0, 0).

(b) Graph the line $x + 4y = 4$. Use a solid line since the inequality uses $\ge$.
Choose a test point not on the line, such as (0, 0). Since $0 + 4(0) \ge 4$ is false, shade the opposite side of the line from (0, 0).

(c) The overlapping region is the solution.

27. $\begin{cases} 2x + y \ge -2 \\ 2x + y \ge \ \ 2 \end{cases}$

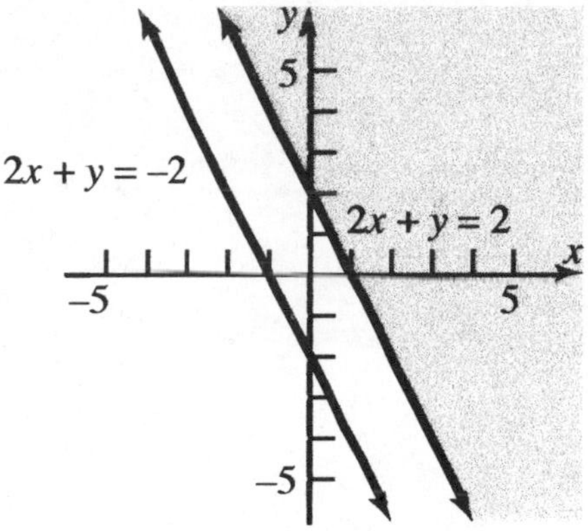

(a) Graph the line $2x + y = -2$. Use a solid line since the inequality uses $\ge$.
Choose a test point not on the line, such as (0, 0). Since $2(0) + 0 \ge -2$ is true, shade the side of the line containing (0, 0).

(b) Graph the line $2x + y = 2$. Use a solid line since the inequality uses $\ge$.
Choose a test point not on the line, such as (0, 0). Since $2(0) + 0 \ge 2$ is false, shade the opposite side of the line from (0, 0).

(c) The overlapping region is the solution.

28. $\begin{cases} x - 4y \le 4 \\ x - 4y \ge 0 \end{cases}$

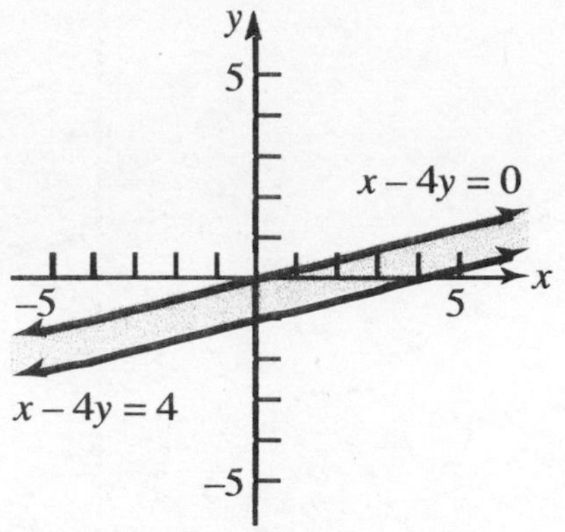

(a) Graph the line $x - 4y = 4$. Use a solid line since the inequality uses $\le$.
Choose a test point not on the line, such as (0, 0). Since $0 - 4(0) \le 4$ is true, shade the side of the line containing (0, 0).

(b) Graph the line $x - 4y = 0$. Use a solid line since the inequality uses $\ge$.
Choose a test point not on the line, such as (1, 0). Since $1 - 4(0) \ge 0$ is true, shade the side of the line containing (1, 0).

(c) The overlapping region is the solution.

29. $\begin{cases} 2x + 3y \ge 6 \\ 2x + 3y \le 0 \end{cases}$

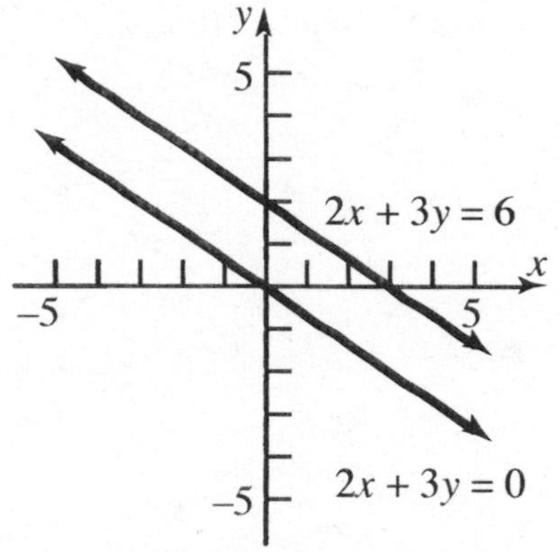

(a) Graph the line $2x + 3y = 6$. Use a solid line since the inequality uses $\ge$.
Choose a test point not on the line, such as (0, 0). Since $2(0) + 3(0) \ge 6$ is false, shade the opposite side of the line from (0, 0).

(b) Graph the line $2x + 3y = 0$. Use a solid line since the inequality uses $\le$.
Choose a test point not on the line, such as (0, 2). Since $2(0) + 3(2) \le 0$ is false, shade the opposite side of the line from (0, 2).

(c) Since the regions do not overlap, the solution is an empty set.

30. $\begin{cases} 2x + y \ge 0 \\ 2x + y \ge 2 \end{cases}$

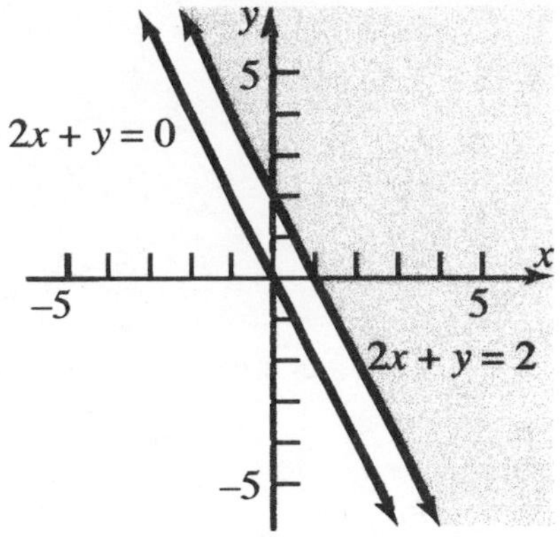

(a) Graph the line $2x + y = 0$. Use a solid line since the inequality uses $\ge$.
Choose a test point not on the line, such as (1, 0). Since $2(1) + 0 \ge 0$ is true, shade the side of the line containing (1, 0).

(b) Graph the line $2x + y = 2$. Use a solid line since the inequality uses $\ge$.
Choose a test point not on the line, such as (0, 0). Since $2(0) + 0 \ge 2$ is false, shade the opposite side of the line from (0, 0).

(c) The overlapping region is the solution.

31. Graph the system of linear inequalities:

$$\begin{cases} x \ge 0 \\ y \ge 0 \\ 2x + y \le 6 \\ x + 2y \le 6 \end{cases}$$

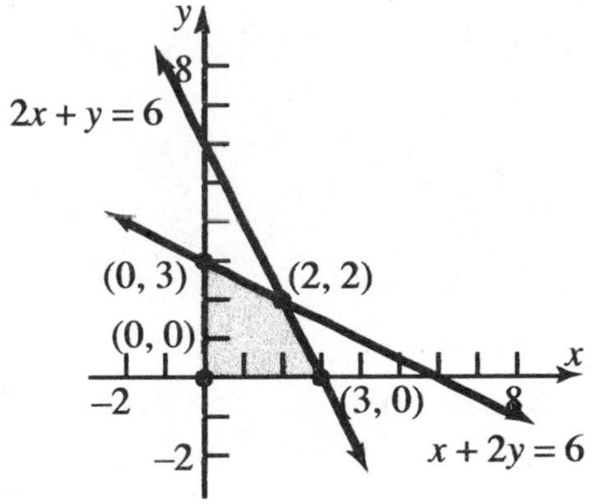

(a) Graph $x \ge 0$; $y \ge 0$. Shaded region is the first quadrant.

(b) Graph the line $2x + y = 6$. Use a solid line since the inequality uses $\le$.
Choose a test point not on the line, such as (0, 0). Since $2(0) + 0 \le 6$ is true, shade the side of the line containing (0, 0).

(c) Graph the line $x + 2y = 6$. Use a solid line since the inequality uses $\le$.
Choose a test point not on the line, such as (0, 0). Since $0 + 2(0) \le 6$ is true, shade the side of the line containing (0, 0).

(d) The overlapping region is the solution.

(e) The graph is bounded.

(f) Find the vertices:
The x-axis and y-axis intersect at (0, 0).
The intersection of $x + 2y = 6$ and the y-axis is (0, 3).
The intersection of $2x + y = 6$ and the x-axis is (3, 0).
To find the intersection of $x + 2y = 6$ and $2x + y = 6$, solve the system:

$$\begin{cases} x+2y=6 & \rightarrow \quad x=6-2y \\ 2x+\ y=6 \end{cases}$$

Substitute and solve:

$$2(6-2y)+y=6 \rightarrow 12-4y+y=6 \rightarrow -3y=-6 \rightarrow y=2$$

$$x=6-2(2)=6-4=2$$

The point of intersection is (2, 2).

The four corner points are (0, 0), (0, 3), (3, 0), and (2, 2

32. Graph the system of linear inequalities:

$$\begin{cases} x \ge 0 \\ y \ge 0 \\ x+\ y \ge 4 \\ 2x+3y \ge 6 \end{cases}$$

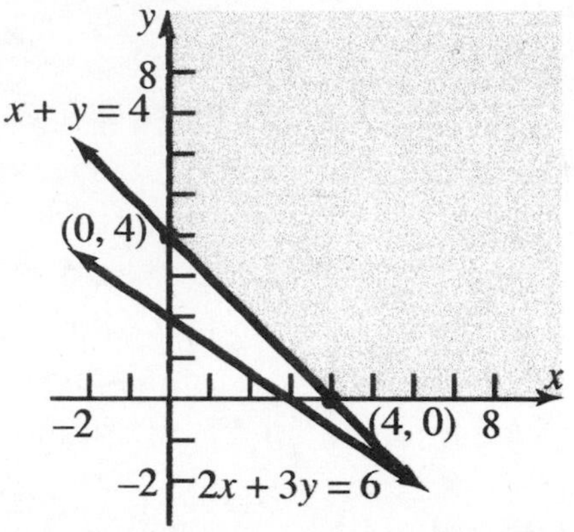

(a) Graph $x \ge 0$; $y \ge 0$. Shaded region is the first quadrant.

(b) Graph the line $x+y=4$. Use a solid line since the inequality uses $\ge$.
Choose a test point not on the line, such as (0, 0). Since $0+0 \ge 4$ is false, shade the opposite side of the line from (0, 0).

(c) Graph the line $2x+3y=6$. Use a solid line since the inequality uses $\ge$.
Choose a test point not on the line, such as (0, 0). Since $2(0)+3(0) \ge 6$ is false, shade the opposite side of the line from (0, 0).

(d) The overlapping region is the solution.

(e) The graph is unbounded.

(f) Find the vertices:
The intersection of $x+y=4$ and the y-axis is (0, 4).
The intersection of $x+y=4$ and the x-axis is (4, 0).
The two corner points are (0, 4), and (4, 0).

33. Graph the system of linear inequalities:

$$\begin{cases} x \ge 0 \\ y \ge 0 \\ x+y \ge 2 \\ 2x+y \ge 4 \end{cases}$$

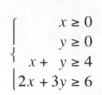

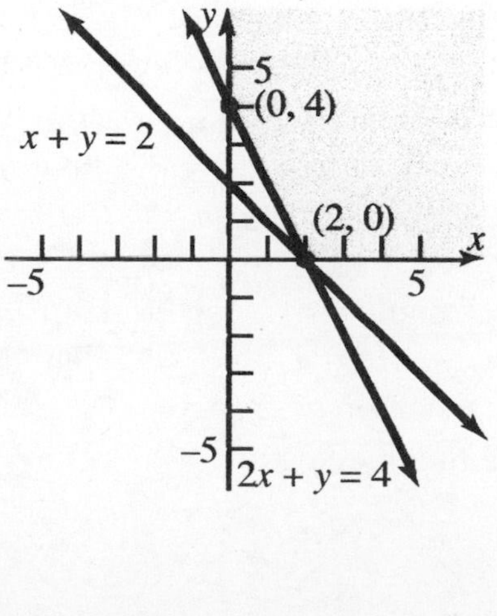

(a) Graph $x \ge 0$; $y \ge 0$. Shaded region is the first quadrant.
(b) Graph the line $x + y = 2$. Use a solid line since the inequality uses $\ge$.
Choose a test point not on the line, such as (0, 0). Since $0 + 0 \ge 2$ is false, shade the opposite side of the line from (0, 0).
(c) Graph the line $2x + y = 4$. Use a solid line since the inequality uses $\ge$.
Choose a test point not on the line, such as (0, 0). Since $2(0) + 0 \ge 4$ is false, shade the opposite side of the line from (0, 0).
(d) The overlapping region is the solution.
(e) The graph is unbounded.
(f) Find the vertices:
The intersection of $x + y = 2$ and the x-axis is (2, 0).
The intersection of $2x + y = 4$ and the y-axis is (0, 4).
The two corner points are (2, 0), and (0, 4).

34. Graph the system of linear inequalities:

$$\begin{cases} x \ge 0 \\ y \ge 0 \\ 3x + y \le 6 \\ 2x + y \le 2 \end{cases}$$

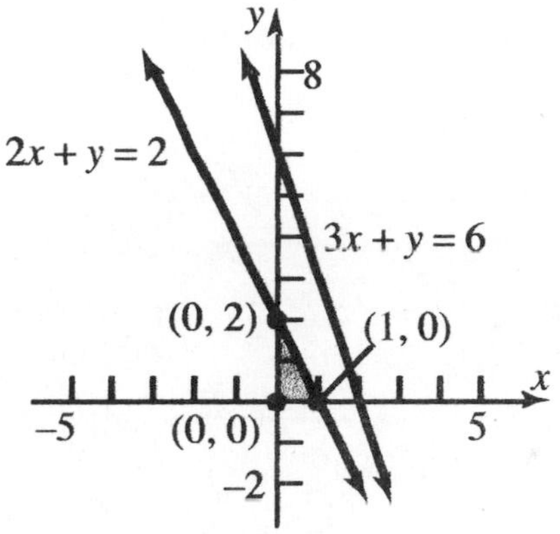

(a) Graph $x \ge 0$; $y \ge 0$. Shaded region is the first quadrant.
(b) Graph the line $3x + y = 6$. Use a solid line since the inequality uses $\le$.
Choose a test point not on the line, such as (0, 0). Since $3(0) + 0 \le 6$ is true, shade the side of the line containing (0, 0).
(c) Graph the line $2x + y = 2$. Use a solid line since the inequality uses $\le$.
Choose a test point not on the line, such as (0, 0). Since $2(0) + 0 \le 2$ is true, shade the side of the line containing (0, 0).
(d) The overlapping region is the solution.
(e) The graph is bounded.
(f) Find the vertices:
The intersection of $x = 0$ and $y = 0$ is (0, 0).
The intersection of $2x + y = 2$ and the x-axis is (1, 0).
The intersection of $2x + y = 2$ and the y-axis is (0, 2).
The three corner points are (0, 0), (1, 0), and (0, 2).

35. Graph the system of linear inequalities:

$$\begin{cases} x \ge 0 \\ y \ge 0 \\ x + y \ge 2 \\ 2x + 3y \le 12 \\ 3x + y \le 12 \end{cases}$$

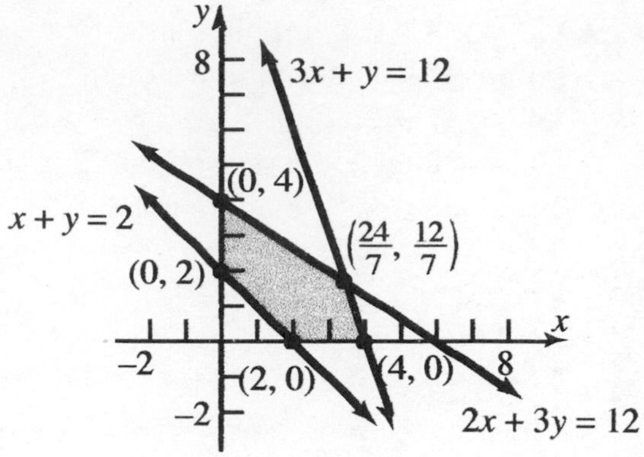

(a) Graph $x \ge 0$; $y \ge 0$. Shaded region is the first quadrant.

(b) Graph the line $x + y = 2$. Use a solid line since the inequality uses $\ge$.
Choose a test point not on the line, such as (0, 0). Since $0 + 0 \ge 2$ is false, shade the opposite side of the line from (0, 0).

(c) Graph the line $2x + 3y = 12$. Use a solid line since the inequality uses $\le$.
Choose a test point not on the line, such as (0, 0). Since $2(0) + 3(0) \le 12$ is true, shade the side of the line containing (0, 0).

(d) Graph the line $3x + y = 12$. Use a solid line since the inequality uses $\le$.
Choose a test point not on the line, such as (0, 0). Since $3(0) + 0 \le 12$ is true, shade the side of the line containing (0, 0).

(e) The overlapping region is the solution.

(f) The graph is bounded.

(g) Find the vertices:
The intersection of $x + y = 2$ and the y-axis is (0, 2).
The intersection of $x + y = 2$ and the x-axis is (2, 0).
The intersection of $2x + 3y = 12$ and the y-axis is (0, 4).
The intersection of $3x + y = 12$ and the x-axis is (4, 0).
To find the intersection of $2x + 3y = 12$ and $3x + y = 12$, solve the system:

$$\begin{cases} 2x + 3y = 12 \\ 3x + y = 12 \quad \rightarrow \quad y = 12 - 3x \end{cases}$$

Substitute and solve:

$$2x + 3(12 - 3x) = 12 \rightarrow 2x + 36 - 9x = 12$$

$$-7x = -24 \rightarrow x = \frac{24}{7}$$

$$y = 12 - 3\left(\frac{24}{7}\right) = 12 - \frac{72}{2} = \frac{12}{7}$$

The point of intersection is $\left(\frac{24}{7}, \frac{12}{7}\right)$.

The five corner points are (0, 2), (0, 4), (2, 0), (4, 0), and $\left(\frac{24}{7}, \frac{12}{7}\right)$.

36. Graph the system of linear inequalities:

$$\begin{cases} x \ge 0 \\ y \ge 0 \\ x + y \ge 2 \\ x + y \le 10 \\ 2x + y \le 3 \end{cases}$$

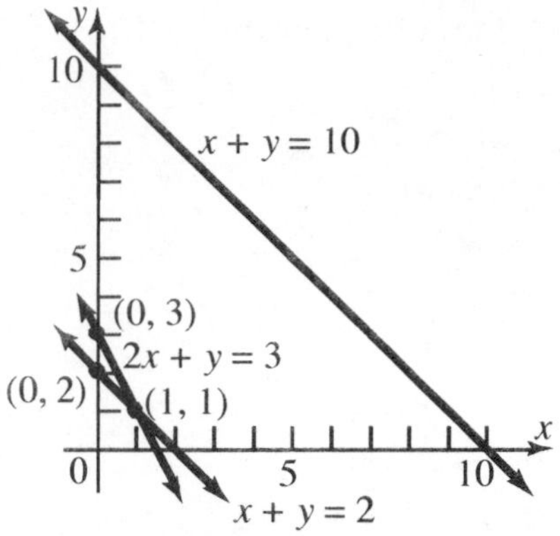

(a) Graph $x \ge 0$; $y \ge 0$. Shaded region is the first quadrant.
(b) Graph the line $x + y = 2$. Use a solid line since the inequality uses $\ge$.
Choose a test point not on the line, such as (0, 0). Since $0 + 0 \ge 2$ is false, shade the opposite side of the line from (0, 0).
(c) Graph the line $x + y = 10$. Use a solid line since the inequality uses $\le$.
Choose a test point not on the line, such as (0, 0). Since $0 + 0 \le 10$ is true, shade the side of the line containing (0, 0).
(d) Graph the line $2x + y = 3$. Use a solid line since the inequality uses $\le$.
Choose a test point not on the line, such as (0, 0). Since $2(0) + 0 \le 3$ is true, shade the side of the line containing (0, 0).
(e) The overlapping region is the solution.
(f) The graph is bounded.
(g) Find the vertices:
The intersection of $x + y = 2$ and the y-axis is (0, 2).
The intersection of $2x + y = 3$ and the y-axis is (0, 3).
To find the intersection of $2x + y = 3$ and $x + y = 2$, solve the system:

$$\begin{cases} 2x + y = 3 \\ x + y = 2 \quad \rightarrow \quad y = 2 - x \end{cases}$$

Substitute and solve:

$$2x + 2 - x = 3 \rightarrow x = 1$$

$$y = 2 - 1 = 1$$

The point of intersection is (1, 1).
The three corner points are (0, 2), (0, 3), and (1, 1).

37. Graph the system of linear inequalities:

$$\begin{cases} x \geq 0 \\ y \geq 0 \\ x + y \geq 2 \\ x + y \leq 8 \\ 2x + y \leq 10 \end{cases}$$

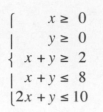

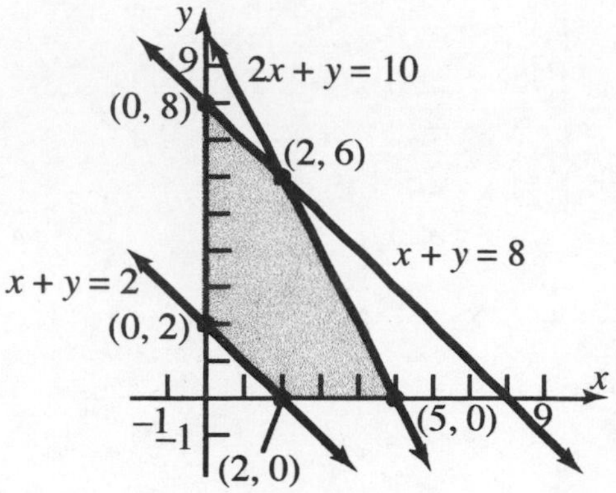

(a) Graph $x \geq 0$; $y \geq 0$. Shaded region is the first quadrant.
(b) Graph the line $x + y = 2$. Use a solid line since the inequality uses $\geq$.
Choose a test point not on the line, such as (0, 0). Since $0 + 0 \geq 2$ is false, shade the opposite side of the line from (0, 0).
(c) Graph the line $x + y = 8$. Use a solid line since the inequality uses $\leq$.
Choose a test point not on the line, such as (0, 0). Since $0 + 0 \leq 8$ is true, shade the side of the line containing (0, 0).
(d) Graph the line $2x + y = 10$. Use a solid line since the inequality uses $\leq$.
Choose a test point not on the line, such as (0, 0). Since $2(0) + 0 \leq 10$ is true, shade the side of the line containing (0, 0).
(e) The overlapping region is the solution.
(f) The graph is bounded.
(g) Find the vertices:
The intersection of $x + y = 2$ and the y-axis is (0, 2).
The intersection of $x + y = 2$ and the x-axis is (2, 0).
The intersection of $x + y = 8$ and the y-axis is (0, 8).
The intersection of $2x + y = 10$ and the x-axis is (5, 0).
To find the intersection of $x + y = 8$ and $2x + y = 10$, solve the system:

$$\begin{cases} x + y = 8 & \rightarrow \quad y = 8 - x \\ 2x + y = 10 \end{cases}$$

Substitute and solve:

$$2x + 8 - x = 10 \rightarrow x = 2$$

$$y = 8 - 2 = 6$$

The point of intersection is (2, 6).
The five corner points are (0, 2), (0, 8), (2, 0), (5, 0), and (2, 6).

38. Graph the system of linear inequalities:

$$\begin{cases} x \ge 0 \\ y \ge 0 \\ x + y \ge 2 \\ x + y \le 8 \\ x + 2y \ge 1 \end{cases}$$

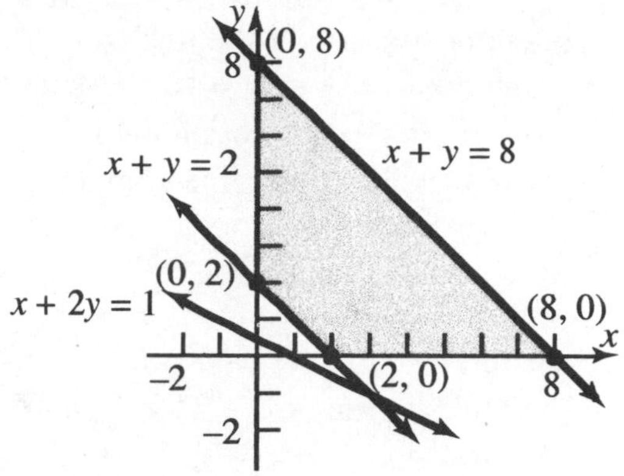

(a) Graph $x \ge 0$; $y \ge 0$. Shaded region is the first quadrant.
(b) Graph the line $x + y = 2$. Use a solid line since the inequality uses $\ge$.
Choose a test point not on the line, such as (0, 0). Since $0 + 0 \ge 2$ is false, shade the opposite side of the line from (0, 0).
(c) Graph the line $x + y = 8$. Use a solid line since the inequality uses $\le$.
Choose a test point not on the line, such as (0, 0). Since $0 + 0 \le 8$ is true, shade the side of the line containing (0, 0).
(d) Graph the line $x + 2y = 1$. Use a solid line since the inequality uses $\ge$.
Choose a test point not on the line, such as (0, 0). Since $0 + 2(0) \ge 1$ is false, shade the opposite side of the line from (0, 0).
(e) The overlapping region is the solution.
(f) The graph is bounded.
(g) Find the vertices:
The intersection of $x + y = 2$ and the y-axis is (0, 2).
The intersection of $x + y = 2$ and the x-axis is (2, 0).
The intersection of $x + y = 8$ and the y-axis is (0, 8).
The intersection of $x + y = 8$ and the x-axis is (8, 0).
The four corner points are (0, 2), (0, 8), (2, 0), and (8, 0).

39. Graph the system of linear inequalities:

$$\begin{cases} x \ge 0 \\ y \ge 0 \\ x + 2y \ge 1 \\ x + 2y \le 10 \end{cases}$$

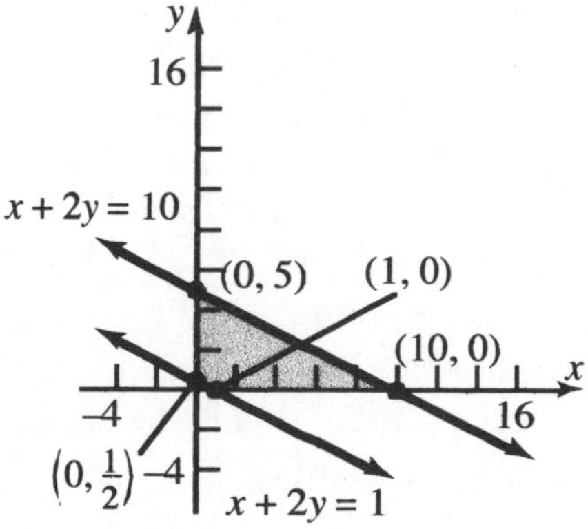

(a) Graph $x \ge 0$; $y \ge 0$. Shaded region is the first quadrant.
(b) Graph the line $x + 2y = 1$. Use a solid line since the inequality uses $\ge$.
Choose a test point not on the line, such as (0, 0). Since $0 + 2(0) \ge 1$ is false, shade the opposite side of the line from (0, 0).
(c) Graph the line $x + 2y = 10$. Use a solid line since the inequality uses $\le$.
Choose a test point not on the line, such as (0, 0). Since $0 + 2(0) \le 10$ is true, shade the side of the line containing (0, 0).
(d) The overlapping region is the solution.
(e) The graph is bounded.
(f) Find the vertices:
The intersection of $x + 2y = 1$ and the y-axis is (0, 0.5).
The intersection of $x + 2y = 1$ and the x-axis is (1, 0).
The intersection of $x + 2y = 10$ and the y-axis is (0, 5).
The intersection of $x + 2y = 10$ and the x-axis is (10, 0).
The four corner points are (0, 0.5), (0, 5), (1, 0), and (10, 0).

40. Graph the system of linear inequalities:

$$\begin{cases} x \ge 0 \\ y \ge 0 \\ x + 2y \ge 1 \\ x + 2y \le 10 \\ x + y \ge 2 \\ x + y \le 8 \end{cases}$$

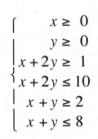

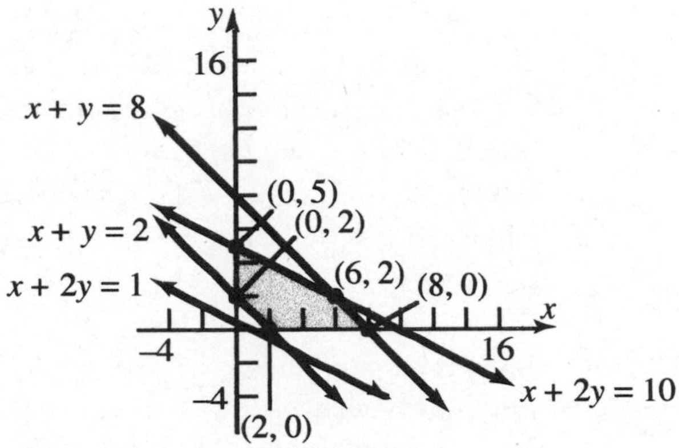

(a) Graph $x \ge 0$; $y \ge 0$. Shaded region is the first quadrant.
(b) Graph the line $x + 2y = 1$. Use a solid line since the inequality uses $\ge$.
Choose a test point not on the line, such as (0, 0). Since $0 + 2(0) \ge 1$ is false, shade the opposite side of the line from (0, 0).
(c) Graph the line $x + 2y = 10$. Use a solid line since the inequality uses $\le$.
Choose a test point not on the line, such as (0, 0). Since $0 + 2(0) \le 10$ is true, shade the side of the line containing (0, 0).
(d) Graph the line $x + y = 2$. Use a solid line since the inequality uses $\ge$.
Choose a test point not on the line, such as (0, 0). Since $0 + 0 \ge 2$ is false, shade the opposite side of the line from (0, 0).
(e) Graph the line $x + y = 8$. Use a solid line since the inequality uses $\le$.
Choose a test point not on the line, such as (0, 0). Since $0 + 0 \le 8$ is true, shade the side of the line containing (0, 0).
(f) The overlapping region is the solution.
(g) The graph is bounded.
(h) Find the vertices:
The intersection of $x + y = 2$ and the y-axis is (0, 2).
The intersection of $x + y = 2$ and the x-axis is (2, 0).

The intersection of $x+y=2$ and the x-axis is (2, 0).
The intersection of $x+2y=10$ and the y-axis is (0, 5).
The intersection of $x+y=8$ and the x-axis is (8, 0).
To find the intersection of $x+y=8$ and $x+2y=10$, solve the system:

$$\begin{cases} x+y=8 & \rightarrow \quad y=8-x \\ x+2y=10 \end{cases}$$

Substitute and solve:

$$x+2(8-x)=10 \rightarrow x+16-2x=10 \rightarrow -x=-6 \rightarrow x=6 \rightarrow y=8-6=2$$

The point of intersection is (6, 2).
The five corner points are (0, 2), (0, 5), (2, 0), (8, 0), and (6, 2).

41. The system of linear inequalities is:

$$\begin{cases} x \ge 0 \\ y \ge 0 \\ x \le 4 \\ x+y \le 6 \end{cases}$$

42. The system of linear inequalities is:

$$\begin{cases} x \ge 0 \\ y \ge 0 \\ x \le 6 \\ y \le 5 \\ x+y \ge 2 \end{cases}$$

43. The system of linear inequalities is:

$$\begin{cases} x \ge 0 \\ y \ge 15 \\ x \le 20 \\ x+y \le 50 \\ x-y \le 0 \end{cases}$$

44. The system of linear inequalities is:

$$\begin{cases} x \ge 0 \\ y \le 6 \\ x \le 5 \\ 3x+4y \ge 12 \\ 2x-y \le 8 \end{cases}$$

45. (a) Let x = the amount invested in Treasury bills.
Let y = the amount invested in corporate bonds.

The constraints are:

$x \ge 0, y \ge 0$	A non-negative amount must be invested.
$x+y \le 50000$	Total investment cannot exceed $50,000.
$y \le 10000$	Amount invested in corporate bonds must not exceed $10,000.
$x \ge 35000$	Amount invested in Treasury bills must be at least $35,000.
$x > y$	Amount invested in Treasury bills must be greater than the amount invested in corporate bonds.

(b) Graph the system.

$$\begin{cases} x \ge 0 \\ y \ge 0 \\ x+y \le 50000 \\ y \le 10000 \\ x \ge 35000 \\ x > y \end{cases}$$

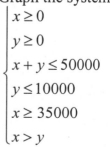

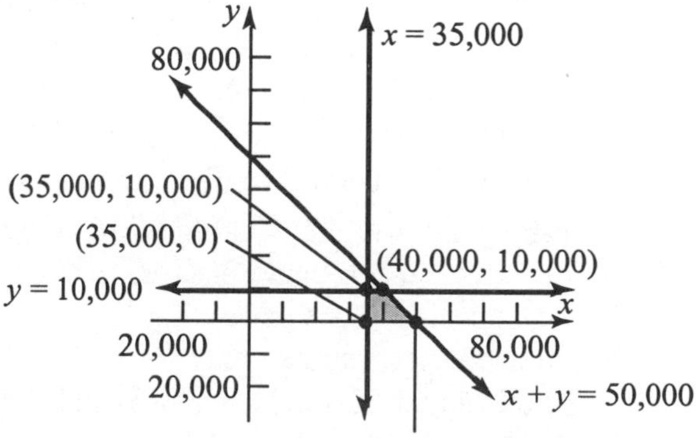

The corner points are (35000, 0), (35000, 10000), (40000, 10000), (50000, 0).

46. (a) Let x = the # of standard model trucks.
Let y = the # of deluxe model trucks.
The constraints are:

$x \geq 0, y \geq 0$	A non-negative number of trucks must be manufactured.
$2x + 3y \leq 80$	Total painting hours worked cannot exceed 80.
$3x + 4y \leq 120$	Total detailing hours worked cannot exceed 120.

(b) Graph the system.

$$\begin{cases} x \geq 0 \\ y \geq 0 \\ 2x + 3y \leq 80 \\ 3x + 4y \leq 120 \end{cases}$$

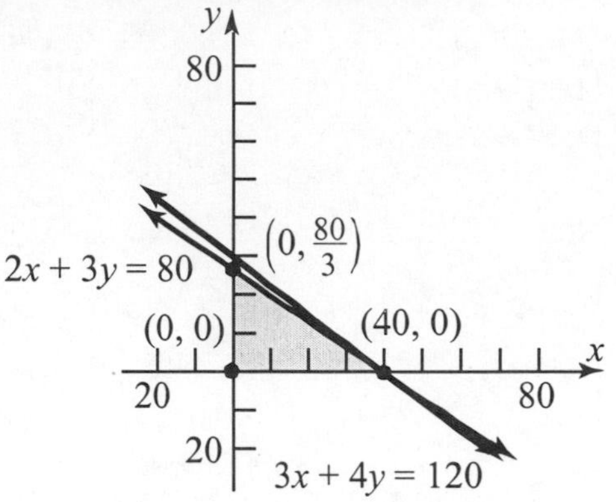

The corner points are (0, 0), (0, 25), (40, 0).

47. (a) Let x = the # of packages of the economy blend.
Let y = the # of packages of the superior blend.
The constraints are:

$x \geq 0, y \geq 0$	A non-negative # of packages must be produced.
$4x + 8y \leq 75 \cdot 16$	Total amount of grade A coffee cannot exceed 75 pounds. (Note: 75 pounds = (75)(16) ounces.)
$12x + 8y \leq 120 \cdot 16$	Total amount of grade B coffee cannot exceed 120 pounds. (Note: 120 pounds = (120)(16) ounces.)

We can simplify the equations

$$4x + 8y \leq 75 \cdot 16 \rightarrow x + 2y \leq 75 \cdot 4 \rightarrow x + 2y \leq 300$$
$$12x + 8y \leq 120 \cdot 16 \rightarrow 3x + 2y \leq 120 \cdot 4 \rightarrow 3x + 2y \leq 480$$

(b) Graph the system.

$$\begin{cases} x \geq 0 \\ y \geq 0 \\ x + 2y \leq 300 \\ 3x + 2y \leq 480 \end{cases}$$

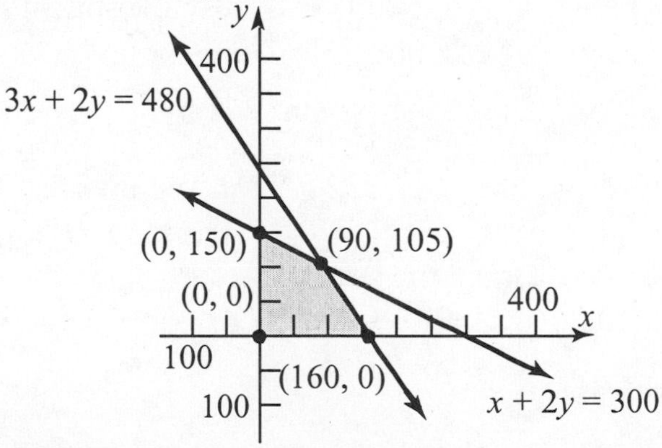

The corner points are (0, 0), (0, 150), (90, 105), (160, 0).

48. (a) Let x = the # of lower priced packages.
Let y = the # of quality packages.

The constraints are:

$x \ge 0, y \ge 0$	A non-negative # of packages must be produced.
$8x + 6y \le 120 \cdot 16$	Total amount of peanuts cannot exceed 120 pounds. (Note: 120 pounds = (120)(16) ounces.)
$4x + 6y \le 90 \cdot 16$	Total amount of cashews cannot exceed 90 pounds. (Note: 90 pounds = (90)(16) ounces.)

We can simplify the equations

$$8x + 6y \le 120 \cdot 16 \rightarrow 4x + 3y \le 120 \cdot 4 \rightarrow 4x + 3y \le 480$$
$$4x + 6y \le 90 \cdot 16 \rightarrow 2x + 3y \le 90 \cdot 4 \rightarrow 2x + 3y \le 360$$

(b) Graph the system.

$$\begin{cases} x \ge 0 \\ y \ge 0 \\ 4x + 3y \le 480 \\ 2x + 3y \le 360 \end{cases}$$

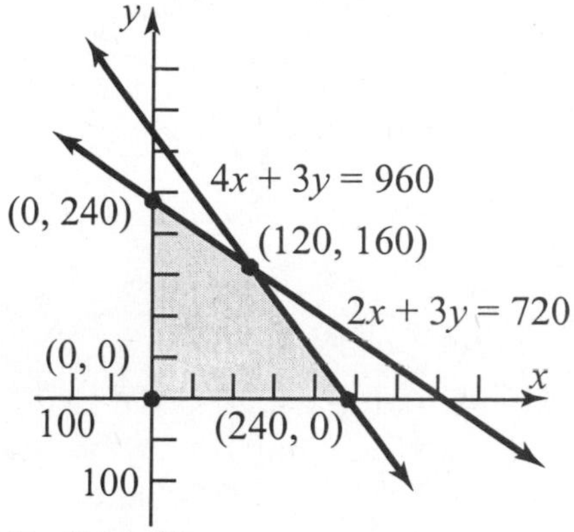

The corner points are (0, 0), (0, 120), (60, 80), (120, 0).

49. (a) Let x = the # of microwaves.
Let y = the # of printers.

The constraints are:

$x \ge 0, y \ge 0$	A non-negative # of items must be shipped.
$30x + 20y \le 1600$	Total cargo weight cannot exceed 1600 pounds.
$2x + 3y \le 150$	Total cargo volume cannot exceed 150 cubic feet.

(b) Graph the system.

$$\begin{cases} x \ge 0 \\ y \ge 0 \\ 30x + 20y \le 1600 \\ 2x + 3y \le 150 \end{cases}$$

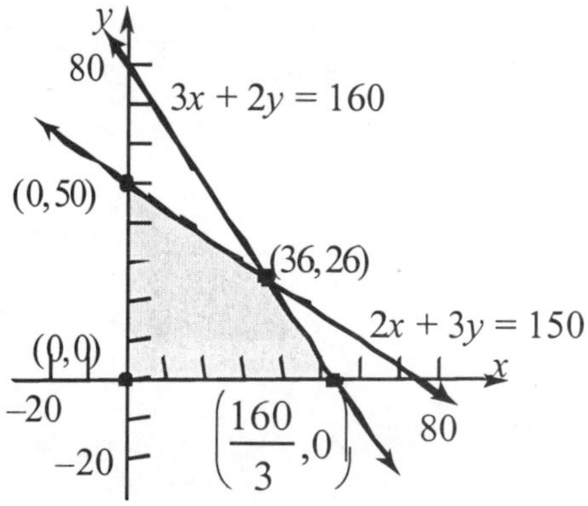

The corner points are (0, 0), (0, 50), (36, 26), (53.3, 0).

Chapter 12

Systems of Equations and Inequalities

12.9 Linear Programming

1. $z = x + y$

Vertex	Value of $z = x + y$
(0, 3)	$z = 0 + 3 = 3$
(0, 6)	$z = 0 + 6 = 6$
(5, 6)	$z = 5 + 6 = 11$
(5, 2)	$z = 5 + 2 = 7$
(4, 0)	$z = 4 + 0 = 4$

The maximum value is 11 at (5, 6), and the minimum value is 3 at (0, 3).

2. $z = 2x + 3y$

Vertex	Value of $z = 2x + 3y$
(0, 3)	$z = 2(0) + 3(3) = 9$
(0, 6)	$z = 2(0) + 3(6) = 18$
(5, 6)	$z = 2(5) + 3(6) = 28$
(5, 2)	$z = 2(5) + 3(2) = 16$
(4, 0)	$z = 2(4) + 3(0) = 8$

The maximum value is 28 at (5, 6), and the minimum value is 8 at (4, 0).

3. $z = x + 10y$

Vertex	Value of $z = x + 10y$
(0, 3)	$z = 0 + 10(3) = 30$
(0, 6)	$z = 0 + 10(6) = 60$
(5, 6)	$z = 5 + 10(6) = 65$
(5, 2)	$z = 5 + 10(2) = 25$
(4, 0)	$z = 4 + 10(0) = 4$

The maximum value is 65 at (5, 6), and the minimum value is 4 at (4, 0).

4. $z = 10x + y$

Vertex	Value of $z = 10x + y$
(0, 3)	$z = 10(0) + 3 = 3$
(0, 6)	$z = 10(0) + 6 = 6$
(5, 6)	$z = 10(5) + 6 = 56$
(5, 2)	$z = 10(5) + 2 = 52$
(4, 0)	$z = 10(4) + 0 = 40$

The maximum value is 56 at (5, 6), and the minimum value is 3 at (0, 3).

5. $z = 5x + 7y$

Vertex	Value of $z = 5x + 7y$
(0, 3)	z = 5(0) + 7(3) = 21
(0, 6)	z = 5(0) + 7(6) = 42
(5, 6)	z = 5(5) + 7(6) = 67
(5, 2)	z = 5(5) + 7(2) = 39
(4, 0)	z = 5(4) + 7(0) = 20

The maximum value is 67 at (5, 6), and the minimum value is 20 at (4, 0).

6. $z = 7x + 5y$

Vertex	Value of $z = 7x + 5y$
(0, 3)	z = 7(0) + 5(3) = 15
(0, 6)	z = 7(0) + 5(6) = 30
(5, 6)	z = 7(5) + 5(6) = 65
(5, 2)	z = 7(5) + 5(2) = 45
(4, 0)	z = 7(4) + 5(0) = 28

The maximum value is 65 at (5, 6), and the minimum value is 15 at (0, 3).

7. Maximize $z = 2x + y$
Subject to $x \geq 0, \quad y \geq 0, \quad x + y \leq 6, \quad x + y \geq 1$
Graph the constraints.

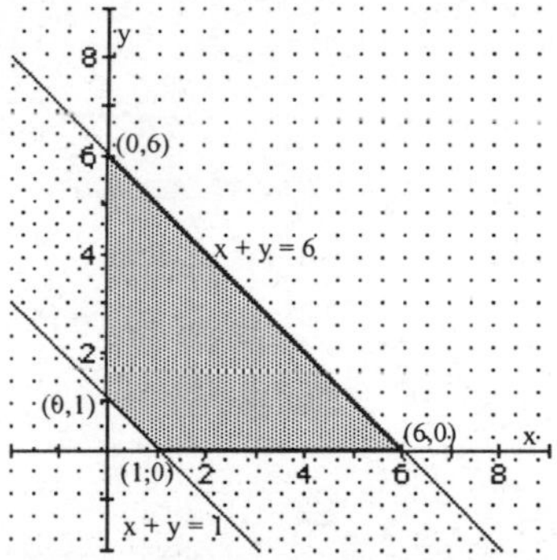

The corner points are (0, 1), (1, 0), (0, 6), (6, 0).
Evaluate the objective function:

Vertex	Value of $z = 2x + y$
(0, 1)	z = 2(0) + 1 = 1
(0, 6)	z = 2(0) + 6 = 6
(1, 0)	z = 2(1) + 0 = 2
(6, 0)	z = 2(6) + 0 = 12

The maximum value is 12 at (6, 0).

8. Maximize $z = x + 3y$
Subject to $x \geq 0,\ \ y \geq 0,\ \ x + y \geq 3,\ \ x \leq 5,\ \ y \leq 7$
Graph the constraints.

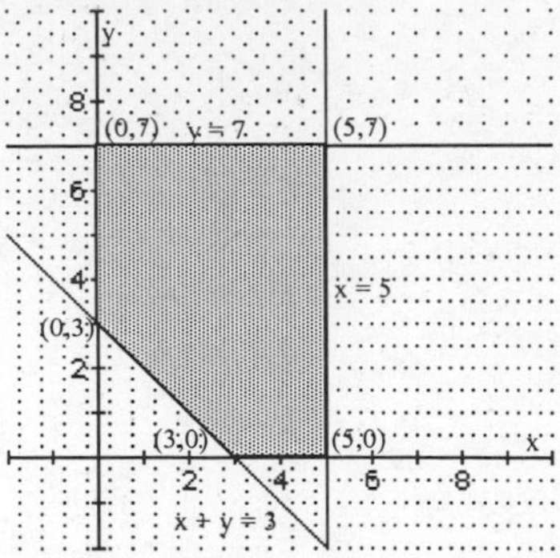

The corner points are (0, 3), (3, 0), (0, 7), (5, 0), (5, 7).
Evaluate the objective function:

Vertex	Value of $z = x + 3y$
(0, 3)	z = 0 + 3(3) = 9
(0, 7)	z = 0 + 3(7) = 21
(3, 0)	z = 3 + 3(0) = 3
(5, 0)	z = 5 + 3(0) = 5
(5, 7)	z = 5 + 3(7) = 26

The maximum value is 26 at (5, 7).

9. Minimize $z = 2x + 5y$
Subject to $x \geq 0,\ \ y \geq 0,\ \ x + y \geq 2,\ \ x \leq 5,\ \ y \leq 3$
Graph the constraints.

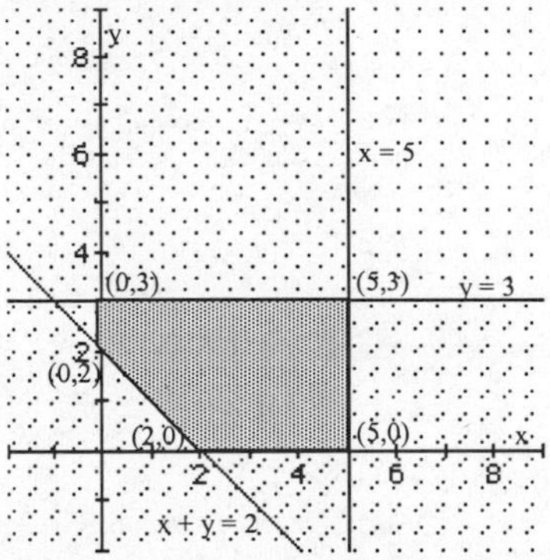

The corner points are (0, 2), (2, 0), (0, 3), (5, 0), (5, 3).
Evaluate the objective function:

Vertex	Value of $z = 2x + 5y$
(0, 2)	z = 2(0) + 5(2) = 10
(0, 3)	z = 2(0) + 5(3) = 15
(2, 0)	z = 2(2) + 5(0) = 4
(5, 0)	z = 2(5) + 5(0) = 10
(5, 3)	z = 2(5) + 5(3) = 25

The minimum value is 4 at (2, 0).

10. Minimize $z = 3x + 4y$
Subject to $x \ge 0$, $y \ge 0$, $2x + 3y \ge 6$, $x + y \le 8$
Graph the constraints.

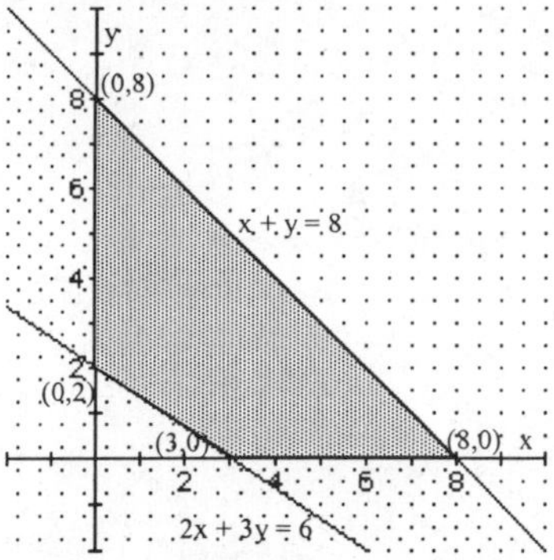

The corner points are (0, 2), (3, 0), (0, 8), (8, 0).
Evaluate the objective function:

Vertex	Value of $z = 3x + 4y$
(0, 2)	z = 3(0) + 4(2) = 8
(0, 8)	z = 3(0) + 4(8) = 32
(3, 0)	z = 3(3) + 4(0) = 9
(8, 0)	z = 3(8) + 4(0) = 24

The minimum value is 8 at (0, 2).

11. Maximize $z = 3x + 5y$
Subject to $x \ge 0$, $y \ge 0$, $x + y \ge 2$, $2x + 3y \le 12$, $3x + 2y \le 12$
Graph the constraints.

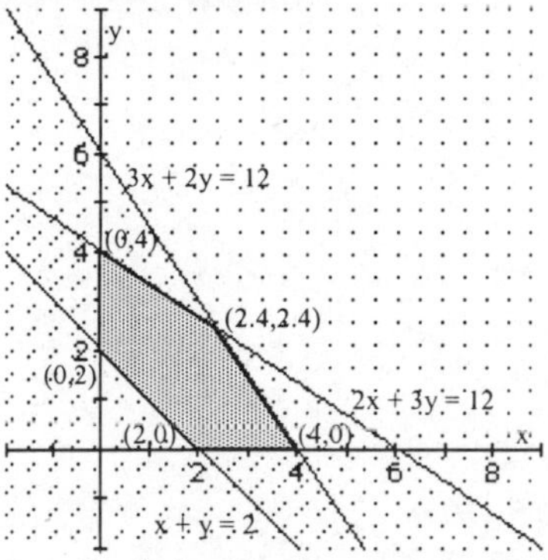

To find the intersection of $2x + 3y = 12$ and $3x + 2y = 12$, solve the system:

$$\begin{cases} 2x + 3y = 12 \\ 3x + 2y = 12 \quad \rightarrow \quad y = 6 - \dfrac{3}{2}x \end{cases}$$

Substitute and solve:

$$2x + 3\left(6 - \frac{3}{2}x\right) = 12 \rightarrow 2x + 18 - \frac{9}{2}x = 12 \rightarrow -\frac{5}{2}x = -6$$

$$x = \frac{12}{5} \qquad y = 6 - \frac{3}{2}\left(\frac{12}{5}\right) = 6 - \frac{18}{5} = \frac{12}{5}$$

The point of intersection is $(2.4, 2.4)$.

The corner points are (0, 2), (2, 0), (0, 4), (4, 0), (2.4, 2.4).

Evaluate the objective function:

Vertex	Value of $z = 3x + 5y$
(0, 2)	$z = 3(0) + 5(2) = 10$
(0, 4)	$z = 3(0) + 5(4) = 20$
(2, 0)	$z = 3(2) + 5(0) = 6$
(4, 0)	$z = 3(4) + 5(0) = 12$
(2.4,2.4)	$z = 3(2.4) + 5(2.4) = 19.2$

The maximum value is 20 at (0, 4).

12. Maximize $z = 5x + 3y$

Subject to $x \geq 0,\ \ y \geq 0,\ \ x + y \geq 2,\ \ x + y \leq 8,\ \ 2x + y \leq 10$

Graph the constraints.

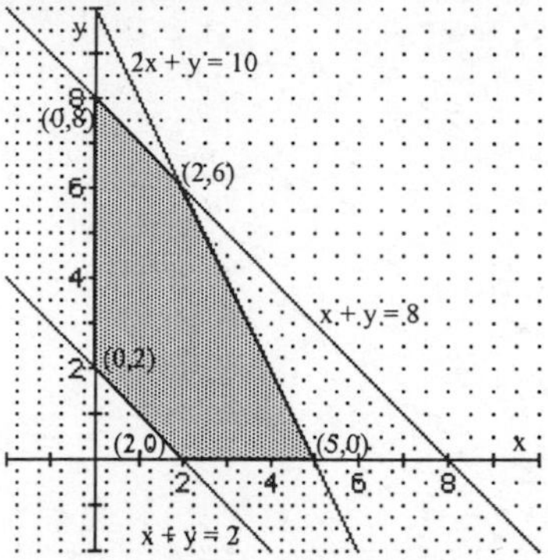

To find the intersection of $x + y = 8$ and $2x + y = 10$, solve the system:

$$\begin{cases} x + y = 8 & \rightarrow \quad y = 8 - x \\ 2x + y = 10 \end{cases}$$

Substitute and solve:

$$2x + 8 - x = 10$$

$$x = 2 \qquad\qquad y = 8 - 2 = 6$$

The point of intersection is (2, 6).

The corner points are (0, 2), (2, 0), (0, 8), (5, 0), (2, 6).

Evaluate the objective function:

Vertex	Value of $z = 5x + 3y$
(0, 2)	$z = 5(0) + 3(2) = 6$
(0, 8)	$z = 5(0) + 3(8) = 24$
(2, 0)	$z = 5(2) + 3(0) = 10$
(5, 0)	$z = 5(5) + 3(0) = 25$
(2, 6)	$z = 5(2) + 3(6) = 28$

The maximum value is 28 at (2, 6).

13. Minimize $z = 5x + 4y$
Subject to $x \ge 0,\ \ y \ge 0,\ \ x + y \ge 2,\ \ 2x + 3y \le 12,\ \ 3x + y \le 12$
Graph the constraints.

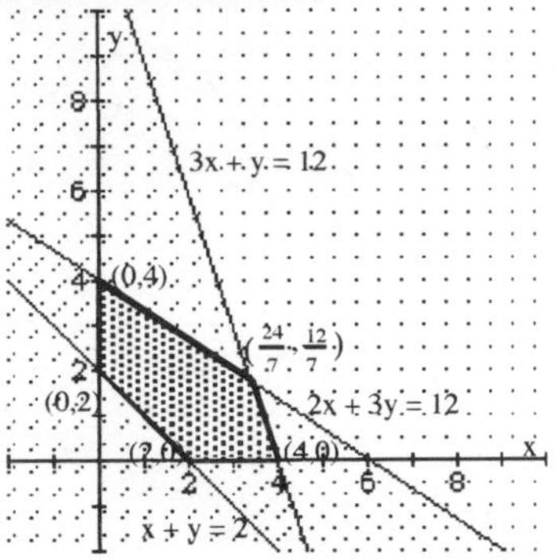

To find the intersection of $2x + 3y = 12$ and $3x + y = 12$, solve the system:

$$\begin{cases} 2x + 3y = 12 \\ 3x + \ \ y = 12 \quad \rightarrow \quad y = 12 - 3x \end{cases}$$

Substitute and solve:

$$2x + 3(12 - 3x) = 12 \rightarrow 2x + 36 - 9x = 12 \rightarrow -7x = -24 \rightarrow x = \frac{24}{7}$$

$$y = 12 - 3\left(\frac{24}{7}\right) = 12 - \frac{72}{7} = \frac{12}{7}$$

The point of intersection is $\left(\frac{24}{7}, \frac{12}{7}\right)$.

The corner points are (0, 2), (2, 0), (0, 4), (4, 0), $\left(\frac{24}{7}, \frac{12}{7}\right)$.

Evaluate the objective function:

Vertex	Value of $z = 5x + 4y$
(0, 2)	z = 5(0) + 4(2) = 8
(0, 4)	z = 5(0) + 4(4) = 16
(2, 0)	z = 5(2) + 4(0) = 10
(4, 0)	z = 5(4) + 4(0) = 20
$\left(\frac{24}{7}, \frac{12}{7}\right)$	$z = 5\left(\frac{24}{7}\right) + 4\left(\frac{12}{7}\right) = \frac{120}{7} + \frac{48}{7} = \frac{168}{7} = 24$

The minimum value is 8 at (0, 2).

14. Minimize $z = 2x + 3y$

Subject to $x \geq 0,\ \ y \geq 0,\ \ x + y \geq 3,\ \ x + y \leq 9,\ \ x + 3y \geq 6$

Graph the constraints.

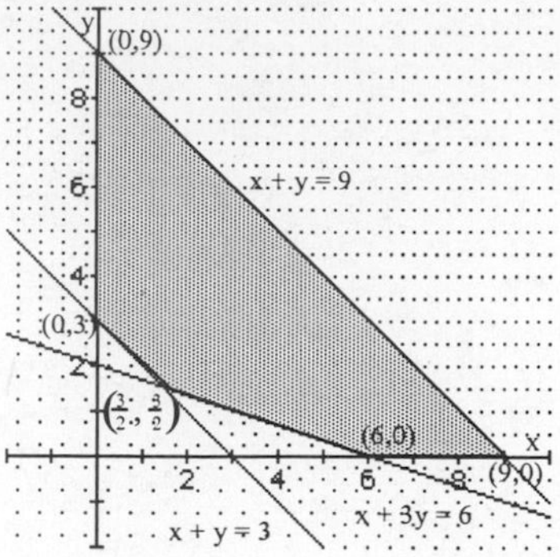

To find the intersection of $x + y = 3$ and $x + 3y = 6$, solve the system:

$$\begin{cases} x + \ y = 3 & \rightarrow \quad y = 3 - x \\ x + 3y = 6 \end{cases}$$

Substitute and solve:

$$x + 3(3 - x) = 6 \rightarrow x + 9 - 3x = 6 \rightarrow -2x = -3$$

$$x = 1.5 \qquad y = 3 - 1.5 = 1.5$$

The point of intersection is $(1.5, 1.5)$.

The corner points are (0, 3), (6, 0), (0, 9), (9, 0), $(1.5, 1.5)$.

Evaluate the objective function:

Vertex	Value of $z = 2x + 3y$
(0, 3)	z = 2(0) + 3(3) = 9
(0, 9)	z = 2(0) + 3(9) = 27
(6, 0)	z = 2(6) + 3(0) = 12
(9, 0)	z = 2(9) + 3(0) = 18
$(1.5, 1.5)$	$z = 2(1.5) + 3(1.5) = 3 + 4.5 = 7.5$

The minimum value is 7.5 at $(1.5, 1.5)$.

15. Maximize $z = 5x + 2y$

Subject to $x \geq 0,\ \ y \geq 0,\ \ x + y \leq 10,\ \ 2x + y \geq 10,\ \ x + 2y \geq 10$

Graph the constraints.

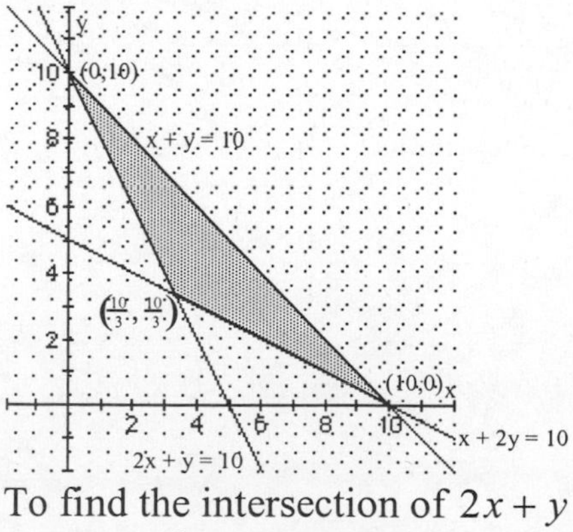

To find the intersection of $2x + y = 10$ and $x + 2y = 10$, solve the system:

$$\begin{cases} 2x + \ y = 10 & \rightarrow \quad y = 10 - 2x \\ \ x + 2y = 10 \end{cases}$$

Substitute and solve:

$$x+2(10-2x)=10 \rightarrow x+20-4x=10 \rightarrow -3x=-10 \rightarrow x=\frac{10}{3}$$

$$y=10-2\left(\frac{10}{3}\right)=10-\frac{20}{3}=\frac{10}{3}$$

The point of intersection is $\left(\frac{10}{3},\frac{10}{3}\right)$.

The corner points are (0, 10), (10, 0), $\left(\frac{10}{3},\frac{10}{3}\right)$.

Evaluate the objective function:

Vertex	Value of $z=5x+2y$
(0, 10)	$z=5(0)+2(10)=20$
(10, 0)	$z=5(10)+2(0)=50$
$\left(\frac{10}{3},\frac{10}{3}\right)$	$z=5\left(\frac{10}{3}\right)+2\left(\frac{10}{3}\right)=\frac{50}{3}+\frac{20}{3}=\frac{70}{3}=23\frac{1}{3}$

The maximum value is 50 at (10, 0).

16. Maximize $z=2x+4y$

Subject to $x\ge 0,\ \ y\ge 0,\ \ x+y\le 9,\ \ 2x+y\ge 4$

Graph the constraints.

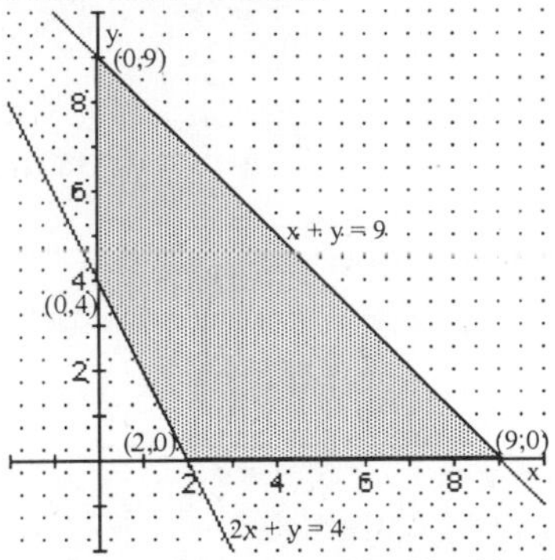

The corner points are (0, 9), (9, 0), (0, 4), (2, 0).

Evaluate the objective function:

Vertex	Value of $z=2x+4y$
(0, 9)	$z=2(0)+4(9)=36$
(9, 0)	$z=2(9)+4(0)=18$
(0, 4)	$z=2(0)+4(4)=16$
(2, 0)	$z=2(2)+4(0)=4$

The maximum value is 36 at (0, 9).

17. Let x = the number of downhill skis produced.

Let y = the number of cross-country skis produced.

The total profit is: $P=70x+50y$. Profit is to be maximized; thus, this is the objective function.

The constraints are:

$x\ge 0,\ \ y\ge 0$ A positive number of skis must be produced.

$2x+y\le 40$ Only 40 hours of manufacturing time is available.

$x+y\le 32$ Only 32 hours of finishing time is available.

Graph the constraints.

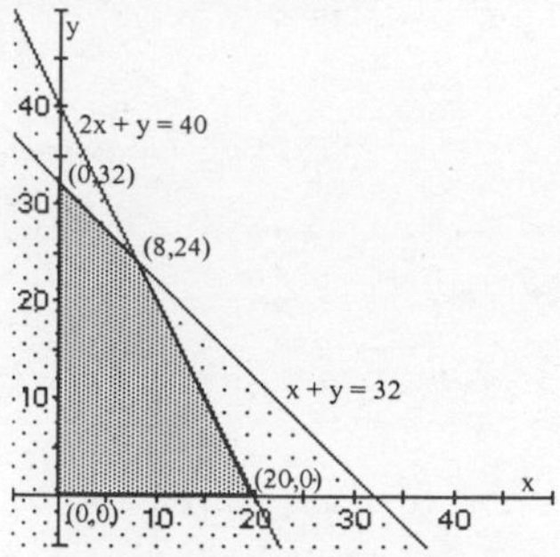

To find the intersection of $x + y = 32$ and $2x + y = 40$, solve the system:

$$\begin{cases} x + y = 32 & \rightarrow \quad y = 32 - x \\ 2x + y = 40 \end{cases}$$

Substitute and solve:

$$2x + 32 - x = 40 \rightarrow x = 8 \rightarrow y = 32 - 8 = 24$$

The point of intersection is (8, 24).

The corner points are (0, 0), (0, 32), (20, 0), (8, 24).

Evaluate the objective function:

Vertex	Value of $P = 70x + 50y$
(0, 0)	P = 70(0) + 50(0) = 0
(0, 32)	P = 70(0) + 50(32) = 1600
(20, 0)	P = 70(20) + 50(0) = 1400
(8, 24)	P = 70(8) + 50(24) = 1760

The maximum profit is \$1760, when 8 downhill skis and 24 cross-country skis are produced.

With the increase of the manufacturing time to 48 hours, we do the following:

The constraints are:

$x \geq 0, \ y \geq 0$ A positive number of skis must be produced.

$2x + y \leq 48$ Only 48 hours of manufacturing time is available.

$x + y \leq 32$ Only 32 hours of finishing time is available.

Graph the constraints.

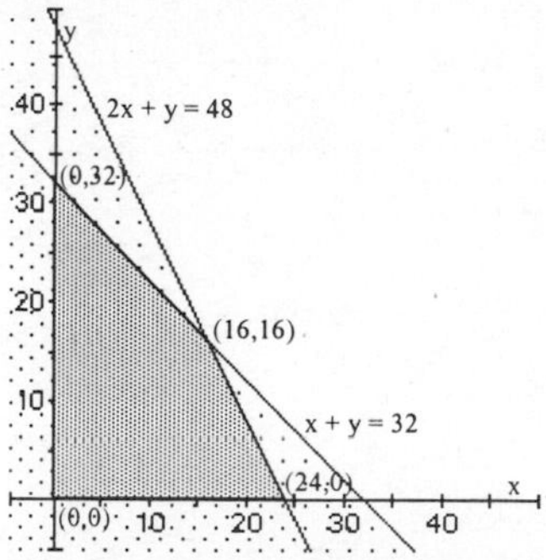

To find the intersection of $x + y = 32$ and $2x + y = 48$, solve the system:

$$\begin{cases} x + y = 32 & \rightarrow \quad y = 32 - x \\ 2x + y = 48 \end{cases}$$

Substitute and solve:

$$2x + 32 - x = 48 \rightarrow x = 16 \rightarrow y = 32 - 16 = 16$$

The point of intersection is (16, 16).

The corner points are (0, 0), (0, 32), (24, 0), (16, 16).

Evaluate the objective function:

Vertex	Value of $P = 70x + 50y$
(0, 0)	P = 70(0) + 50(0) = 0
(0, 32)	P = 70(0) + 50(32) = 1600
(24, 0)	P = 70(24) + 50(0) = 1680
(16, 16)	P = 70(16) + 50(16) = 1920

The maximum profit is \$1920, when 16 downhill skis and 16 cross-country skis are produced.

18. Let x = the number of acres of soybeans planted.
Let y = the number of acres of wheat planted.
The total profit is: $P = 180x + 100y$. Profit is to be maximized; thus, this is the objective function.
The constraints are:

$x \geq 0,\ \ y \geq 0$	A non-negative number of acres must be planted.
$x + y \leq 70$	Acres available to plant.
$60x + 30y \leq 1800$	Money available for preparation.
$3x + 4y \leq 120$	Total workdays available.

Graph the constraints.

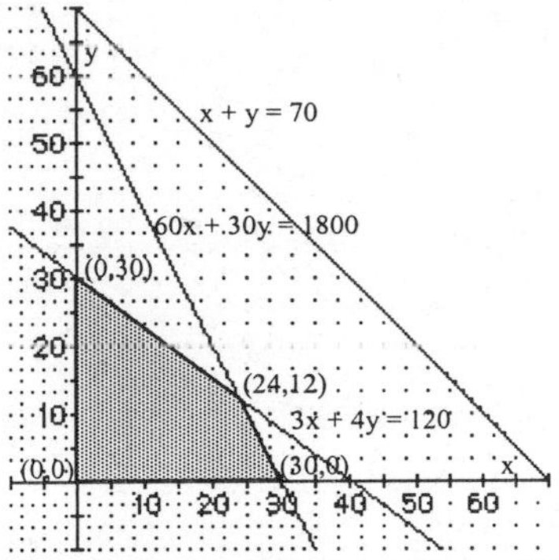

To find the intersection of $60x + 30y = 1800$ and $3x + 4y = 120$, solve the system:

$$\begin{cases} 60x + 30y = 1800 & \rightarrow \quad 2x + y = 60 \quad \rightarrow \quad y = 60 - 2x \\ 3x + 4y = 120 \end{cases}$$

Substitute and solve:

$$3x + 4(60 - 2x) = 120 \rightarrow 3x + 240 - 8x = 120 \rightarrow -5x = -120 \rightarrow x = 24$$

$$y = 60 - 2(24) = 12$$

The point of intersection is (24, 12).

The corner points are (0, 0), (0, 30), (30, 0), (24, 12).

Evaluate the objective function:

Vertex	Value of $P = 180x + 100y$
(0, 0)	P = 180(0) + 100(0) = 0
(0, 30)	P = 180(0) + 100(30) = 3000
(30, 0)	P = 180(30) + 100(0) = 5400
(24, 12)	P = 180(24) + 100(12) = 5520

The maximum profit is \$5520, when 24 acres of soybeans and 12 acres of wheat are planted.

With the increase of the preparation costs to $2400, we do the following:
The constraints are:

$x \geq 0,\ \ y \geq 0$	A non-negative number of acres must be planted.
$x + y \leq 70$	Acres available to plant.
$60x + 30y \leq 2400$	Money available for preparation.
$3x + 4y \leq 120$	Total workdays available.

Graph the constraints.

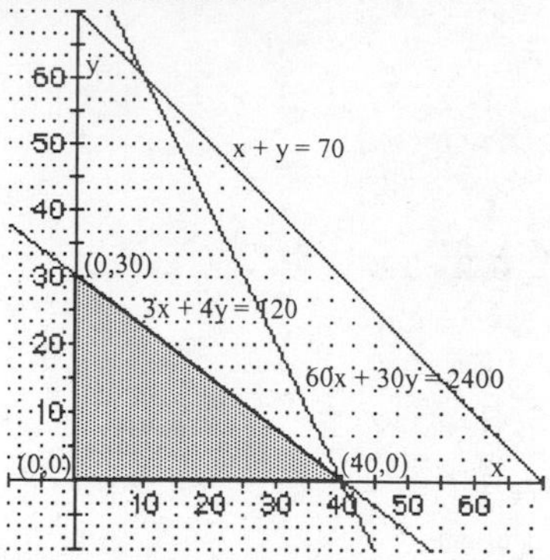

The corner points are (0, 0), (0, 30), (40, 0).
Evaluate the objective function:

Vertex	Value of $P = 180x + 100y$
(0, 0)	P = 180(0) + 100(0) = 0
(0, 30)	P = 180(0) + 100(30) = 3000
(40, 0)	P = 180(40) + 100(0) = 7200

The maximum profit is $7200, when 40 acres of soybeans and 0 acres of wheat are planted.

19. Let x = the number of acres of corn planted.
Let y = the number of acres of soybeans planted.
The total profit is: $P = 250x + 200y$. Profit is to be maximized; thus, this is the objective function.
The constraints are:

$x \geq 0,\ \ y \geq 0$	A non-negative number of acres must be planted.
$x + y \leq 100$	Acres available to plant.
$60x + 40y \leq 1800$	Money available for cultivation costs.
$60x + 60y \leq 2400$	Money available for labor costs.

Graph the constraints.

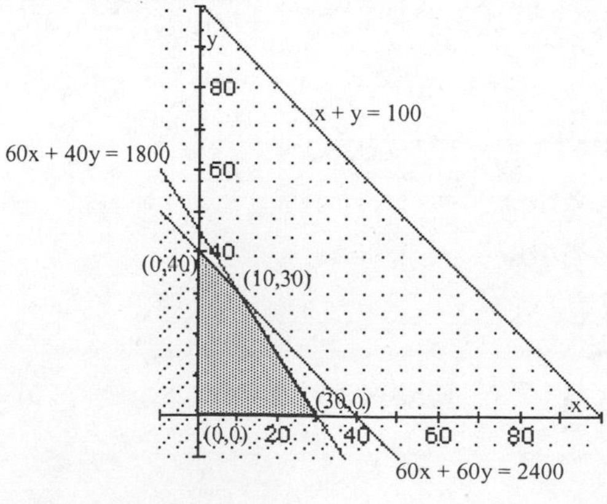

To find the intersection of $60x + 40y = 1800$ and $60x + 60y = 2400$, solve the system:

$$\begin{cases} 60x + 40y = 1800 & \rightarrow \quad 60x = 1800 - 40y \\ 60x + 60y = 2400 \end{cases}$$

Substitute and solve:

$$1800 - 40y + 60y = 2400 \rightarrow 20y = 600 \rightarrow y = 30$$

$$60x = 1800 - 40(30) \rightarrow 60x = 600 \rightarrow x = 10$$

The point of intersection is (10, 30).

The corner points are (0, 0), (0, 40), (30, 0), (10, 30).

Evaluate the objective function:

Vertex	Value of $P = 250x + 200y$
(0, 0)	$P = 250(0) + 200(0) = 0$
(0, 40)	$P = 250(0) + 200(40) = 8000$
(30, 0)	$P = 250(30) + 200(0) = 7500$
(10, 30)	$P = 250(10) + 200(30) = 8500$

The maximum profit is \$8500, when 10 acres of corn and 30 acres of soybeans are planted.

20. Let x = the number of ounces of Supplement A to be taken.

Let y = the number of ounces of Supplement B to be taken.

The total cost is: $C = 1.5x + y$. Cost is to be minimized; thus, this is the objective function.

The constraints are:

$x \geq 0,\ y \geq 0$ A non-negative number of ounces must be taken.

$5x + 2y \geq 60$ Carbohydrates needed in diet.

$3x + 2y \geq 45$ Protein needed in diet.

$4x + y \geq 30$ Fat needed in diet.

Graph the constraints.

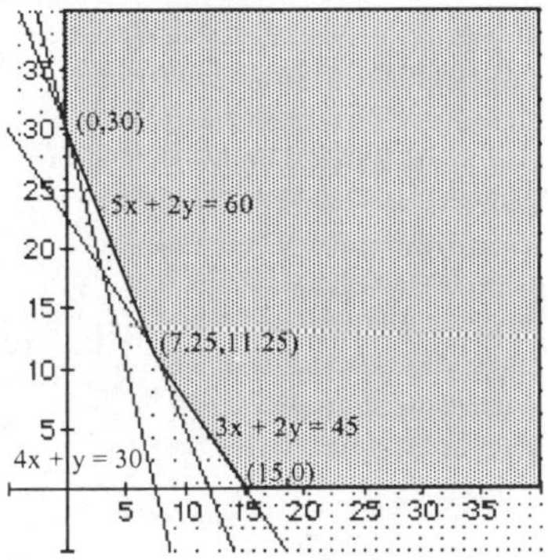

To find the intersection of $5x + 2y = 60$ and $3x + 2y = 45$, solve the system:

$$\begin{cases} 5x + 2y = 60 & \rightarrow \quad 2y = 60 - 5x \\ 3x + 2y = 45 \end{cases}$$

Substitute and solve:

$$3x + 60 - 5x = 45 \rightarrow -2x = -15 \rightarrow x = 7.5$$

$$2y = 60 - 5(7.5) = 22.5 \quad \rightarrow \quad y = 11.25$$

The point of intersection is (7.5, 11.25).

The corner points are (0, 30), (15, 0), (7.5, 11.25).

Evaluate the objective function:

Vertex	Value of $C = 1.5x + y$
(0, 30)	$C = 1.5(0) + 30 = 30$
(15, 0)	$C = 1.5(15) + 0 = 22.5$
(7.5, 11.25)	$C = 1.5(7.5) + 11.25 = 22.5$

The minimum cost is \$22.50, when 15 ounces of Supplement A and 0 ounces of Supplement B are used in the diet or when 7.5 ounces of Supplement A and 11.25 ounces of Supplement B are used in the diet.

21. Let x = the number of hours that machine 1 is operated.
Let y = the number of hours that machine 2 is operated.
The total cost is: $C = 50x + 30y$. Cost is to be minimized; thus, this is the objective function.
The constraints are:

$x \ge 0,\ y \ge 0$	A positive number of hours must be used.
$x \le 10$	10 hours available on machine 1.
$y \le 10$	10 hours available on machine 2.
$60x + 40y \ge 240$	At least 240 8-inch plyers must be produced.
$70x + 20y \ge 140$	At least 140 6-inch plyers must be produced.

Graph the constraints.

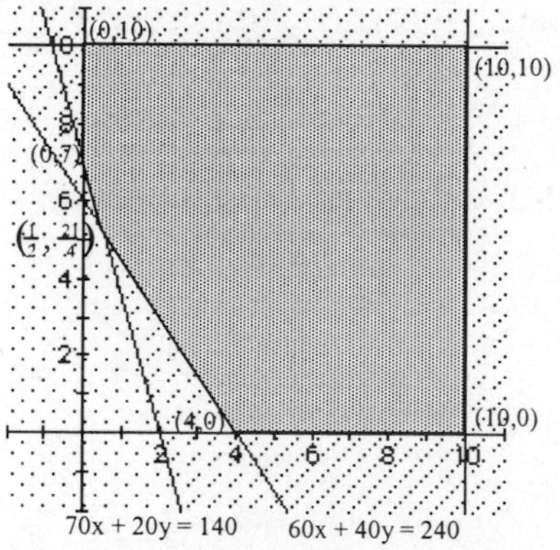

To find the intersection of $60x + 40y = 240$ and $70x + 20y = 140$, solve the system:

$$\begin{cases} 60x + 40y = 240 \\ 70x + 20y = 140 \end{cases} \rightarrow \quad 20y = 140 - 70x$$

Substitute and solve:

$$60x + 2(140 - 70x) = 240 \rightarrow 60x + 280 - 140x = 240$$

$$-80x = -40 \rightarrow x = 0.5$$

$$20y = 140 - 70(0.5) \rightarrow 20y = 105 \rightarrow y = 5.25$$

The point of intersection is $(0.5, 5.25)$.

The corner points are (0, 7), (0, 10), (4, 0), (10, 0), (10, 10), $(0.5, 5.25)$.

Evaluate the objective function:

Vertex	Value of $C = 50x + 30y$
(0, 7)	C = 50(0) + 30(7) = 210
(0, 10)	C = 50(0) + 30(10) = 300
(4, 0)	C = 50(4) + 30(0) = 200
(10, 0)	C = 50(10) + 30(0) = 500
(10, 10)	C = 50(10) + 30(10) = 800
(0.5, 5.25)	C = 50(0.5) + 30(5.25) = 182.50

The minimum cost is \$182.50, when machine 1 is used for 0.5 hours and machine 2 is used for 5.25 hours.

22. Let x = the number of newer trees.
Let y = the number of older trees.
The total cost is: $C = 15x + 20y$. Cost is to be minimized; thus, this is the objective function.

The constraints are:

$x \geq 0,\ \ y \geq 0$ A non-negative number of trees must be pruned.
$x + y \geq 25$ Must prune at least 25 trees.
$x + y \leq 50$ There are only 50 trees in the orchard.
$x + 1.5y \geq 30$ Contract is for at least 30 hours.

Graph the constraints.

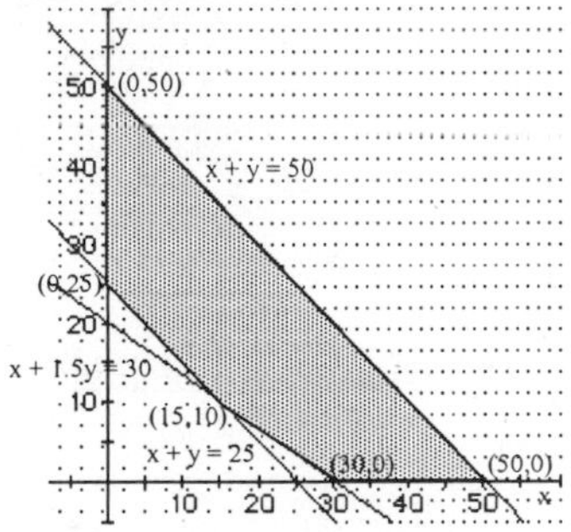

To find the intersection of $x + y = 25$ and $x + 1.5y = 30$, solve the system:

$$\begin{cases} x + y = 25 \\ x + 1.5y = 30 \end{cases} \rightarrow \quad x = 30 - 1.5y$$

Substitute and solve:

$$30 - 1.5y + y = 25$$

$$-0.5y = -5 \rightarrow y = 10 \rightarrow x = 30 - 1.5(10) = 15$$

The point of intersection is (15, 10).

The corner points are (0, 25), (0, 50), (30, 0), (50, 0), (15, 10).

Evaluate the objective function:

Vertex	Value of $C = 15x + 20y$
(0, 25)	C = 15(0) + 20(25) = 500
(0, 50)	C = 15(0) + 20(50) = 1000
(30, 0)	C = 15(30) + 20(0) = 450
(50, 0)	C = 15(50) + 20(0) = 750
(15, 10)	C = 15(15) + 20(10) = 425

The minimum cost is \$425, when 15 newer trees and 10 older trees are pruned.

23. Let x = the number of pounds of ground beef.
Let y = the number of pounds of ground pork.
The total cost is: $C = 0.75x + 0.45y$. Cost is to be minimized; thus, this is the objective function.
The constraints are:

$x \geq 0,\ y \geq 0$ A positive number of pounds must be used.
$x \leq 200$ Only 200 pounds of ground beef are available.
$y \geq 50$ At least 50 pounds of ground pork must be used.
$0.75x + 0.60y \geq 0.70(x + y) \rightarrow 0.05x \geq 0.10y$ Leanness condition to be met.

Graph the constraints.

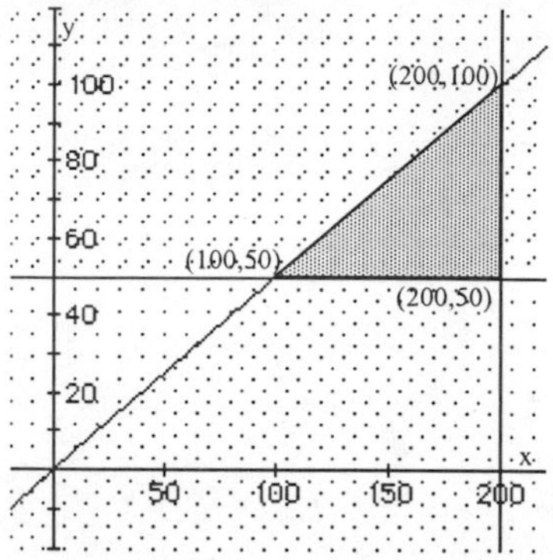

The corner points are (100, 50), (200, 50), (200, 100).
Evaluate the objective function:

Vertex	Value of $C = 0.75x + 0.45y$
(100, 50)	C = 0.75(100) + 0.45(50) = 97.50
(200, 50)	C = 0.75(200) + 0.45(50) = 172.50
(200,100)	C = 0.75(200) + 0.45(100) = 195.00

The minimum cost is $97.50, when 100 pounds of ground beef and 50 pounds of ground pork are used.

24. Let x = the amount invested in junk bonds.
Let y = the amount invested in Treasury bills.
The total income is: $I = 0.09x + 0.07y$. Income is to be maximized; thus, this is the objective function.
The constraints are:

$x \geq 0,\ y \geq 0$ A non-negative amount must be invested.
$x + y \leq 20000$ Total investment cannot exceed $20,000.
$x \leq 12000$ Amount invested in junk bonds must not exceed $12,000.
$y \geq 8000$ Amount invested in Treasury bills must be at least $8,000.
(a) $y \geq x$ Amount invested in Treasury bills must be equal to or greater than the amount invested in junk bonds.

Graph the constraints.

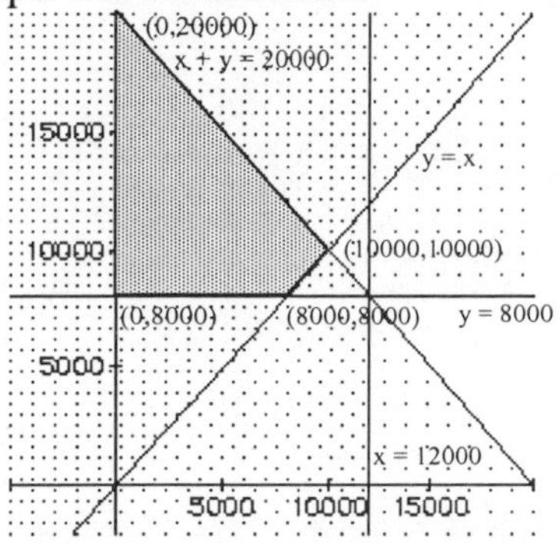

The corner points are (0, 20000), (0, 8000), (8000, 8000), (10000, 10000).
Evaluate the objective function:

Vertex	Value of $I = 0.09x + 0.07y$
(0, 20000)	I = 0.09(0) + 0.07(20000) = 1400
(0, 8000)	I = 0.09(0) + 0.07(8000) = 560
(8000, 8000)	I = 0.09(8000) + 0.07(8000) = 1280
(10000, 10000)	I = 0.09(10000) + 0.07(10000) = 1600

The maximum income is $1600, when $10,000 is invested in junk bonds and $10,000 is invested in Treasury bills.

(b) $y \le x$ Amount invested in Treasury bills must not exceed the amount invested in junk bonds.

Graph the constraints.

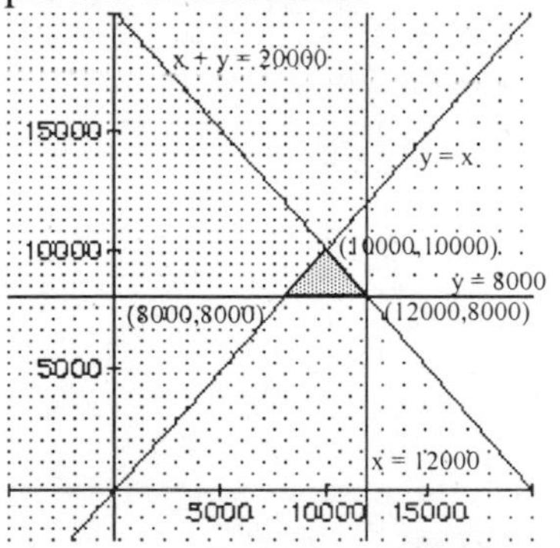

The corner points are (12000, 8000), (8000, 8000), (10000, 10000).
Evaluate the objective function:

Vertex	Value of $I = 0.09x + 0.07y$
(12000, 8000)	I = 0.09(12000) + 0.07(8000) = 1640
(8000, 8000)	I = 0.09(8000) + 0.07(8000) = 1280
(10000, 10000)	I = 0.09(10000) + 0.07(10000) = 1600

The maximum income is $1640, when $12,000 is invested in junk bonds and $8,000 is invested in Treasury bills.

25. Let x = the number of racing skates manufactured.
Let y = the number of figure skates manufactured.
The total profit is: $P = 10x + 12y$. Profit is to be maximized; thus, this is the objective function.
The constraints are:

$x \geq 0,\ y \geq 0$	A positive number of skates must be manufactured.
$6x + 4y \leq 120$	Only 120 hours are available for fabrication.
$x + 2y \leq 40$	Only 40 hours are available for finishing.

Graph the constraints.

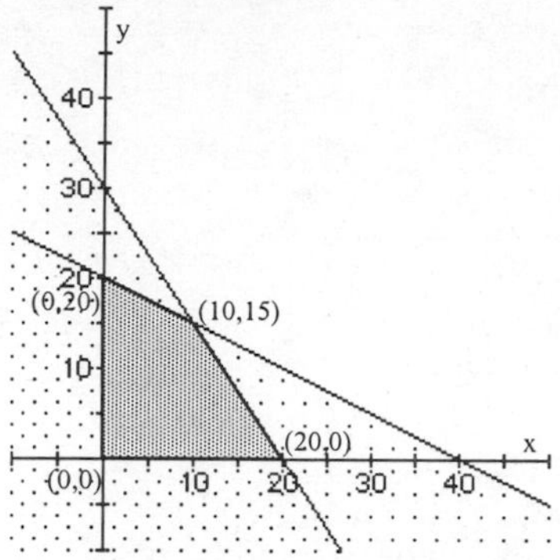

To find the intersection of $6x + 4y = 120$ and $x + 2y = 40$, solve the system:

$$\begin{cases} 6x + 4y = 120 \\ x + 2y = 40 \quad \rightarrow \quad x = 40 - 2y \end{cases}$$

Substitute and solve:

$$6(40 - 2y) + 4y = 120 \rightarrow 240 - 12y + 4y = 120$$

$$-8y = -120 \rightarrow y = 15 \rightarrow x = 40 - 2(15) = 10$$

The point of intersection is (10, 15).
The corner points are (0, 0), (0, 20), (20, 0), (10, 15).
Evaluate the objective function:

Vertex	Value of $P = 10x + 12y$
(0, 0)	$P = 10(0) + 12(0) = 0$
(0, 20)	$P = 10(0) + 12(20) = 240$
(20, 0)	$P = 10(20) + 12(0) = 200$
(10, 15)	$P = 10(10) + 12(15) = 280$

The maximum profit is \$280, when 10 racing skates and 15 figure skates are produced.

26. Let x = the amount placed in the AAA bond.
Let y = the amount placed in a CD.
The total return is: $R = 0.08x + 0.04y$. Return is to be maximized; thus, this is the objective function.
The constraints are:

$x \geq 0,\ y \geq 0$	A positive amount must be invested in each.
$x + y \leq 50000$	Total investment cannot exceed \$50,000.
$x \leq 20000$	Investment in the AAA bond cannot exceed \$20,000.
$y \geq 15000$	Investment in the CD must be at least \$15,000.
$y \geq x$	Investment in the CD must exceed or equal the investment in the bond.

Graph the constraints.

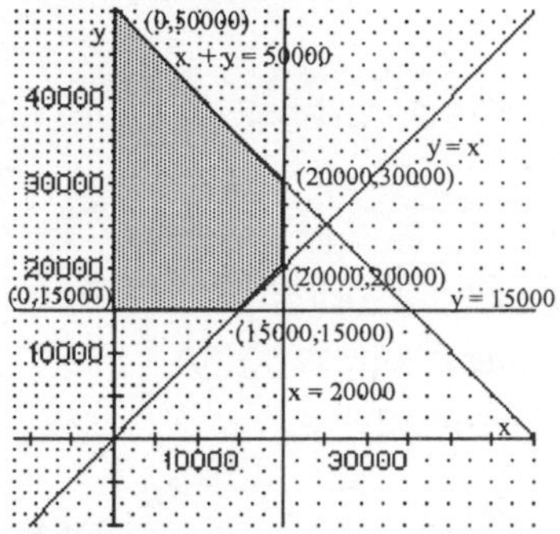

The corner points are (0, 50000), (0, 15000), (15000,15000), (20000,20000), (20000, 30000).

Evaluate the objective function:

Vertex	Value of $R = 0.08x + 0.04y$
(0, 50000)	R = 0.08(0) + 0.04(50000) = 2000
(0, 15000)	R = 0.08(0) + 0.04(15000) = 600
(15000, 15000)	R = 0.08(15000) + 0.04(15000) = 1800
(20000, 20000)	R = 0.08(20000) + 0.04(20000) = 2400
(20000, 30000)	R = 0.08(20000) + 0.04(30000) = 2800

The maximum return is $2800, when $20,000 is invested in a AAA bond and $30,000 is invested in a CD.

27. Let x = the number of metal fasteners.
Let y = the number of plastic fasteners.
The total cost is: $C = 9x + 4y$. Cost is to be minimized; thus, this is the objective function.
The constraints are:

$x \geq 2,\ y \geq 2$	At least 2 of each fastener must be made.
$x + y \geq 6$	At least 6 fasteners are needed.
$4x + 2y \leq 24$	Only 24 hours are available.

Graph the constraints.

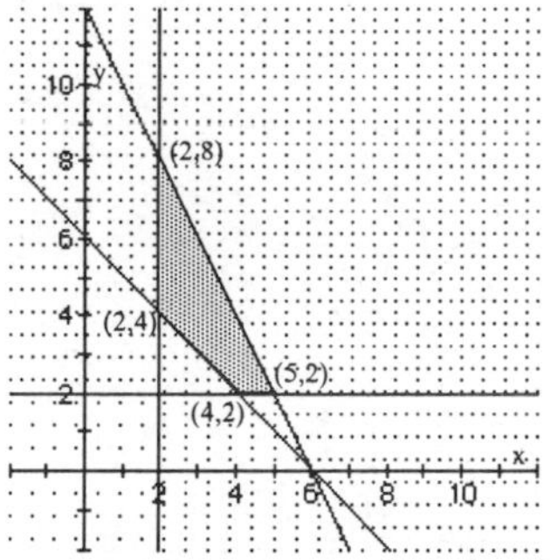

The corner points are (2, 4), (2, 8), (4, 2), (5, 2).

Evaluate the objective function:

Vertex	Value of $C = 9x + 4y$
(2, 4)	C = 9(2) + 4(4) = 34
(2, 8)	C = 9(2) + 4(8) = 50
(4, 2)	C = 9(4) + 4(2) = 44
(5, 2)	C = 9(5) + 4(2) = 53

The minimum cost is $34, when 2 metal fasteners and 4 plastic fasteners are ordered.

28. Let x = the amount of "Gourmet Dog".
Let y = the amount of "Chow Hound".
The total cost is: $C = 0.40x + 0.32y$. Cost is to be minimized; thus, this is the objective function.
The constraints are:

$x \geq 0,\ \ y \geq 0$	A non-negative number of cans must be purchased.
$20x + 35y \geq 1175$	At least 1175 units of vitamins per month.
$75x + 50y \geq 2375$	At least 2375 calories per month.
$x + y \leq 60$	Storage space for 60 cans.

Graph the constraints.

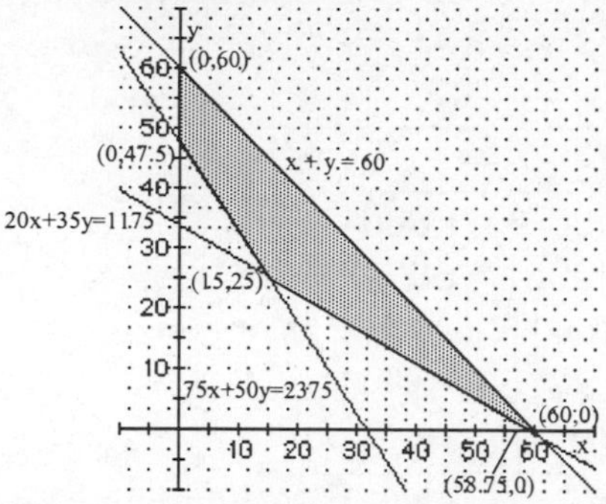

The corner points are (0, 47.5), (0, 60), (60, 0), (58.75, 0), (15, 25).
Evaluate the objective function:

Vertex	Value of $C = 0.40x + 0.32y$
(0, 47.5)	C = 0.40(0) + 0.32(47.5) = 15.20
(0, 60)	C = 0.40(0) + 0.32(60) = 19.20
(60, 0)	C = 0.40(60) + 0.32(0) = 24.00
(58.75, 0)	C = 0.40(58.75) + 0.32(0) = 23.50
(15, 25)	C = 0.40(15) + 0.32(25) = 14.00

The minimum cost is \$14, when 15 cans of "Gourmet Dog" and 25 cans of "Chow Hound" are purchased.

29. Let x = the number of first-class seats.
Let y = the number of coach seats.
The constraints are:

$8 \leq x \leq 16$	Restriction on first-class seats.
$80 \leq y \leq 120$	Restriction on coach seats.

(a) $\dfrac{x}{y} \leq \dfrac{1}{12}$ Ratio of seats.

If $y = 120$, then $\dfrac{x}{120} \leq \dfrac{1}{12} \rightarrow 12x \leq 120 \rightarrow x \leq 10$

The maximum revenue will be obtained with 120 coach seats and 10 first-class seats. (Note that the first-class seats meet their constraint.)

(b) $\dfrac{x}{y} \leq \dfrac{1}{8}$ Ratio of seats.

If $y = 120$, then $\dfrac{x}{120} \leq \dfrac{1}{8} \rightarrow 8x \leq 120 \rightarrow x \leq 15$

The maximum revenue will be obtained with 120 coach seats and 15 first-class seats. (Note that the first-class seats meet their constraint.)

30. Let x = the number of ounces of Supplement A.
Let y = the number of ounces of Supplement B.
The total cost is: $C = 0.06x + 0.08y$. Cost is to be minimized; thus, this is the objective function.

The constraints are:

$x \geq 0, \ y \geq 0$	A non-negative number of ounces must be purchased.
$5x + 25y \geq 50$	At least 50 units of vitamin I.
$25x + 10y \geq 90$	At least 90 units of vitamin II.
$10x + 10y \geq 60$	At least 60 units of vitamin III.
$35x + 20y \geq 100$	At least 100 units of vitamin IV.

Graph the constraints.

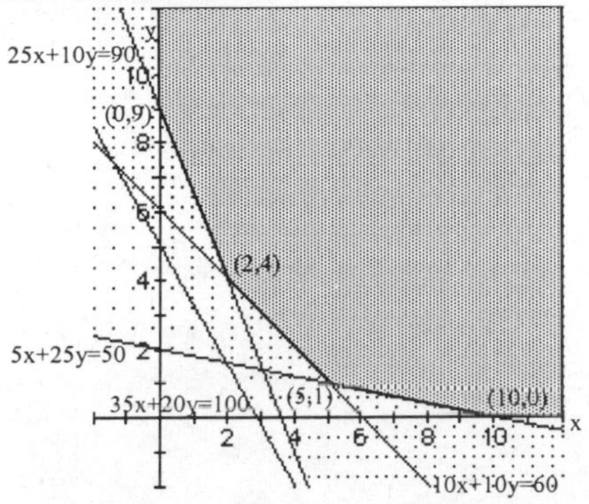

The corner points are (0, 9), (2, 4), (5, 1), (10, 0).

Evaluate the objective function:

Vertex	Value of $C = 0.06x + 0.08y$
(0, 9)	C = 0.06(0) + 0.08(9) = 0.72
(2, 4)	C = 0.06(2) + 0.08(4) = 0.44
(5, 1)	C = 0.06(5) + 0.08(1) = 0.38
(10, 0)	C = 0.06(10) + 0.08(0) = 0.60

The minimum cost is \$0.38, when 5 ounces of Supplement A, and 1 ounce of Supplement B are used.

Chapter 12

Systems of Equations and Inequalities

12.R Chapter Review

1. Solve the first equation for y, substitute into the second equation and solve:

$$\begin{cases} 2x - y = 5 \quad \rightarrow \quad y = 2x - 5 \\ 5x + 2y = 8 \end{cases}$$

$$5x + 2(2x - 5) = 8 \rightarrow 5x + 4x - 10 = 8$$

$$9x = 18 \rightarrow x = 2 \rightarrow y = 2(2) - 5 = 4 - 5 = -1$$

The solution is $x = 2,\ y = -1$.

2. Solve the second equation for y, substitute into the first equation and solve:

$$\begin{cases} 2x + 3y = 2 \\ 7x - y = 3 \quad \rightarrow \quad y = 7x - 3 \end{cases}$$

$$2x + 3(7x - 3) = 2 \rightarrow 2x + 21x - 9 = 2$$

$$23x = 11 \quad \rightarrow \quad x = \frac{11}{23} \rightarrow y = 7\left(\frac{11}{23}\right) - 3 = \frac{77}{23} - \frac{69}{23} = \frac{8}{23}$$

The solution is $x = \frac{11}{23},\ y = \frac{8}{23}$.

3. Solve the second equation for x, substitute into the first equation and solve:

$$\begin{cases} 3x - 4y = 4 \\ x - 3y = \frac{1}{2} \quad \rightarrow \quad x = 3y + \frac{1}{2} \end{cases}$$

$$3\left(3y + \frac{1}{2}\right) - 4y = 4 \rightarrow 9y + \frac{3}{2} - 4y = 4 \rightarrow 5y = \frac{5}{2} \rightarrow y = \frac{1}{2} \rightarrow x = 3\left(\frac{1}{2}\right) + \frac{1}{2} = 2$$

The solution is $x = 2,\ y = \frac{1}{2}$.

4. Solve the first equation for y, substitute into the second equation and solve:

$$\begin{cases} 2x + y = 0 \quad \rightarrow \quad y = -2x \\ 5x - 4y = -\frac{13}{2} \end{cases}$$

$$5x - 4(-2x) = -\frac{13}{2} \rightarrow 5x + 8x = -\frac{13}{2} \rightarrow 13x = -\frac{13}{2} \quad \rightarrow \quad x = -\frac{1}{2} \rightarrow y = -2\left(-\frac{1}{2}\right) = 1$$

The solution is $x = -\frac{1}{2},\ y = 1$.

5. Solve the first equation for x, substitute into the second equation and solve:

$$\begin{cases} x-2y-4=0 & \rightarrow \quad x=2y+4 \\ 3x+2y-4=0 \end{cases}$$

$$3(2y+4)+2y-4=0 \rightarrow 6y+12+2y-4=0$$

$$8y=-8 \rightarrow y=-1 \rightarrow x=2(-1)+4=2$$

The solution is $x=2,\ y=-1$.

6. Solve the first equation for x, substitute into the second equation and solve:

$$\begin{cases} x-3y+5=0 & \rightarrow \quad x=3y-5 \\ 2x+3y-5=0 \end{cases}$$

$$2(3y-5)+3y-5=0 \rightarrow 6y-10+3y-5=0$$

$$9y=15 \rightarrow y=\frac{5}{3} \rightarrow x=3\left(\frac{5}{3}\right)-5=0$$

The solution is $x=0,\ y=\frac{5}{3}$.

7. Substitute the first equation into the second equation and solve:

$$\begin{cases} y=2x-5 \\ x=3y+4 \end{cases}$$

$$x=3(2x-5)+4 \rightarrow x=6x-15+4$$

$$-5x=-11 \rightarrow x=\frac{11}{5} \rightarrow y=2\left(\frac{11}{5}\right)-5=-\frac{3}{5}$$

The solution is $x=\frac{11}{5},\ y=-\frac{3}{5}$.

8. Substitute the first equation into the second equation and solve:

$$\begin{cases} x=5y+2 \\ y=5x+2 \end{cases}$$

$$y=5(5y+2)+2 \rightarrow y=25y+10+2$$

$$-24y=12 \rightarrow y=-\frac{1}{2} \rightarrow x=5\left(-\frac{1}{2}\right)+2=-\frac{5}{2}+2=-\frac{1}{2}$$

The solution is $x=-\frac{1}{2},\ y=-\frac{1}{2}$.

9. Multiply each side of the first equation by 5 and each side of the second equation by 30 and add to eliminate y:

$$\begin{cases} x-\ y+4=0 & \xrightarrow{5} & 5x-5y+20=0 \\ \frac{1}{2}x+\frac{1}{6}y+\frac{2}{5}=0 & \xrightarrow{30} & \underline{15x+5y+12=0} \\ & & 20x \qquad +32=0 \end{cases}$$

$$20x=-32 \rightarrow x=-\frac{8}{5}$$ Substitute and solve for y: $-\frac{8}{5}-y+4=0 \rightarrow y=\frac{12}{5}$

The solution of the system is $x=-\frac{8}{5},\ y=\frac{12}{5}$.

10. Solve the second equation for y, substitute into the first equation and solve:

$$\begin{cases} x+\frac{1}{4}y=2 \\ y+4x+2=0 \quad \rightarrow \quad y=-4x-2 \end{cases}$$

$$x+\frac{1}{4}(-4x-2)=2$$

$$x-x-\frac{1}{2}=2 \rightarrow 0=\frac{5}{2}$$

There is no solution to the system. The system of equations is inconsistent.

11. Rewrite each equation and add to eliminate y:

$$\begin{cases} x-2y-8=0 \quad \longrightarrow \quad x-2y=8 \\ 2x+2y-10=0 \quad \longrightarrow \quad 2x+2y=10 \end{cases}$$

$$3x = 18$$

$$x=6$$

Substitute and solve for y:

$$6-2y=8 \rightarrow -2y=2 \rightarrow y=-1$$

The solution of the system is $x=6,\ y=-1$.

12. Rewrite each equation and add to eliminate y:

$$\begin{cases} x-3y+\frac{7}{2}=0 \quad \longrightarrow \quad x-3y=-\frac{7}{2} \\ \frac{1}{2}x+3y-5=0 \quad \longrightarrow \quad \frac{1}{2}x+3y=5 \end{cases}$$

$$\frac{3}{2}x = \frac{3}{2}$$

$$x=1$$

Substitute and solve for y:

$$\frac{1}{2}(1)+3y=5 \rightarrow 3y=\frac{9}{2} \rightarrow y=\frac{3}{2}$$

The solution of the system is $x=1,\ y=\frac{3}{2}$.

13. Solve the first equation for y, substitute into the second equation and solve:

$$\begin{cases} y-2x=11 \quad \rightarrow \quad y=2x+11 \\ 2y-3x=18 \end{cases}$$

$$2(2x+11)-3x=18$$

$$4x+22-3x=18 \rightarrow x=-4 \rightarrow y=2(-4)+11=3$$

The solution is $x=-4,\ y=3$.

14. Multiply each side of the second equation by 2 and add to eliminate y:

$$\begin{cases} 3x - 4y - 12 = 0 \\ 5x + 2y + 6 = 0 \end{cases} \begin{array}{c} \longrightarrow \\ \xrightarrow{2} \end{array} \begin{array}{r} 3x - 4y = 12 \\ \underline{10x + 4y = -12} \\ 13x \quad = 0 \\ x = 0 \end{array}$$

Substitute and solve for y:

$$3(0) - 4y = 12 \ \rightarrow \ -4y = 12 \ \rightarrow \ y = -3$$

The solution is $x = 0,\ y = -3$.

15. Multiply each side of the first equation by 2 and each side of the second equation by 3 and add to eliminate y:

$$\begin{cases} 2x + 3y - 13 = 0 \\ 3x - 2y \quad = 0 \end{cases} \begin{array}{c} \xrightarrow{2} \\ \xrightarrow{3} \end{array} \begin{array}{r} 4x + 6y - 26 = 0 \\ \underline{9x - 6y \quad = 0} \\ 13x \quad - 26 = 0 \\ 13x = 26 \\ x = 2 \end{array}$$

Substitute and solve for y:

$$3(2) - 2y = 0$$
$$-2y = -6$$
$$y = 3$$

The solution of the system is $x = 2,\ y = 3$.

16. Multiply each side of the first equation by 5 and each side of the second equation by –4 and add to eliminate x:

$$\begin{cases} 4x + 5y = 21 \\ 5x + 6y = 42 \end{cases} \begin{array}{c} \xrightarrow{5} \\ \xrightarrow{-4} \end{array} \begin{array}{r} 20x + 25y = 105 \\ \underline{-20x - 24y = -168} \\ y = -63 \end{array}$$

Substitute and solve for x:

$$4x + 5(-63) = 21$$
$$4x - 315 = 21$$
$$4x = 336$$
$$x = 84$$

The solution of the system is $x = 84,\ y = -63$.

17. Multiply each side of the second equation by –3 and add to eliminate x:

$$\begin{cases} 3x - 2y = 8 \\ x - \frac{2}{3}y = 12 \end{cases} \begin{array}{c} \longrightarrow \\ \xrightarrow{-3} \end{array} \begin{array}{r} 3x - 2y = 8 \\ \underline{-3x + 2y = -36} \\ 0 = -28 \end{array}$$

The system has no solution, so the system is inconsistent.

18. Multiply each side of the first equation by –2 and add to eliminate x:

$$\begin{cases} 2x+\ 5y=10 \xrightarrow{-2} & -4x-10y=-20 \\ 4x+10y=15 \longrightarrow & \underline{\ \ 4x+10y=\ \ 15} \\ & \qquad 0=-5 \end{cases}$$

The system has no solution, so the system is inconsistent.

19. Multiply each side of the first equation by –2 and add to the second equation to eliminate x; and multiply each side of the first equation by –3 and add to the third equation to eliminate x:

$$\begin{cases} x+2y-\ z=\ \ 6 \xrightarrow{-2} -2x-4y+2z=-12 \\ 2x-\ y+3z=-13 \longrightarrow \underline{\ \ 2x-\ y+3z=-13} \\ 3x-2y+3z=-16 \qquad -5y+5z=-25 \xrightarrow{-1/5} y-z=5 \end{cases}$$

$$\xrightarrow{-3} -3x-6y+3z=-18$$
$$\longrightarrow \underline{\ \ 3x-2y+3z=-16}$$
$$-8y+6z=-34$$

Multiply each side of the first result by 8 and add to the second result to eliminate y:

$$y-z=\ \ 5 \xrightarrow{8} 8y-8z=\ \ 40$$
$$-8y+6z=-34 \longrightarrow \underline{-8y+6z=-34}$$
$$-2z=\ \ 6$$
$$z=-3$$

Substituting and solving for the other variables:

$$y-(-3)=5 \qquad x+2(2)-(-3)=6$$
$$y=2 \qquad x+4+3=6$$
$$x=-1$$

The solution is $x=-1,\ y=2,\ z=-3$.

20. Add the first equation and the second equation to eliminate z; and multiply each side of the first equation by 2 and add to the third equation to eliminate z:

$$\begin{cases} x+5y-\ z=2 \longrightarrow x+5y-z=2 \\ 2x+\ y+\ z=7 \longrightarrow \underline{2x+\ y+z=7} \\ x-\ y+2z=11 \qquad 3x+6y\ \ =9 \xrightarrow{-1/3} -x-2y=-3 \end{cases}$$

$$\xrightarrow{2} 2x+10y-2z=4$$
$$\longrightarrow \underline{\ \ x-\ \ y+2z=11}$$
$$3x+9y\ \ =15 \xrightarrow{1/3} x+3y=5$$

Add the two results to eliminate x:

$$-x-2y=-3$$
$$\underline{x+3y=\ \ 5}$$
$$y=\ \ 2$$

Substituting and solving for the other variables:

$$x+3(2)=5 \qquad 2(-1)+2+z=7$$
$$x+6=5 \qquad -2+2+z=7$$
$$x=-1 \qquad z=7$$

The solution is $x=-1,\ y=2,\ z=7$.

21. $A+C=\begin{bmatrix}1 & 0\\ 2 & 4\\ -1 & 2\end{bmatrix}+\begin{bmatrix}3 & -4\\ 1 & 5\\ 5 & -2\end{bmatrix}=\begin{bmatrix}4 & -4\\ 3 & 9\\ 4 & 0\end{bmatrix}$

22. $A-C=\begin{bmatrix}1 & 0\\ 2 & 4\\ -1 & 2\end{bmatrix}-\begin{bmatrix}3 & -4\\ 1 & 5\\ 5 & -2\end{bmatrix}=\begin{bmatrix}-2 & 4\\ 1 & -1\\ -6 & 4\end{bmatrix}$

23. $6A=6\cdot\begin{bmatrix}1 & 0\\ 2 & 4\\ -1 & 2\end{bmatrix}=\begin{bmatrix}6 & 0\\ 12 & 24\\ -6 & 12\end{bmatrix}$

24. $-4B=-4\cdot\begin{bmatrix}4 & -3 & 0\\ 1 & 1 & -2\end{bmatrix}=\begin{bmatrix}-16 & 12 & 0\\ -4 & -4 & 8\end{bmatrix}$

25. $AB=\begin{bmatrix}1 & 0\\ 2 & 4\\ -1 & 2\end{bmatrix}\cdot\begin{bmatrix}4 & -3 & 0\\ 1 & 1 & -2\end{bmatrix}=\begin{bmatrix}4 & -3 & 0\\ 12 & -2 & -8\\ -2 & 5 & -4\end{bmatrix}$

26. $BA=\begin{bmatrix}4 & -3 & 0\\ 1 & 1 & -2\end{bmatrix}\cdot\begin{bmatrix}1 & 0\\ 2 & 4\\ -1 & 2\end{bmatrix}=\begin{bmatrix}-2 & -12\\ 5 & 0\end{bmatrix}$

27. $CB=\begin{bmatrix}3 & -4\\ 1 & 5\\ 5 & -2\end{bmatrix}\cdot\begin{bmatrix}4 & -3 & 0\\ 1 & 1 & -2\end{bmatrix}=\begin{bmatrix}8 & -13 & 8\\ 9 & 2 & -10\\ 18 & -17 & 4\end{bmatrix}$

28. $BC=\begin{bmatrix}4 & -3 & 0\\ 1 & 1 & -2\end{bmatrix}\cdot\begin{bmatrix}3 & -4\\ 1 & 5\\ 5 & -2\end{bmatrix}=\begin{bmatrix}9 & -31\\ -6 & 5\end{bmatrix}$

29. Augment the matrix with the identity and use row operations to find the inverse:

$$A=\begin{bmatrix}4 & 6\\ 1 & 3\end{bmatrix}\rightarrow\left[\begin{array}{cc|cc}4 & 6 & 1 & 0\\ 1 & 3 & 0 & 1\end{array}\right]$$

$$\rightarrow\left[\begin{array}{cc|cc}1 & 3 & 0 & 1\\ 4 & 6 & 1 & 0\end{array}\right]\rightarrow\left[\begin{array}{cc|cc}1 & 3 & 0 & 1\\ 0 & -6 & 1 & -4\end{array}\right]\rightarrow\left[\begin{array}{cc|cc}1 & 3 & 0 & 1\\ 0 & 1 & -\frac{1}{6} & \frac{2}{3}\end{array}\right]\rightarrow\left[\begin{array}{cc|cc}1 & 0 & \frac{1}{2} & -1\\ 0 & 1 & -\frac{1}{6} & \frac{2}{3}\end{array}\right]$$

Interchange r_1 and r_2 $\quad R_2=-4r_1+r_2 \quad R_2=-\frac{1}{6}r_2 \quad R_1=-3r_2+r_1$

$$A^{-1}=\begin{bmatrix}\frac{1}{2} & -1\\ -\frac{1}{6} & \frac{2}{3}\end{bmatrix}$$

30. Augment the matrix with the identity and use row operations to find the inverse:

$$A=\begin{bmatrix}-3 & 2\\ 1 & -2\end{bmatrix}\rightarrow\left[\begin{array}{cc|cc}-3 & 2 & 1 & 0\\ 1 & -2 & 0 & 1\end{array}\right]$$

$$\rightarrow \left[\begin{array}{rr|rr} 1 & -2 & 0 & 1 \\ -3 & 2 & 1 & 0 \end{array}\right] \rightarrow \left[\begin{array}{rr|rr} 1 & -2 & 0 & 1 \\ 0 & -4 & 1 & 3 \end{array}\right] \rightarrow \left[\begin{array}{rr|rr} 1 & -2 & 0 & 1 \\ 0 & 1 & -\frac{1}{4} & -\frac{3}{4} \end{array}\right] \rightarrow \left[\begin{array}{rr|rr} 1 & 0 & -\frac{1}{2} & -\frac{1}{2} \\ 0 & 1 & -\frac{1}{4} & -\frac{3}{4} \end{array}\right]$$

Interchange r_1 and r_2 $\qquad R_2 = 3r_1 + r_2 \qquad R_2 = -\frac{1}{4}r_2 \qquad R_1 = 2r_2 + r_1$

$$A^{-1} = \begin{bmatrix} -\frac{1}{2} & -\frac{1}{2} \\ -\frac{1}{4} & -\frac{3}{4} \end{bmatrix}$$

31. Augment the matrix with the identity and use row operations to find the inverse:

$$A = \begin{bmatrix} 1 & 3 & 3 \\ 1 & 2 & 1 \\ 1 & -1 & 2 \end{bmatrix} \rightarrow \left[\begin{array}{rrr|rrr} 1 & 3 & 3 & 1 & 0 & 0 \\ 1 & 2 & 1 & 0 & 1 & 0 \\ 1 & -1 & 2 & 0 & 0 & 1 \end{array}\right]$$

$$\rightarrow \left[\begin{array}{rrr|rrr} 1 & 3 & 3 & 1 & 0 & 0 \\ 0 & -1 & -2 & -1 & 1 & 0 \\ 0 & -4 & -1 & -1 & 0 & 1 \end{array}\right] \rightarrow \left[\begin{array}{rrr|rrr} 1 & 3 & 3 & 1 & 0 & 0 \\ 0 & 1 & 2 & 1 & -1 & 0 \\ 0 & -4 & -1 & -1 & 0 & 1 \end{array}\right] \rightarrow \left[\begin{array}{rrr|rrr} 1 & 0 & -3 & -2 & 3 & 0 \\ 0 & 1 & 2 & 1 & -1 & 0 \\ 0 & 0 & 7 & 3 & -4 & 1 \end{array}\right]$$

$R_2 = -r_1 + r_2$, $R_3 = -r_1 + r_3$ $\qquad R_2 = -r_2$ $\qquad R_1 = -3r_2 + r_1$, $R_3 = 4r_2 + r_3$

$$\rightarrow \left[\begin{array}{rrr|rrr} 1 & 0 & -3 & -2 & 3 & 0 \\ 0 & 1 & 2 & 1 & -1 & 0 \\ 0 & 0 & 1 & \frac{3}{7} & -\frac{4}{7} & \frac{1}{7} \end{array}\right] \rightarrow \left[\begin{array}{rrr|rrr} 1 & 0 & 0 & -\frac{5}{7} & \frac{9}{7} & \frac{3}{7} \\ 0 & 1 & 0 & \frac{1}{7} & \frac{1}{7} & -\frac{2}{7} \\ 0 & 0 & 1 & \frac{3}{7} & -\frac{4}{7} & \frac{1}{7} \end{array}\right] \longrightarrow A^{-1} = \begin{bmatrix} -\frac{5}{7} & \frac{9}{7} & \frac{3}{7} \\ \frac{1}{7} & \frac{1}{7} & -\frac{2}{7} \\ \frac{3}{7} & -\frac{4}{7} & \frac{1}{7} \end{bmatrix}$$

$R_3 = \frac{1}{7}r_3$ $\qquad R_1 = 3r_3 + r_1$, $R_2 = -2r_3 + r_2$

32. Augment the matrix with the identity and use row operations to find the inverse:

$$A = \begin{bmatrix} 3 & 1 & 2 \\ 3 & 2 & -1 \\ 1 & 1 & 1 \end{bmatrix} \rightarrow \left[\begin{array}{rrr|rrr} 3 & 1 & 2 & 1 & 0 & 0 \\ 3 & 2 & -1 & 0 & 1 & 0 \\ 1 & 1 & 1 & 0 & 0 & 1 \end{array}\right]$$

$$\rightarrow \left[\begin{array}{rrr|rrr} 1 & 1 & 1 & 0 & 0 & 1 \\ 3 & 2 & -1 & 0 & 1 & 0 \\ 3 & 1 & 2 & 1 & 0 & 0 \end{array}\right] \rightarrow \left[\begin{array}{rrr|rrr} 1 & 1 & 1 & 0 & 0 & 1 \\ 0 & -1 & -4 & 0 & 1 & -3 \\ 0 & -2 & -1 & 1 & 0 & -3 \end{array}\right] \rightarrow \left[\begin{array}{rrr|rrr} 1 & 1 & 1 & 0 & 0 & 1 \\ 0 & 1 & 4 & 0 & -1 & 3 \\ 0 & -2 & -1 & 1 & 0 & -3 \end{array}\right]$$

Interchange r_1 and r_2 $\qquad R_2 = -3r_1 + r_2$, $R_3 = -3r_1 + r_3$ $\qquad R_2 = -r_2$

$$\rightarrow \left[\begin{array}{rrr|rrr} 1 & 0 & -3 & 0 & 1 & -2 \\ 0 & 1 & 4 & 0 & -1 & 3 \\ 0 & 0 & 7 & 1 & -2 & 3 \end{array}\right] \rightarrow \left[\begin{array}{rrr|rrr} 1 & 0 & -3 & 0 & 1 & -2 \\ 0 & 1 & 4 & 0 & -1 & 3 \\ 0 & 0 & 1 & \frac{1}{7} & -\frac{2}{7} & \frac{3}{7} \end{array}\right] \rightarrow \left[\begin{array}{rrr|rrr} 1 & 0 & 0 & \frac{3}{7} & \frac{1}{7} & -\frac{5}{7} \\ 0 & 1 & 0 & -\frac{4}{7} & \frac{1}{7} & \frac{9}{7} \\ 0 & 0 & 1 & \frac{1}{7} & -\frac{2}{7} & \frac{3}{7} \end{array}\right]$$

$R_1 = -r_2 + r_1$, $R_3 = 2r_2 + r_3$ $\qquad R_3 = \frac{1}{7}r_3$ $\qquad R_1 = 3r_3 + r_1$, $R_2 = -4r_3 + r_2$

$$A^{-1} = \begin{bmatrix} \frac{3}{7} & \frac{1}{7} & -\frac{5}{7} \\ -\frac{4}{7} & \frac{1}{7} & \frac{9}{7} \\ \frac{1}{7} & -\frac{2}{7} & \frac{3}{7} \end{bmatrix}$$

33. Augment the matrix with the identity and use row operations to find the inverse:

$$A=\begin{bmatrix}4 & -8\\ -1 & 2\end{bmatrix} \rightarrow \left[\begin{array}{cc|cc}4 & -8 & 1 & 0\\ -1 & 2 & 0 & 1\end{array}\right]$$

$$\rightarrow \left[\begin{array}{cc|cc}-1 & 2 & 0 & 1\\ 4 & -8 & 1 & 0\end{array}\right] \rightarrow \left[\begin{array}{cc|cc}-1 & 2 & 0 & 1\\ 0 & 0 & 1 & 4\end{array}\right] \rightarrow \left[\begin{array}{cc|cc}1 & -2 & 0 & -1\\ 0 & 0 & 1 & 4\end{array}\right]$$

Interchange r_1 and r_2; $R_2 = 4r_1 + r_2$; $R_1 = -r_1$

There is no inverse because there is no way to obtain the identity on the left side. The matrix is singular.

34. Augment the matrix with the identity and use row operations to find the inverse:

$$A=\begin{bmatrix}-3 & 1\\ -6 & 2\end{bmatrix} \rightarrow \left[\begin{array}{cc|cc}-3 & 1 & 1 & 0\\ -6 & 2 & 0 & 1\end{array}\right]$$

$$\rightarrow \left[\begin{array}{cc|cc}1 & -\frac{1}{3} & -\frac{1}{3} & 0\\ -6 & 2 & 0 & 1\end{array}\right] \rightarrow \left[\begin{array}{cc|cc}1 & -\frac{1}{3} & -\frac{1}{3} & 0\\ 0 & 0 & -2 & 1\end{array}\right]$$

$R_1 = -\frac{1}{3}r_1$; $R_2 = 6r_1 + r_2$

There is no inverse because there is no way to obtain the identity on the left side. The matrix is singular.

35. $\begin{cases} 3x - 2y = 1 \\ 10x + 10y = 5 \end{cases}$ can be written as: $\left[\begin{array}{cc|c}3 & -2 & 1\\ 10 & 10 & 5\end{array}\right]$

$$\rightarrow \left[\begin{array}{cc|c}3 & -2 & 1\\ 1 & 16 & 2\end{array}\right] \rightarrow \left[\begin{array}{cc|c}1 & 16 & 2\\ 3 & -2 & 1\end{array}\right] \rightarrow \left[\begin{array}{cc|c}1 & 16 & 2\\ 0 & -50 & -5\end{array}\right] \rightarrow \left[\begin{array}{cc|c}1 & 16 & 2\\ 0 & 1 & \frac{1}{10}\end{array}\right] \rightarrow \left[\begin{array}{cc|c}1 & 0 & \frac{2}{5}\\ 0 & 1 & \frac{1}{10}\end{array}\right]$$

$R_2 = -3r_1 + r_2$; Interchange r_1 and r_2; $R_2 = -3r_1 + r_2$; $R_2 = -\frac{1}{50}r_2$; $R_1 = -16r_2 + r_1$

The solution is $x = \dfrac{2}{5}, y = \dfrac{1}{10}$.

36. $\begin{cases} 3x + 2y = 6 \\ x - y = -\dfrac{1}{2} \end{cases}$ can be written as: $\left[\begin{array}{cc|c}3 & 2 & 6\\ 1 & -1 & -\frac{1}{2}\end{array}\right]$

$$\rightarrow \left[\begin{array}{cc|c}1 & -1 & -\frac{1}{2}\\ 3 & 2 & 6\end{array}\right] \rightarrow \left[\begin{array}{cc|c}1 & -1 & -\frac{1}{2}\\ 0 & 5 & \frac{15}{2}\end{array}\right] \rightarrow \left[\begin{array}{cc|c}1 & -1 & -\frac{1}{2}\\ 0 & 1 & \frac{3}{2}\end{array}\right] \rightarrow \left[\begin{array}{cc|c}1 & 0 & 1\\ 0 & 1 & \frac{3}{2}\end{array}\right]$$

Interchange r_1 and r_2; $R_2 = -3r_1 + r_2$; $R_2 = \frac{1}{5}r_2$; $R_1 = r_2 + r_1$

The solution is $x = 1, y = \dfrac{3}{2}$.

37. $\begin{cases} 5x+6y-3z = 6 \\ 4x-7y-2z=-3 \\ 3x+y-7z=1 \end{cases}$ can be written as: $\left[\begin{array}{ccc|c} 5 & 6 & -3 & 6 \\ 4 & -7 & -2 & -3 \\ 3 & 1 & -7 & 1 \end{array}\right]$

$$\rightarrow \left[\begin{array}{ccc|c} 1 & 13 & -1 & 9 \\ 4 & -7 & -2 & -3 \\ 3 & 1 & -7 & 1 \end{array}\right] \rightarrow \left[\begin{array}{ccc|c} 1 & 13 & -1 & 9 \\ 0 & -59 & 2 & -39 \\ 0 & -38 & -4 & -26 \end{array}\right] \rightarrow \left[\begin{array}{ccc|c} 1 & 13 & -1 & 9 \\ 0 & 1 & -\frac{2}{59} & \frac{39}{59} \\ 0 & -38 & -4 & -26 \end{array}\right]$$

$R_1 = -r_2 + r_1$ $\quad R_2 = -4r_1 + r_2$, $R_3 = -3r_1 + r_3$ $\quad R_2 = -\frac{1}{59}r_2$

$$\rightarrow \left[\begin{array}{ccc|c} 1 & 0 & -\frac{33}{59} & \frac{24}{59} \\ 0 & 1 & -\frac{2}{59} & \frac{39}{59} \\ 0 & 0 & -\frac{312}{59} & -\frac{52}{59} \end{array}\right] \rightarrow \left[\begin{array}{ccc|c} 1 & 0 & -\frac{33}{59} & \frac{24}{59} \\ 0 & 1 & -\frac{2}{59} & \frac{39}{59} \\ 0 & 0 & 1 & \frac{1}{6} \end{array}\right] \rightarrow \left[\begin{array}{ccc|c} 1 & 0 & 0 & \frac{1}{2} \\ 0 & 1 & 0 & \frac{2}{3} \\ 0 & 0 & 1 & \frac{1}{6} \end{array}\right]$$

$R_1 = -13r_2 + r_1$, $R_3 = 38r_2 + r_3$ $\quad R_3 = -\frac{59}{312}r_3$ $\quad R_1 = \frac{33}{59}r_3 + r_1$, $R_2 = \frac{2}{59}r_3 + r_2$

The solution is $x = \frac{1}{2}, y = \frac{2}{3}, z = \frac{1}{6}$.

38. $\begin{cases} 2x+y+z=5 \\ 4x-y-3z=1 \\ 8x+y-z=5 \end{cases}$ can be written as: $\left[\begin{array}{ccc|c} 2 & 1 & 1 & 5 \\ 4 & -1 & -3 & 1 \\ 8 & 1 & -1 & 5 \end{array}\right]$

$$\rightarrow \left[\begin{array}{ccc|c} 2 & 1 & 1 & 5 \\ 0 & -3 & -5 & -9 \\ 0 & -3 & -5 & -15 \end{array}\right] \rightarrow \left[\begin{array}{ccc|c} 1 & \frac{1}{2} & \frac{1}{2} & \frac{5}{2} \\ 0 & 1 & \frac{5}{3} & 3 \\ 0 & -3 & -5 & -15 \end{array}\right] \rightarrow \left[\begin{array}{ccc|c} 1 & 0 & -\frac{1}{3} & 1 \\ 0 & 1 & \frac{5}{3} & 3 \\ 0 & 0 & 0 & -6 \end{array}\right]$$

$R_2 = -2r_1 + r_2$, $R_3 = -4r_1 + r_3$ $\quad R_1 = \frac{1}{2}r_1$, $R_2 = -\frac{1}{3}r_2$ $\quad R_1 = -\frac{1}{2}r_2 + r_1$, $R_3 = 3r_2 + r_3$

There is no solution; the system is inconsistent.

39. $\begin{cases} x \quad\quad -2z = 1 \\ 2x+3y \quad = -3 \\ 4x-3y-4z = 3 \end{cases}$ can be written as: $\left[\begin{array}{ccc|c} 1 & 0 & -2 & 1 \\ 2 & 3 & 0 & -3 \\ 4 & -3 & -4 & 3 \end{array}\right]$

$$\rightarrow \left[\begin{array}{ccc|c} 1 & 0 & -2 & 1 \\ 0 & 3 & 4 & -5 \\ 0 & -3 & 4 & -1 \end{array}\right] \rightarrow \left[\begin{array}{ccc|c} 1 & 0 & -2 & 1 \\ 0 & 1 & \frac{4}{3} & -\frac{5}{3} \\ 0 & -3 & 4 & -1 \end{array}\right] \rightarrow \left[\begin{array}{ccc|c} 1 & 0 & -2 & 1 \\ 0 & 1 & \frac{4}{3} & -\frac{5}{3} \\ 0 & 0 & 8 & -6 \end{array}\right]$$

$R_2 = -2r_1 + r_2$, $R_3 = -4r_1 + r_3$ $\quad R_2 = \frac{1}{3}r_2$ $\quad R_3 = 3r_2 + r_3$

$$\rightarrow \left[\begin{array}{ccc|c} 1 & 0 & -2 & 1 \\ 0 & 1 & \frac{4}{3} & -\frac{5}{3} \\ 0 & 0 & 1 & -\frac{3}{4} \end{array}\right] \rightarrow \left[\begin{array}{ccc|c} 1 & 0 & 0 & -\frac{1}{2} \\ 0 & 1 & 0 & -\frac{2}{3} \\ 0 & 0 & 1 & -\frac{3}{4} \end{array}\right]$$

$R_3 = \frac{1}{8}r_3$ $\quad R_1 = 2r_3 + r_1$, $R_2 = -\frac{4}{3}r_3 + r_2$

The solution is $x = -\frac{1}{2}, y = -\frac{2}{3}, z = -\frac{3}{4}$.

40. $\begin{cases} x+2y-z=2 \\ 2x-2y+z=-1 \\ 6x+4y+3z=5 \end{cases}$ can be written as: $\left[\begin{array}{rrr|r} 1 & 2 & -1 & 2 \\ 2 & -2 & 1 & -1 \\ 6 & 4 & 3 & 5 \end{array}\right]$

$$\rightarrow \left[\begin{array}{rrr|r} 1 & 2 & -1 & 2 \\ 0 & -6 & 3 & -5 \\ 0 & -8 & 9 & -7 \end{array}\right] \rightarrow \left[\begin{array}{rrr|r} 1 & 2 & -1 & 2 \\ 0 & 1 & -\frac{1}{2} & \frac{5}{6} \\ 0 & -8 & 9 & -7 \end{array}\right] \rightarrow \left[\begin{array}{rrr|r} 1 & 0 & 0 & \frac{1}{3} \\ 0 & 1 & -\frac{1}{2} & \frac{5}{6} \\ 0 & 0 & 5 & -\frac{1}{3} \end{array}\right]$$

$R_2=-2r_1+r_2$ $\quad R_2=-\frac{1}{6}r_2$ $\quad R_1=-2r_2+r_1$

$R_3=-6r_1+r_3$ $\quad R_3=8r_2+r_3$

$$\rightarrow \left[\begin{array}{rrr|r} 1 & 0 & 0 & \frac{1}{3} \\ 0 & 1 & -\frac{1}{2} & \frac{5}{6} \\ 0 & 0 & 1 & -\frac{1}{15} \end{array}\right] \rightarrow \left[\begin{array}{rrr|r} 1 & 0 & 0 & \frac{1}{3} \\ 0 & 1 & 0 & \frac{4}{5} \\ 0 & 0 & 1 & -\frac{1}{15} \end{array}\right]$$

$R_3=\frac{1}{5}r_3$ $\quad R_2=\frac{1}{2}r_3+r_2$

The solution is $x=\dfrac{1}{3}, y=\dfrac{4}{5}, z=-\dfrac{1}{15}$.

41. $\begin{cases} x-y+z=0 \\ x-y-5z=6 \\ 2x-2y+z=1 \end{cases}$ can be written as: $\left[\begin{array}{rrr|r} 1 & -1 & 1 & 0 \\ 1 & -1 & -5 & 6 \\ 2 & -2 & 1 & 1 \end{array}\right]$

$$\rightarrow \left[\begin{array}{rrr|r} 1 & -1 & 1 & 0 \\ 0 & 0 & -6 & 6 \\ 0 & 0 & -1 & 1 \end{array}\right] \rightarrow \left[\begin{array}{rrr|r} 1 & -1 & 1 & 0 \\ 0 & 0 & 1 & -1 \\ 0 & 0 & -1 & 1 \end{array}\right] \rightarrow \left[\begin{array}{rrr|r} 1 & -1 & 0 & 1 \\ 0 & 0 & 1 & -1 \\ 0 & 0 & 0 & 0 \end{array}\right] \rightarrow \begin{cases} x=y+1 \\ z=-1 \end{cases}$$

$R_2=-r_1+r_2$ $\quad R_2=-\frac{1}{6}r_2$ $\quad R_1=-r_2+r_1$

$R_3=-2r_1+r_3$ $\quad R_3=r_2+r_3$

The solution is $x=y+1$, $z=-1$, y is any real number..

42. $\begin{cases} 4x-3y+5z=0 \\ 2x+4y-3z=0 \\ 6x+2y+z=0 \end{cases}$ can be written as: $\left[\begin{array}{rrr|r} 4 & -3 & 5 & 0 \\ 2 & 4 & -3 & 0 \\ 6 & 2 & 1 & 0 \end{array}\right]$

$$\rightarrow \left[\begin{array}{rrr|r} 1 & -\frac{3}{4} & \frac{5}{4} & 0 \\ 2 & 4 & -3 & 0 \\ 6 & 2 & 1 & 0 \end{array}\right] \rightarrow \left[\begin{array}{rrr|r} 1 & -\frac{3}{4} & \frac{5}{4} & 0 \\ 0 & \frac{11}{2} & -\frac{11}{2} & 0 \\ 0 & \frac{13}{2} & -\frac{13}{2} & 0 \end{array}\right] \rightarrow \left[\begin{array}{rrr|r} 1 & -\frac{3}{4} & \frac{5}{4} & 0 \\ 0 & 1 & -1 & 0 \\ 0 & 1 & -1 & 0 \end{array}\right] \rightarrow \left[\begin{array}{rrr|r} 1 & 0 & \frac{1}{2} & 0 \\ 0 & 1 & -1 & 0 \\ 0 & 0 & 0 & 0 \end{array}\right]$$

$R_1=\frac{1}{4}r_1$ $\quad R_2=-2r_1+r_2$ $\quad R_2=\frac{2}{11}r_2$ $\quad R_1=\frac{3}{4}r_2+r_1$

$R_3=-6r_1+r_3$ $\quad R_3=\frac{2}{13}r_3$ $\quad R_3=-r_2+r_3$

The solution is $x=-\dfrac{1}{2}z$, $y=z$, z is any real number.

43. $\begin{cases} x-y-z-t=1 \\ 2x+y+z+2t=3 \\ x-2y-2z-3t=0 \\ 3x-4y+z+5t=-3 \end{cases}$ can be written as: $\left[\begin{array}{rrrr|r} 1 & -1 & -1 & -1 & 1 \\ 2 & 1 & 1 & 2 & 3 \\ 1 & -2 & -2 & -3 & 0 \\ 3 & -4 & 1 & 5 & -3 \end{array}\right]$

$$\rightarrow\left[\begin{array}{rrrr|r} 1 & -1 & -1 & -1 & 1 \\ 0 & 3 & 3 & 4 & 1 \\ 0 & -1 & -1 & -2 & -1 \\ 0 & -1 & 4 & 8 & -6 \end{array}\right] \rightarrow \left[\begin{array}{rrrr|r} 1 & -1 & -1 & -1 & 1 \\ 0 & -1 & -1 & -2 & -1 \\ 0 & 3 & 3 & 4 & 1 \\ 0 & -1 & 4 & 8 & -6 \end{array}\right] \rightarrow \left[\begin{array}{rrrr|r} 1 & -1 & -1 & -1 & 1 \\ 0 & 1 & 1 & 2 & 1 \\ 0 & 3 & 3 & 4 & 1 \\ 0 & -1 & 4 & 8 & -6 \end{array}\right]$$

$R_2 = -2r_1 + r_2$ Interchange r_2 and r_3 $R_2 = -r_2$

$R_3 = -r_1 + r_3$

$R_4 = -3r_1 + r_4$

$$\rightarrow\left[\begin{array}{rrrr|r} 1 & 0 & 0 & 1 & 2 \\ 0 & 1 & 1 & 2 & 1 \\ 0 & 0 & 0 & -2 & -2 \\ 0 & 0 & 5 & 10 & -5 \end{array}\right] \rightarrow \left[\begin{array}{rrrr|r} 1 & 0 & 0 & 1 & 2 \\ 0 & 1 & 1 & 2 & 1 \\ 0 & 0 & 0 & 1 & 1 \\ 0 & 0 & 1 & 2 & -1 \end{array}\right] \rightarrow \left[\begin{array}{rrrr|r} 1 & 0 & 0 & 1 & 2 \\ 0 & 1 & 1 & 2 & 1 \\ 0 & 0 & 1 & 2 & -1 \\ 0 & 0 & 0 & 1 & 1 \end{array}\right]$$

$R_1 = r_2 + r_1$ $R_3 = -\frac{1}{2}r_3$ Interchange r_3 and r_4

$R_3 = -3r_2 + r_3$ $R_4 = \frac{1}{5}r_4$

$R_4 = r_2 + r_4$

$$\rightarrow\left[\begin{array}{rrrr|r} 1 & 0 & 0 & 1 & 2 \\ 0 & 1 & 0 & 0 & 2 \\ 0 & 0 & 1 & 2 & -1 \\ 0 & 0 & 0 & 1 & 1 \end{array}\right] \rightarrow \left[\begin{array}{rrrr|r} 1 & 0 & 0 & 0 & 1 \\ 0 & 1 & 0 & 0 & 2 \\ 0 & 0 & 1 & 0 & -3 \\ 0 & 0 & 0 & 1 & 1 \end{array}\right]$$

$R_2 = -r_3 + r_2$ $R_1 = -r_4 + r_1$

$R_3 = -2r_4 + r_3$

The solution is $x = 1, y = 2, z = -3, t = 1$.

44. $\begin{cases} x - 3y + 3z - t = 4 \\ x + 2y - z = -3 \\ x + 3z + 2t = 3 \\ x + y + 5z = 6 \end{cases}$ can be written as: $\left[\begin{array}{rrrr|r} 1 & -3 & 3 & -1 & 4 \\ 1 & 2 & -1 & 0 & -3 \\ 1 & 0 & 3 & 2 & 3 \\ 1 & 1 & 5 & 0 & 6 \end{array}\right]$

$$\rightarrow\left[\begin{array}{rrrr|r} 1 & -3 & 3 & -1 & 4 \\ 0 & 5 & -4 & 1 & -7 \\ 0 & 3 & 0 & 3 & -1 \\ 0 & 4 & 2 & 1 & 2 \end{array}\right] \rightarrow \left[\begin{array}{rrrr|r} 1 & -3 & 3 & -1 & 4 \\ 0 & 1 & -\frac{4}{5} & \frac{1}{5} & -\frac{7}{5} \\ 0 & 3 & 0 & 3 & -1 \\ 0 & 4 & 2 & 1 & 2 \end{array}\right] \rightarrow \left[\begin{array}{rrrr|r} 1 & 0 & \frac{3}{5} & -\frac{2}{5} & -\frac{1}{5} \\ 0 & 1 & -\frac{4}{5} & \frac{1}{5} & -\frac{7}{5} \\ 0 & 0 & \frac{12}{5} & \frac{12}{5} & \frac{16}{5} \\ 0 & 0 & \frac{26}{5} & \frac{1}{5} & \frac{38}{5} \end{array}\right]$$

$R_2 = -r_1 + r_2$ $R_2 = \frac{1}{5}r_2$ $R_1 = 3r_2 + r_1$

$R_3 = -r_1 + r_3$ $R_3 = -3r_2 + r_3$

$R_4 = -r_1 + r_4$ $R_4 = -4r_2 + r_4$

$$\rightarrow\left[\begin{array}{rrrr|r} 1 & 0 & \frac{3}{5} & -\frac{2}{5} & -\frac{1}{5} \\ 0 & 1 & -\frac{4}{5} & \frac{1}{5} & -\frac{7}{5} \\ 0 & 0 & 1 & 1 & \frac{4}{3} \\ 0 & 0 & \frac{26}{5} & \frac{1}{5} & \frac{38}{5} \end{array}\right] \rightarrow \left[\begin{array}{rrrr|r} 1 & 0 & 0 & -1 & -1 \\ 0 & 1 & 0 & 1 & -\frac{1}{3} \\ 0 & 0 & 1 & 1 & \frac{4}{3} \\ 0 & 0 & 0 & -5 & \frac{2}{3} \end{array}\right] \rightarrow \left[\begin{array}{rrrr|r} 1 & 0 & 0 & -1 & -1 \\ 0 & 1 & 0 & 1 & -\frac{1}{3} \\ 0 & 0 & 1 & 1 & \frac{4}{3} \\ 0 & 0 & 0 & 1 & -\frac{2}{15} \end{array}\right]$$

$R_3 = \frac{5}{12}r_3$ $R_1 = -\frac{3}{5}r_3 + r_1$ $R_4 = -\frac{1}{5}r_4$

$R_2 = \frac{4}{5}r_3 + r_2$

$R_4 = -\frac{26}{5}r_3 + r_4$

$$\rightarrow\left[\begin{array}{cccc|c} 1 & 0 & 0 & 0 & -\frac{17}{15} \\ 0 & 1 & 0 & 0 & -\frac{1}{5} \\ 0 & 0 & 1 & 0 & \frac{22}{15} \\ 0 & 0 & 0 & 1 & -\frac{2}{15} \end{array}\right]$$

$R_1 = r_4 + r_1$

$R_2 = -r_4 + r_2$

$R_3 = -r_4 + r_3$

The solution is $x = -\dfrac{17}{15}, y = -\dfrac{1}{5}, z = \dfrac{22}{15}, t = -\dfrac{2}{15}$.

45. Evaluating the determinant:

$$\begin{vmatrix} 3 & 4 \\ 1 & 3 \end{vmatrix} = 3(3) - 4(1) = 9 - 4 = 5$$

46. Evaluating the determinant:

$$\begin{vmatrix} -4 & 0 \\ 1 & 3 \end{vmatrix} = -4(3) - 1(0) = -12 - 0 = -12$$

47. Evaluating the determinant:

$$\begin{vmatrix} 1 & 4 & 0 \\ -1 & 2 & 6 \\ 4 & 1 & 3 \end{vmatrix} = 1\begin{vmatrix} 2 & 6 \\ 1 & 3 \end{vmatrix} - 4\begin{vmatrix} -1 & 6 \\ 4 & 3 \end{vmatrix} + 0\begin{vmatrix} -1 & 2 \\ 4 & 1 \end{vmatrix}$$

$$= 1[2(3) - 6(1)] - 4[-1(3) - 6(4)] + 0[-1(1) - 2(4)]$$

$$= 1(6 - 6) - 4(-3 - 24) + 0(-1 - 8)$$

$$= 1(0) - 4(-27) + 0(-9) = 0 + 108 + 0 = 108$$

48. Evaluating the determinant:

$$\begin{vmatrix} 2 & 3 & 10 \\ 0 & 1 & 5 \\ -1 & 2 & 3 \end{vmatrix} = 2\begin{vmatrix} 1 & 5 \\ 2 & 3 \end{vmatrix} - 3\begin{vmatrix} 0 & 5 \\ -1 & 3 \end{vmatrix} + 10\begin{vmatrix} 0 & 1 \\ -1 & 2 \end{vmatrix}$$

$$= 2[1(3) - 2(5)] - 3[0(3) - (-1)(5)] + 10[0(2) - (-1)(1)]$$

$$= 2(3 - 10) - 3(0 + 5) + 10(0 + 1) = 2(-7) - 3(5) + 10(1)$$

$$= -14 - 15 + 10 = -19$$

49. Evaluating the determinant:

$$\begin{vmatrix} 2 & 1 & -3 \\ 5 & 0 & 1 \\ 2 & 6 & 0 \end{vmatrix} = 2\begin{vmatrix} 0 & 1 \\ 6 & 0 \end{vmatrix} - 1\begin{vmatrix} 5 & 1 \\ 2 & 0 \end{vmatrix} + (-3)\begin{vmatrix} 5 & 0 \\ 2 & 6 \end{vmatrix}$$

$$= 2(0 - 6) - 1(0 - 2) + (-3)(30 - 0) = -12 + 2 - 90 = -100$$

50. Evaluating the determinant:

$$\begin{vmatrix} -2 & 1 & 0 \\ 1 & 2 & 3 \\ -1 & 4 & 2 \end{vmatrix} = -2\begin{vmatrix} 2 & 3 \\ 4 & 2 \end{vmatrix} - 1\begin{vmatrix} 1 & 3 \\ -1 & 2 \end{vmatrix} + 0\begin{vmatrix} 1 & 2 \\ -1 & 4 \end{vmatrix}$$

$$= -2(4-12) - 1(2+3) + 0(4+2) = 16 - 5 + 0 = 11$$

51. Set up and evaluate the determinants to use Cramer's Rule:

$$\begin{cases} x - 2y = 4 \\ 3x + 2y = 4 \end{cases}$$

$$D = \begin{vmatrix} 1 & -2 \\ 3 & 2 \end{vmatrix} = 1(2) - 3(-2) = 2 + 6 = 8$$

$$D_x = \begin{vmatrix} 4 & -2 \\ 4 & 2 \end{vmatrix} = 4(2) - 4(-2) = 8 + 8 = 16$$

$$D_y = \begin{vmatrix} 1 & 4 \\ 3 & 4 \end{vmatrix} = 1(4) - 4(3) = 4 - 12 = -8$$

Find the solutions by Cramer's Rule: $x = \dfrac{D_x}{D} = \dfrac{16}{8} = 2 \qquad y = \dfrac{D_y}{D} = \dfrac{-8}{8} = -1$

52. Set up and evaluate the determinants to use Cramer's Rule:

$$\begin{cases} x - 3y = -5 \\ 2x + 3y = 5 \end{cases}$$

$$D = \begin{vmatrix} 1 & -3 \\ 2 & 3 \end{vmatrix} = 1(3) - 2(-3) = 3 + 6 = 9$$

$$D_x = \begin{vmatrix} -5 & -3 \\ 5 & 3 \end{vmatrix} = -5(3) - 5(-3) = -15 + 15 = 0$$

$$D_y = \begin{vmatrix} 1 & -5 \\ 2 & 5 \end{vmatrix} = 1(5) - 2(-5) = 5 + 10 = 15$$

Find the solutions by Cramer's Rule: $x = \dfrac{D_x}{D} = \dfrac{0}{9} = 0 \qquad y = \dfrac{D_y}{D} = \dfrac{15}{9} = \dfrac{5}{3}$

53. Set up and evaluate the determinants to use Cramer's Rule:

$$\begin{cases} 2x + 3y = 13 \\ 3x - 2y = 0 \end{cases}$$

$$D = \begin{vmatrix} 2 & 3 \\ 3 & -2 \end{vmatrix} = -4 - 9 = -13$$

$$D_x = \begin{vmatrix} 13 & 3 \\ 0 & -2 \end{vmatrix} = -26 - 0 = -26$$

$$D_y = \begin{vmatrix} 2 & 13 \\ 3 & 0 \end{vmatrix} = 0 - 39 = -39$$

Find the solutions by Cramer's Rule: $x = \dfrac{D_x}{D} = \dfrac{-26}{-13} = 2 \qquad y = \dfrac{D_y}{D} = \dfrac{-39}{-13} = 3$

54. Set up and evaluate the determinants to use Cramer's Rule:

$$\begin{cases} 3x-4y= & 12 \\ 5x+2y= & -6 \end{cases}$$

$$D=\begin{vmatrix} 3 & -4 \\ 5 & 2 \end{vmatrix}=6+20=26$$

$$D_x=\begin{vmatrix} 12 & -4 \\ -6 & 2 \end{vmatrix}=24-24=0$$

$$D_y=\begin{vmatrix} 3 & 12 \\ 5 & -6 \end{vmatrix}=-18-60=-78$$

Find the solutions by Cramer's Rule: $x=\dfrac{D_x}{D}=\dfrac{0}{26}=0 \qquad y=\dfrac{D_y}{D}=\dfrac{-78}{26}=-3$

55. Set up and evaluate the determinants to use Cramer's Rule:

$$\begin{cases} x+2y-z= & 6 \\ 2x-y+3z= & -13 \\ 3x-2y+3z= & -16 \end{cases}$$

$$D=\begin{vmatrix} 1 & 2 & -1 \\ 2 & -1 & 3 \\ 3 & -2 & 3 \end{vmatrix}=1\begin{vmatrix} -1 & 3 \\ -2 & 3 \end{vmatrix}-2\begin{vmatrix} 2 & 3 \\ 3 & 3 \end{vmatrix}+(-1)\begin{vmatrix} 2 & -1 \\ 3 & -2 \end{vmatrix}$$

$$=1(-3+6)-2(6-9)-1(-4+3)=3+6+1=10$$

$$D_x=\begin{vmatrix} 6 & 2 & -1 \\ -13 & -1 & 3 \\ -16 & -2 & 3 \end{vmatrix}=6\begin{vmatrix} -1 & 3 \\ -2 & 3 \end{vmatrix}-2\begin{vmatrix} -13 & 3 \\ -16 & 3 \end{vmatrix}+(-1)\begin{vmatrix} -13 & -1 \\ -16 & -2 \end{vmatrix}$$

$$=6(-3+6)-2(-39+48)-1(26-16)=18-18-10=-10$$

$$D_y=\begin{vmatrix} 1 & 6 & -1 \\ 2 & -13 & 3 \\ 3 & -16 & 3 \end{vmatrix}=1\begin{vmatrix} -13 & 3 \\ -16 & 3 \end{vmatrix}-6\begin{vmatrix} 2 & 3 \\ 3 & 3 \end{vmatrix}+(-1)\begin{vmatrix} 2 & -13 \\ 3 & -16 \end{vmatrix}$$

$$=1(-39+48)-6(6-9)-1(-32+39)=9+18-7=20$$

$$D_z=\begin{vmatrix} 1 & 2 & 6 \\ 2 & -1 & -13 \\ 3 & -2 & -16 \end{vmatrix}=1\begin{vmatrix} -1 & -13 \\ -2 & -16 \end{vmatrix}-2\begin{vmatrix} 2 & -13 \\ 3 & -16 \end{vmatrix}+6\begin{vmatrix} 2 & -1 \\ 3 & -2 \end{vmatrix}$$

$$=1(16-26)-2(-32+39)+6(-4+3)=-10-14-6=-30$$

Find the solutions by Cramer's Rule:

$$x=\frac{D_x}{D}=\frac{-10}{10}=-1 \qquad y=\frac{D_y}{D}=\frac{20}{10}=2 \qquad z=\frac{D_z}{D}=\frac{-30}{10}=-3$$

56. Set up and evaluate the determinants to use Cramer's Rule:

$$\begin{cases} x-y+z= & 8 \\ 2x+3y-z= & -2 \\ 3x-y-9z= & 9 \end{cases}$$

$$D=\begin{vmatrix} 1 & -1 & 1 \\ 2 & 3 & -1 \\ 3 & -1 & -9 \end{vmatrix}=1\begin{vmatrix} 3 & -1 \\ -1 & -9 \end{vmatrix}-(-1)\begin{vmatrix} 2 & -1 \\ 3 & -9 \end{vmatrix}+1\begin{vmatrix} 2 & 3 \\ 3 & -1 \end{vmatrix}$$

$$=1(-27-1)+1(-18+3)+1(-2-9)=-28-15-11=-54$$

$$D_x = \begin{vmatrix} 8 & -1 & 1 \\ -2 & 3 & -1 \\ 9 & -1 & -9 \end{vmatrix} = 8\begin{vmatrix} 3 & -1 \\ -1 & -9 \end{vmatrix} - (-1)\begin{vmatrix} -2 & -1 \\ 9 & -9 \end{vmatrix} + 1\begin{vmatrix} -2 & 3 \\ 9 & -1 \end{vmatrix}$$
$$= 8(-27-1) + 1(18+9) + 1(2-27) = -224 + 27 - 25 = -222$$

$$D_y = \begin{vmatrix} 1 & 8 & 1 \\ 2 & -2 & -1 \\ 3 & 9 & -9 \end{vmatrix} = 1\begin{vmatrix} -2 & -1 \\ 9 & -9 \end{vmatrix} - 8\begin{vmatrix} 2 & -1 \\ 3 & -9 \end{vmatrix} + 1\begin{vmatrix} 2 & -2 \\ 3 & 9 \end{vmatrix}$$
$$= 1(18+9) - 8(-18+3) + 1(18+6) = 27 + 120 + 24 = 171$$

$$D_z = \begin{vmatrix} 1 & -1 & 8 \\ 2 & 3 & -2 \\ 3 & -1 & 9 \end{vmatrix} = 1\begin{vmatrix} 3 & -2 \\ -1 & 9 \end{vmatrix} - (-1)\begin{vmatrix} 2 & -2 \\ 3 & 9 \end{vmatrix} + 8\begin{vmatrix} 2 & 3 \\ 3 & -1 \end{vmatrix}$$
$$= 1(27-2) + 1(18+6) + 8(-2-9) = 25 + 24 - 88 = -39$$

Find the solutions by Cramer's Rule:

$$x = \frac{D_x}{D} = \frac{-222}{-54} = \frac{37}{9} \qquad y = \frac{D_y}{D} = \frac{171}{-54} = -\frac{19}{6} \qquad z = \frac{D_z}{D} = \frac{-39}{-54} = \frac{13}{18}$$

57. Find the partial fraction decomposition:

$$\frac{6}{x(x-4)} = \frac{A}{x} + \frac{B}{x-4} \quad \text{(Multiply both sides by } x(x-4).)$$
$$6 = A(x-4) + Bx$$

Let $x = 4$: then $6 = A(4-4) + B(4) \rightarrow 4B = 6 \rightarrow B = \frac{3}{2}$

Let $x = 0$: then $6 = A(0-4) + B(0) \rightarrow -4A = 6 \rightarrow A = -\frac{3}{2}$

$$\frac{6}{x(x-4)} = \frac{\left(-\frac{3}{2}\right)}{x} + \frac{\left(\frac{3}{2}\right)}{x-4}$$

58. Find the partial fraction decomposition:

$$\frac{x}{(x+2)(x-3)} = \frac{A}{x+2} + \frac{B}{x-3} \quad \text{(Multiply both sides by } (x+2)(x-3).)$$
$$x = A(x-3) + B(x+2)$$

Let $x = -2$: then $-2 = A(-2-3) + B(-2+2) \rightarrow -5A = -2 \rightarrow A = \frac{2}{5}$

Let $x = 3$: then $3 = A(3-3) + B(3+2) \rightarrow 5B = 3 \rightarrow B = \frac{3}{5}$

$$\frac{x}{(x+2)(x-3)} = \frac{\left(\frac{2}{5}\right)}{x+2} + \frac{\left(\frac{3}{5}\right)}{x-3}$$

59. Find the partial fraction decomposition:

$$\frac{x-4}{x^2(x-1)}=\frac{A}{x}+\frac{B}{x^2}+\frac{C}{x-1} \text{ (Multiply both sides by } x^2(x-1).)$$

$$x-4=Ax(x-1)+B(x-1)+Cx^2$$

Let $x=1$: then $1-4=A(1)(1-1)+B(1-1)+C(1)^2 \rightarrow -3=C \rightarrow C=-3$

Let $x=0$: then $0-4=A(0)(0-1)+B(0-1)+C(0)^2 \rightarrow -4=-B \rightarrow B=4$

Let $x=2$: then $2-4=A(2)(2-1)+B(2-1)+C(2)^2 \rightarrow -2=2A+B+4C$

$$\rightarrow 2A=-2-4-4(-3) \rightarrow 2A=6 \rightarrow A=3$$

$$\frac{x-4}{x^2(x-1)}=\frac{3}{x}+\frac{4}{x^2}+\frac{-3}{x-1}$$

60. Find the partial fraction decomposition:

$$\frac{2x-6}{(x-2)^2(x-1)}=\frac{A}{x-2}+\frac{B}{(x-2)^2}+\frac{C}{x-1} \text{ (Multiply both sides by } (x-2)^2(x-1).)$$

$$2x-6=A(x-2)(x-1)+B(x-1)+C(x-2)^2$$

Let $x=1$: then $2(1)-6=A(1-2)(1-1)+B(1-1)+C(1-2)^2$

$$\rightarrow -4=C \rightarrow C=-4$$

Let $x=2$: then $2(2)-6=A(2-2)(2-1)+B(2-1)+C(2-2)^2 \rightarrow -2=B$

Let $x=0$: then $2(0)-6=A(0-2)(0-1)+B(0-1)+C(0-2)^2$

$$\rightarrow -6=2A-B+4C \rightarrow -6=2A-(-2)+4(-4)$$

$$\rightarrow 2A=8 \rightarrow A=4$$

$$\frac{2x-6}{(x-2)^2(x-1)}=\frac{4}{x-2}+\frac{-2}{(x-2)^2}+\frac{-4}{x-1}$$

61. Find the partial fraction decomposition:

$$\frac{x}{(x^2+9)(x+1)}=\frac{A}{x+1}+\frac{Bx+C}{x^2+9} \text{ (Multiply both sides by } (x+1)(x^2+9).)$$

$$x=A(x^2+9)+(Bx+C)(x+1)$$

Let $x=-1$: then $-1=A((-1)^2+9)+(B(-1)+C)(-1+1)$

$$\rightarrow -1=A(10)+(-B+C)(0) \rightarrow -1=10A \rightarrow A=-\frac{1}{10}$$

Let $x=1$: then $1=A(1^2+9)+(B(1)+C)(1+1) \rightarrow 1=10A+2B+2C$

$$\rightarrow 1=10\left(-\frac{1}{10}\right)+2B+2C \rightarrow 2=2B+2C \rightarrow B+C=1$$

Let $x=0$: then $0=A(0^2+9)+(B(0)+C)(0+1) \rightarrow 0=9A+C$

$$\rightarrow 0=9\left(-\frac{1}{10}\right)+C \rightarrow C=\frac{9}{10} \; B=1-C \rightarrow B=1-\frac{9}{10} \rightarrow B=\frac{1}{10}$$

$$\frac{x}{(x^2+9)(x+1)}=\frac{-\left(\frac{1}{10}\right)}{x+1}+\frac{\left(\frac{1}{10}x+\frac{9}{10}\right)}{x^2+9}$$

62. Find the partial fraction decomposition:

$$\frac{3x}{(x-2)(x^2+1)}=\frac{A}{x-2}+\frac{Bx+C}{x^2+1}$$ (Multiply both sides by $(x-2)(x^2+1)$.)

$$3x = A(x^2+1)+(Bx+C)(x-2)$$

Let $x=2$: then $3(2)=A((2)^2+1)+(B(2)+C)(2-2)$

$$\rightarrow 6=5A \rightarrow A=\frac{6}{5}$$

Let $x=0$: then $3(0)=A(0^2+1)+(B(0)+C)(0-2) \rightarrow 0=A-2C$

$$\rightarrow \quad 0=\frac{6}{5}-2C \rightarrow 2C=\frac{6}{5} \rightarrow C=\frac{3}{5}$$

Let $x=1$: then $3(1)=A(1^2+1)+(B(1)+C)(1-2) \rightarrow 3=2A-B-C$

$$\rightarrow \quad 3=2\left(\frac{6}{5}\right)-B-\frac{3}{5} \rightarrow B=-\frac{6}{5}$$

$$\frac{3x}{(x-2)(x^2+1)}=\frac{\left(\frac{6}{5}\right)}{x-2}+\frac{\left(-\frac{6}{5}x+\frac{3}{5}\right)}{x^2+1}$$

63. Find the partial fraction decomposition:

$$\frac{x^3}{(x^2+4)^2}=\frac{Ax+B}{x^2+4}+\frac{Cx+D}{(x^2+4)^2}$$ (Multiply both sides by $(x^2+4)^2$.)

$$x^3=(Ax+B)(x^2+4)+Cx+D$$

$$x^3=Ax^3+Bx^2+4Ax+4B+Cx+D$$

$$x^3=Ax^3+Bx^2+(4A+C)x+4B+D$$

$$A=1$$

$$B=0$$

$$4A+C=0 \rightarrow 4(1)+C=0 \rightarrow C=-4$$

$$4B+D=0 \rightarrow 4(0)+D=0 \rightarrow D=0$$

$$\frac{x^3}{(x^2+4)^2}=\frac{x}{x^2+4}+\frac{-4x}{(x^2+4)^2}$$

64. Find the partial fraction decomposition:

$$\frac{x^3+1}{(x^2+16)^2}=\frac{Ax+B}{x^2+16}+\frac{Cx+D}{(x^2+16)^2}$$ (Multiply both sides by $(x^2+16)^2$.)

$$x^3+1=(Ax+B)(x^2+16)+Cx+D$$

$$x^3+1=Ax^3+Bx^2+16Ax+16B+Cx+D$$

$$x^3+1=Ax^3+Bx^2+(16A+C)x+16B+D$$

$$A = 1$$

$$B = 0$$

$$16A + C = 0 \rightarrow 16(1) + C = 0 \rightarrow C = -16$$

$$16B + D = 1 \rightarrow 16(0) + D = 1 \rightarrow D = 1$$

$$\frac{x^3 + 1}{(x^2 + 16)^2} = \frac{x}{x^2 + 16} + \frac{-16x + 1}{(x^2 + 16)^2}$$

65. Find the partial fraction decomposition:

$$\frac{x^2}{(x^2 + 1)(x^2 - 1)} = \frac{x^2}{(x^2 + 1)(x - 1)(x + 1)} = \frac{A}{x - 1} + \frac{B}{x + 1} + \frac{Cx + D}{x^2 + 1}$$

(Multiply both sides by $(x - 1)(x + 1)(x^2 + 1)$.)

$$x^2 = A(x + 1)(x^2 + 1) + B(x - 1)(x^2 + 1) + (Cx + D)(x - 1)(x + 1)$$

Let $x = 1$: then $1^2 = A(1 + 1)(1^2 + 1) + B(1 - 1)(1^2 + 1) + (C(1) + D)(1 - 1)(1 + 1)$

$$\rightarrow 1 = 4A \rightarrow A = \frac{1}{4}$$

Let $x = -1$: then

$$(-1)^2 = A(-1 + 1)((-1)^2 + 1) + B(-1 - 1)((-1)^2 + 1) + (C(-1) + D)(-1 - 1)(-1 + 1)$$

$$\rightarrow 1 = -4B \rightarrow B = -\frac{1}{4}$$

Let $x = 0$: then

$$0^2 = A(0 + 1)(0^2 + 1) + B(0 - 1)(0^2 + 1) + (C(0) + D)(0 - 1)(0 + 1)$$

$$\rightarrow 0 = A - B - D \rightarrow 0 = \frac{1}{4} - \left(-\frac{1}{4}\right) - D \rightarrow D = \frac{1}{2}$$

Let $x = 2$: then

$$2^2 = A(2 + 1)(2^2 + 1) + B(2 - 1)(2^2 + 1) + (C(2) + D)(2 - 1)(2 + 1)$$

$$\rightarrow 4 = 15A + 5B + 6C + 3D \rightarrow 4 = 15\left(\frac{1}{4}\right) + 5\left(-\frac{1}{4}\right) + 6C + 3\left(\frac{1}{2}\right)$$

$$\rightarrow 6C = 4 - \frac{15}{4} + \frac{5}{4} - \frac{3}{2} \rightarrow 6C = 0 \rightarrow C = 0$$

$$\frac{x^2}{(x^2 + 1)(x^2 - 1)} = \frac{x^2}{(x^2 + 1)(x - 1)(x + 1)} = \frac{\left(\frac{1}{4}\right)}{x - 1} + \frac{-\left(\frac{1}{4}\right)}{x + 1} + \frac{\left(\frac{1}{2}\right)}{x^2 + 1}$$

66. Find the partial fraction decomposition:

$$\frac{4}{(x^2 + 4)(x^2 - 1)} = \frac{4}{(x^2 + 4)(x - 1)(x + 1)} = \frac{A}{x - 1} + \frac{B}{x + 1} + \frac{Cx + D}{x^2 + 4}$$

(Multiply both sides by $(x - 1)(x + 1)(x^2 + 4)$.)

$$4 = A(x + 1)(x^2 + 4) + B(x - 1)(x^2 + 4) + (Cx + D)(x - 1)(x + 1)$$

Let $x=1$: then $4=A(1+1)(1^2+4)+B(1-1)(1^2+4)+(C(1)+D)(1-1)(1+1)$

$$\to 4=10A \to A=\frac{2}{5}$$

Let $x=-1$: then

$$4=A(-1+1)((-1)^2+4)+B(-1-1)((-1)^2+4)+ (C(-1)+D)(-1-1)(-1+1)$$

$$\to 4=-10B \to B=-\frac{2}{5}$$

Let $x=0$: then

$$4=A(0+1)(0^2+4)+B(0-1)(0^2+4)+(C(0)+D)(0-1)(0+1)$$

$$\to 4=4A-4B-D \to 4=\frac{8}{5}-\left(-\frac{8}{5}\right)-D \to D=-\frac{4}{5}$$

Let $x=2$: then

$$4=A(2+1)(2^2+4)+B(2-1)(2^2+4)+(C(2)+D)(2-1)(2+1)$$

$$\to 4=24A+8B+6C+3D \to 4=24\left(\frac{2}{5}\right)+8\left(-\frac{2}{5}\right)+6C+3\left(-\frac{4}{5}\right)$$

$$\to 6C=4-\frac{48}{5}+\frac{16}{5}+\frac{12}{5} \to 6C=0 \to C=0$$

$$\frac{4}{(x^2+4)(x^2-1)}=\frac{4}{(x^2+4)(x-1)(x+1)}=\frac{\left(\frac{2}{5}\right)}{x-1}+\frac{-\left(\frac{2}{5}\right)}{x+1}+\frac{-\left(\frac{4}{5}\right)}{x^2+4}$$

67. Solve the first equation for y, substitute into the second equation and solve:

$$\begin{cases} 2x+y+3=0 \to y=-2x-3 \\ x^2+y^2=5 \end{cases}$$

$$x^2+(-2x-3)^2=5 \to x^2+4x^2+12x+9=5$$

$$5x^2+12x+4=0 \to (5x+2)(x+2)=0$$

$$x=-\frac{2}{5} \quad \text{or } x=-2$$

$$y=-\frac{11}{5} \qquad y=1$$

Solutions: $\left(-\frac{2}{5},-\frac{11}{5}\right),(-2,1)$.

68. Add the equations to eliminate y, and solve:

$$\begin{cases} x^2+y^2=16 \\ 2x-y^2=-8 \end{cases}$$

$$x^2+2x=8$$

$$x^2+2x-8=0 \to (x+4)(x-2)=0$$

$$x=-4 \text{ or } x=2$$

If $x=-4$: $(-4)^2+y^2=16 \rightarrow y^2=0 \rightarrow y=0$

If $x=2$: $(2)^2+y^2=16 \rightarrow y^2=12 \rightarrow y=\pm\sqrt{12}=\pm 2\sqrt{3}$

Solutions: $(-4,0),\ (2,2\sqrt{3}),\ (2,-2\sqrt{3})$.

69. Multiply each side of the second equation by 2 and add the equations to eliminate xy:

$$\begin{cases} 2xy+y^2=10 \longrightarrow & 2xy+y^2=10 \\ -xy+3y^2=2 \xrightarrow{2} & -2xy+6y^2=4 \end{cases}$$

$$7y^2=14 \rightarrow y^2=2 \rightarrow y=\pm\sqrt{2}$$

If $y=\sqrt{2}$: $2x(\sqrt{2})+(\sqrt{2})^2=10 \rightarrow 2\sqrt{2}x=8 \rightarrow x=\dfrac{8}{2\sqrt{2}}=2\sqrt{2}$

If $y=-\sqrt{2}$: $2x(-\sqrt{2})+(-\sqrt{2})^2=10 \rightarrow -2\sqrt{2}x=8 \rightarrow x=\dfrac{8}{-2\sqrt{2}}=-2\sqrt{2}$

Solutions: $(2\sqrt{2},\sqrt{2}),\ (-2\sqrt{2},-\sqrt{2})$

70. Multiply each side of the first equation by –2 and add the equations to eliminate y:

$$\begin{cases} 3x^2-y^2=1 \xrightarrow{-2} & -6x^2+2y^2=-2 \\ 7x^2-2y^2=5 \longrightarrow & 7x^2-2y^2=5 \end{cases}$$

$$x^2=3$$

$$x=\pm\sqrt{3}$$

If $x=\sqrt{3}$: $3(\sqrt{3})^2-y^2=1 \rightarrow -y^2=-8 \rightarrow y=\pm\sqrt{8}=\pm 2\sqrt{2}$

If $x=-\sqrt{3}$: $3(-\sqrt{3})^2-y^2=1 \rightarrow -y^2=-8 \rightarrow y=\pm\sqrt{8}=\pm 2\sqrt{2}$

Solutions: $(\sqrt{3},2\sqrt{2}),\ (\sqrt{3},-2\sqrt{2}),\ (-\sqrt{3},2\sqrt{2}),\ (-\sqrt{3},-2\sqrt{2})$

71. Substitute into the second equation into the first equation and solve:

$$\begin{cases} x^2+y^2=6y \\ x^2=3y \end{cases}$$

$3y+y^2=6y \rightarrow y^2-3y=0 \rightarrow y(y-3)=0 \rightarrow y=0$ or $y=3$

If $y=0$: $x^2=3(0) \rightarrow x^2=0 \rightarrow x=0$

If $y=3$: $x^2=3(3) \rightarrow x^2=9 \rightarrow x=\pm 3$

Solutions: (0, 0), (–3, 3), (3, 3)

72. Multiply each side of the second equation by –1 and add the equations to eliminate y:

$$\begin{cases} 2x^2+y^2=9 \longrightarrow & 2x^2+y^2=9 \\ x^2+y^2=9 \xrightarrow{-1} & -x^2-y^2=-9 \end{cases}$$

$$x^2=0$$

$$x=0$$

If $x=0$: $0^2+y^2=9 \rightarrow y^2=9 \rightarrow y=\pm 3$

Solutions: (0, 3), (0, –3)

73. Factor the second equation, solve for x, substitute into the first equation and solve:

$$\begin{cases} 3x^2+4xy+5y^2=8 \\ x^2+3xy+2y^2=0 \end{cases} \rightarrow (x+2y)(x+y)=0 \rightarrow x=-2y \text{ or } x=-y$$

Substitute $x=-2y$ and solve:

$$\begin{aligned} 3x^2+4xy+5y^2&=8 \\ 3(-2y)^2+4(-2y)y+5y^2&=8 \\ 12y^2-8y^2+5y^2&=8 \\ 9y^2&=8 \\ y^2&=\frac{8}{9} \\ y&=\pm\frac{2\sqrt{2}}{3} \end{aligned}$$

If $y=\frac{2\sqrt{2}}{3}$: $x=-2\left(\frac{2\sqrt{2}}{3}\right)=\frac{-4\sqrt{2}}{3}$

If $y=\frac{-2\sqrt{2}}{3}$: $x=-2\left(\frac{-2\sqrt{2}}{3}\right)=\frac{4\sqrt{2}}{3}$

Substitute $x=-y$ and solve:

$$\begin{aligned} 3x^2+4xy+5y^2&=8 \\ 3(-y)^2+4(-y)y+5y^2&=8 \\ 3y^2-4y^2+5y^2&=8 \\ 4y^2&=8 \\ y^2&=2 \\ y&=\pm\sqrt{2} \end{aligned}$$

If $y=\sqrt{2}$: $x=-\sqrt{2}$

If $y=-\sqrt{2}$: $x=\sqrt{2}$

Solutions: $\left(\frac{-4\sqrt{2}}{3},\frac{2\sqrt{2}}{3}\right),\left(\frac{4\sqrt{2}}{3},\frac{-2\sqrt{2}}{3}\right),\left(-\sqrt{2},\sqrt{2}\right),\left(\sqrt{2},-\sqrt{2}\right)$

74. Multiply each side of the first equation by 2 and each side of the second equation by 3 and add to eliminate the constant:

$$\begin{cases} 3x^2+2xy-2y^2=6 \xrightarrow{2} 6x^2+4xy-4y^2=12 \\ xy-2y^2=-4 \xrightarrow{3} \underline{\quad 3xy-6y^2=-12} \end{cases}$$

$$6x^2+7xy-10y^2=0$$

$$(6x-5y)(x+2y)=0$$

$$x=\frac{5}{6}y \text{ or } x=-2y$$

Substitute $x=\frac{5}{6}y$ and solve:

$$\frac{5}{6}y\cdot y-2y^2=-4$$

$$-\frac{7}{6}y^2=-4 \rightarrow y^2=\frac{24}{7}$$

$$y=\pm\frac{2\sqrt{42}}{7}$$

If $y=\frac{2\sqrt{42}}{7}$: $x=\frac{5}{6}\cdot\frac{2\sqrt{42}}{7}=\frac{5\sqrt{42}}{21}$

If $y=-\frac{2\sqrt{42}}{7}$: $x=\frac{5}{6}\cdot\frac{-2\sqrt{42}}{7}=-\frac{5\sqrt{42}}{21}$

Substitute $x=-2y$ and solve:

$$\begin{aligned} -2y\cdot y-2y^2&=-4 \\ -4y^2&=-4 \\ y^2&=1 \\ y&=\pm1 \end{aligned}$$

If $y=1$: $x=-2$

If $y=-1$: $x=2$

Solutions: $\left(\frac{5\sqrt{42}}{21},\frac{2\sqrt{42}}{7}\right)\left(-\frac{5\sqrt{42}}{21},-\frac{2\sqrt{42}}{7}\right),(-2,1),(2,-1)$

75. Multiply each side of the second equation by –y and add the equations to eliminate y:

$$\begin{cases} x^2 - 3x + y^2 + y = -2 \\ \dfrac{x^2 - x}{y} + y + 1 = 0 \end{cases} \quad \begin{aligned} &\longrightarrow \quad x^2 - 3x + y^2 + y = -2 \\ &\xrightarrow{-y} \quad \underline{-x^2 + x - y^2 - y = 0} \\ &\qquad\quad -2x \qquad\qquad = -2 \\ &\qquad\qquad\qquad\qquad x = 1 \end{aligned}$$

If $x = 1$: $\quad 1^2 - 3(1) + y^2 + y = -2 \rightarrow y^2 + y = 0 \rightarrow y(y+1) = 0$

$\rightarrow y = 0$ or $y = -1$

Note that $y \neq 0$ because that would cause division by zero in the original equation.
Solution: $(1, -1)$

76. Multiply each side of the second equation by –x and add the equations to eliminate x:

$$\begin{cases} x^2 + x + y^2 = y + 2 \\ x + 1 = \dfrac{2 - y}{x} \end{cases} \quad \begin{aligned} &\longrightarrow \quad x^2 + x + y^2 = y + 2 \\ &\xrightarrow{-x} \quad \underline{-x^2 - x \qquad = y - 2} \end{aligned}$$

$$y^2 = 2y \rightarrow y^2 - 2y = 0 \rightarrow y(y-2) = 0$$

$$y = 0 \text{ or } y = 2$$

If $y = 0$: $\quad x^2 + x + 0^2 = 0 + 2 \rightarrow x^2 + x - 2 = 0 \rightarrow (x-1)(x+2) = 0$

$\rightarrow x = 1$ or $x = -2$

If $y = 2$: $\quad x^2 + x + 2^2 = 2 + 2 \rightarrow x^2 + x = 0 \rightarrow x(x+1) = 0$

$\rightarrow x = 0$ or $x = -1$

Note that $x \neq 0$ because that would cause division by zero in the original equation.
Solutions: $(1, 0), (-2, 0), (-1, 2)$

77. Graph the system of linear inequalities:

$$\begin{cases} -2x + y \le 2 \\ x + y \ge 2 \end{cases}$$

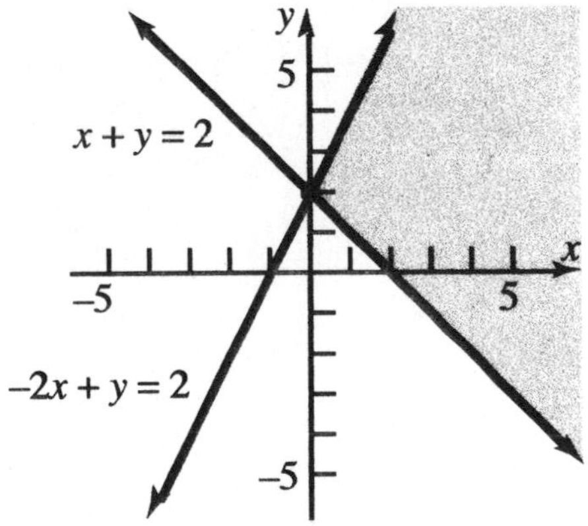

(a) Graph the line $-2x + y = 2$. Use a solid line since the inequality uses $\le$.
Choose a test point not on the line, such as $(0, 0)$. Since $-2(0) + 0 \le 2$ is true, shade the side of the line containing $(0, 0)$.

(b) Graph the line $x + y = 2$. Use a solid line since the inequality uses $\ge$.
Choose a test point not on the line, such as $(0, 0)$. Since $0 + 0 \ge 2$ is false, shade the opposite side of the line from $(0, 0)$.

(c) The overlapping region is the solution.

(d) The graph is unbounded.

(e) Find the vertices:
To find the intersection of $x + y = 2$ and $-2x + y = 2$, solve the system:

$$\begin{cases} x + y = 2 \quad \rightarrow \quad x = 2 - y \\ -2x + y = 2 \end{cases}$$

Substitute and solve:

$$-2(2-y)+y=2 \rightarrow -4+2y+y=2 \rightarrow 3y=6 \rightarrow y=2$$

$$x=2-2=0$$

The point of intersection is (0, 2).

The corner point is (0, 2).

78. Graph the system of linear inequalities:

$$\begin{cases} x-2y \le 6 \\ 2x+y \ge 2 \end{cases}$$

(a) Graph the line $x-2y=6$. Use a solid line since the inequality uses $\le$.
Choose a test point not on the line, such as (0, 0). Since $0-2(0) \le 6$ is true, shade the side of the line containing (0, 0).

(b) Graph the line $2x+y=2$. Use a solid line since the inequality uses $\ge$.
Choose a test point not on the line, such as (0, 0). Since $2(0)+0 \ge 2$ is false, shade the opposite side of the line from (0, 0).

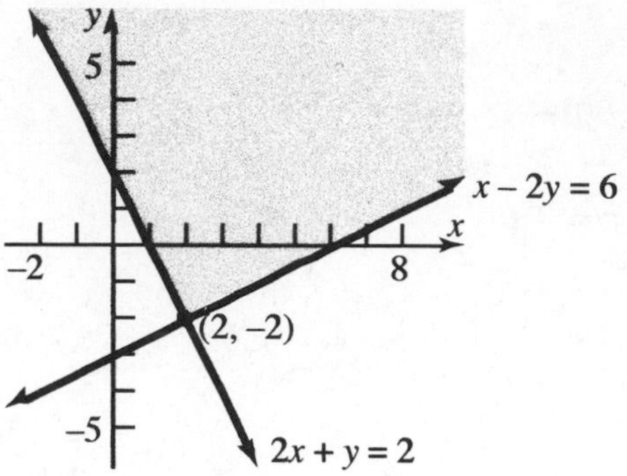

(c) The overlapping region is the solution.

(d) The graph is unbounded.

(e) Find the vertices:
To find the intersection of $x-2y=6$ and $2x+y=2$, solve the system:

$$\begin{cases} x-2y=6 & \rightarrow \quad x=2y+6 \\ 2x+y=2 \end{cases}$$

Substitute and solve:

$$2(2y+6)+y=2 \rightarrow 4y+12+y=2 \rightarrow 5y=-10 \rightarrow y=-2$$

$$x=2(-2)+6=2$$

The point of intersection is (2, –2).

The corner point is (2, –2).

79. Graph the system of linear inequalities:

$$\begin{cases} x \ge 0 \\ y \ge 0 \\ x + y \le 4 \\ 2x + 3y \le 6 \end{cases}$$

(a) Graph $x \ge 0$; $y \ge 0$. Shaded region is the first quadrant.

(b) Graph the line $x + y = 4$. Use a solid line since the inequality uses $\le$.
Choose a test point not on the line, such as (0, 0). Since $0 + 0 \le 4$ is true, shade the side of the line containing (0, 0).

(c) Graph the line $2x + 3y = 6$. Use a solid line since the inequality uses $\le$.
Choose a test point not on the line, such as (0, 0). Since $2(0) + 3(0) \le 6$ is true, shade the side of the line containing (0, 0).

(d) The overlapping region is the solution.

(e) The graph is bounded.

(f) Find the vertices:
The x-axis and y-axis intersect at (0, 0).
The intersection of $2x + 3y = 6$ and the y-axis is (0, 2).
The intersection of $2x + 3y = 6$ and the x-axis is (3, 0).
The three corner points are (0, 0), (0, 2), and (3, 0).

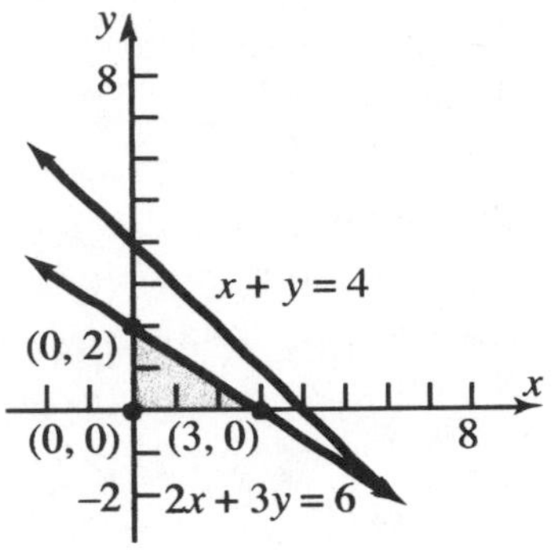

80. Graph the system of linear inequalities:

$$\begin{cases} x \ge 0 \\ y \ge 0 \\ 3x + y \ge 6 \\ 2x + y \ge 2 \end{cases}$$

(a) Graph $x \ge 0$; $y \ge 0$. Shaded region is the first quadrant.

(b) Graph the line $3x + y = 6$. Use a solid line since the inequality uses $\ge$.
Choose a test point not on the line, such as (0, 0). Since $3(0) + 0 \ge 6$ is false, shade the opposite side of the line from (0, 0).

(c) Graph the line $2x + y = 2$. Use a solid line since the inequality uses $\ge$.
Choose a test point not on the line, such as (0, 0). Since $2(0) + 0 \ge 2$ is false, shade the opposite side of the line from (0, 0).

(d) The overlapping region is the solution.

(e) The graph is unbounded.

(f) Find the vertices:
The intersection of $3x + y = 6$ and the y-axis is (0, 6).

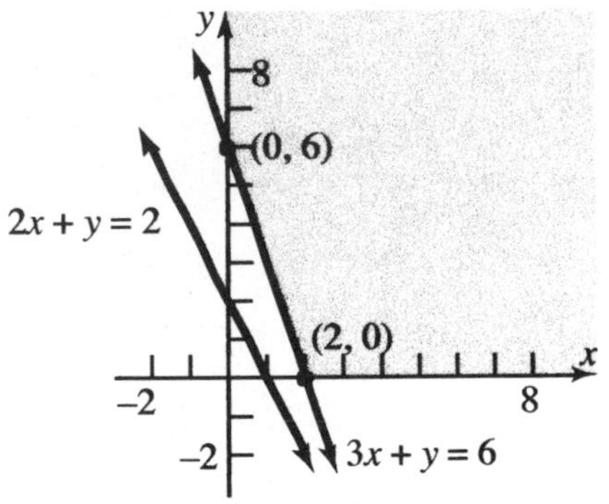

The intersection of $3x + y = 6$ and the x-axis is (2, 0).
The two corner points are (0, 6), and (2, 0).

81. Graph the system of linear inequalities:

$$\begin{cases} x \ge 0 \\ y \ge 0 \\ 2x + y \le 8 \\ x + 2y \ge 2 \end{cases}$$

(a) Graph $x \ge 0$; $y \ge 0$. Shaded region is the first quadrant.
(b) Graph the line $2x + y = 8$. Use a solid line since the inequality uses $\le$.
Choose a test point not on the line, such as (0, 0). Since $2(0) + 0 \le 8$ is true, shade the side of the line containing (0, 0).

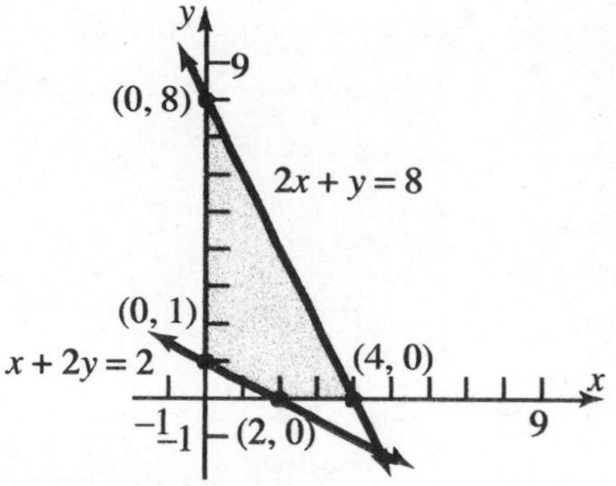

(c) Graph the line $x + 2y = 2$. Use a solid line since the inequality uses $\ge$.
Choose a test point not on the line, such as (0, 0). Since $0 + 2(0) \ge 2$ is false, shade the opposite side of the line from (0, 0).
(d) The overlapping region is the solution.
(e) The graph is bounded.
(f) Find the vertices:
The intersection of $x + 2y = 2$ and the y-axis is (0, 1).
The intersection of $x + 2y = 2$ and the x-axis is (2, 0).
The intersection of $2x + y = 8$ and the y-axis is (0, 8).
The intersection of $2x + y = 8$ and the x-axis is (4, 0).
The four corner points are (0, 1), (0, 8), (2, 0), and (4, 0).

82. Graph the system of linear inequalities:

$$\begin{cases} x \ge 0 \\ y \ge 0 \\ 3x + y \le 9 \\ 2x + 3y \ge 6 \end{cases}$$

(a) Graph $x \ge 0$; $y \ge 0$. Shaded region is the first quadrant.
(b) Graph the line $3x + y = 9$. Use a solid line since the inequality uses $\le$.
Choose a test point not on the line, such as (0, 0). Since $3(0) + 0 \le 9$ is true, shade the side of the line containing (0, 0).
(c) Graph the line $2x + 3y = 6$. Use a solid line since the inequality uses $\ge$.
Choose a test point not on the line, such as (0, 0). Since $2(0) + 3(0) \ge 6$ is false, shade the opposite side of the line from (0, 0).

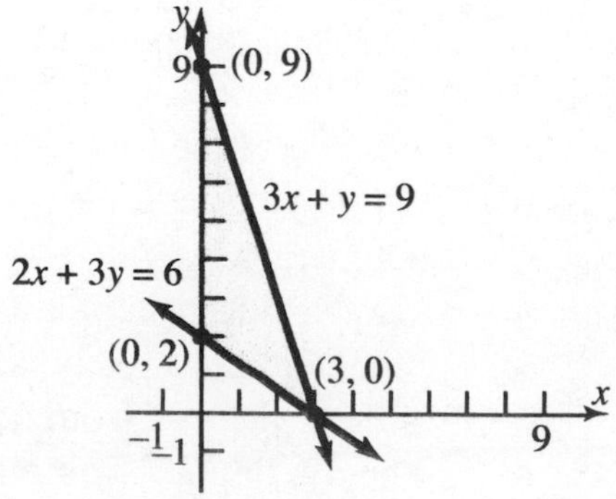

(d) The overlapping region is the solution.
(e) The graph is bounded.
(f) Find the vertices:
The intersection of $2x+3y=6$ and the y-axis is (0, 2).
The intersection of $2x+3y=6$ and the x-axis is (3, 0).
The intersection of $3x+y=9$ and the y-axis is (0, 9).
The intersection of $3x+y=9$ and the x-axis is (3, 0).
The three corner points are (0, 2), (0, 9), and (3, 0).

83. Graph the system of inequalities:
$$\begin{cases} x^2+y^2 \le 16 \\ x+y \ge 2 \end{cases}$$
(a) Graph the circle $x^2+y^2=16$. Use a solid line since the inequality uses $\le$. Choose a test point not on the circle, such as (0, 0). Since $0^2+0^2 \le 16$ is true, shade the side of the circle containing (0, 0).
(b) Graph the line $x+y=2$. Use a solid line since the inequality uses $\ge$. Choose a test point not on the line, such as (0, 0). Since $0+0 \ge 2$ is false, shade the opposite side of the line from (0, 0).

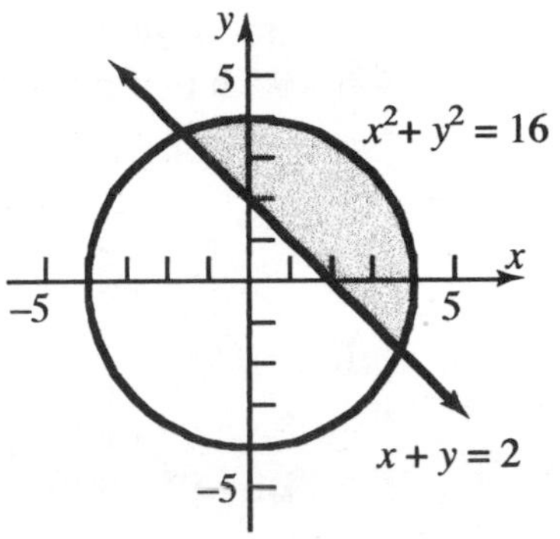

(c) The overlapping region is the solution.

84. Graph the system of inequalities:
$$\begin{cases} y^2 \le x-1 \\ x-y \le 3 \end{cases}$$
(a) Graph the parabola $y^2=x-1$. Use a solid line since the inequality uses $\le$. Choose a test point not on the parabola, such as (0, 0). Since $0^2 \le 0-1$ is false, shade the opposite side of the parabola from (0, 0).
(b) Graph the line $x-y=3$. Use a solid line since the inequality uses $\le$. Choose a test point not on the line, such as (0, 0). Since $0-0 \le 3$ is true, shade the same side of the line as (0, 0).

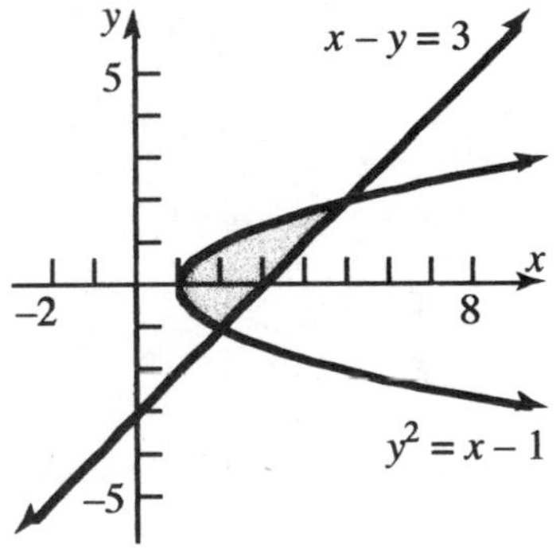

(c) The overlapping region is the solution.

85. Graph the system of inequalities:

$$\begin{cases} y \le x^2 \\ xy \le 4 \end{cases}$$

(a) Graph the parabola $y = x^2$. Use a solid line since the inequality uses $\le$. Choose a test point not on the parabola, such as (1, 2). Since $2 \le 1^2$ is false, shade the opposite side of the parabola from (1, 2).

(b) Graph the hyperbola $xy = 4$. Use a solid line since the inequality uses $\le$. Choose a test point not on the hyperbola, such as (1, 2). Since $1 \cdot 2 \le 4$ is true, shade the same side of the hyperbola as (1, 2).

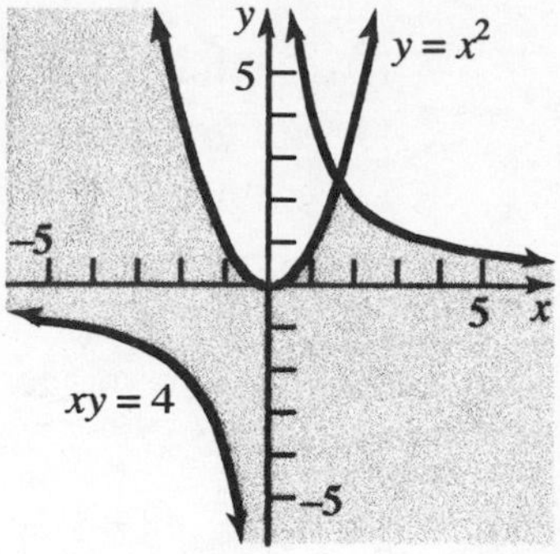

(c) The overlapping region is the solution.

86. Graph the system of inequalities:

$$\begin{cases} x^2 + y^2 \ge 1 \\ x^2 + y^2 \le 4 \end{cases}$$

(a) Graph the circle $x^2 + y^2 = 1$. Use a solid line since the inequality uses $\ge$. Choose a test point not on the circle, such as (0, 0). Since $0^2 + 0^2 \ge 1$ is false, shade the opposite side of the circle from (0, 0).

(b) Graph the circle $x^2 + y^2 = 4$. Use a solid line since the inequality uses $\le$. Choose a test point not on the circle, such as (0, 0). Since $0^2 + 0^2 \le 4$ is true, shade the same side of the circle as (0, 0).

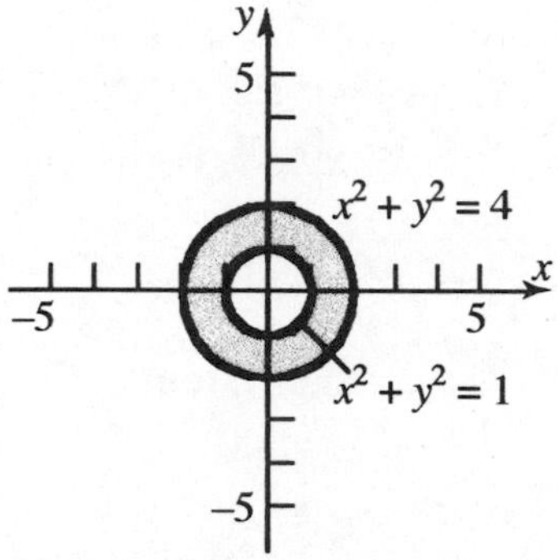

(c) The overlapping region is the solution.

87. Maximize $z = 3x + 4y$ Subject to $x \ge 0,\ \ y \ge 0,\ \ 3x + 2y \ge 6,\ \ x + y \le 8$

Graph the constraints.

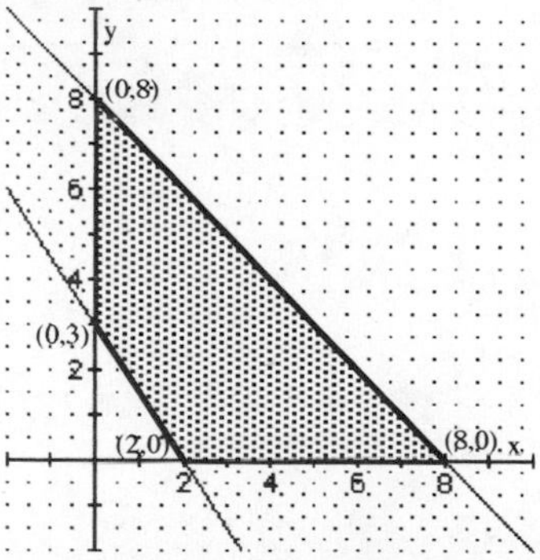

The corner points are (0, 3), (2, 0), (0, 8), (8, 0).

Evaluate the objective function:

Vertex	Value of $z = 3x + 4y$
(0, 3)	z = 3(0) + 4(3) = 12
(0, 8)	z = 3(0) + 4(8) = 32
(2, 0)	z = 3(2) + 4(0) = 6
(8, 0)	z = 3(8) + 4(0) = 24

The maximum value is 32 at (0, 8).

88. Maximize $z = 2x + 4y$ Subject to $x \ge 0$, $y \ge 0$, $x + y \le 6$, $x \ge 2$
Graph the constraints.

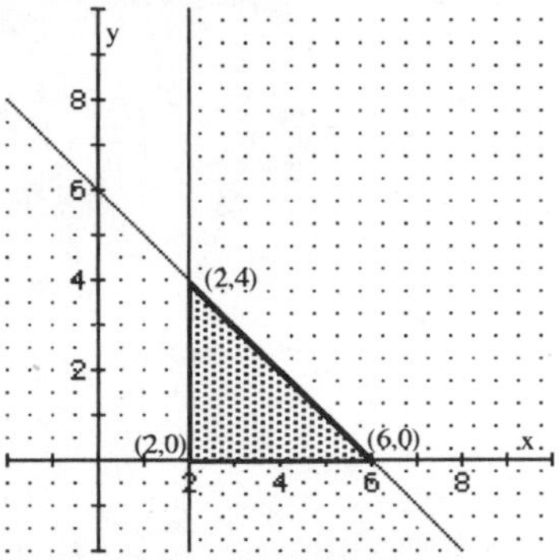

The corner points are (2, 4), (2, 0), (6, 0).

Evaluate the objective function:

Vertex	Value of $z = 2x + 4y$
(2, 4)	$z = 2(2) + 4(4) = 20$
(2, 0)	$z = 2(2) + 4(0) = 4$
(6, 0)	$z = 2(6) + 4(0) = 12$

The maximum value is 20 at (2, 4).

89. Minimize $z = 3x + 5y$
Subject to $x \ge 0$, $y \ge 0$, $x + y \ge 1$, $3x + 2y \le 12$, $x + 3y \le 12$
Graph the constraints.

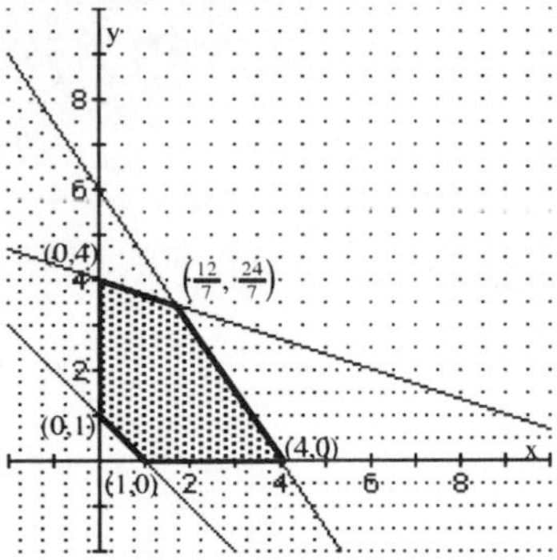

To find the intersection of $3x + 2y = 12$ and $x + 3y = 12$, solve the system:

$$\begin{cases} 3x + 2y = 12 \\ x + 3y = 12 \quad \rightarrow \quad x = 12 - 3y \end{cases}$$

Substitute and solve:

$$3(12 - 3y) + 2y = 12 \rightarrow 36 - 9y + 2y = 12 \rightarrow -7y = -24 \rightarrow y = \frac{24}{7}$$

$$x = 12 - 3\left(\frac{24}{7}\right) = 12 - \frac{72}{7} = \frac{12}{7}$$

The point of intersection is $\left(\frac{12}{7}, \frac{24}{7}\right)$.

The corner points are (0, 1), (1, 0), (0, 4), (4, 0), $\left(\frac{12}{7}, \frac{24}{7}\right)$.

Evaluate the objective function:

Vertex	Value of $z = 3x + 5y$
(0, 1)	$z = 3(0) + 5(1) = 5$
(0, 4)	$z = 3(0) + 5(4) = 20$
(1, 0)	$z = 3(1) + 5(0) = 3$
(4, 0)	$z = 3(4) + 5(0) = 12$
$\left(\frac{12}{7}, \frac{24}{7}\right)$	$z = 3\left(\frac{12}{7}\right) + 5\left(\frac{24}{7}\right) = \frac{36}{7} + \frac{120}{7} = \frac{156}{7} \approx 22.3$

The minimum value is 3 at (1, 0).

90. Minimize $z = 3x + y$

Subject to $x \ge 0,\ \ y \ge 0,\ \ x \le 8,\ \ y \le 6,\ \ 2x + y \ge 4$

Graph the constraints.

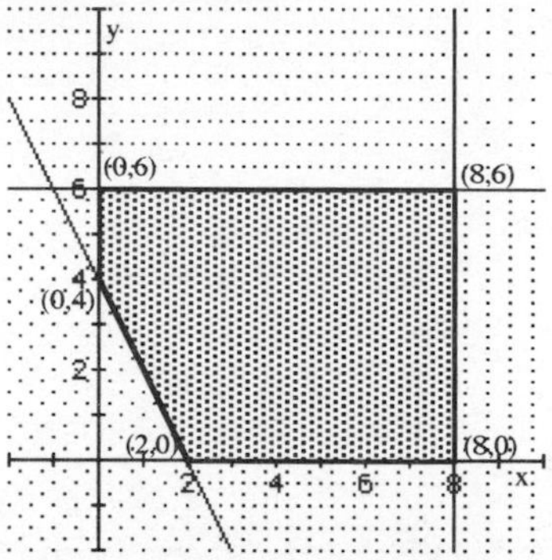

The corner points are (0, 4), (2, 0), (0, 6), (8, 0), (8, 6).

Evaluate the objective function:

Vertex	Value of $z = 3x + y$
(0, 6)	$z = 3(0) + 6 = 6$
(0, 4)	$z = 3(0) + 4 = 4$
(2, 0)	$z = 3(2) + 0 = 6$
(8, 0)	$z = 3(8) + 0 = 24$
(8, 6)	$z = 3(8) + 6 = 30$

The minimum value is 4 at (0, 4).

91. Maximize $z = 5x + 4y$ Subject to $x \ge 0,\ \ y \ge 0,\ \ x + 2y \ge 2,\ \ 3x + 4y \le 12,\ \ y \ge x$

Graph the constraints.

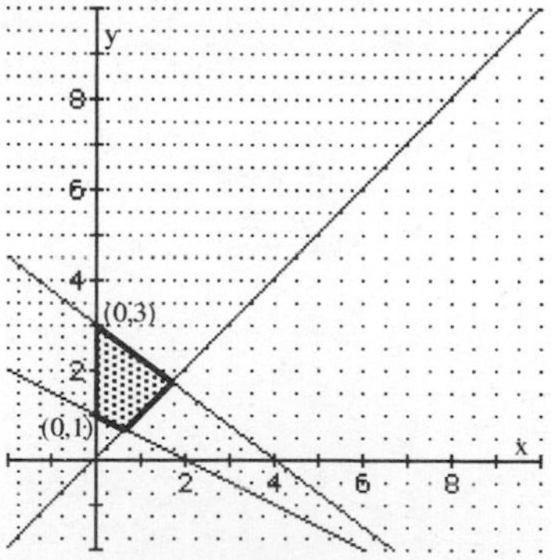

To find the intersection of $x + 2y = 2$ and $y = x$, substitute and solve:

$$x + 2x = 2 \rightarrow 3x = 2 \rightarrow x = \frac{2}{3} \rightarrow y = \frac{2}{3}$$

The point of intersection is $\left(\frac{2}{3}, \frac{2}{3}\right)$.

To find the intersection of $y = x$ and $3x + 4y = 12$, substitute and solve:

$$3x + 4x = 12 \rightarrow 7x = 12 \rightarrow x = \frac{12}{7} \rightarrow y = \frac{12}{7}$$

The point of intersection is $\left(\frac{12}{7}, \frac{12}{7}\right)$.

The corner points are (0, 1), (0, 3), $\left(\frac{2}{3}, \frac{2}{3}\right)$, $\left(\frac{12}{7}, \frac{12}{7}\right)$.

Evaluate the objective function:

Vertex	Value of $z = 5x + 4y$
(0, 1)	z = 5(0) + 4(1) = 4
(0, 3)	z = 5(0) + 4(3) = 12
$\left(\frac{2}{3}, \frac{2}{3}\right)$	$z = 5\left(\frac{2}{3}\right) + 4\left(\frac{2}{3}\right) = \frac{18}{3} = 6$
$\left(\frac{12}{7}, \frac{12}{7}\right)$	$z = 5\left(\frac{12}{7}\right) + 4\left(\frac{12}{7}\right) = \frac{108}{7} \approx 15.43$

The maximum value is $\frac{108}{7}$ at $\left(\frac{12}{7}, \frac{12}{7}\right)$.

92. Maximize $z = 4x + 5y$ Subject to $x \geq 0$, $y \geq 0$, $2x + 3y \geq 6$, $x \geq y$, $2x + y \leq 12$

Graph the constraints.

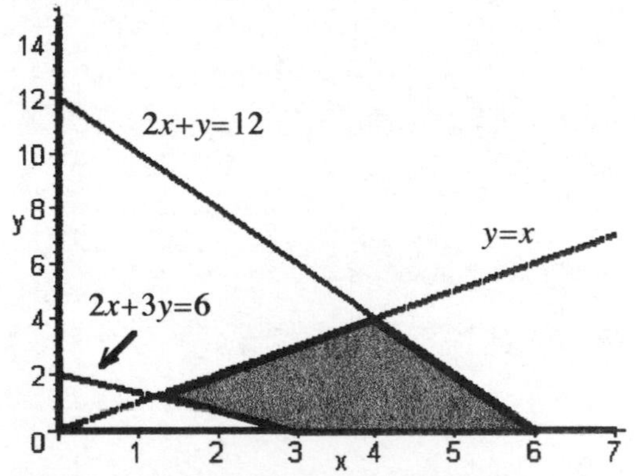

The corner points are (1.2, 1.2), (3,0),4, 4), (6, 0).

Evaluate the objective function:

Vertex	Value of $z = 4x + 5y$
(1.2,1.2)	z = 4(1.2) + 5(1.2) = 10.8
(3, 0)	z = 4(4) + 5(0) = 16
(4, 4)	z = 4(4) + 5(4) = 36
(6, 0)	z = 4(6) + 5(0) = 24

The maximum value is 36 at (4, 4).

93. Multiply each side of the first equation by –2 and eliminate x:

$$\begin{cases} 2x + 5y = 5 \xrightarrow{-2} \\ 4x + 10y = A \longrightarrow \end{cases} \quad \begin{array}{r} -4x - 10y = -10 \\ 4x + 10y = \quad A \\ \hline 0 = A - 10 \end{array}$$

If there are to be infinitely many solutions, the sum in elimination should be 0 = 0. Therefore, $A - 10 = 0$ or $A = 10$.

94. Multiply each side of the first equation by –2 and eliminate x:

$$\begin{cases} 2x + 5y = 5 \xrightarrow{-2} \\ 4x + 10y = A \longrightarrow \end{cases} \quad \begin{array}{r} -4x - 10y = -10 \\ 4x + 10y = \quad A \\ \hline 0 = A - 10 \end{array}$$

If the system is to be inconsistent, the sum in elimination should be 0 = any number except 0. Therefore, $A - 10 \neq 0$ or $A \neq 10$.

95. when $x = 1,\ y = (1)^2 + b(1) + c = 2 \rightarrow 1 + b + c = 2 \rightarrow b + c = 1$

when $x = -1,\ y = (-1)^2 + b(-1) + c = 3 \rightarrow 1 - b + c = 3 \rightarrow -b + c = 2$

so we have the system $\begin{cases} b + c = 1 \\ -b + c = 2 \end{cases}$

subtracting the first equation from the second equation yields

$$\begin{array}{r} b + c = 1 \\ -(-b + c = 2) \\ \hline 2b = -1 \end{array} \quad \therefore b = -0.5$$

Back-substituting we get: $-0.5 + c = 1 \rightarrow c = 1.5$

Therefore, $y = x^2 - 0.5x + 1.5$, which satisfies the given conditions.

96. when $x = 1,\ y = (1)^2 + b(1) + c = 3 \rightarrow 1 + b + c = 3 \rightarrow b + c = 2$

when $x = 3,\ y = (3)^2 + b(3) + c = 3 \rightarrow 9 + 3b + c = 5 \rightarrow 3b + c = -4$

so we have the system $\begin{cases} b + c = 2 \\ 3b + c = -4 \end{cases}$

subtracting these equations yields

$$\begin{array}{r} b + c = 2 \\ -(3b + c = -4) \\ \hline -2b = 6 \end{array}$$

$$\therefore b = \frac{6}{-2} = -3$$

back substituting into the equation $b + c = 2$, we get $-3 + c = 2 \rightarrow c = 5$

Therefore, $y = x^2 - 3x + 5$, which satisfies the given conditions.

97. $y = ax^2 + bx + c$

At (0, 1) the equation becomes:

$$1 = a(0)^2 + b(0) + c$$
$$c = 1$$

At (1, 0) the equation becomes:

$$0 = a(1)^2 + b(1) + c$$
$$0 = a + b + c$$
$$a + b + c = 0$$

At (–2, 1) the equation becomes:

$$1 = a(-2)^2 + b(-2) + c = 4a - 2b + c \rightarrow 4a - 2b + c = 1$$

The system of equations is:

$$\begin{cases} a + b + c = 0 \\ 4a - 2b + c = 1 \\ c = 1 \end{cases}$$

Substitute $c = 1$ into the first and second equations and simplify:

$$\begin{cases} a + b + 1 = 0 \rightarrow a + b = -1 \rightarrow a = -b - 1 \\ 4a - 2b + 1 = 1 \rightarrow 4a - 2b = 0 \end{cases}$$

Solve the first equation for a, substitute into the second equation and solve:

$$4(-b - 1) - 2b = 0$$
$$-4b - 4 - 2b = 0$$
$$-6b = 4 \rightarrow b = -\frac{2}{3} \rightarrow a = \frac{2}{3} - 1 = -\frac{1}{3}$$

The quadratic function is $y = -\frac{1}{3}x^2 - \frac{2}{3}x + 1$.

98. $x^2 + y^2 + Dx + Ey + F = 0$

At (0, 1) the equation becomes:

$$0^2 + 1^2 + D(0) + E(1) + F = 0$$
$$E + F = -1$$

At (1, 0) the equation becomes:

$$1^2 + 0^2 + D(1) + E(0) + F = 0$$
$$D + F = -1$$

At (–2, 1) the equation becomes:

$$(-2)^2 + 1^2 + D(-2) + E(1) + F = 0$$
$$-2D + E + F = -5$$

The system of equations is:

$$\begin{cases} E + F = -1 \\ D + F = -1 \\ -2D + E + F = -5 \end{cases}$$

Substitute $E + F = -1$ into the third equation and solve for D:

$$-2D + (-1) = -5 \rightarrow -2D = -4 \rightarrow D = 2$$

Substitute and solve:

$$2 + F = -1 \rightarrow F = -3$$
$$E + (-3) = -1 \rightarrow E = 2$$

The equation of the circle is $x^2 + y^2 + 2x + 2y - 3 = 0$.

99. Let x = the number of pounds of coffee that costs \$3.00 per pound.
Let y = the number of pounds of coffee that costs \$6.00 per pound.
Then $x + y = 100$ represents the total amount of coffee in the blend.
The value of the blend will be represented by the equation: $3x + 6y = 3.90(100)$.
Solve the system of equations:

$$\begin{cases} x + y = 100 & \rightarrow \quad y = 100 - x \\ 3x + 6y = 390 \end{cases}$$

Solve by substitution:

$$3x + 6(100 - x) = 390 \rightarrow 3x + 600 - 6x = 390$$
$$-3x = -210 \rightarrow x = 70$$
$$y = 100 - 70 = 30$$

The blend is made up of 70 pounds of the \$3 per pound coffee and 30 pounds of the \$6 per pound coffee.

100. Let x = the number of acres of corn.
Let y = the number of acres of soybeans.
Then $x + y = 1000$ represents the total acreage on the farm.
The total cost will be represented by the equation: $65x + 45y = 54325$.
Solve the system of equations:

$$\begin{cases} x + y = 1000 & \rightarrow \quad y = 1000 - x \\ 65x + 45y = 54325 \end{cases}$$

Solve by substitution:

$$65x + 45(1000 - x) = 54325 \rightarrow 65x + 45000 - 45x = 54325$$
$$20x = 9325 \rightarrow x = 466.25 \rightarrow y = 1000 - 466.25 \rightarrow y = 533.75$$

Corn should be planted on 466.25 acres and soybeans should be planted on 533.75 acres.

101. Let x = the number of small boxes.
Let y = the number of medium boxes.
Let z = the number of large boxes.
Oatmeal raisin equation: $x + 2y + 2z = 15$
Chocolate chip equation: $x + y + 2z = 10$
Shortbread equation: $y + 3z = 11$
Multiply each side of the second equation by -1 and add to the first equation to eliminate x:

$$\begin{cases} x + 2y + 2z = 15 & \longrightarrow & x + 2y + 2z = 15 \\ x + y + 2z = 10 & \xrightarrow{-1} & \underline{-x - y - 2z = -10} \\ y + 3z = 11 & & y \quad = 5 \end{cases}$$

Substituting and solving for the other variables:

$$5 + 3z = 11 \qquad x + 5 + 2(2) = 10$$
$$3z = 6 \qquad x + 9 = 10$$
$$z = 2 \qquad x = 1$$

1 small box, 5 medium boxes, and 2 large boxes of cookies should be purchased.

102. (a) Let x = the number of lower priced packages.
Let y = the number of quality packages.
Peanut inequality: $8x + 6y \le 120(16) \rightarrow 8x + 6y \le 1920$
Cashew inequality: $4x + 6y \le 72(16) \rightarrow 4x + 6y \le 1152$
The system of inequalities is:

$$\begin{cases} x \ge 0 \\ y \ge 0 \\ 8x + 6y \le 1920 \\ 4x + 6y \le 1152 \end{cases}$$

(b) Graphing:

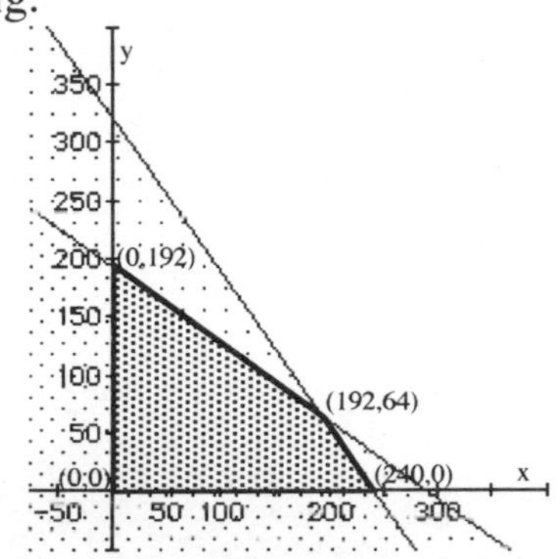

To find the intersection of $8x + 6y = 1920$ and $4x + 6y = 1152$, solve the system:

$$\begin{cases} 8x + 6y = 1920 \\ 4x + 6y = 1152 \end{cases} \rightarrow 6y = 1152 - 4x$$

Substitute and solve:

$$8x + 1152 - 4x = 1920$$

$$4x = 768 \rightarrow x = 192 \rightarrow 6y = 1152 - 4(192) = 384 \rightarrow y = 64$$

The corner points are (0, 0), (0, 192), (240, 0), and (192, 64).

103. Let x = the length of the lot.
Let y = the width of the lot.
Perimeter equation: $2x + 2y = 68$
Diagonal equation: $x^2 + y^2 = 26^2$
Solve the system of equations:

$$\begin{cases} 2x + 2y = 68 \rightarrow y = 34 - x \\ x^2 + y^2 = 676 \end{cases}$$

Solve by substitution:

$$x^2 + (34 - x)^2 = 676 \rightarrow x^2 + 1156 - 68x + x^2 = 676$$

$$2x^2 - 68x + 480 = 0 \rightarrow x^2 - 34x + 240 = 0$$

$$(x - 24)(x - 10) = 0 \rightarrow x = 24 \text{ or } x = 10$$

$$y = 10 \text{ or } y = 24$$

The dimensions of the lot are 24 feet by 10 feet.

104. Let x = the height of the window.
Let y = the width of the window.
Area equation: $xy = 4$
Diagonal equation: $x^2 + y^2 = \left(2\sqrt{2}\right)^2$
Solve the system of equations:
$$\begin{cases} xy = 4 & \rightarrow \quad y = \dfrac{4}{x} \\ x^2 + y^2 = 8 \end{cases}$$
Solve by substitution:
$$x^2 + \left(\frac{4}{x}\right)^2 = 8 \rightarrow x^2 + \frac{16}{x^2} = 8 \rightarrow x^4 + 16 = 8x^2$$
$$x^4 - 8x^2 + 16 = 0 \rightarrow \left(x^2 - 4\right)^2 = 0 \rightarrow x^2 = 4$$
$$x = 2 \text{ or } x = -2$$
$$y = 2 \qquad y = -2$$
The dimensions of the window are 2 feet by 2 feet. (Dimensions must be positive.)

105. Let x = the length of one leg.
Let y = the length of the other leg.
Perimeter equation: $x + y + 6 = 14$
Pythagorean equation: $x^2 + y^2 = 6^2$
Solve the system of equations:
$$\begin{cases} x + y = 8 & \rightarrow \quad y = 8 - x \\ x^2 + y^2 = 36 \end{cases}$$
Solve by substitution:
$$x^2 + (8 - x)^2 = 36 \rightarrow x^2 + 64 - 16x + x^2 = 36$$
$$2x^2 - 16x + 28 = 0 \rightarrow x^2 - 8x + 14 = 0$$
$$x = \frac{8 \pm \sqrt{64 - 56}}{2} = \frac{8 \pm \sqrt{8}}{2} = \frac{8 \pm 2\sqrt{2}}{2} = 4 \pm \sqrt{2}$$
$$\text{If } x = 4 - \sqrt{2}, \text{ then } y = 8 - 4 + \sqrt{2} = 4 + \sqrt{2}$$
$$\text{If } x = 4 + \sqrt{2}, \text{ then } y = 8 - 4 - \sqrt{2} = 4 - \sqrt{2}$$
The legs are $4 + \sqrt{2}$ and $4 - \sqrt{2}$.

106. Let x = the length of the two equal sides in the isosceles triangle.
Let y = the length of the base.
The perimeter of the triangle: $x + x + y = 18$
Since the altitude to the base y is 6, the Pythagorean theorem will produce another equation: $\left(\frac{y}{2}\right)^2 + 6^2 = x^2$

Solve the system of equations:

$$\begin{cases} 2x + y = 18 \quad \rightarrow \quad y = 18 - 2x \\ \dfrac{y^2}{4} + 36 = x^2 \end{cases}$$

Solve the first equation for y, substitute into the second equation and solve:

$$\frac{(18-2x)^2}{4} + 36 = x^2 \rightarrow \frac{324 - 72x + 4x^2}{4} + 36 = x^2$$

$$81 - 18x + x^2 + 36 = x^2 \rightarrow -18x = -117 \rightarrow x = 6.5$$

$$y = 18 - 2(6.5) = 5$$

The base of the triangle is 5 inches.

107. Let x = the length of the side of the smaller square.
Then $2x$ = the length of the side of the larger square.
The needed fencing is $4x + 8x = 12x$.
Solve the area equation:

$$x^2 + (2x)^2 = 5000 \rightarrow 5x^2 = 5000 \rightarrow x^2 = 1000 \rightarrow x = 10\sqrt{10}$$

$$12x = 120\sqrt{10} \approx 379.5 \text{ feet of fence are needed.}$$

108. Let x = the amount Katy receives.
Let y = the amount Mike receives.
Let z = the amount Danny receives.
Let w = the amount that Colleen receives.
Conditions:

$$x + y + z + w = 45$$

$$y = 2x$$

$$w = x$$

$$z = \frac{1}{2}x$$

Solve by substitution:

$$x + y + z + w = 45$$

$$x + 2x + x + \frac{1}{2}x = 45 \rightarrow \frac{9}{2}x = 45 \rightarrow x = 10$$

Katy receives \$10, Mike receives \$20, Danny receives \$5, and Colleen receives \$10.

109. Let x = the speed of the boat in still water.
Let y = the speed of the river current.
Let d = the distance from Chiritza to the Flotel Orellana (100 kilometers)

	Rate	Time	Distance
trip downstream	$x + y$	$\frac{5}{2}$	100
trip downstream	$x - y$	3	100

The system of equations is:

$$\begin{cases} (x+y)\left(\frac{5}{2}\right)=100 & \rightarrow \quad 5x+5y=200 \\ (x-y)(3)=d & \rightarrow \quad 3x-3y=100 \end{cases}$$

$$5x+5y=200 \xrightarrow{3} \quad 15x+15y=600$$
$$3x-3y=100 \xrightarrow{5} \quad \underline{+\ 15x-15y=500}$$
$$30x=1100$$

$$\therefore x=\frac{1100}{30}=\frac{110}{3}$$

$$\rightarrow 3\left(\frac{110}{3}\right)-3y=100 \rightarrow 110-3y=100 \rightarrow 10=3y \rightarrow y=\frac{10}{3}$$

The speed of the boat $=\frac{110}{3}\approx 36.67$ km/hr ; the speed of the current $=\frac{10}{3}\approx 3.33$ km/hr.

110. Let x = the speed of the plane in still air. (475 miles per hour)
Let y = the speed of the jet stream.
Let d = the distance from Chicago to Ft. Lauderdale.
The jet stream flows from Chicago to Ft. Lauderdale because the time is shorter in that direction.

	Rate	Time	Distance
Chicago to Ft. Lauderdale	$x+y$	$\frac{5}{2}$	d
Ft. Lauderdale to Chicago	$x-y$	$\frac{17}{6}$	d

The system of equations is:

$$\begin{cases} (x+y)\left(\frac{5}{2}\right)=d & \rightarrow \quad 5x+5y=2d \\ (x-y)\left(\frac{17}{6}\right)=d & \rightarrow \quad 17x-17y=6d \end{cases}$$

Substitute 475 for x and solve:

$$\begin{cases} 5(475)+5y=2d & \rightarrow \quad 2375+\ 5y=2d \\ 17(475)-17y=6d & \rightarrow \quad 8075-17y=6d \end{cases}$$

$$8075-17y=3(2375+5y)$$

$$8075-17y=7125+15y \rightarrow 950=32y \rightarrow y\approx 29.69$$

The speed of the jet stream is approximately 29.69 miles per hour.

111. Let x = the number of hours for Bruce to do the job alone.
Let y = the number of hours for Bryce to do the job alone.
Let z = the number of hours for Marty to do the job alone.
Then $\frac{1}{x}$ represents the fraction of the job that Bruce does in one hour.
$\frac{1}{y}$ represents the fraction of the job that Bryce does in one hour.
$\frac{1}{z}$ represents the fraction of the job that Marty does in one hour.

The equation representing Bruce and Bryce working together is:

$$\frac{1}{x}+\frac{1}{y}=\frac{1}{\left(\frac{4}{3}\right)}=\frac{3}{4}=0.75$$

The equation representing Bryce and Marty working together is:

$$\frac{1}{y}+\frac{1}{z}=\frac{1}{\left(\frac{8}{5}\right)}=\frac{5}{8}=0.675$$

The equation representing Bruce and Marty working together is:

$$\frac{1}{x}+\frac{1}{z}=\frac{1}{\left(\frac{8}{3}\right)}=0.375$$

Solve the system of equations:

$$\begin{cases} x^{-1}+y^{-1}=0.75 \\ y^{-1}+z^{-1}=0.675 \\ x^{-1}+z^{-1}=0.375 \end{cases}$$

Let $u=x^{-1},\ v=y^{-1},\ w=z^{-1}$

$$\begin{cases} u+v=0.75 & \rightarrow & u=0.75-v \\ v+w=0.675 & \rightarrow & w=0.675-v \\ u+w=0.375 \end{cases}$$

Substitute into the third equation and solve:

$$0.75-v+0.675-v=0.375 \rightarrow -2v=-1 \rightarrow v=0.5$$

$$u=0.75-0.5=0.25$$

$$w=0.675-0.5=0.125$$

Solve for x, y, and z: $x=4,\ y=2,\ z=8$ (reciprocals)

Bruce can do the job in 4 hours, Bryce in 2 hours, and Marty in 8 hours.

112. Let x = the number of dancing girls produced.
Let y = the number of mermaids produced.
The total profit is: $P=25x+30y$. Profit is to be maximized; thus, this is the objective function.
The constraints are:

$x\ge 0,\ y\ge 0$	A non-negative number of figurines must be produced.
$3x+3y\le 90$	90 hours are available for molding.
$6x+4y\le 120$	120 hours are available for painting.
$2x+3y\le 60$	60 hours are available for glazing.

Graph the constraints.

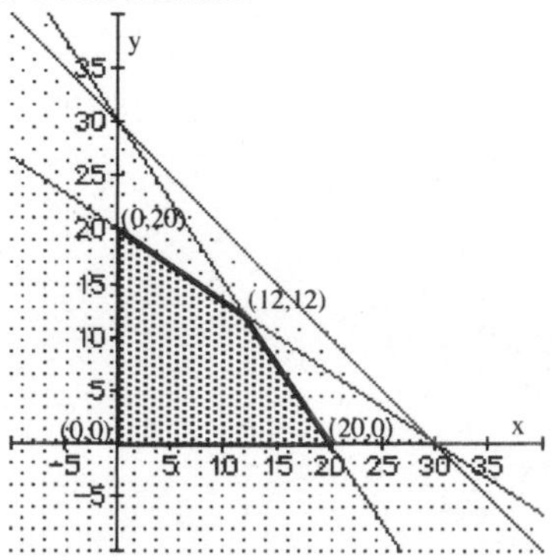

To find the intersection of $6x + 4y = 120$ and $2x + 3y = 60$, solve the system:

$$\begin{cases} 6x + 4y = 120 \\ 2x + 3y = 60 \quad \rightarrow \quad 2x = 60 - 3y \end{cases}$$

Substitute and solve:

$$3(2x) + 4y = 120 \rightarrow 3(60 - 3y) + 4y = 120$$

$$180 - 9y + 4y = 120 \rightarrow -5y = -60 \rightarrow y = 12$$

$$2x = 60 - 3(12) = 24 \rightarrow x = 12$$

The point of intersection is (12, 12).

The corner points are (0, 0), (0, 20), (20, 0), (12, 12).

Evaluate the objective function:

Vertex	Value of $P = 25x + 30y$
(0, 0)	$P = 25(0) + 30(0) = 0$
(0, 20)	$P = 25(0) + 30(20) = 600$
(20, 0)	$P = 25(20) + 30(0) = 500$
(12, 12)	$P = 25(12) + 30(12) = 660$

The maximum profit is $660, when 12 dancing girl and 12 mermaid figurines are produced each day.

To determine the excess, evaluate each constraint at x = 12 and y = 12:

Molding: $3x + 3y = 3(12) + 3(12) = 36 + 36 = 72$

Painting: $6x + 4y = 6(12) + 4(12) = 72 + 48 = 120$

Glazing: $2x + 3y = 2(12) + 3(12) = 24 + 36 = 60$

Painting and glazing are at their capacity. Molding has 18 more hours available, since only 72 of the 90 hours are used.

113. Let x = the number of gasoline engines produced each week.

Let y = the number of diesel engines produced each week.

The total cost is: $C = 450x + 550y$. Cost is to be minimized; thus, this is the objective function.

The constraints are:

$20 \le x \le 60$ number of gasoline engines needed and capacity each week.

$15 \le y \le 40$ number of diesel engines needed and capacity each week.

$x + y \ge 50$ number of engines produced to prevent layoffs.

Graph the constraints.

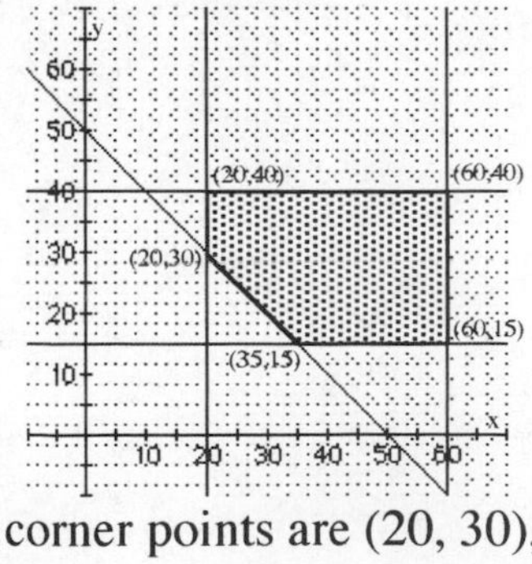

The corner points are (20, 30), (20, 40), (35, 15), (60, 15), (60, 40).

Evaluate the objective function:

Vertex	Value of $C = 450x + 550y$
(20, 30)	$C = 450(20) + 550(30) = 25{,}500$
(20, 40)	$C = 450(20) + 550(40) = 31{,}000$
(35, 15)	$C = 450(35) + 550(15) = 24{,}000$
(60, 15)	$C = 450(60) + 550(15) = 35{,}250$
(60, 40)	$C = 450(60) + 550(40) = 49{,}000$

The minimum cost is $24,000, when 35 gasoline engines and 15 diesel engines are produced.
The excess capacity is 15 gasoline engines, since only 20 gasoline engines had to be delivered.

Chapter 13

Sequences; Induction; The Binomial Theorem

13.1 Sequences

1. $a_1 = 1,\ a_2 = 2,\ a_3 = 3,\ a_4 = 4,\ a_5 = 5$

2. $a_1 = 2,\ a_2 = 5,\ a_3 = 10,\ a_4 = 17,\ a_5 = 26$

3. $a_1 = \frac{1}{1+2} = \frac{1}{3},\ a_2 = \frac{2}{2+2} = \frac{2}{4} = \frac{1}{2},\ a_3 = \frac{3}{3+2} = \frac{3}{5},\ a_4 = \frac{4}{4+2} = \frac{4}{6} = \frac{2}{3},$
$a_5 = \frac{5}{5+2} = \frac{5}{7}$

4. $a_1 = \frac{2\cdot 1+1}{2\cdot 1} = \frac{3}{2},\ a_2 = \frac{2\cdot 2+1}{2\cdot 2} = \frac{5}{4},\ a_3 = \frac{2\cdot 3+1}{2\cdot 3} = \frac{7}{6},\ a_4 = \frac{2\cdot 4+1}{2\cdot 4} = \frac{9}{8},$
$a_5 = \frac{2\cdot 5+1}{2\cdot 5} = \frac{11}{10}$

5. $a_1 = (-1)^{1+1}(1^2) = 1,\ a_2 = (-1)^{2+1}(2^2) = -4,\ a_3 = (-1)^{3+1}(3^2) = 9,$
$a_4 = (-1)^{4+1}(4^2) = -16,\ a_5 = (-1)^{5+1}(5^2) = 25$

6. $a_1 = (-1)^{1-1}\left(\frac{1}{2\cdot 1-1}\right) = 1,\ a_2 = (-1)^{2-1}\left(\frac{2}{2\cdot 2-1}\right) = -\frac{2}{3},\ a_3 = (-1)^{3-1}\left(\frac{3}{2\cdot 3-1}\right) = \frac{3}{5},$
$a_4 = (-1)^{4-1}\left(\frac{4}{2\cdot 4-1}\right) = -\frac{4}{7},\ a_5 = (-1)^{5-1}\left(\frac{5}{2\cdot 5-1}\right) = \frac{5}{9}$

7. $a_1 = \frac{2^1}{3^1+1} = \frac{2}{4} = \frac{1}{2},\ a_2 = \frac{2^2}{3^2+1} = \frac{4}{10} = \frac{2}{5},\ a_3 = \frac{2^3}{3^3+1} = \frac{8}{28} = \frac{2}{7},$
$a_4 = \frac{2^4}{3^4+1} = \frac{16}{82} = \frac{8}{41},\ a_5 = \frac{2^5}{3^5+1} = \frac{32}{244} = \frac{8}{61}$

8. $a_1 = \left(\frac{4}{3}\right)^1 = \frac{4}{3},\ a_2 = \left(\frac{4}{3}\right)^2 = \frac{16}{9},\ a_3 = \left(\frac{4}{3}\right)^3 = \frac{64}{27},\ a_4 = \left(\frac{4}{3}\right)^4 = \frac{256}{81},$
$a_5 = \left(\frac{4}{3}\right)^5 = \frac{1024}{243}$

9. $a_1 = \dfrac{(-1)^1}{(1+1)(1+2)} = \dfrac{-1}{2\cdot 3} = \dfrac{-1}{6},\ a_2 = \dfrac{(-1)^2}{(2+1)(2+2)} = \dfrac{1}{3\cdot 4} = \dfrac{1}{12},$

$$a_3 = \frac{(-1)^3}{(3+1)(3+2)} = \frac{-1}{4\cdot 5} = \frac{-1}{20},\ a_4 = \frac{(-1)^4}{(4+1)(4+2)} = \frac{1}{5\cdot 6} = \frac{1}{30},$$

$$a_5 = \frac{(-1)^5}{(5+1)(5+2)} = \frac{-1}{6\cdot 7} = -\frac{1}{42}$$

10. $a_1 = \dfrac{3^1}{1} = \dfrac{3}{1} = 3,\ a_2 = \dfrac{3^2}{2} = \dfrac{9}{2},\ a_3 = \dfrac{3^3}{3} = \dfrac{27}{3} = 9,\ a_4 = \dfrac{3^4}{4} = \dfrac{81}{4},\ a_5 = \dfrac{3^5}{5} = \dfrac{243}{5}$

11. $a_1 = \dfrac{1}{e^1} = \dfrac{1}{e},\ a_2 = \dfrac{2}{e^2},\ a_3 = \dfrac{3}{e^3},\ a_4 = \dfrac{4}{e^4},\ a_5 = \dfrac{5}{e^5}$

12. $a_1 = \dfrac{1^2}{2^1} = \dfrac{1}{2},\ a_2 = \dfrac{2^2}{2^2} = 1,\ a_3 = \dfrac{3^2}{2^3} = \dfrac{9}{8},\ a_4 = \dfrac{4^2}{2^4} = \dfrac{16}{16} = 1,\ a_5 = \dfrac{5^2}{2^5} = \dfrac{25}{32}$

13. $\dfrac{n}{n+1}$

14. $\dfrac{1}{n(n+1)}$

15. $\dfrac{1}{2^{n-1}}$

16. $\left(\dfrac{2}{3}\right)^n$

17. $(-1)^{n+1}$

18. $\left(\dfrac{1}{n}\right)^{(-1)^n}$

19. $(-1)^{n+1}n$

20. $(-1)^{n+1}2n$

21. $a_1 = 2,\ a_2 = 3+2 = 5,\ a_3 = 3+5 = 8,\ a_4 = 3+8 = 11,\ a_5 = 3+11 = 14$

22. $a_1 = 3,\ a_2 = 4-3 = 1,\ a_3 = 4-1 = 3,\ a_4 = 4-3 = 1,\ a_5 = 4-1 = 3$

23. $a_1 = -2,\ a_2 = 2+(-2) = 0,\ a_3 = 3+0 = 3,\ a_4 = 4+3 = 7,\ a_5 = 5+7 = 12$

24. $a_1 = 1,\ a_2 = 2-1 = 1,\ a_3 = 3-1 = 2,\ a_4 = 4-2 = 2,\ a_5 = 5-2 = 3$

25. $a_1 = 5,\ a_2 = 2\cdot 5 = 10,\ a_3 = 2\cdot 10 = 20,\ a_4 = 2\cdot 20 = 40,\ a_5 = 2\cdot 40 = 80$

26. $a_1 = 2,\ a_2 = -2,\ a_3 = -(-2) = 2,\ a_4 = -2,\ a_5 = -(-2) = 2$

27. $a_1 = 3,\ a_2 = \dfrac{3}{2},\ a_3 = \dfrac{\left(\frac{3}{2}\right)}{3} = \dfrac{1}{2},\ a_4 = \dfrac{\left(\frac{1}{2}\right)}{4} = \dfrac{1}{8},\ a_5 = \dfrac{\left(\frac{1}{8}\right)}{5} = \dfrac{1}{40}$

28. $a_1 = -2,\ a_2 = 2+3(-2) = -4,\ a_3 = 3+3(-4) = -9,\ a_4 = 4+3(-9) = -23,$

$$a_5 = 5+3(-23) = -64$$

29. $a_1 = 1,\ a_2 = 2,\ a_3 = 2\cdot 1 = 2,\ a_4 = 2\cdot 2 = 4,\ a_5 = 4\cdot 2 = 8$

30. $a_1 = -1,\ a_2 = 1,\ a_3 = -1 + 3 \cdot 1 = 2,\ a_4 = 1 + 4 \cdot 2 = 9,\ a_5 = 2 + 5 \cdot 9 = 47$

31. $a_1 = A,\ a_2 = A + d,\ a_3 = (A + d) + d = A + 2d,\ a_4 = (A + 2d) + d = A + 3d,$
$a_5 = (A + 3d) + d = A + 4d$

32. $a_1 = A,\ a_2 = rA,\ a_3 = r(rA) = r^2 A,\ a_4 = r\left(r^2 A\right) = r^3 A,\ a_5 = r\left(r^3 A\right) = r^4 A$

33. $a_1 = \sqrt{2},\ a_2 = \sqrt{2 + \sqrt{2}},\ a_3 = \sqrt{2 + \sqrt{2 + \sqrt{2}}},\ a_4 = \sqrt{2 + \sqrt{2 + \sqrt{2 + \sqrt{2}}}},$
$a_5 = \sqrt{2 + \sqrt{2 + \sqrt{2 + \sqrt{2 + \sqrt{2}}}}}$

34. $a_1 = \sqrt{2},\ a_2 = \sqrt{\dfrac{2^{1/2}}{2}} = \left(2^{-1/2}\right)^{1/2} = 2^{-1/4} = \dfrac{1}{2^{1/4}},\ a_3 = \sqrt{\dfrac{2^{-1/4}}{2}} = \left(2^{-5/4}\right)^{1/2} = 2^{-5/8} = \dfrac{1}{2^{5/8}},$

$a_4 = \sqrt{\dfrac{2^{-5/8}}{2}} = \left(2^{-13/8}\right)^{1/2} = 2^{-13/16} = \dfrac{1}{2^{13/16}},\ a_5 = \sqrt{\dfrac{2^{-13/16}}{2}} = \left(2^{-29/16}\right)^{1/2} = 2^{-29/32} = \dfrac{1}{2^{29/32}}$

35. $\sum_{k=1}^{10} 5 = \underbrace{5 + 5 + 5 + \ldots + 5}_{10 \text{ times}} = 50$

36. $\sum_{k=1}^{20} 8 = \underbrace{8 + 8 + 8 + \ldots + 8}_{20 \text{ times}} = 20(8) = 160$

37. $\sum_{k=1}^{6} k = 1 + 2 + 3 + 4 + 5 + 6 = 21$

38. $\sum_{k=1}^{4} (-k) = (-1) + (-2) + (-3) + (-4) = -10$

39. $\sum_{k=1}^{5} (5k + 3) = 8 + 13 + 18 + 23 + 28 = 90$

40. $\sum_{k=1}^{6} (3k - 7) = -4 + (-1) + 2 + 5 + 8 + 11 = 21$

41. $\sum_{k=1}^{3} (k^2 + 4) = 5 + 8 + 13 = 26$

42. $\sum_{k=0}^{4} (k^2 - 4) = -4 + (-3) + 0 + 5 + 12 = 10$

43. $\sum_{k=1}^{6} (-1)^k 2^k = (-1)^1 \cdot 2^1 + (-1)^2 \cdot 2^2 + (-1)^3 \cdot 2^3 + (-1)^4 \cdot 2^4 + (-1)^5 \cdot 2^5 + (-1)^6 \cdot 2^6$
$= -2 + 4 - 8 + 16 - 32 + 64 = 42$

44. $\sum_{k=1}^{4} (-1)^k 3^k = (-1)^1 \cdot 3^1 + (-1)^2 \cdot 3^2 + (-1)^3 \cdot 3^3 + (-1)^4 \cdot 3^4 = -3 + 9 - 27 + 81 = 60$

45. $\sum_{k=1}^{4} (k^3 - 1) = 0 + 7 + 26 + 63 = 96$

46. $\sum_{k=0}^{3} (k^3 + 2) = 2 + 3 + 10 + 29 = 44$

47. $\sum_{k=1}^{n}(k+2) = 3+4+5+6+\cdots+(n+2)$

48. $\sum_{k=1}^{n}(2k+1) = 3+5+7+9+\cdots+(2n+1)$

49. $\sum_{k=1}^{n}\frac{k^2}{2} = \frac{1}{2}+2+\frac{9}{2}+8+\frac{25}{2}+\cdots+\frac{n^2}{2}$

50. $\sum_{k=1}^{n}(k+1)^2 = 2^2+3^2+4^2+\cdots+(n+1)^2 = 4+9+16+\cdots+(n+1)^2$

51. $\sum_{k=0}^{n}\frac{1}{3^k} = 1+\frac{1}{3}+\frac{1}{9}+\frac{1}{27}+\cdots+\frac{1}{3^n}$

52. $\sum_{k=0}^{n}\left(\frac{3}{2}\right)^k = \left(\frac{3}{2}\right)^0+\left(\frac{3}{2}\right)^1+\left(\frac{3}{2}\right)^2+\cdots+\left(\frac{3}{2}\right)^n = 1+\frac{3}{2}+\frac{9}{4}+\cdots+\left(\frac{3}{2}\right)^n$

53. $\sum_{k=0}^{n-1}\frac{1}{3^{k+1}} = \frac{1}{3}+\frac{1}{9}+\frac{1}{27}+\cdots+\frac{1}{3^n}$

54. $\sum_{k=0}^{n-1}(2k+1) = 1+3+5+7+\cdots+(2(n-1)+1) = 1+3+5+7+\cdots+(2n-1)$

55. $\sum_{k=2}^{n}(-1)^k\ln k = \ln 2-\ln 3+\ln 4-\ln 5+\cdots+(-1)^n\ln n$

56. $\sum_{k=3}^{n}(-1)^{k+1}2^k = (-1)^4 2^3+(-1)^5 2^4+(-1)^6 2^5+\cdots+(-1)^{n+1}2^n$

$= 2^3-2^4+2^5-2^6+\cdots+(-1)^{n+1}2^n$

57. $1+2+3+\cdots+20 = \sum_{k=1}^{20}k$

58. $1^3+2^3+3^3+\cdots+8^3 = \sum_{k=1}^{8}k^3$

59. $\frac{1}{2}+\frac{2}{3}+\frac{3}{4}+\cdots+\frac{13}{13+1} = \sum_{k=1}^{13}\frac{k}{k+1}$

60. $1+3+5+7+\cdots+[2(12)-1] = \sum_{k=1}^{12}(2k-1)$

61. $1-\frac{1}{3}+\frac{1}{9}-\frac{1}{27}+\cdots+(-1)^6\left(\frac{1}{3^6}\right) = \sum_{k=0}^{6}(-1)^k\left(\frac{1}{3^k}\right)$

62. $\frac{2}{3}-\frac{4}{9}+\frac{8}{27}+\cdots+(-1)^{11+1}\left(\frac{2}{3}\right)^{11}=\sum_{k=1}^{11}(-1)^{k+1}\left(\frac{2}{3}\right)^{k}$

63. $3+\frac{3^2}{2}+\frac{3^3}{3}+\cdots+\frac{3^n}{n}=\sum_{k=1}^{n}\frac{3^k}{k}$

64. $\frac{1}{e}+\frac{2}{e^2}+\frac{3}{e^3}+\cdots+\frac{n}{e^n}=\sum_{k=1}^{n}\frac{k}{e^k}$

65. $a+(a+d)+(a+2d)+\cdots+(a+nd)=\sum_{k=0}^{n}(a+kd)$

66. $a+ar+ar^2+\cdots+ar^{n-1}=\sum_{k=1}^{n}ar^{k-1}$

67. $B_1=1.01(3000)-100=\$2930$

68. $B_1=1.005(18500)-534.47=\$18,058.03$

69. $p_1=1.03(2000)+20=2080;\qquad p_2=1.03(2080)+20=2162.4$

70. $p_1=0.9(250)+15=240;\qquad p_2=0.9(240)+15=231$

71. $a_1=1,\ a_2=1,\ a_3=2,\ a_4=3,\ a_5=5,\ a_6=8,\ a_7=13,\ a_8=21,\ a_n=a_{n-1}+a_{n-2}$
$a_8=a_7+a_6=13+8=21$
After 7 months there are 21 mature pairs of rabbits.

72. (a) $u_1=\frac{(1+\sqrt{5})^1-(1-\sqrt{5})^1}{2^1\sqrt{5}}=\frac{1+\sqrt{5}-1+\sqrt{5}}{2\sqrt{5}}=\frac{2\sqrt{5}}{2\sqrt{5}}=1$

$u_2=\frac{(1+\sqrt{5})^2-(1-\sqrt{5})^2}{2^2\sqrt{5}}=\frac{1+2\sqrt{5}+5-1+2\sqrt{5}-5}{4\sqrt{5}}=\frac{4\sqrt{5}}{4\sqrt{5}}=1$

(b) $$u_{n+1}+u_n=\frac{(1+\sqrt{5})^{n+1}-(1-\sqrt{5})^{n+1}}{2^{n+1}\sqrt{5}}+\frac{(1+\sqrt{5})^n-(1-\sqrt{5})^n}{2^n\sqrt{5}}$$
$$=\frac{(1+\sqrt{5})^{n+1}-(1-\sqrt{5})^{n+1}+2(1+\sqrt{5})^n-2(1-\sqrt{5})^n}{2^{n+1}\sqrt{5}}$$
$$=\frac{(1+\sqrt{5})^n[1+\sqrt{5}+2]-(1-\sqrt{5})^n[1-\sqrt{5}+2]}{2^{n+1}\sqrt{5}}$$
$$=\frac{(1+\sqrt{5})^n[3+\sqrt{5}]-(1-\sqrt{5})^n[3-\sqrt{5}]}{2^{n+1}\sqrt{5}}$$
$$=\frac{(1+\sqrt{5})^{n+2}\frac{(3+\sqrt{5})}{(1+\sqrt{5})^2}-(1-\sqrt{5})^{n+2}\frac{(3-\sqrt{5})}{(1-\sqrt{5})^2}}{2^{n+1}\sqrt{5}}$$

$$=\frac{\left(1+\sqrt{5}\right)^{n+2}\dfrac{\left(3+\sqrt{5}\right)}{\left(6+2\sqrt{5}\right)}-\left(1-\sqrt{5}\right)^{n+2}\dfrac{\left(3-\sqrt{5}\right)}{\left(6-2\sqrt{5}\right)}}{2^{n+1}\sqrt{5}}$$

$$=\frac{\left(1+\sqrt{5}\right)^{n+2}\frac{1}{2}-\left(1-\sqrt{5}\right)^{n+2}\frac{1}{2}}{2^{n+1}\sqrt{5}}=\frac{\left(1+\sqrt{5}\right)^{n+2}-\left(1-\sqrt{5}\right)^{n+2}}{2^{n+2}\sqrt{5}}=u_{n+2}$$

(c) Since $u_1=1,\ u_2=1,\ u_{n+2}=u_{n+1}+u_n,\ \{u_n\}$ is the Fibonacci sequence.

73. 1, 1, 2, 3, 5, 8, 13 This is the Fibonacci sequence.

74. a) $u_1=1,\ u_2=1,\ u_3=2,\ u_4=3,\ u_5=5,\ u_6=8,\ u_7=13,\ u_8=21,$
$u_9=34,\ u_{10}=55$

b) $\frac{u_2}{u_1}=\frac{1}{1}=1,\ \frac{u_3}{u_2}=\frac{2}{1}=1,\ \frac{u_4}{u_3}=\frac{3}{2}=1.5,\ \frac{u_5}{u_4}=\frac{5}{3}=1.67,\ \frac{u_6}{u_5}=\frac{8}{5}=1.6,$
$\frac{u_7}{u_6}=\frac{13}{8}=1.625,\ \frac{u_8}{u_7}=\frac{21}{13}=1.615,\ \frac{u_9}{u_8}=\frac{34}{21}=1.619,$
$\frac{u_{10}}{u_9}=\frac{55}{34}=1.618,\ \frac{u_{11}}{u_{10}}=\frac{89}{55}=1.618$

c) 1.618

d) $\frac{u_1}{u_2}=\frac{1}{1}=1,\ \frac{u_2}{u_3}=\frac{1}{2}=0.5,\ \frac{u_3}{u_4}=\frac{2}{3}=0.667,\ \frac{u_4}{u_5}=\frac{3}{5}=0.6,$
$\frac{u_5}{u_6}=\frac{5}{8}=0.625,\ \frac{u_6}{u_7}=\frac{8}{13}=0.615,\ \frac{u_7}{u_8}=\frac{13}{21}=0.619,$
$\frac{u_8}{u_9}=\frac{21}{34}=0.618,\ \frac{u_9}{u_{10}}=\frac{34}{55}=0.618,\ \frac{u_{10}}{u_{11}}=\frac{55}{89}=0.618$

e) 0.618

75. To show that $1+2+3+...+(n-1)+n=\frac{n(n+1)}{2}$

Let

$S=1+2+3+............+(n-1)+n,$ we can reverse the order to get

$+S=n+(n-1)+(n-2)+...+2+1,$ now add these two lines to get

$$2S=\underbrace{[1+n]+[2+(n-1)]+[3+(n-2)]+......+[(n-1)+2]+[n+1]}_{\text{n terms}}$$

So we have

$$2S=\underbrace{[1+n]+[1+n]+[1+n]+....+[n+1]+[n+1]}_{\text{n terms}}=n\cdot[n+1]$$

$$\therefore\ S=\frac{n\cdot(n+1)}{2}$$

76. Answers will vary.

Chapter 13

Sequences; Induction; The Binomial Theorem

13.2 Arithmetic Sequences

1. $d = a_{n+1} - a_n = (n+1+4) - (n+4) = n+5-n-4 = 1$
   $a_1 = 1+4 = 5,\ a_2 = 2+4 = 6,\ a_3 = 3+4 = 7,\ a_4 = 4+4 = 8$

2. $d = a_{n+1} - a_n = (n+1-5) - (n-5) = n-4-n+5 = 1$
   $a_1 = 1-5 = -4,\ a_2 = 2-5 = -3,\ a_3 = 3-5 = -2,\ a_4 = 4-5 = -1$

3. $d = a_{n+1} - a_n = (2(n+1)-5) - (2n-5) = 2n+2-5-2n+5 = 2$
   $a_1 = 2\cdot 1 - 5 = -3,\ a_2 = 2\cdot 2 - 5 = -1,\ a_3 = 2\cdot 3 - 5 = 1,\ a_4 = 2\cdot 4 - 5 = 3$

4. $d = a_{n+1} - a_n = (3(n+1)+1) - (3n+1) = 3n+3+1-3n-1 = 3$
   $a_1 = 3\cdot 1 + 1 = 4,\ a_2 = 3\cdot 2 + 1 = 7,\ a_3 = 3\cdot 3 + 1 = 10,\ a_4 = 3\cdot 4 + 1 = 13$

5. $d = a_{n+1} - a_n = (6-2(n+1)) - (6-2n) = 6-2n-2-6+2n = -2$
   $a_1 = 6 - 2\cdot 1 = 4,\ a_2 = 6 - 2\cdot 2 = 2,\ a_3 = 6 - 2\cdot 3 = 0,\ a_4 = 6 - 2\cdot 4 = -2$

6. $d = a_{n+1} - a_n = (4-2(n+1)) - (4-2n) = 4-2n-2-4+2n = -2$
   $a_1 = 4 - 2\cdot 1 = 2,\ a_2 = 4 - 2\cdot 2 = 0,\ a_3 = 4 - 2\cdot 3 = -2,\ a_4 = 4 - 2\cdot 4 = -4$

7. $d = a_{n+1} - a_n = \left(\frac{1}{2} - \frac{1}{3}(n+1)\right) - \left(\frac{1}{2} - \frac{1}{3}n\right) = \frac{1}{2} - \frac{1}{3}n - \frac{1}{3} - \frac{1}{2} + \frac{1}{3}n = -\frac{1}{3}$
   $a_1 = \frac{1}{2} - \frac{1}{3}\cdot 1 = \frac{1}{6},\ a_2 = \frac{1}{2} - \frac{1}{3}\cdot 2 = -\frac{1}{6},\ a_3 = \frac{1}{2} - \frac{1}{3}\cdot 3 = -\frac{1}{2},\ a_4 = \frac{1}{2} - \frac{1}{3}\cdot 4 = -\frac{5}{6}$

8. $d = a_{n+1} - a_n = \left(\frac{2}{3} + \frac{1}{4}(n+1)\right) - \left(\frac{2}{3} + \frac{1}{4}n\right) = \frac{2}{3} + \frac{1}{4}n + \frac{1}{4} - \frac{2}{3} - \frac{1}{4}n = \frac{1}{4}$
   $a_1 = \frac{2}{3} + \frac{1}{4}\cdot 1 = \frac{11}{12},\ a_2 = \frac{2}{3} + \frac{1}{4}\cdot 2 = \frac{7}{6},\ a_3 = \frac{2}{3} + \frac{1}{4}\cdot 3 = \frac{17}{12},\ a_4 = \frac{2}{3} + \frac{1}{4}\cdot 4 = \frac{5}{3}$

9. $d = a_{n+1} - a_n = \ln 3^{n+1} - \ln 3^n = (n+1)\ln 3 - n\ln 3 = \ln 3(n+1-n) = \ln 3$
   $a_1 = \ln 3^1 = \ln 3,\ a_2 = \ln 3^2 = 2\ln 3,\ a_3 = \ln 3^3 = 3\ln 3,\ a_4 = \ln 3^4 = 4\ln 3$

10. $d = a_{n+1} - a_n = e^{\ln(n+1)} - e^{\ln n} = (n+1) - n = 1$
    $a_1 = e^{\ln 1} = 1,\ a_2 = e^{\ln 2} = 2,\ a_3 = e^{\ln 3} = 3,\ a_4 = e^{\ln 4} = 4$

11. $a_n = a + (n-1)d = 2 + (n-1)3 = 2 + 3n - 3 = 3n - 1$
$a_5 = 3 \cdot 5 - 1 = 14$

12. $a_n = a + (n-1)d = -2 + (n-1)4 = -2 + 4n - 4 = 4n - 6$
$a_5 = 4 \cdot 5 - 6 = 14$

13. $a_n = a + (n-1)d = 5 + (n-1)(-3) = 5 - 3n + 3 = 8 - 3n$
$a_5 = 8 - 3 \cdot 5 = -7$

14. $a_n = a + (n-1)d = 6 + (n-1)(-2) = 6 - 2n + 2 = 8 - 2n$
$a_5 = 8 - 2 \cdot 5 = -2$

15. $a_n = a + (n-1)d = 0 + (n-1)\frac{1}{2} = \frac{1}{2}n - \frac{1}{2}$
$a_5 = \frac{1}{2} \cdot 5 - \frac{1}{2} = 2$

16. $a_n = a + (n-1)d = 1 + (n-1)\left(-\frac{1}{3}\right) = 1 - \frac{1}{3}n + \frac{1}{3} = \frac{4}{3} - \frac{1}{3}n$
$a_5 = \frac{4}{3} - \frac{1}{3} \cdot 5 = \frac{4}{3} - \frac{5}{3} = -\frac{1}{3}$

17. $a_n = a + (n-1)d = \sqrt{2} + (n-1)\sqrt{2} = \sqrt{2} + \sqrt{2}n - \sqrt{2} = \sqrt{2}n$
$a_5 = 5\sqrt{2}$

18. $a_n = a + (n-1)d = 0 + (n-1)\pi = \pi n - \pi$
$a_5 = 5\pi - \pi = 4\pi$

19. $a_1 = 2, \ d = 2, \ a_n = a + (n-1)d$
$a_{12} = 2 + (12-1)2 = 2 + 11(2) = 2 + 22 = 24$

20. $a_1 = -1, \ d = 2, \ a_n = a + (n-1)d$
$a_8 = -1 + (8-1)2 = -1 + 7(2) = -1 + 14 = 13$

21. $a_1 = 1, \ d = -2 - 1 = -3, \ a_n = a + (n-1)d$
$a_{10} = 1 + (10-1)(-3) = 1 + 9(-3) = 1 - 27 = -26$

22. $a_1 = 5, \ d = 0 - 5 = -5, \ a_n = a + (n-1)d$
$a_9 = 5 + (9-1)(-5) = 5 + 8(-5) = 5 - 40 = -35$

23. $a_1 = a, \ d = (a+b) - a = b, \ a_n = a + (n-1)d$
$a_8 = a + (8-1)b = a + 7b$

24. $a_1 = 2\sqrt{5},\ d = 4\sqrt{5} - 2\sqrt{5} = 2\sqrt{5},\ a_n = a + (n-1)d$

$a_7 = 2\sqrt{5} + (7-1)2\sqrt{5} = 2\sqrt{5} + 6\left(2\sqrt{5}\right) = 2\sqrt{5} + 12\sqrt{5} = 14\sqrt{5}$

25. $a_8 = a + 7d = 8 \qquad a_{20} = a + 19d = 44$

Solve the system of equations:

$8 - 7d + 19d = 44$

$12d = 36 \rightarrow d = 3 \rightarrow a = 8 - 7(3) = 8 - 21 = -13$

Recursive formula: $a_1 = -13 \qquad a_n = a_{n-1} + 3$

26. $a_4 = a + 3d = 3 \qquad a_{20} = a + 19d = 35$

Solve the system of equations:

$3 - 3d + 19d = 35$

$16d = 32 \rightarrow d = 2 \rightarrow a = 3 - 3(2) = 3 - 6 = -3$

Recursive formula: $a_1 = -3 \qquad a_n = a_{n-1} + 2$

27. $a_9 = a + 8d = -5 \qquad a_{15} = a + 14d = 31$

Solve the system of equations:

$-5 - 8d + 14d = 31 \rightarrow 6d = 36 \rightarrow d = 6$

$a = -5 - 8(6) = -5 - 48 = -53$

Recursive formula: $a_1 = -53 \qquad a_n = a_{n-1} + 6$

28. $a_8 = a + 7d = 4 \qquad a_{18} = a + 17d = -96$

Solve the system of equations:

$4 - 7d + 17d = -96 \rightarrow 10d = -100 \rightarrow d = -10$

$a = 4 - 7(-10) = 4 + 70 = 74$

Recursive formula: $a_1 = 74 \qquad a_n = a_{n-1} - 10$

29. $a_{15} = a + 14d = 0 \qquad a_{40} = a + 39d = -50$

Solve the system of equations:

$-14d + 39d = -50 \rightarrow 25d = -50 \rightarrow d = -2$

$a = -14(-2) = 28$

Recursive formula: $a_1 = 28 \qquad a_n = a_{n-1} - 2$

30. $a_5 = a + 4d = -2 \qquad a_{13} = a + 12d = 30$

Solve the system of equations:

$-2 - 4d + 12d = 30 \rightarrow 8d = 32 \rightarrow d = 4$

$a = -2 - 4(4) = -18$

Recursive formula: $a_1 = -18 \qquad a_n = a_{n-1} + 4$

31. $a_{14} = a + 13d = -1 \qquad a_{18} = a + 17d = -9$

Solve the system of equations:

$$-1 - 13d + 17d = -9$$

$$4d = -8 \rightarrow d = -2 \rightarrow a = -1 - 13(-2) = -1 + 26 = 25$$

Recursive formula: $a_1 = 25 \qquad a_n = a_{n-1} - 2$

32. $a_{12} = a + 11d = 4 \qquad a_{18} = a + 17d = 28$

Solve the system of equations:

$$4 - 11d + 17d = 28$$

$$6d = 24 \rightarrow d = 4 \rightarrow a = 4 - 11(4) = 4 - 44 = -40$$

Recursive formula: $a_1 = -40 \qquad a_n = a_{n-1} + 4$

33. $S_n = \frac{n}{2}(a + a_n) = \frac{n}{2}(1 + (2n - 1)) = \frac{n}{2}(2n) = n^2$

34. $S_n = \frac{n}{2}(a + a_n) = \frac{n}{2}(2 + 2n) = n + n^2$

35. $S_n = \frac{n}{2}(a + a_n) = \frac{n}{2}(7 + (2 + 5n)) = \frac{n}{2}(9 + 5n) = \frac{9}{2}n + \frac{5}{2}n^2$

36. $S_n = \frac{n}{2}(a + a_n) = \frac{n}{2}(-1 + (4n - 5)) = \frac{n}{2}(4n - 6) = 2n^2 - 3n$

37. $a_1 = 2, \; d = 4 - 2 = 2, \; a_n = a + (n - 1)d$

$$70 = 2 + (n - 1)2 \rightarrow 70 = 2 + 2n - 2 \rightarrow 70 = 2n \rightarrow n = 35$$

$$S_n = \frac{n}{2}(a + a_n) = \frac{35}{2}(2 + 70) = \frac{35}{2}(72) = 35(36) = 1260$$

38. $a_1 = 1, \; d = 3 - 1 = 2, \; a_n = a + (n - 1)d$

$$59 = 1 + (n - 1)2 \rightarrow 59 = 1 + 2n - 2 \rightarrow 60 = 2n \rightarrow n = 30$$

$$S_n = \frac{n}{2}(a + a_n) = \frac{30}{2}(1 + 59) = 15(60) = 900$$

39. $a_1 = 5, \; d = 9 - 5 = 4, \; a_n = a + (n - 1)d$

$$49 = 5 + (n - 1)4 \rightarrow 49 = 5 + 4n - 4 \rightarrow 48 = 4n \rightarrow n = 12$$

$$S_n = \frac{n}{2}(a + a_n) = \frac{12}{2}(5 + 49) = 6(54) = 324$$

40. $a_1 = 2, \; d = 5 - 2 = 3, \; a_n = a + (n - 1)d$

$$41 = 2 + (n - 1)3 \rightarrow 41 = 2 + 3n - 3 \rightarrow 42 = 3n \rightarrow n = 14$$

$$S_n = \frac{n}{2}(a + a_n) = \frac{14}{2}(2 + 41) = 7(43) = 301$$

41. Using the sum of the sequence feature:

42. Using the sum of the sequence feature:

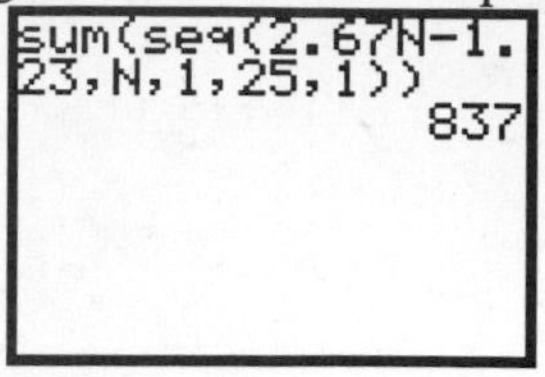

43.
$$d = 5.2 - 2.8 = 2.4$$
$$a = 2.8$$
$$36.4 = 2.8 + (n-1)2.4$$
$$36.4 = 2.8 + 2.4n - 2.4$$
$$36 = 2.4n$$
$$n = 15$$
$$a_n = 2.8 + (n-1)2.4 = 2.8 + 2.4n - 2.4 = 2.4n + 0.4$$

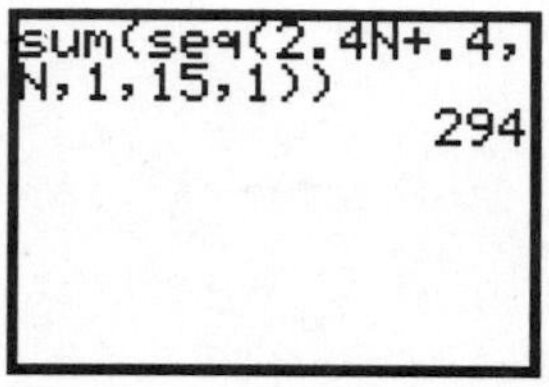

44.
$$d = 7.3 - 5.4 = 1.9$$
$$a = 5.4$$
$$32 = 5.4 + (n-1)1.9$$
$$32 = 5.4 + 1.9n - 1.9$$
$$28.5 = 1.9n$$
$$n = 15$$
$$a_n = 5.4 + (n-1)1.9 = 5.4 + 1.9n - 1.9 = 1.9n + 3.5$$

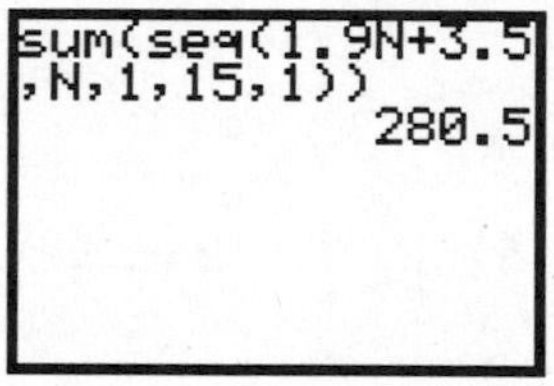

45.
$$d = 7.48 - 4.9 = 2.58$$
$$a = 4.9$$
$$66.82 = 4.9 + (n-1)2.58$$
$$66.82 = 4.9 + 2.58n - 2.58$$
$$64.5 = 2.58n$$
$$n = 25$$
$$a_n = 4.9 + (n-1)2.58 = 4.9 + 2.58n - 2.58$$
$$a_n = 2.58n + 2.32$$

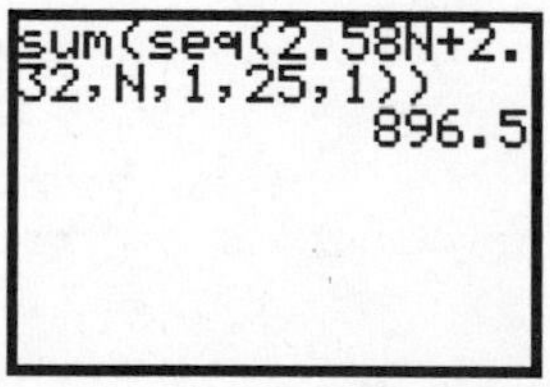

46. $d = 6.9 - 3.71 = 3.19$

$a = 3.71$

$80.27 = 3.71 + (n-1)3.19$

$80.27 = 3.71 + 3.19n - 3.19$

$79.75 = 3.19n$

$n = 25$

$a_n = 3.71 + (n-1)3.19 = 3.71 + 3.19n - 3.19$

$a_n = 3.19n + 0.52$

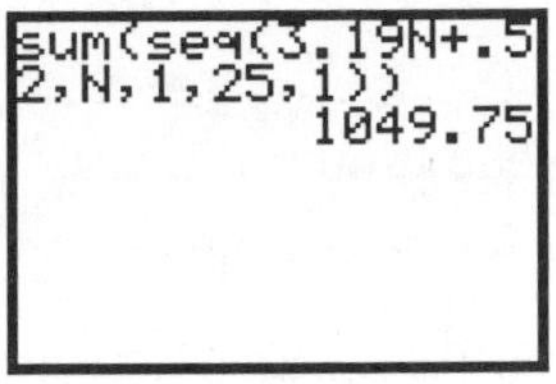

47. Find the common difference of the terms and solve the system of equations:

$(2x+1)-(x+3) = d \rightarrow x - 2 = d$

$(5x+2)-(2x+1) = d \rightarrow 3x + 1 = d$

$3x + 1 = x - 2 \rightarrow 2x = -3 \rightarrow x = -1.5$

48. Find the common difference of the terms and solve the system of equations:

$(3x+2)-(2x) = d \rightarrow x + 2 = d$

$(5x+3)-(3x+2) = d \rightarrow 2x + 1 = d$

$2x + 1 = x + 2 \rightarrow x = 1$

49. The total number of seats is: $S = 25 + 26 + 27 + \cdots$

This is the sum of an arithmetic sequence with $d = 1$, $a = 25$, and $n = 30$.

Find the sum of the sequence:

$$S_{30} = \frac{30}{2}\left[2(25) + (30-1)(1)\right] = 15(50+29) = 15(79) = 1185$$

There are 1185 seats in the theater.

50. The total number of seats is: $S = 15 + 17 + 19 + \cdots$

This is the sum of an arithmetic sequence with $d = 2$, $a = 15$, and $n = 40$.

Find the sum of the sequence:

$$S_{40} = \frac{40}{2}\left[2(15) + (40-1)(2)\right] = 20(30+78) = 20(108) = 2160$$

The corner section has 2160 seats.

51. The lighter colored tiles have 20 tiles in the bottom row and 1 tile in the top row. The number decreases by 1 as we move up the triangle. This is an arithmetic sequence with $a_1 = 20$, $d = -1$, and $n = 20$. Find the sum:

$$S = \frac{20}{2}\left[2(20) + (20-1)(-1)\right] = 10(40-19) = 10(21) = 210 \text{ lighter tiles.}$$

The darker colored tiles have 19 tiles in the bottom row and 1 tile in the top row. The number decreases by 1 as we move up the triangle. This is an arithmetic sequence with $a_1 = 19$, $d = -1$, and $n = 19$. Find the sum:

$$S = \frac{19}{2}\left[2(19) + (19-1)(-1)\right] = \frac{19}{2}(38-18) = \frac{19}{2}(20) = 190 \text{ darker tiles.}$$

52. The number of bricks required decreases by 2 on each successive step. This is an arithmetic sequence with $a_1 = 100$, $d = -2$, and $n = 30$.

(a) The number of bricks for the top step is:

$$a_{30} = a_1 + (n-1)d = 100 + (30-1)(-2) = 100 + 29(-2) = 100 - 58 = 42$$

42 bricks are required for the top step.

(b) The total number of bricks required is the sum of the sequence:

$$S = \frac{30}{2}[100 + 42] = 15(142) = 2130$$

2130 bricks are required to build the staircase.

53. Find n in an arithmetic sequence with $a_1 = 10$, $d = 4$, $s_n = 2040$.

$$s_n = \frac{n}{2}[2a_1 + (n-1)d] \rightarrow 2040 = \frac{n}{2}[2(10) + (n-1)4]$$

$$4080 = n[20 + 4n - 4] \rightarrow 4080 = n(4n + 16)$$

$$4080 = 4n^2 + 16n \rightarrow 1020 = n^2 + 4n$$

$$n^2 + 4n - 1020 = 0 \rightarrow (n + 34)(n - 30) = 0 \rightarrow n = -34 \text{ or } n = 30$$

There are 30 rows in the corner section of the stadium.

54. The yearly salaries form an arithmetic sequence with:

$a_1 = 35000$, $d = 1400$, $s_n = 280,000$.

Find the number of years for the total salary to equal $280,000.

$$s_n = \frac{n}{2}[2a_1 + (n-1)d]$$

$$280,000 = \frac{n}{2}[2(35000) + (n-1)1400] \rightarrow 280,000 = n[35000 + 700n - 700]$$

$$280,000 = n(700n + 34300)$$

$$280,000 = 700n^2 + 34300n \rightarrow 400 = n^2 + 49n \rightarrow n^2 + 49n - 400 = 0$$

$$n = \frac{-49 \pm \sqrt{49^2 - 4(1)(-400)}}{2(1)} = \frac{-49 \pm \sqrt{4001}}{2} \approx \frac{-49 \pm 63.25}{2}$$

$n \approx 7.13$ or $n \approx -56.13$

It takes about 7.13 years to have an aggregate salary of $280,000.

55. Answers will vary.

Chapter 13

Sequences; Induction; The Binomial Theorem

13.3 Geometric Sequences; Geometric Series

1. $r = \dfrac{3^{n+1}}{3^n} = 3^{n+1-n} = 3$

   $a_1 = 3^1 = 3,\ a_2 = 3^2 = 9,\ a_3 = 3^3 = 27,\ a_4 = 3^4 = 81$

2. $r = \dfrac{(-5)^{n+1}}{(-5)^n} = (-5)^{n+1-n} = -5$

   $a_1 = (-5)^1 = -5,\ a_2 = (-5)^2 = 25,\ a_3 = (-5)^3 = -125,\ a_4 = (-5)^4 = 625$

3. $r = \dfrac{-3\left(\frac{1}{2}\right)^{n+1}}{-3\left(\frac{1}{2}\right)^{n}} = \left(\dfrac{1}{2}\right)^{n+1-n} = \dfrac{1}{2}$

   $a_1 = -3\left(\dfrac{1}{2}\right)^1 = -\dfrac{3}{2},\ a_2 = -3\left(\dfrac{1}{2}\right)^2 = -\dfrac{3}{4},\ a_3 = -3\left(\dfrac{1}{2}\right)^3 = -\dfrac{3}{8},\ a_4 = -3\left(\dfrac{1}{2}\right)^4 = -\dfrac{3}{16}$

4. $r = \dfrac{\left(\frac{5}{2}\right)^{n+1}}{\left(\frac{5}{2}\right)^{n}} = \left(\dfrac{5}{2}\right)^{n+1-n} = \dfrac{5}{2}$

   $a_1 = \left(\dfrac{5}{2}\right)^1 = \dfrac{5}{2},\ a_2 = \left(\dfrac{5}{2}\right)^2 = \dfrac{25}{4},\ a_3 = \left(\dfrac{5}{2}\right)^3 = \dfrac{125}{8},\ a_4 = \left(\dfrac{5}{2}\right)^4 = \dfrac{625}{16}$

5. $r = \dfrac{\left(\frac{2^{n+1-1}}{4}\right)}{\left(\frac{2^{n-1}}{4}\right)} = \dfrac{2^n}{2^{n-1}} = 2^{n-(n-1)} = 2$

   $a_1 = \dfrac{2^{1-1}}{4} = \dfrac{2^0}{2^2} = 2^{-2} = \dfrac{1}{4},\ a_2 = \dfrac{2^{2-1}}{4} = \dfrac{2^1}{2^2} = 2^{-1} = \dfrac{1}{2},\ a_3 = \dfrac{2^{3-1}}{4} = \dfrac{2^2}{2^2} = 1,$

   $a_4 = \dfrac{2^{4-1}}{4} = \dfrac{2^3}{2^2} = 2$

6. $r = \dfrac{\left(\dfrac{3^{n+1}}{9}\right)}{\left(\dfrac{3^n}{9}\right)} = \dfrac{3^{n+1}}{3^n} = 3^{n+1-n} = 3$

$a_1 = \dfrac{3^1}{9} = \dfrac{1}{3},\ a_2 = \dfrac{3^2}{9} = \dfrac{9}{9} = 1,\ a_3 = \dfrac{3^3}{9} = \dfrac{27}{9} = 3,\ a_4 = \dfrac{3^4}{9} = \dfrac{81}{9} = 9$

7. $r = \dfrac{2^{\left(\frac{n+1}{3}\right)}}{2^{\left(\frac{n}{3}\right)}} = 2^{\left(\frac{n+1}{3} - \frac{n}{3}\right)} = 2^{1/3}$

$a_1 = 2^{1/3},\ a_2 = 2^{2/3},\ a_3 = 2^{3/3} = 2,\ a_4 = 2^{4/3}$

8. $r = \dfrac{3^{2(n+1)}}{3^{2n}} = 3^{2n+2-2n} = 3^2 = 9$

$a_1 = 3^{2\cdot 1} = 9,\ a_2 = 3^{2\cdot 2} = 3^4 = 81,\ a_3 = 3^{2\cdot 3} = 3^6 = 729,\ a_4 = 3^{2\cdot 4} = 3^8 = 6561$

9. $r = \dfrac{\left(\dfrac{3^{n+1-1}}{2^{n+1}}\right)}{\left(\dfrac{3^{n-1}}{2^n}\right)} = \dfrac{3^n}{3^{n-1}} \cdot \dfrac{2^n}{2^{n+1}} = 3^{n-(n-1)} \cdot 2^{n-(n+1)} = 3 \cdot 2^{-1} = \dfrac{3}{2}$

$a_1 = \dfrac{3^{1-1}}{2^1} = \dfrac{3^0}{2} = \dfrac{1}{2},\ a_2 = \dfrac{3^{2-1}}{2^2} = \dfrac{3^1}{2^2} = \dfrac{3}{4},\ a_3 = \dfrac{3^{3-1}}{2^3} = \dfrac{3^2}{2^3} = \dfrac{9}{8},$

$a_4 = \dfrac{3^{4-1}}{2^4} = \dfrac{3^3}{2^4} = \dfrac{27}{16}$

10. $r = \dfrac{\left(\dfrac{2^{n+1}}{3^{n+1-1}}\right)}{\left(\dfrac{2^n}{3^{n-1}}\right)} = \dfrac{3^{n-1}}{3^n} \cdot \dfrac{2^{n+1}}{2^n} = 3^{n-1-n} \cdot 2^{n+1-n} = 3^{-1} \cdot 2 = \dfrac{2}{3}$

$a_1 = \dfrac{2^1}{3^{1-1}} = \dfrac{2}{3^0} = \dfrac{2}{1} = 2,\ a_2 = \dfrac{2^2}{3^{2-1}} = \dfrac{4}{3},\ a_3 = \dfrac{2^3}{3^{3-1}} = \dfrac{8}{3^2} = \dfrac{8}{9}, a_4 = \dfrac{2^4}{3^{4-1}} = \dfrac{16}{3^3} = \dfrac{16}{27}$

11. $\{n+2\}$ Arithmetic
$d = (n+1+2) - (n+2) = n+3-n-2 = 1$

12. $\{2n-5\}$ Arithmetic
$d = 2(n+1) - 5 - (2n-5) = 2n+2-5-2n+5 = 2$

13. $\{4n^2\}$ Examine the terms of the sequence: 4, 16, 36, 64, 100, ...
There is no common difference; there is no common ratio; neither.

14. $\{5n^2+1\}$ Examine the terms of the sequence: 6, 21, 46, 81, 126, ...
There is no common difference; there is no common ratio; neither.

15. $\left\{3-\frac{2}{3}n\right\}$ Arithmetic

$$d=\left(3-\frac{2}{3}(n+1)\right)-\left(3-\frac{2}{3}n\right)=3-\frac{2}{3}n-\frac{2}{3}-3+\frac{2}{3}n=-\frac{2}{3}$$

16. $\left\{8-\frac{3}{4}n\right\}$ Arithmetic

$$d=\left(8-\frac{3}{4}(n+1)\right)-\left(8-\frac{3}{4}n\right)=8-\frac{3}{4}n-\frac{3}{4}-8+\frac{3}{4}n=-\frac{3}{4}$$

17. 1, 3, 6, 10, ... Neither
There is no common difference or common ratio.

18. 2, 4, 6, 8, ... Arithmetic
The common difference is 2.

19. $\left\{\left(\frac{2}{3}\right)^n\right\}$ Geometric

$$r=\frac{\left(\frac{2}{3}\right)^{n+1}}{\left(\frac{2}{3}\right)^n}=\left(\frac{2}{3}\right)^{n+1-n}=\frac{2}{3}$$

20. $\left\{\left(\frac{5}{4}\right)^n\right\}$ Geometric

$$r=\frac{\left(\frac{5}{4}\right)^{n+1}}{\left(\frac{5}{4}\right)^n}=\left(\frac{5}{4}\right)^{n+1-n}=\frac{5}{4}$$

21. $-1, -2, -4, -8, \ldots$ Geometric $r=\frac{-2}{-1}=\frac{-4}{-2}=\frac{-8}{-4}=2$

22. 1,1,2,3,5,8, ... Neither There is no common difference; there is no common ratio.

23. $\left\{3^{n/2}\right\}$ Geometric

$$r=\frac{3^{\left(\frac{n+1}{2}\right)}}{3^{\left(\frac{n}{2}\right)}}=3^{\left(\frac{n+1}{2}-\frac{n}{2}\right)}=3^{1/2}$$

24. $\left\{(-1)^n\right\}$ Geometric

$$r=\frac{(-1)^{n+1}}{(-1)^n}=(-1)^{n+1-n}=-1$$

25. $a_5=2\cdot 3^{5-1}=2\cdot 3^4=2\cdot 81=162$ $\quad a_n=2\cdot 3^{n-1}$

26. $a_5=-2\cdot 4^{5-1}=-2\cdot 4^4=-2\cdot 256=-512$ $\quad a_n=-2\cdot 4^{n-1}$

27. $a_5 = 5(-1)^{5-1} = 5(-1)^4 = 5 \cdot 1 = 5 \qquad a_n = 5 \cdot (-1)^{n-1}$

28. $a_5 = 6(-2)^{5-1} = 6(-2)^4 = 6 \cdot 16 = 96 \qquad a_n = 6 \cdot (-2)^{n-1}$

29. $a_5 = 0 \cdot \left(\frac{1}{2}\right)^{5-1} = 0 \cdot \left(\frac{1}{2}\right)^4 = 0 \qquad a_n = 0 \cdot \left(\frac{1}{2}\right)^{n-1} = 0$

30. $a_5 = 1 \cdot \left(-\frac{1}{3}\right)^{5-1} = 1 \cdot \left(-\frac{1}{3}\right)^4 = \frac{1}{81} \qquad a_n = 1 \cdot \left(-\frac{1}{3}\right)^{n-1} = \left(-\frac{1}{3}\right)^{n-1}$

31. $a_5 = \sqrt{2} \cdot \left(\sqrt{2}\right)^{5-1} = \sqrt{2} \cdot \left(\sqrt{2}\right)^4 = \sqrt{2} \cdot 4 = 4\sqrt{2} \qquad a_n = \sqrt{2} \cdot \left(\sqrt{2}\right)^{n-1} = \left(\sqrt{2}\right)^n$

32. $a_5 = 0 \cdot \left(\frac{1}{\pi}\right)^{5-1} = 0 \cdot \left(\frac{1}{\pi}\right)^4 = 0 \qquad a_n = 0 \cdot \left(\frac{1}{\pi}\right)^{n-1} = 0$

33. $a = 1,\ r = \frac{1}{2},\ n = 7 \qquad a_7 = 1 \cdot \left(\frac{1}{2}\right)^{7-1} = \left(\frac{1}{2}\right)^6 = \frac{1}{64}$

34. $a = 1,\ r = 3,\ n = 8 \qquad a_8 = 1 \cdot 3^{8-1} = 3^7 = 2187$

35. $a = 1,\ r = -1,\ n = 9 \qquad a_7 = 1 \cdot (-1)^{9-1} = (-1)^8 = 1$

36. $a = -1,\ r = -2,\ n = 10 \qquad a_{10} = -1 \cdot (-2)^{10-1} = -1 \cdot (-2)^9 = -1(-512) = 512$

37. $a = 0.4,\ r = 0.1,\ n = 8 \qquad a_7 = 0.4 \cdot (0.1)^{8-1} = 0.4(0.1)^7 = 0.00000004$

38. $a = 0.1,\ r = 10,\ n = 7 \qquad a_7 = 0.1 \cdot 10^{7-1} = 0.1(10)^6 = 100{,}000$

39. $a = \frac{1}{4},\ r = 2 \qquad S_n = a\left(\frac{1-r^n}{1-r}\right) = \frac{1}{4}\left(\frac{1-2^n}{1-2}\right) = -\frac{1}{4}\left(1-2^n\right)$

40. $a = \frac{3}{9} = \frac{1}{3},\ r = 3 \qquad S_n = a\left(\frac{1-r^n}{1-r}\right) = \frac{1}{3}\left(\frac{1-3^n}{1-3}\right) = \frac{1}{3}\left(\frac{1-3^n}{-2}\right) = -\frac{1}{6}\left(1-3^n\right)$

41. $a = \frac{2}{3},\ r = \frac{2}{3} \qquad S_n = a\left(\frac{1-r^n}{1-r}\right) = \frac{2}{3}\left(\frac{1-\left(\frac{2}{3}\right)^n}{1-\frac{2}{3}}\right) = \frac{2}{3}\left(\frac{1-\left(\frac{2}{3}\right)^n}{\frac{1}{3}}\right) = 2\left(1-\left(\frac{2}{3}\right)^n\right)$

42. $a = 4,\ r = 3 \qquad S_n = a\left(\frac{1-r^n}{1-r}\right) = 4\left(\frac{1-3^n}{1-3}\right) = 4\left(\frac{1-3^n}{-2}\right) = -2\left(1-3^n\right)$

43. $a = -1,\ r = 2 \quad S_n = a\left(\dfrac{1-r^n}{1-r}\right) = -1\left(\dfrac{1-2^n}{1-2}\right) = 1-2^n$

44. $a = 2,\ r = \dfrac{3}{5} \quad S_n = a\left(\dfrac{1-r^n}{1-r}\right) = 2\left(\dfrac{1-\left(\frac{3}{5}\right)^n}{1-\frac{3}{5}}\right) = 2\left(\dfrac{1-\left(\frac{3}{5}\right)^n}{\left(\frac{2}{5}\right)}\right) = 5\left(1-\left(\frac{3}{5}\right)^n\right)$

45. Using the sum of the sequence feature:

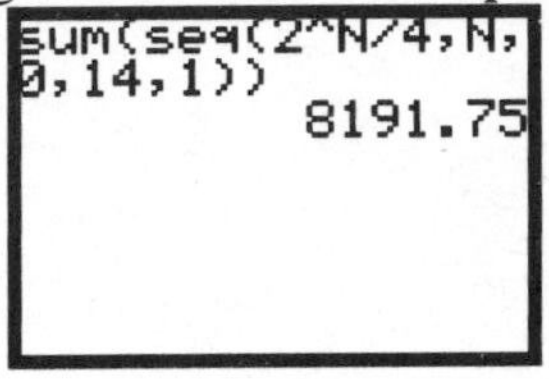

46. Using the sum of the sequence feature:

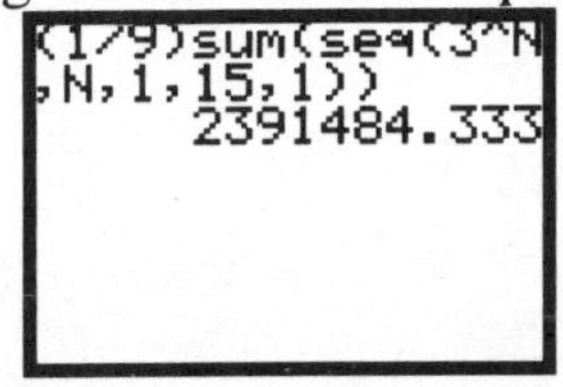

47. Using the sum of the sequence feature:

48. Using the sum of the sequence feature:

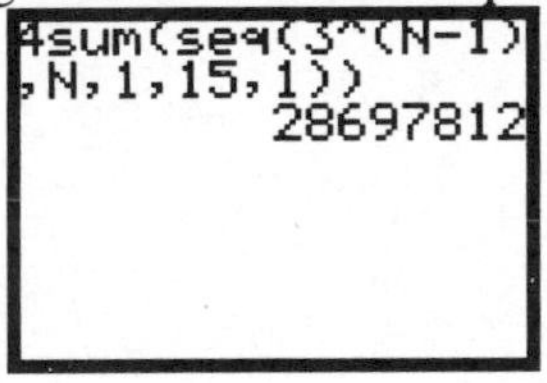

49. Using the sum of the sequence feature:

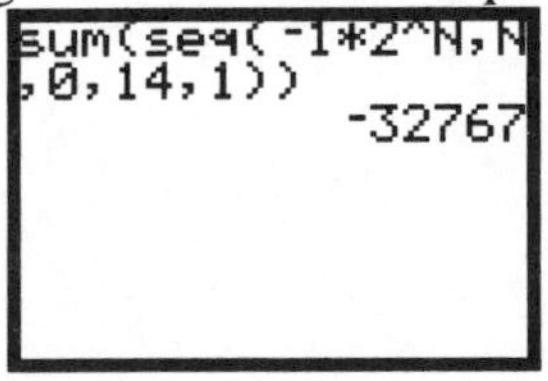

50. Using the sum of the sequence feature:

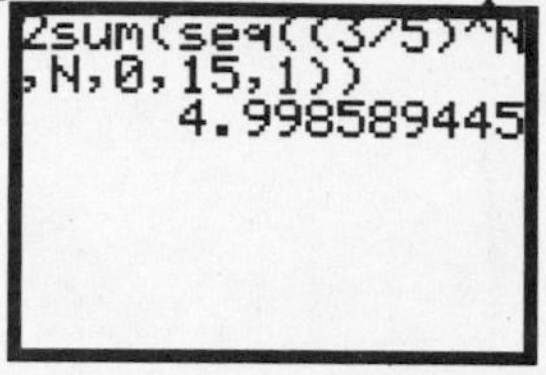

51.

$a=1,\ r=\frac{1}{3}$ Since $|r|<1,\ S_n=\frac{a}{1-r}=\frac{1}{\left(1-\frac{1}{3}\right)}=\frac{1}{\left(\frac{2}{3}\right)}=\frac{3}{2}$

52.

$a=2,\ r=\frac{2}{3}$ Since $|r|<1,\ S_n=\frac{a}{1-r}=\frac{2}{\left(1-\frac{2}{3}\right)}=\frac{2}{\left(\frac{1}{3}\right)}=6$

53.

$a=8,\ r=\frac{1}{2}$ Since $|r|<1,\ S_n=\frac{a}{1-r}=\frac{8}{\left(1-\frac{1}{2}\right)}=\frac{8}{\left(\frac{1}{2}\right)}=16$

54.

$a=6,\ r=\frac{1}{3}$ Since $|r|<1,\ S_n=\frac{a}{1-r}=\frac{6}{\left(1-\frac{1}{3}\right)}=\frac{6}{\left(\frac{2}{3}\right)}=9$

55.

$a=2,\ r=-\frac{1}{4}$ Since $|r|<1,\ S_n=\frac{a}{1-r}=\frac{2}{\left(1-\left(-\frac{1}{4}\right)\right)}=\frac{2}{\left(\frac{5}{4}\right)}=\frac{8}{5}$

56.

$a=1,\ r=-\frac{3}{4}$ Since $|r|<1,\ S_n=\frac{a}{1-r}=\frac{1}{\left(1-\left(-\frac{3}{4}\right)\right)}=\frac{1}{\left(\frac{7}{4}\right)}=\frac{4}{7}$

57.

$a=5,\ r=\frac{1}{4}$ Since $|r|<1,\ S_n=\frac{a}{1-r}=\frac{5}{\left(1-\frac{1}{4}\right)}=\frac{5}{\left(\frac{3}{4}\right)}=\frac{20}{3}$

58.

$$a = 8,\ r = \frac{1}{3} \quad \text{Since } |r| < 1,\ S_n = \frac{a}{1-r} = \frac{8}{\left(1-\frac{1}{3}\right)} = \frac{8}{\left(\frac{2}{3}\right)} = 12$$

59.

$$a = 6,\ r = -\frac{2}{3} \quad \text{Since } |r| < 1,\ S_n = \frac{a}{1-r} = \frac{6}{\left(1-\left(-\frac{2}{3}\right)\right)} = \frac{6}{\left(\frac{5}{3}\right)} = \frac{18}{5}$$

60.

$$a = 4,\ r = -\frac{1}{2} \quad \text{Since } |r| < 1,\ S_n = \frac{a}{1-r} = \frac{4}{\left(1-\left(-\frac{1}{2}\right)\right)} = \frac{4}{\left(\frac{3}{2}\right)} = \frac{8}{3}$$

61. Find the common ratio of the terms and solve the system of equations:

$$\frac{x+2}{x} = r$$

$$\frac{x+3}{x+2} = r$$

$$\frac{x+2}{x} = \frac{x+3}{x+2} \rightarrow x^2 + 4x + 4 = x^2 + 3x \rightarrow x = -4$$

62. Find the common ratio of the terms and solve the system of equations:

$$\frac{x}{x-1} = r$$

$$\frac{x+2}{x} = r$$

$$\frac{x+2}{x} = \frac{x}{x-1} \rightarrow x^2 + x - 2 = x^2 \rightarrow x = 2$$

63. This is a geometric series with $a = \$18,000$, $r = 1.05$, $n = 5$. Find the 5th term:

$$a_5 = 18000(1.05)^{5-1} = 18000(1.05)^4 = \$21,879.11$$

64. This is a geometric series with $a = \$15,000$, $r = 0.85$, $n = 6$. Find the 6th term:

$$a_6 = 15000(0.85)^{6-1} = 15000(0.85)^5 = \$6655.58$$

65. (a) Find the 10th term of the geometric sequence:

$$a = 2,\ r = 0.9,\ n = 10 \qquad a_{10} = 2(0.9)^{10-1} = 2(0.9)^9 = 0.775 \text{ feet}$$

(b) Find n when $a_n < 1$:

$$2(0.9)^{n-1} < 1 \rightarrow (0.9)^{n-1} < 0.5$$

$$(n-1)\log 0.9 < \log 0.5 \rightarrow n-1 > \frac{\log 0.5}{\log 0.9} \rightarrow n > \frac{\log 0.5}{\log 0.9} + 1 = 7.58$$

On the 8th swing the arc is less than 1 foot.

(c) Find the sum of the first 15 swings:

$$S_{15}=2\left(\frac{1-(0.9)^{15}}{1-0.9}\right)=2\left(\frac{1-(0.9)^{15}}{0.1}\right)=20\left(1-(0.9)^{15}\right)=15.88\text{ feet}$$

(d) Find the infinite sum of the geometric series:

$$S=\frac{2}{1-0.9}=\frac{2}{0.1}=20\text{ feet}$$

66. (a) Find the 3rd term of the geometric sequence:

$a=24,\ r=0.8,\ n=3 \qquad a_3=24(0.8)^{3-1}=24(0.8)^2=15.36$ feet

(b) The height after the nth bounce is: $a_n=24(0.8)^{n-1}$

(c) Find n when $a_n<0.5$:

$$24(0.8)^{n-1}<0.5\rightarrow(0.8)^{n-1}<0.020833\rightarrow(n-1)\log 0.8<\log 0.020833$$

$$n-1>\frac{\log 0.020833}{\log 0.8}\rightarrow n>\frac{\log 0.020833}{\log 0.8}+1=18.35$$

On the 19th bounce the height is less than 0.5 feet.

(d) Find the infinite sum of the geometric series:

$S=\frac{24}{1-0.8}=\frac{24}{0.2}=120$ feet on the upward bounce.

For the downward motion of the ball:

$$S=\frac{30}{1-0.8}=\frac{30}{0.2}=150\text{ feet}$$

The total distance the ball travels is 120 + 150 = 270 feet.

67. This is an ordinary annuity with $P=\$100$ and $n=(12)(30)=360$ payment periods.

The interest rate per period is $\frac{.12}{12}=.01$. Thus,

$$A=100\left[\frac{\left[1+\frac{.12}{12}\right]^{360}-1}{\left(\frac{.12}{12}\right)}\right]=\$349496.41$$

68. This is an ordinary annuity with $P=\$400$ and $n=(12)(3)=36$ payment periods.

The interest rate per period is $\frac{.10}{12}=.008\overline{3}$. Thus,

$$A=400\left[\frac{\left[1+\frac{.10}{12}\right]^{36}-1}{\left(\frac{.10}{12}\right)}\right]=\$16712.73$$

69. This is an ordinary annuity with $P=\$500$ and $n=(4)(20)=80$ payment periods.

The interest rate per period is $\frac{.08}{4}=.02$. Thus,

$$A = 500\left[\frac{\left[1+\frac{.08}{4}\right]^{80} - 1}{\left(\frac{.08}{4}\right)}\right] = \$96885.98$$

70. This is an ordinary annuity with $P = \$1000$ and $n = (2)(15) = 30$ payment periods. The interest rate per period is $\frac{.10}{2} = .05$. Thus,

$$A = 1000\left[\frac{\left[1+\frac{.10}{2}\right]^{30} - 1}{\left(\frac{.10}{2}\right)}\right] = \$66438.85$$

71. This is an ordinary annuity with $A = \$50000$ and $n = (12)(10) = 120$ payment periods. The interest rate per period is $\frac{.06}{12} = .005$. Thus,

$$50000 = P\left[\frac{\left[1+\frac{.06}{12}\right]^{120} - 1}{\left(\frac{.06}{12}\right)}\right] \longrightarrow P = 50000\left[\frac{\left(\frac{.06}{12}\right)}{\left[1+\frac{.06}{12}\right]^{120} - 1}\right] = \$305.10$$

72. This is an ordinary annuity with $A = \$150000$ and $n = (12)(18) = 216$ payment periods. The interest rate per period is $\frac{.08}{12} = .00\bar{6}$. Thus,

$$150000 = P\left[\frac{\left[1+\frac{.08}{12}\right]^{216} - 1}{\left(\frac{.08}{12}\right)}\right] \longrightarrow P = 150000\left[\frac{\left(\frac{.08}{12}\right)}{\left[1+\frac{.08}{12}\right]^{216} - 1}\right] = \$312.44$$

73. Both options are geometric sequences:

Option A: $a = \$20{,}000;\quad r = 1.06;\quad n = 5$

$$a_5 = 20{,}000(1.06)^{5-1} = 20{,}000(1.06)^4 = \$25{,}250$$

$$S_5 = 20000\left(\frac{1-(1.06)^5}{1-1.06}\right) = \$112{,}742$$

Option B: $a = \$22{,}000;\quad r = 1.03;\quad n = 5$

$$a_5 = 22{,}000(1.03)^{5-1} = 22{,}000(1.03)^4 = \$24{,}761$$

$$S_5 = 22000\left(\frac{1-(1.03)^5}{1-1.03}\right) = \$116{,}801$$

Option A provides more money in the 5th year, while Option B provides the greatest total amount of money over the 5 year period.

74. Find the sum of each sequence:
A: Arithmetic series with: $a = \$1000, \quad d = -1, \quad n = 1000$
Find the sum of the arithmetic series:
$$S_{1000} = \frac{1000}{2}(1000+1) = 500(1001) = \$500{,}500$$
B: This is a geometric sequence with $a = 1, \quad r = 2, \quad n = 19$.
Find the sum of the geometric series:
$$S_{19} = 1\left(\frac{1-2^{19}}{1-2}\right) = \frac{1-2^{19}}{-1} = 2^{19} - 1 = \$524{,}287$$
B results in more money.

75. Option 1: Total Salary $= \$2{,}000{,}000(7) + \$100{,}000(7) = \$14{,}700{,}000$
Option 2: Geometric series with: $a = \$2{,}000{,}000, \quad r = 1.045, \quad n = 7$
Find the sum of the geometric series:
$$S = 2{,}000{,}000\left(\frac{1-(1.045)^7}{1-1.045}\right) = \$16{,}038{,}304$$
Option 3: Arithmetic series with: $a = \$2{,}000{,}000, \quad d = \$95{,}000, \quad n = 7$
Find the sum of the arithmetic series:
$$S_7 = \frac{7}{2}(2(2{,}000{,}000) + (7-1)(95{,}000)) = \$15{,}995{,}000$$
Option 2 provides the most money; Option 1 provides the least money.

76. Given: $a = 1000, \ r = 0.9$
Find n when $a_n < 0.01$:
$$1000(0.9)^{n-1} < 0.01 \rightarrow (0.9)^{n-1} < 0.00001$$
$$(n-1)\log(0.9) < \log(0.00001) \rightarrow n-1 > \frac{\log(0.00001)}{\log(0.9)} \rightarrow n > \frac{\log(0.00001)}{\log(0.9)} + 1 = 110.27$$
On the 111th day or December 20, 1998, the amount will be less than \$0.01.
Find the sum of the geometric series:
$$S_{110} = a\left(\frac{1-r^n}{1-r}\right) = 1000\left(\frac{1-(0.9)^{110}}{1-0.9}\right) = 1000\left(\frac{1-(0.9)^{110}}{0.1}\right) = \$9999.91$$

77. This is a geometric sequence with $a = 1, \quad r = 2, \quad n = 64$.
Find the sum of the geometric series:
$$S_{64} = 1\left(\frac{1-2^{64}}{1-2}\right) = \frac{1-2^{64}}{-1} = 2^{64} - 1 = 1.845 \times 10^{19} \text{ grains}$$

78. This is an infinite geometric series with $a=\frac{1}{4}$, $r=\frac{1}{4}$.
Find the sum of the infinite geometric series:

$$S=\frac{\left(\frac{1}{4}\right)}{\left(1-\frac{1}{4}\right)}=\frac{\left(\frac{1}{4}\right)}{\left(\frac{3}{4}\right)}=\frac{1}{3}$$

$\therefore\ \frac{1}{3}$ of the square is eventually shaded.

79. The common ratio, $r=0.90<1$. The sum is: $S=\frac{1}{1-0.9}=\frac{1}{0.10}=10$.
The multiplier is 10.

80. The common ratio, $r=0.95<1$. The sum is: $S=\frac{1}{1-0.95}=\frac{1}{0.05}=20$.
The multiplier is 20.

81. This is an infinite geometric series with $a=4$, and $r=\frac{1.03}{1.09}$.

Find the sum: $\text{Price}=\frac{4}{\left(1-\frac{1.03}{1.09}\right)}=\$72.67$.

82. This is an infinite geometric series with $a=2.5$, and $r=\frac{1.04}{1.11}$.

Find the sum: $\text{Price}=\frac{2.5}{\left(1-\frac{1.04}{1.11}\right)}=\$39.64$.

83. – 85. Answers will vary.

Chapter 13

Sequences; Induction; The Binomial Theorem

13.4 Mathematical Induction

1. I: $n=1$: $2 \cdot 1 = 2$ and $1(1+1) = 2$

   II: If $2+4+6+\cdots+2k = k(k+1)$

   then $2+4+6+\cdots+2k+2(k+1)$

   $$= [2+4+6+\cdots+2k]+2(k+1) = k(k+1)+2(k+1)$$
   $$= (k+1)(k+2)$$

   Conditions I and II are satisfied; the statement is true.

2. I: $n=1$: $4 \cdot 1 - 3 = 1$ and $1(2 \cdot 1 - 1) = 1$

   II: If $1+5+9+\cdots+(4k-3) = k(2k-1)$

   then $1+5+9+\cdots+(4k-3)+(4(k+1)-3)$

   $$= [1+5+9+\cdots+(4k-3)]+4k+4-3 = k(2k-1)+4k+1$$
   $$= 2k^2 - k + 4k + 1 = 2k^2 + 3k + 1 = (k+1)(2k+1)$$

   Conditions I and II are satisfied; the statement is true.

3. I: $n=1$: $1+2=3$ and $\frac{1}{2} \cdot 1(1+5) = 3$

   II: If $3+4+5+\cdots+(k+2) = \frac{1}{2} \cdot k(k+5)$

   then $3+4+5+\cdots+(k+2)+[(k+1)+2]$

   $$= [3+4+5+\cdots+(k+2)]+(k+3) = \frac{1}{2} \cdot k(k+5)+(k+3)$$
   $$= \frac{1}{2}k^2 + \frac{5}{2}k + k + 3 = \frac{1}{2}k^2 + \frac{7}{2}k + 3 = \frac{1}{2} \cdot \left(k^2+7k+6\right)$$
   $$= \frac{1}{2} \cdot (k+1)(k+6)$$

   Conditions I and II are satisfied; the statement is true.

4. I: $n=1$: $2 \cdot 1 + 1 = 3$ and $1(1+2) = 3$

   II: If $3+5+7+\cdots+(2k+1) = k(k+2)$

   then $3+5+7+\cdots+(2k+1)+[2(k+1)+1]$

   $$= [3+5+7+\cdots+(2k+1)]+(2k+3) = k(k+2)+(2k+3)$$
   $$= k^2+2k+2k+3 = k^2+4k+3 = (k+1)(k+3)$$

   Conditions I and II are satisfied; the statement is true.

5. I: $n=1:\ 3\cdot 1-1=2$ and $\frac{1}{2}\cdot 1(3\cdot 1+1)=2$

II: If $2+5+8+\cdots+(3k-1)=\frac{1}{2}\cdot k(3k+1)$

then $2+5+8+\cdots+(3k-1)+[3(k+1)-1]$

$$=[2+5+8+\cdots+(3k-1)]+(3k+2)=\frac{1}{2}\cdot k(3k+1)+(3k+2)$$

$$=\frac{3}{2}k^2+\frac{1}{2}k+3k+2=\frac{3}{2}k^2+\frac{7}{2}k+2=\frac{1}{2}\cdot\left(3k^2+7k+4\right)$$

$$=\frac{1}{2}\cdot(k+1)(3k+4)$$

Conditions I and II are satisfied; the statement is true.

6. I: $n=1:\ 3\cdot 1-2=1$ and $\frac{1}{2}\cdot 1(3\cdot 1-1)=1$

II: If $1+4+7+\cdots+(3k-2)=\frac{1}{2}\cdot k(3k-1)$

then $1+4+7+\cdots+(3k-2)+[3(k+1)-2]$

$$=[1+4+7+\cdots+(3k-2)]+(3k+1)=\frac{1}{2}\cdot k(3k-1)+(3k+1)$$

$$=\frac{3}{2}k^2-\frac{1}{2}k+3k+1=\frac{3}{2}k^2+\frac{5}{2}k+1=\frac{1}{2}\cdot\left(3k^2+5k+2\right)$$

$$=\frac{1}{2}\cdot(k+1)(3k+2)$$

Conditions I and II are satisfied; the statement is true.

7. I: $n=1:\ 2^{1-1}=1$ and $2^1-1=1$

II: If $1+2+2^2+\cdots+2^{k-1}=2^k-1$

then $1+2+2^2+\cdots+2^{k-1}+2^{k+1-1}$

$$=\left[1+2+2^2+\cdots+2^{k-1}\right]+2^k=2^k-1+2^k$$

$$=2\cdot 2^k-1=2^{k+1}-1$$

Conditions I and II are satisfied; the statement is true.

8. I: $n=1:\ 3^{1-1}=1$ and $\frac{1}{2}(3^1-1)=1$

II: If $1+3+3^2+\cdots+3^{k-1}=\frac{1}{2}\cdot(3^k-1)$

then $1+3+3^2+\cdots+3^{k-1}+3^{k+1-1}$

$$=\left[1+3+3^2+\cdots+3^{k-1}\right]+3^k=\frac{1}{2}\cdot(3^k-1)+3^k$$

$$=\frac{1}{2}\cdot 3^k-\frac{1}{2}+3^k=\frac{3}{2}\cdot 3^k-\frac{1}{2}=\frac{1}{2}\cdot\left(3\cdot 3^k-1\right)=\frac{1}{2}\left(3^{k+1}-1\right)$$

Conditions I and II are satisfied; the statement is true.

9. I: $n=1$: $4^{1-1}=1$ and $\frac{1}{3}\cdot\left(4^1-1\right)=1$

II: If $1+4+4^2+\cdots+4^{k-1}=\frac{1}{3}\cdot\left(4^k-1\right)$

then $1+4+4^2+\cdots+4^{k-1}+4^{k+1-1}$

$$=\left[1+4+4^2+\cdots+4^{k-1}\right]+4^k=\frac{1}{3}\cdot\left(4^k-1\right)+4^k$$

$$=\frac{1}{3}\cdot 4^k-\frac{1}{3}+4^k=\frac{4}{3}\cdot 4^k-\frac{1}{3}=\frac{1}{3}\left(4\cdot 4^k-1\right)=\frac{1}{3}\cdot\left(4^{k+1}-1\right)$$

Conditions I and II are satisfied; the statement is true.

10. I: $n=1$: $5^{1-1}=1$ and $\frac{1}{4}\cdot\left(5^1-1\right)=1$

II: If $1+5+5^2+\cdots+5^{k-1}=\frac{1}{4}\cdot\left(5^k-1\right)$

then $1+5+5^2+\cdots+5^{k-1}+5^{k+1-1}$

$$=\left[1+5+5^2+\cdots+5^{k-1}\right]+5^k=\frac{1}{4}\cdot\left(5^k-1\right)+5^k$$

$$=\frac{1}{4}\cdot 5^k-\frac{1}{4}+5^k=\frac{5}{4}\cdot 5^k-\frac{1}{4}=\frac{1}{4}\left(5\cdot 5^k-1\right)=\frac{1}{4}\cdot\left(5^{k+1}-1\right)$$

Conditions I and II are satisfied; the statement is true.

11. I: $n=1$: $\frac{1}{1(1+1)}=\frac{1}{2}$ and $\frac{1}{1+1}=\frac{1}{2}$

II: If $\frac{1}{1\cdot 2}+\frac{1}{2\cdot 3}+\frac{1}{3\cdot 4}+\cdots+\frac{1}{k(k+1)}=\frac{k}{k+1}$

then $\frac{1}{1\cdot 2}+\frac{1}{2\cdot 3}+\frac{1}{3\cdot 4}+\cdots+\frac{1}{k(k+1)}+\frac{1}{(k+1)(k+1+1)}$

$$=\left[\frac{1}{1\cdot 2}+\frac{1}{2\cdot 3}+\frac{1}{3\cdot 4}+\cdots+\frac{1}{k(k+1)}\right]+\frac{1}{(k+1)(k+2)}$$

$$=\frac{k}{k+1}+\frac{1}{(k+1)(k+2)}=\frac{k}{k+1}\cdot\frac{k+2}{k+2}+\frac{1}{(k+1)(k+2)}$$

$$=\frac{k^2+2k+1}{(k+1)(k+2)}=\frac{(k+1)(k+1)}{(k+1)(k+2)}=\frac{k+1}{k+2}$$

Conditions I and II are satisfied; the statement is true.

12. I: $n=1$: $\frac{1}{(2\cdot 1-1)(2\cdot 1+1)}=\frac{1}{3}$ and $\frac{1}{2\cdot 1+1}=\frac{1}{3}$

II: If $\frac{1}{1\cdot 3}+\frac{1}{3\cdot 5}+\frac{1}{5\cdot 7}+\cdots+\frac{1}{(2k-1)(2k+1)}=\frac{k}{2k+1}$

then $\dfrac{1}{1\cdot 3}+\dfrac{1}{3\cdot 5}+\dfrac{1}{5\cdot 7}+\cdots+\dfrac{1}{(2k-1)(2k+1)}+\dfrac{1}{(2(k+1)-1)(2(k+1)+1)}$

$$=\left[\frac{1}{1\cdot 3}+\frac{1}{3\cdot 5}+\frac{1}{5\cdot 7}+\cdots+\frac{1}{(2k-1)(2k+1)}\right]+\frac{1}{(2k+1)(2k+3)}$$

$$=\frac{k}{2k+1}+\frac{1}{(2k+1)(2k+3)}=\frac{k}{2k+1}\cdot\frac{2k+3}{2k+3}+\frac{1}{(2k+1)(2k+3)}$$

$$=\frac{2k^2+3k+1}{(2k+1)(2k+3)}=\frac{(k+1)(2k+1)}{(2k+1)(2k+3)}=\frac{k+1}{2k+3}$$

Conditions I and II are satisfied; the statement is true.

13. I: $n=1$: $1^2=1$ and $\dfrac{1}{6}\cdot 1(1+1)(2\cdot 1+1)=1$

II: If $1^2+2^2+3^2+\cdots+k^2=\dfrac{1}{6}\cdot k(k+1)(2k+1)$

then $1^2+2^2+3^2+\cdots+k^2+(k+1)^2$

$$=\left[1^2+2^2+3^2+\cdots+k^2\right]+(k+1)^2=\frac{1}{6}k(k+1)(2k+1)+(k+1)^2$$

$$=(k+1)\left[\frac{1}{6}k(2k+1)+k+1\right]=(k+1)\left[\frac{1}{3}k^2+\frac{1}{6}k+k+1\right]$$

$$=(k+1)\left[\frac{1}{3}k^2+\frac{7}{6}k+1\right]=\frac{1}{6}(k+1)\left[2k^2+7k+6\right]$$

$$=\frac{1}{6}\cdot(k+1)(k+2)(2k+3)$$

Conditions I and II are satisfied; the statement is true.

14. I: $n=1$: $1^3=1$ and $\dfrac{1}{4}\cdot 1^2(1+1)^2=1$

II: If $1^3+2^3+3^3+\cdots+k^3=\dfrac{1}{4}k^2(k+1)^2$

then $1^3+2^3+3^3+\cdots+k^3+(k+1)^3$

$$=\left[1^3+2^3+3^3+\cdots+k^3\right]+(k+1)^3=\frac{1}{4}k^2(k+1)^2+(k+1)^3$$

$$=(k+1)^2\left[\frac{1}{4}k^2+k+1\right]=\frac{1}{4}(k+1)^2\left[k^2+4k+4\right]$$

$$=\frac{1}{4}\cdot(k+1)^2(k+2)^2$$

Conditions I and II are satisfied; the statement is true.

15. I: $n=1:\ 5-1=4$ and $\frac{1}{2}\cdot 1(9-1)=4$

II: If $4+3+2+\cdots+(5-k)=\frac{1}{2}\cdot k(9-k)$

then $4+3+2+\cdots+(5-k)+(5-(k+1))$

$$=[4+3+2+\cdots+(5-k)]+(4-k)=\frac{1}{2}k(9-k)+(4-k)$$

$$=\frac{9}{2}k-\frac{1}{2}k^2+4-k=-\frac{1}{2}k^2+\frac{7}{2}k+4=-\frac{1}{2}\cdot[k^2-7k-8]$$

$$=-\frac{1}{2}\cdot(k+1)(k-8)=\frac{1}{2}\cdot(k+1)(8-k)=\frac{1}{2}\cdot(k+1)[9-(k+1)]$$

Conditions I and II are satisfied; the statement is true.

16. I: $n=1:\ -(1+1)=-2$ and $-\frac{1}{2}\cdot 1(1+3)=-2$

II: If $-2-3-4-\cdots-(k+1)=-\frac{1}{2}\cdot k(k+3)$

then $-2-3-4-\cdots-(k+1)-((k+1)+1)$

$$=[-2-3-4-\cdots-(k+1)]-(k+2)=-\frac{1}{2}\cdot k(k+3)-(k+2)$$

$$=-\frac{1}{2}k^2-\frac{3}{2}k-k-2=-\frac{1}{2}k^2-\frac{5}{2}k-2=-\frac{1}{2}\cdot[k^2+5k+4]$$

$$=-\frac{1}{2}\cdot(k+1)(k+4)$$

Conditions I and II are satisfied; the statement is true.

17. I: $n=1:\ 1(1+1)=2$ and $\frac{1}{3}\cdot 1(1+1)(1+2)=2$

II: If $1\cdot 2+2\cdot 3+3\cdot 4+\cdots+k(k+1)=\frac{1}{3}\cdot k(k+1)(k+2)$

then $1\cdot 2+2\cdot 3+3\cdot 4+\cdots+k(k+1)+(k+1)(k+1+1)$

$$=[1\cdot 2+2\cdot 3+3\cdot 4+\cdots+k(k+1)]+(k+1)(k+2)$$

$$=\frac{1}{3}\cdot k(k+1)(k+2)+(k+1)(k+2)=(k+1)(k+2)\left[\frac{1}{3}k+1\right]$$

$$=\frac{1}{3}\cdot(k+1)(k+2)(k+3)$$

Conditions I and II are satisfied; the statement is true.

18. I: $n=1$: $(2\cdot 1-1)(2\cdot 1)=2$ and $\frac{1}{3}\cdot 1(1+1)(4\cdot 1-1)=2$

II: If $1\cdot 2+3\cdot 4+5\cdot 6+\cdots+(2k-1)(2k)=\frac{1}{3}\cdot k(k+1)(4k-1)$

then $1\cdot 2+3\cdot 4+5\cdot 6+\cdots+(2k-1)(2k)+(2(k+1)-1)(2(k+1))$

$$=[1\cdot 2+3\cdot 4+5\cdot 6+\cdots+(2k-1)(2k)]+(2k+1)(k+1)\cdot 2$$

$$=\frac{1}{3}k(k+1)(4k-1)+2(k+1)(2k+1)=(k+1)\left[\frac{1}{3}\cdot k(4k-1)+2(2k+1)\right]$$

$$=(k+1)\left[\frac{4}{3}k^2-\frac{1}{3}k+4k+2\right]=\frac{1}{3}\cdot(k+1)\left(4k^2-k+12k+6\right)$$

$$=\frac{1}{3}(k+1)\left(4k^2+11k+6\right)=\frac{1}{3}\cdot(k+1)(k+2)(4k+3)$$

Conditions I and II are satisfied; the statement is true.

19. I: $n=1$: $1^2+1=2$ is divisible by 2

II: If k^2+k is divisible by 2

then $(k+1)^2+(k+1)=k^2+2k+1+k+1=(k^2+k)+(2k+2)$

Since k^2+k is divisible by 2 and $2k+2$ is divisible by 2, then $(k+1)^2+(k+1)$ is divisible by 2.

Conditions I and II are satisfied; the statement is true.

20. I: $n=1$: $1^3+2\cdot 1=3$ is divisible by 3

II: If k^3+2k is divisible by 3

then $(k+1)^3+2(k+1)=k^3+3k^2+3k+1+2k+2=(k^3+2k)+(3k^2+3k+3)$

Since k^3+2k is divisible by 3 and $3k^2+3k+3$ is divisible by 3, then $(k+1)^3+2(k+1)$ is divisible by 3.

Conditions I and II are satisfied; the statement is true.

21. I: $n=1$: $1^2-1+2=2$ is divisible by 2

II: If k^2-k+2 is divisible by 2

then $(k+1)^2-(k+1)+2=k^2+2k+1-k-1+2=(k^2-k+2)+(2k)$

Since k^2-k+2 is divisible by 2 and $2k$ is divisible by 2, then $(k+1)^2-(k+1)+2$ is divisible by 2.

Conditions I and II are satisfied; the statement is true.

22. I: $n=1$: $1(1+1)(1+2)=6$ is divisible by 6

II: If $k(k+1)(k+2)$ is divisible by 6

then $(k+1)(k+1+1)(k+1+2)=(k+1)(k+2)(k+3)$

$=k(k+1)(k+2)+3(k+1)(k+2)$. $k(k+1)(k+2)$ is divisible by 6 and either $k+1$ or $k+2$ is even. Thus, $3(k+1)(k+2)$ is divisible by 6.

Conditions I and II are satisfied; the statement is true.

23. I: $n = 1$: If $x > 1$ then $x^1 = x > 1$.
II: Assume, for any natural number k, that if $x > 1$, then $x^k > 1$.
Show that if $x^k > 1$, then $x^{k+1} > 1$:
$$x^{k+1} = x^k \cdot x > 1 \cdot x = x > 1$$
$$\uparrow$$
$$(x^k > 1)$$
Conditions I and II are satisfied; the statement is true.

24. I: $n = 1$: If $0 < x < 1$ then $0 < x^1 < 1$.
II: Assume, for any natural number k, that if $0 < x < 1$, then $0 < x^k < 1$.
Show that if $0 < x < 1$, then $0 < x^{k+1} < 1$:
$$0 < x^{k+1} = x^k \cdot x < 1 \cdot x = x < 1$$
Thus, $0 < x^{k+1} < 1$.
Conditions I and II are satisfied; the statement is true.

25. I: $n = 1$: $a - b$ is a factor of $a^1 - b^1 = a - b$.
II: If $a - b$ is a factor of $a^k - b^k$
Show that $a - b$ is a factor of $a^{k+1} - b^{k+1} = a \cdot a^k - b \cdot b^k$
$$= a \cdot a^k - a \cdot b^k + a \cdot b^k - b \cdot b^k = a\left(a^k - b^k\right) + b^k(a - b)$$
Since $a - b$ is a factor of $a^k - b^k$ and $a - b$ is a factor of $a - b$, then $a - b$ is a factor of $a^{k+1} - b^{k+1}$.
Conditions I and II are satisfied; the statement is true.

26. I: $n = 1$: $a + b$ is a factor of $a^{2\cdot1+1} + b^{2\cdot1+1} = a^3 + b^3$.
II: If $a + b$ is a factor of $a^{2k+1} + b^{2k+1}$
Show that $a + b$ is a factor of $a^{2(k+1)+1} + b^{2(k+1)+1} = a^{2k+3} + b^{2k+3}$
$$= a^2 \cdot a^{2k+1} + a^2 \cdot b^{2k+1} - a^2 \cdot b^{2k+1} + b^{2k+3}$$
$$= a^2\left(a^{2k+1} + b^{2k+1}\right) - b^{2k+1}(a^2 - b^2)$$
Since $a + b$ is a factor of $a^{2k+1} + b^{2k+1}$ and $a + b$ is a factor of $a^2 - b^2$, then $a + b$ is a factor of $a^{2k+3} + b^{2k+3}$.
Conditions I and II are satisfied; the statement is true.

27. $n = 1$: $1^2 - 1 + 41 = 41$ is a prime number.
$n = 41$: $41^2 - 41 + 41 = 41^2$ is not a prime number.

28. II: If $2 + 4 + 6 + \cdots + 2k = k^2 + k + 2$
then $2 + 4 + 6 + \cdots + 2k + 2(k+1)$
$$= [2 + 4 + 6 + \cdots + 2k] + 2k + 2 = k^2 + k + 2 + 2k + 2$$
$$= (k^2 + 2k + 1) + (k + 1) + 2 = (k+1)^2 + (k+1) + 2$$
I: $n = 1$: $2 \cdot 1 = 2$ and $1^2 + 1 + 2 = 4 \neq 2$

29. I: $n=1$: $ar^{1-1}=a$ and $a\left(\frac{1-r^1}{1-r}\right)=a$

II: If $a+ar+ar^2+\cdots+ar^{k-1}=a\left(\frac{1-r^k}{1-r}\right)$

then $a+ar+ar^2+\cdots+ar^{k-1}+ar^{k+1-1}$

$$=\left[a+ar+ar^2+\cdots+ar^{k-1}\right]+ar^k=a\left(\frac{1-r^k}{1-r}\right)+ar^k$$

$$=\frac{a(1-r^k)+ar^k(1-r)}{1-r}=\frac{a-ar^k+ar^k-ar^{k+1}}{1-r}=a\left(\frac{1-r^{k+1}}{1-r}\right)$$

Conditions I and II are satisfied; the statement is true.

30. I: $n=1$: $a+(1-1)d=a$ and $1\cdot a+d\frac{1(1-1)}{2}=a$

II: If $a+(a+d)+(a+2d)+\cdots+[a+(k-1)d]=ka+d\frac{k(k-1)}{2}$

then $a+(a+d)+(a+2d)+\cdots+[a+(k-1)d]+(a+kd)$

$$=[a+(a+d)+(a+2d)+\cdots+[a+(k-1)d]]+(a+kd)$$

$$=ka+d\frac{k(k-1)}{2}+(a+kd)=(k+1)a+d\left[\frac{k(k-1)}{2}+k\right]$$

$$=(k+1)a+d\left[\frac{k^2-k+2k}{2}\right]=(k+1)a+d\left[\frac{k^2+k}{2}\right]$$

$$=(k+1)a+d\left[\frac{(k+1)k}{2}\right]$$

Conditions I and II are satisfied; the statement is true.

31. I: $n=4$: The number of diagonals of a quadrilateral is $\frac{1}{2}\cdot 4(4-3)=2$

II: Assume that for any integer k the number of diagonals of a convex polygon with k sides (k vertices) is $\frac{1}{2}\cdot k(k-3)$. A convex polygon with $k+1$ sides ($k+1$ vertices) consists of a convex polygon with k sides (k vertices) plus a triangle for a total of $k+1$ vertices. The number of diagonals of this convex polygon consists of the original ones plus $k-1$ additional ones, namely, $\frac{1}{2}\cdot k(k-3)+(k-1)=\frac{1}{2}k^2-\frac{3}{2}k+k-1=\frac{1}{2}k^2-\frac{1}{2}k-1$

$$=\frac{1}{2}\cdot(k^2-k-2)=\frac{1}{2}\cdot(k+1)(k-2)$$

Conditions I and II are satisfied; the statement is true.

32. I: $n = 3$: $(3-2)\cdot 180° = 180°$ which is the sum of the angles of a triangle.

II: Assume that for any integer k the sum of the angles of a convex polygon with k sides is $(k-2)\cdot 180°$. A convex polygon with $k+1$ sides consists of a convex polygon with k sides plus a triangle. Thus the sum of the angles is $(k-2)\cdot 180° + 180° = (k-1)\cdot 180°$.

Conditions I and II are satisfied; the statement is true.

33. Answers will vary.

Chapter 13

Sequences; Induction; The Binomial Theorem

13.5 The Binomial Theorem

1. $\binom{5}{3} = \frac{5!}{3!\,2!} = \frac{5 \cdot 4 \cdot 3 \cdot 2 \cdot 1}{3 \cdot 2 \cdot 1 \cdot 2 \cdot 1} = \frac{5 \cdot 4}{2 \cdot 1} = 10$

2. $\binom{7}{3} = \frac{7!}{3!\,4!} = \frac{7 \cdot 6 \cdot 5 \cdot 4 \cdot 3 \cdot 2 \cdot 1}{3 \cdot 2 \cdot 1 \cdot 4 \cdot 3 \cdot 2 \cdot 1} = \frac{7 \cdot 6 \cdot 5}{3 \cdot 2 \cdot 1} = 35$

3. $\binom{7}{5} = \frac{7!}{5!\,2!} = \frac{7 \cdot 6 \cdot 5 \cdot 4 \cdot 3 \cdot 2 \cdot 1}{5 \cdot 4 \cdot 3 \cdot 2 \cdot 1 \cdot 2 \cdot 1} = \frac{7 \cdot 6}{2 \cdot 1} = 21$

4. $\binom{9}{7} = \frac{9!}{7!\,2!} = \frac{9 \cdot 8 \cdot 7 \cdot 6 \cdot 5 \cdot 4 \cdot 3 \cdot 2 \cdot 1}{7 \cdot 6 \cdot 5 \cdot 4 \cdot 3 \cdot 2 \cdot 1 \cdot 2 \cdot 1} = \frac{9 \cdot 8}{2 \cdot 1} = 36$

5. $\binom{50}{49} = \frac{50!}{49!\,1!} = \frac{50 \cdot 49!}{49! \cdot 1} = \frac{50}{1} = 50$

6. $\binom{100}{98} = \frac{100!}{98!\,2!} = \frac{100 \cdot 99 \cdot 98!}{98! \cdot 2 \cdot 1} = \frac{100 \cdot 99}{2 \cdot 1} = 4950$

7. $\binom{1000}{1000} = \frac{1000!}{1000!\,0!} = \frac{1}{1} = 1$

8. $\binom{1000}{0} = \frac{1000!}{0!1000!} = \frac{1}{1} = 1$

9. $\binom{55}{23} = \frac{55!}{23!\,32!} = 1.866442159 \times 10^{15}$

10. $\binom{60}{20} = \frac{60!}{20!\,40!} = 4.191844506 \times 10^{15}$

11. $\binom{47}{25} = \frac{47!}{25!\,22!} = 1.483389769 \times 10^{13}$

12. $\binom{37}{19} = \frac{37!}{19!\,18!} = 1.76726319 \times 10^{10}$

13. $(x+1)^5 = \binom{5}{0}x^5 + \binom{5}{1}x^4 + \binom{5}{2}x^3 + \binom{5}{3}x^2 + \binom{5}{4}x^1 + \binom{5}{5}x^0$
$= x^5 + 5x^4 + 10x^3 + 10x^2 + 5x + 1$

14. $(x-1)^5 = \binom{5}{0}x^5 + \binom{5}{1}(-1)x^4 + \binom{5}{2}(-1)^2x^3 + \binom{5}{3}(-1)^3x^2 + \binom{5}{4}(-1)^4x^1 + \binom{5}{5}(-1)^5x^0$
$= x^5 - 5x^4 + 10x^3 - 10x^2 + 5x - 1$

15. $(x-2)^6 = \binom{6}{0}x^6 + \binom{6}{1}x^5(-2) + \binom{6}{2}x^4(-2)^2 + \binom{6}{3}x^3(-2)^3 + \binom{6}{4}x^2(-2)^4$
$+\binom{6}{5}x(-2)^5 + \binom{6}{6}x^0(-2)^6$
$= x^6 + 6x^5(-2) + 15x^4 \cdot 4 + 20x^3(-8) + 15x^2 \cdot 16 + 6x \cdot (-32) + 64$
$= x^6 - 12x^5 + 60x^4 - 160x^3 + 240x - 192x + 64$

16. $(x+3)^5 = \binom{5}{0}x^5 + \binom{5}{1}x^4(3) + \binom{5}{2}x^3(3)^2 + \binom{5}{3}x^2(3)^3 + \binom{5}{4}x^1(3)^4 + \binom{5}{5}x^0(3)^5$
$= x^5 + 5x^4(3) + 10x^3 \cdot 9 + 10x^2(27) + 5x \cdot 81 + 243$
$= x^5 + 15x^4 + 90x^3 + 270x^2 + 405x + 243$

17. $(3x+1)^4 = \binom{4}{0}(3x)^4 + \binom{4}{1}(3x)^3 + \binom{4}{2}(3x)^2 + \binom{4}{3}(3x) + \binom{4}{4}$
$= 81x^4 + 4 \cdot 27x^3 + 6 \cdot 9x^2 + 4 \cdot 3x + 1 = 81x^4 + 108x^3 + 54x^2 + 12x + 1$

18. $(2x+3)^5 = \binom{5}{0}(2x)^5 + \binom{5}{1}(2x)^4 \cdot 3 + \binom{5}{2}(2x)^3 \cdot 3^2 + \binom{5}{3}(2x)^2 \cdot 3^3$
$+\binom{5}{4} \cdot 2x \cdot 3^4 + \binom{5}{5} \cdot 3^5$
$= 32x^5 + 5 \cdot 16x^4 \cdot 3 + 10 \cdot 8x^3 \cdot 9 + 10 \cdot 4x^2 \cdot 27 + 5 \cdot 2x \cdot 81 + 243$
$= 32x^5 + 240x^4 + 720x^3 + 1080x^2 + 810x + 243$

19. $(x^2+y^2)^5 = \binom{5}{0}(x^2)^5(y^2)^0 + \binom{5}{1}(x^2)^4(y^2) + \binom{5}{2}(x^2)^3(y^2)^2 + \binom{5}{3}(x^2)^2(y^2)^3$
$+\binom{5}{4}x^2(y^2)^4 + \binom{5}{5}(y^2)^5$
$= x^{10} + 5x^8y^2 + 10x^6y^4 + 10x^4y^6 + 5x^2y^8 + y^{10}$

20. $(x^2-y^2)^6 = \binom{6}{0}(x^2)^6(-y^2)^0 + \binom{6}{1}(x^2)^5(-y^2) + \binom{6}{2}(x^2)^4(-y^2)^2 + \binom{6}{3}(x^2)^3(-y^2)^3$
$\binom{6}{4}(x^2)^2(-y^2)^4 + \binom{6}{5}x^2(-y^2)^5 + \binom{6}{6}(-y^2)^6$
$= x^{12} - 6x^{10}y^2 + 15x^8y^4 - 20x^6y^6 + 15x^4y^8 - 6x^2y^{10} + y^{12}$

21. $$\left(\sqrt{x}+\sqrt{2}\right)^6=\binom{6}{0}\left(\sqrt{x}\right)^6\left(\sqrt{2}\right)^0+\binom{6}{1}\left(\sqrt{x}\right)^5\left(\sqrt{2}\right)^1+\binom{6}{2}\left(\sqrt{x}\right)^4\left(\sqrt{2}\right)^2+\binom{6}{3}\left(\sqrt{x}\right)^3\left(\sqrt{2}\right)^3$$
$$\binom{6}{4}\left(\sqrt{x}\right)^2\left(\sqrt{2}\right)^4+\binom{6}{5}\left(\sqrt{x}\right)\left(\sqrt{2}\right)^5+\binom{6}{6}\left(\sqrt{x}\right)^0\left(\sqrt{2}\right)^6$$
$$=x^3+6\sqrt{2}x^{5/2}+15\cdot 2x^2+20\cdot 2\sqrt{2}x^{3/2}+15\cdot 4x+6\cdot 4\sqrt{2}x^{1/2}+8$$
$$=x^3+6\sqrt{2}x^{5/2}+30x^2+40\sqrt{2}x^{3/2}+60x+24\sqrt{2}x^{1/2}+8$$

22. $$\left(\sqrt{x}-\sqrt{3}\right)^4=\binom{4}{0}\left(\sqrt{x}\right)^4\left(-\sqrt{3}\right)^0+\binom{4}{1}\left(\sqrt{x}\right)^3\left(-\sqrt{3}\right)^1+\binom{4}{2}\left(\sqrt{x}\right)^2\left(-\sqrt{3}\right)^2$$
$$+\binom{4}{3}\left(\sqrt{x}\right)\left(-\sqrt{3}\right)^3+\binom{4}{4}\left(\sqrt{x}\right)^0\left(-\sqrt{3}\right)^4$$
$$=x^2-4\sqrt{3}x^{3/2}+6\cdot 3x-4\cdot 3\sqrt{3}x^{1/2}+9=x^2-4\sqrt{3}x^{3/2}+18x-12\sqrt{3}x^{1/2}+9$$

23. $$(ax+by)^5=\binom{5}{0}(ax)^5+\binom{5}{1}(ax)^4\cdot by+\binom{5}{2}(ax)^3(by)^2+\binom{5}{3}(ax)^2(by)^3$$
$$+\binom{5}{4}ax(by)^4+\binom{5}{5}(by)^5$$
$$=a^5x^5+5a^4x^4by+10a^3x^3b^2y^2+10a^2x^2b^3y^3+5axb^4y^4+b^5y^5$$

24. $$(ax-by)^4=\binom{4}{0}(ax)^4+\binom{4}{1}(ax)^3(-by)+\binom{4}{2}(ax)^2(-by)^2+\binom{4}{3}(ax)(-by)^3$$
$$+\binom{4}{4}(-by)^4$$
$$=a^4x^4-4a^3x^3by+6a^2x^2b^2y^2-4axb^3y^3+b^4y^4$$

25. $n=10,\ \ j=4,\ \ x=x,\ \ a=3$
$$\binom{10}{4}x^6\cdot 3^4=\frac{10!}{4!\,6!}\cdot 81x^6=\frac{10\cdot 9\cdot 8\cdot 7}{4\cdot 3\cdot 2\cdot 1}\cdot 81x^6=17{,}010x^6$$
The coefficient of x^6 is 17,010.

26. $n=10,\ \ j=7,\ \ x=x,\ \ a=-3$
$$\binom{10}{7}x^3\cdot(-3)^7=\frac{10!}{7!\,3!}\cdot -2187x^3=\frac{10\cdot 9\cdot 8}{3\cdot 2\cdot 1}\cdot -2187x^3=-262{,}440x^3$$
The coefficient of x^3 is $-262{,}440$.

27. $n=12,\ \ j=5,\ \ x=2x,\ \ a=-1$
$$\binom{12}{5}(2x)^7\cdot(-1)^5=\frac{12!}{5!\,7!}\cdot 128x^7(-1)=\frac{12\cdot 11\cdot 10\cdot 9\cdot 8}{5\cdot 4\cdot 3\cdot 2\cdot 1}\cdot(-128)x^7=-101{,}376x^7$$
The coefficient of x^7 is $-101{,}376$.

28. $n = 12,\ j = 9,\ x = 2x,\ a = 1$

$$\binom{12}{9}(2x)^3 \cdot (1)^9 = \frac{12!}{9!\,3!} \cdot 8x^3(1) = \frac{12 \cdot 11 \cdot 10}{3 \cdot 2 \cdot 1} \cdot 8x^3 = 1760x^3$$

The coefficient of x^3 is 1760.

29. $n = 9,\ j = 2,\ x = 2x,\ a = 3$

$$\binom{9}{2}(2x)^7 \cdot 3^2 = \frac{9!}{2!\,7!} \cdot 128x^7(9) = \frac{9 \cdot 8}{2 \cdot 1} \cdot 128x^7 \cdot 9 = 41{,}472x^7$$

The coefficient of x^7 is 41,472.

30. $n = 9,\ j = 7,\ x = 2x,\ a = -3$

$$\binom{9}{7}(2x)^2 \cdot (-3)^7 = \frac{9!}{7!\,2!} \cdot 4x^2(-2187) = \frac{9 \cdot 8}{2 \cdot 1} \cdot 4x^2 \cdot -2187 = -314{,}928x^2$$

The coefficient of x^2 is $-314{,}928$.

31. $n = 7,\ j = 4,\ x = x,\ a = 3$

$$\binom{7}{4}x^3 \cdot 3^4 = \frac{7!}{4!\,3!} \cdot 81x^3 = \frac{7 \cdot 6 \cdot 5}{3 \cdot 2 \cdot 1} \cdot 81x^3 = 2835x^3$$

32. $n = 7,\ j = 2,\ x = x,\ a = -3$

$$\binom{7}{2}x^5 \cdot (-3)^2 = \frac{7!}{2!\,5!} \cdot 9x^5 = \frac{7 \cdot 6}{2 \cdot 1} \cdot 9x^5 = 189x^5$$

33. $n = 9,\ j = 2,\ x = 3x,\ a = -2$

$$\binom{9}{2}(3x)^7 \cdot (-2)^2 = \frac{9!}{2!\,7!} \cdot 2187x^7 \cdot 4 = \frac{9 \cdot 8}{2 \cdot 1} \cdot 8748x^7 = 314{,}928x^7$$

34. $n = 8,\ j = 5,\ x = 3x,\ a = 2$

$$\binom{8}{5}(3x)^3 \cdot (2)^5 = \frac{8!}{5!\,3!} \cdot 27x^3 \cdot 32 = \frac{8 \cdot 7 \cdot 6}{3 \cdot 2 \cdot 1} \cdot 864x^3 = 48{,}384x^3$$

35. The constant term in $\binom{12}{j}\left(x^2\right)^{12-j}\left(\frac{1}{x}\right)^j$ occurs when:

$2(12 - j) = j \rightarrow 24 - 2j = j \rightarrow 3j = 24 \rightarrow j = 8$.

Evaluate the 9th term:

$$\binom{12}{8}\left(x^2\right)^4 \cdot \left(\frac{1}{x}\right)^8 = \frac{12!}{8!\,4!}x^8 \cdot \frac{1}{x^8} = \frac{12 \cdot 11 \cdot 10 \cdot 9}{4 \cdot 3 \cdot 2 \cdot 1}x^0 = 495$$

36. The constant term in $\binom{9}{j}(x)^{9-j}\left(-\frac{1}{x^2}\right)^j$ occurs when:

$9 - j = 2j \rightarrow 9 = 3j \rightarrow j = 3$.

Evaluate the 4th term:

$$\binom{9}{3}(x)^6 \cdot \left(-\frac{1}{x^2}\right)^3 = \frac{9!}{3!\,6!}x^6 \cdot -\frac{1}{x^6} = -\frac{9 \cdot 8 \cdot 7}{3 \cdot 2 \cdot 1}x^0 = -84$$

37. The x^4 term in $\binom{10}{j}(x)^{10-j}\left(\frac{-2}{\sqrt{x}}\right)^j$ occurs when:

$$10-j-\tfrac{1}{2}j=4 \;\rightarrow\; -\tfrac{3}{2}j=-6 \;\rightarrow\; j=4.$$

Evaluate the 5th term:

$$\binom{10}{4}(x)^6\cdot\left(\frac{-2}{\sqrt{x}}\right)^4=\frac{10!}{6!\,4!}x^6\cdot\frac{16}{x^2}=\frac{10\cdot 9\cdot 8\cdot 7}{4\cdot 3\cdot 2\cdot 1}\cdot 16x^4=3360x^4$$

The coefficient is 3360.

38. The x^2 term in $\binom{8}{j}\left(\sqrt{x}\right)^{8-j}\left(\frac{3}{\sqrt{x}}\right)^j$ occurs when:

$$\tfrac{1}{2}(8-j)-\tfrac{1}{2}j=2 \;\rightarrow\; 4-\tfrac{1}{2}j-\tfrac{1}{2}j=2 \;\rightarrow\; -j=-2 \;\rightarrow\; j=2.$$

Evaluate the 3rd term:

$$\binom{8}{2}\left(\sqrt{x}\right)^6\cdot\left(\frac{3}{\sqrt{x}}\right)^2=\frac{8!}{6!\,2!}x^3\cdot\frac{9}{x}=\frac{8\cdot 7}{2\cdot 1}\cdot 9x^2=252x^2$$

The coefficient is 252.

39. $(1.001)^5=\left(1+10^{-3}\right)^5=\binom{5}{0}\cdot 1^5+\binom{5}{1}\cdot 1^4\cdot 10^{-3}+\binom{5}{2}\cdot 1^3\cdot\left(10^{-3}\right)^2+\binom{5}{3}\cdot 1^2\cdot\left(10^{-3}\right)^3+\ldots$

$$=1+5(0.001)+10(0.000001)+10(0.000000001)+\ldots$$
$$=1+0.005+0.000010+0.000000010+\ldots$$
$$=1.00501 \quad \text{(correct to 5 decimal places)}$$

40. $(0.998)^6=(1-0.002)^6=\binom{6}{0}\cdot 1^6+\binom{6}{1}\cdot 1^5\cdot(-0.002)+\binom{6}{2}\cdot 1^4\cdot(-0.002)^2$

$$+\binom{6}{3}\cdot 1^3\cdot(-0.002)^3+\ldots$$
$$=1+6(-0.002)+15(0.000004)+20(-0.000000008)+\ldots$$
$$=1-0.012+0.000060-0.000000160+\ldots$$
$$=0.98806 \quad \text{(correct to 5 decimal places)}$$

41. $\binom{n}{n-1}=\dfrac{n!}{(n-1)!(n-(n-1))!}=\dfrac{n!}{(n-1)!(1)!}=n$

$$\binom{n}{n}=\frac{n!}{n!(n-n)!}=\frac{n!}{n!\,0!}=\frac{n!}{n!\cdot 1}=\frac{n!}{n!}=1$$

42. $\binom{n}{j}=\dfrac{n!}{j!(n-j)!}=\dfrac{n!}{(n-j)!(n-(n-j))!}=\dfrac{n!}{(n-j)!\,j!}=\binom{n}{n-j}$

43. Show that $\binom{n}{0}+\binom{n}{1}+\ldots+\binom{n}{n}=2^n$

$$2^n=(1+1)^n$$
$$=\binom{n}{0}\cdot 1^n+\binom{n}{1}\cdot 1^{n-1}\cdot 1+\binom{n}{2}\cdot 1^{n-2}\cdot 1^2+\ldots+\binom{n}{n}\cdot 1^{n-n}\cdot 1^n$$
$$=\binom{n}{0}+\binom{n}{1}+\ldots+\binom{n}{n}$$

44. Show that $\binom{n}{0}-\binom{n}{1}+\binom{n}{2}-\ldots+(-1)^n\binom{n}{n}=0$

$$0=(1-1)^n$$
$$=\binom{n}{0}\cdot 1^n+\binom{n}{1}\cdot 1^{n-1}\cdot(-1)+\binom{n}{2}\cdot 1^{n-2}\cdot(-1)^2+\ldots+\binom{n}{n}\cdot 1^{n-n}\cdot(-1)^n$$
$$=\binom{n}{0}-\binom{n}{1}+\binom{n}{2}-\ldots+(-1)^n\binom{n}{n}$$

45. $$\binom{5}{0}\left(\frac{1}{4}\right)^5+\binom{5}{1}\left(\frac{1}{4}\right)^4\left(\frac{3}{4}\right)+\binom{5}{2}\left(\frac{1}{4}\right)^3\left(\frac{3}{4}\right)^2+\binom{5}{3}\left(\frac{1}{4}\right)^2\left(\frac{3}{4}\right)^3$$
$$+\binom{5}{4}\left(\frac{1}{4}\right)\left(\frac{3}{4}\right)^4+\binom{5}{5}\left(\frac{3}{4}\right)^5=\left(\frac{1}{4}+\frac{3}{4}\right)^5=(1)^5=1$$

46. $12!=479{,}001{,}600=4.790016\times 10^8$

$20!=2.432902008\times 10^{18}$

$25!=1.551121004\times 10^{25}$

$$12!\approx\sqrt{2\cdot 12\pi}\left(\frac{12}{e}\right)^{12}\left(1+\frac{1}{12\cdot 12-1}\right)\approx\sqrt{24\pi}(54782414.52)(1.006993007)$$
$$\approx 479013972.4$$

$$20!\approx\sqrt{2\cdot 20\pi}\left(\frac{20}{e}\right)^{20}\left(1+\frac{1}{12\cdot 20-1}\right)\approx\sqrt{40\pi}(2.161276221\times 10^{17})(1.0041841)$$
$$\approx 2.43292403\times 10^{18}$$

$$25!\approx\sqrt{2\cdot 25\pi}\left(\frac{25}{e}\right)^{25}\left(1+\frac{1}{12\cdot 25-1}\right)\approx\sqrt{50\pi}(1.233497203\times 10^{24})(1.003344482)$$
$$\approx 1.551129917\times 10^{25}$$

Chapter 13

Sequences; Induction; The Binomial Theorem

13.R Chapter Review

1. $a_1 = (-1)^1 \frac{1+3}{1+2} = -\frac{4}{3}$, $a_2 = (-1)^2 \frac{2+3}{2+2} = \frac{5}{4}$, $a_3 = (-1)^3 \frac{3+3}{3+2} = -\frac{6}{5}$,
$a_4 = (-1)^4 \frac{4+3}{4+2} = \frac{7}{6}$, $a_5 = (-1)^5 \frac{5+3}{5+2} = -\frac{8}{7}$

2. $a_1 = (-1)^{1+1}(2\cdot 1+3) = 5$, $a_2 = (-1)^{2+1}(2\cdot 2+3) = -7$, $a_3 = (-1)^{3+1}(2\cdot 3+3) = 9$,
$a_4 = (-1)^{4+1}(2\cdot 4+3) = -11$, $a_5 = (-1)^{5+1}(2\cdot 5+3) = 13$

3. $a_1 = \frac{2^1}{1^2} = \frac{2}{1} = 2$, $a_2 = \frac{2^2}{2^2} = \frac{4}{4} = 1$, $a_3 = \frac{2^3}{3^2} = \frac{8}{9}$, $a_4 = \frac{2^4}{4^2} = \frac{16}{16} = 1$, $a_5 = \frac{2^5}{5^2} = \frac{32}{25}$

4. $a_1 = \frac{e^1}{1} = e$, $a_2 = \frac{e^2}{2}$, $a_3 = \frac{e^3}{3}$, $a_4 = \frac{e^4}{4}$, $a_5 = \frac{e^5}{5}$

5. $a_1 = 3$, $a_2 = \frac{2}{3}\cdot 3 = 2$, $a_3 = \frac{2}{3}\cdot 2 = \frac{4}{3}$, $a_4 = \frac{2}{3}\cdot\frac{4}{3} = \frac{8}{9}$, $a_5 = \frac{2}{3}\cdot\frac{8}{9} = \frac{16}{27}$

6. $a_1 = 4$, $a_2 = -\frac{1}{4}\cdot 4 = -1$, $a_3 = -\frac{1}{4}\cdot -1 = \frac{1}{4}$, $a_4 = -\frac{1}{4}\cdot\frac{1}{4} = -\frac{1}{16}$, $a_5 = -\frac{1}{4}\cdot -\frac{1}{16} = \frac{1}{64}$

7. $a_1 = 2$, $a_2 = 2-2 = 0$, $a_3 = 2-0 = 2$, $a_4 = 2-2 = 0$, $a_5 = 2-0 = 2$

8. $a_1 = -3$, $a_2 = 4+(-3) = 1$, $a_3 = 4+1 = 5$, $a_4 = 4+5 = 9$, $a_5 = 4+9 = 13$

9. $\{n+5\}$ Arithmetic
$d = (n+1+5)-(n+5) = n+6-n-5 = 1$
$S_n = \frac{n}{2}[6+n+5] = \frac{n}{2}(n+11)$

10. $\{4n+3\}$ Arithmetic
$d = (4(n+1)+3)-(4n+3) = 4n+4+3-4n-3 = 4$
$S_n = \frac{n}{2}[7+4n+3] = \frac{n}{2}(4n+10) = 2n^2+5n$

11. $\{2n^3\}$ Examine the terms of the sequence: 2, 16, 54, 128, 250, ...
There is no common difference; there is no common ratio; neither.

12. $\{2n^2-1\}$ Examine the terms of the sequence: 1, 7, 17, 31, 49, ...
There is no common difference; there is no common ratio; neither.

13. $\{2^{3n}\}$ Geometric $r=\dfrac{2^{3(n+1)}}{2^{3n}}=\dfrac{2^{3n+3}}{2^{3n}}=2^{3n+3-3n}=2^3=8$

$$S_n=8\left(\frac{1-8^n}{1-8}\right)=8\left(\frac{1-8^n}{-7}\right)=\frac{8}{7}\left(8^n-1\right)$$

14. $\{3^{2n}\}$ Geometric $r=\dfrac{3^{2(n+1)}}{3^{2n}}=\dfrac{3^{2n+2}}{3^{2n}}=3^{2n+2-2n}=3^2=9$

$$S_n=9\left(\frac{1-9^n}{1-9}\right)=9\left(\frac{1-9^n}{-8}\right)=\frac{9}{8}\left(9^n-1\right)$$

15. 0, 4, 8, 12, ... Arithmetic $d=4-0=4$

$$S_n=\frac{n}{2}\left(2(0)+(n-1)4\right)=\frac{n}{2}\left(4(n-1)\right)=2n(n-1)$$

16. $1,-3,-7,-11,\ldots$ Arithmetic $d=-3-1=-4$

$$S_n=\frac{n}{2}\left(2(1)+(n-1)(-4)\right)=\frac{n}{2}\left(2-4n+4\right)=\frac{n}{2}(6-4n)=3n-2n^2$$

17. $3,\dfrac{3}{2},\dfrac{3}{4},\dfrac{3}{5},\dfrac{3}{16},\ldots$ Geometric $r=\dfrac{\left(\frac{3}{2}\right)}{3}=\dfrac{3}{2}\cdot\dfrac{1}{3}=\dfrac{1}{2}$

$$S_n=3\left(\frac{1-\left(\frac{1}{2}\right)^n}{1-\frac{1}{2}}\right)=3\left(\frac{1-\left(\frac{1}{2}\right)^n}{\left(\frac{1}{2}\right)}\right)=6\left(1-\left(\frac{1}{2}\right)^n\right)$$

18. $5,-\dfrac{5}{3},\dfrac{5}{9},-\dfrac{5}{27},\dfrac{5}{81},\ldots$ Geometric $r=\dfrac{\left(-\frac{5}{3}\right)}{5}=-\dfrac{5}{3}\cdot\dfrac{1}{5}=-\dfrac{1}{3}$

$$S_n=5\left(\frac{1-\left(-\frac{1}{3}\right)^n}{1-\left(-\frac{1}{3}\right)}\right)=5\left(\frac{1-\left(-\frac{1}{3}\right)^n}{\left(\frac{4}{3}\right)}\right)=\frac{15}{4}\left(1-\left(-\frac{1}{3}\right)^n\right)$$

19. Neither. There is no common difference or common ratio.

20. $\dfrac{3}{2},\dfrac{5}{4},\dfrac{7}{6},\dfrac{9}{8},\dfrac{11}{10},\ldots$ Neither. There is no common difference or common ratio.

21. $\sum_{k=1}^{5}(k^2+12)=13+16+21+28+37=115$

22. $\sum_{k=1}^{3}(k+2)^2=9+16+25=50$

23. $\sum_{k=1}^{10}(3k-9)=\sum_{k=1}^{10}3k-\sum_{k=1}^{10}9=3\sum_{k=1}^{10}k-\sum_{k=1}^{10}9=3\left(\frac{10(10+1)}{2}\right)-10(9)=165-90=75$

24. $\sum_{k=1}^{9}(-2k+8)=\sum_{k=1}^{9}-2k+\sum_{k=1}^{9}8=-2\sum_{k=1}^{9}k+\sum_{k=1}^{9}8=-2\left(\frac{9(1+9)}{2}\right)+9(8)=-90+72=-18$

25. $\sum_{k=1}^{7}\left(\tfrac{1}{3}\right)^k=\frac{1}{3}\left(\frac{1-\left(\frac{1}{3}\right)^7}{1-\frac{1}{3}}\right)=\frac{1}{3}\left(\frac{1-\left(\frac{1}{3}\right)^7}{\frac{2}{3}}\right)=\frac{1}{2}\left(1-\frac{1}{2187}\right)=\frac{1}{2}\cdot\frac{2186}{2187}=\frac{1093}{2187}$

26. $\sum_{k=1}^{10}(-2)^k=-2\left(\frac{1-(-2)^{10}}{1-(-2)}\right)=-2\left(\frac{1-1024}{3}\right)=-\frac{2}{3}(-1023)=682$

27. Arithmetic $a_1=3,\ d=4,\ a_n=a+(n-1)d$
$a_9=3+(9-1)4=3+8(4)=3+32=35$

28. Arithmetic $a_1=1,\ d=-2,\ a_n=a+(n-1)d$
$a_8=1+(8-1)(-2)=1+7(-2)=1-14=-13$

29. Geometric $a=1,\ r=\frac{1}{10},\ n=11$ $a_{11}=1\cdot\left(\frac{1}{10}\right)^{11-1}=\left(\frac{1}{10}\right)^{10}=\frac{1}{10{,}000{,}000{,}000}$

30. Geometric $a=1,\ r=2,\ n=11$ $a_{11}=1\cdot(2)^{11-1}=(2)^{10}=1024$

31. Arithmetic $a_1=\sqrt{2},\ d=\sqrt{2},\ n=9,\ a_n=a+(n-1)d$
$a_9=\sqrt{2}+(9-1)\sqrt{2}=\sqrt{2}+8\sqrt{2}=9\sqrt{2}$

32. Geometric $a_1=\sqrt{2},\ d=\sqrt{2},\ n=9,\ a_n=ar^{n-1}$
$a_9=\sqrt{2}\left(\sqrt{2}\right)^{9-1}=\sqrt{2}\left(\sqrt{2}\right)^8=\sqrt{2}\cdot16=16\sqrt{2}$

33. $a_7=a+6d=31$ $a_{20}=a+19d=96$
Solve the system of equations:

$$31-6d+19d=96$$
$$13d=65$$
$$d=5$$
$$a=31-6(5)=31-30=1$$

General formula: $\{5n-4\}$

34. $a_8 = a + 7d = -20 \qquad a_{17} = a + 16d = -47$

Solve the system of equations:

$$-20 - 7d + 16d = -47$$
$$9d = -27$$
$$d = -3$$
$$a = -20 - 7(-3) = -20 + 21 = 1$$

General formula: $\{-3n + 4\}$

35. $a_{10} = a + 9d = 0 \qquad a_{18} = a + 17d = 8$

Solve the system of equations:

$$-9d + 17d = 8$$
$$8d = 8$$
$$d = 1$$
$$a = -9(1) = -9$$

General formula: $\{n - 10\}$

36. $a_{12} = a + 11d = 30 \qquad a_{22} = a + 21d = 50$

Solve the system of equations:

$$30 - 11d + 21d = 50$$
$$10d = 20$$
$$d = 2$$
$$a = 30 - 11(2) = 30 - 22 = 8$$

General formula: $\{2n + 6\}$

37.

$a = 3,\ r = \frac{1}{3}$ Since $|r| < 1,\ S_n = \frac{a}{1-r} = \frac{3}{\left(1 - \frac{1}{3}\right)} = \frac{3}{\left(\frac{2}{3}\right)} = \frac{9}{2}$

38.

$a = 2,\ r = \frac{1}{2}$ Since $|r| < 1,\ S_n = \frac{a}{1-r} = \frac{2}{\left(1 - \frac{1}{2}\right)} = \frac{2}{\left(\frac{1}{2}\right)} = 4$

39.

$a = 2,\ r = -\frac{1}{2}$ Since $|r| < 1,\ S_n = \frac{a}{1-r} = \frac{2}{\left(1 - \left(-\frac{1}{2}\right)\right)} = \frac{2}{\left(\frac{3}{2}\right)} = \frac{4}{3}$

40.

$a = 6,\ r = -\frac{2}{3}$ Since $|r| < 1,\ S_n = \frac{a}{1-r} = \frac{6}{\left(1 - \left(-\frac{2}{3}\right)\right)} = \frac{6}{\left(\frac{5}{3}\right)} = \frac{18}{5}$

41.

$a=4,\ r=\frac{1}{2}$ Since $|r|<1$, $S_n=\frac{a}{1-r}=\frac{4}{\left(1-\frac{1}{2}\right)}=\frac{4}{\left(\frac{1}{2}\right)}=8$

42.

$a=3,\ r=-\frac{3}{4}$ Since $|r|<1$, $S_n=\frac{a}{1-r}=\frac{3}{\left(1-\left(-\frac{3}{4}\right)\right)}=\frac{3}{\left(\frac{7}{4}\right)}=\frac{12}{7}$

43. I: $n=1$: $3\cdot 1=3$ and $\frac{3\cdot 1}{2}(1+1)=3$

II: If $3+6+9+\cdots+3k=\frac{3k}{2}(k+1)$

then $3+6+9+\cdots+3k+3(k+1)$

$=[3+6+9+\cdots+3k]+3(k+1)=\frac{3k}{2}(k+1)+3(k+1)$

$=(k+1)\left(\frac{3k}{2}+3\right)=\frac{3}{2}(k+1)(k+2)$

Conditions I and II are satisfied; the statement is true.

44. I: $n=1$: $4\cdot 1-2=2$ and $2(1)^2=2$

II: If $2+6+10+\cdots+(4k-2)=2k^2$

then $2+6+10+\cdots+(4k-2)+(4(k+1)-2)$

$=[2+6+10+\cdots+(4k-2)]+4k+2=2k^2+4k+2$

$=2\left(k^2+2k+1\right)=2(k+1)^2$

Conditions I and II are satisfied; the statement is true.

45. I: $n=1$: $2\cdot 3^{1-1}=2$ and $3^1-1=2$

II: If $2+6+18+\cdots+2\cdot 3^{k-1}=3^k-1$

then $2+6+18+\cdots+2\cdot 3^{k-1}+2\cdot 3^{k+1-1}$

$=\left[2+6+18+\cdots+2\cdot 3^{k-1}\right]+2\cdot 3^k=3^k-1+2\cdot 3^k$

$=3\cdot 3^k-1=3^{k+1}-1$

Conditions I and II are satisfied; the statement is true.

46. I: $n=1$: $3\cdot 2^{1-1}=3$ and $3\left(2^1-1\right)=3$

II: If $3+6+12+\cdots+3\cdot 2^{k-1}=3\left(2^k-1\right)$

then $3+6+12+\cdots+3\cdot 2^{k-1}+3\cdot 2^{k+1-1}$

$=\left[3+6+12+\cdots+3\cdot 2^{k-1}\right]+3\cdot 2^k=3\left(2^k-1\right)+3\cdot 2^k$

$=3\cdot\left(2^k-1+2^k\right)=3\left(2\cdot 2^k-1\right)=3\left(2^{k+1}-1\right)$

Conditions I and II are satisfied; the statement is true.

47. I: $n=1$: $(3\cdot 1-2)^2=1$ and $\frac{1}{2}\cdot 1(6\cdot 1^2-3\cdot 1-1)=1$

II: If $1^2+4^2+7^2+\cdots+(3k-2)^2=\frac{1}{2}\cdot k\left(6k^2-3k-1\right)$

then $1^2+4^2+7^2+\cdots+(3k-2)^2+\left(3(k+1)-2\right)^2$

$$=\left[1^2+4^2+7^2+\cdots+(3k-2)^2\right]+(3k+1)^2$$

$$=\frac{1}{2}\cdot k\left(6k^2-3k-1\right)+(3k+1)^2$$

$$=\frac{1}{2}\cdot\left[6k^3-3k^2-k+18k^2+12k+2\right]=\frac{1}{2}\cdot\left[6k^3+15k^2+11k+2\right]$$

$$=\frac{1}{2}\cdot(k+1)\left[6k^2+9k+2\right]=\frac{1}{2}\cdot(k+1)\left[6k^2+12k+6-3k-3-1\right]$$

$$=\frac{1}{2}\cdot(k+1)\left[6(k^2+2k+1)-3(k+1)-1\right]$$

$$=\frac{1}{2}\cdot(k+1)\left[6(k+1)^2-3(k+1)-1\right]$$

Conditions I and II are satisfied; the statement is true.

48. I: $n=1$: $1(1+2)=3$ and $\frac{1}{6}\cdot(1+1)(2\cdot 1+7)=3$

II: If $1\cdot 3+2\cdot 4+3\cdot 5+\cdots+k(k+2)=\frac{k}{6}(k+1)(2k+7)$

then $1\cdot 3+2\cdot 4+3\cdot 5+\cdots+k(k+2)+(k+1)(k+1+2)$

$$=\left[1\cdot 3+2\cdot 4+3\cdot 5+\cdots+k(k+2)\right]+(k+1)(k+3)$$

$$=\frac{k}{6}(k+1)(2k+7)+(k+1)(k+3)=\frac{(k+1)}{6}\left(2k^2+7k+6k+18\right)$$

$$=\frac{(k+1)}{6}\left(2k^2+13k+18\right)=\frac{(k+1)}{6}(k+2)(2k+9)$$

Conditions I and II are satisfied; the statement is true.

49. $(x+2)^5=\binom{5}{0}x^5+\binom{5}{1}x^4\cdot 2+\binom{5}{2}x^3\cdot 2^2+\binom{5}{3}x^2\cdot 2^3+\binom{5}{4}x^1\cdot 2^4+\binom{5}{5}\cdot 2^5$

$$=x^5+5\cdot 2x^4+10\cdot 4x^3+10\cdot 8x^2+5\cdot 16x+1\cdot 32$$

$$=x^5+10x^4+40x^3+80x^2+80x+32$$

50. $(x-3)^4=\binom{4}{0}x^4+\binom{4}{1}x^3(-3)+\binom{4}{2}x^2(-3)^2+\binom{4}{3}x(-3)^3+\binom{4}{4}x^0(-3)^4$

$$=x^4+4(-3)x^3+6\cdot 9x^2+4(-27)x+81$$

$$=x^4-12x^3+54x^2-108x+81$$

51. $(2x+3)^5=\binom{5}{0}(2x)^5+\binom{5}{1}(2x)^4\cdot 3+\binom{5}{2}(2x)^3\cdot 3^2+\binom{5}{3}(2x)^2\cdot 3^3$

$$+\binom{5}{4}(2x)^1\cdot 3^4+\binom{5}{5}\cdot 3^5$$

$= 32x^5 + 5\cdot 16x^4 \cdot 3 + 10\cdot 8x^3 \cdot 9 + 10\cdot 4x^2 \cdot 27 + 5\cdot 2x\cdot 81 + 1\cdot 243$
$= 32x^5 + 240x^4 + 720x^3 + 1080x^2 + 810x + 243$

52. $(3x-4)^4 = \binom{4}{0}(3x)^4 + \binom{4}{1}(3x)^3(-4) + \binom{4}{2}(3x)^2(-4)^2 + \binom{4}{3}(3x)(-4)^3 + \binom{4}{4}(-4)^4$
$= 81x^4 + 4\cdot 27x^3(-4) + 6\cdot 9x^2\cdot 16 + 4\cdot 3x(-64) + 1\cdot 256$
$= 81x^4 - 432x^3 + 864x^2 - 768x + 256$

53. $n = 9,\ j = 2,\ x = x,\ a = 2$
$\binom{9}{2}x^7\cdot 2^2 = \frac{9!}{2!\,7!}\cdot 4x^7 = \frac{9\cdot 8}{2\cdot 1}\cdot 4x^7 = 144x^7$
The coefficient of x^7 is 144.

54. $n = 8,\ j = 5,\ x = x,\ a = -3$
$\binom{8}{5}x^3(-3)^5 = \frac{8!}{5!\,3!}(-243)x^3 = \frac{8\cdot 7\cdot 6}{3\cdot 2\cdot 1}(-243)x^3 = -13{,}608x^3$
The coefficient of x^3 is $-13{,}608$.

55. $n = 7,\ j = 5,\ x = 2x,\ a = 1$
$\binom{7}{5}(2x)^2\cdot 1^5 = \frac{7!}{5!\,2!}\cdot 4x^2(1) = \frac{7\cdot 6}{2\cdot 1}\cdot 4x^2 = 84x^2$
The coefficient of x^2 is 84.

56. $n = 8,\ j = 2,\ x = 2x,\ a = 1$
$\binom{8}{2}(2x)^6\cdot 1^2 = \frac{8!}{2!\,6!}\cdot 64x^6(1) = \frac{8\cdot 7}{2\cdot 1}\cdot 64x^6 = 1792x^6$
The coefficient of x^6 is 1792.

57. This is an arithmetic sequence with $a = 80,\ d = -3,\ n = 25$
(a) $a_{25} = 80 + (25-1)(-3) = 80 - 72 = 8$ bricks
(b) $S_{25} = \frac{25}{2}(80+8) = 25(44) = 1100$ bricks
1100 bricks are needed to build the steps.

58. This is an arithmetic sequence with $a = 30,\ d = -1,\ a_n = 15$

$15 = 30 + (n-1)(-1) \rightarrow -15 = -n + 1 \rightarrow -16 = -n \rightarrow n = 16$
$S_{16} = \frac{16}{2}(30+15) = 8(45) = 360$ tiles
360 tiles are required to make the trapezoid.

59. This is an ordinary annuity with $P = \$200$ and $n = (12)(20) = 240$ payment periods.

The interest rate per period is $\dfrac{.10}{12} = .008\overline{3}$. Thus,

$$A = 200\left[\frac{\left[1+\frac{.10}{12}\right]^{240} - 1}{\left(\frac{.10}{12}\right)}\right] = \$151873.77$$

60. This is an ordinary annuity with $P = \$500$ and $n = (4)(30) = 120$ payment periods.

The interest rate per period is $\dfrac{.08}{4} = .02$. Thus

$$A = 500\left[\frac{\left[1+\frac{.08}{4}\right]^{120} - 1}{\left(\frac{.08}{4}\right)}\right] = \$244129.08$$

61. This is a geometric sequence with $a = 20,\ r = \dfrac{3}{4}$.

(a) After striking the ground the third time, the height is $20\left(\dfrac{3}{4}\right)^3 = \dfrac{135}{16} \approx 8.44$ feet.

(b) After striking the ground the nth time, the height is $20\left(\dfrac{3}{4}\right)^n$ feet.

(c) If the height is less than 6 inches or 0.5 feet, then:

$$0.5 = 20\left(\frac{3}{4}\right)^n \to 0.025 = \left(\frac{3}{4}\right)^n \to \log 0.025 = n\log\left(\frac{3}{4}\right) \to n = \frac{\log 0.025}{\log\left(\frac{3}{4}\right)} \approx 12.82$$

The height is less than 6 inches after the 13th strike.

(d) Since this is a geometric sequence with $|r| < 1$, the distance is the sum of the two infinite geometric series - the distances going down plus the distances going up.

Distance going down: $S_{down} = \dfrac{20}{\left(1-\frac{3}{4}\right)} = \dfrac{20}{\left(\frac{1}{4}\right)} = 80$ feet.

Distance going up: $S_{up} = \dfrac{15}{\left(1-\frac{3}{4}\right)} = \dfrac{15}{\left(\frac{1}{4}\right)} = 60$ feet.

The total distance traveled is 140 feet.

62. This is a geometric sequence with $a = 20{,}000,\ r = 1.04,\ n = 5$.
Find the fifth term of the sequence:

$$a_5 = 20000(1.04)^{5-1} = 20000(1.04)^4 = \$23{,}397.17$$

The salary in the fifth year will be \$23,397.17.

Chapter 14

Counting and Probability

14.1 Sets and Counting

1. $A \cup B = \{1, 3, 5, 7, 9\} \cup \{1, 5, 6, 7\} = \{1, 3, 5, 6, 7, 9\}$

2. $A \cup C = \{1, 3, 5, 7, 9\} \cup \{1, 2, 4, 6, 8, 9\} = \{1, 2, 3, 4, 5, 6, 7, 8, 9\}$

3. $A \cap B = \{1, 3, 5, 7, 9\} \cap \{1, 5, 6, 7\} = \{1, 5, 7\}$

4. $A \cap C = \{1, 3, 5, 7, 9\} \cap \{1, 2, 4, 6, 8, 9\} = \{1, 9\}$

5. $$\begin{aligned}(A \cup B) \cap C &= (\{1, 3, 5, 7, 9\} \cup \{1, 5, 6, 7\}) \cap \{1, 2, 4, 6, 8, 9\} \\ &= \{1, 3, 5, 6, 7, 9\} \cap \{1, 2, 4, 6, 8, 9\} \\ &= \{1, 6, 9\}\end{aligned}$$

6. $$\begin{aligned}&(A \cap C) \cup (B \cap C) \\ &\quad = (\{1, 3, 5, 7, 9\} \cap \{1, 2, 4, 6, 8, 9\}) \cup (\{1, 5, 6, 7\} \cap \{1, 2, 4, 6, 8, 9\}) \\ &\quad = \{1, 9\} \cup \{1, 6\} = \{1, 6, 9\}\end{aligned}$$

7. $$\begin{aligned}(A \cap B) \cup C &= (\{1, 3, 5, 7, 9\} \cap \{1, 5, 6, 7\}) \cup \{1, 2, 4, 6, 8, 9\} \\ &= \{1, 5, 7\} \cup \{1, 2, 4, 6, 8, 9\} \\ &= \{1, 2, 4, 5, 6, 7, 8, 9\}\end{aligned}$$

8. $$\begin{aligned}(A \cup B) \cup C &= (\{1, 3, 5, 7, 9\} \cup \{1, 5, 6, 7\}) \cup \{1, 2, 4, 6, 8, 9\} \\ &= \{1, 3, 5, 6, 7, 9\} \cup \{1, 2, 4, 6, 8, 9\} = \{1, 2, 3, 4, 5, 6, 7, 8, 9\}\end{aligned}$$

9. $$\begin{aligned}&(A \cup C) \cap (B \cup C) \\ &\quad = (\{1, 3, 5, 7, 9\} \cup \{1, 2, 4, 6, 8, 9\}) \cap (\{1, 5, 6, 7\} \cup \{1, 2, 4, 6, 8, 9\}) \\ &\quad = \{1, 2, 3, 4, 5, 6, 7, 8, 9\} \cap \{1, 2, 4, 5, 6, 7, 8, 9\} \\ &\quad = \{1, 2, 4, 5, 6, 7, 8, 9\}\end{aligned}$$

10. $$\begin{aligned}(A \cap B) \cap C &= (\{1, 3, 5, 7, 9\} \cap \{1, 5, 6, 7\}) \cap \{1, 2, 4, 6, 8, 9\} \\ &= \{1, 5, 7\} \cap \{1, 2, 4, 6, 8, 9\} = \{1\}\end{aligned}$$

11. $\overline{A} = \{0, 2, 6, 7, 8\}$ 12. $\overline{C} = \{0, 2, 5, 7, 8, 9\}$

13. $\overline{A \cap B} = \overline{\{1, 3, 4, 5, 9\} \cap \{2, 4, 6, 7, 8\}} = \overline{\{4\}} = \{0, 1, 2, 3, 5, 6, 7, 8, 9\}$

14. $\overline{B \cup C} = \overline{\{2, 4, 6, 7, 8\} \cup \{1, 3, 4, 6\}} = \overline{\{1, 2, 3, 4, 6, 7, 8\}} = \{0, 5, 9\}$

15. $\overline{A} \cup \overline{B} = \{0, 2, 6, 7, 8\} \cup \{0, 1, 3, 5, 9\} = \{0, 1, 2, 3, 5, 6, 7, 8, 9\}$

16. $\overline{B} \cap \overline{C} = \{0, 1, 3, 5, 9\} \cap \{0, 2, 5, 7, 8. 9\} = \{0, 5, 9\}$

17. $\overline{A \cap \overline{C}} = \overline{\{1, 3, 4, 5, 9\} \cap \{0, 2, 5, 7, 8, 9\}} = \overline{\{5, 9\}} = \{0, 1, 2, 3, 4, 6, 7, 8\}$

18. $\overline{\overline{B} \cup C} = \overline{\{0, 1, 3, 5, 9\} \cup \{1, 3, 4, 6\}} = \overline{\{0, 1, 3, 4, 5, 6, 9\}} = \{2, 7, 8\}$

19. $\overline{A \cup B \cup C} = \overline{\{1, 3, 4, 5, 9\} \cup \{2, 4, 6, 7, 8\} \cup \{1, 3, 4, 6\}}$
$= \overline{\{1, 2, 3, 4, 5, 6, 7, 8, 9\}} = \{0\}$

20. $\overline{A \cap B \cap C} = \overline{\{1, 3, 4, 5, 9\} \cap \{2, 4, 6, 7, 8\} \cap \{1, 3, 4, 6\}} = \overline{\{4\}}$
$= \{0, 1, 2, 3, 5, 6, 7, 8, 9\}$

21. $\{a\}, \{b\}, \{c\}, \{d\}, \{a, b\}, \{a, c\}, \{a, d\}, \{b, c\}, \{b, d\}, \{c, d\}, \{a, b, c\}, \{a, b, d\},$
$\{a, c, d\}, \{b, c, d\}, \{a, b, c, d\}, \varnothing$

22. $\{a\}, \{b\}, \{c\}, \{d\}, \{e\}, \{a, b\}, \{a, c\}, \{a, d\}, \{a, e\}, \{b, c\}, \{b, d\}, \{b, e\}, \{c, d\},$
$\{c, e\}, \{d, e\}, \{a, b, c\}, \{a, b, d\}, \{a, b, e\}, \{a, c, d\}, \{a, c, e\}, \{a, d, e\}, \{b, c, d\},$
$\{b, c, e\}, \{b, d, e\}, \{c, d, e\}, \{a, b, c, d\}, \{a, b, c, e\}, \{a, c, d, e\}, \{a, b, d, e\},$
$\{b, c, d, e\}, \{a, b, c, d, e\}, \varnothing$

23. $n(A) = 15, n(B) = 20, n(A \cap B) = 10$
$n(A \cup B) = n(A) + n(B) - n(A \cap B) = 15 + 20 - 10 = 25$

24. $n(A) = 20, n(B) = 40, n(A \cup B) = 35$
$n(A \cup B) = n(A) + n(B) - n(A \cap B)$
$35 = 20 + 40 - n(A \cap B)$
$n(A \cap B) = 20 + 40 - 35 = 25$

25. $n(A \cup B) = 50, n(A \cap B) = 10, n(B) = 20$
$n(A \cup B) = n(A) + n(B) - n(A \cap B)$
$50 = n(A) + 20 - 10$
$40 = n(A)$

26. $n(A \cup B) = 60,\ n(A \cap B) = 40,\ n(A) = n(B)$

$$n(A \cup B) = n(A) + n(B) - n(A \cap B)$$
$$60 = n(A) + n(A) - 40$$
$$100 = 2n(A)$$
$$n(A) = 50$$

27. From the figure:

$$n(A) = 15 + 3 + 5 + 2 = 25$$

28. From the figure: $n(B) = 10 + 3 + 5 + 2 = 20$

29. From the figure:

$$n(A \text{ or } B) = n(A \cup B) = n(A) + n(B) - n(A \cap B) = 25 + 20 - 8 = 37$$

30. From the figure: $n(A \text{ and } B) = n(A \cap B) = 3 + 5 = 8$

31. From the figure:

$$n(A \text{ but not } C) = n(A) - n(A \cap C) = 25 - 7 = 18$$

32. From the figure: $n(\overline{A}) = 10 + 2 + 15 + 4 = 31$

33. From the figure:

$$n(A \text{ and } B \text{ and } C) = n(A \cap B \cap C) = 5$$

34. From the figure:

$$n(A \text{ or } B \text{ or } C) = n(A \cup B \cup C) = 15 + 3 + 5 + 2 + 10 + 2 + 15 = 52$$

35. Let $A = \{\text{those who will purchase a major appliance}\}$

$B = \{\text{those who will buy a car}\}$

$n(U) = 500,\ \ n(A) = 200,\ \ n(B) = 150,\ \ n(A \cap B) = 25$

$n(A \cup B) = n(A) + n(B) - n(A \cap B) = 200 + 150 - 25 = 325$

$n(\text{purchase neither}) = 500 - 325 = 175$

$n(\text{purchase only a car}) = 150 - 25 = 125$

36. Let $A = \{\text{those who will attend Summer Session I}\}$

$B = \{\text{those who will attend Summer Session II}\}$

$n(A) = 200,\ \ n(B) = 150,\ \ n(A \cap B) = 75,\ \ n\left(\overline{A \cup B}\right) = 275$

$n(A \cup B) = n(A) + n(B) - n(A \cap B) = 200 + 150 - 75 = 275$

$n(U) = n(A \cup B) + n\left(\overline{A \cup B}\right) = 275 + 275 = 550$

550 students participated in the survey.

37. Construct a Venn diagram:

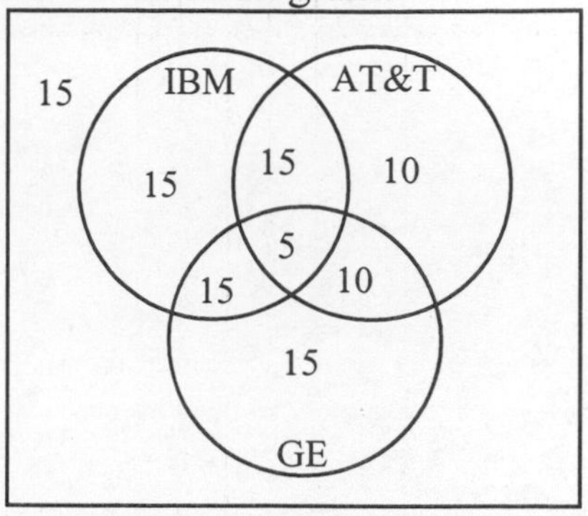

(a) 15
(b) 15
(c) 15
(d) 25
(e) 40

38. Construct a Venn diagram:

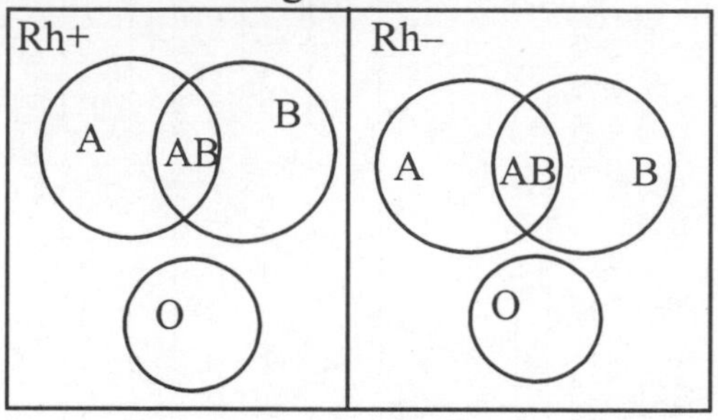

There are 8 different kinds of blood: A-Rh+, B-Rh+, AB-Rh+, O-Rh+, A-Rh–, B-Rh–, AB-Rh–, O-Rh–

39. (a) $n(\text{married}) = n(\text{married, spouse present}) + n(\text{married, spouse absent})$
$= 54{,}654 + 3{,}232 = 57{,}886$ thousand

(b) $n(\text{widowed or divorced}) = n(\text{widowed}) + n(\text{divorced})$
$= 2{,}686 + 8{,}208 = 10{,}894$ thousand

(c) $n(\text{married, spouse absent or widowed or divorced})$
$= n(\text{married, spouse absent}) + n(\text{widowed}) + n(\text{divorced})$
$= 3{,}232 + 2{,}686 + 8{,}208 = 14{,}126$ thousand

40. (a) $n(\text{married}) = n(\text{married, spouse present}) + n(\text{married, spouse absent})$
$= 54{,}626 + 4{,}122 = 58{,}748$ thousand

(b) $n(\text{widowed or divorced}) = n(\text{widowed}) + n(\text{divorced})$
$= 11{,}056 + 11{,}107 = 22{,}163$ thousand

(c) $n(\text{married, spouse absent or widowed or divorced})$
$= n(\text{married, spouse absent}) + n(\text{widowed}) + n(\text{divorced})$
$= 4{,}122 + 11{,}056 + 11{,}107 = 26{,}285$ thousand

41. Answers will vary.

42. Answers will vary.

Chapter 14

Counting and Probability

14.2 Permutations and Combinations

1. $P(6,2)=\dfrac{6!}{(6-2)!}=\dfrac{6!}{4!}=\dfrac{6\cdot5\cdot4!}{4!}=30$

2. $P(7,2)=\dfrac{7!}{(7-2)!}=\dfrac{7!}{5!}=\dfrac{7\cdot6\cdot5!}{5!}=42$

3. $P(4,4)=\dfrac{4!}{(4-4)!}=\dfrac{4!}{0!}=\dfrac{4\cdot3\cdot2\cdot1}{1}=24$

4. $P(8,8)=\dfrac{8!}{(8-8)!}=\dfrac{8!}{0!}=\dfrac{8\cdot7\cdot6\cdot5\cdot4\cdot3\cdot2\cdot1}{1}=40320$

5. $P(7,0)=\dfrac{7!}{(7-0)!}=\dfrac{7!}{7!}=1$

6. $P(9,0)=\dfrac{9!}{(9-0)!}=\dfrac{9!}{9!}=1$

7. $P(8,4)=\dfrac{8!}{(8-4)!}=\dfrac{8!}{4!}=\dfrac{8\cdot7\cdot6\cdot5\cdot4!}{4!}=1680$

8. $P(8,3)=\dfrac{8!}{(8-3)!}=\dfrac{8!}{5!}=\dfrac{8\cdot7\cdot6\cdot5!}{5!}=336$

9. $C(8,2)=\dfrac{8!}{(8-2)!\,2!}=\dfrac{8!}{6!\,2!}=\dfrac{8\cdot7\cdot6!}{6!\cdot2\cdot1}=28$

10. $C(8,6)=\dfrac{8!}{(8-6)!\,6!}=\dfrac{8!}{2!\,6!}=\dfrac{8\cdot7\cdot6!}{6!\cdot2\cdot1}=28$

11. $C(7,4)=\dfrac{7!}{(7-4)!\,4!}=\dfrac{7!}{3!\,4!}=\dfrac{7\cdot6\cdot5\cdot4!}{4!\cdot3\cdot2\cdot1}=35$

12. $C(6,2)=\dfrac{6!}{(6-2)!\,2!}=\dfrac{6!}{4!\,2!}=\dfrac{6\cdot5\cdot4!}{4!\cdot2\cdot1}=15$

13. $C(15,15)=\dfrac{15!}{(15-15)!\,15!}=\dfrac{15!}{0!\,15!}=\dfrac{15!}{15!\cdot1}=1$

14. $C(18,1)=\dfrac{18!}{(18-1)!\,1!}=\dfrac{18!}{17!\,1!}=\dfrac{18\cdot17!}{17!\cdot1}=18$

15. $C(26,13)=\dfrac{26!}{(26-13)!\,13!}=\dfrac{26!}{13!\,13!}=10{,}400{,}600$

16. $C(18,9)=\dfrac{18!}{(18-9)!\,9!}=\dfrac{18!}{9!\,9!}=48620$

17. {*abc*, *abd*, *abe*, *acb*, *acd*, *ace*, *adb*, *adc*, *ade*, *aeb*, *aec*, *aed*, *bac*, *bad*, *bae*, *bca*, *bcd*, *bce*, *bda*, *bdc*, *bde*, *bea*, *bec*, *bed*, *cab*, *cad*, *cae*, *cba*, *cbd*, *cbe*, *cda*, *cdb*, *cde*, *cea*, *ceb*, *ced*, *dab*, *dac*, *dae*, *dba*, *dbc*, *dbe*, *dca*, *dcb*, *dce*, *dea*, *deb*, *dec*, *eab*, *eac*, *ead*, *eba*, *ebc*, *ebd*, *eca*, *ecb*, *ecd*, *eda*, *edb*, *edc*}

$$P(5,3)=\frac{5!}{(5-3)!}=\frac{5!}{2!}=\frac{5\cdot4\cdot3\cdot2!}{2!}=60$$

18. {*ab*, *ac*, *ad*, *ae*, *ba*, *bc*, *bd*, *be*, *ca*, *cb*, *cd*, *ce*, *da*, *db*, *dc*, *de*, *ea*, *eb*, *ec*, *ed*}

$$P(5,2)=\frac{5!}{(5-2)!}=\frac{5!}{3!}=\frac{5\cdot4\cdot3!}{3!}=20$$

19. {123, 124, 132, 134, 142, 143, 213, 214, 231, 234, 241, 243, 312, 314, 321, 324, 341, 342, 412, 413, 421, 423, 431, 432}

$$P(4,3)=\frac{4!}{(4-3)!}=\frac{4!}{1!}=\frac{4\cdot3\cdot2\cdot1}{1}=24$$

20. {123, 124, 125, 126, 132, 134, 135, 136, 142, 143, 145, 146, 152, 153, 154, 156, 162, 163, 164, 165, 213, 214, 215, 216, 231, 234, 235, 236, 241, 243, 245, 246, 251, 253, 254, 256, 261, 263, 264, 265, 312, 314, 315, 316, 321, 324, 325, 326, 341, 342, 345, 346, 351, 352, 354, 356, 361, 362, 364, 365, 412, 413, 415, 416, 421, 423, 425, 426, 431, 432, 435, 436, 451, 452, 453, 456, 461, 462, 463, 465, 512, 513, 514, 516, 521, 523, 524, 526, 531, 532, 534, 536, 541, 542, 543, 546, 561, 562, 563, 564, 612, 613, 614, 615, 621, 623, 624, 625, 631, 632, 634, 635, 641, 642, 643, 645, 651, 652, 653, 654}

$$P(6,3)=\frac{6!}{(6-3)!}=\frac{6!}{3!}=\frac{6\cdot5\cdot4\cdot3!}{3!}=120$$

21. {*abc*, *abd*, *abe*, *acd*, *ace*, *ade*, *bcd*, *bce*, *bde*, *cde*}

$$C(5,3)=\frac{5!}{(5-3)!\,3!}=\frac{5\cdot4\cdot3!}{2\cdot1\cdot3!}=10$$

22. {*ab*, *ac*, *ad*, *ae*, *bc*, *bd*, *be*, *cd*, *ce*, *de*}

$$C(5,2)=\frac{5!}{(5-2)!\,2!}=\frac{5\cdot4\cdot3!}{2\cdot1\cdot3!}=10$$

23. {123, 124, 134, 234} $C(4,3)=\dfrac{4!}{(4-3)!\,3!}=\dfrac{4\cdot3!}{1!\,3!}=4$

24. {123, 124, 125, 126, 134, 135, 136, 145, 146, 156, 234, 235, 236, 245, 246, 256, 345, 346, 356, 456}

$$C(6,3) = \frac{6!}{(6-3)!\,3!} = \frac{6\cdot 5\cdot 4\cdot 3!}{3\cdot 2\cdot 1\cdot 3!} = 20$$

25. There are 5 choices of shirts and 3 choices of ties; there are (5)(3) = 15 combinations.

26. There are 3 choices of blouses and 5 choices of skirts; there are (3)(5) = 15 different outfits.

27. There are 4 choices for the first letter in the code and 4 choices for the second letter in the code; there are (4)(4) = 16 possible two-letter codes.

28. There are 5 choices for the first letter in the code and 5 choices for the second letter in the code; there are (5)(5) = 25 possible two-letter codes.

29. There are two choices for each of three positions; there are (2)(2)(2) = 8 possible three-digit numbers.

30. There are ten choices for each of three positions; there are (10)(10)(10) = 1000 possible three-digit numbers.

31. To line up the four people, there are 4 choices for the first position, 3 choices for the second position, 2 choices for the third position, and 1 choice for the fourth position. Thus there are (4)(3)(2)(1) = 24 possible ways four people can be lined up.

32. To stack the five boxes, there are 5 choices for the first position, 4 choices for the second position, 3 choices for the third position, 2 choices for the fourth position, and 1 choice for the fifth position. Thus, there are (5)(4)(3)(2)(1) = 120 possible ways five boxes can be stacked up.

33. Since no letter can be repeated, there are 5 choices for the first letter, 4 choices for the second letter, and 3 choices for the third letter. Thus, there are (5)(4)(3) = 60 possible three-letter codes.

34. Since no letter can be repeated, there are 6 choices for the first letter, 5 choices for the second letter, 4 choices for the third letter, and 3 choices for the fourth letter. Thus, there are (6)(5)(4)(3) = 360 possible three-letter codes.

35. There are 26 possible one-letter names. There are (26)(26) = 676 possible two-letter names. There are (26)(26)(26) = 17576 possible three-letter names. Thus, there are 26 + 676 + 17576 = 18,278 possible companies that can be listed on the New York Stock Exchange.

36. There are (26)(26)(26)(26) = 456,976 possible four-letter names. There are (26)(26)(26)(26)(26) = 11,881,376 possible five-letter names. Thus, there are 456,976 + 11,881,376 = 12,338,352 possible companies that can be listed on the NASDAQ.

37. A committee of 4 from a total of 7 students is given by:

$$C(7,4)=\frac{7!}{(7-4)!\,4!}=\frac{7!}{3!\,4!}=\frac{7\cdot 6\cdot 5\cdot 4!}{3\cdot 2\cdot 1\cdot 4!}=35$$

35 committees are possible.

38. A committee of 3 from a total of 8 professors is given by:

$$C(8,3)=\frac{8!}{(8-3)!\,3!}=\frac{8!}{5!\,3!}=\frac{8\cdot 7\cdot 6\cdot 5!}{3\cdot 2\cdot 1\cdot 5!}=56$$

56 committees are possible.

39. There are 2 possible answers for each question. Therefore, there are $2^{10}=1024$ different possible arrangements of the answers.

40. There are 4 possible answers for each question. Therefore, there are $4^5=1024$ different possible arrangements of the answers.

41. There are 9 choices for the first digit, and 10 choices for each of the other three digits. Thus, there are (9)(10)(10)(10) = 9000 possible four-digit numbers.

42. There are 8 choices for the first digit, and 10 choices for each of the other four digits. Thus, there are (8)(10)(10)(10)(10) = 80,000 possible five-digit numbers.

43. There are 5 choices for the first position, 4 choices for the second position, 3 choices for the third position, 2 choices for the fourth position, and 1 choice for the fifth position. Thus, there are (5)(4)(3)(2)(1) = 120 possible arrangements of the books.

44. (a) There are 26 choices for each of the first two positions, and 10 choices for each of the next four positions. Thus, there are (26)(26)(10)(10)(10)(10) = 6,760,000 possible license plates.
(b) There are 26 choices for each of the first two positions, 10 choices for the first digit, 9 choices for the second digit, 8 choices for the third digit, and 7 choices for the fourth digit. Thus, there are (26)(26)(10)(9)(8)(7) = 3,407,040 possible license plates.
(c) There are 26 choices for the first letter, 25 choices for the second letter, 10 choices for the first digit, 9 choices for the second digit, 8 choices for the third digit, and 7 choices for the fourth digit. Thus, there are (26)(25)(10)(9)(8)(7) = 3,276,000 possible license plates.

45. There are 8 choices for the DOW stocks, 15 choices for the NASDAQ stocks, and 4 choices for the global stocks. Thus, there are (8)(15)(4) = 480 different portfolios.

46. There are 50 choices for the first number, 50 choices for the second number, and 50 choices for the third number. Thus, there are (50)(50)(50) = 125,000 different lock combinations.

47. The first person can have any of 365 days, the second person can have any of the remaining 364 days. Thus, there are (365)(364) = 132,860 possible ways two people can have different birthdays.

48. The first person can have any of 365 days, the second person can have any of the remaining 364 days, the third person can have any of the remaining 363 days, the fourth person can have any of the remaining 362 days, and the fifth person can have any of the remaining 361 days. Thus, there are $(365)(364)(363)(362)(361) = 6.302555019 \times 10^{12}$ possible ways five people can have different birthdays.

49. Choosing 2 boys from the 4 boys can be done C(4,2) ways, and choosing 3 girls from the 8 girls can be done in C(8,3) ways. Thus, there are a total of:

$$C(4,2)\cdot C(8,3) = \frac{4!}{(4-2)!\,2!}\cdot\frac{8!}{(8-3)!\,3!} = \frac{4!}{2!\,2!}\cdot\frac{8!}{5!\,3!}$$

$$= \frac{4\cdot 3!}{2\cdot 1\cdot 2\cdot 1}\cdot\frac{8\cdot 7\cdot 6\cdot 5!}{5!\,3!} = 336$$

50. The committee is made up of 2 of 4 administrators, 3 of 8 faculty, and 5 of 20 students. The number of possible committees is:

$$C(4,2)\cdot C(8,3)\cdot C(20,5) = \frac{4!}{(4-2)!\,2!}\cdot\frac{8!}{(8-3)!\,3!}\cdot\frac{20!}{(20-5)!\,5!}$$

$$= \frac{4!}{2!\,2!}\cdot\frac{8!}{5!\,3!}\cdot\frac{20!}{15!\,5!} = \frac{4!}{2\cdot 1\cdot 2\cdot 1}\cdot\frac{8\cdot 7\cdot 6\cdot 5!}{5\cdot 4!\,3!}\cdot\frac{20\cdot 19\cdot 18\cdot 17\cdot 16\cdot 15!}{15!\,5!}$$

$$= 5{,}209{,}344 \text{ possible committees}$$

51. This is a permutation with repetition. There are $\frac{9!}{2!\,2!} = 90{,}720$ different words.

52. This is a permutation with repetition. There are $\frac{11!}{2!\,2!\,2!} = 4{,}989{,}600$ different words.

53. (a) $C(7,2)\cdot C(3,1) = 21\cdot 3 = 63$
(b) $C(7,3) = 35$
(c) $C(3,3) = 1$

54. (a) $C(15,5)\cdot C(10,0) = \frac{15!}{10!\,5!}\cdot\frac{10!}{0!\,10!} = \frac{15\cdot 14\cdot 13\cdot 12\cdot 11\cdot 10!}{10!\cdot 5\cdot 4\cdot 3\cdot 2\cdot 1} = 3003$
(b) $C(15,3)\cdot C(10,2) = \frac{15!}{12!\,3!}\cdot\frac{10!}{8!\,2!} = \frac{15\cdot 14\cdot 13\cdot 12!}{12!\cdot 3\cdot 2\cdot 1}\cdot\frac{10\cdot 9\cdot 8!}{8!\cdot 2\cdot 1} = 20475$
(c) $C(15,4)\cdot C(10,1) + C(15,5)\cdot C(10,0) = \frac{15\cdot 14\cdot 13\cdot 12\cdot 11!}{11!\cdot 4\cdot 3\cdot 2\cdot 1}\cdot\frac{10\cdot 9}{9!\cdot 1} + 3003 = 16653$

Chapter 14

Counting and Probability

14.3 Probability

1. Probabilities must be between 0 and 1, inclusive. Thus, 0, 0.01, 0.35, and 1 are probabilities.

2. Probabilities must be between 0 and 1, inclusive. Thus, $\frac{1}{2}, \frac{3}{4}, \frac{2}{3}$, and 0 are probabilities.

3. All the probabilities are between 0 and 1.
The sum of the probabilities is $0.2 + 0.3 + 0.1 + 0.4 = 1$.
This is a probability model.

4. All the probabilities are between 0 and 1.
The sum of the probabilities is $0.4 + 0.3 + 0.1 + 0.2 = 1$.
This is a probability model.

5. All the probabilities are between 0 and 1.
The sum of the probabilities is $0.3 + 0.2 + 0.1 + 0.3 = 0.9$.
This is not a probability model.

6. One probability is not between 0 and 1.
This is not a probability model.

7. The sample space is: $S = \{HH, HT, TH, TT\}$.
Each outcome is equally likely to occur; so $P(E) = \frac{n(E)}{n(S)}$.
The probabilities are: $P(HH) = \frac{1}{4}$, $P(HT) = \frac{1}{4}$, $P(TH) = \frac{1}{4}$, $P(TT) = \frac{1}{4}$.

8. The sample space is: $S = \{HH, HT, TH, TT\}$.
Each outcome is equally likely to occur; so $P(E) = \frac{n(E)}{n(S)}$.
The probabilities are: $P(HH) = \frac{1}{4}$, $P(HT) = \frac{1}{4}$, $P(TH) = \frac{1}{4}$, $P(TT) = \frac{1}{4}$.

9. The sample space of tossing two fair coins and a fair die is:
$$S = \{HH1, HH2, HH3, HH4, HH5, HH6, HT1, HT2, HT3, HT4, HT5, HT6, TH1, TH2, TH3, TH4, TH5, TH6, TT1, TT2, TT3, TT4, TT5, TT6\}$$
There are 24 equally likely outcomes and the probability of each is $\frac{1}{24}$.

10. The sample space of tossing a fair coin, a fair die, and a fair coin is:

$$S = \{H1H, H2H, H3H, H4H, H5H, H6H, H1T, H2T, H3T, H4T, H5T, H6T, T1H, T2H, T3H, T4H, T5H, T6H, T1T, T2T, T3T, T4T, T5T, T6T\}$$

There are 24 equally likely outcomes and the probability of each is $\frac{1}{24}$.

11. The sample space for tossing three fair coins is:

$$S = \{HHH, HHT, HTH, THH, HTT, THT, TTH, TTT\}$$

There are 8 equally likely outcomes and the probability of each is $\frac{1}{8}$.

12. The sample space for tossing one fair coin three times is:

$$S = \{HHH, HHT, HTH, THH, HTT, THT, TTH, TTT\}$$

There are 8 equally likely outcomes and the probability of each is $\frac{1}{8}$.

13. The sample space is:

S = {1 Yellow, 1 Red, 1 Green, 2 Yellow, 2 Red, 2 Green, 3 Yellow, 3 Red, 3 Green, 4 Yellow, 4 Red, 4 Green}

There are 12 equally likely events and the probability of each is $\frac{1}{12}$. The probability of getting a 2 or 4 followed by a Red is $P(2\text{ Red}) + P(4\text{ Red}) = \frac{1}{12} + \frac{1}{12} = \frac{1}{6}$.

14. The sample space is:

S = {Forward Yellow, Forward Red, Forward Green, Backward Yellow, Backward Red, Backward Green}

There are 6 equally likely events and the probability of each is $\frac{1}{6}$. The probability of getting Forward followed by Yellow or Green is:

$P(\text{Forward Yellow}) + P(\text{Forward Green}) = \frac{1}{6} + \frac{1}{6} = \frac{1}{3}$.

15. The sample space is:

S = {1 Yellow Forward, 1 Yellow Backward, 1 Red Forward, 1 Red Backward, 1 Green Forward, 1 Green Backward, 2 Yellow Forward, 2 Yellow Backward, 2 Red Forward, 2 Red Backward, 2 Green Forward, 2 Green Backward, 3 Yellow Forward, 3 Yellow Backward, 3 Red Forward, 3 Red Backward, 3 Green Forward, 3 Green Backward, 4 Yellow Forward, 4 Yellow Backward, 4 Red Forward, 4 Red Backward, 4 Green Forward, 4 Green Backward}

There are 24 equally likely events and the probability of each is $\frac{1}{24}$. The probability of getting a 1, followed by a Red or Green, followed by a Backward is

$P(1\text{ Red Backward}) + P(1\text{ Green Backward}) = \frac{1}{24} + \frac{1}{24} = \frac{1}{12}$.

16. The sample space is:
S = {Yellow 1 Forward, Yellow 1 Backward, Red 1 Forward, Red 1 Backward, Green 1 Forward, Green 1 Backward, Yellow 2 Forward, Yellow 2 Backward, Red 2 Forward, Red 2 Backward, Green 2 Forward, Green 2 Backward, Yellow 3 Forward, Yellow 3 Backward, Red 3 Forward, Red 3 Backward, Green 3 Forward, Green 3 Backward, Yellow 4 Forward, Yellow 4 Backward, Red 4 Forward, Red 4 Backward, Green 4 Forward, Green 4 Backward}
There are 24 equally likely events and the probability of each is $\frac{1}{24}$. The probability of getting a Yellow, followed by a 2 or 4, followed by a Forward is
$P(\text{Yellow 2 Forward}) + P(\text{Yellow 4 Forward}) = \frac{1}{24} + \frac{1}{24} = \frac{1}{12}$.

17. The sample space is:
S = {1 1 Yellow, 1 1 Red, 1 1 Green, 1 2 Yellow, 1 2 Red, 1 2 Green, 1 3 Yellow, 1 3 Red, 1 3 Green, 1 4 Yellow, 1 4 Red, 1 4 Green, 2 1 Yellow, 2 1 Red, 2 1 Green, 2 2 Yellow, 2 2 Red, 2 2 Green, 2 3 Yellow, 2 3 Red, 2 3 Green, 2 4 Yellow, 2 4 Red, 2 4 Green, 3 1 Yellow, 3 1 Red, 3 1 Green, 3 2 Yellow, 3 2 Red, 3 2 Green, 3 3 Yellow, 3 3 Red, 3 3 Green, 3 4 Yellow, 3 4 Red, 3 4 Green, 4 1 Yellow, 4 1 Red, 4 1 Green, 4 2 Yellow, 4 2 Red, 4 2 Green, 4 3 Yellow, 4 3 Red, 4 3 Green, 4 4 Yellow, 4 4 Red, 4 4 Green}
There are 48 equally likely events and the probability of each is $\frac{1}{48}$. The probability of getting a 2, followed by a 2 or 4, followed by a Red or Green is
$P(2\ 2\ \text{Red}) + P(2\ 4\ \text{Red}) + P(2\ 2\ \text{Green}) + P(2\ 4\ \text{Green}) = \frac{1}{48} + \frac{1}{48} + \frac{1}{48} + \frac{1}{48} = \frac{1}{12}$

18. The sample space is:
S = {Forward 11, Forward 12, Forward 13, Forward 14, Forward 21, Forward 22, Forward 23, Forward 24, Forward 31, Forward 32, Forward 33, Forward 34, Forward 41, Forward 42, Forward 43, Forward 44, Backward 11, Backward 12, Backward 13, Backward 14, Backward 21, Backward 22, Backward 23, Backward 24, Backward 31, Backward 32, Backward 33, Backward 34, Backward 41, Backward 42, Backward 43, Backward 44}
There are 32 equally likely events and the probability of each is $\frac{1}{32}$. The probability of getting a Forward, followed by a 1 or 3, followed by a 2 or 4 is
$P(\text{Forward } 12) + P(\text{Forward } 14) + P(\text{Forward } 32) + P(\text{Forward } 34)$
$= \frac{1}{32} + \frac{1}{32} + \frac{1}{32} + \frac{1}{32} = \frac{1}{8}$

19. A, B, C, F

20. A

21. B

22. F

23. Let $P(\text{tails}) = x$, then $P(\text{heads}) = 4x$

$$x + 4x = 1 \rightarrow 5x = 1 \rightarrow x = \frac{1}{5} \quad P(\text{tails}) = \frac{1}{5}, \quad P(\text{heads}) = \frac{4}{5}$$

24. Let $P(\text{heads}) = x$, then $P(\text{tails}) = 2x$

$$x + 2x = 1 \rightarrow 3x = 1 \rightarrow x = \frac{1}{3} \quad P(\text{heads}) = \frac{1}{3}, \quad P(\text{tails}) = \frac{2}{3}$$

25. $P(2) = P(4) = P(6) = x \qquad P(1) = P(3) = P(5) = 2x$

$$P(1) + P(2) + P(3) + P(4) + P(5) + P(6) = 1$$

$$2x + x + 2x + x + 2x + x = 1 \rightarrow 9x = 1 \rightarrow x = \frac{1}{9}$$

$$P(2) = P(4) = P(6) = \frac{1}{9} \qquad P(1) = P(3) = P(5) = \frac{2}{9}$$

26. $P(1) = P(2) = P(3) = P(4) = P(5) = x \qquad P(6) = 0$

$$P(1) + P(2) + P(3) + P(4) + P(5) + P(6) = 1$$

$$x + x + x + x + x + 0 = 1 \rightarrow 5x = 1 \rightarrow x = \frac{1}{5}$$

$$P(1) = P(2) = P(3) = P(4) = P(5) = \frac{1}{5} \qquad P(6) = 0$$

27. $P(E) = \dfrac{n(E)}{n(S)} = \dfrac{n\{1,2,3\}}{10} = \dfrac{3}{10}$

28. $P(F) = \dfrac{n(F)}{n(S)} = \dfrac{n\{3, 5, 9, 10\}}{10} = \dfrac{4}{10} = \dfrac{2}{5}$

29. $P(E) = \dfrac{n(E)}{n(S)} = \dfrac{n\{2,4,6,8,10\}}{10} = \dfrac{5}{10} = \dfrac{1}{2}$

30. $P(F) = \dfrac{n(F)}{n(S)} = \dfrac{n\{1, 3, 5, 7, 9\}}{10} = \dfrac{5}{10} = \dfrac{1}{2}$

31. $P(\text{white}) = \dfrac{n(\text{white})}{n(S)} = \dfrac{5}{5+10+8+7} = \dfrac{5}{30} = \dfrac{1}{6}$

32. $P(\text{black}) = \dfrac{n(\text{black})}{n(S)} = \dfrac{7}{5+10+8+7} = \dfrac{7}{30}$

33. The sample space is: S = {BBB, BBG, BGB, GBB, BGG, GBG, GGB, GGG}

$$P(3\text{ boys}) = \frac{n(3\text{ boys})}{n(S)} = \frac{1}{8}$$

34. The sample space is: S = {BBB, BBG, BGB, GBB, BGG, GBG, GGB, GGG}

$$P(3\text{ girls}) = \frac{n(3\text{ girls})}{n(S)} = \frac{1}{8}$$

35. The sample space is:
S = {BBBB, BBBG, BBGB, BGBB, GBBB, BBGG, BGBG, GBBG, BGGB, GBGB, GGBB, BGGG, GBGG, GGBG, GGGB, GGGG}
$P(1\text{ girl, }3\text{ boys}) = \frac{n(1\text{ girl, }3\text{ boys})}{n(S)} = \frac{4}{16} = \frac{1}{4}$

36. The sample space is:
S = {BBBB, BBBG, BBGB, BGBB, GBBB, BBGG, BGBG, GBBG, BGGB, GBGB, GGBB, BGGG, GBGG, GGBG, GGGB, GGGG}
$P(2\text{ girl, }2\text{ boys}) = \frac{n(2\text{ girl, }2\text{ boys})}{n(S)} = \frac{6}{16} = \frac{3}{8}$

37. $P(\text{sum of two die is 7}) = \frac{n(\text{sum of two die is 7})}{n(S)}$
$= \frac{n\{1,6\text{ or }2,5\text{ or }3,4\text{ or }4,3\text{ or }5,2\text{ or }6,1\}}{n(S)} = \frac{6}{36} = \frac{1}{6}$

38. $P(\text{sum of two die is 11}) = \frac{n(\text{sum of two die is 11})}{n(S)} = \frac{n\{5,6\text{ or }6,5\}}{n(S)} = \frac{2}{36} = \frac{1}{18}$

39. $P(\text{sum of two die is 3}) = \frac{n(\text{sum of two die is 3})}{n(S)} = \frac{n\{1,2\text{ or }2,1\}}{n(S)} = \frac{2}{36} = \frac{1}{18}$

40. $P(\text{sum of two die is 12}) = \frac{n(\text{sum of two die is 12})}{n(S)} = \frac{n\{6,6\}}{n(S)} = \frac{1}{36}$

41. $P(A \cup B) = P(A) + P(B) - P(A \cap B) = 0.25 + 0.45 - 0.15 = 0.55$

42. $P(A \cap B) = P(A) + P(B) - P(A \cup B) = 0.25 + 0.45 - 0.6 = 0.1$

43. $P(A \cup B) = P(A) + P(B) = 0.25 + 0.45 = 0.70$

44. $P(A \cap B) = 0$

45. $P(A \cup B) = P(A) + P(B) - P(A \cap B)$
$0.85 = 0.60 + P(B) - 0.05$
$P(B) = 0.85 - 0.60 + 0.05 = 0.30$

46. $P(A \cup B) = P(A) + P(B) - P(A \cap B)$
$0.65 = P(A) + 0.30 - 0.15$
$P(A) = 0.65 - 0.30 + 0.15 = 0.50$

47. $P(\text{not victim}) = 1 - P(\text{victim}) = 1 - 0.253 = 0.747$

48. $P(\text{not victim}) = 1 - P(\text{victim}) = 1 - 0.056 = 0.944$

49. $P(\text{not in 70's}) = 1 - P(\text{in 70's}) = 1 - 0.3 = 0.7$

50. $P(\text{not in 30's}) = 1 - P(\text{in 30's}) = 1 - 0.04 = 0.96$

51. $P(\text{white or green}) = P(\text{white}) + P(\text{green}) = \dfrac{n(\text{white}) + n(\text{green})}{n(S)} = \dfrac{9+8}{9+8+3} = \dfrac{17}{20}$

52. $P(\text{white or orange}) = P(\text{white}) + P(\text{orange}) = \dfrac{n(\text{white}) + n(\text{orange})}{n(S)} = \dfrac{9+3}{9+8+3}$
$= \dfrac{12}{20} = \dfrac{3}{5}$

53. $P(\text{not white}) = 1 - P(\text{white}) = 1 - \dfrac{n(\text{white})}{n(S)} = 1 - \dfrac{9}{20} = \dfrac{11}{20}$

54. $P(\text{not green}) = 1 - P(\text{green}) = 1 - \dfrac{n(\text{green})}{n(S)} = 1 - \dfrac{8}{20} = \dfrac{12}{20} = \dfrac{3}{5}$

55. $P(\text{strike or one}) = P(\text{strike}) + P(\text{one}) = \dfrac{n(\text{strike}) + n(\text{one})}{n(S)} = \dfrac{3+1}{8} = \dfrac{4}{8} = \dfrac{1}{2}$

56. $P(100 \text{ or } 30) = P(100) + P(30) = \dfrac{n(100) + n(30)}{n(S)} = \dfrac{1+1}{20} = \dfrac{2}{20} = \dfrac{1}{10}$

57. There are 30 households out of 100 with an income of \$30,000 or more.
$P(E) = \dfrac{n(E)}{n(S)} = \dfrac{n(30{,}000 \text{ or more})}{n(\text{total households})} = \dfrac{30}{100} = \dfrac{3}{10}$

58. There are 65 households out of 100 with an income between \$10,000 and \$29,999.
$P(E) = \dfrac{n(E)}{n(S)} = \dfrac{n(10{,}000 \text{ to } 29{,}999)}{n(\text{total households})} = \dfrac{65}{100} = \dfrac{13}{20} = 0.65$

59. There are 40 households out of 100 with an income of less than \$20,000.
$P(E) = \dfrac{n(E)}{n(S)} = \dfrac{n(\text{less than } \$20{,}000)}{n(\text{total households})} = \dfrac{40}{100} = \dfrac{2}{5}$

60. There are 60 households out of 100 with an income of \$20,000 or more.
$P(E) = \dfrac{n(E)}{n(S)} = \dfrac{n(\$20{,}000 \text{ or more})}{n(\text{total households})} = \dfrac{60}{100} = \dfrac{3}{5}$

61. (a) $P(1 \text{ or } 2) = P(1) + P(2) = 0.24 + 0.33 = 0.57$
(b) $P(1 \text{ or more}) = P(1) + P(2) + P(3) + P(4 \text{ or more})$
$= 0.24 + 0.33 + 0.21 + 0.17 = 0.95$
(c) $P(3 \text{ or fewer}) = P(0) + P(1) + P(2) + P(3) = 0.05 + 0.24 + 0.33 + 0.21 = 0.83$
(d) $P(3 \text{ or more}) = P(3) + P(4 \text{ or more}) = 0.21 + 0.17 = 0.38$
(e) $P(\text{less than } 2) = P(0) + P(1) = 0.05 + 0.24 = 0.29$
(f) $P(\text{less than } 1) = P(0) = 0.05$
(g) $P(1, 2, \text{ or } 3) = P(1) + P(2) + P(3) = 0.24 + 0.33 + 0.21 = 0.78$

(h) $P(2 \text{ or more}) = P(2) + P(3) + P(4 \text{ or more}) = 0.33 + 0.21 + 0.17 = 0.71$

62. (a) $P(\text{at most } 2) = P(0) + P(1) + P(2) = 0.10 + 0.15 + 0.20 = 0.45$
(b) $P(\text{at least } 2) = P(2) + P(3) + P(4 \text{ or more}) = 0.20 + 0.24 + 0.31 = 0.75$
(c) $P(\text{at least } 1) = 1 - P(0) = 1 - 0.10 = 0.90$

63. (a)
$$\begin{aligned} P(\text{freshman or female}) &= P(\text{freshman}) + P(\text{female}) - P(\text{freshman and female}) \\ &= \frac{n(\text{freshman}) + n(\text{female}) - n(\text{freshman and female})}{n(S)} \\ &= \frac{18 + 15 - 8}{33} = \frac{25}{33} \end{aligned}$$
(b)
$$\begin{aligned} P(\text{sophomore or male}) &= P(\text{sophomore}) + P(\text{male}) - P(\text{sophomore and male}) \\ &= \frac{n(\text{sophomore}) + n(\text{male}) - n(\text{sophomore and male})}{n(S)} \\ &= \frac{15 + 18 - 8}{33} = \frac{25}{33} \end{aligned}$$

64. (a)
$$\begin{aligned} P(\text{female or under } 40) &= P(\text{female}) + P(\text{under } 40) - P(\text{female and under } 40) \\ &= \frac{n(\text{female}) + n(\text{under } 40) - n(\text{female and under } 40)}{n(S)} \\ &= \frac{4 + 5 - 2}{13} = \frac{7}{13} \end{aligned}$$
(b)
$$\begin{aligned} P(\text{male or over } 40) &= P(\text{male}) + P(\text{over } 40) - P(\text{male and over } 40) \\ &= \frac{n(\text{male}) + n(\text{over } 40) - n(\text{male and over } 40)}{n(S)} \\ &= \frac{9 + 8 - 6}{13} = \frac{11}{13} \end{aligned}$$

65.
$$\begin{aligned} P(\text{at least 2 with same birthday}) &= 1 - P(\text{none with same birthday}) \\ &= 1 - \frac{n(\text{different birthdays})}{n(S)} \\ &= 1 - \frac{365 \cdot 364 \cdot 363 \cdot 362 \cdot 361 \cdot 360 \cdot \ldots \cdot 354}{365^{12}} \\ &= 1 - 0.833 \\ &= 0.167 \end{aligned}$$

66.
$$\begin{aligned} P(\text{at least 2 with same birthday}) &= 1 - P(\text{none with same birthday}) \\ &= 1 - \frac{n(\text{different birthdays})}{n(S)} \\ &= 1 - \frac{365 \cdot 364 \cdot 363 \cdot 362 \cdot 361 \cdot 360 \cdot \ldots \cdot 331}{365^{35}} \\ &= 1 - 0.1856 = 0.8144 \end{aligned}$$

67. The sample space for picking 5 out of 10 numbers in a particular order contains
$$P(10,5) = \frac{10!}{(10-5)!} = \frac{10!}{5!} = 30{,}240 \text{ possible outcomes.}$$
One of these is the desired outcome. Thus, the probability of winning is:

$$P(E)=\frac{n(E)}{n(S)}=\frac{n(\text{winning})}{n(\text{total possible outcomes})}=\frac{1}{30240}$$

68. The sample space is the number of ways of choosing members for the committee:

$$C(14,6)=\frac{14!}{(14-6)!\cdot 6!}=\frac{14!}{8!\,6!}=3003$$

The number of ways of choosing 0 supervisors from 2:

$$C(2,0)=\frac{2!}{(2-0)!\cdot 0!}=\frac{2!}{2!\,0!}=1$$

The number of ways of choosing 2 skilled laborers from 5:

$$C(5,2)=\frac{5!}{(5-2)!\cdot 2!}=\frac{5!}{3!\,2!}=10$$

The number of ways of choosing 4 unskilled laborers from 7:

$$C(7,4)=\frac{7!}{(7-4)!\cdot 4!}=\frac{7!}{3!\,4!}=35$$

Using the multiplication principle:

$$P(2\text{ skilled and }4\text{ unskilled})=\frac{1\cdot 10\cdot 35}{3003}=\frac{350}{3003}\approx 0.1166$$

69. (a) $P(3\text{ heads})=\dfrac{C(5,3)}{2^5}=\dfrac{10}{32}=\dfrac{5}{16}$

(b) $P(0\text{ heads})=\dfrac{C(5,0)}{2^5}=\dfrac{1}{32}$

70. (a) $P(1\text{ tail})=\dfrac{C(4,1)}{2^4}=\dfrac{4}{16}=\dfrac{1}{4}$

(b) $P(\text{no more than 1 tail})=P(0\text{ tails})+P(1\text{ tail})=\dfrac{1+4}{2^4}=\dfrac{5}{16}$

71. (a)

$$\begin{aligned}P(\text{sum}=7\text{ three times})&=P(\text{sum}=7)\cdot P(\text{sum}=7)\cdot P(\text{sum}=7)\\&=\frac{1}{6}\cdot\frac{1}{6}\cdot\frac{1}{6}=\frac{1}{216}\end{aligned}$$

(b)

$$\begin{aligned}P(\text{sum}&=7\text{ or }11\text{ at least twice})\\&=P(\text{sum}=7\text{ or }11)\cdot P(\text{sum}=7\text{ or }11)\cdot P(\text{sum}\neq 7\text{ or }11)+\\&\qquad P(\text{sum}=7\text{ or }11)\cdot P(\text{sum}=7\text{ or }11)\cdot P(\text{sum}=7\text{ or }11)\\&=\frac{8}{36}\cdot\frac{8}{36}\cdot\frac{28}{36}+\frac{8}{36}\cdot\frac{8}{36}\cdot\frac{8}{36}=0.049\end{aligned}$$

72. (a) $P(\text{sum}\neq 2)=1-P(\text{sum}=2)=1-\dfrac{1}{36}=\dfrac{35}{36}$

$P(\text{sum}\neq 2\text{ on 5 tosses})=\left(\dfrac{35}{36}\right)^5=0.8686$

(b) $P(\text{sum}\neq 7)=1-P(\text{sum}=7)=1-\dfrac{6}{36}=\dfrac{30}{36}=\dfrac{5}{6}$

$P(\text{sum}\neq 7\text{ on 5 tosses})=\left(\dfrac{5}{6}\right)^5=0.4019$

73. $P(\text{all 5 defective}) = \dfrac{n(\text{5 defective})}{n(S)} = \dfrac{1}{C(30,5)} = 7.02 \times 10^{-6}$

$P(\text{at least 2 defective}) = 1 - (P(\text{none defective}) + P(\text{one defective}))$

$$= 1 - \left(\frac{C(5,0) \cdot C(25,5)}{C(30,5)} + \frac{C(5,1) \cdot C(25,4)}{C(30,5)} \right) = 1 - 0.817 = 0.183$$

74. $P(\text{30 nondefective}) = \dfrac{n(\text{30 nondefective chosen from 40})}{n(S)}$

$$= \frac{C(40,30)}{C(50,30)} = 1.7986 \times 10^{-5}$$

75. $P(\text{one of 5 coins is valued at more than \$10,000}) = \dfrac{C(49,4) \cdot C(1,1)}{C(50,5)} = 0.1$

Chapter 14

Counting and Probability

14.R Chapter Review

1. $A \cup B = \{1, 3, 5, 7\} \cup \{3, 5, 6, 7, 8\} = \{1, 3, 5, 6, 7, 8\}$

2. $B \cup C = \{3, 5, 6, 7, 8\} \cup \{2, 3, 7, 8, 9\} = \{2, 3, 5, 6, 7, 8, 9\}$

3. $A \cap C = \{1, 3, 5, 7\} \cap \{2, 3, 7, 8, 9\} = \{3, 7\}$

4. $A \cap B = \{1, 3, 5, 7\} \cap \{3, 5, 6, 7, 8\} = \{3, 5, 7\}$

5. $\overline{A} \cup \overline{B} = \overline{\{1, 3, 5, 7\}} \cup \overline{\{3, 5, 6, 7, 8\}} = \{2, 4, 6, 8, 9\} \cup \{1, 2, 4, 9\} = \{1, 2, 4, 6, 8, 9\}$

6. $\overline{B} \cap \overline{C} = \overline{\{3, 5, 6, 7, 8\}} \cap \overline{\{2, 3, 7, 8. 9\}} = \{1, 2, 4, 9\} \cap \{1, 4, 5, 6\} = \{1, 4\}$

7. $\overline{B \cap C} = \overline{\{3, 5, 6, 7, 8\} \cap \{2, 3, 7, 8, 9\}} = \overline{\{3, 7, 8\}} = \{1, 2, 4, 5, 6, 9\}$

8. $\overline{A \cup B} = \overline{\{1, 3, 5, 7\} \cup \{3, 5, 6, 7, 8\}} = \overline{\{1, 3, 5, 6, 7, 8\}} = \{2, 4, 9\}$

9. $n(A) = 8,\ n(B) = 12,\ n(A \cap B) = 3$
   $n(A \cup B) = n(A) + n(B) - n(A \cap B) = 8 + 12 - 3 = 17$

10. $n(A) = 12,\ n(A \cup B) = 30,\ n(A \cap B) = 6$
    $n(A \cup B) = n(A) + n(B) - n(A \cap B)$
    $30 = 12 + n(B) - 6$
    $n(B) = 30 - 12 + 6 = 24$

11. From the figure:
    $n(A) = 20 + 2 + 6 + 1 = 29$

12. From the figure:
    $n(A \text{ or } B) = 20 + 2 + 6 + 1 + 5 + 0 = 34$

13. From the figure:
    $n(A \text{ and } C) = n(A \cap C) = 1 + 6 = 7$

14. From the figure:
    $n(\text{not in } B) = 20 + 1 + 4 + 20 = 45$

15. From the figure:

$n(\text{neither in } A \text{ nor in } C) = n(\overline{A \cup C}) = 20 + 5 = 25$

16. From the figure:

$n(\text{in } B \text{ but not in } C) = 2 + 5 = 7$

17. $5! = 5 \cdot 4 \cdot 3 \cdot 2 \cdot 1 = 120$

18. $6! = 6 \cdot 5 \cdot 4 \cdot 3 \cdot 2 \cdot 1 = 720$

19. $P(8,3) = \dfrac{8!}{(8-3)!} = \dfrac{8!}{5!} = \dfrac{8 \cdot 7 \cdot 6 \cdot 5!}{5!} = 336$

20. $P(7,3) = \dfrac{7!}{(7-3)!} = \dfrac{7!}{4!} = \dfrac{7 \cdot 6 \cdot 5 \cdot 4!}{4!} = 210$

21. $C(8,3) = \dfrac{8!}{(8-3)!\,3!} = \dfrac{8!}{5!\,3!} = \dfrac{8 \cdot 7 \cdot 6 \cdot 5!}{5! \cdot 3 \cdot 2 \cdot 1} = 56$

22. $C(7,3) = \dfrac{7!}{(7-3)!\,3!} = \dfrac{7!}{4!\,3!} = \dfrac{7 \cdot 6 \cdot 5 \cdot 4!}{4! \cdot 3 \cdot 2 \cdot 1} = 35$

23. There are 2 choices of material, 3 choices of color, and 10 choices of size. The complete assortment would have: $2 \cdot 3 \cdot 10 = 60$ suits.

24. This is a permutation of 5 items taken 5 at a time. There are

$P(5,5) = \dfrac{5!}{(5-5)!} = \dfrac{5!}{0!} = 5! = 120$ possible wirings.

25. There are two possible outcomes for each game or

$2 \cdot 2 \cdot 2 \cdot 2 \cdot 2 \cdot 2 \cdot 2 = 2^7 = 128$ outcomes for 7 games.

26. There are two possible outcomes for each game or

$2 \cdot 2 \cdot 2 \cdot 2 \cdot 2 \cdot 2 = 2^6 = 64$ outcomes for 6 games.

27. Since order is significant, this is a permutation.

$P(9,4) = \dfrac{9!}{(9-4)!} = \dfrac{9!}{5!} = \dfrac{9 \cdot 8 \cdot 7 \cdot 6 \cdot 5!}{5!} = 3024$ ways to seat 4 people in 9 seats.

28. Since order is significant, this is a permutation.

$P(4,4) = \dfrac{4!}{(4-4)!} = \dfrac{4!}{0!} = \dfrac{4 \cdot 3 \cdot 2 \cdot 1}{1} = 24$ arrangements of the letters in ROSE.

29. Choose 4 runners - order is not significant:

$C(8,4) = \dfrac{8!}{(8-4)!\,4!} = \dfrac{8!}{4!\,4!} = \dfrac{8 \cdot 7 \cdot 6 \cdot 5 \cdot 4!}{4 \cdot 3 \cdot 2 \cdot 1 \cdot 4!} = 70$ ways a squad can be chosen.

30. Choose 3 problems - order is not significant:

$C(10,3) = \dfrac{10!}{(10-3)!\,3!} = \dfrac{10!}{7!\,3!} = \dfrac{10 \cdot 9 \cdot 8 \cdot 7!}{3 \cdot 2 \cdot 1 \cdot 7!} = 120$ different tests are possible.

31. Choose 14 teams 2 at a time:
$$C(14,2) = \frac{14!}{(14-2)!\,2!} = \frac{14!}{12!\,2!} = \frac{14\cdot 13\cdot 12!}{12!\cdot 2\cdot 1} = 91 \text{ ways to pair 14 teams.}$$

32. (a) Since order is important, this is a permutation:
$$P(5,5)\cdot P(5,5) = \frac{5!}{(5-5)!}\cdot\frac{5!}{(5-5!} = 5!\cdot 5! = 120\cdot 120 = 14400 \text{ different arrangements.}$$
(b) There would be $5\cdot 5\cdot 4\cdot 4\cdot 3\cdot 3\cdot 2\cdot 2\cdot 1\cdot 1 = 14400$ different arrangements.

33. There are $8\cdot 10\cdot 10\cdot 10\cdot 10\cdot 10\cdot 2 = 1{,}600{,}000$ possible phone numbers.

34. There are $5\cdot 3\cdot 4 = 60$ different types of homes that can be built.

35. There are $24\cdot 9\cdot 10\cdot 10\cdot 10 = 216{,}000$ possible license plates.

36. There are $2^8 = 256$ different numbers.

37. Since there are repeated letters:
$$\frac{7!}{2!\cdot 2!} = \frac{7\cdot 6\cdot 5\cdot 4\cdot 3\cdot 2\cdot 1}{2\cdot 1\cdot 2\cdot 1} = 1260 \text{ different words can be formed.}$$

38. Since there are repeated colors:
$$\frac{10!}{4!\cdot 3!\cdot 2!\cdot 1!} = \frac{10\cdot 9\cdot 8\cdot 7\cdot 6\cdot 5\cdot 4\cdot 3\cdot 2\cdot 1}{4\cdot 3\cdot 2\cdot 1\cdot 3\cdot 2\cdot 1\cdot 2\cdot 1\cdot 1} = 12600 \text{ different vertical arrangements.}$$

39. (a) $C(9,4)\cdot C(9,3)\cdot C(9,2) = 126\cdot 84\cdot 36 = 381{,}024$ committees can be formed.
(b) $C(9,4)\cdot C(5,3)\cdot C(2,2) = 126\cdot 10\cdot 1 = 1260$ committees can be formed.

40. (a) $C(5,1)\cdot C(8,3) = \dfrac{5!}{(5-1)!1!}\cdot\dfrac{8!}{(8-3)!3!} = 5\cdot 56 = 280$ committees containing exactly 1 man.
(b) $C(5,2)\cdot C(8,2) = 10\cdot 28 = 280$ committees containing exactly 2 women.
(c) $C(5,1)\cdot C(8,3) + C(5,2)\cdot C(8,2) + C(5,3)\cdot C(8,1) = 280 + 280 + 10\cdot 8 = 640$ committees containing at least 1 man.

41. (a) $365\cdot 364\cdot 363\cdot 362\cdot \ldots \cdot 348 = 8.634628387\times 10^{45}$
(b) $P(\text{no one has same birthday}) = \dfrac{365\cdot 364\cdot 363\cdot 362\cdot \ldots \cdot 348}{365^{18}} = 0.6531 = 65.31\%$
(c) $P(\text{at least 2 have same birthday}) = 1 - P(\text{no one has same birthday})$
$= 1 - 0.6531 = 0.3469 = 34.69\%$

42. (a) $P(\text{heart disease}) = 0.321$
(b) $P(\text{not heart disease}) = 1 - P(\text{heart disease}) = 1 - 0.321 = 0.679$

43. (a) $P(\text{unemployed}) = 0.054 = 5.4\%$
(b) $P(\text{not unemployed}) = 1 - P(\text{unemployed}) = 1 - 0.054 = 0.946 = 94.6\%$

44. $P(40\text{ watt}) = \dfrac{n(40\text{ watt})}{n(\text{bulbs})} = \dfrac{3}{20}$

$P(\text{not }75\text{ watt}) = 1 - P(75\text{ watt}) = 1 - \dfrac{n(75\text{ watt})}{n(\text{bulbs})} = 1 - \dfrac{11}{20} = \dfrac{9}{20}$

45. $P(\$1\text{ bill}) = \dfrac{n(\$1\text{ bill})}{n(S)} = \dfrac{4}{9}$

46. $P(\text{ROSE}) = \dfrac{1}{4}\cdot\dfrac{1}{3}\cdot\dfrac{1}{2}\cdot\dfrac{1}{1} = \dfrac{1}{24}$

47. Let S be all possible selections, let D be a card that is divisible by 5, and let PN be a 1 or a prime number.

$n(S) = 100$

$n(D) = 20$ (There are 20 numbers divisible by 5 between 1 and 100.)

$n(PN) = 26$ (There are 25 prime numbers less than or equal to 100.)

$P(D) = \dfrac{n(D)}{n(S)} = \dfrac{20}{100} = \dfrac{1}{5} = 0.2$

$P(PN) = \dfrac{n(PN)}{n(S)} = \dfrac{26}{100} = \dfrac{13}{50} = 0.26$

48. (a) $P(3\text{ Merlot}) = \dfrac{C(5,3)}{C(12,3)} = \dfrac{10}{220} = \dfrac{1}{22} \approx 0.0455$

(b) $P(2\text{ Merlot, }1\text{ Cabernet}) = \dfrac{C(5,2)\cdot C(7,1)}{C(12,3)} = \dfrac{10\cdot 7}{220} = \dfrac{70}{220} = \dfrac{7}{22} \approx 0.3182$

(c) $P(3\text{ Cabernet}) = \dfrac{C(7,3)}{C(12,3)} = \dfrac{35}{220} = \dfrac{7}{44} \approx 0.1591$

49. (a) $P(5\text{ heads}) = \dfrac{n(5\text{ heads})}{n(S)} = \dfrac{C(10,5)}{2^{10}} = \dfrac{\left(\dfrac{10!}{5!5!}\right)}{1024} = \dfrac{252}{1024} \approx 0.2461$

(b) $P(\text{all heads}) = \dfrac{n(\text{all heads})}{n(S)} = \dfrac{1}{2^{10}} = \dfrac{1}{1024} = 0.00098$

50. (a) $P(T \cup B) = P(T) + P(B) - P(T \cap B) = 0.6 + 0.1 - 0.02 = 0.68$

(b)

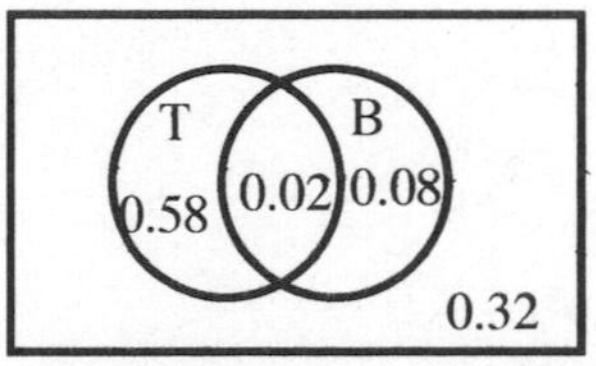

$P(T\text{ and not }B) = 0.58$

(c) $P(\overline{T \cup B}) = 1 - P(T \cup B) = 1 - 0.68 = 0.32$

Graphing Utilities

A.1 The Viewing Rectangle

1. (- 1, 4)

2. (3, 4)

3. (3, 1)

4. (- 6, - 4)

5.
$X\min = -6$
$X\max = 6$
$X\text{scl} = 2$
$Y\min = -4$
$Y\max = 4$
$Y\text{scl} = 2$

6.
$X\min = -3$
$X\max = 3$
$X\text{scl} = 1$
$Y\min = -2$
$Y\max = 2$
$Y\text{scl} = 1$

7.
$X\min = -6$
$X\max = 6$
$X\text{scl} = 2$
$Y\min = -1$
$Y\max = 3$
$Y\text{scl} = 1$

8.
$X\min = -9$
$X\max = 9$
$X\text{scl} = 3$
$Y\min = -12$
$Y\max = 4$
$Y\text{scl} = 4$

9.
$X\min = 3$
$X\max = 9$
$X\text{scl} = 1$
$Y\min = 2$
$Y\max = 10$
$Y\text{scl} = 2$

10.
$X\min = -22$
$X\max = -10$
$X\text{scl} = 2$
$Y\min = 4$
$Y\max = 8$
$Y\text{scl} = 1$

11.
$X\min = -11$
$X\max = 5$
$X\text{scl} = 1$
$Y\min = -3$
$Y\max = 6$
$Y\text{scl} = 1$

12.
$X\min = -3$
$X\max = 7$
$X\text{scl} = 1$
$Y\min = -4$
$Y\max = 9$
$Y\text{scl} = 1$

13.
$X\min = -30$
$X\max = 50$
$X\text{scl} = 10$
$Y\min = -90$
$Y\max = 50$
$Y\text{scl} = 10$

14.
$X\min = -90$
$X\max = 30$
$X\text{scl} = 10$
$Y\min = -50$
$Y\max = 70$
$Y\text{scl} = 10$

15.
$X\min = -10$
$X\max = 110$
$X\text{scl} = 10$
$Y\min = -10$
$Y\max = 160$
$Y\text{scl} = 10$

16.
$X\min = -20$
$X\max = 110$
$X\text{scl} = 10$
$Y\min = -10$
$Y\max = 60$
$Y\text{scl} = 10$

17. $P_1 = (1,3); P_2 = (5,15)$

$$\begin{aligned} d(P_1,P_2) &= \sqrt{(5-1)^2 + (15-3)^2} \\ &= \sqrt{(4)^2 + (12)^2} \\ &= \sqrt{16+144} \\ &= \sqrt{160} = 2\sqrt{10} \end{aligned}$$

18. $P_1 = (-8,-4); P_2 = (2,3)$

$$\begin{aligned} d(P_1,P_2) &= \sqrt{(2-(-8))^2 + (3-(-4))^2} \\ &= \sqrt{(10)^2 + (7)^2} \\ &= \sqrt{100+49} \\ &= \sqrt{149} \end{aligned}$$

19. $P_1 = (-4,6); P_2 = (4,-8)$

$$\begin{aligned} d(P_1,P_2) &= \sqrt{(4-(-4))^2 + (-8-6)^2} \\ &= \sqrt{(8)^2 + (-14)^2} \\ &= \sqrt{64+196} \\ &= \sqrt{260} = 2\sqrt{65} \end{aligned}$$

20. $P_1 = (0,6); P_2 = (3,-8)$

$$\begin{aligned} d(P_1,P_2) &= \sqrt{(3-0)^2 + (-8-6)^2} \\ &= \sqrt{(3)^2 + (-14)^2} \\ &= \sqrt{9+196} \\ &= \sqrt{205} \end{aligned}$$

Graphing Utilities

A.2 Using a Graphing Utility to Graph Equations

1. (a) $y = x + 2$

$X\min = -5$

$X\max = 5$

$X\text{scl} = 1$

$Y\min = -4$

$Y\max = 4$

$Y\text{scl} = 1$

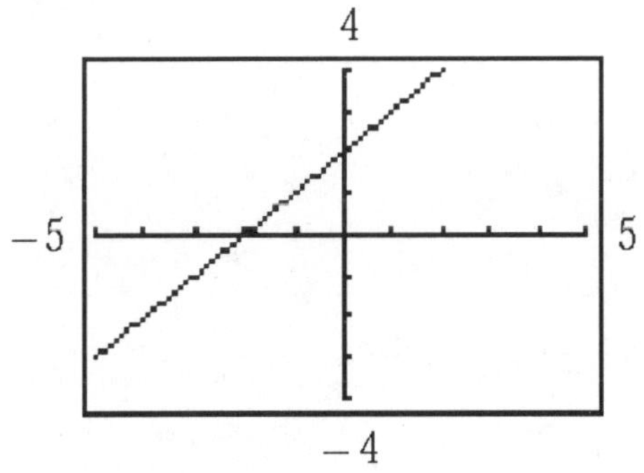

(b)

$X\min = -10$

$X\max = 10$

$X\text{scl} = 1$

$Y\min = -8$

$Y\max = 8$

$Y\text{scl} = 1$

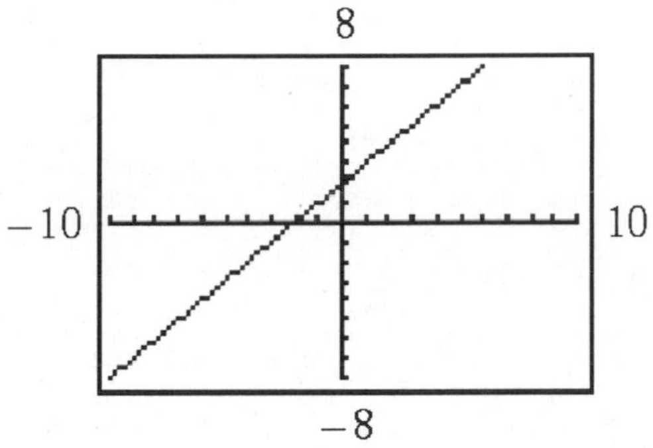

(c)

$X\min = -10$

$X\max = 10$

$X\text{scl} = 2$

$Y\min = -8$

$Y\max = 8$

$Y\text{scl} = 2$

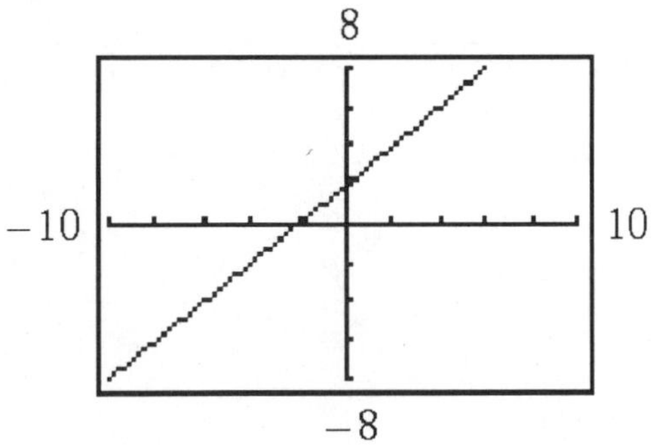

(d)

$X\min = -5$

$X\max = 5$

$X\text{scl} = 1$

$Y\min = -20$

$Y\max = 20$

$Y\text{scl} = 5$

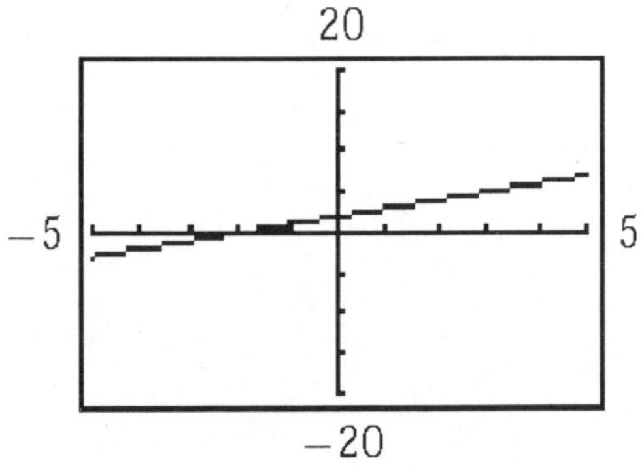

2. (a) $y = x - 2$

$X\min = -5$

$X\max = 5$

$X\text{scl} = 1$

$Y\min = -4$

$Y\max = 4$

$Y\text{scl} = 1$

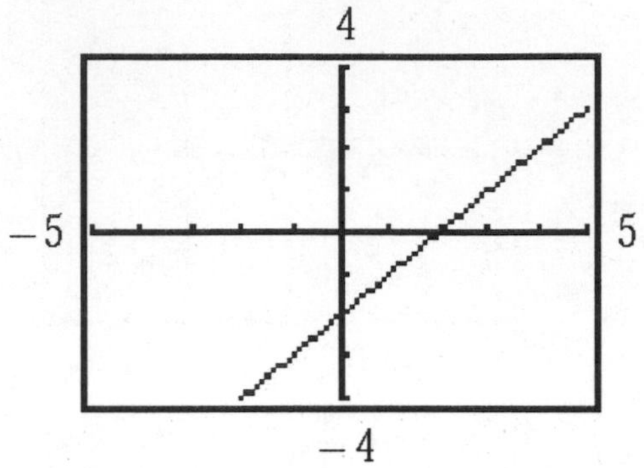

(b)

$X\min = -10$

$X\max = 10$

$X\text{scl} = 1$

$Y\min = -8$

$Y\max = 8$

$Y\text{scl} = 1$

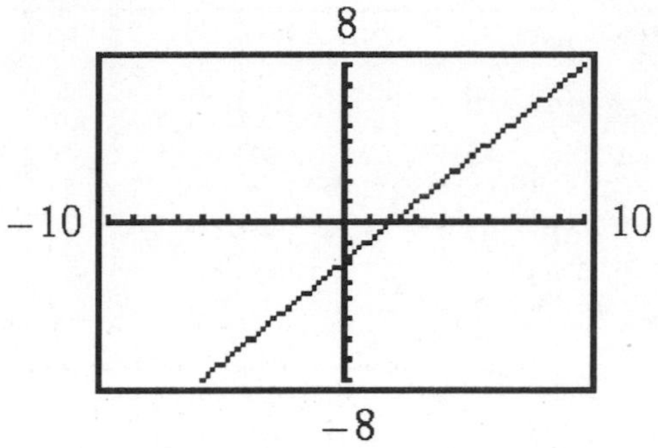

(c)

$X\min = -10$

$X\max = 10$

$X\text{scl} = 2$

$Y\min = -8$

$Y\max = 8$

$Y\text{scl} = 2$

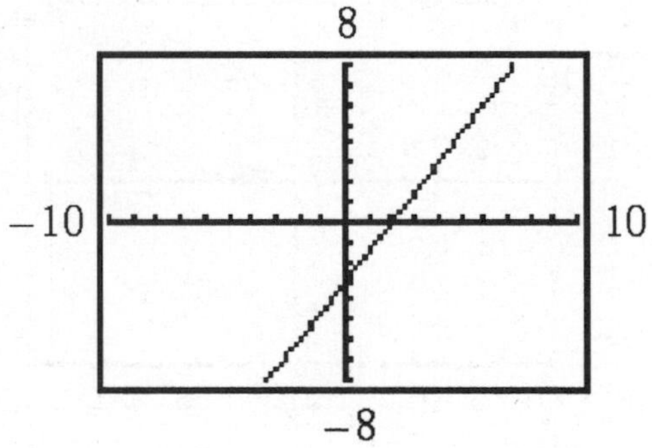

(d)

$X\min = -5$

$X\max = 5$

$X\text{scl} = 1$

$Y\min = -20$

$Y\max = 20$

$Y\text{scl} = 5$

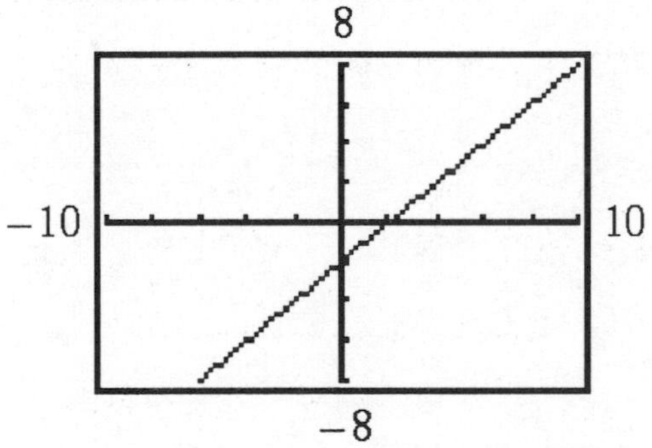

3. (a) $y = -x + 2$

$X\min = -5$

$X\max = 5$

$X\text{scl} = 1$

$Y\min = -4$

$Y\max = 4$

$Y\text{scl} = 1$

4

−5 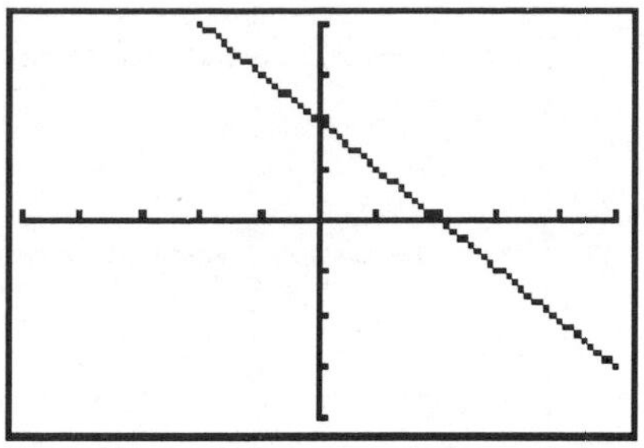 5

−4

(b)

$X\min = -10$

$X\max = 10$

$X\text{scl} = 1$

$Y\min = -8$

$Y\max = 8$

$Y\text{scl} = 1$

8

−10 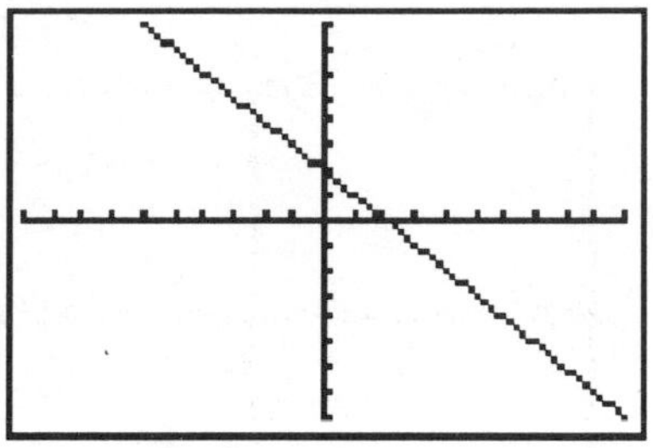 10

−8

(c)

$X\min = -10$

$X\max = 10$

$X\text{scl} = 2$

$Y\min = -8$

$Y\max = 8$

$Y\text{scl} = 2$

8

−10 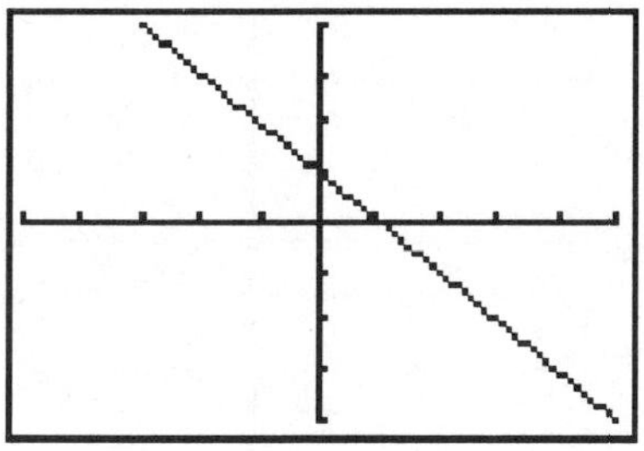 10

−8

(d)

$X\min = -5$

$X\max = 5$

$X\text{scl} = 1$

$Y\min = -20$

$Y\max = 20$

$Y\text{scl} = 5$

20

−5 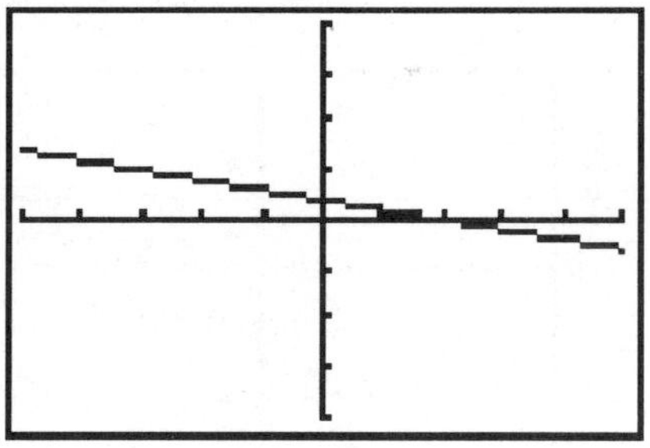 5

−20

4. (a) $y = -x - 2$

$X\min = -5$

$X\max = 5$

$X\text{scl} = 1$

$Y\min = -4$

$Y\max = 4$

$Y\text{scl} = 1$

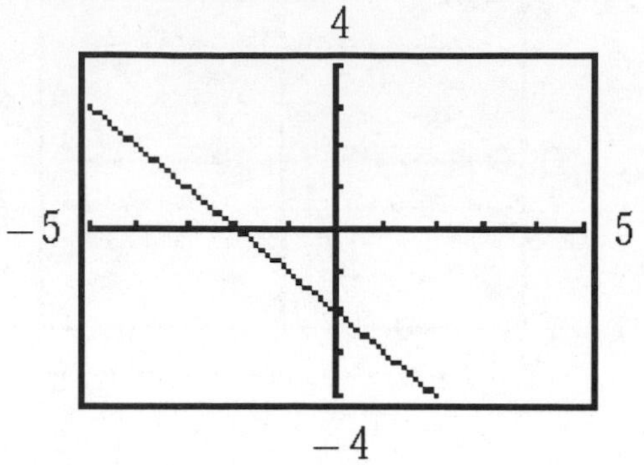

(b)

$X\min = -10$

$X\max = 10$

$X\text{scl} = 1$

$Y\min = -8$

$Y\max = 8$

$Y\text{scl} = 1$

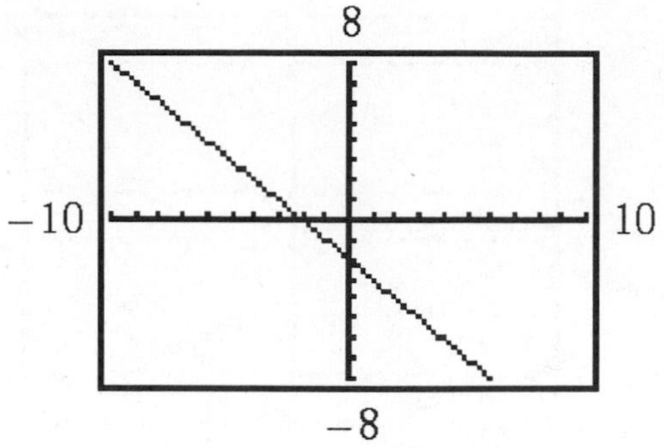

(c)

$X\min = -10$

$X\max = 10$

$X\text{scl} = 2$

$Y\min = -8$

$Y\max = 8$

$Y\text{scl} = 2$

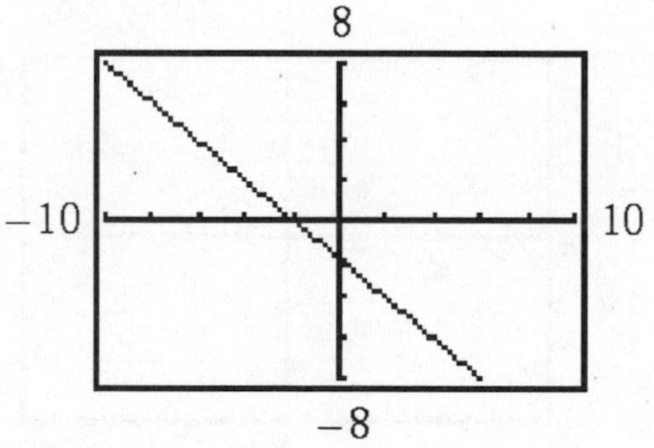

(d)

$X\min = -5$

$X\max = 5$

$X\text{scl} = 1$

$Y\min = -20$

$Y\max = 20$

$Y\text{scl} = 5$

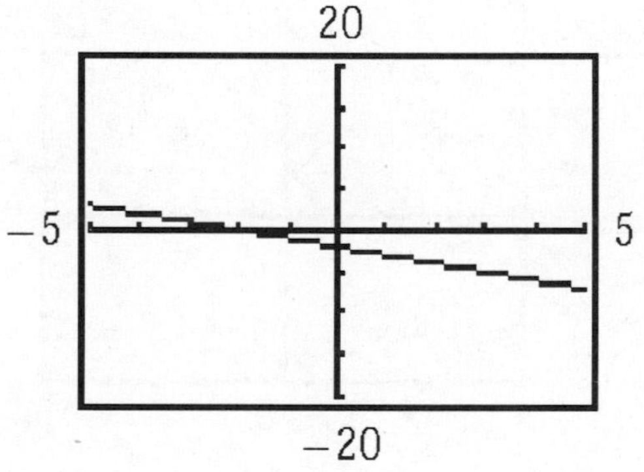

5. (a) $y = 2x + 2$

$X\min = -5$

$X\max = 5$

$X\text{scl} = 1$

$Y\min = -4$

$Y\max = 4$

$Y\text{scl} = 1$

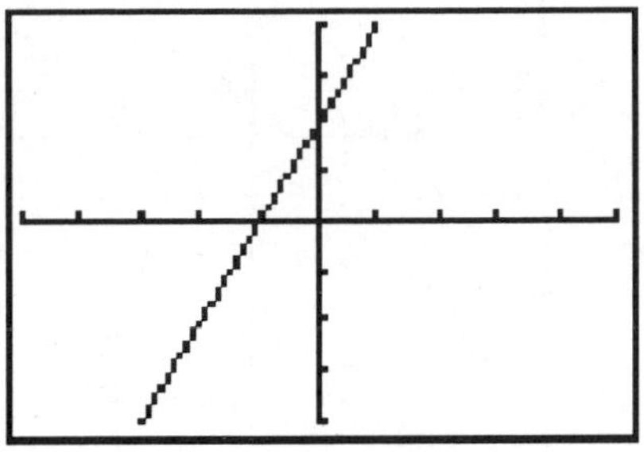

(b)

$X\min = -10$

$X\max = 10$

$X\text{scl} = 1$

$Y\min = -8$

$Y\max = 8$

$Y\text{scl} = 1$

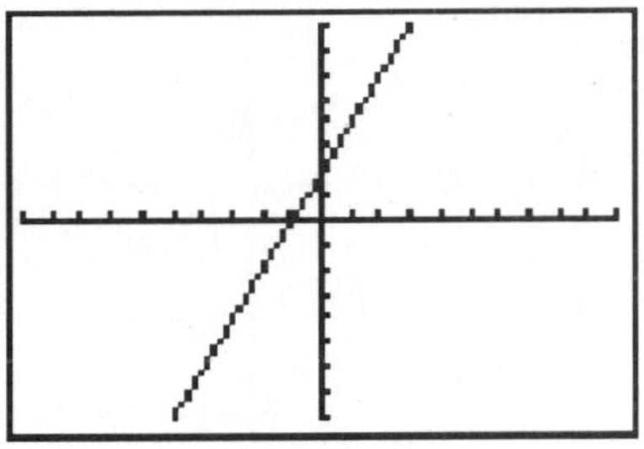

(c)

$X\min = -10$

$X\max = 10$

$X\text{scl} = 2$

$Y\min = -8$

$Y\max = 8$

$Y\text{scl} = 2$

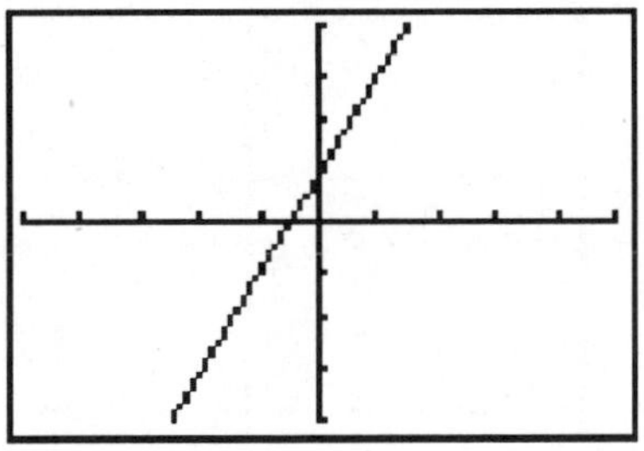

(d)

$X\min = -5$

$X\max = 5$

$X\text{scl} = 1$

$Y\min = -20$

$Y\max = 20$

$Y\text{scl} = 5$

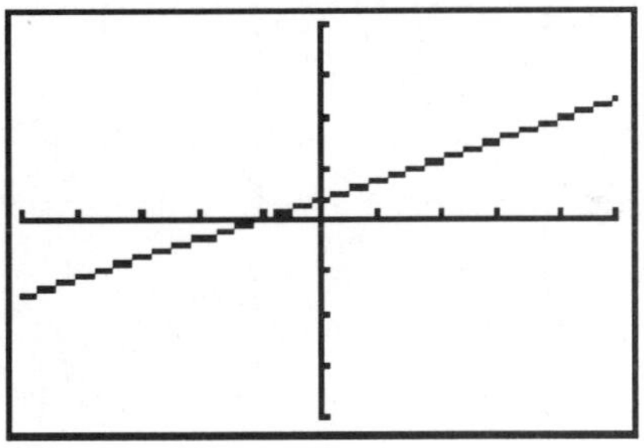

6. (a) $y = 2x - 2$

$X\min = -5$

$X\max = 5$

$X\text{scl} = 1$

$Y\min = -4$

$Y\max = 4$

$Y\text{scl} = 1$

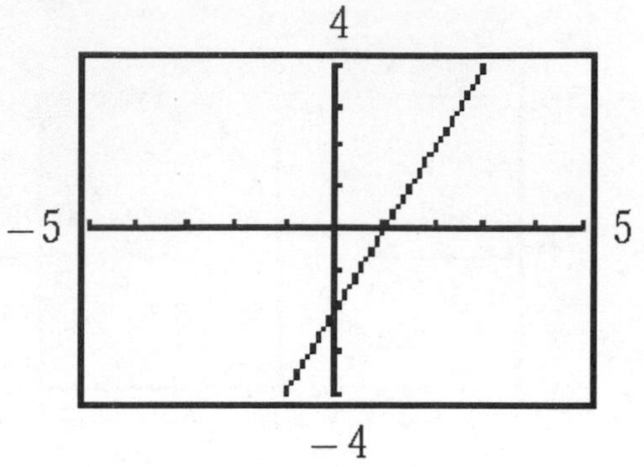

(b)

$X\min = -10$

$X\max = 10$

$X\text{scl} = 1$

$Y\min = -8$

$Y\max = 8$

$Y\text{scl} = 1$

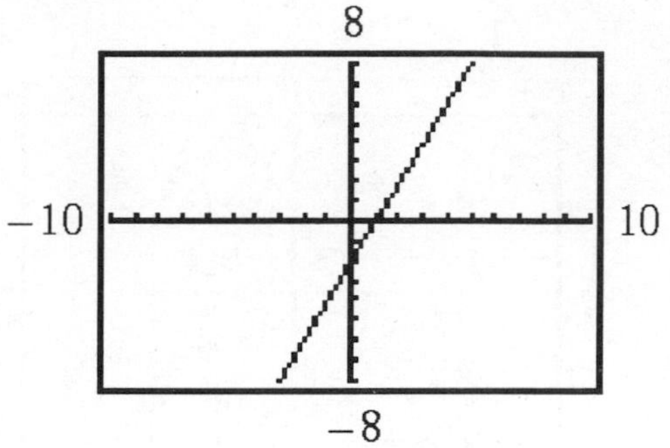

(c)

$X\min = -10$

$X\max = 10$

$X\text{scl} = 2$

$Y\min = -8$

$Y\max = 8$

$Y\text{scl} = 2$

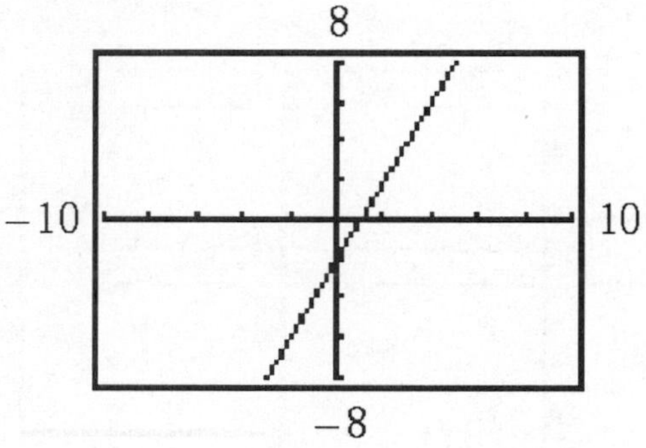

(d)

$X\min = -5$

$X\max = 5$

$X\text{scl} = 1$

$Y\min = -20$

$Y\max = 20$

$Y\text{scl} = 5$

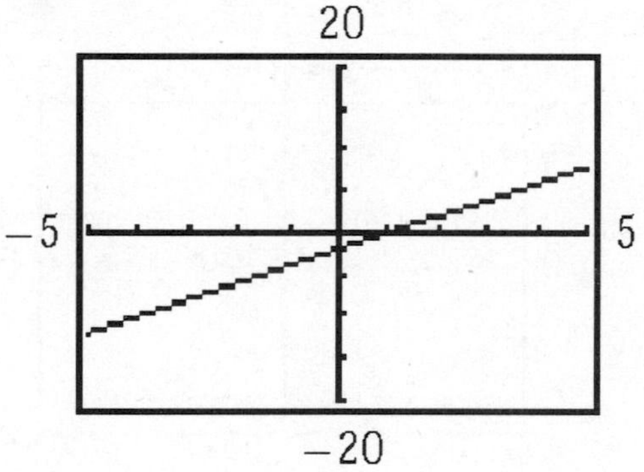

7. (a) $y = -2x + 2$

$X\min = -5$

$X\max = 5$

$X\text{scl} = 1$

$Y\min = -4$

$Y\max = 4$

$Y\text{scl} = 1$

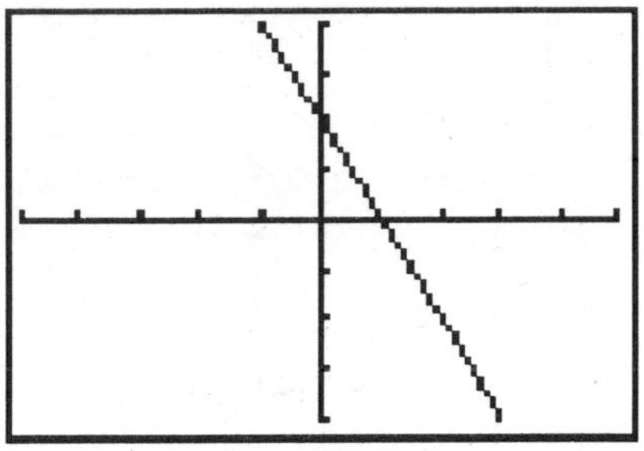

(b)

$X\min = -10$

$X\max = 10$

$X\text{scl} = 1$

$Y\min = -8$

$Y\max = 8$

$Y\text{scl} = 1$

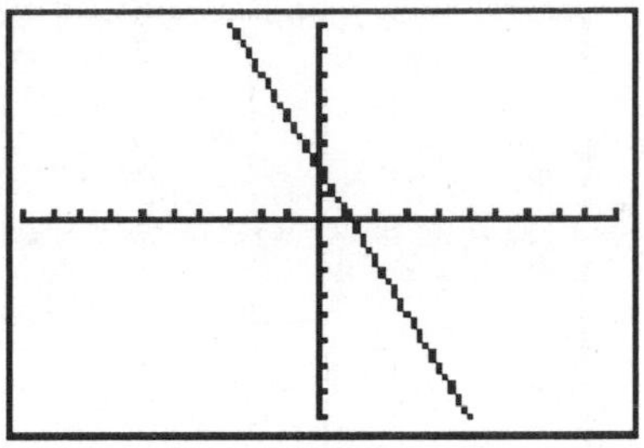

(c)

$X\min = -10$

$X\max = 10$

$X\text{scl} = 2$

$Y\min = -8$

$Y\max = 8$

$Y\text{scl} = 2$

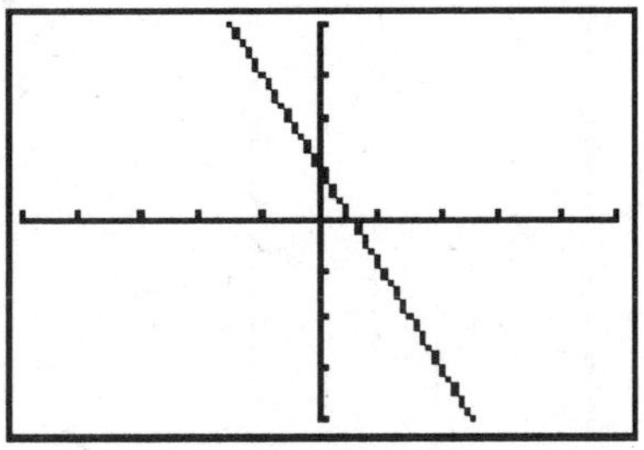

(d)

$X\min = -5$

$X\max = 5$

$X\text{scl} = 1$

$Y\min = -20$

$Y\max = 20$

$Y\text{scl} = 5$

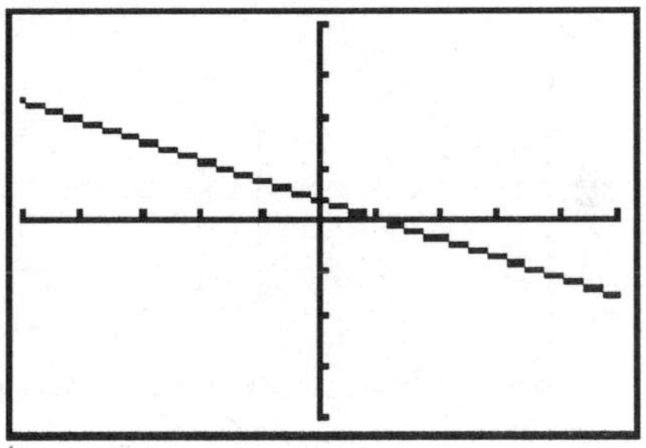

8. (a) $y = -2x - 2$

$X\min = -5$

$X\max = 5$

$X\text{scl} = 1$

$Y\min = -4$

$Y\max = 4$

$Y\text{scl} = 1$

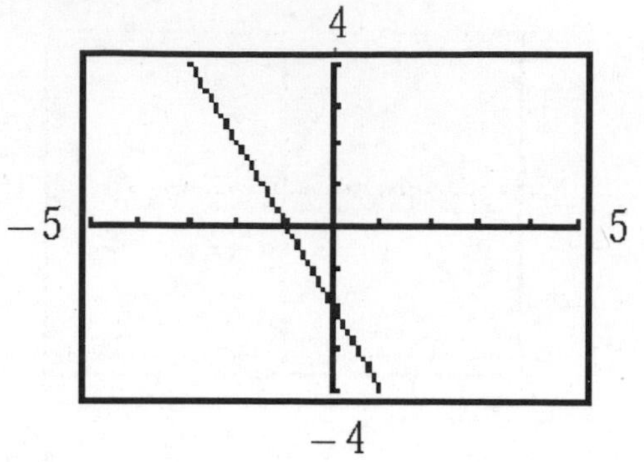

(b)

$X\min = -10$

$X\max = 10$

$X\text{scl} = 1$

$Y\min = -8$

$Y\max = 8$

$Y\text{scl} = 1$

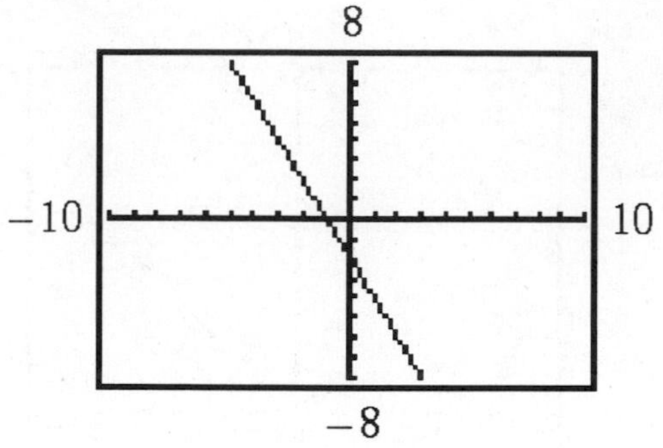

(c)

$X\min = -10$

$X\max = 10$

$X\text{scl} = 2$

$Y\min = -8$

$Y\max = 8$

$Y\text{scl} = 2$

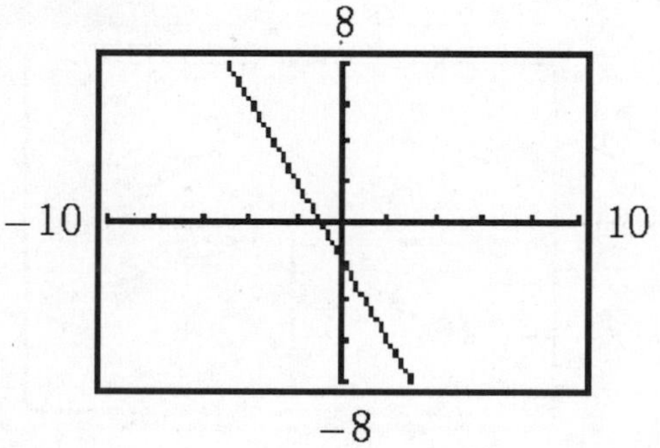

(d)

$X\min = -5$

$X\max = 5$

$X\text{scl} = 1$

$Y\min = -20$

$Y\max = 20$

$Y\text{scl} = 5$

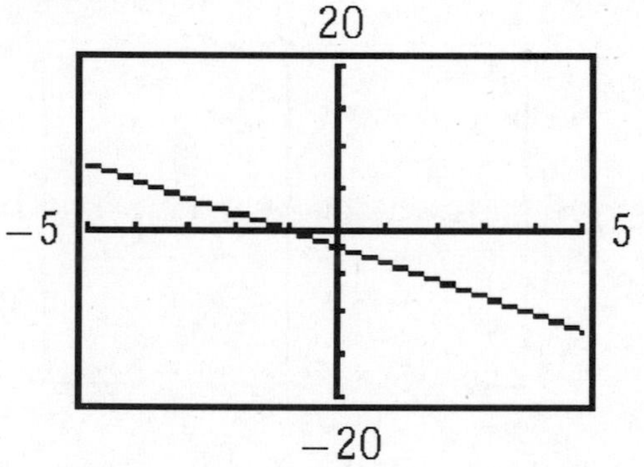

9. (a) $y = x^2 + 2$

$X\min = -5$

$X\max = 5$

$X\text{scl} = 1$

$Y\min = -4$

$Y\max = 4$

$Y\text{scl} = 1$

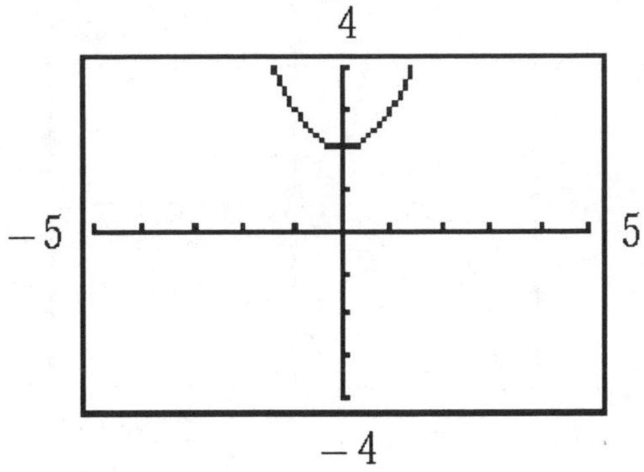

(b)

$X\min = -10$

$X\max = 10$

$X\text{scl} = 1$

$Y\min = -8$

$Y\max = 8$

$Y\text{scl} = 1$

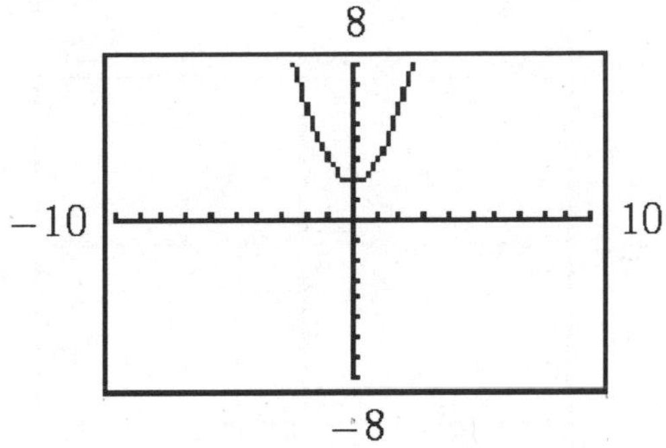

(c)

$X\min = -10$

$X\max = 10$

$X\text{scl} = 2$

$Y\min = -8$

$Y\max = 8$

$Y\text{scl} = 2$

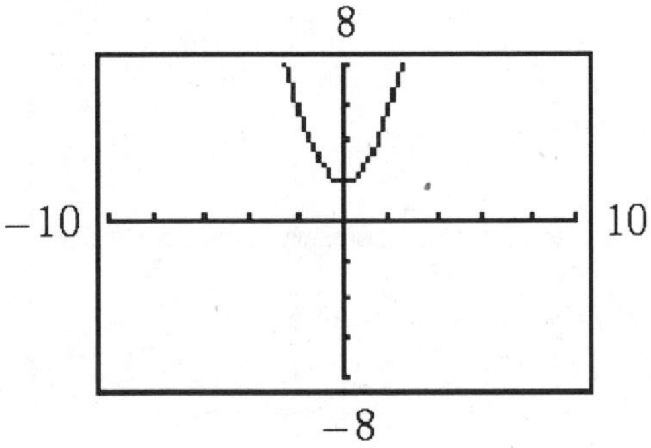

(d)

$X\min = -5$

$X\max = 5$

$X\text{scl} = 1$

$Y\min = -20$

$Y\max = 20$

$Y\text{scl} = 5$

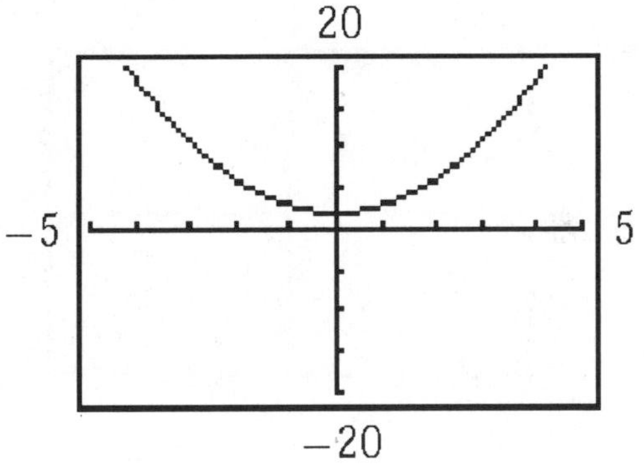

10. (a) $y = x^2 - 2$

$X\min = -5$
$X\max = 5$
$X\text{scl} = 1$
$Y\min = -4$
$Y\max = 4$
$Y\text{scl} = 1$

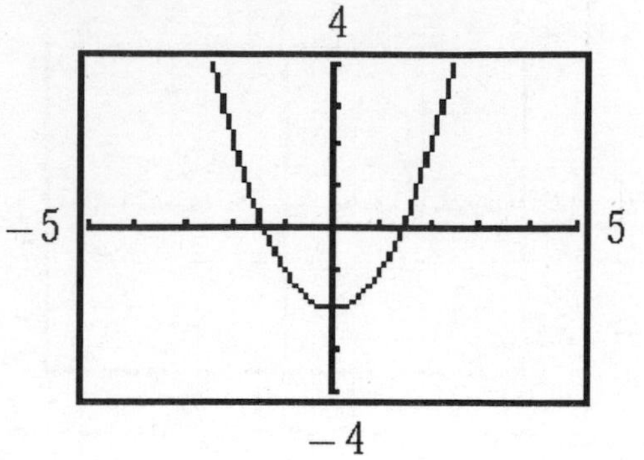

(b)

$X\min = -10$
$X\max = 10$
$X\text{scl} = 1$
$Y\min = -8$
$Y\max = 8$
$Y\text{scl} = 1$

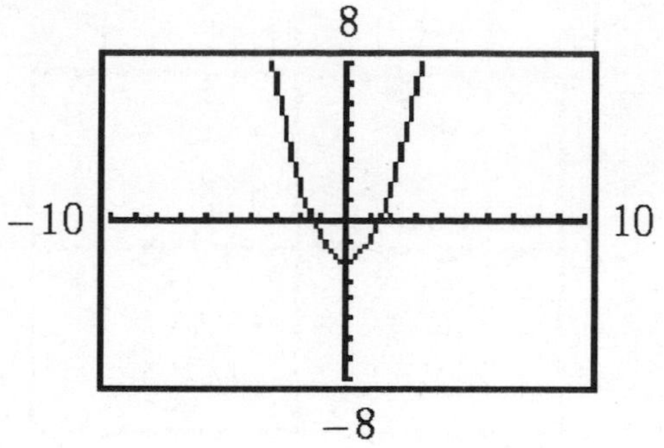

(c)

$X\min = -10$
$X\max = 10$
$X\text{scl} = 2$
$Y\min = -8$
$Y\max = 8$
$Y\text{scl} = 2$

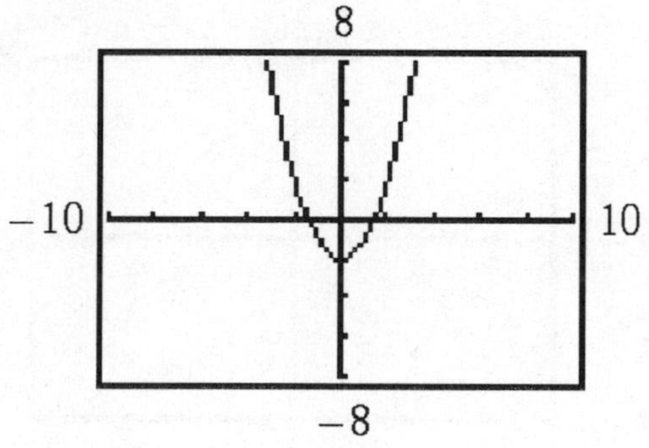

(d)

$X\min = -5$
$X\max = 5$
$X\text{scl} = 1$
$Y\min = -20$
$Y\max = 20$
$Y\text{scl} = 5$

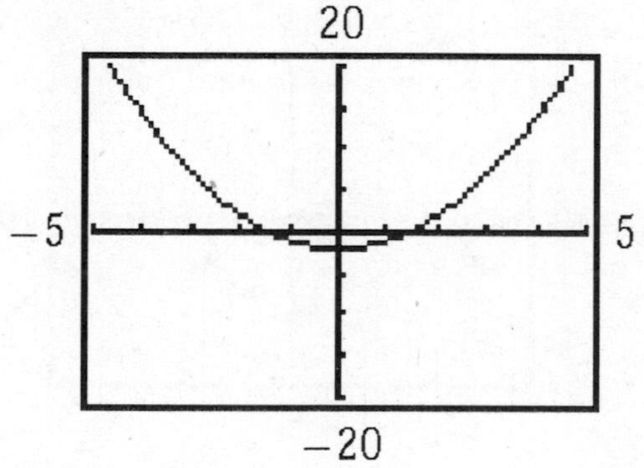

11. (a) $y = -x^2 + 2$

$X\min = -5$

$X\max = 5$

$X\text{scl} = 1$

$Y\min = -4$

$Y\max = 4$

$Y\text{scl} = 1$

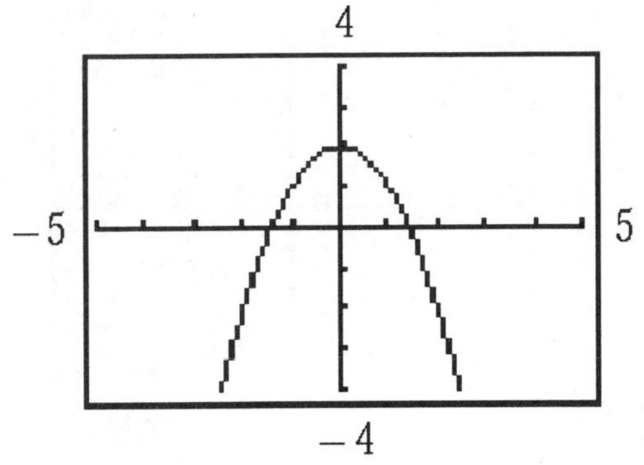

(b)

$X\min = -10$

$X\max = 10$

$X\text{scl} = 1$

$Y\min = -8$

$Y\max = 8$

$Y\text{scl} = 1$

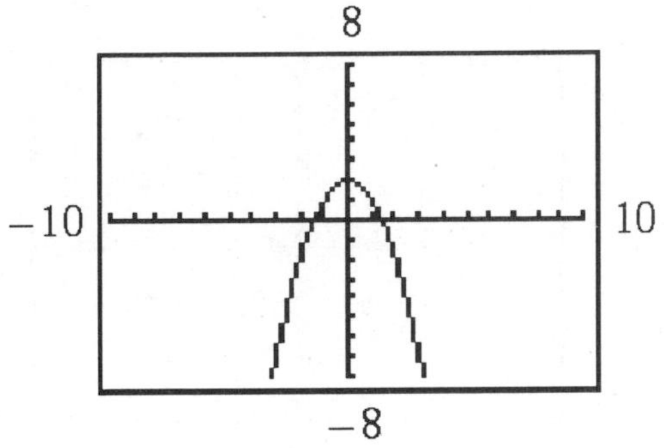

(c)

$X\min = -10$

$X\max = 10$

$X\text{scl} = 2$

$Y\min = -8$

$Y\max = 8$

$Y\text{scl} = 2$

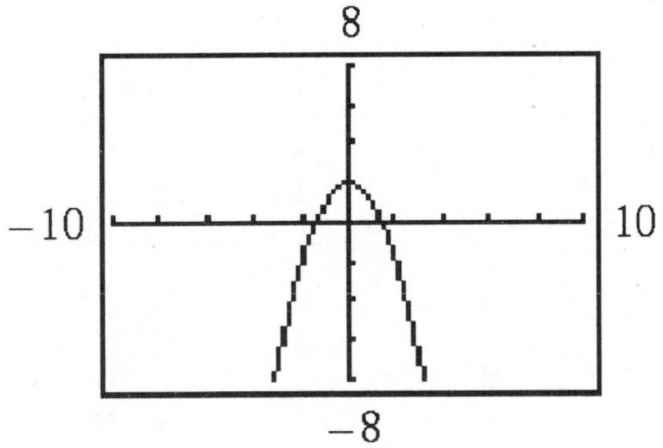

(d)

$X\min = -5$

$X\max = 5$

$X\text{scl} = 1$

$Y\min = -20$

$Y\max = 20$

$Y\text{scl} = 5$

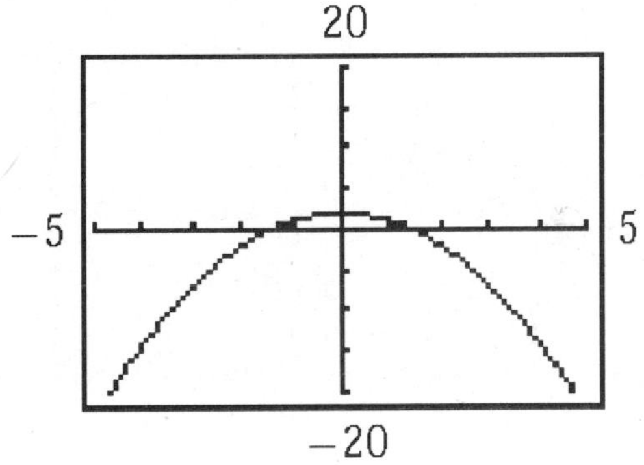

12. (a) $y = -x^2 - 2$

$X\min = -5$

$X\max = 5$

$X\text{scl} = 1$

$Y\min = -4$

$Y\max = 4$

$Y\text{scl} = 1$

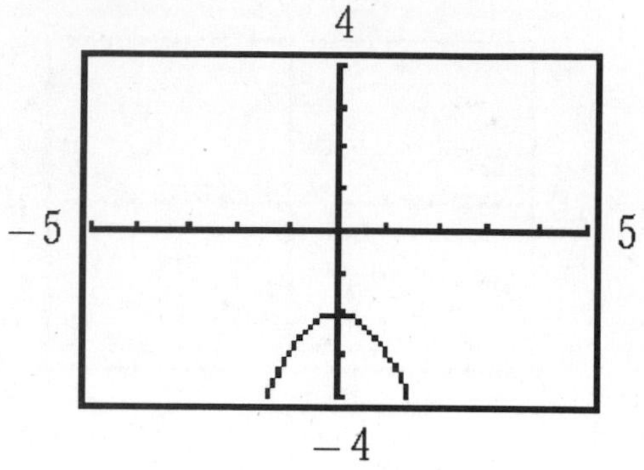

(b)

$X\min = -10$

$X\max = 10$

$X\text{scl} = 1$

$Y\min = -8$

$Y\max = 8$

$Y\text{scl} = 1$

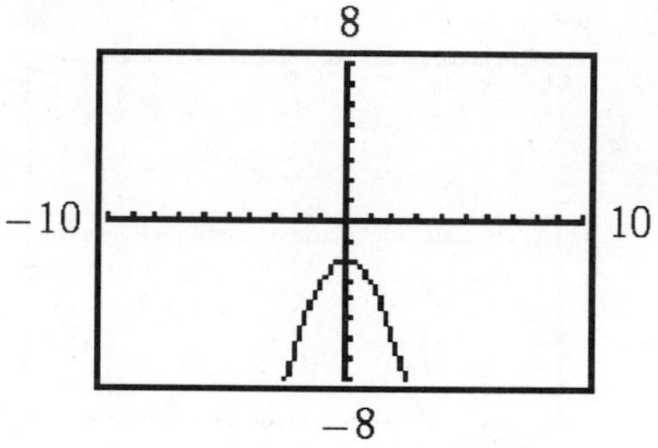

(c)

$X\min = -10$

$X\max = 10$

$X\text{scl} = 2$

$Y\min = -8$

$Y\max = 8$

$Y\text{scl} = 2$

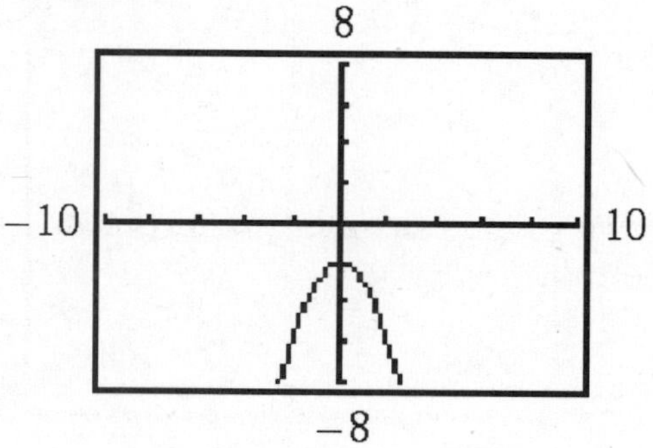

(d)

$X\min = -5$

$X\max = 5$

$X\text{scl} = 1$

$Y\min = -20$

$Y\max = 20$

$Y\text{scl} = 5$

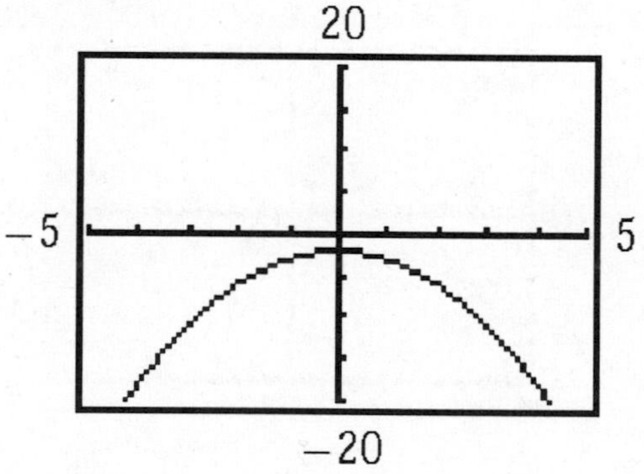

13. (a) $3x + 2y = 6$

$X\min = -5$

$X\max = 5$

$X\text{scl} = 1$

$Y\min = -4$

$Y\max = 4$

$Y\text{scl} = 1$

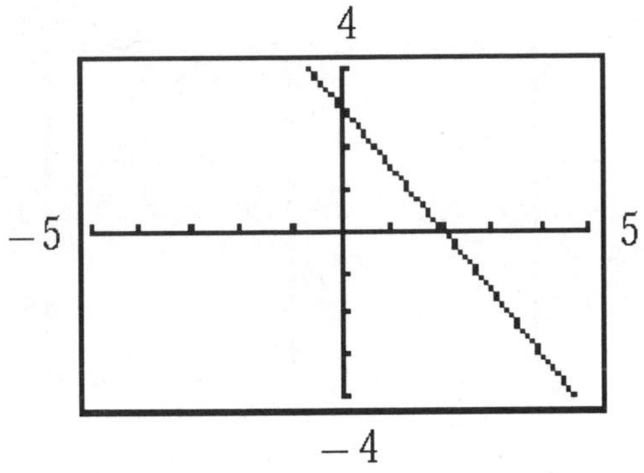

(b)

$X\min = -10$

$X\max = 10$

$X\text{scl} = 1$

$Y\min = -8$

$Y\max = 8$

$Y\text{scl} = 1$

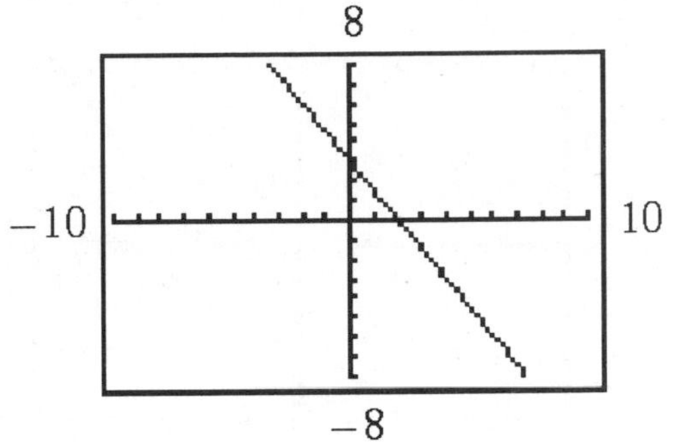

(c)

$X\min = -10$

$X\max = 10$

$X\text{scl} = 2$

$Y\min = -8$

$Y\max = 8$

$Y\text{scl} = 2$

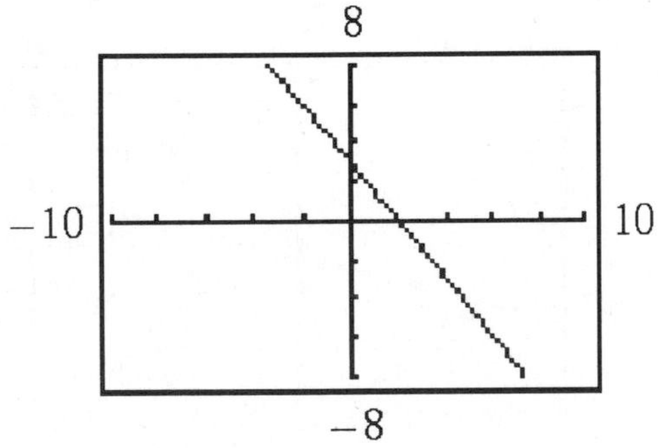

(d)

$X\min = -5$

$X\max = 5$

$X\text{scl} = 1$

$Y\min = -20$

$Y\max = 20$

$Y\text{scl} = 5$

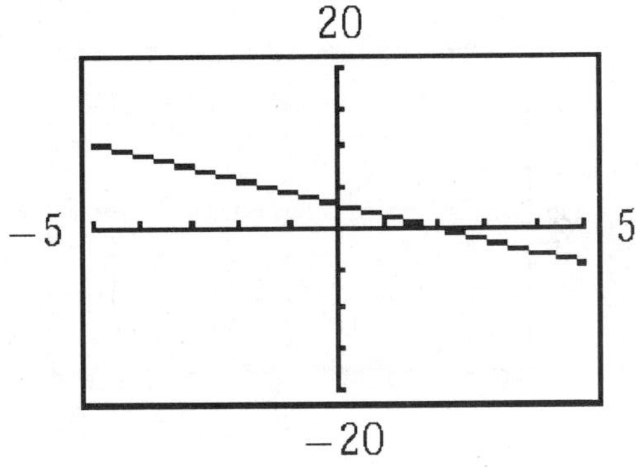

14. (a) $3x-2y=6$

$X\min=-5$
$X\max=5$
$X\text{scl}=1$
$Y\min=-4$
$Y\max=4$
$Y\text{scl}=1$

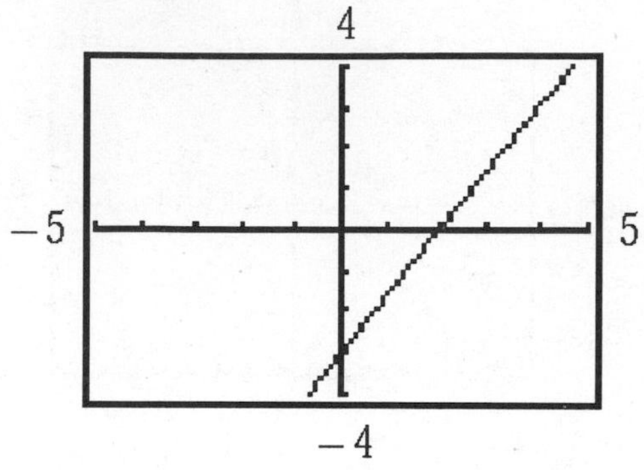

(b)

$X\min=-10$
$X\max=10$
$X\text{scl}=1$
$Y\min=-8$
$Y\max=8$
$Y\text{scl}=1$

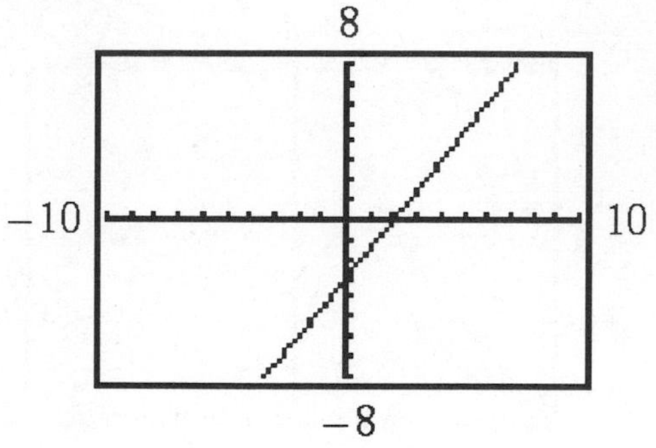

(c)

$X\min=-10$
$X\max=10$
$X\text{scl}=2$
$Y\min=-8$
$Y\max=8$
$Y\text{scl}=2$

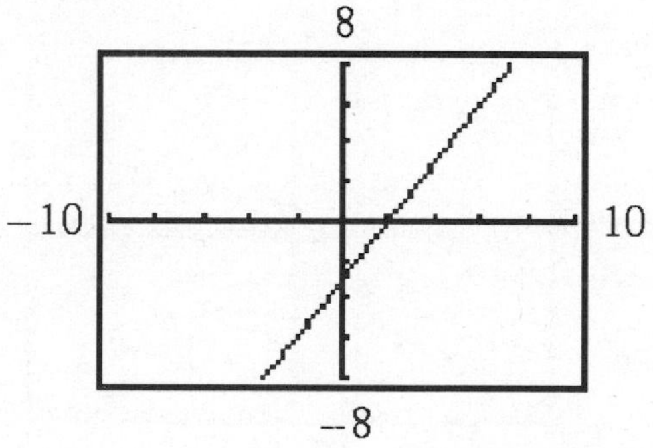

(d)

$X\min=-5$
$X\max=5$
$X\text{scl}=1$
$Y\min=-20$
$Y\max=20$
$Y\text{scl}=5$

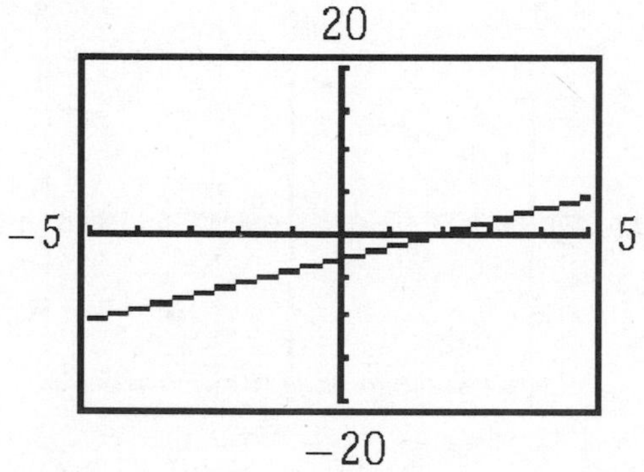

15. (a) $-3x+2y=6$

$X\min=-5$

$X\max=5$

$X\text{scl}=1$

$Y\min=-4$

$Y\max=4$

$Y\text{scl}=1$

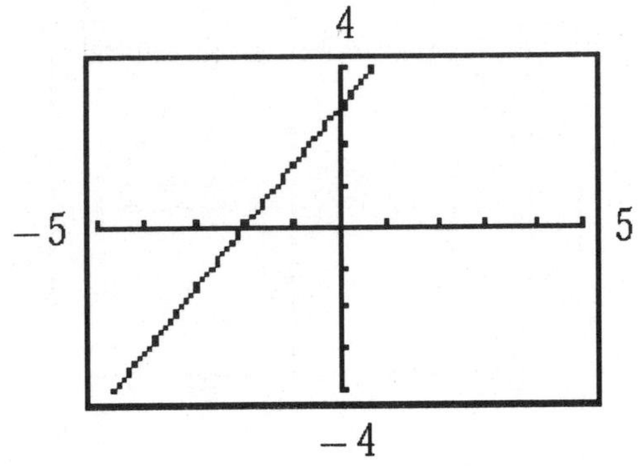

(b)

$X\min=-10$

$X\max=10$

$X\text{scl}=1$

$Y\min=-8$

$Y\max=8$

$Y\text{scl}=1$

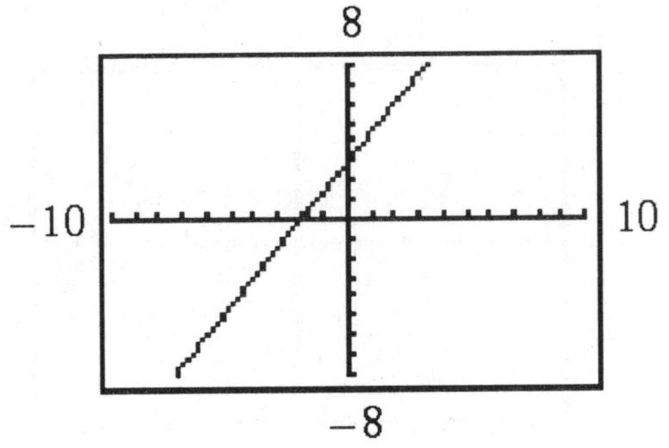

(c)

$X\min=-10$

$X\max=10$

$X\text{scl}=2$

$Y\min=-8$

$Y\max=8$

$Y\text{scl}=2$

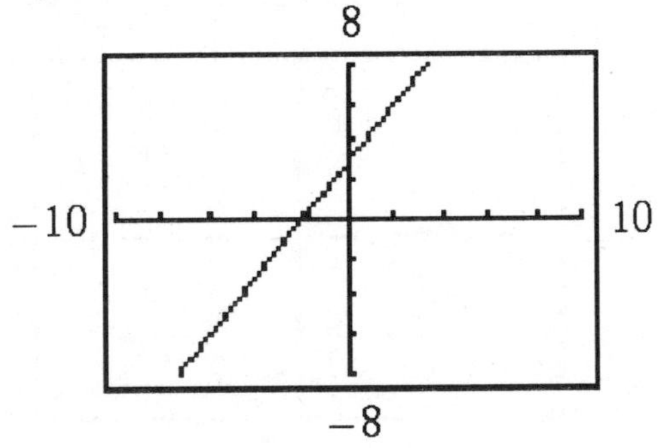

(d)

$X\min=-5$

$X\max=5$

$X\text{scl}=1$

$Y\min=-20$

$Y\max=20$

$Y\text{scl}=5$

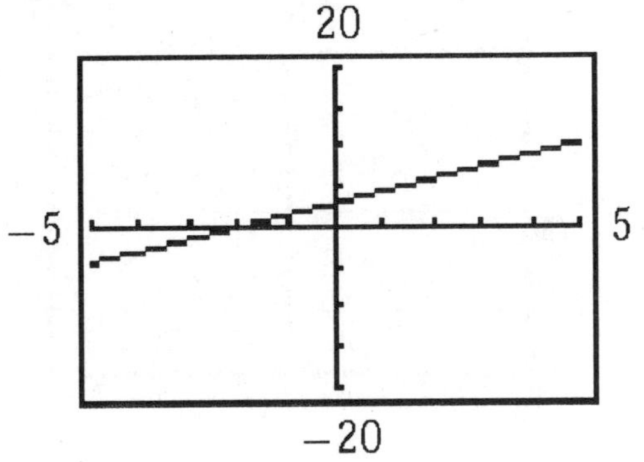

16. (a) $-3x - 2y = 6$

$X\min = -5$
$X\max = 5$
$X\text{scl} = 1$
$Y\min = -4$
$Y\max = 4$
$Y\text{scl} = 1$

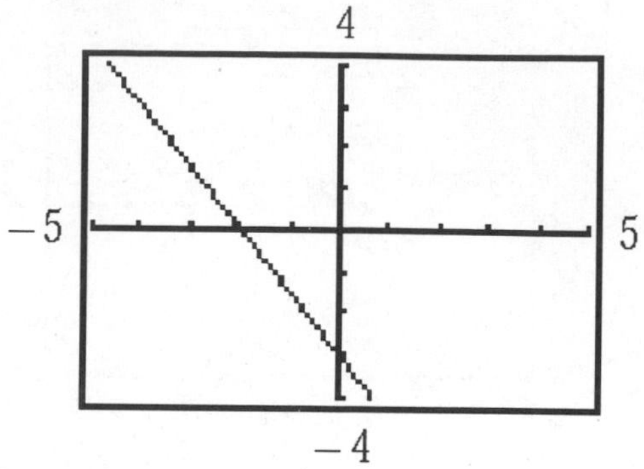

(b)

$X\min = -10$
$X\max = 10$
$X\text{scl} = 1$
$Y\min = -8$
$Y\max = 8$
$Y\text{scl} = 1$

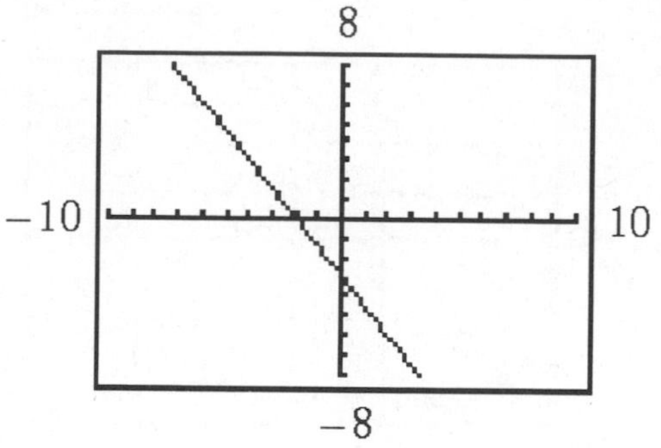

(c)

$X\min = -10$
$X\max = 10$
$X\text{scl} = 2$
$Y\min = -8$
$Y\max = 8$
$Y\text{scl} = 2$

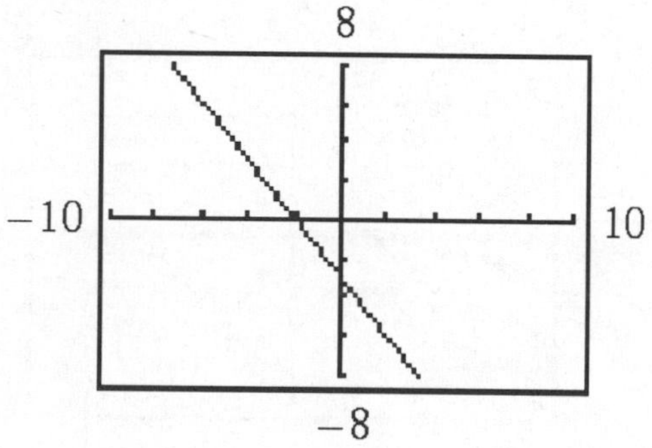

(d)

$X\min = -5$
$X\max = 5$
$X\text{scl} = 1$
$Y\min = -20$
$Y\max = 20$
$Y\text{scl} = 5$

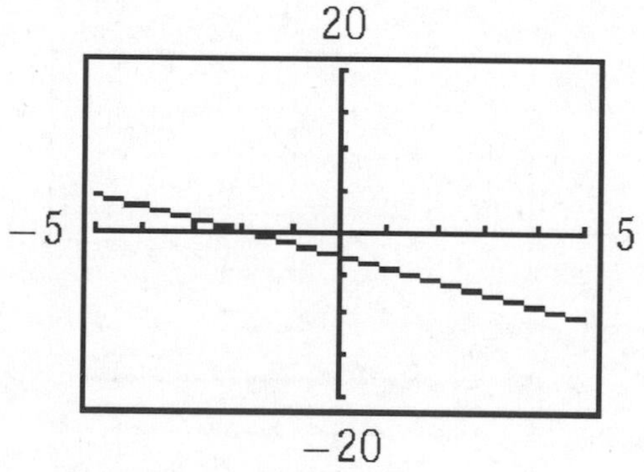

17. $y = x + 2;\quad -3 \le x \le 3$

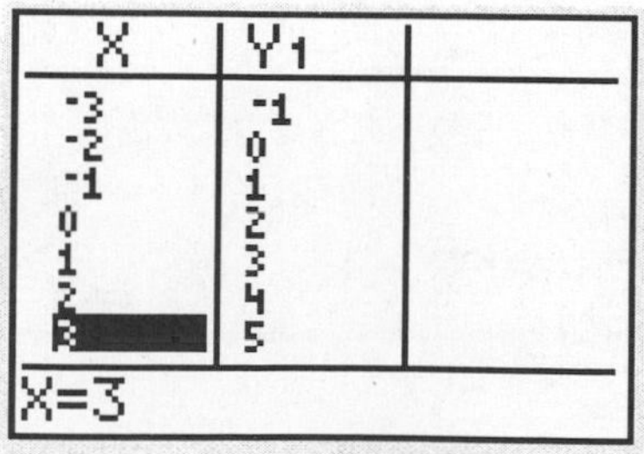

18. $y = x - 2;\quad -3 \le x \le 3$

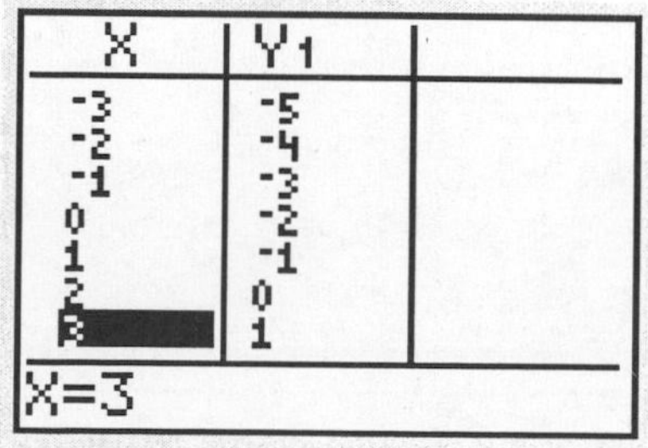

19. $y = -x + 2; \quad -3 \le x \le 3$

X	Y_1
-3	5
-2	4
-1	3
0	2
1	1
2	0
3	-1

X=3

20. $y = -x - 2; \quad -3 \le x \le 3$

X	Y_1
-3	1
-2	0
-1	-1
0	-2
1	-3
2	-4
3	-5

X=3

21. $y = 2x + 2; \quad -3 \le x \le 3$

X	Y_1
-3	-4
-2	-2
-1	0
0	2
1	4
2	6
3	8

X=3

22. $y = 2x - 2; \quad -3 \le x \le 3$

X	Y_1
-3	-8
-2	-6
-1	-4
0	-2
1	0
2	2
3	4

X=3

23. $y = -2x + 2; \quad -3 \le x \le 3$

X	Y_1
-3	8
-2	6
-1	4
0	2
1	0
2	-2
3	-4

X=3

24. $y = -2x - 2; \quad -3 \le x \le 3$

X	Y_1
-3	4
-2	2
-1	0
0	-2
1	-4
2	-6
3	-8

X=3

25. $y = x^2 + 2; \quad -3 \le x \le 3$

X	Y_1
-3	11
-2	6
-1	3
0	2
1	3
2	6
3	11

X=3

26. $y = x^2 - 2; \quad -3 \le x \le 3$

X	Y_1
-3	7
-2	2
-1	-1
0	-2
1	-1
2	2
3	7

X=3

27. $y = -x^2 + 2; \quad -3 \le x \le 3$

X	Y_1
-3	-7
-2	-2
-1	1
0	2
1	1
2	-2
3	-7

X=3

28. $y = -x^2 - 2; \quad -3 \le x \le 3$

X	Y_1
-3	-11
-2	-6
-1	-3
0	-2
1	-3
2	-6
3	-11

X=3

29. $3x + 2y = 6; \quad -3 \le x \le 3$

X	Y_1
-3	7.5
-2	6
-1	4.5
0	3
1	1.5
2	0
3	-1.5

X=3

30. $3x - 2y = 6; \quad -3 \le x \le 3$

X	Y_1
-3	-7.5
-2	-6
-1	-4.5
0	-3
1	-1.5
2	0
3	1.5

X=3

31. $-3x + 2y = 6; \quad -3 \le x \le 3$

X	Y_1
-3	-1.5
-2	0
-1	1.5
0	3
1	4.5
2	6
3	7.5

X=3

32. $-3x - 2y = 6; \quad -3 \le x \le 3$

X	Y_1
-3	1.5
-2	0
-1	-1.5
0	-3
1	-4.5
2	-6
3	-7.5

X=3

Graphing Utilities

A.3 Using a Graphing Utility to Locate Intercepts and Check for Symmetry

1. $y = x^2 + 4x + 2$

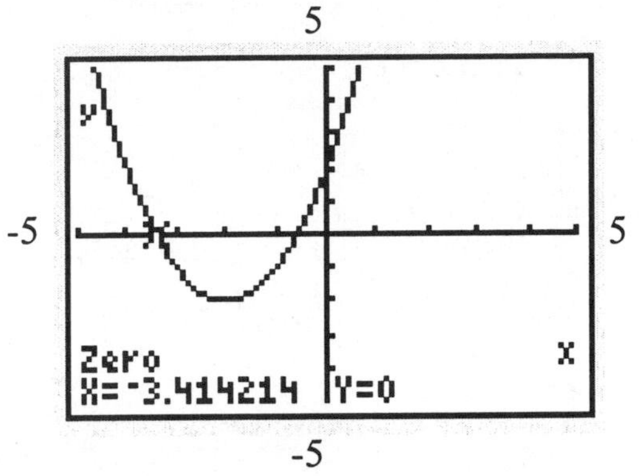

The smaller x-intercept is $x \approx -3.41$.

2. $y = x^2 + 4x - 3$

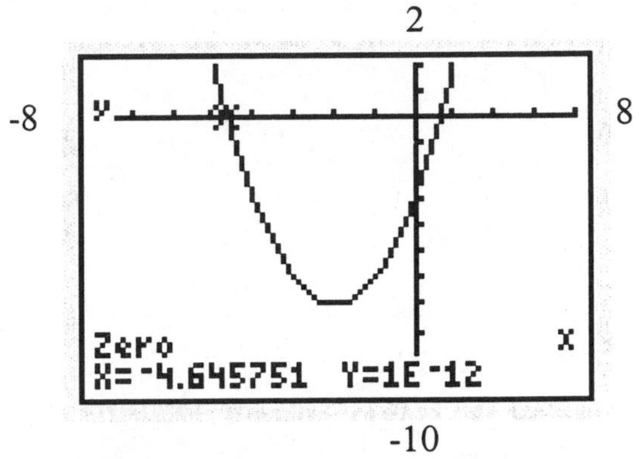

The smaller x-intercept is $x \approx -4.65$.

3. $y = 2x^2 + 4x + 1$

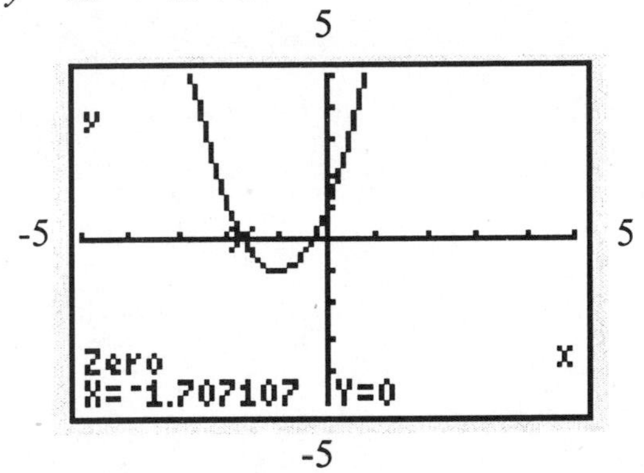

The smaller x-intercept is $x \approx -1.71$.

4. $y = 3x^2 + 5x + 1$

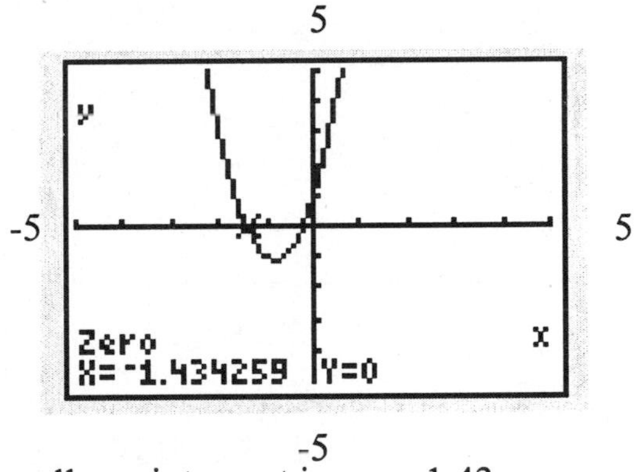

The smaller x-intercept is $x \approx -1.43$.

5. $y = 2x^2 - 3x - 1$

5

-5 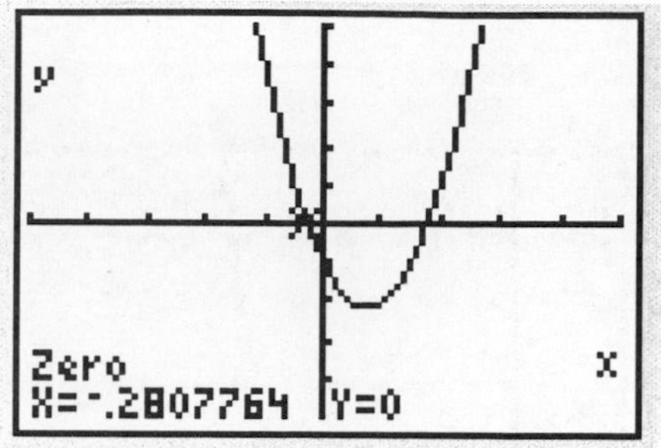 5

-5

The smaller x-intercept is $x \approx -0.28$.

6. $y = 2x^2 - 4x - 1$

5

-5 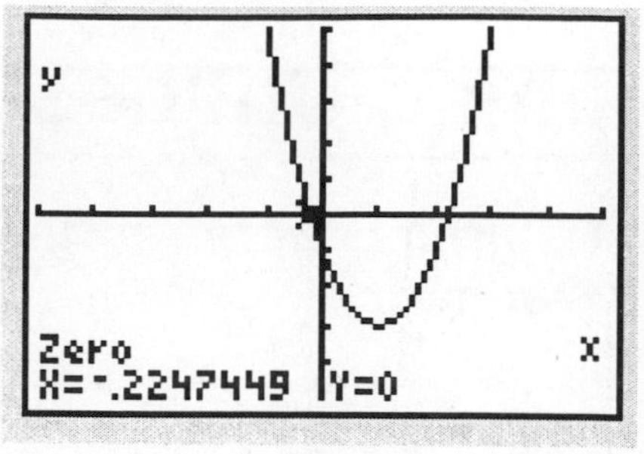 5

-5

The smaller x-intercept is $x \approx -0.22$.

7. $y = x^3 + 3.2x^2 - 16.83x - 5.31$

60

-10 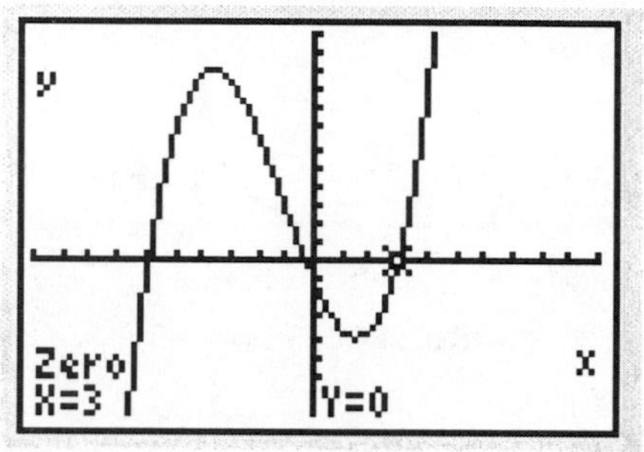 10

-40

The positive x-intercept is $x = 3$.

8. $y = x^3 + 3.2x^2 - 7.25x - 6.3$

60

-10 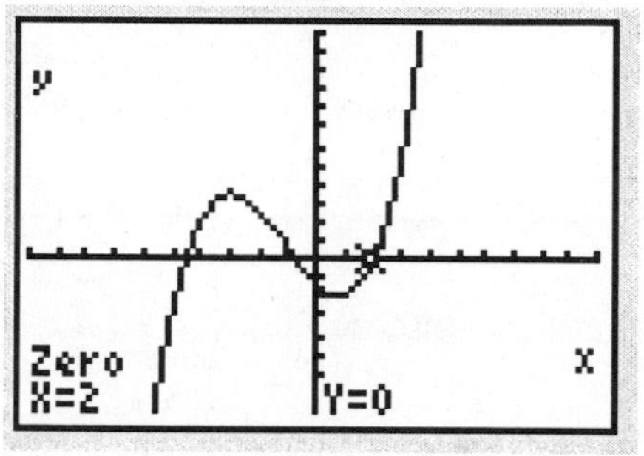 10

-40

The positive x-intercept is $x = 2$.

9. $y = x^4 - 1.4x^3 - 33.71x^2 + 23.94x + 292.41$

400

-10 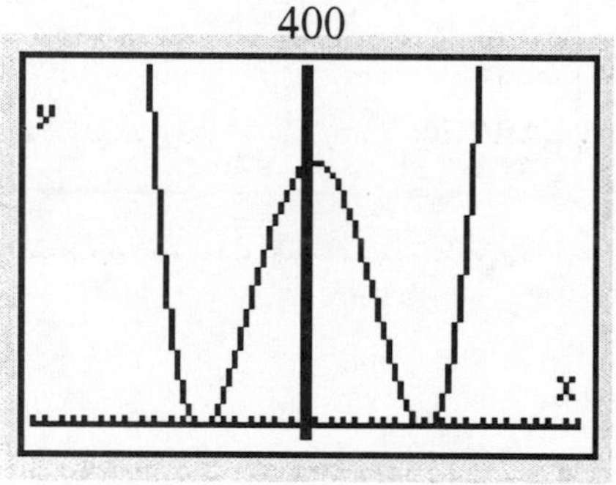 10

-10

We zoom in on the positive x-intercept:

50

2 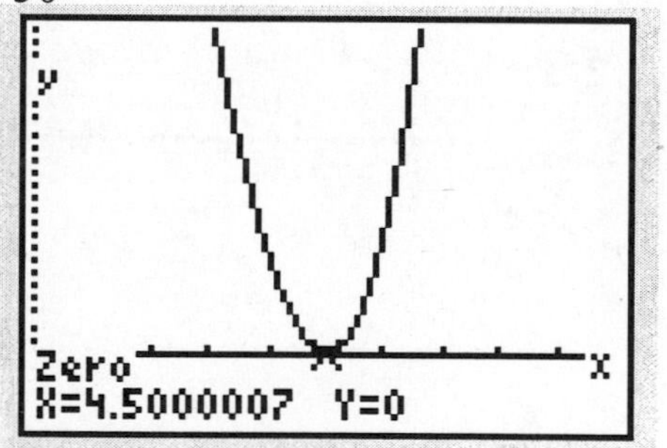 7

-10

The positive x-intercept is $x \approx 4.50$.

10. $y = x^4 + 1.2x^3 - 7.46x^2 - 4.692x + 15.2881$

50

-10 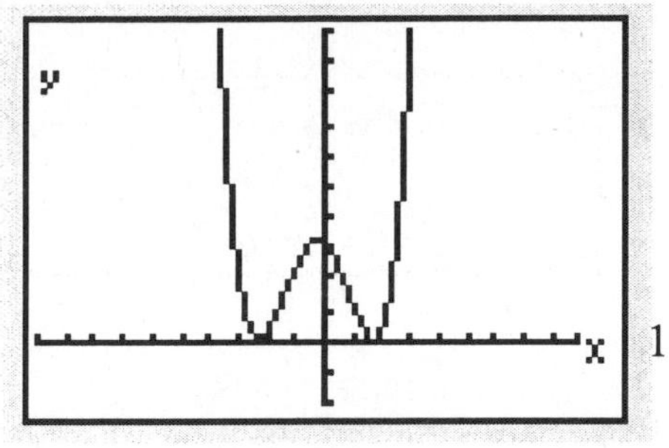 10

-10

We zoom in on the positive x-intercept:

12

-1 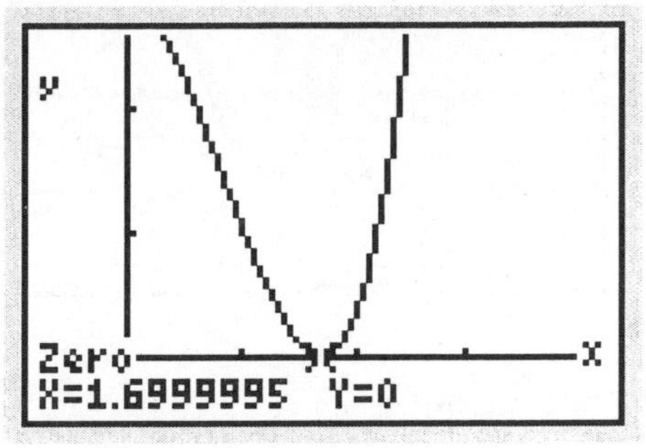 4

-2

The positive x-intercept is $x \approx 1.70$.

11. $y = \pi x^3 - (8.88\pi + 1)x^2 - (42.066\pi - 8.88)x + 42.066$

300

-10 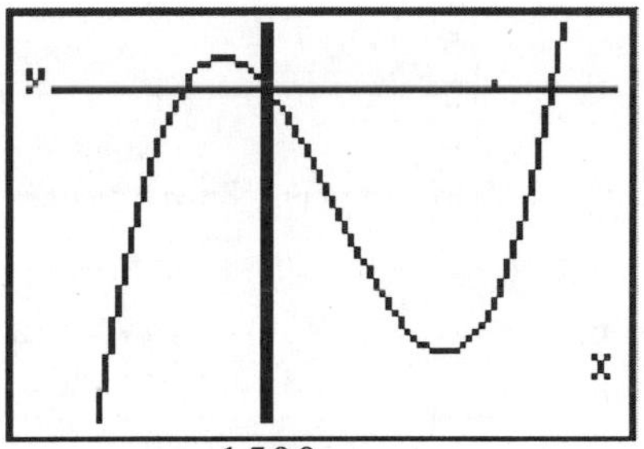 25

-1500

We zoom in on the positive x-intercepts:

218

-2 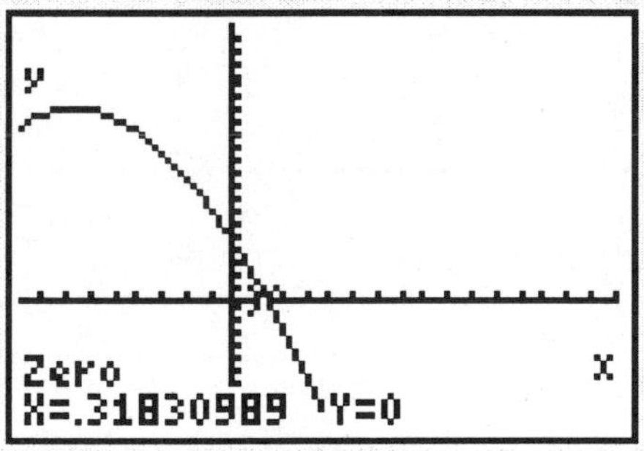 4

-100

The smallest positive x-intercept is $x \approx 0.32$.

We zoom in on the positive x-intercepts:

500

7 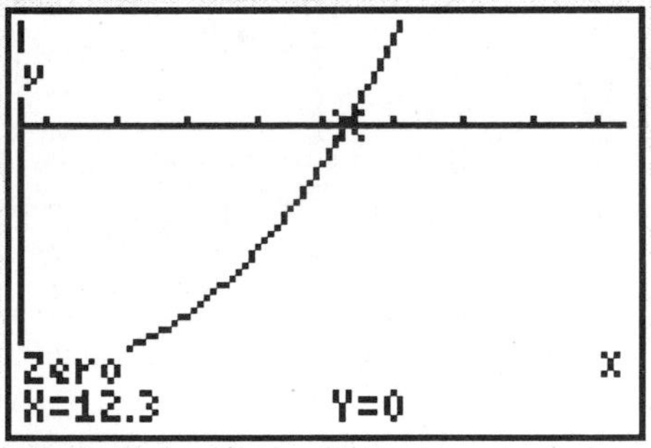 16

-1455

The largest positive x-intercept is $x \approx 12.3$.

12. $y = \pi x^3 - (5.63\pi + 2)x^2 - (108.392\pi - 11.26)x + 216.784$

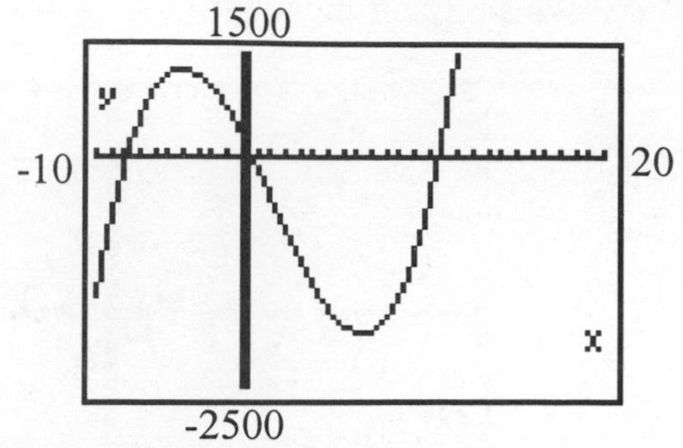

We zoom in on the positive x-intercepts:

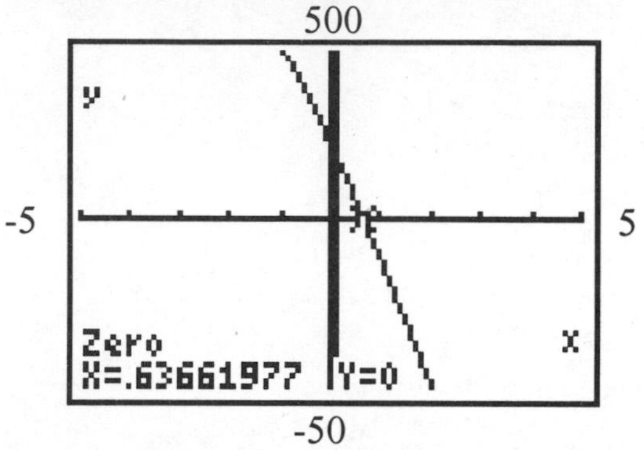

The smallest positive x-intercept is $x \approx 0.64$.

We zoom in on the positive x-intercepts:

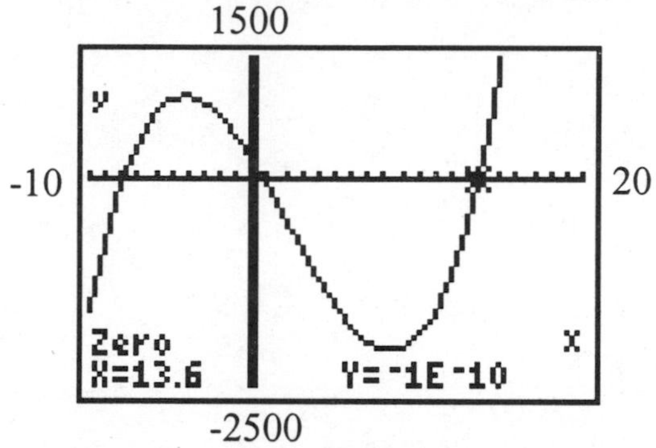

The largest positive x-intercept is $x \approx 13.60$.

13. $y = x^3 + 19.5x^2 - 1021x + 1000.5$

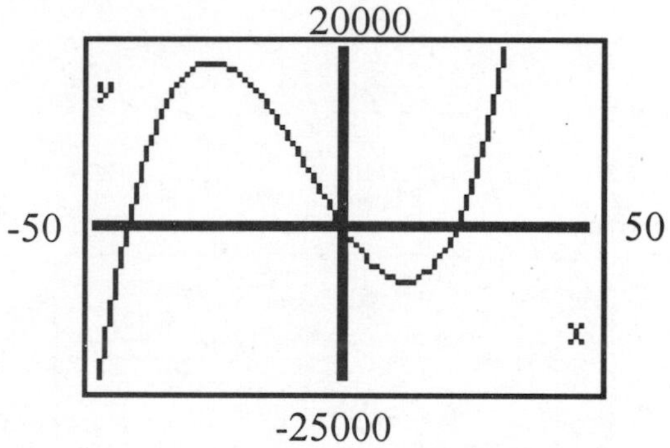

We zoom in on the positive x-intercepts:

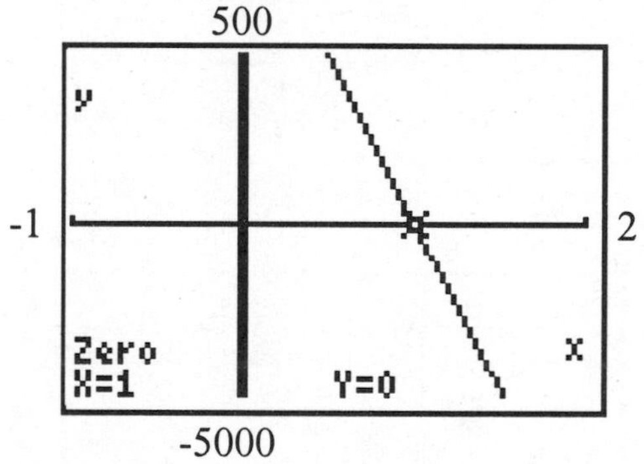

The smallest positive x-intercept is $x = 1$.

We zoom in on the positive x-intercepts:

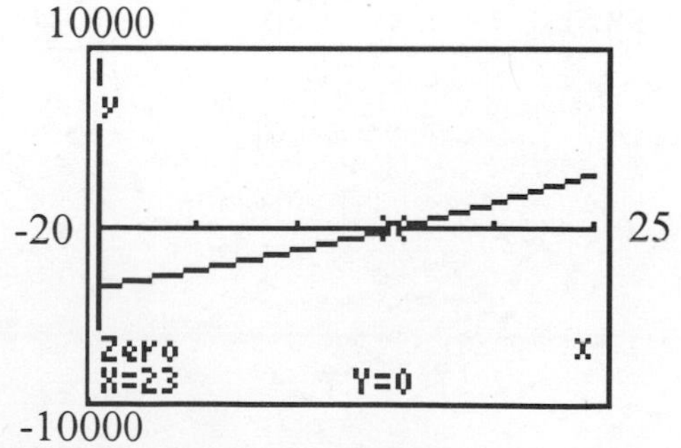

The largest positive x-intercept is $x = 23$.

14. $y = x^3 + 14.2x^2 - 4.8x - 12.4$

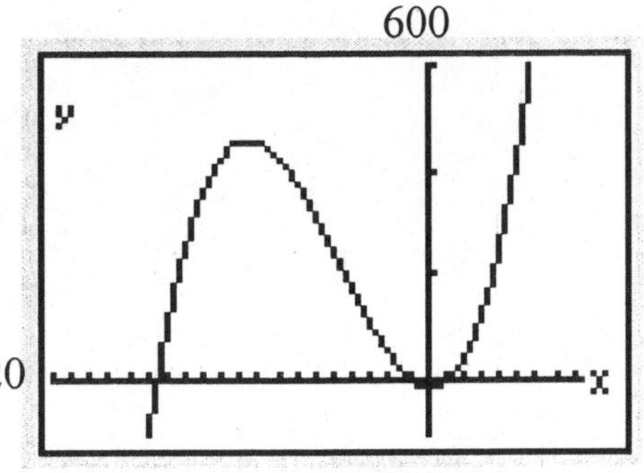

We zoom in on the positive x-intercept:

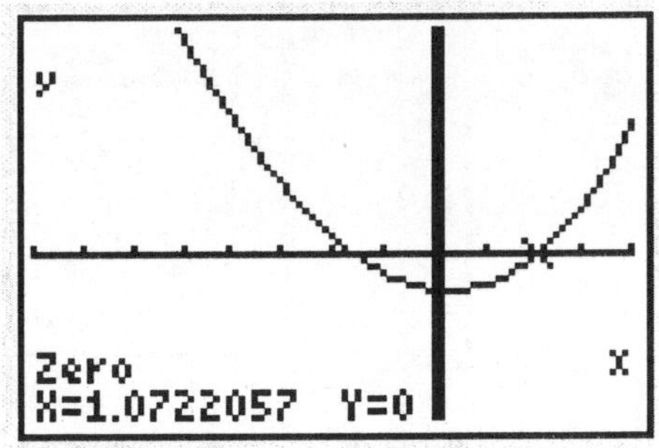

The positive x-intercept is $x \approx 1.07$.

15. x-intercepts: (- 1.5, 0); (1.5, 0)

y-intercept: (0, -2)

y-axis symmetry

16. x-intercept: (0, 0)

y-intercept: (0, 0)

origin symmetry

17. x-intercepts: none

y-intercept: none

origin symmetry

18. x-intercept: none

y-intercept: none

x-axis symmetry

Graphing Utilities

A.5 Square Screens

1. yes

$X\min = -3$

$X\max = 3$

$X\text{scl} = 2$

$Y\min = -2$

$Y\max = 2$

$Y\text{scl} = 2$

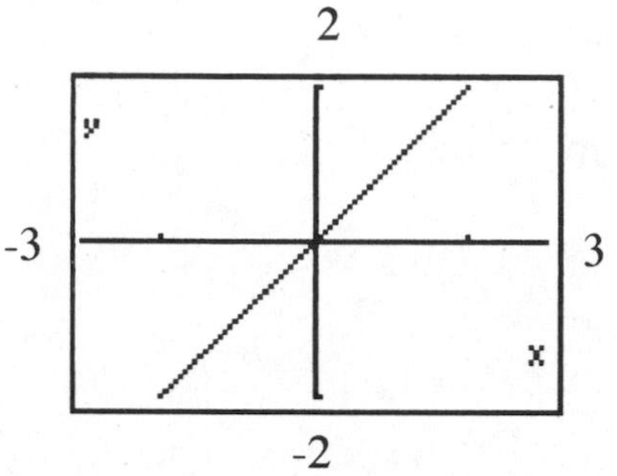

2. no

$X\min = -5$

$X\max = 5$

$X\text{scl} = 1$

$Y\min = -4$

$Y\max = 4$

$Y\text{scl} = 1$

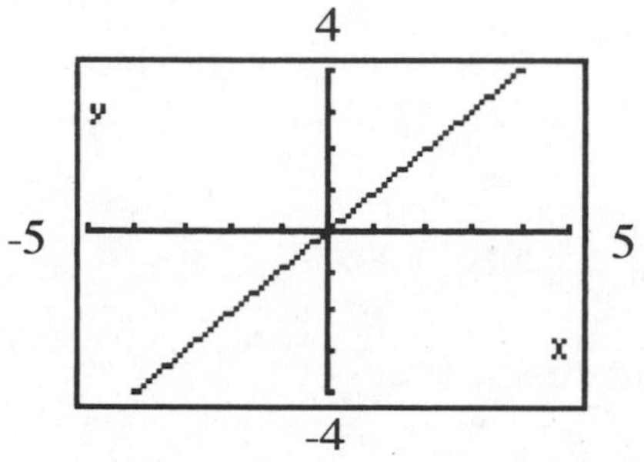

3. yes

$X\min = 0$

$X\max = 9$

$X\text{scl} = 3$

$Y\min = -2$

$Y\max = 4$

$Y\text{scl} = 2$

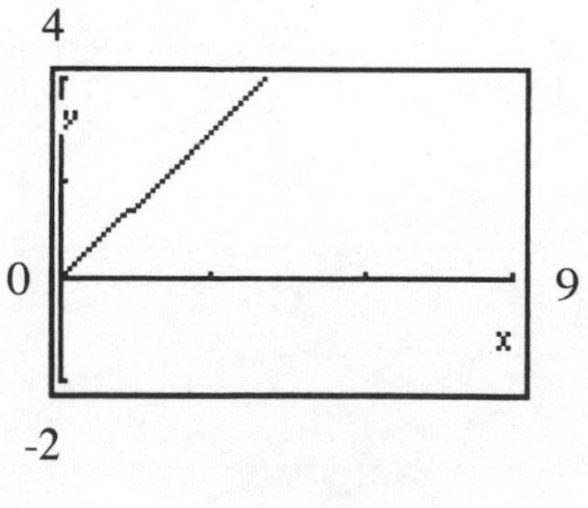

4. yes

$X\min = -6$

$X\max = 6$

$X\text{scl} = 1$

$Y\min = -4$

$Y\max = 4$

$Y\text{scl} = 2$

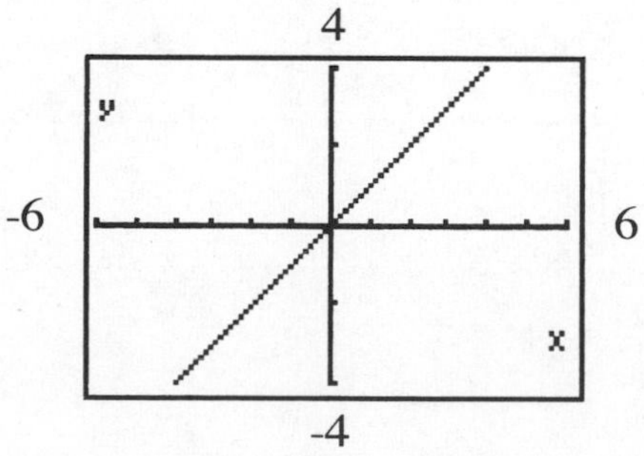

5. no

$X\min = -6$
$X\max = 6$
$X\text{scl} = 1$
$Y\min = -2$
$Y\max = 2$
$Y\text{scl} = 0.5$

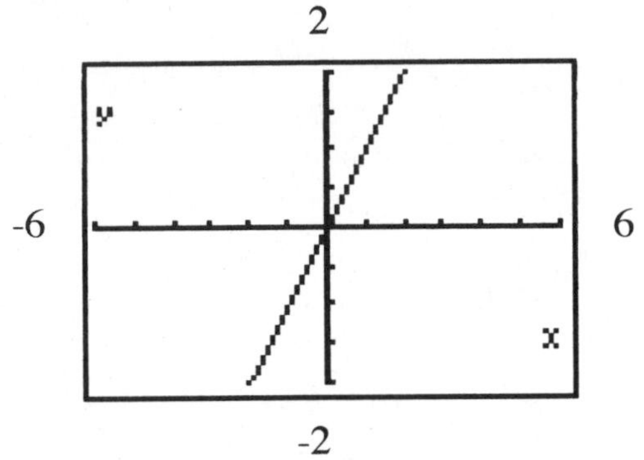

6. yes

$X\min = -6$
$X\max = 6$
$X\text{scl} = 2$
$Y\min = -4$
$Y\max = 4$
$Y\text{scl} = 1$

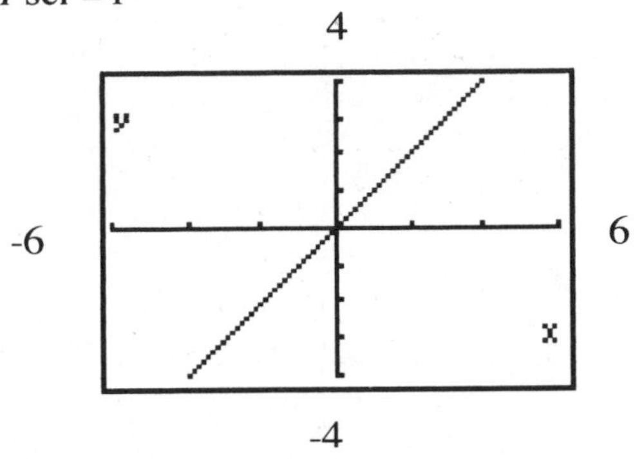

7. yes

$X\min = 0$
$X\max = 9$
$X\text{scl} = 1$
$Y\min = -2$
$Y\max = 4$
$Y\text{scl} = 1$

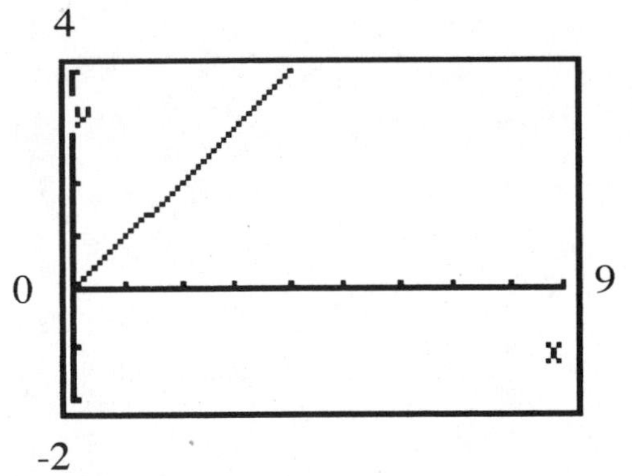

8. yes

$X\min = -6$
$X\max = 6$
$X\text{scl} = 2$
$Y\min = -4$
$Y\max = 4$
$Y\text{scl} = 2$

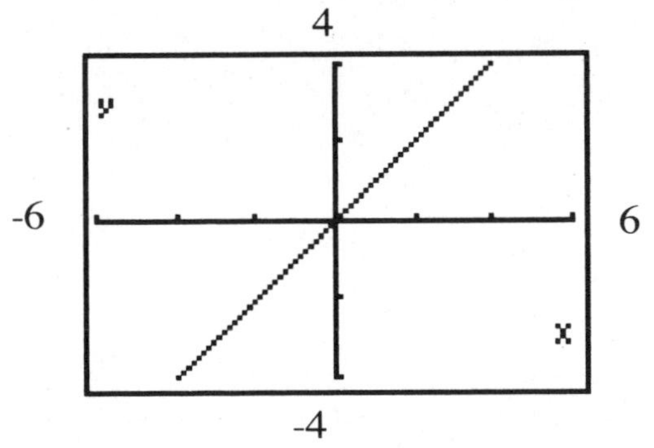

9. One possible answer:

$X\min = -4$

$X\max = 8$

$X\text{scl} = 1$

$Y\min = 4$

$Y\max = 12$

$Y\text{scl} = 1$

10. One possible answer:

$X\min = -6$

$X\max = 12$

$X\text{scl} = 2$

$Y\min = -2$

$Y\max = 10$

$Y\text{scl} = 2$